OFFICIAL
RUGBY UNION
CLUB DIRECTORY
1994-95

COURAGE
CLUBS CHAMPIONSHIP

OFFICIAL

RUGBY UNION
CLUB DIRECTORY
1994-95

Edited by Bill Mitchell

Tony Williams Publications

Copyright: Tony Williams Publications

Published in Great Britain by Tony Williams
Publications, 24a Queen Square, North Curry,
Taunton, Somerset TA3 6LE

The publishers wish to confirm that the views
expressed in articles and reviews in this directory
are not necessarily those of the R.F.U., Courage
Ltd or Michael Humphreys & Partners Ltd.

Typeset by Interface (South West) Ltd 0392 444045

Printed and bound in Great Britain by
B.A.S. Printers, Orange Lane, Over Wallop,
Stockbridge, Hampshire SO20 8JD

Trade Sales & Distribution: Little Red Witch
Books 0823 490080

ISBN 1-869833-23-6

Cover Photograph supplied by Colorsport.
Bath on the rampage as they clinch another title

PUBLISHER'S FOREWORD

by Tony Williams

The unanimous chorus of approval given to last season's Courage Rugby Union Club Directory was extremely satisfying to all who have developed the concept over the last seven yars.

The Courage Club Championship now has substantial records from which Steve McCormack has supplied many excellent statistics, while Joe McCabe's photos seem to get better and better each season.

Many National League clubs have appointed well organised, enthusiastic and helpful Press Officers but you will see which clubs are not so well organised from the club sections in this Directory.

Sadly it is the supporters of these clubs who suffer as their clubs' contributions to the book often do not match their status within the game.

If all clubs managed to forward team photos, action pictures, programmes and players details as requested the club section in the Directory would quickly become more consistent and obviously even more enjoyable.

However it's early days and, having seen our 'Non-League Football Club Directory' grow to 1,200 pages in its seventeen years life span, we are sure that its Rugby Union brother will develop just as successfully.

It's interesting to see there is now a Rugby Union Programme Club, plus Rugby fanzines and a developing band of Rugby enthusiasts who 'collect' Courage League Club grounds as they tour the country enjoying this sport.

Most members of the massive Courage Championship are becoming more and more determined to be successful and consequently standards on and off the field are improving anually.

Recording this development is a sheer pleasure and I must say the knowledge and expertise of Editor Bill Mitchell has proved invaluable.

Hopefully the 1994-95 season will prove just as enjoyable for us all.

Tony Williams

A WELCOME FROM THE RFU

by Dennis H Easby

President
The Rugby Football Union

Whilst an exciting new season approaches us, culminating with the Rugby World Cup in South Africa, the immediate concern of most is the domestic scene.

Of all competitions the one that attracts the most attention is the Courage Clubs Championship. Each club strives to win its league and looks forward to promotion in the next season. The Courage League dominates the domestic scene for the majority of clubs.

The administration of a league which is the largest in the world can only succeed if supported by careful planning, up to date reporting and assessment of league positions. The Rugby Football Union are indebted to all those who administer the leagues throughout England.

I am particularly delighted to be able to write this welcome as the first President who has represented Berkshire County — a county whose capital, Reading, has been the home of Courage for many years. Courage with their generous support of our game have, over the last few years, increased the support and interest in club rugby and all that is good in our game — competitive rugby played with spirit — with new friendships being formed both on and off the field.

We are grateful to Courage for their continued support and together we look forward to another exciting year.

Dennis H Easby

A WELCOME FROM COURAGE

by Michael Foster

**Executive Chairman,
Courage Ltd**

Courage and Rugby Union have been closely linked for the last seven years. Over that period of time, not only have standards risen at both grass roots and National levels, but the popularity of the game is now at an all time high.

However, we are not prepared to rest on our laurels. Over the next season we will be making conscious efforts to expand our support of rugby clubs to develop further links — on and off the pitch. At the other end of the scale we will continue our support of the England squad as they prepare for the 1995 World Cup in South Africa.

As the game continues to grow, obviously the amount of work that is generated also increases. Without the many administrators who voluntarily donate so much of their time to rugby, the league structure that we have seen develop would grind to a halt — our thanks to them all. The vital role of the referee and touch judge should also be acknowledged.

The relationship between Courage and the Rugby Football Union remains a mutually beneficial one as both ultimately have a single objective — the continued expansion of rugby at all levels. Long may it continue.

Best wishes for a successful 1994-95 season.

Michael Foster

Courage Ltd Business Unit Addresses

BROOKLANDS
Brooklands Business Park, Vickers Drive South,
Weybridge, Surrey. KT13 0YU
Tel: 0932 350088
Fax: 0932 336268
Business Unit Director John McAlister
General Sales Manager Steve Cannan

CHELMSFORD
Montrose Road, Dukes Park Estate, Springfield,
Chelmsford. CM2 6TE
Tel: 0245 460888
Fax: 0245 462558
Business Unit Director Les Bailey
General Sales Manager Mike Crawshaw

EAST ANGLIA
Unit C & D, Frenbury Estate, Hellesdon Park Road,
Norwich. NR6 5DP
Tel: 0603 482328
Fax: 0603 482329
Business Unit Director John Drake
General Sales Manager Steve Parker

EAST MIDLANDS
Lodge Way, Harlestone Road, Northampton. NN5 7UU
Tel: 0604 752452
Fax: 0604 580411
Business Unit Director Patrick Ryan
General Sales Manager Ian Webb

ELLAND
Huddersfield Road, Elland, Nr. Halifax. HX5 9JP
Tel: 0422 375555
Fax: 0422 373347
Business Unit Director Colin Lund
General Sales Manager David Marchbank-Smith

LEWES
Daveys Lane, Brook Road, Lewes, E. Sussex. BN7 2BQ
Tel: 0273 473116
Fax: 0273 473353
Business Unit Director Steve Goodyear
General Sales Manager Dave Brown

LONDON CENTRAL
Wyke Road, Bow Lane, London. E3 2PC
Tel: 081 986 9833
Fax: 081 986 0702
Business Unit Director Keith Hogg
Fax: 081 986 0750
General Sales Manager Dan Townsend

LONDON NORTH
Brantwood Road, Tottenham, London. N17 0EE
Tel: 081 808 1106
Fax: 081 808 4938
Business Unit Director Don Steen
General Sales Manager Ken Nicol

LONDON SOUTH
Unit 19, Merton Industrial Park, Jubilee Way, Merton,
London. SW19 3XY
Tel: 081 540 8282
Fax: 081 542 0047
Business Unit Director John Randle
General Sales Manager Murray Roberts

MAIDSTONE
Medway House, Bircholt Road, Parkwood, Maidstone,
Kent. ME15 9XJ
Tel: 0622 671311
Fax: 0622 677494
Business Unit Director Mark Gerken
General Sales Manager Matt Scott

MANCHESTER
Monsall Road, Newton Heath, Manchester. M10 8PA
Tel: 061 205 2345
Fax: 061 205 8634
Business Unit Director Nick Cullen
General Sales Manager Steve Turner

NEWARK
The Brewery, Northgate, Newark-on-Trent, Notts.
NG24 1HD
Tel: 0636 612688
Fax: 0636 612802
Business Unit Director Mike Langford
General Sales Manager Nick Rust

NORTH EAST
Eastern Avenue, Team Valley Trading Estate, Gateshead,
Tyne & Wear. NE11 0UU
Tel: 091 487 8897
Fax: 091 482 5037
Business Unit Director Jon Gillespie
General Sales Manager Trevor North

PRESTON
Unit 147, Brierley Road, Walton Summit, Bamber Bridge,
Preston. PR5 8AH
Tel: 0772 697755
Fax: 0772 697797
Business Unit Director Nigel Woodland
General Sales Manager Mike Thomas

SOLENT
Reliant Close, Chandlers Ford Ind. Estate, Chandlers Ford,
Hants. SO5 3ND
Tel: 0703 260144
Fax: 0703 260766
Business Unit Director Simon Jackson
General Sales Manager Ian Squires

SOUTH WEST
North Road, Lee Mill Industrial Estate, Ivybridge, Devon.
PC21 9PB
Tel: 0752 690680
Fax: 0752 894725
Business Unit Driector Paul Hoffman
General Sales Manager Roger Fergus

TADCASTER
The Brewery, Tadcaster, North Yorks. LS24 9SA
Tel: 0937 832091
Fax: 0937 530362
Business Unit Director John O'Brien
General Sales Manager John Thorn

THAMES VALLEY
Imperial Way, Basingstoke Road, Reading, Berks.
RG2 0RS
Tel: 0734 869696
Fax: 0734 876202
Business Unit Director Keith Quinn
General Sales Manager James Vyvyan-Robinson

WEST
St. Brendan's Way, Bristol. BS11 9EZ
Tel: 0272 825321
Fax: 0272 826539
Business Unit Director Mark Todd
General Sales Manager Tony Bird

WEST MIDLANDS
30, First Avenue, Pensnett Trading Estate, Kingswinford,
Brierley Hill, West Mids. GY6 7NA
Tel: 0384 400001
Fax: 0384 291061
Business Unit Director Steve Hollender
General Sales Manager John Barclay

WINSFORD
Road 1, Winsford Industrial Estate, Winsford, Cheshire.
CW7 3PQ
Tel: 0606 863366
Fax: 0606 557634
Business Unit Director Stephen Paul
General Sales Manager Mike Charlton

PRINCIPAL FIXTURES 1994-95

AUGUST 1994
Sa 27th   Heineken Leagues (1) Divs 1 & 2 (Wal)
         Selkirk Sevens (Sco)
SEPTEMBER 1994
Sa 3rd   Bath v Barbarians (Centenary Match) (Bath)
         Heineken Leagues (2) Divs 1 & 2 (Wal)
         Heineken Leagues (2) Divs 3 to 5 (Wal)
Su 4th   Kelso Sevens (Sco)
Tu 6th   French Barbarians v Barbarians (Paris
         University Club, Stade Charlety, Paris)
We 7th   Heineken Leagues (3) Divs 1 & 2 (Wal)
Sa 10th   Courage Leagues (1) Divs 1 & 2 (Eng)
         Courage Leagues (1) Divs 3 & 4 (Eng)
         Pilkington Cup Round 1 (Eng)
         Pilkington Shield Round 1 (Eng)
         Heineken Leagues (2) Divs 3 to 5 (Wal)
         McEwan's National Leagues (1) (Sco)
Sa 17th   ROMANIA v WALES (World Cup)(Bucharest)
         Courage Leagues (2) Divs 1 & 2 (Eng)
         Courage Leagues (2) Divs 3 & 4 (Eng)
         Courage Leagues (1) All others (Eng)
         SWALEC Cup 1st Round (Wal)
         Heineken Leagues (3) Divs 3 to 5 (Wal)
         McEwan's National Leagues (2) (Sco)
         Insurance Corporation Leagues (1) 1 to 4 (Ire)
Sa 24th   Courage Leagues (3) Divs 1 & 2 (Eng)
         Courage Leagues (3) Divs 3 & 4 (Eng)
         Courage Leagues (2) All others (Eng)
         Heineken Leagues (4) Divs 1 to 4 (Wal)
         McEwan's National Leagues (3) (Sco)
         Insurance Corporation Leagues (2) 1 to 4 (Ire)
Su 25th   Insurance Corporation League Div 1 (Ire)
         Garryowen v Shannon
OCTOBER 1994
Sa 1st   ITALY v ROMANIA (World Cup)(TBA)
         Courage Leagues (4) Divs 1 & 2 (Eng)
         Courage Leagues (4) Divs 3 & 4 (Eng)
         Courage Leagues (3) All others (Eng)
         Heineken Leagues (5) Divs 1 to 4 (Wal)
         Heineken Leagues (4) Div 5 (Wal)
         McEwan's National Leagues (4) (Sco)
         Insurance Corporation Leagues (3) 1 to 4 (Ire)
Tu 4th   Newport v Barbarians (Newport)
Sa 8th   Courage Leagues (5) Divs 1 & 2 (Eng)
         Pilkington Cup Round 2 (Eng)
         Pilkington Shield Round 2 (Eng)
         Heineken Leagues (6) Divs 3 & 4 (Wal)
         Heineken Leagues (5) Div 5 (Wal)
         McEwan's National Leagues (5) (Sco)
         Insurance Corporation Leagues (4) 1 to 4 (Ire)
Su 9th   Insurance Corporation League Div 1 (Ire)
         Young Munster v Garryowen
We 12th   WALES v ITALY (World Cup)(Cardiff)
Sa 15th   Courage Leagues (6) Divs 1 & 2 (Eng)
         Courage Leagues (5) Divs 3 & 4 (Eng)
         Courage Leagues (4) All others (Eng)
         Heineken Leagues (6) Divs 1 & 2 (Wal)
         Heineken Leagues (7) Divs 3 & 4 (Wal)
         Heienken Leagues (6) Div 5 (Wal)
         McEwan's National Leagues (6) (Sco)
         Insurance Corporation League (5) 1 to 4 (Ire)
Su 16th   Insurance Corporation League Div 1 (Ire)
         Sunday's Well v Shannon
Sa 22nd   Cardiff v South Africa (Cardiff)
         Courage Leagues (7) Divs 1 & 2 (Eng)
         Courage Leagues (6) Divs 3 & 4 (Eng)
         Courage Leagues (5) All others (Eng)
         SWALEC Cup Round 2 (Wal)
         Heineken Leagues (8) Divs 3 & 4 (Wal)
         Scotland & Ireland Dist & Prov matches:
         South of Scotland v Ulster (TBA)
         Glasgow v Leinster (TBA)
         Connacht v North & Midlands (Galway)
         Munster v Edinburgh (TBA)
We 26th   Wales 'A' v South Africa (Newport)
Sa 29th   Llanelli v South Africa (Llanelli)
         Courage Leagues (8) Divs 1 & 2 (Eng)
         Courage Leagues (7) Divs 3 & 4 (Eng)
         Courage Leagues (6) All others (Eng)
         Heineken Leagues (7) Divs 1 & 2 (Wal)
         Heineken Leagues (9) Divs 3 & 4 (Wal)
         Heineken Leagues (7) Div 5 (Wal)

         Scotland & Ireland Dist & Prov matches:
         Leinster v South of Scotland (Dublin)
         Ulster v Glasgow (Belfast)
         North & Midlands v Munster (TBA)
         Edinburgh v Connacht (TBA)
NOVEMBER 1994
Tu 1st   Irish Development XV v Namibia (Ire)
We 2nd   Neath v South Africa (Neath)
Th 4th   Bridgend v Canterbury (Bridgend)
Sa 5th   IRELAND v NAMIBIA (Dublin)
         Swansea v South Africa (Swansea)
         Oxford University v Romania (Oxford)
         Courage Leagues (9) Divs 1 & 2 (Eng)
         Pilkington Cup Round 3 (Eng)
         Pilkington Shield Round 3 (Eng)
         Heineken Leagues (8) Divs 1 & 2 (Wal)
         Heineken Leagues (10) Divs 3 & 4 (Wal)
         Heineken Leagues (8) Div 5 (Wal)
         McEwan's National League (7) (Sco)
Mo 7th   Leinster v Canterbury (Lansdowne Road, Dublin)
Tu 8th   Cambridge University v Romania (Cambridge)
We 9th   Scotland 'A' v South Africa (Melrose)
         Irish Universities v Namibia (Ire)
         Cornwall v Canterbury (Redruth or Camborne)
Sa 12th   ENGLAND v ROMANIA (Twickenham)
         Scottish Combined Districts v South Africa
         (Glasgow)
         Leinster v Namibia (Dublin)
         Courage Leagues (8) Divs 3 & 4 (Eng)
         West Hartlepool v Canterbury (West Hartlepool)
         Heineken Leagues (9) Divs 1 & 2 (Wal)
         Heineken Leagues (10) Divs 3 & 4 (Wal)
         Heineken Leagues (9) Div 5 (Wal)
         Irish Interprovincial matches:
         Munster v Ulster (TBA)
         Connacht v Exiles (Galway)
Tu 15th   Scottish Selection v South Africa (Aberdeen)
         Moseley v Canterbury (Moseley)
We 16th   Oxford University v R V Stanley's XV (Oxford)
Th 17th   Coventry v Canterbury (Coventry)
Sa 19th   SCOTLAND v SOUTH AFRICA (Murrayfield)
         CIS Divisional Championships (Eng):
         South West v London & SE (Bristol)
         North v Midlands (Otley)
         County Championship matches (Eng)
         Gloucester v Canterbury (Gloucester)
         SWALEC Cup Round 3 (Wal)
         Heineken Leagues (10) Divs 1 & 2 (Wal)
         Irish Interprovincial matches:
         Leinster v Exiles (Dublin)
         Ulster v Connacht (Belfast)
Tu 22nd   Pontypridd v South Africa (Pontypridd)
         Bristol v Canterbury (Bristol)
We 23rd   Cambridge University v Steele-Bodger's XV
         (Grange Road, Cambridge)
Fr 25th   Ulster v Canterbury (Ravenhill, Belfast)
Sa 26th   WALES v SOUTH AFRICA (Cardiff)
         CIS Divisional Championships (Eng):
         London & SE v North (Wasps, Sudbury)
         Midlands v South West (Leicester)
         County Championship matches (Eng)
         Pilkington Shield Round 4 (Eng)
         McEwan's National League (8) (Sco)
         Irish Interprovincial matches:
         Exiles v Munster (TBA)
         Connacht v Leinster (Galway)
Tu 29th   Combined Irish Provinces v South Africa
         (Belfast - under floodlights)
DECEMBER 1994
Sa 3rd   BARBARIANS v SOUTH AFRICA (Dublin)
         CIS Divisional Championships (Eng):
         London & SE v Midlands (Wasps, Sudbury)
         North v South West (Sale)
         County Championship matches (Eng)
         Heineken Leagues (11) Divs 1 & 2 (Wal)
         Heineken Leagues (12) Divs 3 & 4 (Wal)
         Heineken Leagues (10) Div 5 (Wal)
         Scottish Inter District matches:
         South v Scottish Exiles (TBA)
         Glasgow v North & Midlands (TBA)
Tu 6th   Oxford v Cambridge (Twickenham)
         Oxford v Cambridge Under 21s (Stoop

Memorial Ground, Twickenham - am)
England Emerging Players v Canada (Bath)
Sa 10th ENGLAND v CANADA (Twickenham)
County Championship matches (Eng)
Heineken Leagues (12) Divs 1 & 2 (Wal)
Heineken Leagues (13) Divs 3 & 4 (Wal)
Heineken Leagues (11) Div 5 (Wal)
Scottish Inter District matches:
North & Midlands v Edinburgh (TBA)
Scottish Exiles v Glasgow (TBA)
Irish Interprovincial matches:
Exiles v Ulster (TBA)
Leinster v Munster (Dublin)

We 14th Scottish Inter District match:
South v Edinburgh (TBA)

Sa 17th Pilkington Cup Round 5 (Eng)
Pilkington Shield Round 5 (Eng)
SWALEC Cup Round 4 (Wal)
Scottish Inter District matches:
Edinburgh v Glasgow (TBA)
North & Midlands v South (TBA)
Irish Interprovincial matches:
Ulster v Leinster (Belfast)
Munster v Connacht (TBA)

We 21st Scottish Inter District match:
Scottish Exiles v North & Midlands (TBA)

Sa 24th Heineken Leagues (13) Divs 1 & 2 (Wal)
Scottish Inter District matches:
Glasgow v South (TBA)
Edinburgh v Scottish Exiles (TBA)

Tu 27th Leicester v Barbarians (Leicester)
Sa 31st Scotland International Trial (Murrayfield)
Heineken Leagues (14) Divs 1 & 2 (Wal)

JANUARY 1995
Sa 7th Scotland 'A' v Italy (Sco)
Courage Leagues (10) Divs 1 & 2 (Eng)
Courage Leagues (9) Divs 3 & 4 (Eng)
Courage Leagues (7) All others (Eng)
Heineken Leagues (15) Divs 1 & 2 (Wal)
Heineken Leagues (14) Divs 3 & 4 (Wal)
Heineken Leagues (12) Div 5 (Wal)
Insurance Corporation Leagues (6) 1 to 4 (Ire)

Su 8th Insurance Corporation League Div 1 (Ire)
Garryowen v Sunday's Well

Sa 14th Courage Leagues (11) Divs 1 & 2 (Eng)
Courage Leagues (10) Divs 3 & 4 (Eng)
Courage Leagues (8) All others (Eng)
Heineken Leagues (15) Divs 3 & 4 (Wal)
Heineken Leagues (13) Div 5 (Wal)
McEwan's National Leagues (9) (Sco)
Insurance Corporation Leagues (7) 1 to 4 (Ire)

Fr 20th Ireland 'A' v England 'A' (Dublin)
Sa 21st IRELAND v ENGLAND (Dublin)
FRANCE v WALES (Paris)
Scotland 'A' v France 'A' (Sco)

Sa 28th Pilkington Cup Round 5 (Eng)
Pilkington Shield Round 6 (Eng)
SWALEC Cup Round 5 (Wal)
McEwan's National Leagues (10) (Sco)

FEBRUARY 1995
Fr 3rd England 'A' v France 'A' (Eng)
Scotland 'A' v Ireland 'A' (Sco)
Scotland v Ireland (Under 21s - Sco)

Sa 4th ENGLAND v FRANCE (Twickenham)
SCOTLAND v IRELAND (Murrayfield)
Heineken Leagues (16) Divs 1 to 4 (Wal)
Heineken Leagues (14) Div 5 (Wal)

Tu/We 7/8 Heineken Leagues (17) Divs 1 & 2 (Wal)
Sa 11th Courage Leagues (12) Divs 1 & 2 (Eng)
Courage Leagues (11) Divs 3 & 4 (Eng)
Courage Leagues (9) All others (Eng)
Heineken Leagues (17) Divs 3 & 4 (Wal)
Heineken Leagues (15) Divs 5 (Wal)Wal)
McEwan's National Leagues (11) (Sco)
Insurance Corporation Leagues (8) 1 to 4 (Ire)

Su 12th Insurance Corporation League Div 1 (Ire)
Cork Constitution v Shannon(Ire)

Fr 17th France 'A' v Wales 'A' (Fra)
France v Scotland (Under 21s - Fra)

Sa 18th WALES v ENGLAND (Cardiff)
FRANCE v SCOTLAND (Paris)
Insurance Corporation Leagues (9) 1 to 4 (Ire)

Sa 25th Pilkington Cup Quarter-finals (Eng)
Pilkington Shield Quarter-finals (Eng)
Courage Leagues (13) Divs 3 & 4 (Eng)
Courage Leagues (10) All others (Eng)
Heineken Leagues (18) Divs 1 to 4 (Wal)
Heineken Leagues (16) Div 5 (Wal)
McEwan's National Leagues (12) (Sco)

Insurance Corporation Leagues Divs 3 & 4 (Ire)
Highfield v University College Cork (Div 3)
Queens University Belfast v Sligo (Div 4)
University College Galway v Dublin University (Div 4)

MARCH 1995
Fr 3rd Scotland v Wales (Under 21s - Sco)
Heineken Leagues (19) Div 3 (Wal)

Sa 4th SCOTLAND v WALES (Murrayfield)
FRANCE v IRELAND (Paris)
Courage Leagues (13) Divs 1 & 2 (Eng)
Courage Leagues (13) Divs 3 & 4 (Eng)
Courage Leagues (11) All others (Eng)

We 8th East Midlands v Barbarians (Northampton)
Sa 11th County Championship Semi-finals (Eng)
Heineken Leagues (19) Divs 1,2 & 4 (Wal)
Heineken Leagues (17) Div 5 (Wal)
McEwan's National Leagues (13) (Sco)
Insurance Corporation Leagues(10) 1 to 4 (Ire))

Su 12th Insurance Corporation League Div 1 (Ire)
Sunday's Well v Cork Constitution

Fr 17th Wales 'A' v Ireland 'A' (Wal)
Wales v Ireland (Under 21's - Wal)

Sa 18th ENGLAND v SCOTLAND (Twickenham)
WALES v IRELAND (Cardiff)

Su 19th England 'A' v Italy 'A' (Eng)
We 22nd BUSA Final (Twickenham)
Sa/Su 25-26 Cathay Pacific Hong Kong Sevens (HongKong)
Sa 25th Courage Leagues (14) Divs 1 & 2 (Eng)
Courage Leagues (14) Divs 3 & 4 (Eng)
Courage Leagues (12) All others (Eng)
Daily Mail Schools Day (Twickenham)
SWALEC Cup Round 5 (Wal)
Heineken Leagues (18) Div 5 (Wal)
McEwan's National Leagues stand-by day (Sco)

APRIL 1995
Sa 1st Pilkington Cup Semi-finals (Eng)
Pilkington Shield Semi-finals (Eng)
Courage Leagues (15) Divs 3 & 4 (Eng)
Royal Navy v The Army (Twickenham)
Heineken Leagues (20) Divs 1 to 4 (Wal)
Heineken Leagues (19) Div 5 (Wal)
Insurance Corporation League (11) 1 to 4
Gala Sevens (Sco)
Scotland v Italy (Under 21s - Sco)

Sa 8th Courage Leagues (15) Divs 1 & 2 (Eng)
Courage Leagues (16) Divs 3 & 4 (Eng)
Courage Leagues (13) All others (Eng)
SWALEC Cup Quarter-finals (Wal)
Heineken Leagues (20) Div 5 (Wal)
Melrose Sevens (Sco)

We 12th The Army v Royal Air Force (Twickenham)
Sa 15th Courage Leagues (16) Divs 1 & 2 (Eng)
Courage Leagues (17) Divs 3 & 4 (Eng)
Cardiff v Barbarians (Cardiff)
Heineken Leagues (21) Divs 1 to 5 (Wal)
Hawick Sevens (Sco)

Su 16th Earlston Sevens (Sco)
Mo 17th Swansea v Barbarians (Swansea)
We 19th Royal Navy v Royal Air Force (Twickenham)
Sa 22nd County Championship Final (Twickenham)
County Championship Under 21s Final
(Twickenham curtain raiser)
Courage Leagues (17) Divs 1 & 2 (Eng)
SWALEC Cup Semi-finals (Wal)
Jed-Forest Sevens (Sco)

Sa 29th Courage Leagues (18) Divs 1 & 2 (Eng)
Courage Leagues (18) Divs 3 & 4 (Eng)
Heineken Leagues (22) Divs 1 to 5 (Wal)
Langholm Sevens (Sco)

MAY 1995
Sa 6th Pilkington Cup Final (Twickenham)
Pilkington Shield Final (Twickenham -
curtain raiser)
SWALEC Cup Final (National Stadium, Cardiff)
France v Wales (Under 21s - Fra)

Sa 13th Middlesex Seven-a-Sides Finals

Abbreviations:
TBA - to be announced
Eng - England
Fra - France
Ire - Ireland
Sco - Scotland
Wal - Wales
(-) - Figures in brackets where league and cup dates are listed denote the number of the round being played.

REVIEW OF THE SEASON

by Bill Mitchell

IT SEEMS hard to believe it but the Courage Leagues are only seven seasons old. To many of us it has seemed like a life time and even the changes from the old formula in the top four leagues to the highly desirable home and away fixtures system seemed as if they had been with us since time immemorial after only a few weeks of action.

This is not as easy as it sounds since clubs depend for sponsorship on being able to rub shoulders with the best, while the top dogs need more fixtures to keep their bank managers happy. But the choice is there and the nettle needs to be grasped. Reduce or have a situation where the best players in the country will be unable to perform to the best of their ability in a physical game which places huge demands on players' full fitness.

The one thing no-one can legislate out of existence is the continued success of Bath, whose 14-6 win over Leicester in early April virtually ended the campaign as a contest with the men from 'The Rec' finally finishing six points clear of the only team to defeat them during the season. Early in May they met again at Twickenham in the Pilkington Cup final and Bath won a thoroughly shoddy match 21-9, which tarnished the reputations of both clubs and Bath's Team of the Year award at a prestigeous ceremony a few days later was seen by many as not being in the best interests of the game. The superb record of Melrose was thought to have made them a better choice.

Of the other top league clubs most praiseworthy were the efforts of third placed Wasps, the greatly improved Bristol and Orrell, who survived several anxious moments bravely. Gloucester under the influence of Barry Corless cannot remain sleeping giants for long, whilst we had to say farewell to London Irish and Newcastle Gosforth, who strove gallantly enough but in the end were just not up to it.

Next season Sale and West Hartlepool will be back amongst the elite, the former having drawn their final game of the season on 'West's' patch to win a title race which had been led by the Durham side for most of the campaign, although it was points differential that was needed to separate them. Their only challengers — after a good effort at that — were Saracens, whose last game home defeat at the hands of London Scottish meant that the Exiles survived for another season at that level after a campaign which they would wish to forget; they had looked doomed at an early stage but survived and Sale can thank them also for a late home victory over West Hartlepool, which inspired their ultimate title win.

This left the short straws in the hands of Rugby (relegated for a second successive season after losing unluckily at Moseley also on the last day) and Otley, who also put up a valiant fight.

A famous name will be one of the sides to fill the vacancy left by the latter two as Coventry won the League Three title by two points from Bill Beaumont's Fylde, who also ascend, but that was after a hard slog which also involved Bedford and Blackheath. At the foot of the table Havant and Redruth — the latter from the early weeks of the season — never seemed likely to escape, which is a great pity as both Hampshire and Cornwall could do with some rated national clubs.

The scene at the top of League Four was crystallised at a very early stage and bookies stopped taking bets on promotion long before Christmas, when the only question was how Clifton and Harrogate would finish. In the event the former ended the season as the senior leagues' only unbeaten club, their only blemishes being two draws — against Harrogate, who also had the consolation of being promoted for a second successive season. Clifton through the kicking of Simon Hogg and speed of John Phillips cornered all the national scoring awards into the bargain.

Relegation from that league to the area leagues was not without its heartbreaks as Sheffield and Sudbury finally had to descend. The South Yorkshire club could have stayed put had they won their final match instead of drawing 18-18 at Liverpool St Helens, while Sudbury's late rally faded in the last two outings.

The replacement from Five North is Rotherham, who are keen to show their local citizens that their best footballing choice is Clifton Lane and not Millmoor. If they keep up their momentum it will become a 'no contest' and they did superbly well to shade top spot by a point from Preston Grasshoppers, Wade Dooley's club which once again missed out narrowly on promotion.

In that league there were no other challengers for the top spot with all the other teams looking anxiously downwards and a final table produced a siuation where two points separated seven teams with the short straws going to Durham City (on points differential from Kendal and Nuneaton) and Bradford & Bingley. The fixtures organisers were left with massive headaches for the rest of the leagues as both Durham and Bradford are Northern clubs, which left adjustments needed in all manner of areas.

The latter was a problem which also existed south of the Humber as two London and South East outfits — Southend and Maidstone — comfortably occupied the last two places and in fact one has to go to High Wycombe in ninth position to find the least successful South West club in the division.

However, the Five South title was always — except for a brief 'blip' through a narrow mid-season loss at Weston-super-Mare — going to Reading and they should also be formidable opposition in the new season for all League Four clubs.

To end our leagues review we must not forget those clubs, who have gained senior status as a result of winning the top leagues of their respective divisions, and these show how amply justified are the claims of the leagues' protagonists that every ambitious club has a chance of achieving its highest ambitions. In all four cases of promotion new names will appear among those who are trying to take on the elite and this can only be for the good of the game.

Into League Five North come the Yorkshire side Upper Wharfedale after a superb season along with Coventry's doughty near neighbours Barkers' Butts — not a pub team but a serious outfit that has been challenging for the right to meet top sides for many seasons.

In Five South we have Barking from London's East End, who wave the game's flag defiantly in the area where West Ham United are kings. They prove that rugby has no such thing as a 'no-go' area. In contrast Henley from Oxfordshire's commuter belt is best known for its annual Royal Regatta and other rowing occasions, but their rugby club usually wins the county cup and has plenty of unfulfilled ambitions, which it intends to achieve. Good luck to all of you!

Once again we have stuck our necks out with some forecasts:

League One:
Champions: Bath. Relegation: West Hartlepool and Orrell.

League Two:
Champions: Moseley. Promotion: Saracens: Relegation: London Irish and Fylde.

League Three:
Champions: Bedford. Promotion: Rosslyn Park. Relegation: Morley and Harrogate.

League Four:
Champions: Liverpool St Helens. Promotion: Leeds. Relegation: Askeans and Broughton Park.

League Five North:
Champions: Preston Grasshoppers.

League Five South:
Champions: Lydney.

No offence is meant to anyone but we hope to do better than the less than 40 per cent success rate in our last forecast!

RFU AWARDS

The following were awarded at the inaugural RFU Awards Dinner at the
Royal Lancaster Hotel, London
on 9 May 1994

PLAYER OF THE SEASON
Nigel Redman
(Bath and South West)

YOUNG PLAYER OF THE SEASON
Andy Diprose
(Saracens)

TRY OF THE SEASON
Mike Harrison
for Yorkshire v Durham, CIS Insurance County Final
*(The Award is based on the quality of the rugby in scoring the try
rather than the significance of the try)*

UNSUNG HERO
Malcolm Werrett
(Twickenham groundsman)

The nominations and winners for these Awards
were selected by a panel appointed by the RFU.

The panel was:

Chairman, Rugby Union Writers Club — Chris Jones (Evening Standard)
RFU National Promotions Officer — Alan Black
BBC Television — Chris Rea
Hon. Asst. England Manager & U21 Manager — John Elliott

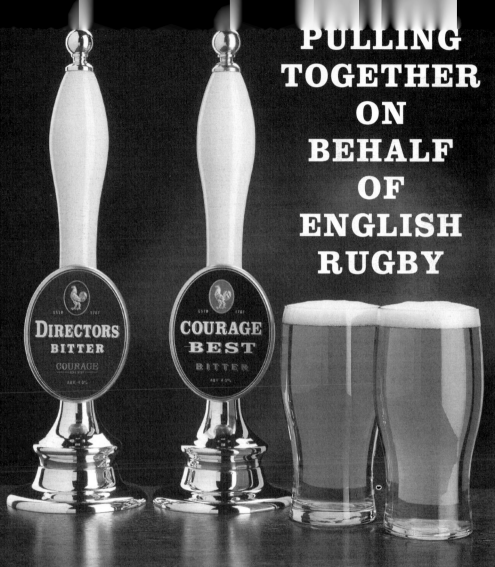

PULLING TOGETHER ON BEHALF OF ENGLISH RUGBY

**Proud Sponsors of
The Courage Clubs Championship
and the England Squad**

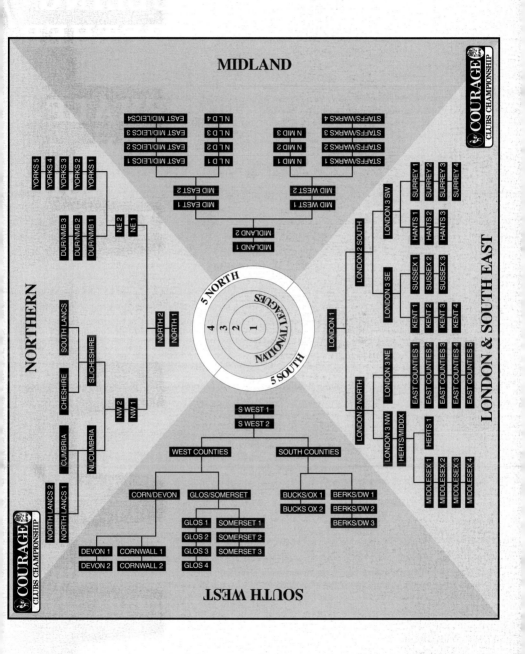

MIDLAND

NORTHERN

LONDON & SOUTH EAST

SOUTH WEST

COURAGE CLUBS CHAMPIONSHIP

NATIONAL LEAGUES
1
2
3
4
5 NORTH
5 SOUTH

YORKS 5
YORKS 4
YORKS 3
YORKS 2
YORKS 1

DUR/NMB 3
DUR/NMB 2
DUR/NMB 1

NE 2
NE 1

SOUTH LANCS

CHESHIRE

S/L CHESHIRE

NORTH 2
NORTH 1

NW 2
NW 1

CUMBRIA

NL/CUMBRIA

NORTH LANCS 2
NORTH LANCS 1

CORN/DEVON

DEVON 1   CORNWALL 1
DEVON 2   CORNWALL 2

GLOS/SOMERSET

GLOS 1   SOMERSET 1
GLOS 2   SOMERSET 2
GLOS 3   SOMERSET 3
GLOS 4

WEST COUNTIES

S WEST 1
S WEST 2

SOUTH COUNTIES

BUCKS/OX 1   BERKS/DW 1
BUCKS OX 2   BERKS/DW 2
              BERKS/DW 3

EAST MID/LEICS4
EAST MID/LEICS 3
EAST MID/LEICS 2
EAST MID/LEICS 1

N L D 4
N L D 3
N L D 2
N L D 1

STAFFS/WARKS 4
STAFFS/WARKS 3
STAFFS/WARKS 2
STAFFS/WARKS 1

N MID 3
N MID 2
N MID 1

MID EAST 2
MID EAST 1

MID WEST 2
MID WEST 1

MIDLAND 2
MIDLAND 1

LONDON 3 SW

LONDON 3 SE

LONDON 3 NE

LONDON 3 NW
HERTS/MIDDX

LONDON 2 SOUTH

LONDON 2 NORTH

LONDON 1

SURREY 1
SURREY 2
SURREY 3
SURREY 4

HANTS 1
HANTS 2
HANTS 3

SUSSEX 1
SUSSEX 2
SUSSEX 3

KENT 1
KENT 2
KENT 3
KENT 4

EAST COUNTIES 1
EAST COUNTIES 2
EAST COUNTIES 3
EAST COUNTIES 4
EAST COUNTIES 5

HERTS 1

MIDDLESEX 1
MIDDLESEX 2
MIDDLESEX 3
MIDDLESEX 4

COURAGE CLUBS CHAMPIONSHIP

15

THE COURAGE CLUBS CHAMPIONSHIP REGULATIONS 1994-95

1 **Description**

The Competition shall be called "The English Clubs Rugby Union Championship" (hereinafter referred to as "the Competition") and shall be open to Clubs in membership with the Rugby Football Union (hereinafter called "the RFU"). All matches in the Competition shall be played under the Laws of Rugby Union Football and shall comply with the Rules and Regulations of the RFU.

2 **Organising Committee**

The Competition will be organised by the Competition Sub-Committee of the RFU (hereinafter referred to as "the Committee") whose decision shall be binding and final on any matter not provided for in and on the interpretation of these Regulations.

3 **Delegation of Administration**

a) The Committee appoints the RFU Senior Clubs Association Committee as the Organising Committee of National Leagues 1, 2, 3 and 4 (see Appendix 1).

b) The Committee appoints the RFU Divisions as the organising Committees of all Leagues within their Divisions.

c) The Committee will be the organising Committee of National Leagues 5 North and South.

d) The Committee (in respect of National Leagues 5 North and South), the RFU Senior Clubs Association and the RFU Divisions shall, subject to Regulation 18(a) of these Regulations, deal with all disputes, transgressions and complaints as laid down by Regulation 19.

4 **Structure**

a) **National**

There shall be four National Leagues 1, 2, 3 and 4, comprising 10 Clubs each, unless agreed otherwise by the Committee.

b) **Areas**

(i) The Northern and Midland RFU Divisions shall combine to provide one National League 5 North and the London and South East and South West RFU Divisions shall combine to provide one National League 5 South each comprised of thirteen Clubs, unless agreed otherwise by the Committee.

(ii) Promotion from the National Leagues 5 North and South shall be to National League 4.

c) **RFU Divisions**

(i) Each of the RFU Divisions shall have a first League.

(ii) Promotion from the Northern Division League 1 and the Midland Division League 1 shall be to the National League 5 North and from the London and South East Division League 1 and the South West Division League 1 shall be to the National League 5 South.

(iii)The Divisional League structure below Division League 1 in each Division shall be such as shall, with the approval of the Committee, be determined by that Division.

(iv)Leagues shall be comprised of 13 Clubs, except that the lowest two Leagues may, with the consent of the appropriate Divisional Committee, consist of more or less, unless agreed otherwise by the Committee.

d) **General**

(i) Not more than two lower Leagues may support a higher League.

(ii) Only Club first XVs may enter the Competition.

(iii) A Club may only play in any National League 5 or Divisional League according to its RFU Constituent Body allocation.

5 **Club Positions**

The position of a Club in a League shall be established by awarding two points for a win and one point for a draw. In the case of equality, positions shall be determined on the basis of match points scored. A Club with a larger difference between match points for and match points against shall be placed higher in a League than a Club with a smaller difference between match points for and match points against. Should two Clubs have the same number of competition points and the same match points difference, the Club having scored more match points shall be placed higher in the League than the Club having a lesser number of match points for. In the event of the match points for still being unable to establish the position of two Clubs, and if the winning of the Competition or promotion or relegation is involved, the Club who has won the highest number of its League matches shall be placed higher. If this does not establish the position then the Club who has won the most matches, excluding its first League match of the season, then its second League match, until it can be established which is the highest placed Club.

6 **Promotion and Relegation**

a) Where one League supports one League the top two Clubs from the lower League at the end of the season shall be promoted to the higher League, except in National League 1 where the bottom Club will be relegated and in National League 2 the top Club will be promoted.

b) Where two Leagues support one League, the top Club in each of the supporting Leagues at the end of the season shall be promoted to the higher League.

c) After promotion has taken place in accordance with Clauses (a) and (b) above, the requisite number of Clubs shall be relegated (upon the basis prescribed in Clause (d) below) from each League at the end of the season so that the following season there are 10 Clubs in National Leagues 1, 2, 3 and 4, and 13 Clubs in all other Leagues (or such other number of Clubs as there are to be in the lowest two Leagues in each of the RFU Divisions in accordance with Regulation 4(c)(iv) above).

d) Except in the cases of relegation from National League 1 to National League 2, from National League 2 to National League 3 and from National League 3 to National League 4 Clubs shall be relegated on a geographical/Divisional/Constituent Body basis as appropriate.

Note: Given this, and the provisions of Clause (c) above, it is accordingly not possible (except in the cases of relegation from National Leagues 1 where one Club will be relegated, and 2, 3 and 4 where two Clubs will be relegated from each League) to determine how many Clubs are to be relegated from any particular League until it has first been determined at the end of the season (i) how many Clubs are to be relegated from each (in turn) of the Leagues (both National Leagues and Divisional Leagues) higher than that League and (ii) to which League or Leagues the Clubs from those higher Leagues are to be relegated.

e) Notwithstanding the foregoing provisions of this Regulation or the provisions of Regulation 4 above, the Committee may, as it shall in its absolute discretion think fit, at any time (i) disapply, suspend, amend and/or vary the foregoing provisions of this Regulation and/or of Regulation 4 as to promotion and relegation and/or as to the number of Clubs comprising any League or Leagues, and/or (ii) transfer any Club from the League in which it would have been placed by virtue of the application of Clauses (a) to (d) of this Regulation to such other League (whether higher or lower) as the Committee shall think fit. Any action taken or decision made by the Committee under the powers conferred on it by the foregoing provisions of this Clause (e) shall be final and binding.

7 **Fixtures**

a) All League matches shall be played on fixed Saturdays as set out in the Structured Season.

b) All League matches in National Leagues 1, 2, 3 and 4 shall be played on a home and away basis.

c) All League fixture lists shall be prepared by the Organising Committee of the League concerned and submitted to the Clubs comprising the League by the 31st May in each year. A copy shall be sent to the Secretary of the RFU by the same date.

d) Every Club in all League fixtures shall play its bona fide first XV.

8 Eligibility

a) Clubs

(i) Any Club in membership with the RFU may enter the Competition subject to the approval of the Committee and of the appropriate RFU Division according to its RFU Constituent Body allocation.

(ii) Any Club applying to join the Competition shall only be permitted to do so by being placed in the bottom League in its RFU Division.

(iii) The Committee shall have the power to impose conditions upon the membership or continued participation of any Club or Clubs in the Competition. Any Club or Clubs failing to comply with such conditions shall not be entitled to enter the Competition or to continue to participate in it.

b) Players

(i) A Club in a Competition match may only play or select as a replacement, players who hold EFFECTIVE registration for that Club, in accordance with the RFU Registration of Players Regulations.

(ii) A Club may only play or select as a replacement in a Competition match one player who holds EFFECTIVE registration under Regulation 9(b)(ii) of the RFU Registration of Players Regulations.

(iii) A Club may not play or select as a replacement in a match in the Competition any player who has at any time received any material benefit (as defined in Regulation 1.3 of the IRFB Regulations Relating to Amateurism) for playing any form of Rugby Football.

Penalty: A Club shall be deducted two championship points on each occasion that it has been represented by an ineligible player or replacement or been in breach of Regulation 8(b)(i), 8(b)(ii) or 8(b)(iii).

(Warning: The computerised registration list is the only evidence which will be accepted to substantiate a player's EFFECTIVE registration — see Registration Regulation 8).

9 Players in Representative Matches

Where an English representative match involving any National team or any match involving the Senior National Representative Team of one of the other three Home Unions or the CIS Insurance County Championship Semi-finals or Final is played on a date fixed for a League match, any Club which is affected by three or more players or replacements taking part in such representative match may require the League match to be rearranged for a later date. Such rearranged match will be fixed by the Organising Committee of the League concerned.

10 Replacements

In all matches in the Competition replacements are permitted in accordance with the RFU Resolutions relating to the use of replacements.

11 Unplayed, Postponed and Abandoned Matches

a) If weather conditions prevent a match being played or a match is abandoned because of such conditions with less than sixty minutes having been played, the match shall be played or replayed on a date directed by the Organising Committee of the League concerned. If a match is abandoned because of weather conditions when sixty or more minutes have been played, then the score at the moment of abandonment shall stand and be deemed the final score in the match. The referee's decision as to the necessity for abandonment and the number of minutes played at the moment of abandonment shall be final.

b) If the referee finds it necessary to abandon a match for any reason other than weather conditions, then, irrespective of the number of minutes played, the result of that match may be determined by the Organising Committee of the League concerned or that Committee may order the match to be replayed.

c) If a match is abandoned under Clauses (a) or (b) above, the home Club shall supply the secretary of the Organising Committee of the League concerned with the match card duly signed by the referee and stating the exact time of the match abandonment, the existing match score at the time and the reason for the abandonment.

d) In the event of a Competition match not being played the Organising Committee of the League concerned may at its absolute discretion award the Competition points to either side, divide the Competition points equally between the sides or decide that no Competition points shall be awarded. The Organising Committee of the League concerned shall not have the power to award match points.

e) Any Club which is suspended by its County Constituent Body from playing Rugby Union Football for disciplinary reasons will not be permitted to rearrange any League fixtures failing to be played within the period of the suspension. The effects thereof on the non-offending Clubs in the League concerned shall be dealt with by the Organising Committee of the League concerned under Clause (f) below.

f) In the event of a Competition match not being played for whatever reason, whether or not Championship points are awarded to a Club under this Regulation, if that Club be a contender for promotion or relegation at the end of the season, the difference between the match points for and against of all Clubs (other than the offending Club) in the League shall be adjusted to exclude all match points scored in matches played against the offending Club before establishing the final position of each Club in the League in accordance with Regulation 5.

g) In the event of a Club failing to fulfil its League fixtures for reasons unacceptable to the Organising Committee of the League concerned, or if a Club voluntarily withdraws from a League, or if a Club is expelled or suspended from a League or from membership of the Competition, the results of all matches played by it shall be deleted. The final League table positions shall be established under Regulation 5 from all matches played between the remaining Clubs in such League.

12 Completion of Match Result Card

Each Club shall complete a match result card in accordance with the instructions set out in the Administrative Instructions applicable to such Club's League. The Organising Committees are empowered to impose monetary fines for failure to comply with such instructions and non-payment of fines by the due dates may lead to a deduction of two competition points for each such offence. Providing false information on players or replacements taking part in a match shall be a serious offence.

Penalty: A Club shall be deducted eight championship points on each occasion false information has been provided. This will be in addition to any points which may have been deducted if the players or replacements were ineligible.

13 Referees and Touch Judges

a) The referee for each match shall be appointed or provided by the Referees' Society to which the home Club pay a Referees' Society subscription, subject to any appointments made by the RFU.

b) In all matches in National Leagues 1, 2, 3, 4 and 5 North and 5 South two qualified touch judges shall be appointed by the RFU and the RFU Regulation relating to Law 6 shall apply.

c) In all other matches each Club shall provide a competent touch judge who should not be a replacement. In an emergency a replacement may act as a touch judge with the agreement of the referee.

d) If the referee appointed or provided under Regulation 13(a) has not arrived at the agreed kick-off time or if the referee is unable to officiate for the whole of the match for any reason and a replacement referee is available, the captains of the two Clubs concerned may agree that the replacement referee can officiate and the result shall count in the Competition. Such agreement shall thereafter be binding upon the Clubs. If there is no agreement then the match shall not count in the Competition and it must be replayed in accordance with the provisions of Regulation 11(a).

14 Kick-Offs and Delayed Arrivals

All Saturday matches shall start at the home Club's normal kick-off time but shall not be later than 3.00pm in any event. An earlier kick-off time may be arranged by mutual agreement between the two Clubs concerned. Any delay may be reported by the non-offending Club to the Organising Committee of the League concerned and may lead to the match being awarded to the non-offending Club.

15 Clash of Colours/Identification of Players

a) In the event of Clubs having similar or clashing colours the home Club will be responsible for changing its colours, subject to the satisfaction of the appointed referee.

b) The jerseys of teams competing in the Competition should all be numbered or lettered to ensure the correct identification of all players and replacements during a match.

16 Grounds

a) A home Club is responsible for correctly and clearly marking its pitch and it must make proper provision to ensure that (with the exception of the touch judges) all spectators, replacements and officials are kept at a reasonable distance from the field of play.

b) When a late decision as to the fitness of the ground for the playing of a match is necessary, it shall be made by the respective captains of the Clubs involved but if the captains are not able to agree, the decision shall be made by the appointed referee.

c) A late decision is defined as one made within 3 hours of the scheduled kick-off time.

17 Finance

a) Monies provided for the1993-94 Competition and all Competitions thereafter (until otherwise agreed by Courage) shall belong to the Clubs in the Leagues for whom the monies have been provided and shall be distributed in such shares as the Committee shall decide provided always that the Committee may as it shall see fit appropriate for the benefit of Clubs whether or not participating in the Competition and Schools in membership of the ERFSU or distribute for such charitable purposes as the Committee may select not more than 15% of the said monies.

b) Any proposal involving an offer of sponsorship, financial assistance or gift for a League or combination of Leagues must be submitted to the RFU for approval.

c) Gate receipts at a match shall belong to the home Club.

d) The home Club shall be responsible for all match expenses.

e) The away Club shall be responsible for its own travelling and accommodation expenses.

f) Such membership/registration fee may be charged to each participating Club as may from time to time be determined by the Organising Committee of the League concerned with the approval of the Committee.

g) Clubs failing to register claims by the 28th February will not be eligible for payment of sponsorship monies.

18 Disciplinary Powers

a) Without prejudice to the powers of the RFU or the delegation of powers to Constituent Bodies under Rule 12.4, the Committee shall have the power to expel or suspend any Club from membership of the Competition or impose such other penalty as is considered appropriate on any Club for a breach of these Regulations.

b) The Committee shall have the right to delegate disciplinary powers (other than the power to expel or suspend from membership of the Competition) for any breach of these Regulations to an Organising Committee of a League or National League subject to the rights of appeal as hereinafter provided.

c) Specifically an Organising Committee of a League shall have power to discipline any Club participating in such League for breach of any of the Regulations of the Competition by way of loss of match or Competition points, transference of points, review of result or monetary fine, and any such Club may be liable to be placed at the bottom of the League concerned and such Club's results deleted from such League table.

19 Complaints and Appeals

a) Any complaint shall be referred to the Secretary of the League concerned by telephone within 48 hours of knowledge of the occurrence giving rise to the complaint and thereafter submitted in writing within a further 48 hours. The complaining Club shall also send a copy of such complaint in writing within such 48 hours to the other party to the complaint if applicable. The Secretary, on receipt of the written complaint, shall give a ruling within 7 days. If either party to the complaint is dissatisfied with such ruling there shall be a right of appeal to the Organising Committee of the League concerned as set out in Regulation 3 to be given in writing within 7 days of receipt of the Secretary's decision.

b) If either the complaining Club, or the other party to the complaint, or the Club against whom the complaint is made, requires an oral hearing, it shall be requested in writing and the Organising Committee responsible for the League concerned shall, within 72 hours of receiving notice of such request, appoint a time, date and place for the hearing of such complaint.

c) Any party aggrieved at the decision of the Organising Committee may, within seven days of receipt of the decision, appeal in writing to the Secretary of the RFU restating the grounds on which the original appeal was made. The Club shall not be entitled to introduce any further grounds of objection not previously stated to the Organising Committee, nor to lodge a second objection arising from the circumstances on which the objection is based.

The Secretary of the RFU shall refer the objection to the Competition Sub-Committee of the RFU whose decision shall be final and binding. It shall be the sole discretion of the Competition Sub-Committee whether or not to grant a personal hearing.

d) (i) Any party to an appeal (whether made under Regulation 19(b) or 19(c)) shall provide such information or evidence and within such time as the Organising Committee or the Appeal Committee (as the case may be) shall require.

   (ii) Upon a party to an appeal failing to provide such information within the time required, the Organising Committee or the Appeal Committee (as the case may be) shall be entitled to refuse to hear that party when considering the appeal.

e) The Club and/or appellant may be required to pay the cost of the Appeal when a personal hearing is requested and granted.

20 Medical Safety

Whenever possible, the home team should ensure a doctor or other medically qualified person is in attendance throughout the match.

21 Terms and Conditions of Participation

All Clubs participating in the Competition shall at all times comply with each and every of the obligations and requirements entered into by the RFU with third parties, including but not limited to, the sponsors of the Competition under the terms and conditions of the sponsorship agreement. Details of any such obligations and requirements shall be notified by the RFU to participating Clubs as applicable.

22 Copyright

The copyright in the fixture lists of the Competition shall vest in the RFU and must not be reproduced in whole or in part except with the written consent of the RFU.

Organising Committee for National Leagues 1, 2, 3 and 4

The participating Clubs within National Leagues 1, 2, 3 and 4 of the English Clubs Championship within each of the four geographical divisional areas of the RFU shall nominate three members from their respective Divisional Membership who shall constitute the Organising Committee for National Leagues 1, 2, 3 and 4.

The members for 1994/95 are:

J A Allen
60 Dorchester Road,
Leicester LE3 0UF
Tel: 0533 858407 (H)
     0533 471234 (B)
Fax: 0533 471434

R L Ellis,
31 Russell Avenue,
Hartley,
Plymouth PL3 5RB.
Tel: 0752 771237 (H)

R Fawden,
100 Swain's Lane
Highgate,
London N6 6PL.
Tel: 081 348 4753 (H)
      081 348 4254 (B)
Fax: 081 340 2199

R Foster,
27 Carr Lane,
Sandal,
Wakefield,
West Yorkshire WF2 6HJ.
Tel: 0924 250116 (H)
     0924 371501 (B)

F M Gibbon (Chairman),
12 The Green,
Bishopton,
Stockton-on-Tees,
Cleveland TS21 1HF.
Tel: 0740 30410 (H)
     0642 602221 (B)

G W Hancock
191 Ringswell Gardens,
Bath BA1 6BP
Tel: 0225 420532 (H)

N G Hannah,
Gatehouse,
62 Beeston Fields Drive,
Bramcote,
Beeston,
Nottingham NG9 3DD.
Tel: 0602 254798 (H)
     0602 243243 (B)
Fax: 0509 242310

B W Redwood
205 Stoke Lane,
Westbury-on-Trym,
Bristol BS9 3RX
Tel: 0272 684342 (H)
     0272 424273 (B)

D Seabrook,
29 St. Lukes Drive,
Orrell,
Nr. Wigan,
Lancs. WM5 7AU
Tel: 0695 622648 (H)

C Sewell
6 Font Close,
Titchfield Common,
Fareham,
Hampshire PO14 4QH
Tel: 0489 583417 (H)
     0705 563904 (B)

R B Taylor,
82 Bridgwater Drive,
Abington,
Northampton
NN3 3AG.
Tel: 0604 38626 (H)

D Wills,
25 Woodland Gardens,
Isleworth,
Middx. TW7 6LN.
Tel: 081 560 7594 (H)

RFU REGISTRATION OF PLAYERS

Regulations and Operating Procedures — Season 1994/95

These Regulations and Operating Procedures apply to all players making an application to be registered with a Club in membership of the RFU on or after **1st May 1994**. All existing RFU player registrations and eligibility dates remain valid.

1   **Definitions — for the purpose of RFU Registration Regulations and Operating Procedures —**
    a)   **Home Union Player** is a player who has, or has the right to have, as his only or main passport either a passport of the United Kingdom of Great Britain and Northern Ireland or a passport of the Republic of Ireland or a passport issued in the Channel Islands or the Isle of Man.
    b)   **Overseas Player** is any player who is unable to satisfy provisions of 1(a) above.
    c)   **Registrar** is a person appointed annually by the RFU Competition Sub-Committee for each Division/Senior Clubs Association/National Leagues 5 (North and South) responsible for the administration of computerised registration of players. The Registrars for season 1994/95 are as set out in Appendix 1.
    d)   **Registration Date** is the date on which a player's name is added to a Club's computerised registration list.
    e)   **EFFECTIVE Date** is the date when a player's Registration Application becomes EFFECTIVE in accordance with the Registration Regulations.
2   All players competing in the Courage Clubs Championship, the Pilkington Cup and the Pilkington Shield, must be registered on the official Registration Form. Pads of these forms are available from Michael Humphreys & Partners. The first pad in each season will be supplied free of charge. Thereafter pads will only be supplied upon payment of £25 for each pad — cheques to be made payable to 'SPIRE'.
3   (a) The Registration Application Form when fully completed must be submitted to the Registrar as appropriate — see Regulation 1(c). A copy should be retained by the Club.
    (b) In Leagues below National Leagues 1, 2, 3 and 4 forms MUST be submitted to the Registrar by post only.
    (c) In National Leagues 1, 2, 3 and 4 Registration Forms may be submitted either by post or fax. The original Registration Form must be forwarded by first class post to the Registrar within 7 days of the fax being transmitted.
    (d) All relevant sections of the Registration Form MUST be completed and personally signed by the player and the Clubs' officials.
    Registration Forms from 'overseas' players MUST be accompanied by the completed International Rugby Football Board form endorsed by their own Union and, where that player is claiming possession of a British Passport, a copy of documentary evidence.
    No Club playing in National Leagues 1, 2, 3 and 4 may register more than **50 players** at any one time — see Transitional Regulation 9(a)(iv).
    A Club shall not submit a Registration Form on behalf of any player under the age of 18 years.
    Any incomplete forms will be returned to the sender and the registration will not be recorded until these have been resubmitted containing all the information required. Applications carrying false information or per-pro signatures are unacceptable and may render the Club, player and/or official liable to disciplinary action under RFU Rule 5.12, in addition to any statutory penalties that may be imposed under any RFU Competition Regulation.
4   On receipt of the Registration Form, the Registrar will calculate the EFFECTIVE date of registration for the RFU Club Competitions referred to in 1(e) above and enter this date into the computer records.
5   At any point in time a player may only be registered with two Clubs affiliated to the RFU, only one of which can be EFFECTIVE.
6   A Club wishing to register a player from another Club shall submit the pink copy of the new Registration Application Form to the Registrar responsible for the player's new Club. At the same time the white copy of the form must be posted to the Secretary of the player's current Club. On receipt, this must be signed by a Club Official and then forwarded immediately to that Club's Registrar.
    The Registration Date is as defined in Regulation 1(d) providing no valid objection to the registration is received from the current Club within 21 days of the Registrar's receipt of the white copy.
7   Officials of a player's current Club may not refuse to sign the form. If when signing the Registration Form, officials of the player's current Club have objections to the player moving under RFU Regulations concerning unpaid subscriptions or RFU Rule 5.12 or any of the IRFB Regulations Relating to Amateurism, these objections must be submitted in writing to the Secretary of the RFU stating all the grounds upon which the objection is made. The Club shall not be entitled to introduce any further grounds of objection not so stated nor to lodge a second objection arising from the circumstances upon which an objection is based.
8   On or before **1st September** the Registrar will post to each Club a complete list of registered players. This list will show Registration Date, Competition Eligibility Date and movement of players and will be updated on receipt of each new Registration Application Form. A copy of the updated list will only be forwarded

to the Club if a stamped-addressed envelope has been enclosed with the new Registration Form. The Club's computerised registration list is the only evidence that will be accepted to substantiate a player's EFFECTIVE registration.

9 **Registration Regulations**

a) **Registration of Home Union Players**

The Registration Date is as defined in Regulation 1(d), but the registration becomes EFFECTIVE as follows:-

(i) 7 days (exclusive of the period 1st May to 31st July) — for a player who is not registered with any other Club in membership of the RFU and who has not played, during the twelve calendar months immediately preceding his Registration Application, for any Club (other than a student Club or school) in membership of any other National Union.

A player in this section (i) whose Registration Application is with a Club in National Leagues 1, 2, 3 and 4 shall have EFFECTIVE registration on the Registration Date.

(ii) 60 days — (exclusive of the period 1st May to 31st July) after the Registration Date — for players (other than (i) above) who are moving between clubs, both of which are playing in a league BELOW the first Divisional League (ie, Northern Division 1, Midland Division 1, South West Division 1 and London & South East Division 1).

A player in this section (ii) retains EFFECTIVE registration and may play in RFU competition matches for his current club throughout the 60 day period of waiting for EFFECTIVE registration with his new club.

A player in this section (ii) may also within 60 days of his Registration Date request that the Registrar cancel his application — such a request must be received in writing by the Registrar within the 60 day period.

(iii) 120 days — (exclusive of the period 1st May to 31st July) after the Registration Date — for players other than those qualifying in (i) and (ii) above.

A player in this section (iii) may continue to play in RFU competition matches for his current Club throughout the 120 day period of waiting for EFFECTIVE registration with his new club.

A player in this section (iii) may also within 120 days of his Registration Date, request that the Registrar cancel his application — such a request must be received in writing by the Registrar within the 120 day period.

Transitional Regulation

(iv) A player in section (iii) above whose registration is cancelled by his Club under the 50 player maximum registration requirement (see Regulation 3 para 6) will qualify for EFFECTIVE registration with his new Club after 60 days (exclusive of the period 1st May to 31 July) providing the Registrar receives his application and enters it on the Club's computerised registration list on or before 30th October 1994.

NB **With effect from 1st May 1995 the dates referred to at (i), (ii) and (iii) above will be amended to read "1st May to 31st August".**

b) **Registration of 'Overseas' Players**

(i) A Registration Application cannot be made until the player arrives in the Four Home Unions and he submits, duly completed by him and endorsed by his own Union, the IRFB form of statutory declaration (See Appendix 2) giving clearance for him to play outside his own Union.

(ii) The Registration Date is as defined in Regulation 1(d), but the registration becomes EFFECTIVE 180 days (exclusive of the period 1st May to 31st July) after the Registration Date. Any absence from the Home Unions during this waiting period will count towards the 60 days stipulated in (b)(iv).

(iii) When a registered player has maintained EFFECTIVE registration for a consecutive period of 730 days (2 years), he ceases to be subject to the restriction in 8(b)(ii)of the Courage Clubs Championship Regulations and 2(b)(ii) of the Pilkington Cup and Pilkington Shield Regulations.

(iv) The registration of an overseas player will cease to be EFFECTIVE if the player is absent from the Four Home Unions at any time for a total of 60 days or more in any calendar year.

(v) A player who loses his EFFECTIVE registration under 9(b)(iv) has to re-apply and is subject to 9(b)(i) and (ii).

(vi) A player, if moving Clubs, is subject to the restrictions in 9(a)(ii) and (iii) which may run concurrently with the restriction in 9(b)(ii).

(vii) It is the responsibility of a Club to inform the Registrar if a player is absent from the Home Unions for a total of 60 days or more in any calendar year.

NB **With effect from 1st May 1995 the dates referred to at (ii) above will be amended to read — "1st May to 31st August".**

c) **Registration — General**

(i) Any player, however qualified, who is an employee of a Club, or of a Company which is substantially involved in any activity which is related to a Club, may not be registered with that Club unless authorised by the RFU Amateur Status Sub-Committee.

(ii) The registration or qualifying period of any player who is ineligible to play for any other reason under the Rules and Regulations of the RFU, is suspended for the period of that ineligibility. But the right to withdraw a registration is not affected.

24

(iii) The EFFECTIVE registration of any player, who plays in a match in a Club Competition of any other National Union during the period 1st September to 30th April inclusive, shall be discontinued. A player whose registration is discontinued under this Clause may not re-register until he is residing in the Home Unions and must requalify under 9(a)(ii) or 9(a)(iii) if a Home Union player or 9(b)(ii) if an Overseas player.

(iv) A Player who is registered with a Club which withdraws from all RFU Competitions in the season and who wishes during that season to play for another Club in an RFU Competition, must register with that Club in accordance with these Regulations. If the Club withdrawing does not re-enter any RFU Competition for the following season, the player shall be entitled to EFFECTIVE Registration under paragraph 9(a)(i).

(v) A player with EFFECTIVE Registration may request to be deregistered, or a Club may request for a player to be deregistered. On receipt of such a request, which must be in writing, the Registrar will transfer the player's current Club registration to a lapsed registration file. After 120 days, the player shall no longer be registered.

(vi) A player whose registration has been deleted under clause 9(c)(v) may reapply for RFU registration and such registration will be EFFECTIVE on the Registration Date subject to the provision of Clause 9(a)(i).

(vii) A player who is under the age of 22 years on 1st September 1994 may request, in writing, to return to the Club which held his initial RFU registration ("his original Club"). His registration with his original Club will be EFFECTIVE immediately upon receipt of his written request by the Registrar, provided that no subsequent registration of that player shall become EFFECTIVE until the period of 120 days shall have elapsed from the date of the player's registration with and upon his returning to his original Club.

(viii) A Club may not register any player who has at any time received any material benefit (as defined in Regulation 1.3 of the IRFB Regulations Relating to Amateurism) for playing any form of Rugby Football.

10 Any dispute on the application of these Regulations and Operating Procedures by the Registrar must be referred in writing to that Registrar stating all the grounds on which the objection is made. If the dispute is not resolved within 7 days, the Club or player may submit the complaint in writing to the Secretary of the RFU restating the grounds upon which the objection is made. The Club shall not be entitled to introduce any further grounds of objection not previously stated to the Registrar, nor to lodge a second objection arising from the circumstances upon which an objection is based.

The Secretary of the RFU shall refer the objection to the Competition Sub-Committee of the RFU whose decision shall be final and binding.

It shall be at the sole discretion of the Competition Sub-Committee whether or not to grant a personal hearing. The Club and/or player may be requested to pay the cost of any such hearing.

11 The Competition Sub-Committee of the RFU shall have absolute and unfettered discretion to decide on any matter not provided for in and on the interpretation of these Regulations and Operating Procedures and their decision shall be final and binding.

Appendix 1

REGISTRARS — SEASON 1994-95

Senior Clubs Association

DAE Evans
22 Brooks Road, Sutton Coldfield,
West Midlands B71 1HP
Tel: 021 354 8183 Fax: 021 321 3221

National Leagues 5 (North and South)

MJ Wilson
c/o Michael Humphreys & Partners Ltd,
68 South Lambeth Road, Vauxhall,
London SW8 1RL
Tel: 071 820 9911

London & South East Division

MA Ward
3 Rookery Close, Oulton Broad, Lowestoft,
Suffolk NR33 9NZ
Tel: 0502 566169

Midland Division

DI Robins
c/o Russells News Agency, PO Box 183,
Leicester LE3 8BZ
Tel: 0533 332200

South West Division

JD Wooldridge
c/o The First Eleven Sports Agency,
PO Box 11, Reading, Berkshire RG6 3DT
Tel: 0734 311244

Northern Division

R Archer
Brookfield House, Scotland Head, Winlaton,
Tyne & Wear NE21 6PL
Tel: 091 414 3532

THE COURAGE CLUBS CHAMPIONSHIP GENERAL CONTACTS

NATIONAL ADMINISTRATION OFFICE

Michael Humphreys & Partners Ltd.,
68 South Lambeth Road,
Vauxhall,
London SW8 1RL.
Tel: 071 820 9911
Fax: 071 820 9259

Administration Director: Sue Wheeler
Administration Executives: Katie Bullivant
    Theo Chapman

Michael Humphreys & Partners (MH&P) is responsible to the Rugby Football Union for the administration of fixtures, results and league tables for all National Leagues.

MH&P also represents the RFU in liaison with the Committee of each RFU Division of the Championship. The Company is responsible for ensuring that all necessary fixtures have been made and that all promotions and relegations are arranged.

Media Relations Director: Teresa Cash
Media Relations Manager: Sara Jones
Media Relations Executive: Julian Yeomans

MH&P is responsible to the RFU for the overall promotion and media relations with regard to the Courage Clubs Championship. All information regarding fixtures, results and tables for the National Leagues is co-ordinated from MH&P. MH&P will also hold the results and the tables for all other leagues in the Championship. All media information regarding the overall Championship is released from MH&P and all enquiries should be directed to MH&P for any regional information not available from the regional contact.

THE RUGBY FOOTBALL UNION

Roger Godfrey,
The Administrative Secretary,
The Rugby Football Union,
Rugby Road, Twickenham,
Middlesex TW1 1DZ
Tel: 081 892 8161

RFU COMPETITION SUB-COMMITTEE

The Committee will act as a final arbiter in case of all disputes.

Chairman:
John A Jeavons-Fellows,
Shrawley Wood,
Worcester WR6 6TT.
Tel: 0905 621255 (H)
Fax: 0905 621377

NATIONAL MEDIA CONTACTS

DAILY EXPRESS
Ludgate House, 245 Blackfriars Road,
London SE1 9UX
Tel: 071 928 8000

DAILY MAIL
Northcliffe House, 2 Derry Street,
London W8 5TT
Tel: 071 938 6000

DAILY MIRROR
1 Canada Square, Canary Wharf,
London E14 5AP
Tel: 071 293 3000

THE DAILY TELEGRAPH
1 Canada Square, Canary Wharf,
London E14 5AP
Tel: 071 538 5000

THE EUROPEAN
Orbit House, 5 New Fetters Lane,
London EC4A 1AR
Tel: 071 377 4903

EVENING STANDARD
Northcliffe House, 2 Derry Street,
London W8 5TT
Tel: 071 938 6000

THE GUARDIAN
119 Farringdon Road,
London EC1R 3ER
Tel: 071 278 2332

THE INDEPENDENT
1 Canada Square, Canary Wharf,
London E14 5AP (as of Oct '94)
Tel: 071 253 1222

THE DAILY STAR
Ludgate House, 245 Blackfriars Road
London SE1 9UX
Tel: 071 928 8000

THE SUN
PO Box 481, Virginia Street
London E1 9BD
Tel: 071 782 4000

THE TIMES
1 Pennington Street, London E1 9XN
Tel: 071 782 5000

TODAY
1 Virginia Street, London E1 9BS
Tel: 071 782 4600

MAIL ON SUNDAY
Northcliffe House, 2 Derry Street,
London W8 5TT
Tel: 071 938 6000

NEWS OF THE WORLD
1 Virginia Street, London E1 9XR
Tel 071 782 4000

PRESS ASSOCIATION
PA Sport, London House,
Central Park, New Lane,
Leeds LS11 5DZ
Tel: 0532 344411

NATIONAL MEDIA CONTACTS

THE OBSERVER
119 Farringdon Road,
London EC1R 3ER
Tel: 071 278 2332

SUNDAY EXPRESS
Ludgate House, 245 Blackfriars Road,
London SE1 9UX
Tel: 071 928 8000

SUNDAY MIRROR
1 Canada Square, Canary Wharf,
London E14 5AP
Tel: 071 293 3601

SUNDAY TELEGRAPH
1 Canada Square, Canary Wharf,
London E14 5AP
Tel: 071 538 5000

SUNDAY TIMES
1, Pennington Street, London E1 9XW
Tel: 071 782 5000

THE PEOPLE
1 Canada Square, Canary Wharf,
London E14 5AP
Tel: 071 293 3201

INDEPENDENT ON SUNDAY
1 Canada Square, Canary Wharf,
London E14 5AP (as of Oct '94)
Tel: 071 253 1222

ITN NEWS
200 Grays Inn Road, London WC1X 8XZ
Tel: 071 833 3000

BBC TV NEWS
Television Centre, Wood Lane,
London W12 7RJ
Tel: 081 576 1914

BBC BREAKFAST NEWS
Room 7039, Television Centre
London W12 8QT
Tel: 081 576 7501 / 6

SKY NEWS & SKY SPORT
6 Centaurs Business Park, Grant Way,
Isleworth, Middlesex TW7 5QD
Tel: 071 705 3000

GMTV
The London Television Centre,
Upper Ground, London SE1 9TT
Tel: 071 827 7000

CHANNEL FOUR NEWS
200 Grays Inn Road,
London WC1X 8XZ
Tel: 071 833 3000

I.R.N.
200 Grays Inn Road,
London WC1X 8XZ
Tel: 071 833 3000

SPORT ON 5
BBC Radio 5, Broadcasting House,
London W1 1AA
Tel: 071 580 4468

THE NATIONAL LEAGUES

LEAGUE 1

LEAGUE 2
PAGE 121

LEAGUE 3
PAGE 167

LEAGUE 4
PAGE 213

NATIONAL LEAGUES STRUCTURE

and immediate supporting leagues

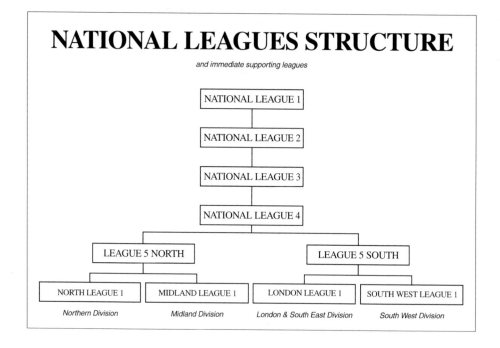

ADMINISTRATIVE INSTRUCTION — NATIONAL LEAGUES 1-4
COURAGE CLUBS CHAMPIONSHIP POSTPONED MATCHES

Matches which have to be postponed should be re-scheduled for the following Saturday. The only exceptions can be when:

a)   One or other side is involved in another National club Competition (i.e. Pilkington Cup).

b)   On or within two days of the re-scheduled date one or other side has three or more players involved in an RFU Divisional match or an English representative match or the full national representative team of another Home Union.

> NB County Cup and County rugby, Services and Student rugby do not take precedence over Courage Clubs Championship matches in National Leagues 1-4.

If any of the above exceptions apply then the match should be played on the first Saturday when they do not.

Where the next or next available Saturday presents another major difficulty to either side then an appeal may be made within two days of the original match date for an alternative date. This appeal must· be made to the Secretary of the Organising Committee. The decision of the Organising Committee is final.

Further to the above, the SCA has laid down guidelines for National League clubs to follow in the case of possible postponements.

– Every effort must be made to play each match.

– In the event of postponement the decision must be left to the latest possible moment.

– The latest possible moment is normally judged by the departure time of the visiting team.

– Ground costs, sponsorship and media considerations should take second place to playing the match.

– If, prior to the day of a match it is considered that the pitch may be unplayable on the day of the match, a referee experienced at the relevant playing standard should be consulted on the fitness of the pitch before any decision is made. (The RFU will help identify a referee if requested.) On match day, if a decision is to be taken prior to the arrival of the visiting team then the match referee should be consulted.

COURAGE NATIONAL LEAGUES
1994-95

LEAGUE 1

BATH
BRISTOL
GLOUCESTER
HARLEQUINS
LEICESTER
NORTHAMPTON
ORRELL
SALE
WASPS
WEST HARTLEPOOL

LEAGUE 2

COVENTRY
FYLDE
LONDON IRISH
LONDON SCOTTISH
MOSELEY
NEWCASTLE GOSFORTH
NOTTINGHAM
SARACENS
WAKEFIELD
WATERLOO

LEAGUE 3

BEDFORD
BLACKHEATH
CLIFTON
EXETER
HARROGATE
MORLEY
OTLEY
RICHMOND
ROSSLYN PARK
RUGBY

LEAGUE 4

ASKEANS
ASPATRIA
BROUGHTON PARK
HAVANT
LEEDS
LIVERPOOL ST HELENS
PLYMOUTH ALBION
READING
REDRUTH
ROTHERHAM

THE COURAGE CLUBS CHAMPIONSHIP 1994-95

NATIONAL LEAGUES: RFU SENIOR CLUBS ASSOCIATION (EXECUTIVE COMMITTEE)

CHAIRMAN

Frank Gibbon,
12 The Green,
Bishopton,
Stockton onTees,
Cleveland TS21 1HF.
Tel: 0740 30410 (H)
    0642 602221 (B)

DEPUTY CHAIRMAN

Bob Taylor,
82 Bridgwater Drive,
Abington,
Northampton NN3 3AG.
Tel: 0604 38626 (H)

HON. SECRETARY

Alwynne Evans,
22 Brooks Road,
Wylde Green,
Sutton Coldfield,
West Midlands B72 1HP.
Tel: 021 354 8183 (H)
    0675 470042 (B)
Fax: 021 321 3221 (H)
    0675 470490 (B)

HON. TREASURER

Brian Baister,
The Cedars,
3 Kidderton Close,
Brindley,
Nantwich,
Cheshire CW5 8JU.
Tel: 0270 74465 (H)
    0244 350000 x 2003 (B)

MEMBERS

John Allen
60 Dorchester Road, Leicester LE3 0UF
Tel: 0533 858407 (H)
    0533 471234 (B)
Fax: 0533 471434
Neil Hannah,
Gatehouse, 62 Beeston Fields Drive,
Bramcote, Beeston, Nottingham NG9 3DD.
Tel: 0602 254798 (H)
    0602 243243 (B)
Fax: 0509 242310
Ray Ellis,
31 Russell Avenue, Hartley,
Plymouth PL3 5RB.
Tel: 0752 771237 (H)
Roy Fawden,
100 Swains Lane Highgate,
London N6 6PL.
Tel: 081 348 4753 (H)
    081 348 4254 (B)
Fax: 081 340 2199
Geoff Hancock
191 Ringswell Gardens, Bath BA1 6BP
Tel: 0225 420532 (H)
Bill Redwood
205 Stoke Lane, Westbury-on-Trym, Bristol BS9 3RX
Tel: 0272 684342 (H)
    0272 424273
Des Seabrook,
29 St. Lukes Drive, Orrell, Nr. Wigan, Lancs. WM5 7AU
Tel: 0695 622648 (H)
Colin Sewell
6 Font Close, Titchfield Common, Fareham,
Hampshire PO14 4QH
Tel: 0489 583417 (H)
    0705 563904 (B)
Don Wills,
25 Woodland Gardens, Isleworth,
Middx. TW7 6LN.
Tel: 081 560 7594 (H)
Robin Foster,
27 Carr Lane, Sandal, Wakefield,
West Yorkshire WF2 6HJ.
Tel: 0924 250116 (H)
    0924 371501 (B)

COURAGE LEAGUE FIXTURES

1994-95 NATIONAL LEAGUE ONE

September 10 (Week 2)
Bath v Bristol
Leicester v Northampton
Sale v Harlequins
Wasps v Gloucester
West Hartlepool v Orrell

September 17 (Week 3)
Bristol v Sale
Gloucester v West Hartlepool
Harlequins v Wasps
Northampton v Bath
Orrell v Leicester

September 24 (Week 4)
Bath v Orrell
Bristol v Harlequins
Leicester v Gloucester
Sale v Northampton
West Hartlepool v Wasps

October 1 (Week 5)
Gloucester v Bath
Harlequins v West Hartlepool
Northampton v Bristol
Orrell v Sale
Wasps v Leicester

October 8 (Week 6)
Bath v Wasps
Bristol v Orrell
Leicester v West Hartlepool
Northampton v Harlequins
Sale v Gloucester

October 15 (Week 7)
Gloucester v Bristol
Harlequins v Leicester
Orrell v Northampton
Wasps v Sale
West Hartlepool v Bath

October 22 (Week 8)
Bath v Leicester
Bristol v Wasps
Harlequins v Orrell
Northampton v Gloucester
Sale v West Hartlepool

October 29 (Week X2)
Bath v Harlequins
Gloucester v Orrell
Leicester v Sale
Wasps v Northampton
West Hartlepool v Bristol

November 5 (Week 9)
Bristol v Leicester
Harlequins v Gloucester
Northampton v West Hartlepool
Orrell v Wasps
Sale v Bath

January 7 (Week 17)
Bristol v Bath
Gloucester v Wasps
Harlequins v Sale
Northampton v Leicester
Orrell v West Hartlepool

January 14 (Week 18)
Bath v Northampton
Leicester v Orrell
Sale v Bristol
Wasps v Harlequins
West Hartlepool v Gloucester

February 11 (Week 22)
Gloucester v Leicester
Harlequins v Bristol
Northampton v Sale
Orrell v Bath
Wasps v West Hartlepool

March 4 (Week 25)
Bath v Gloucester
Bristol v Northampton
Leicester v Wasps
Sale v Orrell
West Hartlepool v Harlequins

COURAGE LEAGUE FIXTURES

March 25 (Week 28)

Gloucester v Sale
Harlequins v Northampton
Orrell v Bristol
Wasps v Bath
West Hartlepool v Leicester

April 8 (Week 30)

Bath v West Hartlepool
Bristol v Gloucester
Leicester v Harlequins
Northampton v Orrell
Sale v Wasps

April 15 (Week 31)

Gloucester v Northampton
Leicester v Bath
Orrell v Harlequins
Wasps v Bristol
West Hartlepool v Sale

April 22 (Week 32)

Bristol v West Hartlepool
Harlequins v Bath
Northampton v Wasps
Orrell v Gloucester
Sale v Leicester

April 29 (Week X8)

Bath v Sale
Gloucester v Harlequins
Leicester v Bristol
Wasps v Orrell
West Hartlepool v Northampton

COURAGE LEAGUE FIXTURES

1994-95 NATIONAL LEAGUE TWO

September 10 (Week 2)
Coventry v Wakefield
Fylde v Nottingham
London Irish v London Scottish
Moseley v Saracens
Waterloo v Newcastle Gosforth

September 17 (Week 3)
London Scottish v Waterloo
Newcastle Gosforth v Fylde
Nottingham v Coventry
Saracens v London Irish
Wakefield v Moseley

September 24 (Week 4)
Coventry v Newcastle Gosforth
Fylde v London Scottish
Moseley v Nottingham
Wakefield v Saracens
Waterloo v London Irish

October 1 (Week 5)
London Irish v Fylde
London Scottish v Coventry
Newcastle Gosforth v Moseley
Nottingham v Wakefield
Saracens v Waterloo

October 8 (Week 6)
Coventry v London Irish
Fylde v Waterloo
Moseley v London Scottish
Nottingham v Saracens
Wakefield v Newcastle Gosforth

October 15 (Week 7)
London Irish v Moseley
London Scottish v Wakefield
Newcastle Gosforth v Nottingham
Saracens v Fylde
Waterloo v Coventry

October 22 (Week 8)
Coventry v Fylde
Moseley v Waterloo
Newcastle Gosforth v Saracens
Nottingham v London Scottish
Wakefield v London Irish

October 29 (Week X2)
Coventry v Saracens
Fylde v Moseley
London Irish v Nottingham
London Scottish v Newcastle Gosforth
Waterloo v Wakefield

November 5 (Week 9)
Moseley v Coventry
Newcastle Gosforth v London Irish
Nottingham v Waterloo
Saracens v London Scottish
Wakefield v Fylde

January 7 (Week 17)
London Scottish v London Irish
Newcastle Gosforth v Waterloo
Nottingham v Fylde
Saracens v Moseley
Wakefield v Coventry

January 14 (Week 18)
Coventry v Nottingham
Fylde v Newcastle Gosforth
London Irish v Saracens
Moseley v Wakefield
Waterloo v London Scottish

February 11 (Week 22)
London Irish v Waterloo
London Scottish v Fylde
Newcastle Gosforth v Coventry
Nottingham v Moseley
Saracens v Wakefield

March 4 (Week 25)
Coventry v London Scottish
Fylde v London Irish
Moseley v Newcastle Gosforth
Wakefield v Nottingham
Waterloo v Saracens

COURAGE LEAGUE FIXTURES

March 25 (Week 28)

London Irish	v	Coventry
London Scottish	v	Moseley
Newcastle Gosforth	v	Wakefield
Saracens	v	Nottingham
Waterloo	v	Fylde

April 8 (Week 30)

Coventry	v	Waterloo
Fylde	v	Saracens
Moseley	v	London Irish
Nottingham	v	Newcastle Gosforth
Wakefield	v	London Scottish

April 15 (Week 31)

Fylde	v	Coventry
Lonodn Irish	v	Wakefield
London Scottish	v	Nottingham
Saracens	v	Newcastle Gosforth
Waterloo	v	Moseley

April 22 (Week 32)

Moseley	v	Fylde
Newcastle Gosforth	v	London Scottish
Nottingham	v	London Irish
Saracens	v	Coventry
Wakefield	v	Waterloo

April 29 (Week X8)

Coventry	v	Moseley
Fylde	v	Wakefield
London Irish	v	Newcastle Gosforth
London Scottish	v	Saracens
Waterloo	v	Nottingham

COURAGE LEAGUE FIXTURES

1994-95 NATIONAL LEAGUE THREE

September 10 (Week 2)
Clifton v Otley
Morley v Exeter
Richmond v Harrogate
Rosslyn Park v Blackheath
Rugby v Bedford

September 17 (Week 3)
Bedford v Clifton
Blackheath v Rugby
Exeter v Rosslyn Park
Harrogate v Morley
Otley v Richmond

September 24 (Week 4)
Blackheath v Exeter
Morley v Otley
Richmond v Bedford
Rosslyn Park v Harrogate
Rugby v Clifton

October 1 (Week 5)
Bedford v Morley
Clifton v Richmond
Exeter v Rugby
Harrogate v Blackheath
Otley v Rosslyn Park

October 15 (Week 7)
Blackheath v Otley
Exeter v Harrogate
Morley v Clifton
Rosslyn Park v Bedford
Rugby v Richmond

October 22 (Week 8)
Bedford v Blackheath
Clifton v Rosslyn Park
Otley v Exeter
Richmond v Morley
Rugby v Harrogate

October 29 (Week X2)
Blackheath v Clifton
Exeter v Bedford
Harrogate v Otley
Morley v Rugby
Rosslyn Park v Richmond

November 12 (Week 10)
Bedford v Harrogate
Clifton v Exeter
Otley v Rugby
Richmond v Blackheath
Rosslyn Park v Morley

January 7 (Week 17)
Blackheath v Morley
Exeter v Richmond
Harrogate v Clifton
Otley v Bedford
Rugby v Rosslyn Park

January 14 (Week 18)
Clifton v Bedford
Morley v Harrogate
Richmond v Otley
Rosslyn Park v Exeter
Rugby v Blackheath

February 11 (Week 22)
Bedford v Rugby
Backheath v Rosslyn Park
Exeter v Morley
Harrogate v Richmond
Otley v Clifton

February 25 (Week 24)
Blackheath v Harrogate
Morley v Bedford
Richmond v Clifton
Rosslyn Park v Otley
Rugby v Exeter

March 4 (Week 25)
Bedford v Rosslyn Park
Clifton v Morley
Harrogate v Exeter
Otley v Blackheath
Richmond v Rugby

COURAGE LEAGUE FIXTURES

March 25 (Week 28)

Blackheath	v	Bedford
Exeter	v	Otley
Harrogate	v	Rugby
Morley	v	Richmond
Rosslyn Park	v	Clifton

April 1 (Week 29)

Bedford	v	Exeter
Clifton	v	Blackheath
Otley	v	Harrogate
Richmond	v	Rosslyn Park
Rugby	v	Morley

April 8 (Week 30)

Bedford	v	Otley
Clifton	v	Harrogate
Morley	v	Blackheath
Richmond	v	Exeter
Rosslyn Park	v	Rugby

April 15 (Week 31)

Blackheath	v	Richmond
Exeter	v	Clifton
Harrogate	v	Bedford
Morley	v	Rosslyn Park
Rugby	v	Otley

April 29 (Week X8)

Bedford	v	Richmond
Clifton	v	Rugby
Exeter	v	Blackheath
Harrogate	v	Rosslyn Park
Otley	v	Morley

COURAGE LEAGUE FIXTURES

1994-95
NATIONAL LEAGUE
FOUR

September 10 (Week 2)
Aspatria v Leeds
Havant v Redruth
Liverpool St Helens v Broughton Park
Reading v Plymouth
Rotherham v Askeans

September 17 (Week 3)
Askeans v Liverpool St Helens
Broughton Park v Aspatria
Leeds v Havant
Plymouth v Rotherham
Redruth v Reading

September 24 (Week 4)
Askeans v Broughton Park
Havant v Aspatria
Liverpool St Helens v Plymouth
Reading v Leeds
Rotherham v Redruth

October 1 (Week 5)
Aspatria v Reading
Broughton Park v Havant
Leeds v Rotherham
Redruth v Liverpool St Helens
Plymouth v Askeans

October 15 (Week 7)
Askeans v Redruth
Liverpool St Helens v Leeds
Plymouth v Broughton Park
Reading v Havant
Rotherham v Aspatria

October 22 (Week 8)
Aspatria v Liverpool St Helens
Broughton Park v Reading
Havant v Rotherham
Leeds v Askeans
Redruth v Plymouth

October 29 (Week X2)
Askeans v Aspatria
Broughton Park v Redruth
Liverpool St Helens v Havant
Plymouth v Leeds
Rotherham v Reading

November 12 (Week 10)
Aspatria v Plymouth
Havant v Askeans
Leeds v Redruth
Reading v Liverpool St Helens
Rotherham v Broughton Park

January 7 (Week 17)
Askeans v Reading
Broughton Park v Leeds
Liverpool St Helens v Rotherham
Plymouth v Havant
Redruth v Aspatria

January 14 (Week 18)
Askeans v Rotherham
Broughton Park v Liverpool St Helens
Leeds v Aspatria
Plymouth v Reading
Redruth v Havant

February 11 (Week 22)
Aspatria v Broughton Park
Havant v Leeds
Liverpool St Helens v Askeans
Reading v Redruth
Rotherham v Plymouth

February 25 (Week 24)
Aspatria v Havant
Broughton Park v Askeans
Leeds v Reading
Plymouth v Liverpool St Helens
Redruth v Rotherham

March 4 (Week 25)
Askeans v Plymouth
Havant v Broughton Park
Liverpool St Helens v Redruth
Reading v Aspatria
Rotherham v Leeds

COURAGE LEAGUE FIXTURES

March 25 (Week 28)

Aspatria	v	Rotherham
Broughton Park	v	Plymouth
Havant	v	Reading
Leeds	v	Liverpool St Helens
Redruth	v	Askeans

April 1 (Week 29)

Askeans	v	Leeds
Liverpool St Helens	v	Aspatria
Plymouth	v	Redruth
Reading	v	Broughton Park
Rotherham	v	Havant

April 8 (Week 30)

Aspatria	v	Askeans
Havant	v	Liverpool St Helens
Leeds	v	Plymouth
Reading	v	Rotherham
Redruth	v	Broughton Park

April 15 (Week 31)

Askeans	v	Havant
Broughton Park	v	Rotherham
Liverpool St Helens	v	Reading
Plymouth	v	Aspatria
Redruth	v	Leeds

October 29 (Week X8)

Aspatria	v	Redruth
Havant	v	Plymouth
Leeds	v	Broughton Park
Reading	v	Askeans
Rotherham	v	Liverpool St Helens

Unisys and the Courage Clubs Championship

As a major worldwide information services company we are active in many different ways in the community in which we work.

UNISYS
We make it happen.

As part of our extensive 1994 sports programme we are pleased to support the Courage Clubs Championship Directory.

FINAL UNISYS COMPUTER RUGBY UNION STATISTICS 1993-94

These statistics have been collected during the Season for players in all clubs playing first class rugby. They include representative matches, County and Divisional matches, including the Varsity Match and Barbarian fixtures.

UNISYS TOP POINTS SCORERS
(up to and including 7th May 1994)

		Total	Tries	Cons	Pens	DG
1.	Simon Hogg (Clifton)	431	8	59	75	16
2.	Phil Belshaw (Reading	407	7	78	72	
3.	Jez Harris (Leicester)	340	4	43	64	14
4.	Jonathan Callard (Bath)	332	5	41	75	
5.	Guy Gregory (Nottingham)	299	1	27	75	5
6.	Andy Finnie (Bedford)	292		44	64	4
7.	Mark Tainton (Bristol)	290	4	51	54	2
8.	Paul Grayson (Northampton)	269	5	26	58	6
9.	Mark Mapletoft (Rugby)	266	10	45	40	2
10.	Andy Green (Exeter)	265	7	37	49	3
11.	Darren Chapman (Camborne)	262	1	22	69	2
12.	Lee Osborne (Berry Hill)	254	7	21	54	5
13.	Rob Andrew (Wasps)	249	3	27	53	7
14.	Paul Turner (Sale)	244	1	61	34	5
14.	Peter Rutledge (Otley)	244	8	36	44	
16.	Mark Rodgers (Sheffield)	240	5	25	55	
17.	Richard Rowledge (Basingstoke)	238	6	38	43	1
17.	Martin Thompson (Plymouth)	238	5	30	44	7
19.	Paul Larkin (Askeans)	236		28	56	4
20.	Richard Angell (Coventry)	230	4	45	38	2

UNISYS TOP TRY SCORERS

1.	John Phillips (Clifton)	32
2.	Simon Verbickas (Sale)	29
3.	Jim Naylor (Orrell)	25
4.	Ian Pollard (Camborne)	24
4.	Ian McGeever (Reading)	24
6.	Brendan Hanavan (Fylde)	23

UNISYS TOP KICKERS (Tries excluded)

1.	Simon Hogg (Clifton)	391
2.	Phil Belshaw (Reading)	372
3.	Jez Harris (Leicester)	320
4.	Jon Callard (Bath)	307
5.	Guy Gregory (Nottingham)	294

UNISYS TOP DROP KICKERS

1.	Simon Hogg (Clifton)	16
2.	Jez Harris (Leicester)	14
3.	Paul Tincknell (Weston-Super-Mare)	8
3.	Rob Andrew (Wasps)	8
5.	Martin Thompson (Plymouth)	7

COURAGE CHAMPIONSHIP STATISTICS

Compiled by Steve McCormack

DIVISION ONE

	CHAMPIONS	RUNNERS-UP	RELEGATED
1987-88	Leicester	Wasps	Coventry Sale
1988-89	Bath	Gloucester	Waterloo Liverpool St Helens
1989-90	Wasps	Gloucester	Bedford
1990-91	Bath	Wasps	Moseley Liverpool St Helens
1991-92	Bath	Orrell	Nottingham Rosslyn Park
1992-93	Bath	Wasps	Saracens London Scottish West Hartlepool Rugby
1993-94	Bath	Leicester	London Irish Newcastle Gosforth

TEAM RECORDS

Highest score: Bath 76 Bedford 0. 13-1-90
Highest aggregate: Harlequins 71 Bedford 8. 14-10-89
Highest score by a losing side: London Irish 31 Bath 32 30-4-94
Highest Scoring draw: Leicester 22 Rugby 22. 25-4-92
Most consecutive wins: 15 Bath 1992-93 through 1993-94
Most consecutive defeats: 12 Liverpool St Helens 1990-91, Newcastle Gosforth 1993-94
Most points in a season: 431 Bath 1993-94
Most tries in a season: 46 Bath 1993-94
Most conversions in a season: 29 Bath 1989-90
Most penalties in a season: 51 Harlequins 1993-94
Most drop goals in a season: 11 Leicester 1993-94

INDIVIDUAL RECORDS

Most points in a season: 202 Jez Harris Leicester 1993-94
Most tries in a season: 11 A Harriman Harlequins 1987-88, Darren O'Leary Harlequins 1993-94
Most conversions in a season: 29 S Barnes Bath 1989-90
Most penalities in a season: 41 Jez Harris Leicester 1993-94
Most drop goals in a season: 11 Jez Harris Leicester 1993-94
Most points in a match: 31 J Liley Leicester v Rosslyn Park 21- 3-92
Most tries in a match: 4 G Hartley Nottingham v Bedford 18-11-89, A Swift Bath v Bedford 13-1-90,
J Guscott Bath v Bedford 13-1-90. P Hamer Orrell v Rugby 13-3-93,
T Underwood Leicester v Newcastle Gosforth
Most conversions in a match: 10 S Barnes Bath v Bedford 13-1-90
Most penalities in a match: 7 D Pears Harlequins v Rosslyn Park 7-12-91, J Harris Leicester v Bristol
11-12-93 & v Gloucester 29-1-94, R Andrew Wasps v Orrell 11-12-93
Most drop goals in a match: 3 J Steele Northern v Wasps 23-3-91, J Harris Leicester v Wasps 23-11-91

SEASON BY SEASON LEADING SCORERS

	POINTS		TRIES	
1987-88	126	D Hare (Leicester)	11	A Harriman (Harlequins)
1988-89	103	R Andrew (Wasps)	10	J Guscott (Bath)
1989-90	126	J Liley (Leicester)	10	A Swift (Bath)
1990-91	126	R Andrew (Wasps)	9	R Underwood (Leicester) A Harriman (Harlequins)
1991-92	129	J Liley (Leicester)	9	R Underwood (Leicester)
1992-93	122	J Webb (Bath)	7	S Barnes (Bath)
1993-94	202	J Harris (Leicester)	11	D O'Leary (Harlequins)

DIVISION TWO STATISTICS

	CHAMPIONS	RUNNERS-UP	RELEGATED
1987-88	Rosslyn Park	Liverpoool St Helens	None
1988-89	Saracens	Bedford	London Welsh London Scottish
1989-90	Northampton	Liverpool St Helens	None
1990-91	Rugby	London Irish	Richmond Headingley
1991-92	London Scottish	West Hartlepool	Plymouth Albion Liverpool St Helens
1992-93	Newcastle Gosforth	Waterloo	Bedford Rosslyn Park Richmond Blackheath Coventry Fylde Morley
1993-94	Sale	West Hartlepool	Rugby Otley

TEAM RECORDS

Highest score: Sale 88 Otley 9 12-2-94
Highest aggregate: 97 points as above
Highest score by a losing side: 28 Waterloo 28 Plymouth 33 31-3- 90
Highest scoring draw: 24-24 London Scottish v London Welsh 13-4- 88
Most consecutive wins: 15 Saracens 1987-88 through 1988-89
Most consecutive defeats: 12 Liverpool St Helens 1991-92
Most points in a season: 438 Sale 1993-94
Most tries in a season: 57 Newcastle Gosforth 1992-93, Sale 1993-94
Most conversions in a season: 31 Newcastle Gosforth 1992-93
Most penalties in a season: 47 Wakefield, Waterloo 1993-94
Most drop goals in a season: 9 Nottingham 1992-93

INDIVIDUAL RECORDS

Most points in a season: 171 Guy Gregory Nottingham 1993-94
Most tries in a season: 16 Simon Verbickas Sale 1993-94
Most conversions in a season: 31 D Johnson Newcastle Gosforth 1991-92
Most penalities in a season: 43 G Gregory Nottingham 1993-94
Most drop goals in a season: 9 G Gregory Nottingham 1992-93
Most points in a match: 28 D Johnson Newcastle Gosforth v Morley, 11-1-92,
Newcastle Gosforth v Liverpool St Helens 29-2-92
Most tries in a match: 5 Simon Verbickas Sale v Otley 12-2-94
Most conversions in a match: 9 D Johnson Newcastle Gosforth v Liverpool St Helens 29-2-92,
Paul Turner Sale v Otley 12-2-94
Most penalities in a match: 6 11 players have achieved this feat
Most drop goals in a match: 3 M Livesey (Richmond v Northampton) 19-11-88
Murray Walker London Scottish v West Hartlepool 23-4-94

SEASON BY SEASON LEADING SCORES

	POINTS	TRIES
1987-88	75 A Finnie (Bedford)	10 D McLagan (Saracens)
1988-89	138 A Kennedy (Saracens)	7 D McLagan (Saracens)
1989-90	107 I Aitchison (London Irish)	7 J Fallon (Richmond)
1990-91	117 B Mullen (London Irish)	9 L Renwick (London Scottish)
1991-92	147 D Johnson (Newcastle Gosforth)	11 N Grecian (London Scottish)
1992-93	136 D Johnson (Newcastle Gosforth)	7 J Sleightholme (Wakefield)
1993-94	172 G Gregory (Nottingham)	16 S Verbickas (Sale)

DIVISION THREE STATISTICS

	CHAMPIONS	RUNNERS-UP	RELEGATED
1987-88	Wakefield	West Hartlepool	Morley Birmingham
1988-89	Plymouth Albion	Rugby	Maidstone Metropolitan Police
1989-90	London Scottish	Wakefield	London Welsh
1990-91	West Hartlepool	Morley	Metropolitan Police Vale of Lune
1991-92	Richmond	Fylde	Lydney Nuneaton
1992-93	Otley	Havant	Sheffield Leeds Liverpool St Helens Clifton Aspatria Askeans Broughton Park Plymouth
1993-94	Coventry	Fylde	Havant Redruth

TEAM RECORDS

Highest score: Liverpool St Helens 77 Aspatria 5 13-3-93
Highest aggregate: 82 points as above
Highest score by a losing side: 32 Leeds 42 Clifton 32 24-4-93
Highest scoring draw: 18-18 Exeter v West Hartlepool 22-9-90
Most consecutive wins: 11 London Scottish 1989-90
Most consecutive defeats: 11 Maidstone 1988-89
Most points in a season: 406 Coventry 1993-94
Most tries in a season: 48 Rosslyn Park 1993-94
Most conversions in a season: 31 Fylde 1987-88
Most penalties in a season: 50 Bedford 1993-94
Most drop goals in a season: 6 Vale of Lune 1989-90, Broughton Park 1990-91 & 1991-92

INDIVIDUAL RECORDS

Most points in a season: 172 Andy Finnie Bedford 1993-94
Most tries in a season: 12 Brendan Hanavan Fylde 1993-94
Most conversions in a season: 30 S Burnage Fylde 1987-88
Most penalities in a season: 45 Andy Finnie Bedford 1993-94
Most drop goals in a season: 6 A Higgin Vale of Lune 1989-90, A Rimmer Broughton Park 1990-91
Most points in a match: 28, S Burnage Fylde v Birmingham 7-11-87
Most tries in a match: B Hanavan Fylde v Exeter 3-10-87 & v Birmingham 7-11-87 & v Redruth 9-9-94,
S Walklin Plymouth v Birmingham 17-10-87, I Russell Plymouth Albion v Fylde 31-10-87, D Cottrell Clifton v
Askeans 4-1-92, M Sephton Liverpool St Helens v Aspatria 13-3- 93, D Crompton Liverpool St Helens v
Aspatria 13-3-90, M Farrar Otley v Askeans 27-3-94
Most conversions in a match: 9 S Burnage Fylde v Birmingham 7-11- 87
Most penalities in a match: 6 J Stabler West Hartlepool v Metropolitan Police 2-1-88, R Adamson
Wakefield v Vale of Lune 27-2-88, C Howard Rugby v Nuneaton 22-10-88, R Goodliffe Sheffield v London
Scottish 14-10-89, Mark Rodgers Sheffield v Morley 23-2-91, J Clark Richmond v Lydney 14-3-92
Most drop goals in a match: 4 A Rimmer Broughton Park v Sheffield 17-11-90

SEASON BY SEASON LEADING SCORERS

	POINTS	TRIES
1987-88	121 S Burnage (Fylde)	10 B Hanavan (Fylde)
1988-89	123 C Howard (Rugby)	8 S Walklin (Plymouth Albion) D Scully (Wakefield)
1989-90	102 A Higgin (Vale of Lune)	7 M Harrison (Wakefield) B Hananan (Fylde)
1990-91	108 M Rodgers (Sheffield)	9 J Wrigley (West Hartlepool)
1991-92	106 M Jackson (Fylde)	8 M Brain (Clifton)
1992-93	122 A Green (Exeter)	8 M Kelly (Broughton Park) M Sephton (Liverpool)
1993-94	172 Andy Finnie (Bedford)	12 Brendan Hanavan (Fylde)

DIVISION FOUR STATISTICS

	CHAMPIONS	RUNNERS-UP	RELEGATED
1993-94	Clifton	Harrogate	Sheffield Sudbury

TEAM RECORDS

Highest score: Harrogate 78 Aspatria 21 30-4-94
Highest aggregate: 99 points as above
Highest score by a losing side: 23 Liverpool St Helens 30 Askeans 30-10-93
Highest scoring draw: 18-18 Sudbury v Askeans 8-1- 94, Liverpool St Helens v Sheffield 30-4-94
Most consecutive wins: 8 Clifton (twice) 1993-94
Most consecutive defeats: 7 Sheffield 1993-94
Most points in a season: 479 Harrogate 1993-94
Most tries in a season: 60 Harrogate 1993-94
Most conversions in a season: 31 Harrogate 1993-94
Most penalties in a season: 43 Liverpool St Helens, Aspatria 1993-94
Most drop goals in a season: 13 Clifton 1993-94 @HEAD 3 =

INDIVIDUAL RECORDS

Most points in a season: 222 Simon Hogg Clifton 1993-94
Most tries in a season: 16 Jon Phillips Clifton 1993-94
Most conversions in a season: 24 Simon Hogg Clifton 1993-94
Most penalities in a season: Simon Hogg Clifton 1993-94
Most drop goals in a season: 13 Simon Hogg Clifton 1993-94
Most points in a match: Ralph Zoing Harrogate v Plymouth 23-3-94
Most tries in a match: 3 on 8 occasions by 7 players
Most conversions in a match: 6 Ralph Zoing Harrogate v Plymouth 23-3-94
Most penalities in a match: 7 Kevin O'Brien Broughton Park v Liverpool St Helens 22-1-94
Most drop goals in a match: 2 Simon Hogg Clifton v Leeds 30-10-93, Ralph Zoing Harrogate v Askeans
20-11-93, Simon Hogg Clifton v Sheffield 4-12-93, Dan Eddie Leeds v Broughton Park 19-2-94, Richard
Larkin Askeans v Aspatria 9-4-94

SEASON BY SEASON LEADING SCORERS

	POINTS	TRIES
1993-94	222 S Hogg (Clifton)	16 Jon Phillips (Clifton)

MOST TRIES IN A COURAGE DIVISION ONE MATCH

4	G Hartley	Nottingham v Bedford	18-11-89
4	A Swift	Bath v Bedford	13-1-90
4	J Guscott	Bath v Bedford	13-1-90
4	P Hamer	Orrell v Rugby	13-3-93
4	T Underwood	Leicester v Newcastle Gosforth	12-3-94
3	P Shillingford	Moseley v Wasps	5-2-88
3	M Charles	Leicester v Sale	26-3-88
3	A Harriman	Harlequins v Nottingham	1-4-88
3	S Smith	Wasps v Coventry	13-4-88
3	A Harriman	Harlequins v Sale	23-4-88
3	J Guscott	Bath v Moseley	12-11-88
3	M Bailey	Wasps v Moseley	19-11-88
3	J Liley	Leicester v Bedford	23-9-89
3	E Wedderburn	Harlequins v Bedford	14-10-89
3	M Bailey	Wasps v Gloucester	14-10-89
3	D Morgan	Gloucester v Rosslyn Park	11-11-89
3	J Callard	Bath v Bedford	13-1-90
3	C Gerard	Leicester v Moseley	31-3-90
3	P Manley	Orrell v Rosslyn Park	28-4-90
3	D Morris	Orrell v Liverpool St Helens	13-10-90
3	D Morris	Orrell v Northampton	27-10-90
3	R Underwood	Leicester v Northampton	21-1-91
3	A Harriman	Harlequins v Bristol	30-3-91
3	W Carling	Harlequins v Bristol	30-3-91
3	G Childs	Wasps v Liverpool St Helens	20-4-91
3	R Andrew	Wasps v Bristol	27-4-91
3	R Underwood	Leicester v Moseley	27-4-91
3	S Hackney	Leicester v London Irish	4-1-92
3	A Swift	Bath v Leicester	11-1-92
3	R Underwood	Leicester v Rosslyn Park	21-3-92
3	M Lloyd	Bristol v Rugby	28-3-92
3	M Pepper	Nottingham v Rosslyn Park	4-4-92
3	C Oti	Wasps v Bristol	25-4-92
3	S Barnes	Bath v Hartlepool	27-3-93
3	D Eves	Bristol v Rugby	22-3-93
3	I Wynn	Orrell v Wasps	30-4-94

MOST POINTS IN A COURAGE DIVISION ONE MATCH

31	J Liley	Leicester v Rosslyn Park	21-3-92
28	M Strett	Orrel v Rosslyn Park	28-4-90
27	D Pears	Harlequins v Bedford	14-10-89
26	J Liley	Leicester v Bedford	23-9-89
26	S Barnes	Bath v West Hartlepool	27-3-93
26	D Grayson	Northampton v Bristol	2-10-93
24	W Hare	Leicester v Rosslyn Park	19-11-88
24	S Barnes	Bath v Bedford	13-1-90
24	R Andrew	Wasps v Bristol	27-4-91
23	J Salmon	Harlequins v Waterloo	27-2-88
23	R Andrew	Wasps v Rosslyn Park	22-10-88
23	D Pears	Harlequins v Saracens	20-10-90
23	R Andrew	Wasps v Orrell	11-12-93
23	J Harris	Leicester v Gloucester	29-1-94
22	W Hare	Leicester v Sale	26-3-88
22	J Graves	Rosslyn Park v Bedford	31-3-90
22	S Thresher	Harlequins v London Irish	31-10-92
22	J Callard	Bath v Northampton	18-9-93
22	M Corcoran	London Irish v Wasps	26-3-94
21	I Aitchison	Waterloo v Sale	2-1-88
21	D Pears	Harlequins v Rosslyn Park	7-12-91

21	B Rudling	Saracens v Harlequins	21-3-92
21	J Webb	Bath v Rugby	9-1-93
21	J Harris	Leicester v Bristol	11-12-93
21	J Harris	Leicester v Northampton	8-1-94
20	W Hare	Leicester v Waterloo	4-4-88
20	S Thresher	Harlequins v Sale	23-4-88
20	T Smith	Gloucester v Harlequins	12-3-90
20	J Liley	Leicester v London Irish	19-9-92
20	M Appleson	London Scottish v Rugby	31-10-92
20	P Hamer	Orrell v Rugby	13-3-93
20	T Underwood	Leicester v Newcastle Gosforth	12-3-94

MOST TRIES IN A COURAGE DIVISION TWO MATCH

5	S Verbickas	Sale v Otley	12-2-94
3	J Macklin	London Scottish v Northampton	3-10-87
3	O Bluitt	Northampton v Bedford	21-11-87
3	J Roberts	Headingley v Northampton	16-4-88
3	P Rowland	Coventry v London Irish	10-9-88
3	D Kennell	Headingley v Gosforth	14-1-89
3	L Smith	Saracens v Gosforth	22-4-89
3	N Saunders	Plymouth Albion v Blackheath	14-10-89
3	G Robbins	Coventry v Waterloo	13-1-90
3	R Saunders	London Irish v Rugby	13-10-90
3	J Wrigley	West Hartlepool v Moseley	14-12-91
3	P Walton	Newcastle Gosforth v Blackheath	14-12-91
3	J Sleightholme	Wakefield v Blackheath	4-1-92
3	G Clark	Newcastle Gosforth v Liverpool St Helens	29-2-92
3	R Arnold	Newcastle Gosforth v Liverpool St Helens	29-2-92
3	D Spillar	Moseley v Sale	4-4-92
3	R Gee	Coventry v Morley	19-9-92
3	M Walker	Nottingham v Morley	24-10-92
3	M Warr	Sale v Otley	12-2-94

MOST POINTS IN A COURAGE DIVISION TWO MATCH

28	D Johnson	Newcastle Gosforth v Morley	11-1-92
28	D Johnson	Newcastle Gosforth v Liverpool St Helens	29-2-93
26	A Mitchell	London Scottish v Northampton	3-10-87
25	C Howard	Rugby v Newcastle Gosforth	11-11-89
25	A Finnie	Bedford v Coventry	27-3-93
25	C Gregory	Nottingham v Otley	11-9-93
25	S Verbickas	Sale v Otley	12-2-94
24	S Irving	Headingley v London Scottish	12-11-88
24	A Kennedy	Saracens v Northampton	12-11-88
24	N Grecian	London Scottish v Blackheath	16-11-91
23	S Hodgkinson	Nottingham v Blcakheath	26-9-92
23	D Johnson	Newcastle Gosforth v Nottingham	10-10-92
23	G Gregory	Nottingham v Morley	24-10-92
23	G Abraham	Rosslyn Park v Morley	27-3-93
23	R Liley	Wakefield v Rugby	11-9-93
23	P Turner	Sale v Otley	12-2-94
22	G Clark	Gosforth v London Welsh	12-11-88
22	A Kennedy	Saracens v Bedford	19-11-88
22	R Liley	Wakefield v Liverpool St Helens	28-3-92
22	I Aitchison	Waterloo v Blackheath	25-4-92
22	J Graves	Rosslyn Park v Coventry	13-2-93
22	A Tunningley	Saracens v London Scottish	11-12-93
21	A Kennedy	Saracens v London Welsh	22-10-88
21	M Thomas	Coventry v Morley	19-9-92
21	P Turner	Sale v Fylde	19-9-92
21	S Swindells	Waterloo v Nottingham	30-4-94

MOST TRIES IN A COURAGE DIVISION THREE MATCH

4	B Hanavan	Fylde v Exeter	3-10-87
4	S Walklin	Plymouth Albion v Birmingham	17-10-87
4	I Russell	Plymouth Albion v Fylde	31-10-87
4	B Hanavan	Fylde v Birmingham	7-11-87
4	D Cottrell	Clifton v Askeans	4-1-92
4	M Sephton	Liverpool St Helens v Aspatria	13-3-93
4	D Crompton	Liverpool St Helens v Aspatria	13-3-93
4	M Farrar	Otley v Askeans	27-3-93
4	B Hanavan	Fylde v Redruth	9-4-94

MOST POINTS IN A COURAGE DIVISION THREE MATCH

28	S Burnage	Fylde v Birmingham	7-11-87
25	D Cundy	Plymouth Albion v Metropolitan Police	26-11-89
25	M Rodgers	Sheffield v Askians	13-3-93
25	R Angell	Coventry v Redruth	30-4-94
24	C Howard	Rugby v Maidstone	26-11-88
23	J Stabler	West Hartlepool v Broughton Park	9-3-91
22	A Atkinson	Wakefield v Metropolitan Police	24-9-88
22	S Hogg	Clifton v Lydney	28-3-92
22	K O'Brien	Broughton Park v Askeans	11-4-92
22	M Livesey	Richmond v Blackheath	13-11-93
21	J Stabler	West Hartlepool v Sheffield	3-10-87
21	G Hughes	London Welsh v Fylde	13-1-90
21	P Rutledge	Otley v Askians	27-3-93
21	J Hoad	Richmond v Fylde	5-2-94
21	A Finie	Bedford v Coventry	23-4-94
20	S Burnage	Fylde v Exeter	3-10-87
20	R Adamson	Wakefield v Vale of Lune	27-2-88

MOST TRIES IN A COURAGE DIVISION FOUR MATCH

3	J Phillips	Clifton v Leeds	30-10-93
3	J Phillips	Clifton v Sudbury	20-11,93
3	M Wyatt	Clifton v Sudbury	20-11-93
3	J Hopkinson	Harrogate v Broughton Park	11-12-93
3	R Bailey	Plymouth v Broughton Park	12-3-94
3	M Richardson	Aspatria v Plymouth	23-4-94
3	E Atkins	Harrogate v Aspatria	30-4-94
3	P Taylor	Harrogate v Aspatria	30-4-94

MOST POINTS IN A COURAGE DIVISION FOUR MATCH

23	R Zoing	Harrogate v Plymouth	23-3-94
22	M Rogers	Sheffield v Leeds	13-11-93
21	K O'Brien	Broughton Park v Liverpool St Helens	22-1-94
21	R Larkin	Askeans v Aspatria	9-4-94
20	D Breakwell	Leeds v Aspatria	23-10-93
18	S Hogg	Clifton v Sheffield	4-12-93
18	J Cowling	Sudbury v Askeans	8-1-94
18	S Hogg	Clifton v Aspatria	12-2-94
18	S Mason	Liverpool St Helens v Leeds	12-3-94

TOP POINTS SCORERS DIVISION ONE 1993-94 (OVER 50)

PTS	PLAYER	CLUB	T	C	P	D
202	Jez Harris	Leicester	2	18	41	11
178	Jon Callard	Bath	4	25	36	—
161	Mark Tainton	Bristol	—	19	40	1
159	Rob Andrew	Wasps	2	16	38	1
143	Kent Bray	Harlequins	1	12	38	—
132	Paul Grayson	Northampton	2	10	33	1
84	Simon Langford	Orrell	2	10	18	—
82	Tim Smith	Gloucester	—	8	21	1
79	David Johnson	Newcastle	—	5	22	1
75	Michael Corcoran	London Irish	3	3	18	—
65	Gerry Ainscough	Orrell	—	13	13	—
55	Paul Challinor	Harlequins	2	3	12	1
55	Darren O'Leary	Harlequins	11	—	—	—

100 POINTS IN A COURAGE SEASON DIVISION ONE

PTS	PLAYER	CLUB	SEASON	T	C	P	D
202	Jez Harris	Leicester	1993-94	2	18	41	11
178	Jon Callard	Bath	1993-94	4	25	36	—
161	Mark Tainton	Bristol	1993-94	—	19	40	1
159	Rob Andrew	Wasps	1993-94	2	16	38	1
143	Kent Bray	Harlequins	1993-94	1	12	38	—
132	Paul Grayson	Northampton	1993-94	2	10	33	1
129	John Liley	Leicester	1991-92	4	19	25	—
126	Dusty Hare	Leicester	1987-88	—	15	31	1
126	John Liley	Leicester	1989-90	7	16	22	—
126	Rob Andrew	Wasps	1990-91	4	16	26	—
122	Jon Webb	Bath	1992-93	3	19	23	—
120	David Pears	Harlequins	1990-91	1	16	23	5
114	David Pears	Harlequins	1989-90	2	14	24	2
111	Michael Corcoran	London Irish	1992-93	2	4	31	—
110	John Liley	Leicester	1990-91	2	18	22	—
110	John Steele	Northampton	1991-92	—	10	28	2
109	Martin Strett	Orrell	1990-91	1	21	20	—
107	David Pears	Harlequins	1991-92	4	15	21	—
106	John Liley	Leicester	1992-93	2	15	22	—
104	Martin Strett	Orrell	1989-90	4	4	20	—
104	Martin Strett	Orrell	1991-92	1	8	26	2
103	Rob Andrew	Wasps	1988-89	2	13	21	2
103	Stuart Barnes	Bath	1989-90	6	29	7	—
101	Steve Pilgrim	Wasps	1991-92	2	6	27	—

TOP POINTS SCORERS DIVISION TWO 1993-94 (OVER 100)

PTS	PLAYER	CLUB	T	C	P	D
171	Guy Gregory	Nottingham	1	11	43	5
149	Andy Tunningley	Saracens	5	14	31	1
144	Paul Turner	Sale	1	29	24	3
137	Steve Swindells	Waterloo	2	5	39	—
119	Peter Rutledge	Otley	3	10	28	—
115	Mark Mapletoft	Rugby	5	9	22	2
103	John Stabler	West Hartlepool	1	16	20	2

100 POINTS IN A COURAGE SEASON DIVISION TWO

PTS	PLAYER	CLUB	SEASON	T	C	P	D
171	Guy Gregory	Nottingham	1993-94	1	11	43	5
149	Andy Tunningley	Saracens	1993-94	5	14	31	1
147	David Johnson	Newcastle Gosforth	1991-92	1	31	26	3
144	Paul Turner	Sale	1993-94	1	29	24	3
138	Andy Kennedy	Saracens	1988-89	5	14	30	—
137	Steve Swindells	Waterloo	1993-94	2	5	39	—
136	David Johnson	Newcastle Gosforth	1992-93	1	16	30	3
126	Paul Grayson	Waterloo	1992-93	1	8	29	6
124	Nick Grecian	London Scottish	1991-92	11	13	18	—
120	Martin Livesey	Richmond	1989-90	3	24	20	—
119	Peter Rutledge	Otley	1993-94	3	10	28	—
118	John Stabler	West Hartlepool	1991-92	2	16	26	—
117	Brian Mullen	London Irish	1990-91	1	16	22	5
115	Mark Mapletoft	Rugby	1993-94	5	9	22	2
111	Ian Aitchison	London Irish	1989-90	—	18	22	3
106	Guy Gregory	Nottingham	1992-93	1	10	18	9
105	John Steele	Northampton	1989-90	2	11	22	3
103	John Stabler	West Hartlepool	1993-94	1	16	20	2
102	David Pears	Sale	1988-89	3	3	26	2
101	Robert Liley	Wakefield	1992-93	1	9	24	2
100	Chris Howard	Rugby	1989-90	3	17	16	1
100	Brian Mullen	London Irish	1988-89	—	8	25	3

TOP POINTS SCORERS DIVISION THREE 1993-94 (OVER 100)

PTS	PLAYER	CLUB	T	C	P	D
172	Andy Finnie	Bedford	—	14	45	3
151	Richard Angell	Coventry	3	23	29	1
125	Andy Green	Exeter	3	16	24	2
117	Jamie Grayshon	Morley	—	12	28	3
109	Andy Parker	Fylde	3	17	20	—

100 POINTS IN A COURAGE SEASON DIVISION THREE

PTS	PLAYER	CLUB	SEASON	T	C	P	D
172	Andy Finnie	Bedford	1993-94	—	14	45	3
151	Richard Angell	Coventry	1993-94	3	23	29	1
125	Andy Green	Exeter	1993-94	3	16	24	2
123	Chris Howard	Rugby	1988-89	7	19	19	—
122	Andy Green	Exeter	1992-93	—	10	31	3
121	Steve Burnage	Fylde	1987-88	4	30	14	1
121	Peter Rutledge	Otley	1992-93	3	14	26	—
117	Jamie Grayshon	Morley	1993-94	—	12	28	3
109	Andy Parker	Fylde	1993-94	3	17	20	—

108	Martin Livesey	Plymouth	1987-88	2	23	17	1
108	Mark Rodgers	Sheffield	1990-91	7	7	22	—
106	Mike Jackson	Fylde	1991-92	1	12	26	—
105	Ray Adamson	Wakefield	1987-88	1	19	21	—
102	Andy Higgin	Vale of Lune	1989-90	—	9	22	
101	Dominic Cundy	Plymouth	1988-89	1	20	—	
100	Simon Hogg	Clifton	1991-92	2	16	19	1

TOP POINTS SCORERS DIVISION FOUR 1993-94 (OVER 100)

PTS	PLAYER	CLUB	T	C	P	D
222	Simon Hogg	Clifton	3	24	40	13
150	Mark Rodgers	Sheffield	3	12	37	—
140	Simon Mason	Liverpool St Helens	2	16	30	1
129	Mike Scott	Aspatria	1	1	33	1
117	Richard Larkin	Askeans	—	9	29	4
106	Ralph Zoing	Harrogate	1	16	20	3

100 POINTS IN A COURAGE SEASON DIVISION FOUR

PTS	PLAYER	CLUB	SEASON	T	C	P	D
222	Simon Hogg	Clifton	1993-94	3	24	40	13
150	Mark Rodgers	Sheffield	1993-94	3	12	37	—
140	Simon Mason	Liverpool St Helens	1993-94	2	—	30	1
129	Mike Scott	Aspatria	1993-94	1	1	33	1
117	Richard Larkin	Askeans	1993-94	—	9	29	4
106	Ralph Zoing	Harrogate	1993-94	1	16	20	3

MOST CAREER POINTS IN THE COURAGE LEAGUE

620 Martin Livesey, Plymouth (108), Richmond (512)
569 John Stabler, West Hartlepool
564 Kevin Plant, Rotherham
563, Andy Green, Exeter
554 Andy Finnie, Bedford
546 Rob Andrew, Wasps
531 John Liley, Wakefield (22), Leicester (509)
511 Ralph Zoing, Harrogate
508 Simon Hogg, Bristol (115), Clifton (393)
499 Simon Hodgkinson, Nottingham (416), Moseley (83)
490 Tim Smith, Gloucester
490 Jamie Grayshon, Morley
484 David Johnson, Newcastle Gosforth

500 POINTS IN A CAREER FOR ONE CLUB

569 John Stabler, West Hartlepool
564 Kevin Plant, Rotherham
563, Andy Green, Exeter
554 Andy Finnie, Bedford
546 Rob Andrew, Wasps
512 Martin Livesey, Richmond
511 Ralph Zoing, Harrogate
509 John Liley, Leicester

100 POINTS IN A SEASON FOR 3 CLUBS

Paul Grayson — Preston 1991-92, Waterloo 1992-93, Northampton 1993-94

100 POINTS IN A SEASON FOR 2 CLUBS

David Pears — Sale 1988-89, Harlequins 1989-90, 1990-91, 1991-92
Martin Livesey — Plymouth 1987-88, Richmond 1989-90

100 POINTS IN A SEASON ON MOST OCCASIONS

4 John Liley, Leicester
4 David Pears, Sale (1), Harlequins (3)
3 Rob Andrew, Wasps 3 Martin Strett, Orrell
3 Paul Grayson, Preston (1), Waterloo (1), Northampton (1)

MOST TRIES IN A CAREER FOR ONE CLUB

39 Tony Swift, Bath
36 Glyn Melville, Otley
35 Brendan Hanavan, Fylde 35 Paul Scott, Rotherham
33 Mark Wyatt, Clifton 33 Eddie Saunders, Rugby 33 Richard Selkirk, Rotherham
32 Tony Clarke, Morley

MOST CAREER TRIES

39 Tony Swift, Bath
38 Brendan Melville, Fylde (35), Liverpool St Helens (3)
36 Glyn Melville, Otley
35 Paul Scott, Rotherham
33 Mark Wyatt, Clifton 33 Eddie Saunders, Rugby 33 Richard Selkirk, Rotherham
32 Tony Clarke, Morley

MOST CONVERSIONS IN A CAREER FOR ONE CLUB

91 Ralph Zoing, Harrogate
90 Kevin Plant, Rotherham
79 John Stabler, West Hartlepool
74 Martin Livesey, Richmond

MOST CAREER COMVERSIONS

97 Martin Livesey, Plymouth (23), Richmond (74)
91 Ralph Zoing, Harrogate
90 Kevin Plant, Rotherham
79 John Stabler, West Hartlepool
76 John Liley, Wakefield (4), Leicester (72)
65 Stuart Barnes, Bath 65 David Johnson, Newcastle Gosforth
58 Rob Andrew, Wasps
57 Jon Webb, Bristol (16), Bath (41)
53 Tim Smith, Gloucester
52 Chris Howard, Rugby 52 Andy Green, Exeter
51 Jamie Grayshon, Morley
49 David Pears, Sale (3), Harlequins (46)
47 Andy Finnie, Bedford

MOST PENALTIES IN A CAREER FOR ONE CLUB

133 Andy Finnie, Bedford
122 Andy Green, Exeter
119 Rob Andrew, Wasps
118 Tim Smith, Gloucester

MOST CAREER PENALTIES
133 Andy Finnie, Bedford
123, Simon Hodgkinson, Nottingham (100), Moseley (23)
122 Andy Green, Exeter
119 Rob Andrew, Wasps
118 Tim Smith, Gloucester
118 John Stabler, West Hartlepool
117 Martin Livesey, Plymouth (17), Richmond (100)
114 John Graves, Rosslyn Park
111 Jamie Grayshon, Morley
107 Kevin Plant, Rotherham
105 David Johnson, Newcastle Gosforth
103 John Liley, Wakefield (2), Leicester (101)
98 Ian Aitchison, Waterloo (76), London Irish (22)
97 David Pears, Sale (26), Harlequins (71)
95 John Steele, Northampton
95 Ralph Zoing, Harrogate

MOST DROP GOALS IN A CAREER FOR ONE CLUB
22 Jez Harris, Leicester
19 Guy Gregory, Nottingham
17 Simon Hogg, Clifton
16 Andy Finnie, Bedford

MOST CAREER DROP GOALS
22 Jez Harris, Leicester
22 Simon Hogg, Bristol (5), Clifton (17)
19 Guy Gregory, Nottingham
16 Andy Higgin, Vale of Lune (12), Liverpool St Helens (4)
16 Andy Finnie, Bedford
16 Jon King, Blakheath
16 Andy Rimmer, Broughton Park
15 Martin Livesey, Plymouth (1), Richmond (14)
13 Richard Pell, Rugby
12 Andy Green, Exeter
11 Ian Aitchison, Waterloo (8), London Irish (3)
11 John Steele, Northampton
11 Kevin Plant, Rotherham

DIVISION ONE TEAM RECORDS
MOST POINTS IN A SEASON
431, Bath, 1993-94, 1st
425, Leicester, 1993-94, 2nd
362, Wasps, 1993-94, 3rd
355, Bath, 1992-93, 1st
333, Harlequins, 1993-94, 6th
331, Bristol, 1993-94, 4th
327, Orrell, 1993-94, 7th
305, Northampton, 1993-94, 5th
280, Bath, 1990-91, 1st
277, Bath, 1991-92, 1st

NATIONAL LEAGUE ONE

RESULTS AND LEAGUE TABLES
1987-1994
Pages 56-59

MEMBER CLUBS
1994-95

NATIONAL LEAGUE ONE RESULTS

1987-88

		1	2	3	4	5	6	7	8	9	10	11	12
1	Bath		15-9			21-9		14.0		23-18			10-17
2	Bristol				16-21			21-10			37-3	12-12	N/P
3	Coventry	9-9	25-3			12-15			15-20	11-24	24-19		15-10
4	Gloucester	9-16		39-3			18-12	17-9		61-7	13-24		
5	Harlequins		28-22		9-9		9-12		34-8	6-12	66-0		37-4
6	Leicester	24-13	15-10	32-16	N/P						42-15	12-9	39-15
7	Moseley			26-3		11-32	3-21			28-10		19-12	27-3
8	Nottingham	25-15	3-16				13-22	21-12		12-12			
9	Orrell		13-25		9-13		30-6				19-0		30-6
10	Sale	17-46						15-19	3-17			6-14	
11	Wasps	19-15		49-6		17-16			17-9	23-15			
12	Waterloo				16-6				10-9		29-13	13-22	

1988-89

		1	2	3	4	5	6	7	8	9	10	11	12
1	Bath		16-9	19-9					22-16	36-12		16-6	38-9
2	Bristol				18-6		50-14	18-0		15-6			14-3
3	Gloucester		10-11			28-0		37-9	13-6			19-3	
4	Harlequins	9-26		26-11			15-6	38-15					23-24
5	Leicester	15-12	13-12		21-31					15-27	28-15	15-6	
6	Liverpool St. Helens	7-21		9-31		12-23			15-22		12-32		
7	Moseley	0-38				22-13	18-15			10-12	7-13		13-6
8	Nottingham		10-6		12-0	12-12		13-9				9-15	
9	Orrell			6-16	16-15		20-24		12-6			9-9	15-12
10	Rosslyn Park	6-19	18-16	8-26	12-16				9-18	19-13			
11	Wasps		21-9		23-15		16-10	39-10			39-16		
12	Waterloo			15-15		22-34	6-12		9-18		14-24	0-29	

1989-90

		1	2	3	4	5	6	7	8	9	10	11	12
1	Bath		76-0			32-12	26-15	27-9			34-6		
2	Bedford			6-16		8-71		0-24		7-25		3-22	9-44
3	Bristol	13-14			6-13		11-13	13-9			6-15		21-22
4	Gloucester	13-6	37-6			24-9			16-10	41-12	21-21		
5	Harlequins			13-7			15-12		22-27	15-9	19-15		12-9
6	Leicester		60-3		16-26			38-20	15-6		34-6		
7	Moseley			10-16	12-16	22-21			6-22				0-42
8	Nottingham	12-9	47-16		12-3					9-25	6-11	25-12	
9	Orrell	6-9		12-15			33-10	25-13			64-14		
10	Rosslyn Park		45-12			9-23	18-6					13-15	6-14
11	Saracens	9-7	17-12		15-9		33-13		12-6				
12	Wasps	9-18			29-4		29-12		16-12	12-6		24-6	

1990-91

	1	2	3	4	5	6	7	8	9	10	11	12	13
1 Bath				23-3		46-3	11-6			17-9	45-21		15-16
2 Bristol	3-10		15-12		10-6				6-22	3-36		25-6	
3 Gloucester	15-17			38-19			30-12		22-6	9-16		21-16	
4 Harlequins	,38-16				41-12	33-6	21-6			18-6		12-18	
5 Leicester	3-9		18-6	12-15					25-9	15-12	29-6		
6 Liverpool St. Helens		6-7	7-26			7-28		13-23	12-13			3-17	
7 Moseley		9-9			19-43	20-12		10-16			9-19	,9-22	
8 Northampton	10-16	12-9	6-7		18-28				22-15			15-6	
9 Nottingham	9-22			6-19			12-7			16-12		3-28	12-10
10 Orrell				12-9		38-0	16-0	60-0			12-3		12-14
11 Rosslyn Park		16-13	17-12		17-15	39-9		48-0	9-15				
12 Saracens	6-49			7-39			21-6			19-12	13-11		6-15
13 Wasps		46-19	14-9		12-22	51-4		21-21			13-10		

1991-92

	1	2	3	4	5	6	7	8	9	10	11	12	13
1 Bath		9-4	29-9		37-6		15-6	25-15				32-12	
2 Bristol				16-0		14-19	9-15			22-4	48-4		10-33
3 Gloucester		29-15			21-3	22-15	10-17			12-9			15-10
4 Harlequins	18-18		21-18		20-13			23-6	7-10			21-37	
5 Leicester		25-9				36-13	19-22			51-16	22-22		31-12
6 London Irish	21-26			3-39				7-21		12-12	6-6		18-13
7 Northampton				24-14		12-12		12-3		21-12	29-0		28-15
8 Nottingham		0-32	3-14		14-27	9-12	18-9			34-9			
9 Orrell	10-9	23-9	18-12		21-9			20-6				23-0	
10 Rosslyn Park	13-21		12-24					4-22			7-15	6-10	7-15
11 Rugby	0-32		16-19	29-20				9-9	7-21			6-22	
12 Saracens		13-4	12-12		9-20	27-9	9-14	13-12					
13 Wasps	12-24			20-6				11-7	13-12		17-10	6-12	

1992-93

	1	2	3	4	5	6	7	8	9	10	11	12	13
1 Bath				22-6	13-3	42-19	40-6		39-3	16-7		22-11	
2 Bristol	8-13		9-22		15-0				23-11		12-7		19-11
3 Gloucester	0-20			25-5					8-13	21-12	19-5		6-21
4 Harlequins		16-0				47-24	22-22	7-12		35-14		13-15	
5 Leicester			22-21	23-0					9-0		30-3		21-8
6 London Irish		9-7	9-18		14-30			12-3			10-9		25-13
7 London Scottish		8-11	8-3		11-28	28-21		21-34					10-15
8 Northampton	11-8	16-6	16-21		12-13						21-17		55-9
9 Orrell				18-16		8-12	13-10	9-10		66-0	10-11		
10 Rugby		21-32			5-28	1-14	20-45	7-13				3-34	
11 Saracens	13-19			3-18			41-17		6-9	14-9		9-13	
12 Wasps		7-6	19-9		14-13	18-9	10-6	20-12					
13 West Hartlepool	10-38			9-12					39-15	5-6	3-10	6-19	

NATIONAL LEAGUE ONE TABLES

1987-88

	P	W	D	L	F	A	Pts
Leicester	10	9	0	1	225	133	37
Wasps	11	8	1	2	218	136	36
Harlequins	11	6	1	4	261	128	30
Bath	11	6	1	4	197	156	30
Gloucester	10	6	1	3	206	121	29
Orrell	11	5	1	5	192	153	27
Moseley	11	5	0	6	167	170	26
Nottingham	11	4	1	6	146	170	24
Bristol	10	4	1	5	171	145	23
Waterloo	10	4	0	6	123	208	22
Coventry	11	3	1	7	133	246	21
Sale	11	0	0	11	95	374	0

1990-91

	P	W	D	L	F	A	Pts
Bath	12	11	0	1	280	104	22
Wasps	12	9	1	2	252	151	19
Harlequins	12	8	0	4	267	162	16
Leicester	12	8	0	4	244	140	16
Orrell	12	7	0	5	247	105	14
Gloucester	12	6	0	6	207	163	12
Rosslyn Park	12	6	0	6	216	174	12
Nottingham	12	6	0	6	138	194	12
Northampton	12	5	1	6	149	254	11
Saracens	12	5	0	7	151	228	10
Bristol	12	4	1	7	135	219	9
Moseley	12	1	1	10	113	244	3
Liverpool St. H.	12	0	0	12	88	349	0

1988-89

	P	W	D	L	F	A	Pts
Bath	11	10	0	1	263	98	20
Gloucester	11	7	1	3	215	112	15
Wasps	11	7	1	3	206	138	15
Nottingham	11	6	1	4	142	122	13
Orrell	11	6	1	4	148	157	13
Leicester	11	6	1	4	189	199	13
Bristol	11	6	0	5	188	117	12
Harlequins	11	5	0	6	194	184	10
Rosslyn Park	11	5	0	6	172	208	10
Moseley	11	3	0	8	113	242	6
Waterloo	11	1	1	9	120	235	3
Liverpool St. H.	11	1	0	10	116	254	2

1991-92

	P	W	D	L	F	A	PD	Pts
Bath	12	10	1	1	277	126	151	20
Orrell	12	10	0	2	204	95	109	20
Northampton	12	9	1	2	209	136	73	19
Gloucester	12	7	1	4	193	168	11	15
Saracens	12	7	1	4	176	165	11	15
Leicester	12	6	1	5	262	216	46	13
Wasps	12	6	0	6	177	180	-3	12
Harlequins	12	5	1	6	213	207	6	11
London Irish	12	3	3	6	147	237	-90	9
Bristol	12	4	0	8	192	174	18	8
Rugby	12	2	3	7	124	252	-128	7
Nottingham	12	2	1	9	133	204	-71	5
Rosslyn Park	12	0	1	11	111	258	-147	1

1989-90

	P	W	D	L	F	A	Pts
Wasps	11	9	0	2	250	106	18
Gloucester	11	8	1	2	214	139	17
Bath	11	8	0	3	258	104	16
Saracens	11	7	1	3	168	167	15
Leicester	11	6	0	5	248	184	12
Nottingham	11	6	0	5	187	148	12
Harlequins	11	6	0	5	218	180	12
Orrell	11	5	0	6	221	132	10
Bristol	11	4	0	7	136	144	8
Rosslyn Park	11	4	0	7	164	243	8
Moseley	11	2	0	9	138	258	4
Bedford	11	0	0	11	70	467	0

1992-93

	P	W	D	L	F	A	PD	Pts
Bath	12	11	0	1	355	97	258	22
Wasps	12	11	0	1	186	118	118	68
Leicester	12	9	0	3	220	116	104	18
Northampton	12	8	0	4	215	150	65	16
Gloucester	12	6	0	6	173	151	22	12
Bristol	12	6	0	6	148	169	-21	12
London Irish	12	6	0	6	175	223	-48	12
Harlequins	12	5	1	6	197	187	10	11
Orrell	12	5	0	7	175	183	-8	10
London Scottish	12	3	1	8	192	248	-56	7
Saracens	12	3	0	9	137	180	-43	6
West Hartlepool	12	3	0	9	149	236	-87	6
Rugby	12	1	0	11	104	368	-264	2

NATIONAL LEAGUE ONE STATISTICS 1993/94

RESULTS

		1	2	3	4	5	6	7	8	9	10
1	Bath		9-0	46-17	32-13	14-6	28-8	46-3	37-9	13-7	24-8
2	Bristol	10-18		16-12	20-16	40-22	21-8	26-0	22-31	30-17	15-16
3	Gloucester	6-16	6-24		24-20	14-23	9-10	15-9	19-14	30-25	9-9
4	Harlequins	12-14	15-20	38-20		13-25	30-15	12-6	15-7	13-20	22-17
5	Leicester	9-6	21-9	28-8	3-10		38-3	66-5	36-9	23-18	38-6
6	London Irish	31-32	0-16	12-15	7-33	10-22		17-19	13-16	19-6	14-10
7	Newcastle Gosforth	5-29	13-22	12-12	3-22	13-22	9-13		8-28	13-12	16-18
8	Northampton	9-30	22-19	19-3	15-14	19-10	23-12	43-23		9-13	15-17
9	Orrell	15-18	16-13	6-10	21-20	0-18	24-3	42-12	27-6		42-24
10	Wasps	13-19	34-8	29-18	18-15	13-15	21-22	38-21	24-11	28-16	

WEEK BY WEEK POSITIONS

	18/9	25/9	2/10	9/10	13/11	20/11	4/12	11/12	8/1	15/1	29/1	12/2	12/3	26/3	9/4	23/4	30/4
Bath	1	1	1	1	1	1	1	1	1	1	1	1	1	1	1	1	1
Bristol	2	3	6	7	5	7	6	7	6	6	5	7	6	5	4	4	4
Gloucester	5	8	9	9	9	9	8	8	8	5	7	8	7	8	8	8	8
Quins	7	7	5	3	2	3	4	4	4	4	4	4	4	4	6	6	6
Leicester	3	4	2	2	3	2	2	2	2	2	2	2	2	2	2	2	2
London Irish	9	10	8	8	8	8	9	9	9	9	9	9	9	9	9	9	9
Newcastle Gosforth	5	9	10	10	10	10	10	10	10	10	10	10	10	10	10	10	10
Northampton	10	5	3	4	6	6	7	5	7	8	6	5	5	6	5	5	5
Orrell	8	6	7	6	4	4	5	6	5	7	8	6	8	7	7	7	7
Wasps	4	2	4	5	7	5	3	3	3	3	3	3	3	3	3	3	3

PLAYING RECORD AND POINTS BREAKDOWN

								HOME						AWAY				
	P	W	D	L	F	A	Pts	P	W	D	L	F	A	P	W	D	L	F	A
Bath	18	17	0	1	431	181	34	9	9	0	0	249	71	9	8	0	1	182	110
Leicester	18	14	0	4	425	210	28	9	8	0	1	262	74	9	6	0	3	163	136
Wasps	18	10	1	7	362	340	21	9	6	0	3	218	145	9	4	1	4	144	195
Bristol	18	10	0	8	331	276	20	9	6	0	3	200	140	9	4	0	5	131	136
Northampton	18	9	0	9	305	342	18	9	6	0	3	174	126	9	3	0	6	141	201
Harlequins	18	8	0	10	333	287	16	9	5	0	4	170	144	9	3	0	6	163	143
Orrell	18	8	0	10	327	302	16	9	6	0	3	193	124	9	2	0	7	134	178
Gloucester	18	6	2	10	247	356	14	9	4	1	4	132	150	9	2	1	6	115	206
London Irish	18	4	0	14	217	391	8	9	1	0	8	123	188	9	3	0	6	94	203
Newcastle Gosforth	18	2	1	15	190	453	5	9	1	1	7	92	178	9	1	0	8	98	305

PULLING
TOGETHER
ON
BEHALF
OF
ENGLISH
RUGBY

Proud Sponsors of
The Courage Clubs Championship
and the England Squad

BATH RFC

Triple Crown Triumph!

Even by Bath's standards this was a very special season especially as this was probably the hardest one ever, in terms of commitment for the players. The home and away league system introduced this season, plus the divisional and international calls at all levels, proved a great demand on players' time and fitness. It was to the great credit of all the squad, the trainers and coaches and the medical teams that the players took the Courage League Title, the Pilk-Ington Cup and, the icing on the cake, the Middlesex Sevens as well. There have been a few famous 'Farewells' over the season with Gareth Chilcott and Richard Hill hanging up their boots but not lost to the club in important other ways. Jack Rowell too left the stage at Bath that had seen the club transformed over the years, to become the 'Ace of Clubs', and now to take England through to the next World Cup.

Success is not only confined to the 1st XV and all the players in all the teams the club runs, plus all the back up staff in whatever capacity, can look back on the 93-94 season with great pride. A new feature on 'The Rec' next season could well be a Bath emerging players XV, the brain child of Gareth Chilcott and Richard Hill, who, in looking towards the next generation of Bath players, have already had a trial run of their embryo team, with great success so far.

Punters arriving at the Rec from now on can witness, arising arising from the south end, the new and exciting 'Teachers Stand', due to be completed in time for the opening league match against Bristol in early September. The fund raising efforts have been enormous and, with all the hospitality suites now taken or spoken for, the enterprise has been one of the biggest events in the club's history. With the government decision not to allow a supermarket to be built at Lambridge, the resultant loss of expected revenue from that venture, which would, in part at least, have gone into facility improvements on 'The Rec', including the playing surface, means that new ways will have to be found to raise the recessary capital. So, with new faces expected at the Bath Club next season to enhance those already there, the new teachers stand in operation and these titles to defend there is already a buzz of excitement and anticipation about.

The Champions pose at Twickenham before conflicting a mighty 'double'   Photo: Joe McCabe

BATH RFC

COURAGE CLUBS CHAMPIONSHIP
NATIONAL DIVISION ONE 1993-94

No	Date	Opponents	Venue	Result	Point Scorers
1	Sep 11	Bristol	A	W18-10	Catt (2T) Callard (C) Barnes (P) Callard (P)
2	Sep 18	Northampton	A	W37-9	Lumsden (2T) Clarke (T) Callard (T)(4C)(3P)
3	Sep 25	Orrell	A	W18-15	Guscott (T) Callard (T)(C)(P) Barnes (P)
4	Oct 2	Gloucester	H	W46-17	Ubogu (2T) Clarke (T) Guscott (T) Adebayo (T) Hill (T) Callard (5C)(2P)
5	Oct 9	Wasps	A	W19-13	Catt (T) Clarke (T) Callard (3P)
6	Nov 13	Newcastle G	H	W46-3	Clarke (T) Hill(T) Barnsey (T) Dawe (T) Lumsden (T) Callard (2C)(5P) Chilcott (C)
7	Nov 20	Leicester	A	L6-9	Barnes (2P)
8	Dec 4	Quins	A	W14-12	Robinson (T) Barnes (2P) Catt (P)
9	Dec 11	L Irish	H	W28-8	Catt(T) Lloyd(T) De Glanville (T) Hill(T) Callard(C)(2P)
10	Jan 8	Bristol	H	W9-0	Callard (3P)
11	Jan 15	Northampton	A	W30-9	Swift (2T) De Glanville (T)(PT) Callard (2C)(2P)
12	Jan 29	Orrell	H	W13-7	Swift (T) Callard (C)(2P)
13	Feb 12	Gloucester	A	W16-6	Ojomoh (T) Callard (C)(3P)
14	Mar 12	Wasps	H	W24-8	Callard (2T)(C)(3P) Barnes (DG)
15	Mar 26	Newcastle	A	W29-5	Haag (2T) Catt (T) Sanders (T) Callard (3C)(P)
16	Apr 9	Leicester	H	W14-6	Swift (T) Callard (3P)
17	Apr 23	Quins	H	W32-13	Clarke (T) De Glanville (T) Hall (T) Hilton (T) Callard (3C)(2P)
18	Apr 30	L Irish	A	W32-31	Egerton (2T) Woodman (T) Rayner (C)(4P)(DG)

COURAGE RECORDS

Jon Callard breaks Jon Webb's points scoring record for a season. Callard finishes up with 178 easily ahead of Webbs 122 set in 1992-93.

	PTS	T	C	P	D	APPS	AVER
John Callard	178	4	25	36	0	15	11.88
Webb	122	3	19	23	0	10	12.20

Callard also equals Webb's record of 5 penalties in a match.
Tony Swift extends both his division one and Bath record for number of career tries to 39.
Stuart Barnes finishes his Courage League career with the following record.

PLD	T	C	P	D	PTS	AVER
72	21	65	71	9	467	6.49

The points, conversions, penalties and drop goals totals are all career records for Bath.

CLUB PLAYING RECORD 1993-94

National Division: One
Final League Position at end of 1993/94 season: 1st
League Playing Record: P 36, W 29, D 0, L 7, Pts F 895, Pts A 499

COMPETITIONS WON DURING 1993-94

Pilkington Cup Winners   Middlesex 7's Winners

BATH PLAYING SQUAD 1994-95

Full Backs — Callard, Lumsden
Wings — Swift, Adebayo, Lloyd, Sleightholme (from Wakefield), Woodman, Geoghegan (from London Irish)
Centres — De Glanville, Guscott, Bamsey, Stuart, Fox, Webber
Fly Half — Catt, Rayner
Scrum Half — Sanders, Olsen, Nicol (from Dundee HS FP after Christmas)
No 8 — Clarke, Peters, Egerton
Flanker — Hall, Robinson, Ojomoh, Maslen, Adam
Locks — Reed, Redman, Haag, McCoy
Props — Hilton, Ubogu, Mallet, Crompton, Clark
Hookers — Dawe, Atkins, French (from Orrell)

BATH RFC

MATCH BY MATCH PLAYERS BY POSITION

Callard	Swift	De Glanville	Catt	Lumsden	Barnes	Hill	Chilcott	Dawes	Obugu	Haag	Redman	Robinson	Hall	Clarke	Sanders	Adams	Guscott	Adabayo	Barnsey	Ojomoh	Lloyd	Egerton	Mallett
16	15	14	12	11	10	9	1	2	3	4	5	6	7	8	R								
16	15	14		11	10	9	1	2	3	4	5	6	7	8									
16	15	14		11	10	9	1	2	3	4	5	6	7	8		16	12						
16		14	10	11		9	1	2	3	4	5	6	7	8			12	15					
16		14	12	15	10	9	3	2	1	4	5	6	7	8					11				
16	15		14	11	10	9	1	2	3	4	5		8	7				12	6				
	15	12	14	16	10	9	1	2	3	4	5	6	8								11	7	
		14	12	16	10	9	1	2			4	5	6	8	7						11		3
16		12	10	15		14		2	3	4			8	7	9	6			14		11		3
16	15	14	12		10			2	3	4		6	8	7	9					11			
16	15	12	14		10	9		2	3	4			7	8				11	6				
16	15	14	12		10	9		2	3	4		6	7					11	8				
16	15	14	12		10			2	3		4	6	7		9			11	8				
16	15	14	12		10			2			4	6	8	7	9			11					3
16	15		12		10			2		5	4	6	7		9			11	8				3
16	15	14	12		10	9		2	3		4	6	8	7				11					
16	15	14	11		10	9		2	3		4	6	8	7				12					
				16						5					9	6			12			11	8

Match 2 Lewis 12. Match 8 Stuart 15. Match 9 McCoy 5, Hill R, Compton 1. Match 10 Clark 1, McCoy 5. Match 11 Clark 1, Reed 5. Match 12 Clark 1, Reed 5. Match 13 Hilton 1, Reed 5. Match 14 Hilton 1, Reed 5. Match 15, Rayner 14, Olsen R, Hilton 1, Atkins R. Match 16 Hilton 1, Reed 5. Match 17 Hilton 1, Reed 5. Match 18 Woodman 15, Fox 14, Raynor 10, Yates 1, Atkins 2, Maslen 4, Peters 7, Compton 3

Andy Robinson shields the ball with Jon Hall and Ben Clarke in support

Photo: Joe McCabe

BATH FC

COURAGE LEAGUE RECORDS

Biggest Home Win: 76-0 v Bedford 13-1-90 CL1   **Defeat:** 10-17 v Waterloo 12-12-87 CL1
Biggest Away Win: 49-6 v Saracens 27-4-91 CL1   **Defeat:** 15-25 v Nottingham 10-10-87 CL1
Most Tries For in a Match: 14 v Bedforc 13-1-90 CL1
Most Tries Against in a Match: 4 v London Irish 30-4-94 CL1
Most consecutive Wins: 15   **Defeats:** Never had more than one
No of Matches failed to Score: 0   **Clean Sheets:** 6   **Drawn Matches:** 2
Most appearances Forward: 81 Graham Dawe
Most appearances Back: 75 Tony Swift
Most consecutive appearances: 50 Tony Swift 9-9-89 thru 25-9-93
Consecutive match scoring Tries: 4 Tony Swift, Jeremy Guscott
Points: 9 Stuart Barnes, Jon Webb, Jon Callard

INDIVIDUAL SCORING RECORDS

IN A MATCH

Most points: 26 Stuart Barnes v W Hartlepool
27-3-93 Away CL1
Most tries: 4 Jeremy Guscott & Tony Swift
v Bedford 13-1-90 Home CL1
Most conversions: 10 Stuart Barnes v Bedford
13-1-90 Home CL1
Most penalities: 5 Jon Webb v Northampton 7-12-91
Home CL1, v Harlequins 19-9-92 Home CL1,
v Gloucester 13-2-93 Away CL1,
Jon Callard v New Gosforth 13-11-93 Home CL1
Most drop goals: 1 on 13 occassions by 5 players.
Stuart Barnes9, Phil Cue 1, Jonathan Palmer 1,
Jeremy Guscott 1, Ed Raynor 1

IN A SEASON

Most points: 178 Jon Callard 1993-94 CL1
Most tries: 10 Jeremy Guscott 1988-89 CL1,
Tony Swift 1989-90 CL1
Most conversions: 29 Stuart Barnes 1989-90 CL1
Most penalties: 36 Jon Callard 1993-94 CL1
Most drop goals: 2 Stuart Barnes 1987-88, 1988-89,
1990-91

IN A CAREER

Most points: 467 Stuart Barnes 1987-94
Most tries: 39 Tony Swift 1987-94
Most conversions: 65 Stuart Barnes 1987-94
Most penalties: 71 Stuart Barnes 1987-94
Most drop goals: 9 Stuart Barnes 1987-94

COURAGE LEAGUE RECORD

	DIV	PLD	W	D	L	F	T	C	P	D	A	T	C	P	D
87-88	1	11	6	1	4	197	28	14	15	4	156	17	8	20	4
88-89	1	11	10	0	1	263	43	17	17	2	98	6	4	22	0
89-90	1	11	8	0	3	258	44	29	8	0	104	8	6	20	0
90-91	1	12	11	0	1	280	39	23	24	2	104	8	6	20	0
91-92	1	12	10	1	1	277	34	18	33	2	126	10	7	20	4
92-93	1	12	11	0	1	355	42	23	32	1	97	7	4	14	4
93-94	1	18	17	0	1	431	46	27	47	2	181	13	7	32	2
		87	73	2	12	2061	276	151	176	13	866	69	42	148	14

SEASON BY SEASON LEADING SCORERS

	Most Points			Most Tries	
1987-88	40	Phil Cue	4	Tony Swift
1988-89	83	Stuart Barnes	10	Jeremy Guscott
1989-90	103	Stuart Barnes	10	Tony Swift
1990-91	98	Stuart Barnes	6	Tony Swift
1991-92	95	Stuart Barnes	8	Tony Swift
1992-93	122	Jon Webb	7	Stuart Barnes
1993-94	178	Jon Callard	5	Mike Catt, Ben Clarke

BATH FC

COURAGE POINT SCORERS

	APPS	SEASON	PTS	T	C	P	D
J Callard	31	1989-94	234	15	27	37	
A Swift	75	1987-94	164	39			
P de Glanville	43	1990-94	41	9			
M Catt	15	1992-94	28	5		1	
A Lumsden	24+1	1987-94	31	7			
S Barnes	72	1987-94	467	21	65	71	9
R Hill	74+1	1987-94	48	11			
G Chillcott	59	1987-94	14	3	1		
G Dawe	81	1987-94	13	3			
V Ubogo	49+2	1989-94	41	9			
M Haag	39	1988-94	18	4			
N Redman	63	1987-94	31	7			
A Robinson	76	1987-94	30	7			
J Hall	57	1987-94	55	13			
B Clarke	34	1991-94	53	11			
I Sanders	7+3	1990-94	5	1			
I Lewis	8	1991-94	4	1			
J Guscott	57	1987-94	128	26	8		1
G Adams	2+1	1993-94	0				
A Adabayo	29	1989-94	44	10			
J Bamsey	18	1987-94	17	4			
S Ojomoh	22	1990-94	5	1			
M Lloyd	5	1993-94	5	1			
D Egerton	38	1987-94	54	13			
R Stuart	1	1993-94	0				
J Mallett	7+2	1991-94	4	1			
D Crompton	2	1993-94	0				
P McCoy	3	1991-94	0				
C Clark	3	1993-94	0				
A Reed	17	1990-94	0				
D Hilton	7	1992-94	5	1			
E Rayner	2	1993-94	17		1	4	1
M Olson	+1	1993-94	0				
C Atkins	2+2	1991-94	0				
M Woodman	1	1993-94	5	1			
S Fox	1	1993-94	0				
K Yates	1	1993-94	0				
N Maslen	12+3	1987-94	4	1			
E Peters	1	1993-94	0				

BATH FC

Club Details

Colours: Blue, white & black
Change of Colours: White & thin blue/black hoops
Date Founded: 1865
Membership: Total 3,880, Playing Members 100, Junior/Youth/Minis 150
Number of Teams: Senior 3 + U21, Junior 10
Programme Advertising Rates: Various
Any Special Occasions during 1994/95: First Sat v BARBARIANS
100 yrs rugby on The Rec

Ground Details

Ground Address: The Recreation Ground, Bath, BA2 6PW
Telephone: 0225 465328 **Fax:** 0225 443253
Directions: Gt Pulteney ST, City Centre
Capacity: Total 8,500, Seated 1400, Standing 7000
Ticket Prices: Adults £50, OAP/Child £40/£25
Training Nights: Mondays & Wednesdays

Club Officials

President: G W Hancock
Chairman: J M Gaynor
Club Secretary: Major J W Quin, 7 Bennett Street, Bath, BA1 2QJ. Tel: (H) 0225 422505 (W) 0225 422505 (F) 0225 443253
Fixtures Secretary: T D Martland, 22 Gainsborough Gardens, Weston Lane, Bath, BA1 4AJ. Tel: (H) 0225 317801 (W) 0272 674481
Press Officer: K Johnstone, 10 St Michaels Court, Monkton Combe, Bath, BA2 7HA. Tel: (H) 0225 723579 (W) 0225 723579 (Fax) 0225 723579
1993/94 1XV Captain: Jon Hall
Director of Coaching: Brian Ashton
Marketing Executive: G Chilcott

Gareth Chilcott enjoys his last match for Bath against Quins winning away 14-12   Photo: Joe McCabe

Price: £1.00
Pages: 40
Colour throughout
At least 12 original pages each issue
An excellent publication

BRISTOL RFC

Bristol Reach Top Table

At the start of the season most pundits ranked Bristol's chances amongst the 'also rans' but the young players proved them wrong by finishing the League season in fourth place, their best ever position. In addition the club had provided four bright, fresh players to the International scene with scrum half Kyran Bracken, full back Paul Hull and lock Simon Shaw gaining England honours and prop Alan Sharp finally rewarded by Scotland.

Club captain Derek Eves, in his fourth but not last season at the helm, captained the Emerging England Players which also included scrum half Rob Kitchin with centre Mark Denney leading the England Colts.

The League programme couldn't have provided a stronger test than with the visit of neighbours, and League Champions, Bath to the Memorial Ground. Bristol enjoyed the better of the opening half hour before the visitors opened up a gap to secure an 18-10 victory.

Two visits to London gave Bristol their first League points of the season with a comfortable 16-nil victory against London Irish followed by an injury time 20-15 win at Harlequins after being 15 points adrift at the interval.

Northampton proved too strong on their visit with fly half Paul Grayson scoring 19 points for The Saints in their 31-22 victory.

With scrum halves Kyran Bracken and Rob Kitchin both out through injury Bristol had to rely on Mark Newall behind the pack for the visit to Edge Hall Road to play Orrell. With ten minutes of the second half gone Bristol were 13-3 ahead and the pack eased off the throttle. Loose tactical kicking, a touch of panic plus two Ainscough penalties and Orrell were on a roll to clinch the game.

Bristol, working with a coaching panel of three, decided to appoint a new Co-ordinator in October. New Zealander Brian Hanlon, from North Harbour, was given a three year contract in time to take charge of preparations for the visit of Gloucester.

Mark Tainton, Bristol's much critised fly half, held his nerve against the Cherry & Whites to kick three penalties and the conversion of Ralph Knibbs' try to lead his side to a 16-12 victory in a game played in appalling conditions.

But the following week things weren't so pleasant as Engand fly half Rob Andrews notched up 19 points as Wasps surged away in the second half at Sudbury to win 34-8.

Signs of a return to League Two were already clearly marked out for Newcastle Gosforth when they flew to Bristol for what was to be a bad tempered and spiteful game. (The visitors had lock Gareth Adams sent off in the first half for stamping after he had already been warned for punching). Despite an uninspired performance Bristol won 26-nil.

Away defeats at Leicester (21-9) and Bath (9-nil) saw Bristol drop to seventh place in the table. Veteran centre Ralph Knibbs wasn't going to let another defeat spoil his 400th game for the Bristol 1st XV as Harlequins came to the Memorial Ground complete with the BBC Rugby Special cameras and the, then, England manager Geoff Cooke in the stand. Knibbs scored a try in the final quarter to help Bristol to a 20-16 victory and the double over Quins.

Only Northampton (22-19) and Wasps (16-15) were to beat Bristol in the run in and the 40-22 victory over Leicester was a fitting climax to the League season.

In the Pilkington Cup Bristol had a home tie against South West One side Henley. Bristol rarely reached top gear, yet were still able to run in seven tries and never looked in serious danger. For their troubles Bristol were drawn against Bath in the next round which meant another match at the Recreation Ground just 14 days after their League encounter. Bath won this game 14-9 with Tainton kicking three penalties.

Bristol entertained two touring sides during the season and lost to both — The South African Barbarians 45-13 and Auckland 44-8. This season New Zealand side Canterbury will be at the Memorial Ground in November.

Bristol's policy of developing its young players continued with no less than 18 of them making 1st XV debuts during the season. Fly half Mark Tainton notched up 304 points in the campaign to take him to 1501 in his career for the senior side. He becomes the fourth Bristol player to reach 1500. Only Alan Pearn, twice, and Dave Sorrell have scored more than 304 for Bristol in a season. His 161 League points during 1993-94 is a new club record and takes him to 311 in his League Career.

Bristol beat Gloucester 26-5 in the final of the Worthington National Tens at Kingsholm. Wing David John ran in eight tries in the competition.

The club's match programme was voted The Most Improved Programme for 1992/93 by the Rugby Programme Club. This season (1993/94) it was runner up to Llanelli which was the Best Programme, so it can rightly claim to be the Best in England.

BRISTOL RFC

COURAGE CLUBS CHAMPIONSHIP
NATIONAL DIVISION ONE 1993-94

No	Date	Opponents	Venue	Result	Point Scorers
1	Sep 11	Bath	H	L10-18	Saverimutto (T) Tainton (C)(P)
2	Sep 18	L. Irish	A	W16-0	Wring (T) Tainton (1C)(3P)
3	Sep 25	Quins	A	W20-15	Eves (T) Saverimutto (T) Tainton (2C)(2P)
4	Oct 2	Northampton	H	L22-31	Hull (2T)(C) Saverimutto (T) Eves (T)
5	Oct 9	Orrell	A	L13-16	Saverimutto (T) Tainton (C)(2P)
6	Nov 13	Gloucester	H	W16-12	Knibbs (T) Tainton (C)(3P)
7	Nov 20	Wasps	A	L8-34	Bracken (T) Tainton (P)
8	Dec 4	Newcastle	H	W26-0	Hull (T) Saverimutto (T) John (T) Tainton (C)(3P)
9	Dec 11	Leicester	A	L9-21	Tainton (3P)
10	Jan 8	Bath	A	L0-9	
11	Jan 15	L. Irish	H	W21-8	Saverimutto (T) Kitchin (T) Tainton (C)(3P)
12	Jan 29	Quins	H	W20-16	John (T) Blackmore (T) Knibbs (T) Tainton (C)(P)
13	Feb 12	Northampton	A	L19-22	Eves (T) Barrow (T) Tainton (3P)
14	Mar 12	Orrell	H	W30-17	Hull (2T) Bracken (T) Tainton (3C)(3P)
15	Mar 26	Gloucester	A	W24-6	Kitchin (T) Saverimutto (T) Tainton (3C)(DG)
16	Apr 19	Wasps	H	L15-16	Tainton (5P)
17	Apr 23	Newcastle G	A	W22-13	Saverimutto (T) Tainton (C)(4P) KNibbs (DG)
18	Apr 30	Leicester	H	W40-22	Hull (2T) Patten (2T) Denney (T) Tainton (3C)(3P)

ADDITIONAL RESULTS 1993-94

Date	Opponents		V	RES	F	A
4 Sept	Barnstaple		A	W	67	3
16 Oct	Sale		H	L	19	28
30 Oct	Nottingham		A	W	29	3
1 Nov	S A Barbarians	Mon	H	L	13	45
3 Nov	Combined Services	Wed	H	L	7	19
6 Nov	Moseley		A	W	27	9
22 Nov	Auckland	Mon	H	L	7	44
26 Nov	Newbury	Fri	H	W	63	13
(Abandoned 70 mins fog)						
18 Dec	Henley (Pilkington Cup r4)		H	W	46	6
27 Dec	Newport	Mon	A	L	7	53
1 Jan	Clifton		H	W	39	14
15 Jan	London Irish		H	W	10	nil
22 Jan	Bath (Pilkington Cup r5)		A	L	9	14
2 Feb	Bridgend	Wed	A	L	12	29
18 Feb	Cardiff	Fri	H	W	32	12
26 Feb	Aberavon		H	W	20	15
1 Mar	Clifton	Tue	A	W	30	12
4 Mar	Exeter	Fri	A	W	13	6
16 Mar	Pontypridd	Wed	A	L	3	48
4 Apr	Glamorgan Wanderers	Mon	A	W	28	10
16 Apr	Cradiff		A	cancelled		

CLUB PLAYING RECORD 1993-94

National Division: One
Final League Position at end 1993/94 Season: 4th
League Playing Record: P 18, W 10, D 0, L 8,
Pts F 331, Pts A 276
Season Playing Record: P 38, W 22, D 0, L 16,
Pts F 812, Pts A 661

COURAGE RECORDS

Mark Tainton breaks a number of Bristol scoring records in Courage League matches. He started by passing Jon Webbs Bristol career record of 155 points and he finished the season with 300 career points his 161 points for the season beat his own seasonal record of 68 set this previous season.

CAREER	PTS	T	C	P	D	APPS	AVER
Mark Tainton	300		36	74	2	41	7.32
Jon Webb	155	3	16	37		22	7.05

Tainton also broke the seasonal record for conversions and penalties, 19 and 40 respectively. He also extended his career conversions record to 36 and passed Jon Webbs career penalties record of 37 and ended the season with 74.

Alistair Saverimutto broke Pete Stiffs record of 5 tries in a season while Paul Hull's 6 tries for the season saw him pass John Davies's career record of 10 and end the season with 15.

Derek Eves ends the season with the record for the most consecutive division one appearances, 68.

BRISTOL RFC

MATCH BY MATCH PLAYERS BY POSITION

Hull	John	Saverimutto	Wring	Crossland	Tainton	Bracken	Sharp	Regan	Hinkins	Stiff	Shaw	Armstrong	Eves	Barrow	Palmer	Blackmore	Kitchin	Newall	Pearson	Knibbs	Whitehead	Smith	Adams
A	B	C	D	E	F	G	H	I	J	K	L	M	N	O									
A	B	C	D	E	F	G	H		J	R	L	M	N	O	I		K						
A	B	C	D	E	F	G	H		J		L		N	O	I		K	R					
A	B	C	D	E	F		H		J		K	M	N	O	I	L		G					
A	B	C	D	E	F		H		J		K		N	O	I	L		G	M				
A	B	C			F	G		I	J		L	K	N	O					M	D	E	H	
	B	C			F	G		I	J		L		O	N			K	R	M	D	E	H	
A	B	C		E	F		H	I	J				O	N		L		G	M	D			K
A	B	C		E	F		H	I	J	K			O	N				G	M	D			L
A	B	C		E	F		H	I	J	K		M	O	N		L	G			D			
A	B	C		E	F	G		I	J	K		M	N	O		L	R			D			
A	B	C		E	F	G	H	I	J	K		M	N	O						D			
A	B	C			F	G	H	I	J	K		R	O	N		L	E			D			
A	B		D		F	G	H	I	J	K			N	O		L				C			
A	B	C			F	G		I	J	K			O	N		L	E			D			
	B	C			F	G	H	I	J	K			N	O		L	E			D			
A	B	C			F	G	H	I	J	K			N	O		L	E			D			
A	B				F	G	H	I	J	K			O	N		L	E			D			

Also Played: Match 3 Griffin, Lathrope. Match 7 Duggan. Match 11 Smith P. Match 13 Skuse L, Patten M. Match 14 Saltmarsh E, Pattern M. Match 15 Patten M, Smith P. Match 16 Denney A, Patten M. March 17 Patten M. Match 18 Denney C, Lathrope, Patten M

Appearances 1993/94 season (plus replacements)
David John 34
Derek Eves, Mark Tainton 33
David Hinkins 32
Craig Barrow 28
Ralph Knibbs 27 (1)
Alastair Saverimutto 26
Simon Shaw 25
Mark Regan 24 (1)
Paul Hull 22
Bob Armstrong 20
Andy Blackmore 19
Alan Sharp, Pete Smith, Stuart Crossland 17
Ian Patten 16 (1)
Mark Newall 15 (2)
Kyran Bracken 14
Barry Whitehead, Dean Wring 13
Rob Kitchin 11 (2)
David Palmer (1), Joel Pearson (1) 10
Mark Fountaine 8
Andy J Williams, Phil Adams 6

D Andy Williams, Tom Griffin, Andy Cunningham 5
Matt Brain, Mark Denney, Andy Lathrope (4), Althan Ozdemir, Kevin Maggs, Matt Skuse, Huw Duggan 4
Dan Cotterell, Ben Harvey, Nick Marvel, Andy Player, Robin Saltmarsh, Peter Stiff (1), Erick Thillet 3
Sam Dawson 2
James Averis, Alan Burchill, Tony Down, Kris Fulman, Geoff Lewis, Simon Wallis, Matt Whittaker 1

Most Capped Players (including British Lions)
John Pullin 1966-76 — 42
England +7 Lions = 49
Sam Tucker 1922-31 — 27
Mike Rafter 1977-81 — 17
Len Corbett 1921-27 — 16
Billy Johnston 1910-14 — 16
Jonathan Webb 1987-89 — 16

Leading Club Appearances
Alan Morley 1968-85 — 519
Dave Watt 1957-74 — 512
Pete Polledri 1975-89 — 466
Mike Fry 1968-80 — 435
Austin Sheppard 1973-88 — 432
David Tyler 1966-76 — 425

Leading Appearances of Current Players
Ralph Knibbs 1981 — 412
Peter Stiff 1978 — 357
David Palmer 1980 — 263
Derek Eves 1985 — 244
Andy Blackmore 1984 — 234
Huw Duggan 1980 — 230

Leading Scorers 1993/94 season
Mark Tainton Outside half 304pts
Alastair Saverimutto Centre 70pts
Derek Eves Flanker 50pts
Paul Hull Full Back 45pts
David John Wing 45pts
Stuart Crossland Wing 35pts)

BRISTOL RFC

Try Scorers 1993/94 season Alastair Saverimutto 14, Derek Eves 10, David John 9, Paul Hull 8, Stuart Crossland 7, Barry Whitehead 5, Craig Barrow 4, Rob Kitchin 4, Mark Tainton 4, Erick Thillet 4, Dean Wring 3, Ina Patten 3, Kyran Bracken 2, Matt Brain 2, Ralph Knibbs 2, Mark Newall 2, Alan Sharp 2, Robin Saltmarsh 2, Bob Armstrong 1, Andy Blackmore 1, Mark Denney 1, Huw Duggan 1, Mark Fountaine 1, Andy Lathrope 1, Nick Marvel 1, Joel Pearson 1, Mark Regan 1, Simon Shaw 1, Matt Skuse 1, Andy J Williams 1, D Andy Williams 1, Penalty Try 1
Conversions 1993/94 season Mark Tainton 52, James Averis 4, Ralph Knibbs 3, Paul Hull 1, Nick Marval 1, Mark Newall 1
Penalties 1993/94 season Mark Tainton 58   **Drop Goals 1993/94 season** Mark Tainton 2, Paul Hull 1
League Points Scorers 1993/94 Craig Barrow 1T — 5pts, Andy Blackmore 1T — 5pts, Kyran Bracken 2T — 10pts, Mark Denney 1T — 5pts, Derek Eves 3T — 15pts, Paul Hull 7T, 1C, 1DG — 40pts, David John 2T — 10pts, Rob Kitchin 3T — 15pts, Ralph Knibbs 2T — 10pts, Ian Patten 2T — 10pts, Alastair Saverimutto 8T — 40pts, Mark Tainton 19C, 40P, 1DG — 161pts, Dean Wring 1T — 5pts, TOTAL 33T, 20C, 40P, 2DG — 331pts

Representative Honours 1993/94 season

England v New Zealand, Scotland, Ireland — Kyran Bracken
Scotland v England, Ireland, France — Alan Sharp
England tour to South Africa — Paul Hull, Simon Shaw
Scotland tour to Argentina — Alan Sharp
Barbarians tour to Zimbabwe — Derek Eves
England A v New Zealand — Paul Hull, Kyran Bracken
England A v France — Andy Blackmore (rep Paul Hull)
England A v Italy — Andy Blackmore, Paul Hull
Emerging England v New Zealand — Paul Hull
Emerging England v Spain — Derek Eves (capt, rep Rob Kitchin)

Emerging England v Canada — Derek Eves (capt), Rob Kitchin
England Under 21's — Simon Shaw
England Students — Rob Kitchin
England Colts — Mark Deney (capt)
South West v New Zealand — Paul Hull, Andy Blackmore, Kyran Bracken (rep David Hinkins)
South West v Midlands — Kyran Bracken, Andy Blackmore (reps Eves, Hull, Hinkins)
South West v North — Paul Hull, Kyran Bracken, David Hinkins, Derek Eves, Andy Blackmore (reps Simon Shaw)
South West v London — Paul Hull, David Hinkins, Derek Eves, Andy Blackmore
Midlands v South West, London — Craig Barrow
North v Canada — Alastair Saverimutto
Combined Services v New Zealand — Paul Hull, Chris Moore, Stuart Crossland
RAF — Paul Hull, Stuart Crossland
Royal Navy — Bob Armstrong
Gloucestershire — Ian Patten, Andy J Williams
South West under 21's — Sam Dawson, Kris Fulman
Gloucestershire under 21's — Matt Wise, Kevin Maggs, Nick William, James Averis, Matt Long, Nick Evans, Kris Fulman, Matt Norman, Adam Burns, Sam Dawson

BRISTOL PROGRAMME
Pages: 40 (A5),
Price: £1.00
Colour throughout
Different cover photo for each edition.
Original copy on the majority of two page spreads.
Voted 'Best Rugby Union Club Programme in England' 1993-94

BRISTOL RFC

COURAGE LEAGUE RECORDS

Biggest Home Win: 50-14 v Liverpool St Helens 22-4-89 CL1   **Defeat:** 3-36 v Orrell 17-11-90 CL1
Biggest Away Win: 32-0 v Nottingham 16-11-91 CL1, 32-21 v Rugby 27-3-93 CL1
Defeat: 19-46 v Wasps 27-4-91 CL1
Most Tries For in a Match: 10 v Rugby 28-3-92
Most Tries Against in a Match: 8 v Wasps 27-4-91
Most consecutive Wins: 4   Defeats: 7
No. of Matches failed to Score: 2   **Clean Sheets:** 5   **Drawn Matches:** 2
Most appearances Forward: 69 Derek Eves
Most appearances Back: 70 Ralph Knibbs
Most consecutive appearances: 68 Derek Eves 11-3-88 to date
Consecutive match scoring Tries: 3 Alistair Saverimutto
Points: 8 Jon Webb, Mark Tainton

INDIVIDUAL SCORING RECORDS

IN A MATCH

Most points: 17 Jon Webb v Sale 24-10-87 Home CL1, Mark Tainton v Wasps 31-3-90 Home CL1
Most tries: 3, Mike Lloyd v Rugby 28-3-92 Home CL1, Derek Eves v Rugby 27-3-93 Home CL1
Most conversions: 5 Jonathan Webb, v, Sale 24-10-87 Home CL1
Most penalities: 5 Jonathan Webb v Orrell 9-9-89 Away CL1, Mark Tainton v Wasps 31-3-90 Home CL1, v Wasps 19-4-94 Home CL1
Most drop goals: 2 Simon Hogg v Leicester 9-3-91 Home CL1

IN A SEASON

Most points: 161 Mark Tainton 1993-94 CL1
Most tries: 8 Alastair Saverimutto 1993-94 CL1
Most conversions: 19 Mark Tainton 1993-94 CL1
Most penalties: 40 Mark Tainton 1993-94 CL1
Most drop goals: 3 Simon Hogg 1988-89 CL1

IN A CAREER

Most points: 300 Mark Tainton 1987-94
Most tries: 15 Paul Hull 1987-94
Most conversions: 36 Mark Tainton 1987-94
Most penalties: 74 Mark Tainton 1987-94
Most drop goals: 5 Simon Hogg 1987-94

COURAGE LEAGUE RECORD

	DIV	PLD	W	D	L	F	T	C	P	D	A	T	C	P	D
1987-88	1	10	4	1	5	171	22	16	16	1	145	17	13	16	1
1988-89	1	11	6	0	5	188	24	10	21	3	117	13	4	16	3
1989-90	1	11	4	0	7	136	14	4	24	0	144	19	7	18	0
1990-91	1	12	4	1	7	135	16	7	17	2	219	32	20	16	1
1991-92	1	12	4	0	8	192	29	14	13	3	174	23	8	19	3
1992-93	1	12	6	0	6	148	13	7	23	0	169	18	11	15	4
1993-94	1	18	10	0	8	331	33	20	40	2	276	23	13	44	1
		86	38	2	46	1301	151	78	154	11	1244	145	76	144	13

SEASON BY SEASON LEADING SCORES

	Most Points			Most Tries	
1987-88	58	Jon Webb	3	Andy Dun	
1988-89	50	Jon Webb	2	8 players	
1989-90	47	Jon Webb	2	Paul Hull Paul Collings J Davis	
1990-91	35	Simon Hogg	4	Julian Horrobin	
1991-92	29	Mark Tainton	5	Pete Stiff	
1992-93	68	Mark Tainton	3	Derek Eves	
1994-94	161	Mark Tainton	8	Alistair Saverimutto	

BRISTOL RFC

Ground Details

Ground Address: Memorial Ground, Filton Avenue, Horfield, Bristol. BS7 0AQ
Telephone: 0117 951 4448 or 0117 951 4134.
Fax: 0117 951 4226
Bristol Rugby Call Line: 0891 660 226
Directions: M4 Junction 19 to join M32 to Junction 2 Turn right taking B4469 towards Horfield Signposted left at traffic lights into Filton Avenue.
Capacity: 8,500.
Membership: Adults Stand £80, Enclosure £55, Ground £45
OAP/Students/Jnrs Stand £45, Enclosure £30, Ground £25
Car Park £10
Parents who are both members may apply for FREE child membership.
League & Cup games: Stand £8, Enclosure £7, Ground £6
Other Games: Adults Stand £6, Enclosure £5, Ground £4
OAP Stand £4, Enclosure £3.50, Ground £3
Students/Juniors Stand £2, Enclosure £1.50, Ground £1
Training Nights: 1st XV & United — Monday & Wednesday
U21's & Colts — Tuesday & Thursday.

Club Details

Colours: Blue & white.
Change of Colours: White.
Date Founded: 1888.
Membership: Total 1500.
Number of Teams: 1st XV, United, Under 21's, Colts, Juniors U8's through to U17's.
Programme Advertising Rates: On application.

Club Officials

Club President: Arthur Holmes
Club Chairman: Bill Redwood
Hon Secretary: T Wynne Jones, 31 Bromley HeathRoad, Downend, Bristol, BS16 6HY. Tel: (H) 0117 956 9161
Fixture Secretary: Keith Gerrish, 52 West Town Lane, Brislington, Bristol, BS4 5DB. Tel: (H) 0117 977 7009
Club Administrator & Press Officer: David Tyler, , Memorial Ground, Filton Avenue, Bristol, BS7 0AO. Tel: 0117 951 4448 or 0117 951 4134 Fax: 0117 951 4226
Registration Officer: David Tyler, see above
1994/95 1st XV Captain: Derek Eves
1994/95 Club Coach: Brian Hanlon

Back Row: Wynne Jones (Hon Sec), Brian Hanlon (Coach), Paul Lander (Team Sec), Alan Sharp, Mark Regan, Any Lathrope, Stuart Crossland, Peter Smith, Andy J Williams, Peter Stiff, Simon Shaw, Andy Blackmore, Mark Fountaine, Ian Patten, David Hinkins, Andy Williams, Huw Duggan, Tim Griffin, Matt Brrain, Bill Redwood (Chairman), Jeff Lewis (hon Treas), Rick Sellers (Coach)
Seated: David Palmer, David John, Rob Kitchin, Mark Tainton, Mark Denney, Dean Wring, Derek Eves (captain), Arthur Holmes (President), Paul Hull, Mark Newall, Kyran Bracken, Ralph Knibbs, Barry Whitehead

GLOUCESTER RFC

Barrie's new team struggled

Gloucester's first season under the inspirational leadership of Barrie Corless was only one league place away from disaster. It was a struggle all the way and safety was only achieved on the penultimate day of the campaign when Orrell were beaten at Kingsholm in a high scoring game.

It was fortunate that full back Tim Smith was still around and his trusty boot saved many a desperate situation — notably in the 15-12 win at London Irish on March 12th when he scored all the points.

However, the club has a fine youth policy and if only a small handful of youngsters from each season reach the top the future of this home spun famous club will be bright and replacements for the consistent veterans will be found to reinforce key players like Holford, Sims, Cashie, Cummins and Ian Smith.

One hopeful sign was seen in the Pilkington Cup where the quarter-final was reached after wins at Nottingham (29-9) and at home to Northampton (11-6) before Orrell came and conquered (10-3). Gloucester is a sleeping giant which needs to wake up.

CLUB PLAYING RECORD

National League: One
Final League Position at end of 1993-94 season: 8th
League playing record: P 18, W 6, D, 2, L, 10, Pts F 247, Pts A 356
Season playing record (including league matches/Pilkington Cup etc):
P 41, W, 22, D, 2, L 17, Pts F 849, Pts A 610

Dave Sims Gloucester in action against Harlequins

GLOUCESTER RFC

COURAGE CLUBS CHAMPIONSHIP
NATIONAL DIVISION ONE 1992-93

No	Date	Opponents	Venue	Result	Point Scorers
1	Sep 11	Wasps	H	D9-9	Smith(2P) Cummins(DG)
2	Sep 18	Newcastle	A	D12-12	Smith(2P) Beech(2P)
3	Sep 25	Leicester	H	L14-23	Holford(T) T Smith(2P) Beech(P)
4	Oct 2	Bath	A	L17-46	Cummins(T) Holford(T) T Smith(C) Beech(C)(P)
5	Oct 9	L. Irish	H	L9-10	Roberts(3P)
6	Nov 13	Bristol	A	L12-16	Johnson(4P)
7	Nov 20	Northampton	H	W19-14	Deacon(T) Johnson(C)(2P) T Smith(2P)
8	Dec 4	Orrell	A	W10-6	Johnson(T) T Smith(C)(P)
9	Dec 11	Harlequins	H	W24-20	Nicholson(T) Fenley(T) Windo(T) Deacon(T) T Smith(2C)
10	Jan 8	Wasps	A	L18-29	Fenley(T),PT, T Smith(C)(2P)
11	Jan 15	Newcastle G	H	W15-9	Holford(T),PT, T Smith(C)(P)
12	Jan 29	Leicester	A	L8-28	Sims(T) T Smith(P)
13	Feb 12	Bath	H	L6-16	T Smith(P) Cummins(DG)
14	Mar 12	L. Irish	A	W15-12	Smith(4P)(DG)
15	Mar 26	Bristol	H	L6-24	Fenwick(2P)
16	Apr 9	Northampton	A	L3-19	Cummins(DG)
17	Apr 23	Orrell	H	W30-25	Sharp(2T) Morris(T) Fenley(T) T Smith(2C)(2P)
18	Apr 30	Harlequins	A	L20-38	Windo(T) Kearsey(T) I Smith(T) Beech(C) T Smith(P)

Tim Smith extended all his career points records for
Gloucester as he finished leading scorer for the sixth
successive season. Smith remains the only Gloucester
player to have scored 100 Courage points.

	PTS	T	C	P	D	APPS	AVE
Tim Smith	490	6	53	118	1	69	7.10

Damian Cummins' 3 drop goals in the season broke
the record for drop goals in a season of one held by
Mike Hamlin and Neil Matthews.

GLOUCESTER RFC

MATCH BY MATCH PLAYERS BY POSITION

T Smith	Holford	Morris	Caskie	Nicholson	Cummins	Hannaford	Jones	Hawker	Deacon	West	Sims	Ashmead	I Smith	Fowke	Beech	Phillips	Masters	Roberts	Johnson	Fenley	Devereaux	Windo	Glanville
15	14	13	12	11	10	9	1	2	3	4	5	6	7	8									
15	14	13	12	11	10	9	1	2	3	4	5	6	7	8	R								
15	14		12	11	13	9	1	2		5	4	6	7			10	3	8					
15	14		12	11	13	9	3	2		5	4	6	7			10	1	8					
14	13			11	12	9	1	2		5	4		7	6		10	3	8	15				
	14		12	11	13		1	2	3	5		8	7	6				15	10	9	4		
15	14	13	12				1	2	3	4	8	6	7					11	10	9	5		
15	14	13		11				2	3	4	8		7	6					10	9	5		
15	13			11	12			2	3	4	8		7	6					10	9	5	1	
15	14	13	11	12				2	3	5	8		7	6					10	9	4	1	
15	14	13	12	11				2	3	5	8		7	8					10	9	4	1	
15	14	13		11	10			2	3	5	8		7							9	4	1	6
15	14	13		11	10			2	3	5			7	8						9	4	1	6
15	11	14	13	R	10				3	5	8		7							9	4	1	6
	11	13	14		10				3	5	4		7							9	R	1	6
15	14	12	13		10				3	5	4		7							9		1	6
15	14	13	12		10				3	5			7							9	4	1	6
15	14	13	12						3	5			7						10	9	4	1	6

Match 8 Morgan 12, Winder 1. Match 9 Perrin 14. Match 10 Fenwick 9. Match 11 Fenwick 9. Match 12 Morgan 12. Match 13 Maslen 12, Kearsey R, Morgan R. Match 14 Maslin 12, Kearsey 2, Perrin R. Match 15 Kearsey 2, Nicholls 8, Morgan 12, Fenwick 15. Match 16 Kearsey 2, Nicholls 8, Perrin 11. Match 17 Sharp 11, Kearsey 2, Nicholls 8. Match 18 Bedney R, Sharp 11, Kearsey 2, Nicholls 8

MOST CAPPED PLAYERS
Tom Voyce 29
Mike Teague 29
Don Rutherford 15

LEADING APPEARANCES FOR CLUB
Dave Sims, 29, 118, 1993-94
Bruce Fenley, 26, 26, 1993-94
Tim Smith, 26, 312, 1993-94
Don Caskie, 26, 133, 1993-94
Damian Cummins, 26, 155, 1993-94
Ian Smith, 26, 291, 1993-94
Paul Holford, 25, 42, 1993-94

LEADING SCORERS (1993-94)
Tim Smith, Full Back, 172, 2,587
Paul Beech, Fly Half, 58, 123
Paul Holford, Wing, 45, 65
Ashley Johnson, Fly Half, 45, 45
Martin Roberts, Full Back, 41, 383
Andy Sharp, Wing, 40, 40

GLOUCESTER RFC

COURAGE LEAGUE RECORDS

Biggest Home Win: 61-7 v Sale 16-4-88 CL1   **Defeat:** 13-24 v Wasps 13-2-88 CL1, 6-24 v Bristol 26-3-94 CL1
Biggest Away Win: 31-9 v Liverpool St Helens 22-10-88 CL1   **Defeat:** 17-46 v Bath 2-10-93 CL1
Most Tries For in a Match: 11 v Sale 16-4-88 CL1
Most Tries Against in a Match: 6 v Bath 2-10-93 CL1
Most consecutive Wins: 5   **Defeats:** 4
No. of Matches failed to Score: 1   **Clean Sheets:** 1   **Drawn Matches:** 6
Most appearances Forward: 79 Ian Smith   **Most appearances Back:** 69 Tim Smith
Most consecutive appearances: 40 Mike Hamlin 12-11-87 thru 27-4-9?
Consecutive match scoring Tries: 3 Jim Breeze, Mike Hamlin, Tim Smith   **Points:** 15 Tim Smith

INDIVIDUAL SCORING RECORDS

IN A MATCH

Most points: 20 Tim Smith v Harlequins 12-3-90
Home CL1
Most tries: 3 Derek Morgan v Rosslyn Park 11-11-89
Home CL1
Most conversions: 6 Paul Mansell v Sale 16-4-88
Home CL1
Most penalities: 6 Tim Smith v Harlequins 12-3-90
Home CL1
Most drop goals: 1 on 7 occasions by 4 players —
Damian Cummins 3, Mike Hamlin 2,
Neil Matthews 1, Tim Smith 1

IN A SEASON

Most points: 85 Tim Smith 1988-89 CL1
Most tries: 6 Jim Breeze 1987-88 CL1, Mike Hamlin
1988-89 CL1, Derek Morgan 1989-90 CL1
Most conversions: 12 Tim Smith 1988-89 CL1,
1990-91 CL1
Most penalties: 21 Tim Smith 1991-92 CL1
Most drop goals: 1 Mike Hamlin 1989-90 CL1 &
1991-92 CL1, Neil Matthews 1991-92 CL1

IN A CAREER

Most points: 408 Tim Smith 1987-93
Most tries: 15 Derek Morgan 1988-93
Most conversions: 45 Tim Smith 1987-93
Most penalties: 97 Tim Smith 1987-93
Most drop goals: 2 Mike Hamlin 1987-92

COURAGE LEAGUE RECORD

	DIV	PLD	W	D	L	F	T	C	P	D	A	T	C	P	D
1987-88	1	10	6	1	3	206	32	18	14	0	121	9	2	23	4
1088-89	1	11	7	1	3	215	31	14	21	0	112	14	7	13	1
1989-90	1	11	8	1	2	214	32	10	21	1	139	16	9	19	0
1990-91	1	12	6	0	6	207	29	17	19	0	163	19	9	22	1
1991-92	1	12	7	1	4	193	19	12	29	2	168	16	10	26	2
1992-93	1	12	6	0	6	173	17	8	24	0	151	12	5	25	2
1993-94	1	18	6	2	10	247	21	11	36	4	356	29	23	53	2
		86	46	6	34	1455	181	90	164	7	1210	115	65	181	12

SEASON BY SEASON LEADING SCORES

		Most Points		Most Tries
1987-88	42	Nick Marment	6	Jim Breeze
1988-89	85	Tim Smith	6	Mike Hamlin
1989-90	75	Tim Smith	6	Derek Morgan
1990-91	75	Tim Smith	3	Ian Smith Derek Morgan Paul Ashmead Chris Dee
1991-92	81	Tim Smith	5	Simon Morris
1992-93	71	Tim Smith	3	Tim Smith Derek Morgan
1993-94	82	Tim Smith	3	Paul Holford, Ben Fenley

GLOUCESTER RFC

Club Details

Colours: Cherry, white, black
Change of Colours: Black
Date Founded: 1873
Membership: Total 2,400
Membership: Playing members 50, U21's/Colts
Number of Teams: Senior 2, Junior(Youth) 2
Programme Advertising Rates: Various rates from £300
Special occasions during 1994-95: South Africa Tour (1st XV), England U18 vs Australia U18

Ground Details

Ground Address: Kingsholm, Kingsholm Road, Gloucester, GL1 3AX
Telephone: 0452 381087
Fax: 0452 383321
Simple directions to ground: M5 Jcn 11 towards Glos, first r/about right towards Glos/Wates, next r/about left, next r/about straight over, ground 300 yards on right.
Capacity: 12,000 (seated 1,250, standing 10,750).
Ticket Prices: Adult £7.50 (ground) £5.00 (g.stand). OAP/Child £4.00 (ground) £2.50 (g.stand).
Training Nights: Tuesday & Thursday

Club Officials

President: Canon H M Hughes
Chairman: Alan Brinn
Club Secretary: A Doug Wadley, Byeways, Belront Avenue, Hucclecote, Glos, GL3 3SF. Tel: (H) 0452 617202 (W) 0452 383321
Fixtures Secretary: M Nicholls, 90 Kingsholm Road, Gloucester. Tel: 0452 301879 (W) 021 772 6644
Press Officer: Peter Ford, 'Rivermead', Sandhurst Lane, Gloucester, GL2 9AB. Tel: (H) 0452 424101 (W) 0452 523580
Registration Officer: Andy Mitchell, 'The Marsh', Marsh Road, Leonard Stanley, Stonehouse, Gloucester, GL10 3NH. Tel: (H) 0453 822654 (W) 0452 381087
1994/95 1XV Captain: Andrew Deacon
1994/95 1XV Coach: Viv Wooley
Director of Rugby: Barrie Corless
Commercial Manager: Mike Burton

Action from the Harlequins v Gloucester match

TEAMS OF THE SEASON

Courage Rugby Club Directory Statistician Stephen McCormash contacted coaches from the four senior leagues and from these selections compiled four unofficial "Team of the Seasons". Not all coaches replied but these selections give an interesting guide to the form players last season, as seen from the coaches viewpoint.

DIVISION ONE

15 Paul Hull (Bristol) — other votes:- J Callard
14 James Naylor (Orrell) — other votes:- R Underwood (Leics) N Beal (North)
13 Stuart Potter (Leicester) — other votes:- W Carling (Har) G Childs (Wasps)
12 Phil De Glanvile (Bath) — other votes:- D Hopley (Wasps) A Saverimutto (Bristol)
11 Darren O'Leary (Harlequins) — other votes:- T Underwood (Leics) C Oti (Wasps)
10 Stuart Barnes (Bath) — other votes:- R Andrew (Wasps) J Harris (Leics)
9 D Morris (Orrell) — other votes:- K Bracken (Brist) M Dawson (North)
1 J Leonard (Harlequins) — other votes:- A Sharp (Brist)
2 Graham Dawe (Bath) — other votes:- B Moore (Har) K Dunn (Wasps)
3 Victor Ubogo (Bath) — other votes:- P Jings (Gloucs) A Mullins (Har)
4 Nigel Redman (Bath) — other votes:- M Poole (Leics) S Shaw (Bristol) M Haag (Bath)
5 Martin Johnson (Leicester) — other votes:- M Bayfield (North) D Sims (Gloucs)
6 Peter Walton (Northampton) — oter votes:- J Wells (Leics) M Greenwood (Wasps)
7 Neil Back (Leicester) — other votes:- D Eves (Brist) I Smith (Leics)
8 Tim Rodber (Northampton) — other votes:- B Clarke (Bath) D Ryan (Wasps)

DIVISION TWO

15 Steve Swindells (Waterloo) — other votes:- J Mallinder (Sale) A Tunnungley (Sara)
14 Simon Verbickas (Sale) — other votes:- R Thompson (Wake)
13 Diccon Edwards (Wakefield) — other votes:- A Kerr (Mose) A Handley (Water)
12 Phil Hodder (West Hartlepool) — other votes:- M Birt (Sale) P Maynard (Wake) J Buckton (Sara)

11 Jon Sleightholme (Wakefield) — other votes:- K Young (Sale)
10 Paul Turner (Sale) — other votes:- G Gregory (Nott)
9 Dave Scully (Wakefield) — other votes:- M Warr (Sale) J Wrigley (W Hart)
1 Mark Linnet (Moseley) — other votes:- M Whitcombe (Sale) M Beckett (Water)
2 Stuart Mitchell (West Hartlepool) — other votes:- T Garnett (Wake) D West (Nott)
3 Paul Burnell (London Scottish) — other votes:- A Smith (Sale) S Peters (Water)
4 J Dixon (West Hartlepool) — other votes:- P Stewart (Wake) D Baldwin (Sale) C Gray (Nott)
5 J Westgarth (West Hartlepool) — other votes:- M Langley (Sara) S Smith (Rugby)
6 Dave Erskine (Sale) — other votes:- A Diprose (Sara)
7 Richard Hill (Saracens) — other votes:- P Buckton (Water) M Kenrick (Sale)
8 Mike Watson (West Hartlepool) — other votes:- A McFarlane (Sale) M Rennell (Rugby)

DIVISION THREE

15 Martin Livesey (Richmond) — other votes:- I Stewart (Exe) A Parker (Fylde)
14 Brendan Hanavan (Fylde) — other votes:- T Clarke (Mor) M Chatterton (Exe)
13 Mark Lakey (Coventry) — other votes:- T Ashworth (R P) B Whetstone (Bed)
12 Steve Gough (Fylde) — other votes:- D Coyne (Black) M Hutton (Rich)
11 Doug Woodman (Coventry) — other votes:- P Greenwood (Rich) G Anderson (Fylde)
10 Richard Angell (Coventry) — other votes:- A Green (Exe) A Finnie (Bed)
9 Mike Friday (Blackheath) — other votes:- C O'Toole (Fylde)
1 Craig Burns (Fylde) — other votes:- R Gibbins (Exe) P Garrett (Bed)
2 Mark Howe (Bedford) — other votes:- A Moffitt (Fylde) D Addleton (Cov)

3 Warwick Bullock (Coventry) — other votes:- S Rigby (Fylde)
4 Richard Mackie (Coventry) — other votes:- M Fitzgerald (Rich)
5 Paddy O'Neil (Fylde) — other votes:- R Field (Cov) P Carr (Rich)
6 Matt Deans (Bedford) — other votes:- L Crofts (Cov) I Pickup (R P)
7 Willie Phillips (Coventry) — other votes:- P Della-Savina (Rich)
8 Kevin Hickey (Coventry) — other votes:- M Greatorex (Fylde)

DIVISION FOUR

15 David Breakwell (Leeds) — other votes:- S Mason (L S T) A Higgin (Liv St H)
14 Jon Eagle (Leeds) — other votes:- E Atkins (Harr) T Davies (Clift)
13 Kevin Simms (Liverpool St Helens) — other votes:- R Zoing (Har)
12 Kerry Locke (Clifton) — other votes:- P Naivalurua (Clift)
11 Jon Phillips (Clifton) — other votes:- S Lewis (Sudbury) A Speakman (B P) M Sephton (Liv St H)
10 Simon Hogg (Clifton) — other votes:- A Higgin (Liv St H)
9 Graham Eldoy (Liverpool) — other votes:- G Easterby (Harr)
1 Andrew Simpson (Harrogate) — other votes:- A Fisher (Clift) D Bosworth (Sheff) J Russell (B P)
2 Richard Whyley (Harrogate) — other votes:- P Cox (Clift) S Pooley (Ply)
3 Shaun McMain (Sheffield) — other votes:- DF Hall (Harr)
4 Phil Taylor (Harrogate) — other votes:- C Pinnegar (Sudbury) DA Hinton (Liv St H)
5 Chris Blake (Clifton) — other votes:- I Brown (Harr) D Mason (Clift)
6 Steve Baker (Harrogate) — other votes:- N Hargreaves (Leeds) M Richardson (Asp) S Hill (Askeans)
7 Wayne Hone (Clifton) — other votes:- P Griffin (Leeds) I Crapper (Sheff)
8 Mark Wyatt (Clifton) — other votes:- J Hopkinson (Harr) D Gaskell (Liv St H)

HARLEQUIN FC

Review of the Season 1993/94

The 1993/94 season was never going to be easy. Peter Winterbottom and Andrew Harriman had retired, Neil Edwards had moved on, and, as it turned out, injuries were to prevent David Pears and Richard Langhorn from playing more than a handful of games between them.

Take five quality players out of any team and they cannot be replaced overnight. Many of our young players played with plenty of commitment, but experience is so important in the League and at various moments that lack of experience was evident and we lost games we should have won.

However, it is ironic that as a club we are often not given credit in the media for our policy of giving young players a chance. Yet Under 21 players O'Leary, Keyter, Brown, Leach, Madderson, Richardson and Hamilton-Smith all played for the 1st XV in League games and many others turned out for the 1st XV in non-League matches.

League Division 1

Played 18, Won 8, Lost 10, Points For 333, Points Against 287

Having finished 8th in 92/93 we improved by two positions by coming 6th and also became more competitive as a whole. Seven of the games we lost were by fewer than six points; it is these results that we must turn in our favour, and we are very capable of doing so. We had a notable victory at Leicester and at times produced some excellent rugby which was cancelled out on other occasions by some very average performances.

Only three players (Mullins, Thompson, O'Leary) played all 18 games and perhaps surprisingly only one other, Kent Bray, played more than 13 games. Daren O'Leary was comfortably the top try scorer at eleven, and Kent Bray top points scorer with one try, 12 conversions and 38 penalties. In all League games over 30 players were used.

Pilkington Cup

Few who were present at Stoop Memorial Ground will forget our Semi-Final match against Bath in which we lost 25-26 having staged a most remarkable comeback from being 0-19 down. It was a travesty to lose at the end but we showed great character to come from so far behind and we earned respect from our visitors.

Unbelievably, for all our four games in the competition we were drawn at home and victories were achieved against Basingstoke (52-3), West Hartlepool (23-15), Sale (26-13).

Daren O'Leary scores for Quins against London Irish   *Photo: Joe McCabe*

HARLEQUIN FC

COURAGE CLUBS CHAMPIONSHIP
NATIONAL DIVISION ONE 1993-94

No	Date	Opponents	Venue	Result	Point Scorers
1	11/9	L Irish	H	W30-15	O'Leary (2T) Challinor (T)(2C)(2P) Glenister (T)
2	18/9	Wasps	A	L15-18	Leonard (T) Glenister (T) Bray (C)(P)
3	25/9	Bristol	H	L15-20	Bray 5P
4	2/10	Newcastle G	A	W22-3	O'Leary (T) Snow (T) Bray (3P) Challinor (P)
5	9/10	Northampton	H	W15-7	Bray (5P)
6	13/11	Leicester	A	W10-3	O'Leary (T) Carling (T)
7	20/11	Orrell	A	L20-21	O'Leary (T) Challinor (T) Bray (2C)(2P)
8	4/12	Bath	H	L12-14	Bray (4P)
9	11/12	Gloucester	A	L20-24	Bray (T)(C)(P) Kayter (T) Jardine-Brown (T)
10	8/1	L Irish	A	W33-7	Russell (T) Glenister (T) O'Leary (T) Thompson (T) Bray (2C)(3P)
11	15/1	Wasps	H	W22-17	O'Leary (T) Bray (C)(4P) Challinor (DG)
12	29/1	Bristol	A	L16-20	Glenister (T) Snow (T) Bray (2P)
13	12/2	Newcastle	H	W12-6	Challinor (4P)
14	12/3	Northampton	A	L14-15	O'Leary (T) Challinor (3P)
15	26/3	Leicester	H	L13-25	Keyter (T) Challinor (C)(2P)
16	9/4	Orrell	H	L13-20	Keyter (T) Bray (C)(2P)
17	23/4	Bath	A	L13-32	Thompson (T) Bray (C)(2P)
18	30/4	Gloucester	H	W38-20	O'Leary (2T) Carling (T) Keyter (T) Bray (3C)(4P)

CLUB PLAYING RECORD 1993-94

National League: One
Final League Position at end of 1993/94 Season: 6th
League Playing record: P 18, W 8, D 0, L 10, Pts F 333, Pts A 287
Season Playing record (including league matches/Pilkington Cup): P 35, W 18, D 0, L 17, Pts F 811, Pts A 610

COURAGE RECORDS

Andy Mullins was an ever present for the fourth time in 7 Courage League seasons and extended his consecutive league appearances to 42. The last game he missed was in April 91 v Gloucester when Harlequins fielded a reserve team the week before the Pilkington Cup Final.

Kent Bray passed David Pears' record of most points in a season - 120 - in the match v Bath on 23 April.
90-91, D Pears 1T 16C 23P 5DG total 120 points in 10 games 12.00 pt average
93-94, K Bray 1T 12C 38P total 143 points in 16 games 8.94 average
Darren O'Leary equalled Andrew Harriman's record of 11 tries in a Courage League season. O'Leary's 11 tries came in 18 matches, strike rate of 0.61, Harriman's 11 came in just 5 matches, strike rate of 2.2.

HARLEQUIN RFC

MATCH BY MATCH PLAYERS BY POSITION

Bray	Thompson	Carling	O'Leary	Challinor	Glenister	Leonard	Moore	Mullins	Coker	Snow	Sheasby	Pepper	Langhorn	Madderson	Russell	Cassell	Alexander	Simmonds	Dix	Thresher	Keyter	Dear	Brown
15	13	12	11	10	9	1	2	3	4	5	6	7	8										
15	12	13	11	10	9	1	2	3	4		6		8	14	5	7							
15	12	13	11	10		1	2	3	4	5	6		8	14		7							
15	13	12	14	10		1		3			4	8	6			7	11	2	5				
15	12	13	14	10	9	1	2	3			4	8	6			7	11		5	R			
15	13	12	14	10	9	1	2	3			4	7	8		6		11	5					
15	12		11	10	9	1	2	3			4	7		8	14	6	13		5	R			
15	12		14	10	9		2	3	4			7	8		6		11		R	13	5		
15	12		14	10	9			3				8			6		11	2	R		5		
15	12	13	14	10	9	1		3	4			8			6		11	2	R		5		R
15	12	13	14	10	9	1	2	3	8	4					6		11				5		
15	12	13	14	10	9	1	2	3	8	4	6				6		11				5		
	12	13	14	10			2	3	6	4	8					11					5		1
	12	13	14	10	15	1		3	6		8			4	7	11					5		
15	12	14		10			2	3	8	4		7		11	6						5	13	
10	12		15				2	3	8	4			14	7	11			5				13	1
15	12	13	11	10				3	5	4		8			6	7					14		
15	12	13	11	10				3	8	5		7		4	6	2					14		

Match 11 Richardson 7, Match 13 Pears 15, Luxton 9, Richardson 7, Winterbottom R8, Match 14 Luxton 9, Killick 2, Match 15 Luxton 9, Match 16 Luxton 9, Killick R2, Leach R5, Pepper 6, Match 17 Luxton 9, Hamilton-Smith 2, Match 18 Luxton 9, Short R9

PLAYING SQUAD 1993-94

Full Back: K Bray, A Hutchinson, D Pears, D Currie
Wing: D Currie, J Alexander, K Ali, C Madderson, M Molyneux, D O'Leary, A Pinnock
Centre: W Carling, J Keyter, C Short, G Thompson
Fly Half: R Butland, P Challinor
Scrum Half: R Glenister, C Luxton, B Short
Prop: S Brown, A Challis, J Collins, B Fenwell, M Hobley, J Leonard, A Mullins
Hooker: J Hamilton-Smith, N Killick, B Moore, P Simmonds
Lock: M Brown, S Dear, D Dix, A Snow, P Thresher, R Till, D Sibson
Back Row: J Cassell, R Coker, I Desmond, R Jardine-Brown, R Leach, M Pepper, B Richardson, M Russell, C Sheasby

MOST CAPPED PLAYERS
(including British Lions Appearances)
P Winterbottom (Eng), 58 + 6
W Dooley (Eng), 55 + 2
B Moore (Eng), 52 + 4
W Carling (Eng), 49 + 1
I Milne (Scot), 44
A Haden (NZ), 41

LEADING SCORERS
K Gray, Full Back, 153 (13C 39DG 2T)
R Butland, Fly Half, 107 (13C 1DG 21PG 3T)
P Challinor, Fly Half, 102 (8C 3DG 19PG 4T)
D O'Leary, Wing, 70 (14T)
R Glenister, Scrum Half, 41 (6C 1DG 2PG 4T)
J Keyter, Centre, 35 (7T)

HARLEQUIN FC

COURAGE LEAGUE CLUB RECORDS

Highest Winning Score Home: 66 v Sale (66-0) 23.4.87 **Away**: 71 v Bedford (71-8) 14.10.89
Highest Score Against Home: 37 v Saracens (12-37) 14.3.92 **Away**: 38 v Gloucester (19-38) 27.4.91
Most Tries in a match For: 12 v Sale 23.4.87, v Bedford 14.10.89
Against: 6 v Bath 9.9.89, v Gloucester 27,4.91
Most Consecutive Wins: 4 **Defeats:** 4
No of Matches failed to score: 3 **Clean Sheets:** 2 **Drawn Matches:** 3
Most Appearances - Forward: 82 Andy Mullins 87-89 **Back:** 53 Will Carling 87-94
Consecutive Appearances: 42 Andy Mullins 16.11.91 to date
Consecutive Matches Scoring Tries: 3 Andrew Harriman
Points: 10 David Pears (twice)

INDIVIDUAL SCORING RECORDS

IN A MATCH

Most points: 27 David Pears v Bedford 14-10-89 Home CL1

Most tries: 3 Andrew Harriman v Nottingham 1-4-88 Home CL1, v Sale 23-4-88 Home CL1, Mike Wedderburn v Bedford 14-10-89 Away CL1, Andrew Harriman v Bristol 30-3-91 Home CL1, Will Carling v Bristol 30-30-91 Home CL1

Most conversions: 8 David Pears v Bedford 14-10-89 Away CL1

Most penalities: 7 David Pears v Rosslyn Park 7-12-91 Away CL1

Most drop goals: 2 David Pears v Rosslyn Park 13-10-92Home CL1, v Leicester 23-3-91 Away CL1

IN A SEASON

Most points: 143 Kent Bray 1993-94 CL1
Most tries: 11 Andrew Harriman 1987-88 CL1
Most conversions: 16 David Pears 1990-91 CL1
Most penalties: 38 Kent Bray 1993-94 CL1
Most drop goals: 5 David Pears 1990-91 CL1

IN A CAREER

Most points: 354 David Pears 1989-93
Most tries: 22 Andrew Harriman 1987-93
Most conversions: 46 David Pears 1989-93
Most penalties: 71 David Pears 1989-93
Most drop goals: 7 David Pears 1989-93

COURAGE LEAGUE RECORD

Season	Div	Pld	W	D	L	F	T	C	P	D	A	T	C	P	D
87-88	1	11	6	1	4	261	38	26	18	1	128	19	5	11	3
88-89	1	11	5	0	6	194	25	17	18	2	184	23	16	20	
89-90	1	11	6	0	5	218	26	15	26	2	180	22	10	21	3
90-91	1	12	8	0	4	267	32	20	28	5	162	17	8	24	2
91-92	1	12	5	1	6	213	27	15	23	2	207	28	16	18	2
92-93	1	12	5	1	6	197	23	11	19	1	187	17	9	26	2
93-94	1	18	8	0	10	333	29	16	51	1	287	34	18	27	
	7	87	43	3	41	1683	200	120	183	14	1335	160	92	147	13

SEASON BY SEASON LEADING SCORES

	Most Points			Most Tries	
1987-88	58	Stuart Thresher	11	Andrew Harriman	
1988-89	71	Stuart Thresher	4	Mickey Skinner Jon Eagle	
1989-90	114	David Pears	5	Craig Luxton	
1990-91	120	David Pears	9	Andrew Harriman	
1991-92	109	David Pears	4	David Pears	
1992-93	57	Stuart Thresher	3	Will Carling Rob Glenister Paul Challinor Stuart Thresher	
1993-94	143	Kent Bray	11	Daren O'Leary	

HARLEQUIN FC

Troy Coker Quins Australian International vs West Hartlepool, Pilkington Cup　　　　　　　　*Photo: Joe McCabe*

Gavin Thomson supported by Will Carling and Jason Leonard vs Wasps 18th Sept 1993　　　　　*Photo: Joe McCabe*

HARLEQUIN FC

Club Details

Club Colours: light blue, magenta, chocolate, french grey, light green, black
Change of Colours: none
Date Founded: 1866
Membership: Total: 2124, Playing members 56, Junior/Youth/Minis/Students 138, Other 1930
No. of teams: Senior 2, Junior 2
Programme advertising rates: Full Colour £1,000, Black & white £500

Ground Details:

Ground Address: Stoop Memorial Ground, Craneford Way, Twickenham, Middlesex, TW2 7SQ
Ground Tel No: 081 892 0822 Fax: 081 744 2764
Spectator Capacity: Total: 6,500 (increased to 8,500 with additional stands), seated 3,000, standing 3,500
Ticket Prices: Adults: £8, OAP/Child: £3
Training Nights: Tuesdays and Thursdays

Club Officials

Club President: D K Brooks
Club Chairman: R F Looker
Club Secretary: G R Morey, 27 Carter Walk, Penn, Bucks, HP10 8ER. Tel: (H) 0494 814607 (W) 0494 814607 Fax: 0494 815144
Fixtures Secretary: G C Murray, Westow, 25 Barham Road, Wimbledon, London, SW20 0ES. Tel: (H) 081 946 1976 (W) 071 736 1155 Fax: 071 731 6861
Press Officer: Gad Saward, 152 Woodseer Street, London, E1 5HQ. Tel: (H) 071 377 1151 (W) 071 377 1151 Fax: 071 377 1151
Registration Officer: P E Glenister, 47 Bury Lane, Codicote, Hitchen, Herts, SG4 8XX. Tel: (H) 0438 820692
1994/ 95 1st XV Captain: B C Moore
1994/95 Club Coach: K Richardson
Commercial Manager: M L Coley

Will Carling in full flight   *Photo: Joe McCabe*

84

LEICESTER FC

Review of the Season

For 'The Tigers' it was a good, but frustrating, season. Being in second place in the two major competitions was no disgrace but how nicer it would have been if they had won at least one of them.

As it was they shadowed the champions Bath right through the season after being the only ones earlier on to defeat them. In the end the destination of the title depended on their meeting at The Recreation Ground on 9th April, when the home team won a tight game 14-6 and that decided the battle finally in Bath's favour.

There was still another competition to be fought out — The Pilkington Cup — and as both clubs had reached the Twickenham final on 7th May it was hoped that it would be a memorable epic for everyone to savour. It was nothing of the kind and Leicester, as holders, must have been bitterly disappointed at the ultimate 21-9 victory for Bath, who thus won the double, but the fans were the real losers as it was a shocking match, which did nothing to enhance the reputation of the game.

Overall, however, Leicester were a credit to England rugby and contributed well to the national cause with the Underwood brothers, Martin Johnson, Neil Back (at last) and Dean Richards (yet again) being called on by their country. Stuart Potter, Graham Rowntree and Matt Poole were selected for the South Africa tour along with all the others except the unlucky Back and the likes of scrum-half Aadel Kardooni and fly-half Jez Harris were others to be noted by the selectors.

Big developments are taking place at Welford Road and with luck the team should continue to be good enough to justify all the expense.

Leicester FC at Twickenham   *Photo: Joe McCabe*

LEICESTER FC

COURAGE CLUBS CHAMPIONSHIP
NATIONAL DIVISION ONE 1993-94

No	Date	Opponents	Venue	Result	Point Scorers
1	11/9	Northampton	A	L10-19	Underwood (T) Harris (C)(P)
2	18/9	Orrell	H	W23-18	Cockerill (T) Potter (T) Liley (2C)(P) Harris (2DG)
3	25/9	Gloucester	A	W23-14	Hackney (2T) Back (T) Liley (C)(P) Harris (DG)
4	2/10	Wasps	H	W38-6	Back (T) Wells (T) Poole (T) Richards (T) Harris (3C)(3P)(DG)
5	9/10	Newcastle G	A	W22-13	Back (T) Harris (C)(4P)(DG)
6	13/11	Harlequins	H	L3-10	Liley (P)
7	20/11	Bath	H	W9-6	Liley (2P) Harris (DG)
8	4/12	L Irish	A	W22-10	Kardooni (T) Harris(T)(2P)(2DG)
9	11/12	Bristol	H	W21-9	Harris (7P)
10	8/1	Northampton	H	W36-9	Kilford (T) T Underwood (T) Poole (T) Harris (3C)(3P)(2DG)
11	15/1	Orrell	A	W18-0	Boyle (T) Kilford (T) Harris (T)(P)
12	29/1	Gloucester	H	W28-8	T Underwood (T) Harris (1C)(7P)
13	12/2	Wasps	A	W15-13	Harris (4P)(DG)
14	12/3	Newcastle G	H	W66-3	Underwood (4T) Hackney (2T) Back (2T) Robinson (T) Rowntree (T) Harris (5C)(2P)
15	26/3	Quins	A	W25-13	Back (T) Potter (T) Richards (T) Harris (2C)(2P)
16	9/4	Bath	A	L6-14	Harris (2P)
17	23/4	L Irish	H	W38-3	Hackney (T) Potter (T) Boyle (T) Underwood (T) Smith (T) Harris (2C)(3P)
18	30/4	Bristol	A	L22-40	Tarbuck (T) Johnson (T) Reynolds (T) Liley (2C)(P)

COURAGE RECORDS

Jez Harris virtually re-wrote the record book in the 1993-94 season. He broke John Lileys division one record of 129 points in a season and finished on 202 points.

	PTS	T	C	P	D	APP	AVE
J Harris	202	2	18	41	1	11	11.88
J Liley	129	4	19	25	0	11	11.72

His 11 drop goals beat the previous division one record for a season which was 6 by Simon Hodgkinson, Nottingham, and Paul Burke, London Irish.
Harris twice equaled David Pears division one record of 7 penalties in a match and broke the Leicester record of 6 previously held by Dusty Hare.
Harris ended the season with 267 Courage League points for Leicester and passed Dusty Hare to move into 2nd place on Leicester alltime Courage points list behind John Liley.

	PTS	T	C	P	D	APPS	AVE
J Liley	509	13	72	101	0	50+1	10.18
J Harris	267	4	24	45	22	45+1	5.93
D Hare	223	2	22	56	7	18	

Tony Underwood moves past John Liley, 13 tries and finishes the season with 19 career tries in the Courage League for Leicester, 2nd to his brother Rory who has 28.

CLUB PLAYING RECORD 1993-94

National League: One
Final League Position at end of 1993/94 Season: Second
League Playing record: P 18, W 14, D 0, L 4
Season Playing record (including league matches/Pilkington Cup): P 36, W 28, D 0 , L 8

ACHIEVEMENTS/COMPETITIONS WON DURING 93/94 SEASON
Pilkington Cup Finalists

LEICESTER FC

MATCH BY MATCH PLAYERS BY POSITION

Kilford	Hackney	Bates	Potter	Underwood T	Harris	Kardooni	Rowntree	Cockerill	Garforth	Johnson M	Poole	Wells	Back	Richards	Liley	Povoas	Grewcock	Wigley	Hamilton	Underwood R	Gabriel	Malone	Boyle
O	N	M	L	K	J	I	A	B	C	D	E	F	G	H									
	N	M	L	K	J	I	A	B	C	D	E	F	H	G	O	R							
	N	M	L		J	I	A	B	C	D	E		G	H	O	F	R	K					
O	N	M	L		J	I	A	B	C	D	E	F	G	H				K					
O	N	M	L		J	I	A	B	C	D	E	F	G	H						R			
	N	M		K	J		A	B	C	D	E	F	G	H	O						L	I	
	N		L	K	J	I	A	B	C	D	E	F	H	G	O					M			
K	N		L		J	I		B	C	D	E	F		H	O					M	R		
O	N		L	K	J	I	A	B	C	D	E	F	G	H						M			
O	N	M		K	J	I	A	B	C	D	E	F	G	H									
O			L	N	J	I	A		C	D	E		H	G				K					
O			L	N	J	I	A	B	C	D	E	F						K					
O			L	N	J	I	A	B	C	D	E	F	H					K					
O	N			K	J	I	A	B	C		E	F	G	H							R		
O	N	M			J	I	A	B	C	D	E	F	G	H						K			
	K	M	N		J	I	A	B	C	D	E	F		H						O			
O	N	M			K	J	I	A	B	C				F		H				R			
	N														O					R		I	J

Match 11 Wingham F, Richardson RG, Match 12 Tarbuck H, Match 13 Tarbuck G, Match 14 Robinson L, T Smith D, Match 16 Drake-Lee G, Match 17 Wingham RC, Grant D, T Smith E, Richardson G, Match 18 Robinson M, Roke L, Reynolds K, Wingham C, Grant D, T Smith E, Wingham F, Tarbuck G.

MOST CAPPED PLAYERS

(including British Lions Appearances)
R Underwood, 62 + 6, Present
D Richard, 36 + 6, Present
P Wheeler, 41 + 7
P Dodge, 32 + 2
W H Hare, 25
C R Woodward, 21 + 3

LEADING APPEARANCES FOR CLUB

D J Matthews 502, 1955/6-1973/4
S Penny, 491, 1895/6-1910/1
J D Allen, 459, 1960/1-1975/6
D J Norman, 453, 1919/20-1932/3
P W Dodge, 437, 1975-6-1992/3
W D Hare, 394, 1976/7-1988/9

LEICESTER FC

COURAGE LEAGUE RECORDS

Highest Home Win: 66-5 v Newcastle Gosforth 12-3-94 CL1   **Defeat:** 21-31 v Harlequins 26-11-89 CL1
Biggest Away Win: 43-19 v Moseley 27-4-91 CL1   **Defeat:** 6-37 v Bath 11-1-92 CL1
Most Tries For in a Match: 11 v Bedford 23-9-89 CL1
Most Tries Against in a Match: 7 v Bath 11-1-92 CL1
Most consecutive Wins: 9   **Defeats:** 2
No. of Matches failed to Score: 1   **Clean Sheets:** 3   **Drawn Matches:** 2
Most appearances Forward: 72 John Wells
Most appearance Back: 66 Ian Bates
Most consecutive appearances: 32 Darren Garforth 28-3-92 to date
Consecutive match scoring Tries: 3 Rory Underwood, Neil Back
Points: 24 John Liley

INDIVIDUAL SCORING RECORDS

IN A MATCH

Most points: 31 John Liley v Rosslyn Park 21-03-92 Home CL1
Most tries: Tony Underwood v Newcastle Gosforth 12-3-94 Home CL1
Most conversions: 7 John Liley v Rosslyn Park 21-03-92 Home CL1
Most penalities: 7 Jez Harris v Bristol 11-12-93 Home CL1, v Gloucester 29-1-94 Home CL1
Most drop goals: 3 Jez Harris v Wasps 23-11-91 Home CL1

IN A SEASON

Most points: 202 Jez Harris 1993-94 CL1
Most tries: 9 Rory Underwood 1990-91 & 1991-92 CL1
Most conversions: 19 John Liley 1991-92 CL1
Most penalties: 41 Jez Harris 1993-94 CL1
Most drop goals: 11 Jez Harris 1993-94 CL1

IN A CAREER

Most points: 509 John Liley 1988-94
Most tries: 28 Rory Underwood 1987-94
Most conversions: 72 John Liley 1988-94
Most penalties: 101 John Liley 1988-94
Most drop goals: 22 Jez Harris 1987-94

COURAGE LEAGUE RECORD

	DIV	PLD	W	D	L	F	T	C	P	D	A	T	C	P	D
1987-88	1	10	9	0	1	225	21	15	31	6	133	14	10	17	2
1988-89	1	11	6	1	4	189	19	10	29	2	199	25	12	21	4
1989-90	1	11	6	0	5	248	36	16	22	2	184	24	14	17	3
1990-91	1	12	8	0	4	244	29	19	25	5	140	12	7	21	5
1991-92	1	12	6	1	5	262	33	20	26	4	216	26	11	28	2
1992-93	1	12	9	0	3	220	21	17	23	4	116	13	3	14	1
1993-94	1	18	14	0	4	425	41	23	46	11	210	18	9	32	2
		86	58	2	26	1813	200	120	202	34	1198	132	66	150	19

SEASON BY SEASON LEADING SCORES

	Most Points			Most Tries	
1987-88	126	Dusty Hare	5	Barry Evans	
1988-89	97	Dusty Hare	3	Barry Evans D Richards R Underwood	
1989-90	126	John Liley	7	John Liley	
1990-91	110	John Liley	9	Rory Underwood	
1991-92	129	John Liley	7	Rory Underwood	
1992-93	106	John Liley	3	Tony Underwood Nigel Richardson	
1993-94	202	Jez Harris	8	Tony Underwood	

LEICESTER FC

Club Details

Club Colours: Scarlet, green & white hoops
Change of Colours: scarlet with green & white band
Date Founded: 1880
Membership: Total: 10159, Playing members 130, Junior/Youth/Minis 30, Other 10,000
No. of teams: Senior 4, Junior 1
Programme advertising rates: On Application

Ground Details:

Ground Address: Aylestone Road, Leicester, LE2 7LF
Ground Tel No: 541607
Simple Directions to Ground: M1 (Junction 21) A46 towards Leicester. Right at traffic lights to T Junction - left for 2 miles - ground on right.
Spectator Capacity: Total: 13,800, seated 9,200, standing 4,600
Ticket Prices: Adults: £7, OAP/Child £5
Training Nights: Tuesdays and Thursdays

Club Officials

Club President: J T Thomas
Club Chairman: P W G Tom
Club Secretary: J D Allen, 60 Dorchester Road, Leicester, L63 0UF. Tel: (H) 0533 858407 (W) 0533 471234 Fax: 0533 471434
Fixtures Secretary: S H Berry, Hall Lane, Kinoulton, Notts. Tel: (W) 0949 81428
Press Officer: J D Allen
Registration Officer: J D Allen
1994/ 95 1st XV Captain: D Richards
1994/95 Club Coach: I R Smith
Director of Rugby: A D Russ

Tony Underwood **pushes John Hill away in the Pilkington Cup Final**   *Photo: Joe McCabe*

LEICESTER FC

Dean Richards of Leicester & England

Photo: Joe McCabe

NORTHAMPTON FC

Saints Mark Time

After recent seasons full of excitement the post-Corless era of Northampton made a quiet start with nothing exceptional being achieved in either cup or league, the former campaign ending with defeat at Gloucester in the fifth round (11- 6) after Waterloo had been sent packing at Franklin's Gardens in the opening session earmarked for the top clubs.

In the league the Saints were never either in serious trouble nor were they ever in a position to challenge the Bath-Leicester domination, which almost inevitably ended in favour of the former. The highest position reached was fourth on October 2nd and a nadir of eighth was plumbed on January 8th after a bad humiliation at Leicester (36-9). The Tigers thus gained revenge for defeat at Northampton by a convincing 19-10 margin on September 11th. The best results were probably the 31- 22 win at Bristol in October, a 15-14 home win in March against Harlequins and the 19-3 success at home to Gloucester on April 9th when the points were still vital.

The youth team, which won the Whitbread-Rugby World award in 1992-93, was good but it did not reach the same standards as its immediate predecessors. However, it did show that there are plenty of talented youngsters in the pipeline to support the established top club players such as the inter- nationals Tim Rodber, Martin Bayfield, the veteran Gary Pearce and new Scotland flanker Peter Walton — not to mention Nick Beal and Matthew Dawson, who must be close enough to caps themselves.

There are enough good players at Northampton for a real challenge to be mounted for both major competitions in the new season and the club coaches (Paul Larkin, Geoff Wright and Alan Hughes) mean to make sure that the team gets matters right from the start.

Northampton FC 1993-94

NORTHAMPTON FC

COURAGE CLUBS CHAMPIONSHIP
NATIONAL DIVISION ONE 1993-94

No	Date	Opponents	Venue	Result	Point Scorers
1	Sep 11	Leicester	H	W19-10	Packman (T) Grayson (C)(3P) Steele (DG)
2	Sep 18	Bath	A	L9-37	Grayson (3P)
3	Sep 25	L. Irish	H	W23-12	Rodber (T) Fielden(T) Grayson (2C)(3P)
4	Oct 2	Bristol	A	W31-22	Grayson (2T)(2C)(3P)(DG) Walton (T)
5	Oct 9	Quins	A	L7-15	Dawson (T) Grayson (C)
6	Nov 13	Orrell	H	L9-13	Grayson (P) Hunter (2P)
7	Nov 20	Gloucester	A	L14-19	Beal (T) Grayson (3P)
8	Dec 4	Wasps	H	L15-17	Steele (4P)(DG)
9	Dec 11	Newcastle G	A	W28-8	Hunter (T) Beal (T) Dawson (T) Merlin (T) Grayson (C)(2P)
10	Jan 8	Leicester	A	L9-36	Grayson (3P)
11	Jan 15	Bath	H	L9-30	Steele (3P)
12	Jan 29	L. Irish	A	W16-13	Thorneycroft (T) Grayson (C)(3P)
13	Feb 12	Bristol	H	W22-19	Fletcher (T) Grayson (C)(5P)
14	Mar 12	Quins	H	W15-14	Morgan (2T) Grayson (C)(P)
15	Mar 26	Orrell	A	L6-27	Grayson (2P)
16	Apr 9	Gloucester	H	W19-3	Rodber (T) Beal (C)(4P)
17	Apr 23	Wasps	A	L11-24	Moir (T) Beal (P)(DG)
18	Apr 30	Newcastle	H	W43-23	Thorneycroft (T) Steele (T) Walton (T) Bayfield (T) Morgan (T) Beal (3C)(4P)

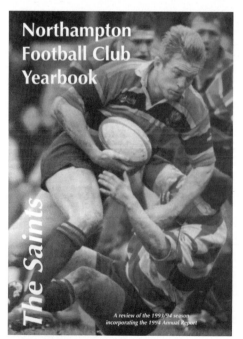

Northampton Football Club Yearbook

The Saints

A review of the 1993/94 season incorporating the 1994 Annual Report

CLUB PLAYING RECORD 1993-94
National League: One
Final League Position at end of 1993/94 saeson: 5th
League playing record: P 18, W 9, D 0, L 9,
Pts F 305, Pts A 342
Season playing record (incl. league matches/Pilkington Cup etc): P 39, W 23, D 1, L 15, Pts F 929, Pts A 642

COMPETITIONS WON DURING 1993-94
Plate Competition Middlesex 7s 1994

YEARBOOK
If we are not succeeding in getting across the message that our game has gone professional in all but name we command a detailed look at the latest Northampton Football Club Yearbook, a thoroughly professional effort. Not only does it cover the efforts of the 1993-94 season in complete detail, but it also provides a wealth of club statistics, player profiles and photographs and anything you would wish to know abou the club — and information about other available facilities. Meanwhile Franklin's Gardens, their traditional home, is building up a reputation as an outstanding Conference Centre, which can cater for ten to 200 people. There are nine syndicate rooms, all of which face the pitch and are light, airy and peaceful. The catering of Ken and Sue Ball is top quality and there is ample parking space.
For further information contact Shobha Aranha on 0664 751543 (phone) or 0604 750061 (fax).

NORTHAMPTON FC

MATCH BY MATCH PLAYERS BY POSITION

Steele	Packman	Beal	Macnaughton	Thorneycroft	Grayson	Dawson	Baldwin	Olver	Pearce	Phillips	Bayfield	Walton	Millhouse	Rodber	Fielden	Webster	Hunter	Fletcher	Steffen	Allen	Foale	Morgan	Edwards
15	14	13	12	11	10	9	1	2	3	4	5	6	7	8									
15	11	13	12	14	10	9	1	2	3	5	4	6	7	8									
15		14	13	11	10	9	1	2	3	4		6	7	8	12	5							
	11			14	10	9	1	2	3	4		6	7	8	12	5	15	13					
	11	13		14	10	9	1	2	3	5		6	7	8	12	4	15						
	14	13		11	10	9	1	2	3	5			7	8	4	15	12	6					
		13	14		10	9	1		3	5		6		8	11	4	15	12	7	R			
10	11			14		9	1	2	3			6			13	4	15	12	8	5			
10	11			14	10	9	1	2	3			6			13	5	15	12	8	4			
	11				10	9	1	2	3	5		6		8	12		15	13	7	R		14	4
10	11					9	1		3	4	5	6	7		12		15	13	8			14	4
		13		11	10	R			3	5			7	8			15	12	R	6		14	4
F	R	E	E			F	R	E	E		F	R	E	E	F	R	E	E					
	12		11	10	9				3	5		6	7				15	13	8	1		14	4
	13	12	11	10	15		1			4			7	8		3						14	5
15	10	12	11				1			4	5	6		8	R		7	3				13	
15	10	12	11						3		5			8		4	7	1				13	
15	10	12	11		9				3	4			7		1				R			13	5

Match 2 Rees R. Match 6 Roworth R. Match 7 Rowarth 2. Match 8 Pask R, Merlin 7. Match 9 Merlin 7. Match 11 Taylor R, Clarke 2. Match 12 Taylor 9, Vollands 1, Clarke 2. Match 13 Clarke 2. Match 15 Juds R, Taylor 9, Clarke 2, Merlin 6. Match 16 Moir 14, Taylor 9, Clarke 2. Match 17 Moir 14, Taylor 9, Clarke 2, Merlin 6. Match 18 Beales 14, Clarke 2, Walton 6, Pask 8.

LEADING SCORERS 1993/94

Paul Grayson, Fly Half — 196
John Steele, Full Back/Fly Half — 111

COURAGE RECORDS

Paul Grayson breaks John Steeles record of most points in a courage season for Northampton. Steele scored 110 points in 1991-92 while Grayson scored 132 points.

	PTS	T	C	P	D	APPS	AVE
Paul Grayson	132	2	10	33	1	13	
John Steele	110	—	10	28	2	11	

Grayson also broke Steeles record for penalties in a season. Steele kicked 28 in 1991-92 while Grayson kicked 33. Grayson Broke John Steeles record for points in a match. Grayson scored 26 points in the away match at Bristol beating the 20 Steele scored v Coventry in March 1990.
Grayson has now scored 100 points in a season for 3 clubs, the 2 previous were Waterloo and Preston Grasshoppers.

NORTHAMPTON FC

	APS	SEASONS	PTS	T	C	P	D
J Steele	58	1988-94	425	5	40	95	11
F Packman	65	1987-94	81	19			
N Beal	28	1992-94	70	3	11	10	3
R McNaughton	29	1991-94	13	3			
H Thorneycroft	56	1987-94	68	15			
P Grayson	13	1993-94	132	2	10	33	1
M Dawson	31+1	1991-94	30	4	1 2	1	
G Baldwin	43	1990-94	9	2			
J Olver	43	1990-94	8	2			
G Pearce	71	1987-94	8	2			
J Phillips	12	1991-94	0				
M Bayfield	30	1991-94	9	2			
P Walton	23	1993-94	10	2			
C Millhouse	10+1	1993-94	0				
T Rodber	44	1989-94	32	7			
M Fielden	9	1993-94	10	2			
R Rees	1+1	1992-94	5	1			
G Webster	8	1993-94	0				
I Hunter	43	1989-94	54	10		3	1
J Fletcher	10	1993-94	5	1			
M Steffert	12+1	1993-94	0				
P Rowarth	10+2	1987-94	0				
S Foale	6+3	1991-94	0				
D Merlin	5+1	1992-94	5	1			
P Pask	29+2	1987-94	5	1			
K Morgan	9	1993-94	15	3			
N Edwards	6	1993-94	0				
B Taylor	9+1	1990-94	0				
A Clarke	8+1	1989-94	0				
M Vollands	1	1993-94	0				
P Miles	+1	1993-94	0				
S Jubs	+1	1993-94	0				
C Moir	2	1993-94	5	1			
A Beales	1	1993-94	0				

NORTHAMPTON FC

COURAGE LEAGUE RECORDS

Biggest Home Win: 55-9 v West Hartlepool 3-4-93 CL1   **Defeat:** 3-50 v London Scottish 3-10-87 CL2
Biggest Away Win: 34-22 v London Scottish 24-4-93 CL1   **Defeat:** 0-60 v Orrell 27-10-90 CL1
Most Tries For in a Match: 8 v Rugby 28-4-90 Home CL1, v W Hartlepool 3-4-93 CL1
Most Tries Against in a Match: 11 v Orrell 27-10-90 CL1
Most consecutive Wins: 7   Defeats: 6
No. of Matches failed to Score: 3   Clean Sheets: 2   Drawn Matches: 4
Most appearances Forward: 71 Gary Pearce
Most appearances Back: 65 Frank Packman
Most consecutive appearances: 31 Frank Packman
Consecutive match scoring Tries: 4 Ian Hunter
Points: 16 John Steele

INDIVIDUAL SCORING RECORDS

IN A MATCH

Most points: 26 Paul Grayson v Bristol 2-10-93 Away CL1
Most tries: 3 Orson Bluitt v Bedford 21-11-88 Away CL2
Most conversions: 6 Nick Beal v West Hartlepool 3-4-93 Home CL1
Most penalities: 5 John Steele v Coventry 10-3-90 Home CL2, v Rugby 29-2-92 Home CL1, Paul Grayson v Bristol 12-2-94 Home CL1
Most drop goals: 3 John Steele v Wasps 23-9-91 Away CL1

IN A SEASON

Most points: 132 Paul Grayson 1993-94 CL1
Most tries: 6 Frank Packman 1988-89 CL2, Harvey Thorneycroft 1992-93 CL1
Most conversions: 11 John Steele 1989-90 CL2
Most penalties: 33 Paul Grayson 1993-94 CL1
Most drop goals: 3 John Steel 1989-90 CL2 & 1990-91 CL1

IN A CAREER

Most points: 425 John Steele 1988-94
Most tries: 19 Frank Packman 1987-94
Most conversions: 40 John Steele 1988-93
Most penalties: 95 John Steele 1988-94
Most drop goals: 11 John Steele 1988-94

COURAGE LEAGUE RECORD

	DIV	PLD	W	D	L	F	T	C	P	D	A	T	C	P	D
1987-88	2	10	1	0	9	81	10	7	9	0	226	33	20	16	2
1988-89	2	11	5	2	4	165	28	10	10	1	131	12	7	17	6
1989-90	2	11	9	1	1	192	23	11	22	4	135	12	6	22	3
1990-91	1	12	5	1	6	149	15	10	20	3	254	38	18	19	3
1991-92	1	12	9	1	2	209	22	11	30	3	136	11	7	23	3
1992-93	1	12	8	0	4	215	24	16	20	1	150	11	4	27	2
1993-94	1	18	9	0	9	305	23	14	50	4	342	34	17	40	6

SEASON BY SEASON LEADING SCORES

	Most Points			Most Tries	
1987-88	27	Phil Larkin	4	Paul Alston	
1988-89	43	John Steele	6	Frank Packman	
1989-90	105	John Steele	4	John Thame Frank Packman	
1990-91	83	John Steele	3	Wayne Shelford	
1991-92	110	John Steele	5	Harvey Thorneycroft	
1992-93	52	John Steele	6	Harvey Thorneycroft	
1993-94	132	Paul Grayson	2	7 players	

NORTHAMPTON FC

Club Details

Colours: Black, green & gold hoops
Change of Colours: White with black, green & gold bands
Nickname: the Saints
Date Founded: 1880
Membership: Total 2,500
Membership: Fees Full £90
Number of Teams: Senior 2
Programme Advertising Rates: via Brian Barron 0604 29483

Ground Details

Ground Address: Franklins Gardens, Weedon Road, Northampton, NN5 5BG.
Telephone: 0604 755149
Fax: 0604 588408
Capacity: Total 8,500, seated 2,000 (covered), temporary (open) 600, standing 5,900.
Ticket Prices: Adult £10 stand, £8 temp, £6 ground, OAP/Child half price.
Training Nights: Tuesday & Thursday

Club Officials

President: R B Taylor
Chairman: M Holmes
Club Secretary: R Horwood, Trinity Pavilion, Abbey Street, Northampton, NN5 5LN. Tel: 0604 755149 (H) 0604 410326 (H) 0604 414131 Club Office 0604 588408
Fixtures Secretary: R B Taylor, c/o Rugby Admin. as Hon. Sec. above. Tel: 0604 38626
Press Officer: R Horwood, as above.
Registration Officer: R Horwood, as above.
1994/95 1XV Captain: Tim Rodber
1994/95 1XV Coaches: Paul Larkin, Geoff Wright, Alan Hughes
Commercial Manager: John Shurvinton, Sturtridge Pavilion, Weedon Road, Northampton, NN5 5BG. Tel: 0604 751543 Fax: 0604 750061

Tim Rodber *Photo: Joe McCabe*

Harve Thorneycroft *Photo: Joe McCabe*

ORRELL RUFC

Review of the Season

A glance through the rugby press at the start of this past season did not make encouraing reading. The majority of the pundits seemed to have Orrell heading towards Courage League Division 2. It has to be said that there were some nervous moments at the club as well. Bob Kimmins, so long the spearhead of Orrell's forwards, finally decided to call it a day after struggling for years with a severe back problem. Neil Hitchen, one of the most difficult of opponents, joined Manchester and Phil Horrocks, the promising centre, was forced, by work commitments, to put his rugby carrer on hold. However, Orrell have always been at their most dangerous when their right to be part of rugby's elite is challenged. A comprehensive defeat of Newcastle Gosforth in the first match of the season was followed by two close defeats to Leicester and Bath.

In many ways it was a result of not having won either of these games when we were good value for victory that led to one of the most disappointing results of the season, am away defeat to London Irish. This was the story of Orrell's season. Losing to poor sides whilst either winning or coming extremely close to the top sides. A look at the final League table confirms this.

A closer look at the results show that whilst Orrell lost on both occasions to Bath and Leicester they also lost four matches to those clubs beneath them in the table. Victory in these matches would have lifted us to third place in the League — a huge difference!

The team also came tantalisingly close to their first ever Pilkington Cup Final appearance losing out in the semi final to mighty Leicester. Even this game could have gone Orrell's way but for one magnificent tackle on Dewi Morris as he looked certain to extend Orrell's early lead to three tries to none. Had Leicester conceded that try it would have been debatable if they could have come back. It is nice to see that Orrell had some representation at Twickenham on the big day as our U21's took to the field in the junior exhibition curtain raiser.

Taking the season as a whole we must be quietly content. Comfortably holding on to League 1 status, the semi finals of the Pilkington Cup, Finalists in the Lancashire Cup, quarter finalists in the National 10's and finishing the season in real style, losing narrowly to Bath in a memorable final at the Middlesex Sevens, make up for some of the disappointments.

1994/95 season promises to be even tougher and Orrell will need to show all their traditional grit and determination. On this season's evidence I think we can feel confident that they will continue to do credit to themselves and to the wider rugby union fraternity.

Orrell RUFC 1993-94   *Photo: Wigan Observer*

ORRELL RUFC

COURAGE CLUBS CHAMPIONSHIP
NATIONAL DIVISION ONE 1993-94

No	Date	Opponents	Venue	Result	Point Scorers
1	Sep 11	Newcastle G	H	W42-12	Naylor (2T) Morris (2T) Taberner (T) Hamer (T) Langford (2P)(2C) Peacock (C)
2	Sep 18	Leicester	A	L18-23	Ashurst (T) Cleary (T) Landford (2C)(2P)
3	Sep 25	Bath	H	L15-18	Langford (5P)
4	Oct 2	L Irish	A	L6-19	Langford (2P)
5	Oct 9	Bristol	H	W16-13	Naylor (T) Ainscough (C)(2P) Langford (P)
6	Nov 13	Northampton	A	W13-9	Cleary (T) Ainscough (C)(2P)
7	Nov 20	Harlequins	H	W21-20	Morris (T) Cleary (T) Ainscough (C)(3P)
8	Dec 4	Gloucester	H	L6-10	Ainscough (P) Peacock (P)
9	Dec 11	Wasps	A	L16-28	Hamer (T) Langford (C)(2P) Peacock (P)
10	Jan 8	Newcastle G	A	L12-13	Hamer (T) Bibby (T) Ainscough (C)
11	Jan 15	Leicester	H	L0-18	
12	Jan 29	Bath	A	L7-13	Morris (T) Langford (C)
13	February 12	L. Irish	H	W24-3	Taberner (T) Wynn (T) Bibby (T) Langford (2C) Ainscough (C)(P)
14	Mar 12	Bristol	A	L17-30	Hayter (T) Hamer (T) Ainscough (2C) Langford (P)
15	Mar 26	Northampton	H	W27-6	Naylor (2T) Johnson (T) Langford (T)(C) Ainscough (C)(P)
16	Apr 9	Quins	A	W20-13	French (T) Johnson (T) Ainscough (C) Langford (C)(2P)
17	Apr 23	Gloucester	A	L25-30	Winstanley (T) Langford (T) Johnson (T) Ainsworth (C)(P) Langford (C)(P)
18	Apr 30	Wasps	H	W42-24	Naylor (2T) Wynn (2T) Johnson (T) French (T) Ainscough (3C)(2P)

COURAGE LEAGUE RECORD

Season	Div	Pld	W	D	L	FOR	T	C	P	DG	AGA	T	C	P	DG
1987-88	1	11	5	1	5	192	24	12	24	0	153	17	5	23	2
1988-89	1	11	6	1	4	148	13	9	24	2	157	14	7	27	2
1989-90	1	11	5	0	6	221	28	17	25	0	132	9	3	28	2
1990-91	1	12	7	0	5	247	34	21	21	2	105	12	6	14	1
1991-92	1	12	10	0	2	204	26	8	26	2	95	8	3	17	2
1992-93	1	12	5	0	7	175	20	6	21	0	183	19	11	22	0
1993-94	1	18	8	0	10	327	36	24	33	0	302	25	18	43	4
		87	46	2	39	1514	181	97	174	6	1127	104	53	174	13

COURAGE RECORDS

Dewi Morris broke Phil Halsall's record of 19 Courage league tries, Morris finished the season with a toal of 21 tries from 48 games since his debut back in 1990. Halsall's 19 tries came in 59 matches.

James Naylor, in his debut season, broke the club record of seven tries in a Courage league season. The previous record of seven was jointly held by Phil Halsall and Dewi Morris.

'Sammy' Southern, Orrells' stalwart prop, holds the record, with 83, of the most appearances in the Courage first division.

Simon Langford's 84 points in the 93-94 season leaves him on 198 Courage league points. Only two Orrell players have passed the 200 point mark, Martin Strett and Gerry Ainscough with 323 and 276 respectively. Orrell used just 27 players in last season's Courage league campaign — the lowest of any first division side.

ORRELL RUFC

MATCH BY MATCH PLAYERS BY POSITION

Taberner	Naylor	Langford	Wynn	Hamer	Peacock	Morris	Ridenaugh	French	Southern	Cusani	Brierley	Ashurst	Manley	Bibby	Ainscough	Hynes	Cleary	Johnson	Cooper	Farr	Hayter	Topping	Winstanley
15	14	13	12	11	10	9	1	2	3	4	5	6	7	8									
15	14	13	12	11		9		2	3	5	4	7	6	R	10	1	8						
15	14	13	12	11		9		2	3	4	5	7	8	R	10	1	6						
15	14	13		11	10	9		2	1	4	5	6	8			3	7	12	R				
15	14	13		11	10	9	1	2	3	4	R	6	7		R		8	12	5				
15	14			11		9		2	1	5	R	7	6		10	3	8	13	4	12			
15	14			11		9		2	3	5	4	6	8		10	1	7	12	13				
15	14			11	R			2	3	5	7	6			10	1	8	13	4	12			
15	14	R		11	10	9		2	3	5		6			1		8	13	4	12	7		
15	14		11	1				2	R	5		6	7		10	1		13	4	12		9	3
15	14	13		11	10	9		2	3	4		7	6			1	8	5	12				
10	14	15	13	11		9		2	3	4		6				1	8	5	12	7			
15	14	13	12	11		9		2	3	4		6			10	1	8	5					
15	14	12	13	11				2	3	4		6	7		10			5			8	9	1
15	14	13	12			9		2	3	4		8	6		10	1	7	11	5				R
	14	15	13	11		9		2	3	4		6	7		10		8	12	5				1
	14	15	13	11				2	3			7			10		6	12	4		8	9	1
	14	15	12	11		9		2	3	4		7			10			13	5	6			1

Also Played: Match 8 Povall. Match 10 Parr. Match 13 Bibby. Match 17 Jackson. Match 18 Parr

'It isn't just a Game'

While the powers at HQ "tut-tut" about the amateur ethos, clubs are fast learning that the only route to survival is through being totally professional and a good example of this is Orrell, who are going to great lengths to sell their club facilities close to the M6 and near Wigan for all manner of social activities.

A wedding? An anniversary? Charity events?

You name it and they have the facilities and location to meet your needs. They can cater for any numbers ranging from ten to 250 people.

So, if you live near the club and need somewhere for a function of any kind why not try Orrell? Better still, try them on a match day (although they are also free to help during any week) and see the high quality entertainment on offer.

For further information phone their Commercial Manager, Jim McEwan, on 0695 632114 (24 hour service).

It isn't just a game!

ORRELL RUFC

COURAGE LEAGUE RECORDS

Highest winning score Home: 66-0 v Rugby 13-3-93 CL1
Highest winning score Away: 36-3 v Bristol 17-11-90 CL1
Highest score against Home: 25-13 v Bristol 14-11-87 CL1
Highest score against Away: 39-3 v Bath 24-10-92 CL1, 39-15 v W Hartlepool 24-4-93 CL1
Most tries in a match: For-11 v Rosslyn Park 28-4-90 CL1, v Northampton 27- 10-90 CL1, v Rugby 13-3-93 CL1
Against-5 v Moseley 10-10-87 CL1, v Bath 19-11-88 CL1, v Bath 24-10-90 CL1, v W Hartlepool 24-4-93 CL1
Most consecutive: Wins-5 Defeats-4 **Clean Sheets:** 6
Failed to score: 2, **Drawn matches:** 2
Most appearances: Forward — 83 Sammy Southern Back — 77 Simon Langford
Consecutive appearances: 39 Sammy Southern 26-9-87 till 17-11-90
Consecutive match scoring tries: 3 Gerry Ainscough, Martin Street, Phil Halsall
Consecutive match scoring points: 17 Martin Street

INDIVIDUAL SCORING RECORDS

IN A MATCH

Most points: 28 Martin Street v Rosslyn Park 28-4-90 Home CL1

Most tries: 4 Paul Hamer v Rugby 13-3-93 Home CL1

Most conversions: 8 Martin Strett v Rosslyn Park 28-4-90 Home CL1

Most penalities: 6 Martin Strett v Gloucester 28-3-92 Home CL1

Most drop goals: 1 on 6 occasions by 2 players. Martin Strett 4, Gerry Ainscough 2

IN A SEASON

Most points: 109 Martin strett 1990-91 CL1
Most tries: 8 James Naylor 1993-94 CL1
Most conversions: 21 Martin Strett 1990-91 CL1
Most penalties: 26 Martin Strett 1991-92 CL1
Most drop goals: 2 Martin Strett 1991-92 CL1

IN A CAREER

Most points: 323 Martin Strett 1988-93
Most tries: 21 Dewi Morris 1990-94
Most conversions: 43 Martin Strett 1988-93
Most penalties: 67 Martin Strett 1988-93
Most drop goals: 4 Martin Strett 1988-93

COURAGE LEAGUE RECORD

	DIV	PLD	W	D	L	F	T	C	P	D	A	T	C	P	D
1987-88	1	11	5	1	5	192	24	12	24	0	153	17	5	23	2
1988-89	1	11	6	1	4	148	13	9	24	2	157	14	7	27	2
1889-90	1	11	5	0	6	221	28	17	25	0	132	9	3	28	2
1990-91	1	12	7	0	5	247	34	21	21	2	105	12	6	14	1
1991-92	1	12	10	0	2	204	26	8	26	2	95	8	3	17	2
1992-93	1	12	5	0	7	175	20	6	21	0	183	19	11	22	0
1993-94	1	18	8	0	10	327	36	24	33	0	302	25	18	43	4
		87	46	2	39	1514	181	97	174	6	1127	104	53	174	13

SEASON BY SEASON LEADING SCORES

	Most Points			Most Tries	
1987-88	72	Gerry Ainscough	6		Gerry Ainscough
1988-89	54	Gerry Ainscough	3		Nigel Heslop
1989-90	104	Martin Strett	5		Paul Manley Nigel Heslop
1990-91	109	Martin Strett	7		Phil Halsall Dewi Morris
1991-92	104	Martin Street	7		Dewi Morris
1992-93	63	Gerry Ainscough	6		Paul Hamer
1993-94	84	Simon Langford	8		James Naylor

ORRELL RUFC

ORRELL'S COURAGE POINT SCORERS

	APS	SEASONS	PTS	T	C	P	D
S Taberner	17	1987-94	52	12			
J Naylor	17	1993-94	40	8			
S Langford	77	1987-94	198	2	25	46	
I Wynn	27+5	1988-94	20	4			
P Hamer	24+1	1992-94	50	10			
A Peacock	5+1	1993-94	8		1	2	
D Morris	48	1990-94	91	21			
M Ridehalgh	4	1992-94	0				
G French	18	1993-94	10	2			
D Southern	83	1987-94	0				
C Cusani	48	1987-94	4	1			
C Brierley	27	1988-94	0				
N Ashurst	39+2	1989-94	31	7			
P Manley	60	1987-94	29	7			
S Bibby	20+3	1988-94	14	3			
G Ainscough	55+1	1987-94	276	10	28	58	2
M Hynes	65	1988-94	4	1			
D Cleary	50+5	1987-94	48	11			
P Johnson	11	1993-94	15	3			
C Cooper	13+1	1993-94	0				
M Farr	7	1993-94	0				
G Povall	1	1993-94	0				
S Hayter	15+1	1989-94	5	1			
D Topping	3	1993-94	0				
P Winstanley	6+1	1988-94	9	2			
H Parr	2+1	1992-94	0				
A Jackson	2	1992-94	0				

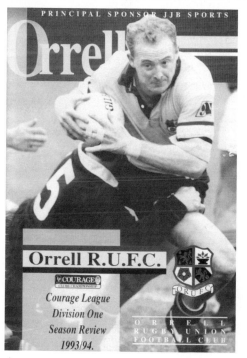

1993-94 Season Review

40 pages with colour throughout
Available on request from club

ORRELL RUFC

Club Details

Colours: Black with amber shirts with red & white facings
Change of Colours: Red with amber, black & white facings
Date Founded: 1927
Membership: Total 1,200, Full 600, Associate 100, Junior/Youth/Minis 350
Membership Fees: Full £45
Number of Teams: Senior 6 Junior/Youth/Minis 7
Programme Advertising Rates: Contact Commercial Manager

Directions: Leave M6 at Jcn 26. Follow signs for Up Holland until Orrell RUFC is signposted - approx 2 miles from M6.
Capacity: Total 6,000, Seated 400, Standing 5,600
Clubhouse Facilities: Members Lounge, Clubroom, 3 Sponsor Suites, Restaurant, Medical Room, Shop, President's Lounge
Training Nights: Mon, Tues, Thurs

Ground Details

Ground Address: Edgehall Raod, Orrell, Nr Wigan WN5 8TL
Telephone: 0695 623193 (Ground) 632114 (Commercial)
Fax: 0695 632116

Despite having his leg pulled Dewi Morris (Orrell & England Scrum Half) clears the ball   Photo: Joe McCabe

SALE FC

Sale back in top flight

It's an indication of Sale's performance last season that they had the best points for and the best defensive record of the Courage Divisions and that on their way to becoming second division champions they broke two Courage records in their 88-9 defeat of Otley.

The season got off to a flying start with wins against London Scottish, Saracens and Waterloo. Defeats at the hands of Otley and Moseley and a point dropped against Wakefield were the hiccups of the first half of the season but it ended on a high with a convincing defeat of the then unbeaten leaders West Hartlepool. In the second half of the season Sale maintained their position in the table behind West Hartlepool despite only one defeat at the hands of bogey side Moseley but with only one game to go Sale found themselves at the top of the league after a surprise defeat for West Hartlepool. Promotion was secure but the last match of the season became the Championship decider. A draw would clinch it for Sale and it has to rank amongst the other significant achievements of the season that the side hung on to an 11-11 score to snatch the Championship. The other achievement that few will forget was the run for their money that Sale gave Harlequins in the process of being knocked out at the quarter final stage of the Pilkington Cup.

Sale FC

Photo: Peter Barton

SALE FC

COURAGE CLUBS CHAMPIONSHIP
NATIONAL DIVISION ONE 1993-94

No	Date	Opponents	Venue	Result	Point Scorers
1	Sep 11	London Scottish	A	W12-3	Turner (4P)
2	Sep 18	Saracens	H	W52-3	Erskine (2T) Young (2T) Kenrick (T) Stocks (T) Mallinder (T) Baldwin (T) Turner (6C)
3	Sep 25	Waterloo	H	W15-6	Birt (2T) Turner (C)(P)
4	Oct 2	Otley	A	L5-9	Baldwin (T)
5	Oct 9	Rugby	H	W16-3	Warr (T) Turner (C)(3P)
6	Nov 13	Moseley	A	L-3-9	Turner (P)
7	Nov 20	Wakefield	H	D11-11	Kenrick (T) Jee (P) Turner (DG)
8	Dec 4	Nottingham	A	W30-9	Duthie (T) Kenrick (T) Diamond (T) Verbickas (T) Turner (2C)(2P)
9	Dec 11	W. Hartlepool	H	W28-12	McCartney (T) Verbickas (T) Warr (T) Turner (2C)(3P)
10	Feb 10	L. Scottish	H	W28-12	Young (T) Verbickas (T) Whitcombe (T) Erskine (T) Jee (C)(P) Turner (P)
11	Jan 15	Saracens	A	W8-3	Verbickas (T) Turner (P)
12	Jan 29	Waterloo	A	W28-10	Verbickas (2T) Diamond (T) Turner (2C)(3P)
13	Feb 12	Otley	H	W88-9	Verbackis (5T) Warr (4T) Whitcombe (T) Turner (T) Mallinder (T) Erskine (T) Young (T) Turner (9C)
14	Mar 12	Rugby	A	W21-8	Verbickas (2T) Mallinder (T) Jee (2P)
15	Mar 26	Moseley	H	L13-16	Verbickas (T) Mallinder (T) Turner (P)
16	Apr 9	Wakefield	A	W28-19	Whitcombe (T) Mallinder (T) Erskine (T) Turner (2C)(P)(2DG)
17	Apr 23	Nottingham	H	W41-7	Baldwin (T) O'Grady (T) Young (T) Birt (T) Verbackis (T) Mallinder (T) Turner (4C)(P)
18	Apr 30	W. Hartlepool	A	D11-11	Verbickas (T) Turner (2P)

COURAGE RECORDS

A record breaking season for Sale who fought their way back to the big time after a 6 season gap. Star of the show was the teenage winger Simon Verbickas who scored 16 tries in 11 appearances after making his debut at Nottingham in December. His 16 set a new division two record for a season beating the 11 scored by Nick Grecian for London Scottish in 1991-92. It easily beat the Sale record of 5 which was held jointly by Jeff Powell and Jim Mallinder. He also broke the records for most points in a match, beating Paul Turners record of 21. This was in the match v Otley where Sale ran in a record 88 points. Turner ended the match with 23 points also breaking his old record. In that match Verbickas became the first Sale player to score a hat trick of tries and went on to score 5 in the match, another division two record. In Turners 23 points were 9 conversions which equalled the division two record set by Newcastle's David Johnson twice in the 1991-92 season. Turners 144 points for the season broke David Pears club record of 102 set in 1988-89 and he took his career record to 198 passing Richard Booths club record of 127.

SEASON RECORD	PTS	T	C	P	D	APPS	AVE
Paul Turner	144	7	29	24	3	17	8.47
David Pears	102	3	3	26	2	8	12.75

CAREER RECORD	PTS	T	C	P	D	APPS	AVE
Paul Turner	198	2	37	32	6	24	8.25
Richard Booth	127	—	17	31	—	21	6.05

CLUB PLAYING RECORD
1993-94 SEASON

National League: Two
Final League Position at end of 1993/94 season: Top
League playing record: P18, W13, D2 L3, Pts F 438, Pts A 160
Season playing record (including league matches/Pilkington Cup etc):
P32, W23, D3, L6, Pts For 928, Pts Against 374

SALE FC

MATCH BY MATCH PLAYERS BY POSITION

Mallinder	Davies	Stocks	Birt	Young	Turner	Warr	Smith P	Diamond	Smith A	Baldwin	Erskine	Duthie	Macfarlane	Kenrick	Hewson	Jee	Parker	O'Grady	Harper	McCartney	Verbickas	Whitcombe	Baxendell
15	14	13	12	11	10	9	1	2	3	4	5	6	7	8									
15	14	13	12	11	10	9	1	2	3	5	4	6	8	7									
15	14		12	11	10	9	1	2	3	5	4	6	8	7	R								
F	R	E	E			F	R	E	E			F	R	E	E								
15		12	13	11	10	9	1		3	5	4		8		2	14		6					
		12	13	11	10		1	2	3			6	8	7	15		4		9	5			
15		12	13	11	10		1	2	3	5		6	8	7	14		4	R	9				
15		13	12	11	10	9	1	2	3	4		6	8	7						5	14		
15		13	12	11	10	9	1	2	3	4	8	6	7							5	14		
			12	11	10	9		2	3	4	6		8		15			7		5	14	1	13
15		13	12	11	10	9		2	3	4	6		8					7		5	14	1	
15			12	11	10	9		2		5	6		8					7		4	14	1	13
15			12	11	10	9		2	3	4	6		8					7		5	14	1	13
15	R		13	11		9		2	3	4	6		8		10			7		5	14	1	12
15			12	11	10	9		2	3	4	6		8				5	7			14	1	13
15	12			11	10	9		2	3	4	6		8					7		5	14	1	13
15			12	11	10			2	3	4	6		8					7	9	5	14	1	13
15			12	11	10	9		2	3	4	6		8					7		5	14	1	13

Also played Match 3 Stansfield 13, Dobson R. Match 5 Greenwood 7. Match 6 Bourne 14.
* half season up to Christmas injured after that

PLAYING SQUAD 1993-94

Full Backs: J Mallinder, D Medley
Wings: K Young, S Verbickas, G Davis
Centres: P J Baxendell, M Birt, G Stocks, P Stansfield, R Davies, G Bourne
Fly Half: P Turner, P Jee, D Callaghan
Scrum Half: M Warr, R Harper
Loose Head: M Whitcombe, P Smith
Tight Head: A Smith, N Wheeler
Hookers: S Diamon, L Hewson, P Curry
Second Row: D Baldwin, R McCartney, G Parker, S Collins, Bob Finney
Back Row: M Kenrick, M Duthie, Dave Erskine, Dylan O'Grady, H Greenwood, M Dobson, I Marshall
No. 8: A Macfarlane

LEADING SCORERS 1993-94

Paul Turner, Fly Half, 244
Simon Verbickas, Wing, 152 (including 29 tries)
Phil Jee, Fly Half, 59
Kevin Young, Wing, 57
Mike Kenrick, Bark Row, 45*
Jim Mallinder, Full Back, 40
Dave Erskine, Back Row, 40

SALE FC

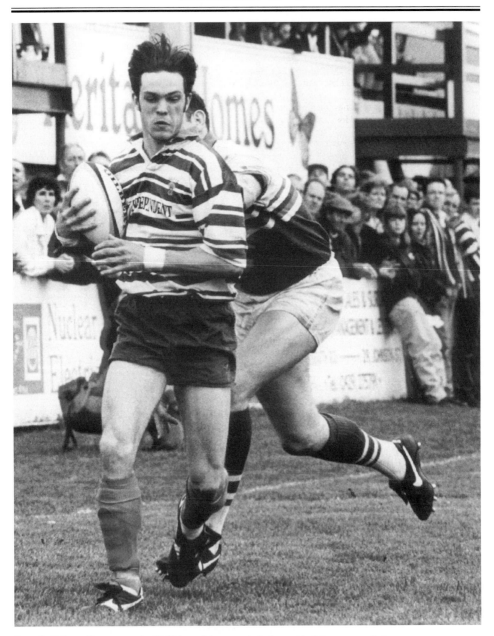

Simon Verbickas on his way to scoring his 29th try of the season in the last match of the season against West Hartlepool

Photo: Peter Barton

SALE FC

COURAGE LEAGUE RECORDS

Biggest Home Win: 88-9 v Otley 12-2-94 CL2   **Defeat:** 17-46 v Bath 28-4-88 CL1
Biggest Away Win: 38-11 v Liverpool St Helens 14-12-91 CL2   **Defeat:** 6-66 v Harlequins 23-4-88 CL1
Most Tries For in a Match: 14 v Otley 12-2-94 CL2
Most Tries Against in a Match: 12 v Harlequins 23-4-88 CL1
Most consecutive Wins: 7   **Defeats:** 11
No. of Matches failed to Score: 3   **Clean Sheets:** 3   **Drawn Matches:** 5
Most appearances Forward: 70 Martin Whitcombe
Most appearances Back: 61 Phil Stansfield
Most consecutive appearances: 39 Phil Stansfield 22-10-88 thru 14-3-92
Consecutive match scoring Tries: 8 Simon Verbickas
Points: 14 Richard Booth

INDIVIDUAL SCORING RECORDS

IN A MATCH

Most Points: 25 Simon Verbickas v Otley 12-2-94 CL2
Most Tries: 5 Simon Verbickas v Otley 12-2-94 CL2
Most Conversions: 9 Paul Turner v Otley 12-2-94 CL2
Most Penalties: 5 David Pears v Headingley 19-11-88 Home CL2, v Gosforth
Most Drop Goals: 2 David Pears v Bedford 22-2-89 Home CL2, Paul Turner v Morley 3-10-92 Home CL2, v, Wakefield 9-4-94 Away CL2

IN A SEASON

Most Points: 144 Paul Turner 1993-94 CL2
Most Tries: 16 Simon Verbickas 1993-94 CL2
Most Conversions: 29 Paul Turner 1993-94 CL2
Most Penalties: 26 David Pears 1988-89 CL2
Most Drop Goals: 3 David Shufflebottom 1990-91 CL2, Paul Turner 1993-94 CL2

IN A CAREER

Most Points: 198 Paul Turner 1992-94
Most Tries: 20 Jim Mallinder 1988-94
Most Conversions: 37 Paul Turner 1992-94
Most Penalties: 32 Paul Turner 1992-94
Most Drop Goals: 6 Paul Turner 1992-94

COURAGE LEAGUE RECORD

	DIV	PLD	W	D	L	F	T	C	P	D	A	T	C	P	D
1987-88	1	11	0	0	11	95	9	4	16	1	375	60	40	15	3
1988-89	2	11	6	0	5	195	18	9	32	3	152	16	8	23	1
1989-90	2	11	4	0	7	153	16	7	25	0	182	23	12	22	0
1990-91	2	12	5	1	6	224	32	15	18	4	156	23	11	8	6
1991-92	2	12	6	0	6	204	23	11	28	2	209	25	11	27	2
1992-93	2	12	7	1	4	237	26	12	22	5	102	5	4	20	3
1993-94	2	18	13	2	3	438	57	30	28	3	160	9	5	32	3
		87	41	4	42	1546	181	88	169	18	1336	161	91	147	18

SEASON BY SEASON LEADING SCORERS

	Most Points			Most Tries
1987-88	49	Graham Jenion	3	Howard Fitto
1988-89	102	David Pears	3	David Pears
1989-90	29	Graham Jension	4	Phil Stansfield
1990-91	92	Richard Booth	5	Jeff Powell
1991-92	79	Matthew Alexander	5	Jim Mallinder
1992-93	63	Phil Jee	7	Mark Warr
1993-94	144	Paul Turner	16	Simon Verbickas

SALE FC

Club Details

Colours: Royal blue & white irregular hoops.
Change of Colours: Red & white irregular hoops.
Date Founded: 1861.
Membership: Total 700, Junior/Youth/Minis 30, Women 1.
Number of Teams: Senior 4, Junior 1.
Programme Advertising Rates: Full £200, Half £100, 1/4 £25.
Special Occasions during 1994/95: North v South West Dec 3, Irish Exiles v Ulster Dec 10, Chesgire U21s v Lancs U21s Dec 7 (Wells)

Ground Details

Ground Address: Hewyood Road, Brooklands, Sale, Cheshire, M33 3WB.
Telephone: 061 973 6348.
Directions: Brooklands Railway Station Manchester/Altrincham line, 500 yards.
Capacity: 3,400, Seated 250, Standing 3,150.
Ticket Prices: Adults £6 (league), £5 (Non0league), OAP/Child £3 (league), £2 (non-league)
Training Nights: Tuesday & Thursday.

Club Officials

Club President: John Gardiner
Club Chairman: Tom Barker
Club secretary: Laura Murrell, 41 Lawrence Road, Altrincham, Cheshire, WA14 4EL. Tel: (H) 061 926 9223 (W) 061 905 6318
Fixture secretary: Tony Dolan, 9 Greenway Road, Timperley, Cheshire. Tel: (H) 061 973 4799 (W) 061 795 0711
Press Officer: Christine Kenrick, 32 Darley Street, Sale, Cheshire, M33 7TB. Tel: (H) 061 962 1365 (W) 061 200 2020
Registration Officer: Peter Tasker, 26 Alcester Road, Sale, Cheshire, M33 3QP.
1994/95 1st XV Captain: Mike Kenrick
1994/95 Director of Coaching: Paul Turner

Richard McCartney   *Photo: Joe McCabe*   *Paul Turner*   *Photo: Joe McCabe*

WASPS FC

Wasps — Muted Sting

The previous season 1992/3 Wasps were joint top of Courage League One, becoming runners up to Bath only on points difference, were Cup Semi finalists, Winners of the Middlesex Sevens and our Under 21's won the National Championship.

This past season, 1993/4, Wasps were third in the Courage League, lost to Bath at the Rec early in the Cup, but their powerful Under 21's again won the National Championship. Most clubs would be quietly satisfied by such an outcome, but Wasps are very disappointed and expect and demand better of themselves.

Led by Dean Ryan and coached by Rob Smith, this season we got an infinitely smaller share of the luck needed to sustain league success and losing to Leicester by an inevitable Jez Harris drop goal well into injury time, losing to Bath with the customary unusual refereeing aberrations, and losing two games through complacently releasing over half the League side for such things as Hong Kong Sevens, did nothing to help. Perhaps the worst piece of bad luck was Norman Hadley (Canada) breaking his leg in a Sunday exhibition game early in the season — such a player would have had a major influence in the second half of the season.

Wasps were delighted that five players went with England to South Africa — Rob Andrew, Steve Bates, Dean Ryan, Damian Hopley and Lawrence Dallaglio. Rob broke all sorts of records, Dean captained the Dirt Trackers and Lawrence Dallaglio showed the incredible promise we already knew he had. The club has for some time recognised that the future and the continuity of success must come from a home nursery of young players and the likes of Dallaglio and Hopley could soon be followed by the current U21 stars like Peter Scrivener, Nick Greenstock, Jon Ufton and Andy Gomarsall. Watch this space....

This coming season poses the problem of reconciling the conflicting requirements of the need for England to compete for the 1995 World Cup in South Africa with fresh and rested players against the need of their clubs, in what may be vital stages of the League, or indeed Cup. Wasps have always given precedence to the primary requirements of England and whatever is eventually devised; the club will wish to do all in its power to ensure that our England representatives get the best possible preparation in the national interest.

WASPS FC

COURAGE CLUBS CHAMPIONSHIP
NATIONAL DIVISION ONE 1993-94

No	Date	Opponents	Venue	Result	Point Scorers
1	Sep 11	Gloucester	A	D9-9	Andrew (3P)
2	Sep 18	Harlequins	H	W18-15	Holmes (T) Hopley (T) Andrew (C)(2P)
3	Sep 25	Newcastle G	H	W38-21	D Hopley (2T) Oti (2T) Andrew (T)(3P)(2C)
4	Oct 2	Leicester	A	L6-38	Andrew (2P)
5	Oct 9	Bath	H	L13-19	Childs (T) Andrew (C)(2P)
6	Nov 13	L. Irish	A	W29-14	Hopley (T) Dallaglio (T) Ryan (T) Bates (T) Andrew (3C)(P)
7	Nov 20	Bristol	H	W34-8	D Hopley (2T) Buzza (T) Andrew (T)(4C)(2P)
8	Dec 4	Northampton	A	W17-15	Shortland (T) Andrew (3P)(DG)
9	Dec 11	Orrel	H	W28-16	Bates (T)
10	Jan 8	Gloucester	H	W29-18	Ryan (T) Shortland (T) Andrew (2C)(5P)
11	Jan 15	Quins	A	L17-22	Oti (T) Andrew (4P)
12	Jan 29	Newcastle G	A	W18-16	Dallaglio (T) White (T) Andrew (C)(2P)
13	Feb 12	Leicester	H	L13-15	P Hopley (T) Andrew (C)(2P)
14	Mar 12	Bath	A	L8-24	Hunter (T) P Hopley (P)
15	Mar 26	L. Irish	H	L21-22	Greenstock (T) Maddock (T)(C)(2P) Davies (DG)
16	Apr 19	Bristol	A	W16-15	Ryan (T) P Hopley (T) Braithwaite (2P)
17	Apr 23	Northampton	H	W24-11	Braithwaite (T)(C)(3P) P Hopley (T) Maddock (P)
18	Apr 30	Orrell	A	L24-42	Probyn (T) Shortland (T) Braithwaite (C)(3P)(DG)

Club Sponsor

UNITED
AIRLINES

WASPS
FOOTBALL
CLUB
Founded in 1867

WASPS
v
NORTHAMPTON

COURAGE CLUBS CHAMPIONSHIP

Saturday, 23rd April, 1994. Kick-off 3.00 p.m.

£1.00

CLUB PLAYING RECORD
1993-94 SEASON
National League: One
Final League Position at end of 1993/94 saeson: 3rd
League playing record: P 18, W 10, D 1, L 7,
Pts F 362, Pts A 340
Season playing record (including league
matches/Pilkington Cup etc):
P 37, W 23, D 1, L 13, Pts F 975, Pts A 668

COMPETITIONS WON DURING
1993-94 SEASON
National Under 21 Champions

MATCH PROGRAMME 1993-94
Price: £1.00
Pages: 32
Black and white with colour cover
At least 10 original features, including three articles.

WASPS FC

MATCH BY MATCH PLAYERS BY POSITION

Buzza	P Hopley	Clough	Childs	Andrew	Skinner	Malloy	Dunn	Probyn	Kinsey	Shortland	Greenwood	White	Wilkins	D Hopley	Davies	Bates	Holmes	Dallaglio	Ryan	Oti	Hunter	Dunston
15	14	13	12	10	9	1	2	3	4	5	6	7	8									
15	14	13	12	10			2	3	4	5	6			13	11	9	1	7	8			
15	14	13		10			2	3	4	5	6			12		9	1	7	8	11		
15	14	13		10	9		2	3	4	5	6			12			1	7	8	11		
15	14	13		10	R		2	3	4		6	7	8	12		9	1	R	5	11		
	14	13	12	10			2	3	4		5	7			15	9	1	6	8			
15	14	13		10			2	3	4	5	6	7		12		9	1		8	11		
15	11	13	12	10			2	3	4	5	6	7		14		9	1		8			
	14			10			2	3	4			7		12	15	9	1	8	5		11	
15	14	13	12	10			2		4	5	6	7				9	1		8	11		3
15	14	13	12	10			2		4	5	6	7				9	1		8	11		3
	11		12	10		1	2		4	5	6	7		13	15	9		R	8		14	3
	14	13		10			2	3		5		7		12	15	9	1	6	8		11	
	14		12					3	4	5		7		13	10	9	1		8		11	
			12					3	4		6				10	9	1		8			
	14	13				1	2	3	4	5		7		12		9		6	8		11	
	11	13	12			1	2	3	4	5		7				9		6	8			
	11		12			1	2	3	4	5	6	7										

Match 1 Abadom 11. Match 4 Green R. Match 6 Wedderburn 11, March 14, Maddock 15, Delaney 2, Emeruwa 6. Match 9 Scrase 13, Dyte 6. Match 11 Delaney R, Wright R. Match 12 Delany R. Match 15 Maddock 15, Adeyems 14, Greenstock 13, Scrase 11, Delaney 2, O'Leary 5, Scrivengr 7. Match 16 Maddock 15, Braithwaite 10. Match 17 Maddock 15, Greenstock 14, Braithwaite 10. Match 18 Wright 9, Maddock 15, Adeyems 14, Greenstock 13, Braithwaite 10, Cook 6

PLAYING SQUAD 1993-94

Hookers: P Delaney, K Dunn, P Green
Scrum Halves: S Bates, A Gomarsall, M Skinner, C Wright
Locks: N Hadley, R Kinsey, S O'Leary, S Shortland
Wings: J Abadom, M Adeyemi, P Hopley, S Hunter, C Oti, M Wedderburn
Full Backs: A Buzza, H Davies, A Maddock
Centres: G Childs, F Clough, N Greenstock, D Hopley, L Scrase
Fly half: R Andrew, C Braithwaite
No 8: M Greenwood, D Ryan, C Wilkins
Props: I Dunston, G Holmes, D Molloy, J Probyn
Flankers: D Cook, L Dallaglio, N Dyte, F Emeruwa, P Scrivener, M White

Individual Player Information

Rob Andrew 64 (incl 5 Lions) (RE-CORD) 1985 to date
Jeff Probyn 37 (RECORD) 1988-1993
Maurice Colclough 33
(incl 8 Lions) 1978-1986
Paul Rendall 28 1984-1991
Roger Uttley 27
(incl 4 Lions) 1973-1980
Huki Davies 21 1981 to date

Leading Appearances for Club

League only — 1993-94 season
Richard Kinsley 18
Phil Hopley 17
Dean Ryan & Kevin Dunn 16
Graham Childs, Steve Bates, Jeff Probyn & Matt Greenwood 15

Leading Scorers 1993-94

Points ONLY for Wasps
Rob Andrew, Fly Half — 201
Chris Braithwaite, Fly Half — 197
Steve Shortland, Lock — 35
Phil Hopley, Wing — 33
Damian Hopley, Centre — 30
Les Jackson, Lock — 30

WASPS FC

COURAGE RECORDS

Despite missing the last 5 matches of the season Rob Andrew broke his own record of points in a season for wasps. He finished the season on 159 beating his own record of 129 set in 1990-91.

SEASON		T	C	P	D	APPS	AVE
1993-94	Rob Andrew	2	16	38	1	13	12.23
1990-91	Rob Andrew	4	16	26	—	12	10.75

Andrew kicked 7 penalties v Orrell in December 1993 to equal the divisional record of David Pears and Jez Harris. The previous best for Wasps was 5 by Nick Stringer, Andrew himself and Steve Pilgrim.

Chris Oti extended his career tries record to 22 from 19 since his debut back in 1988.

Andrew broke Steve Pilgrims record for penalties in a season. Pilgrim kicked 27 in the 1991-92 season, while Andrew ended the season with 38.

Chris Oti supported by Alan Buzza takes on A Adedayo
Photo: Colorsport

WASPS FC

COURAGE LEAGUE RECORDS

Biggest Home Win: 51-4 v Liverpool St Helens 20-4-91 CL1   **Defeat:** 12-24 v Bath 14-3-92 CL1
Biggest Away Win: 44-9 v Bedford 12-3-90   **Defeat:** 24-42 v Orrell 30-4-94 CL1
Most Tries For in a Match: 9 v Coventry 13-4-88 H CL1, v Bedford 12-3-90 A CL1,
v Liverpool St Helens 20-4-91 H CL1
Most Tries Against in a Match: 6 v Orrell 30-4-94 CL1
Most consecutive Wins: 9   **Defeats:** 4
No. of Matches failed to Score: 0   **Clean Sheets:** 2   **Drawn Matches:** 4
Most appearances Forward: 64 Jeff Probyn   **Most appearances Back:** 71 Steve Bates
Most consecutive appearances: 36 R Kinsey 29-2-92 to date
Consecutive Matches scoring Tries: 3 Chris Oti, Simon Smith   **Points:** 16 Rob Andrew

INDIVIDUAL SCORING RECORDS

IN A MATCH

Most points: 24 Rob Andrew v Bristol 27-4-91 H CL1
Most tries: 3 Simon Smith v Coventry 13-4-88 Home CL1, Mark Bailey v Moseley 19-11-88 Home CL1 & v Gloucester 14-10-89 Home CL1, Graham Childs v Liverpool St Helens 20-4-91 Home CL1, Rob Andrew v Bristol 27-4-91 Home CL1, Chris Oti v Bristol 25-4-92 Away CL1
Most conversions: 6 Rob Andrew v Liverpool St Helens 20-4-91 Home CL1, & v Bristol 27-4-91 H CL1
Most penalities: 5 Nick Stringer v Orrel 23-4-88 Home CL1, Rob Andrew v Nottingham 12-11-88 Away CL1 & v Leicester 9-9-89 Home CL1, Steve Pilgrim v Rosslyn park 11-1-92 Away CL1 & v Bristol 25-4-92 Away CL1, 7 Rob Andrew v Orrell 11-12-93 Home CL1
Most drop goals: 1 on 9 occasions by 2 players. Rob Andrew 5, Huw Davies 3, Chris Braithwaite 1

IN A SEASON

Most points: 159 Rob Andrew 1993-94 CL1
Most tries: 7 Mark Bailey 1989-90 CL1, Chris Oti 1990-91 CL1
Most conversions: 16 Rob Andrew 1990-91 + 1993-94 CL1
Most penalties: 38 Rob Andrew 1993-94 CL1
Most drop goals: 2 Rob Andrew 1988-89 CL1

IN A CAREER

Most points: 546 Rob Andrew 1987-94
Most tries: 22 Chris Oti 1988-94
Most conversions: 58 Rob Andrew 1987-94
Most penalties: 119 Rob Andrew 1987-94
Most drop goals: 5 Rob Andrew 1987-94

COURAGE LEAGUE RECORD

	DIV	PLD	W	D	L	F	T	C	P	D	A	T	C	P	D
1987-88	1	11	8	1	2	218	29	12	25	1	136	14	7	21	1
1988-89	1	11	7	1	3	206	24	15	24	2	138	13	7	20	4
1989-90	1	11	9	0	2	250	39	17	20	0	106	9	5	19	1
1990-91	1	12	9	1	2	252	35	17	26	0	151	12	8	25	4
1991-92	1	12	6	0	6	177	18	6	29	2	180	17	8	27	0
1992-93	1	12	11	0	1	186	19	8	24	1	118	6	5	25	1
1993-94	1	18	10	1	7	362	33	19	50	3	340	28	13	50	8
		87	60	4	23	1651	197	94	198	9	1169	99	53	187	19

SEASON BY SEASON LEADING SCORES

	Most Points			**Most Tries**
1987-88	57	Nick Stringer	5	Mark Bailey Simon Smith
1988-89	103	Rob Andrew	4	Mark Bailey
1989-90	90	Rob Andrew	7	Mark Bailey
1990-91	126	Rob Andrew	7	Chris Oti
1991-92	101	Steve Pilgrim	5	Chris Oti
1992-93	53	Alan Buzza	4	Phil Hopley Chris Oti
1993-94	159	Rob Andrew	5	Damian Hopley

WASPS FC

Club Details

Colours: Black with gold wasp on left breast
Change of Colours: Black and gold hoops
Date Founded: 1867
Membership: Total 1600, Full 1,550, Junior/Youth/Minis 100.
Membership: Playing members 300, other 1200
Number of Teams: Senior 7 (incl U21) + 3 ladies, Junior Colts U19s
Programme Advertising Rates: Page £660 + VAT, 1/2 Page £380 + VAT

Ground Details

Ground Address: Repton Avenue, Sudbury, Nr Wembley, Middlesex, HA0 3DW
Telephone: 081 902 4220
Fax: 081 900 2659
Simple directions to ground: To Sudbury Town Stn (Picadilly Line) walk via A404 (Watford Rd) to "Swan" PH, Roundabout, Ground off to right. (London Central 35 mins)
Capacity: 4,500 (seated 1,350, standing 3,150).
Ticket Prices: Adult £6. OAP/Child £3.
Training Nights: Tuesday, Wednesday, Thursday

Club Officials

President: W T Treadwell
Chairman: Sir Patrick Lowry
Club Secretary: I A Mountlake, Nash House, 25 Mount Sion, Tunbridge Wells, Kent, TN1 1TZ. Tel: (H) 0892 511348 (W) 0892 511348
Fixtures Secretary: Don Wills, 25 Woodland Gardens, Isleworth, Middlesex TW7 6LN. Tel: 081 560 7594.
Press Officer: John Gasson, The Manor, Willington, Bedfordshire, MK44 3PX. Tel: (H) 0234 838735 (W) 071 409 3455 Fax: 0234 838314.
Registration Officer: Malcolm Sincalir, 72 The Warren, Heston, Middlesex, TW5 0JN. Tel: 081 570 0595.
1994/95 1XV Captain: Dean Ryan
1994/95 1XV Coach: Rob Smith
Commercial Manager: Sara Rigby
Club Steward: Louis O'Meara
Chairman of Club Council: Sir Peter Yarranton

Damian Hopley chased by Chris Sheesby of Harlequins
Photo: Joe McCabe

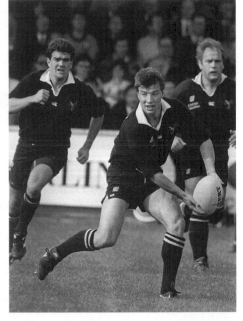

Rob Andrew supported by Steve Bates and Jeff Probin
Photo: Joe McCabe

114

WEST HARTLEPOOL RFC

West back with elite

The objective of promotion back to national league one was achieved at the first attempt, although it was slightly disappointing not to be going up as champions after leading the league for most of the season. The final league game against rivals Sale resulted in an 11-11 draw, Sale taking the title by virtue of a much superior points difference.

The wear and tear of a long league season took its toll towards the end of the season with a couple of disappointing defeats when key players were injured. Coach Dave Stubbs built on the experience gained during the previous season in league one, the players being more "Streetwise" and having the benefit of a generally settled squad.

A feature of the season was three closely contested matches against Yorkshire rivals Wakefield, resulting in a 13-13 draw and an 11-10 win in the league matches and a similar one point win (18-17) in the Pilkington Cup.

WEST HARTLEPOOL RFC

COURAGE CLUBS CHAMPIONSHIP
NATIONAL DIVISION ONE 1993-94

No	Date	Opponents	Venue	Result	Point Scorers
1	Sep 11	Waterloo	H	W30-11	Hodder (T) Wrigley (T) Cooke (T) Stabler (3C)(3P)
2	Sep 18	Rugby	H	W28-19	Watson (T) Dixon (T) Stabler (T)(2C)(3P)
3	Sep 25	Otley	A	W28-11	Cooke (2T) Wrigley (T) Stabler (2C)(3P)
4	Oct 2	Loseley	A	W31-9	Cooke (T) Mitchell (T) Oliphant (T) Ridley (T) Stabler (4C)(P)
5	Oct 9	Wakefield	H	D13-13	Dixon (T) Stabler (C)(2P)
6	Nov 13	Nottingham	A	W17-9	Lancaster (T) Mitchell (T) Stabler (2C)(P)
7	Nov 20	Saracens	A	W14-8	Hodder (T)(DG) Stabler (2P)
8	Dec 4	L Scottish	H	W21-19	P. Evans (T) O. Evans (T) Stabler (C)(2P)(DG)
9	Dec 11	Sale	A	L12-28	Stabler (2P)(DG) Oliphant (P)
10	Jan 8	Waterloo	A	W25-15	Watson (T) Wrigley (T) Evans (T) Oliphant (2C)(2P)
11	Jan 15	Otley	H	W48-20	Evans (2T) Brown (T) Wrigley (T) Hodder (T) Cooke (T)(PT) Oliphant (5P)(C)
12	Jan 29	Rugby	A	W27-6	Lee (T) P. Evans (T) Oliphant (C)(5P)
13	Feb 12	Moseley	A	W16-15	Wrigley (T) Brown (T) Oliphant (2P)
14	Mar 12	Wakefield	A	W11-10	P. Evans (T) Parker (2P)
15	Mar 26	Nottingham	H	L13-23	Wrigley (T) Stabler (C)(P) Oliphant (P)
16	Apr 9	Saracens	H	W22-20	Watson (T) Oliphant (C)(4P) Parker (DG)
17	Apr 23	L. Scottish	A	L22-24	S. Mitchell (T) Watson (T) Oliphant (3P) Parker (DG)
18	Apr 30	Sale	H	D11-11	Watson (T) Oliphant (2P)

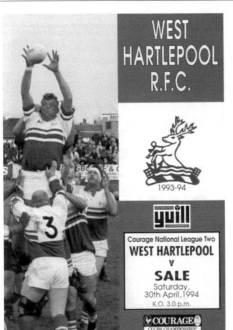

WEST HARTLEPOOL R.F.C.

1993-94

yuill

Courage National League Two
WEST HARTLEPOOL
v
SALE
Saturday,
30th April, 1994
K.O. 3.0 p.m.

COURAGE
CLUBS CHAMPIONSHIP

CLUB PLAYING RECORD
1993-94 SEASON

National Division: Two
Final League Position at end 1993/94 Season: 2nd
League Playing Record: P 18, W 13, D 2, L 3,
Pts F 389, Pts A 271
Season Playing Record (including League
matches/Pilkington cup etc):
P 32, W 22, D 2, L 8, Pts F 653, Pts A 519

MOST CAPPED PLAYERS
C Arvold 16
J Taylor 11

LEADING SCORERS 1993/94
Kevan Oliphant Full Back 135
John Stabler Fly Half 134
Dave Cooke Wing 55
Jonathan Wrigley Scrum Half 50
Mick Watson No. 8 45
Owne Evans Wing 35

PROGRAMME
32 Pages (8 colour) at least eight original pages with
two features and stastistics

WEST HARTLEPOOL RFC

MATCH BY MATCH PLAYERS BY POSITION

Oliphant	Cooke	Lee	Hodder	Ridley	Stabler	Wrigley	Lancaster	S Mitchell	Whitelock	Dixon	Westgarth	P Evans	Brown	Watson	Havery	D Mitchell	O Evans	Aldington	Cook	G Evans	Parker	McManus	Elwin
15	14	13	12	11	10	9	1	2	3	4	5	6	7	8									
15	14	13	12	11	10	9	1	2	3	4	5		7	8	R	6							
F	R	R	E			F	R	E	E			F	R	E	E								
15	14	13	12	11	10	9	1	2	3	4	5	6	7	8									
15	14	13	12		10		1	2	3	4	5	6	7	8	9		11						
15	14	13	12		10	9	1	2	3	5	4	6	7	8			11						
15	14	13	12		10	9	1	2		4	5	8	7			6	11	3	R				
15	14	13	12		10	9	1	2	3	4	5	6	7	8	R		11						
15	11	12	13		10	9	1	2	3	4	5		7	8		6	14						
15	11	13	12		10	9	1	2	3	4	5	6	7	8	R		14						
15		13	12		10		1	2		4	5	6	7	8	9		14	3		11			
15		13	12		10	9	1	2		4	5	6	7	8			14	2		11			
		13	12		10	9	1	2	3	4	5	6	7	8			14			11	15		
15		13			10	9	1	2	3	4	5	8	7			6	14			11		12	
15			12				9	1	2	3	4	5	R	7	8		6	14			11	10	13
15			12				9	1	2	3	4	5		7	8		6		14	11	10	13	
15	11		12				9	1	2	3	4	5	R	7	8		6	14	R			10	13

Also played Match 12 McKinnon R

PLAYING SQUAD 1993-94
Full Back — Kevan Oliphant
Wing — Dave Cooke, Owen Evans, Glynn Evans, Bill Ridley
Centre — Paul Hodder, Craig Lee, Steve McManus
Fly Half — John Stabler, Ashley Parker
Scrum Half — Jonathan Wrigley, Steve Harvey, Steve Cook
Prop — Phil Lancaster, Paul Whitelock, Bruce Aldington
Hooker — Simon Mitchell, Mark Jengelow
Lock — John Dixon, Kevin Westgarth, Jason Malcolm
Flanker — Alan Brown, Dave Mitchell, Paul Evans, Darren McKinnon
No. 8 — Mick Watson

LEADING APPEARANCES FOR CLUB:
Dave Stubbs 685 1966-86
Peter Robinson 573 1972-92
Paul Stacey 514 1972-89
Derek Boyd 362 1973-88
Dave Mitchell 359 1977-91
John Stables 345 1981-94

LEADING APPEARANCES 1993-94
Paul Hodder — 30
Kevan Oliphant — 29
Kevin Westgarth — 27
Alan Brown — 26
John Stables — 25
Phil Lancaster — 25
Simon Mitchell —25

WEST HARTLEPOOL RFC

COURAGE LEAGUE RECORDS

Biggest Home Win: 48-20 v Otley 15-1-94 CL2   **Defeat:** 10-38 v Bath 27-3-93 CL1
Biggest Away Win: 43-6 v Birmingham 6-2-88 CL3   **Defeat:** 9-55 v Northampton 3-4-93 CL1
Most Tries For in a Match: 8 Birmingham 6-2-88 CL3, v Broughton Park 9-3-91 CL3
Most Tries Against in a Match: 8 v Northampton 3-4-93 CL1
Most Consecutive Wins: 9   **Defeats:** 5
No. of Matches failed to Score: 0   **Clean Sheets:** 3   **Drawn Matches:** 6
Most appearances Forward: 75 Phil Lancaster
Most appearances Back: 76 John Stabler
Most consecutive appearances: 64 John Stabler 11-7-89 thru 26-3-94
Consecutive Match scoring Tries: 4 Owain Evans   **Points:** 36 John Stabler

INDIVIDUAL SCORING RECORDS

IN A MATCH

Most Points: 23 John Stabler v Broughton Park O9-O3-91 Home CL3
Most Tries: 3 Owain Evans v Nuneaton 23-O4-88 Home CL3,
Peter Robinson v Vale of Lune O2-O3-91 Away CL3,
John Wrigley v Moseley 14-12-91 Home CL2
Most Conversions: 6 John Stabler v Broughton Park O9-O3-91 Away CL3
Most Penalties: 6 John Stabler v Met Police O6-O1-88 Away CL3
Most Drop Goals: 2 Kevin Oliphant v Vale of Lune O7-11-88 Away CL3,
John Stabler v Sheffield 19-11-88 Home CL3

IN A SEASON

Most Points: 118 John Stabler 1991-92 CL3
Most Tries: 9 John Wrigley 1990-91 CL3
Most Conversions: 19 John Stabler 199O-91 CL3
Most Penalties: 26 John Stabler 1991-92 CL2
Most Drop Goals: 3 John Stabler 1988-89 CL3

IN A CAREER

Most Points: 561 John Stabler 1987-94
Most Tries: 28 Dave Cooke 1987-94
Most Conversions: 79 John Stabler 1987-94
Most Penalties: 118 John Stabler 1987-94
Most Drop Goals: 8 John Stabler 1987-94

COURAGE LEAGUE RECORD

	DIV	PLD	W	D	L	F	T	C	P	D	A	T	C	P	D
1987-88	3	11	10	0	1	249	33	12	27	4	105	11	5	16	1
1988-89	3	11	5	1	5	164	19	11	18	4	133	18	8	14	1
1989-90	3	11	5	2	4	175	20	10	23	2	126	8	4	21	1
1990-91	3	12	10	1	1	282	42	24	21	1	90	13	4	10	0
1991-92	2	12	11	0	1	244	33	17	26	0	89	12	4	11	0
1992-93	1	12	3	0	9	149	14	8	21	0	236	24	1	28	2
1993-94	2	18	13	2	3	389	39	25	43	5	271	22	13	36	9
		87	57	6	24	1652	200	107	179	16	1050	108	49	136	14

SEASON BY SEASON LEADING SCORERS

	Most Points			Most Tries	
1987-88	83	John Stabler	6	Owain Evans	
1988-89	6O	John Stabler	8	Dave Cooke	
1989-9O	65	Gary Armstrong	5	Dave Cooke	
199O-91	87	John Stabler	9	John Wrighley	
1991-92	118	John Stabler	7	John Wrighley	
1992-93	89	John Stabler	3	Alan Brown	
1993-94	103	John Stabler	7	John Wrigley	

WEST HARTLEPOOL RFC

COURAGE RECORDS

Fairly uneventful season on the records front with none of the in a match or in a season records being broken.

In the career records Dave Cooke extended his try scoring record to 28 but is closely followed by Owain Evans and John Wrigley.

	TOTAL	APPS	STRIKE RATE
D Cooke	28	69	0.40
O Evans	25	68	0.36
J Wrigley	23	46	0.50

Kevin Oliphant moves into 2nd place on Wests all time courage league points scorers and becomes the 5th man to pass 100 pts.

John Stabler 569pts 1987-94
Kevin Oliphant 122pts 1987-94
Dave Cooke 119pts 1988-94
Owain Evans 106pts 1987-94
Gary Armstrong 102pts 1989-92

Jonathan Wrigley — West Hartlepool v Waterloo at Westhartlepool

WEST HARTLEPOOL RFC

Club Details

Colours: Red, Green/white shirts, white shorts, green socks.
Change of Colours: Blue & wWhite shirts, white shorts, bue socks.
Date Founded: 1981.
Membership: Total 2,700, Junior/Youth/Minis 300.
Number of Teams: 4 + U21, Junior U19, U18, U17, U16, U15, U14, U13, U12 + Minis

Ground Details

Ground Address: Brierton Lane, Hartlepool, Cleveland TS25 5DR.
Telephone: 0429 272640 (Clubhouse)
0429 233149 (Office).
Fax: 0429 261857.
Directions: From A1 or A19 take the A689 to Hartlepool. Within a mile of first houses turn left into Brierton Lane (opposite Travellers Rest PH). Ground 800 yds on left, after hospital.
Capacity: Total 6,100, Seated 600, Standing 5,500.
Ticket Prices: Adults £5 cup/league games, OAP/Child £2.50 cup/league games.
Training Nights: Tues & Thurs (Senior), Mon 7 Wed (Colts), Sunday (Juniors & Minis).

Club Officials

Club President: Frank Gibbon
Club Chairman: Bob Bateman
Club secretary: Tony Savage, 17 Greenbank Court, Hartelpool, Cleveland, TS26 0HH. Tel: (H)0429 273187 (W)0429 273187 Fax: Club Office 0429 261857
Fixture Secretary: Dave Butcher, 55 Arncliffe Gardens, Hartlepool, Cleveland. Tel: (H) 0429 236886 (W) 0325 300616 Fax: 0325 316007
Press Officer: Steve Smith, 35 Roseberry Road, Hartlepool, Cleveland. Tel: (H) 0429 272160 Fax: Club Office 0429 261857
Registration Officer: see Club secretary
1994/95 1st XV Captain: Paul Hodder
1994/95 Club Coach: Barry Taylor, Dave Stubbs, Dave Stead
Treasurer: Peter Olsen
Promotions & Sponsorship: John Dixon-Barker

Owen Evans scoring a spectacular try against Wakefield

NATIONAL LEAGUE TWO

RESULTS AND LEAGUE TABLES
1987-1994
Pages 122-125

MEMBER CLUBS
1994-95

NATIONAL LEAGUE TWO RESULTS

1987-88

		1	2	3	4	5	6	7	8	9	10	11	12
1	Bedford		6-0	16-25		33-25		21-9	6-6	17-16		15-3	
2	Blackheath						12-16		22-7	19-12	3-4		12-48
3	Gosforth		26-8				14-22		12-14	N/P	12-10		
4	Headingley	7-13	21-9	26-7						38-3		12-12	3-12
5	Liverpool St. Helens		15-0	15-12	6-6		14-0	10-3				3-13	
6	London Irish	12-12			12-32			3-6			17-15		9-27
7	London Scottish		18-9	13-8	6-22					50-3			
8	London Welsh				10-18	10-27	6-13	24-24			22-26		
9	Northampton					9-13	15-13		14-16		3-16	0-22	
10	Richmond	28-25			14-13		9-6					3-22	
11	Rosslyn Park		14-8	14-3			20-3	15-6	16-15		20-12		
12	Saracens	33-4		7-7		10-13		34-0	7-25	22-6		6-6	

1988-89

		1	2	3	4	5	6	7	8	9	10	11	12
1	Bedford		19-99				15-2	9-6	16-6		15-3		
2	Blackheath	12-13			34-10	21-3					31-3	12-6	12-24
3	Coventry		18-2		19-12	7-18				22-10		7-3	
4	Gosforth	16-17				29-14		16-14	34-26		16-4		9-27
5	Headingley	7-7					48-9	22-10	24-0		9-12		3-7
6	London Irish		21-6	6-29	32-7			24-19	18-10		18-8		
7	London Scottish		6-3				16-21			3-3	16-17		
8	London Welsh		15-15	14-21				29-10		0-22	9-16		
9	Northampton	42-3	15-7		13-12	19-7					15-12		4-32
10	Richmond		12-3				18-18	12-32	14-3	15-12			10-27
11	Sale	15-15		23-15	15-24					50-9		10-12	
12	Saracens	50-10	13-6				20-3	19-9	37-4				

1989-90

		1	2	3	4	5	6	7	8	9	10	11	12
1	Blackheath		16-21				28-18	9-10	9-37		0-21		
2	Coventry					13-13	18-25		15-13	21-18	18-10		22-12
3	Gosforth	12-12	0-16				6-27	15-22			22-18		
4	Headingley	31-12	30-22	17-10				15-3			3-9		
5	Liverpool St. Helens	16-3		16-11	10-4			13-13			22-15	10-3	
6	London Irish				25-19	12-23			27-19	12-36			24-33
7	Northampton		24-18				33-21		6-4	12-6	41-25		
8	Plymouth Albion			28-13	9-20	20-3				11-12	21-16		33-28
9	Richmond	15-15		36-3	86-8	6-17						16-7	
10	Rugby			49-9	31-8	6-11	23-10			16-28			28-6
11	Sale	14-18	24-22				19-27	3-16	15-11		20-13		
12	Waterloo	10-19		25-7	9-6			6-12		13-23		12-9	

1990-91

	1	2	3	4	5	6	7	8	9	10	11	12	13
1 Bedford			7-9	16-10	18-19	21-16		10-9			10-10		
2 Blackheath	12-16					13-19	9-19		12-9		14-12	12-7	
3 Coventry		16-4		11-3	20-4			21-9		9-13			26-15
4 Headingley		16-15			9-10		7-18	31-6		11-20			16-13
5 London Irish		21-18					24-16	19-18		29-17		15-9	39-0
6 London Scottish			9-12	30-7	13-17			32-0		27-19			22-16
7 Newcastle/Gosforth	22-7		10-9			12-13			38-3		7-6	6-13	
8 Plymouth	13-3					12-3		19-13	6-28		15-9	13-21	
9 Richmond	28-17		0-13	17-6	18-18	15-40					10-9		
10 Rugby	28-3	18-7					25-8		25-8		28-9		
11 Sale			23-16	42-0	36-24	25-10		20-9		18-26			
12 Wakefield	27-0		32-10	17-9		21-9			20-3		13-10		
13 Waterloo	13-13	3-15					12-10		25-9		17-13	6-14	

1991-92

	1	2	3	4	5	6	7	8	9	10	11	12	13
1 Bedford		52-10					8-9	9-4		6-25	25-4	6-30	
2 Blackheath			21-13	9-6		3-9	31-6		16-20			6-34	
3 Coventry	19-13				15-32			6-30		19-12	21-20		18-24
4 Liverpoool St. H.	6-22		0-19		4-41	6-49				11-38			0-32
5 London Scottish	38-0	36-16						16-11		40-13	31-4		7-6
6 Morley	19-12		12-16		12-13					12-13	9-13		13-21
7 Moseley			12-22	33-3	18-25	19-3			15-10	47-15			
8 Newcastle-Gosforth		30-0		76-4		60-12	20-26		54-21			37-6	
9 Plymouth Alb.	24-9		10-13	25-10	9-10	10-12				10-15			
10 Sale	16,6	10-14						19-15			37-3	3-17	13-15
11 Wakefield		20-6		34-25			14-9	8-18	22-7			24-18	
12 Waterloo			10-6	40-12	22-15	16-9	18-17		12-3				
13 West Hartlepool		21-8					27-4	13-7	21-4		7-0	27-9	

1992-93

	1	2	3	4	5	6	7	8	9	10	11	12	13
1 Bedford			30-156	24-12	25-10			15-9	22-16		9-9	9-9	
2 Blackheath	16-12						9-12	5-46		18-14	3-20		
3 Coventry		38-15		37-10	41-3	19-22			13-18				6-32
4 Fylde		9-9				15-15	5-32			9-22		7-27	14-15
5 Morley		8-23		10-10		6-13	13-36		6-28				12-27
6 Moseley	9-9	23-6					19-16			32-10		3-14	9-12
7 Newcastle/Gosforth	19-13		26-3					28-6		16-3	7-3	17-20	
8 Nottingham			16-10	19-8	78-0	9-5			17-12				19-9
9 Richmond		13-23		29-6		28-21	9-21					11-6	12-16
10 Rosslyn Park	13-16	,32-10		43-24			6-18	24-18		18-8			
11 Sale			24-3	51-3	34-0	6-13		25-8	21-10				
12 Wakefield	27-3		8-0		16-15			22-9		20-15	6-12		
13 Waterloo	28-8	27-6					3-13			12-9	25-24	22-11	

NATIONAL LEAGUE TWO TABLES

1987-88

	P	W	D	L	F	A	Pts
Rosslyn Park	11	8	2	1	155	83	18
Liverpool St. H.	11	8	1	2	154	97	17
Saracens	11	7	2	2	228	86	16
Headingley	11	6	2	3	202	104	14
Bedford	11	6	2	3	152	139	14
Richmond	11	6	0	5	140	156	12
London Scottish	11	4	1	6	141	158	9
London Irish	11	4	1	6	120	177	9
London Welsh	11	3	2	6	153	185	8
Gosforth	10	2	1	7	99	129	5
Blackheath	11	2	0	9	102	187	4
Northampton	11	1	0	9	81	226	2

1990-91

	P	W	D	L	F	A	Pts
Rugby	12	10	0	2	252	146	20
London Irish	12	9	1	2	239	192	19
Wakefield	12	8	0	4	188	109	16
Coventry	12	8	0	4	172	129	16
London Scottish	12	7	0	5	240	178	14
Gosforth	12	6	0	6	169	140	12
Sale	12	5	1	6	224	156	11
Bedford	12	4	2	6	138	203	10
Waterloo	12	4	0	8	134	169	8
Blackheath	12	4	0	8	134	169	8
Plymouth Albion	12	4	0	8	129	210	8
Richmond	12	3	1	8	134	245	7
Headingley	12	3	0	9	125	215	6

1988-89

	P	W	D	L	F	A	Pts
Saracens	11	11	0	0	288	80	22
Bedford	11	6	2	3	141	187	14
Northampton	11	5	2	4	195	152	12
Sale	11	6	0	5	150	143	12
Coventry	11	6	0	5	150	143	12
London Irish	11	5	2	4	194	222	12
Headingley	11	5	1	5	179	136	11
Blackheath	11	4	11	6	181	144	9
Richmond	11	4	1	6	112	216	9
Gosforth	11	4	0	7	176	246	8
London Scottish	11	3	1	7	146	160	7
London Welsh	11	1	1	9	125	235	3

1991-92

	P	W	D	L	F	A	PD	Pts
London Scottish	12	11	0	1	304	130	174	22
West Hartlepool	12	11	0	1	244	89	155	22
Waterloo	12	8	0	4	206	184	22	16
Newcastle Gosf'th	12	7	0	5	371	371	140	231
Wakefield	12	7	0	5	187	194	-7	14
Coventry	12	7	0	5	187	196	-9	14
Moseley	12	6	0	6	215	196	19	12
Sale	12	6	0	6	204	209	-5	12
Morley	12	4	0	8	171	202	-31	8
Bedford	12	4	0	8	168	204	-36	8
Blackheath	12	4	0	8	140	266	-126	8
Plymouth	12	3	0	9	153	209	-56	6
Liverpool St. H.	12	0	0	12	87	418	-331	0

1989-90

	P	W	D	L	F	A	Pts
Northampton	11	9	1	1	192	135	19
Liverpool St. H.	11	8	2	1	154	106	18
Richmond	11	7	1	3	282	135	15
Coventry	11	6	1	4	206	185	13
London Irish	11	6	0	5	228	247	12
Rugby	11	5	0	6	238	172	10
Plymouth Albion	11	5	0	6	206	164	10
Headingley	11	5	0	6	161	226	10
Sale	11	4	0	7	153	182	8
Blackheath	11	3	2	6	141	205	8
Waterloo	11	3	0	8	147	193	6
Gosforth	11	1	1	9	108	266	3

1992-93

	P	W	D	L	F	A	PD	Pts
Newcastle Gosf'th	12	10	0	2	241	106	135	20
Waterloo	12	10	0	2	228	138	90	20
Wakefield	12	8	1	3	186	123	63	17
Nottingham	12	8	0	4	249	154	104	16
Sale	12	7	1	4	237	102	135	15
Moseley	12	6	2	4	184	150	34	14
Bedford	12	6	2	4	186	183	3	14
Rosslyn Park	12	5	0	7	209	199	10	10
Richmond	12	5	0	7	204	196	8	10
Blackheath	12	4	2	6	142	231	-89	10
Coventry	12	3	0	9	192	236	-44	6
Fylde	12	0	3	9	108	290	-182	3
Morley	12	0	1	11	107	374	-267	1

NATIONAL LEAGUE TWO STATISTICS 1993/94

RESULTS

		1	2	3	4	5	6	7	8	9	10
1	L. Scottish		16-8	21-14	3-11	22-11	3-12	12-37	11-37	9-18	24-22
2	Moseley	27-12		17-0	30-22	13-11	9-3	15-16	20-11	6-6	9-31
3	Nottingham	23-18	6-25		25-30	17-16	9-30	18-9	16-13	27-21	9-17
4	Otley	13-6	12-26	12-18		3-3	9-5	9-11	0-22	15-21	11-28
5	Rugby	7-5	6-3	16-14	19-10		8-21	6-30	16-12	3-8	6-27
6	Sale	28-12	13-16	41-7	88-9	16-3		52-3	11-11	15-6	28-12
7	Saracens	6-11	14-10	13-3	31-19	6-3	3-8		20-10	37-0	8-14
8	Wakefield	17-11	13-12	6-6	26-14	48-16	19-28	14-23		47-6	10-11
9	Waterloo	13-17	12-5	8-19	39-16	19-17	10-28	2-12	6-18		15-25
10	W. Hartlepool	21-19	16-15	13-23	48-20	28-19	11-11	22-20	13-13	30-11	

WEEK BY WEEK POSITIONS

	23/9	2/10	9/10	13/11	20/11	4/12	11/12	8/1	15/1	29/1	12/2	12/3	26/3	9/4	23/4	30/4
L. Scottish	7	8	7	8	7	8	9	9	10	10	10	10	10	10	9	8
Moseley	3	5	6	5	8	5	5	6	7	5	5	5	5	5	5	5
Nottingham	9	9	10	10	10	10	10	10	8	9	6	6	6	6	6	6
Otley	4	3	4	6	6	6	7	8	9	8	9	9	9	9	10	10
Rugby	8	6	8	9	9	9	8	5	6	7	7	8	8	8	8	9
Sale	1	2	2	3	2	2	2	3	2	2	2	2	2	2	1	1
Saracens	5	4	3	2	3	3	3	2	3	3	3	3	3	3	3	3
Wakefield	6	7	5	4	4	4	4	4	4	4	4	4	4	4	4	4
Waterloo	10	10	9	7	5	7	6	7	5	6	8	7	7	7	7	7
W Hartlepool	2	1	1	1	1	1	1	1	1	1	1	1	1	1	2	2

PLAYING RECORD AND POINTS BREAKDOWN

	P	W	D	L	F	A	Pts	HOME						AWAY					
								P	W	D	L	F	A	P	W	D	L	F	A
Sale	18	13	2	3	438	160	28	9	0	0	0	292	79	9	0	0	0	146	81
W. Hartlepool	18	13	2	3	389	271	28	9	6	2	1	202	48	9	7	0	2	187	123
Saracens	18	11	1	6	299	238	23	9	7	0	2	138	78	9	4	1	4	161	160
Wakefield	18	8	3	7	347	240	19	9	5	1	3	200	127	9	3	2	4	147	113
Moseley	18	9	1	8	266	220	19	9	6	1	2	146	112	9	3	0	6	120	108
Nottingham	18	8	1	9	254	326	17	9	5	0	4	150	179	9	3	1	5	104	147
Waterloo	18	6	2	10	231	346	14	9	3	1	5	134	157	9	3	1	5	97	189
London Scottish	18	6	0	12	232	325	12	9	4	0	5	121	170	9	2	0	7	111	155
Rugby	18	5	1	12	186	302	11	9	5	0	4	87	130	9	0	1	8	99	172
Otley	18	4	1	13	235	449	9	9	2	1	6	84	140	9	2	0	7	151	309

RUGBY SPECIALISTS Bourne Sports

COURAGE

CRT7.

CRT2.

CRT8.

CRT1.

CRT5.

COURAGE
RUGBY TACKLE   RANGE

CRT1 Rugby Jersey - 100% cotton, long sleeves rugby jersey, embroidered badge, unisex, generous sizes, all our usual quality features, taped inside collar, reinforced seams and snug stretch cuffs, sizes S, M, L, XL.
CRT1. Usual £29.95 **League price £25.00**

CRT2 Rugby Jersey - 100% cotton, long sleeves with all features of CRT1 in alternative design, sizes S, M, L, XL.
CRT2. Usual £29.95 **League price £25.00**

CRT3 Polo Shirt - Fashionable Polo Shirt, comfortable 50/50 poly-cotton fabric with embroidered badge, sizes S, M, L, XL.
CRT3. Usual £13.99 **League price £12.50**

CRT4 Training Jacket - Two Colour Jacket in hard wearing 100% cotton drill with embroidered badge, sizes S, M, L, XL, XXL, not illustrated
CRT4. Usual £24.95 **League price £21.00**

CRT5 Sweatshirt - Heavy fleece sweatshirt, 50/50 poly-cotton in navy with embroidered logo, sizes S, M, L, XL. Usual £17.99 **League price £15.**

CRT6 Hooded Top - Fashionable garment, 50/50 poly-cotton with embroidered badge, sizes S, M, L, XL. **CRT6.** Usual £26.95 **League price £24.**

CRT7 Cap - Pro style cap adjustable to any size, embroidered logo, **£9.95**
CRT7. Usual £9.95 **League price £8.95**

CRT8 T-Shirt - Printed T-Shirt, 50/50 poly-cotton, sizes available S, M, L, XL, XXL **£10.95**
CRT8. Usual £10.95 **League price £8.00**

CRT6.

CRT3.

BOURNE SPORTS

**Bourne Sports, Church Street
Stoke-on-Trent, ST4 1DJ**

Tel: 0782 410411.
Fax: 0782 411072

All orders value £40 and over post free. Other orders plus £3 postage and packing. Send cheque/postal order or telephone your order quoting Access, Visa, American Express, Diners Card, or Switchcard.

Special Prices for Courage League Players

COVENTRY FC

Happy Days are back at Cov!

Only time would tell whether the club had turned the corner. Those few words summed up the pre-season view.

Having been one of the seven relegated sides from National Division 2 in 1992/93, the side finished a fine campaign as Division 3 champions and the question was answered. New playing Administrator Andy Johnson was never afraid to put the accent on youth with the consequence six colts made 1st XV debuts and this allied to experience in the squad made for a much more prosperous season. New recruits Doug Woodman, Julian Horrobin, Mark Douglas, Lee Crofts and Willie Phillips all played magnificent roles in the promotion drive, dovetailing well with other senior members of the side. Fly half Richard Angell passed 200 points in a season for the first time for the club; long serving lock Tony Gulliver passing 350 appearances.

Outside 14 league wins, other excellent results came against 1st Division Northampton and Harlequins and local rivals Rugby and Moseley, whilst a very young side only just lost to Newport over Easter.

After much hard work on and off the field, happier days were certainly here again.

CLUB PLAYING RECORD 1993-94 SEASON

National League: Three
Final League Position at end of 1993/94 season: First
League playing record: P18, W14, D0 L4, Pts F 406, Pts A 259
Season playing record (including league matches/Pilkington Cup etc):
P38, W25, D0, L13, Pts F 874, Pts A 642

Coventry's squad and officials pictured before the title clinching win v Redruth.
Back Row (L to R) — Andy Johnson (Playing Administrator, Bomber Evans (Selector), Warwick, Bullock, Rob Field, Tony Gulliver, Richard Mackie, Lee Crofts, Steve Carter, Mark Douglas, Paul Thomas, Ian Darnell (Coach), Peter Jackson (Hon Sec)
Middle Row — Norman Smith (Match Sec), George Cole (Chairman of Selectors), Rob Hardwick, Dave Addleton, Gareth Tregilgas, Peter Bell (President), Barry Evans (Captain), Gerry Sugrue (Chairman), Kevin Hickey, Mark Lakey, Doug Woodman, John Butler (Hon Fix Sec)
Front Row —Willie Phillips, Richard Angell, Mick Curtis, Richard Gee, Stuart Barden, Simon Dowson, Gareth Mitchell, Elliott Blundell, Jackie Mahon (Physiotherapist)

COVENTRY FC

ACHIEVEMENTS/COMPETITIONS WON DURING 93/94 SEASON
Won 3rd Division Championship
Colts — Warwickshire Country Cup Winners

PLAYING SQUAD 1993-94
Full Back — R Gee, M Thomas, A Parton, D Butler, T Woolman
Wings — B Evans, D Woodman, M Bennett, B Shepherd, P Powis, D Morgan, S Hancox, D Keenan
Centres — N Thomson, G Mitchell, S Chapman, R Rowan, M Brown, S Lloyd-Jones, M Curtis, C Quick, S Barden, I Dee, S Allen, M Lakey, S Hancox
Fly Halves — R Angell, G Mitchell, M Lakey, M Butler
Scrum Halves — M Douglas, S Dowson, E Blundell, B Sylvester, M Butler
Props — G Tregilgas, W Bullock, C Phillips, R Hardwick, D Andreou, P Merritt, G Caswell
Hookers — D Addleton, G. Sharp, T Harrison
Locks — A Gulliver, R Field, D Andreou, R Mackie, L Crofts
No. 8 — K Hickey, R Field, S Carter, K Ferdinand, J Horrobin, C Field
Flankers — S Carter, K Hickey, C Gardener, J Horrobin, P Thomas, K Herbert, L Crofts, P Stone, G Allinson, W. Pillips

MOST CAPPED PLAYERS
(including British Lions Appearances)
Name, No. of caps, Season
D J Duckham, 36, Debut 1969
F E Cotton, 31, Debut 1971
P B Jackson, 20, Debut 1956
P G D Robbins, 19, Debut 1956
J E Owen, 14, Debut 1963
S E Brain, 14, Debut 1984

LEADING APPEARANCES FOR CLUB
Overall
G. H. Cole — 452
Season 1993/94
D Addleton (Hooker) 35
D Woodman (Wing) 33
B Evans (Wing) 32

LEADING SCORERS (1993/94)
R Angell, Fly Half, 230 (4T, 45C, 38P, 2DG)
D Woodman, Wing, 83
K Hickey, No. 8, 75
B Evans, Wing, 75
M Lakey, Centre/Fly Half, 67
R Gee, Fullback, 50

Player of the Year Julian Horrobin

Any player, who within eight months of joining a club is named player of the year, can certainly be said to have arrived with a bang.

The 24 year old flanker and former skipper of Berry Hill made a very big impact almost from the outset. A troublesome knee injury sustained in the final club trial meant Horrobin's debut was slightly delayed, but once fitness and form was re-established the big forward soon became a firm favourite with the Coundon Road faithful. In scoring eight tries in 28 appearances, his bulldoging runs and fine defence became a feature of the season. One memorable, match saving tackle in the close league win at Balckheath will be long remembered by all who witnessed it.

COVENTRY FC

Club Details

Colours: Navy blue & white hoops.
Change of Colours: Dark blue.
Date Founded: 1874
Membership: Total 628. Playing 105, Junior/Youth 65, Other 458
Number of Teams: Senior 3, Junior 4.
Programme Advertising Rates:
Special occasions: 1st XV v Catnerbury (N.Z.) Thursday 17th November 1994.

Ground Details

Ground Address: Barker Butts Lane, Coundon, Coventry, CV6 1DU.
Telephone: 0203 593399/591274
Fax: 0203 601194
Simple directions to ground: From ringroad take the A414 to Birmingham, turn right at traffic lights and follow road across railway line — coming in on the A45 pick up A414, turn left at Holy Head Pub, right at traffic light, ground on right hand side.
Capacity: 9,999. Seated 1,100, Standing 8,900.
Ticket Prices: Adult Ground £5 + seat £1. OAP/Child Ground £3 + seat £1.
Training Nights: Monday & Thursday

Club Officials

President: P. B. Jackson
Chairman: G. Sugrue
Club Secretary: P. B. Jackson, 147 Chester Road, Castle Bromwich, Birmingham, B36 0AE. Tel: 021 747 2498
Fixtures Secretary: J. Butler, 62 Spring Lane, Whittington, Nr Lichfield, Staffs, WS14 9NA. Tel: (H) 0543 432654 (W) 0827 289999
Press Officer: R. Wilkinson, C/o Coventry FC, Barker Butts Lane, Coundon, Coventry, CV6 1DU. Tel: (H) 0203 672151 (W) 0203 661174 Fax: 0203 601194
Registration Officer: L. R. Evans, 4 Croft Close, Wolvey, Nr Kinckley, LE10 3LE. Tel: (H) 0455 220448 (W) 0203 639393
1994/95 1XV Captain: B. Evans
1994/95 1XV Coach: I. Darnell
Commercial Manager: R. Wilkinson
Director of Coaching: A. Johnson

COURAGE RECORDS

Richard Angell broke a number of records in Coventrys championship season.
His 151 points for the season smashed the previous record of 79 set by Steve Thomas back in 1989-90.

	PTS	T	C	P	D	APPS	AVE
Richard Angell	151	3	23	29	—	16	5.50
Steve Thomas	79	6	8	13	—	10	7.90

Angell also passed Thomas's career record of 228 points ending the season on 281.

	PTS	T	C	P	D	APPS	AVE
Richard Angell	281	9	40	51	2	51	5.50
Steve Thomas	228	9	21	50	—	36	6.33

Angell broke Marc Thomas's record for points in a match and conversions as well as Steve Thomas's season and career records for both conversions and penalties.
Doug Woodman in his first season for the club broke the record for most tries in a season. Steve Thomas held the previous record with 6.
Kevin Kickey extended his club career record to 18 thanks to his 7 tries for the season.

COVENTRY FC

COURAGE LEAGUE RECORDS

Biggest Home Win: 60-3 v Redruth 30-4-94 CL3   **Defeat:** 6-32 v Waterloo 26-9-92 CL2
Biggest Away Win: 29-6 v London Irish 10-9-88 CL2   **Defeat:** 6-49 v Wasps 13-4-88 CL1
Most Tries For in a Match: 9 v Redruth 30-4-94 CL3
Most Tries Against in a Match: 9 v Wasps 13-4-88 CL1
Most consecutive Wins: 5   **Defeats:** 6
No. of Matches failed to score: 2   **Clean Sheets:** 3   **Drawn Matches:** 2
Most appearances Forward: 46 John Hyde, Kevin Hickey   **Back:** 51 Mark Lakey, Richard Angell
Most consecutive appearances: 7 Richard Angell
Consecutive matches scoring Tries: 3 Peter Suckling, Steve Thomas, Doug Woodman
Consecutive matches scoring Points: 7 Richard Angell

INDIVIDUAL SCORING RECORDS

IN A MATCH

Most Points: 21 Marc Thomas v Morley 19.9.92
Home CL2, 25 Richard Angell v Redruth 30-4-94 CL3
Most Tries: 3 Pete Rowlands v London Irish 10-9-98
Away CL2, Graham Robbins v Waterloo 13-1-90
Home CL2, Richard Gee v Morley 19-9-92 Home CL2
Most Conversions: 5 Marc Thomas v Morley 19-9-92 Home CL2, Richard Angell v Redruth 30-4-94 CL3
Most Penalties: 6 Steve Thomas v Sale 23-9-89 Away CL2
Most Drop Goals: 2 Mark Lakey v Moseley 3-4-93 Home CL2

IN A SEASON

Most Points: 151 Richard Angell 1993-94 CL3
Most Tries: 9 Doug Woodman 1993-94 CL3
Most Conversions: 23 Richard Angell 1993-94 CL3
Most Penalties: 29 Richard Angell 1993-94 CL3
Most Drop Goals: 4 Mark Lakey 1988-89 CL2

IN A CAREER

Most Points: 281 Richard Angell 1990-94
Most Tries: 18 Kevin Hickey 1988-94
Most Conversions: 40 Richard Angell 1990-94
Most Penalties: 51 Richard Angell 1990-94
Most Drop Goals: 8 Mark Lakey 1987-94

COURAGE LEAGUE RECORD

	DIV	PLD	W	D	L	F	T	C	P	D	A	T	C	P	D
1987-88	1	11	3	1	7	139	14	10	19	2	246	35	17	23	1
1988-89	2	11	6	0	5	150	22	7	12	4	143	16	11	16	3
1989-90	2	11	6	1	4	206	25	11	24	4	185	23	9	21	4
1990-91	2	12	8	0	4	172	23	13	17	1	129	19	10	10	1
1991-92	2	12	7	0	5	187	18	11	29	2	196	22	15	25	1
1992-93	2	12	3	0	9	192	19	15	16	3	236	24	13	26	4
1993-94	3	18	14	0	4	406	47	27	37	2	259	29	12	26	4

SEASON BY SEASON LEADING SCORERS

	Most Points			**Most Tries**
1987-88	28	Martin Fairn	3	Paul Suckling
1988-89	36	Martin Fairn	4	Dick Travers
1989-90	79	Steve Thomas	6	Steve Thomas
1990-91	37	Richard Angell	4	Richard Angell
1991-92	73	Steve Thomas	4	Kevin Hickey Jason Minshull
1992-93	53	Richard Angell	4	Barry Evans
1993-94	151	Richard Angell	9	Doug Woodman

FYLDE RUFC

Fylde Bounce Back!

Fylde bounced straight back after being relegated in 1992/93 deservedly to reclaim their League Two status by finishing runners-up to Coventry. The new coach, Graham Smith, formerly in charge of England Colts, was assisted by Mike Dixon and Paddy Mortimer, and this trio instilled a new spirit which spread throughout the club. Six consecutive League wins at the end of the season included three away from the Woodlands and this enabled Fylde to stay ahead of their rivals. The penultimate game saw the side come from behind to beat Blackheath at The Rectory Field which was followed by a nail-biting victory at Morley to ensure promotion. Brendan Hanavan captained the side by example and re-discovered his try-scoring touch to finish as leading try scorer with 23 whilst full back Andy Parker topped the points table with 169. Fylde also reached the Fifth Round of the Pilkington Cup, a run which included an excellent away win at London Scottish. This season is Fylde's 75th Anniversary season and the club is looking forward with optimism to being back in League Two.

CLUB PLAYING RECORD 1993-94

National League: Two
Final League Position at end of 1993/94 Season: 2nd
League Playing record: P 18, W 13, D 0, L 5, Pts For 339, Pts Against 219
Season Playing record (including league matches/Pilkington Cup): P 35, W 25, D 0, L 10, Pts F 637, Pts A 219

FYLDE RUFC

ACHIEVEMENTS/COMPETITIONS WON DURING 93/94 SEASON:
Runners up National League 3

PLAYING SQUAD 1993-94
Full Back: Andy Parker
Wing: Brendan Hanavan, Greg Anderton, Dave Collinge
Centre: Steve Gough, Paddy Seed, Anthony Greenwood, Andy Russell
Fly Half: Ian Barclay, Simon Taylor
Scrum Half: Chris O'Toole, Andy Rice, Phil Rudd
Prop: Craig Burns, Mike Heys, Rick Frith, Steve Rigby
Hooker: Mike Dixon, Alex Moffat, Andy Liddle
Lock: Paddy O'Neill, Jon Taylor, Dave Young, Shaun Carleton
Flanker: Gareth Russell, Clive Blackburn, Jon Kay, Tim Weighman, Ian Ashton
No 8: Martin Greatorex, Mike Taylor

LEADING SCORERS (1993-94):
Andy Parker, Full back, 169
Brendan Hanavan, Right Wing, 115
Steve Gough, Centre, 76
Ian Barclay, Fly half, 58
Greg Anderton, Left Wing, 45
Chris O'Toole, Scrum half, 40

MOST CAPPED PLAYERS
(including British Lions Appearances)
Bill Beaumont, 34
Malcolm Phillips, 25

COURAGE RECORDS

Captain Brendan Hanavan scored 4 tries in a match for the third time in the home win over Redruth. The 10 tries that Fylde scored equalised the club record, the previousoccasion was v Birmingham back in November 1987.

Hanavan broke his own club record for tries in a season. He scored 12 compared to the 10 he scored in 1987-88.

Fylde finished the season with the impressive home record of:-

PLD	W	D	L	F	T	C	P	D	A	T	C	P	D
9	9	0	0	206	28	12	13	1	66	4	2	15	1

The points and tries against were the lowest in any of the 4 divisions.

FYLDE RUFC

Club Details

Club Colours: Claret, gold & white
Change of Colours: Maroon
Date Founded: 1919
Membership: Total: 1350, Playing members 150, Junior/Youth/Minis 100, Other 1,100
No. of teams: Senior 5, Junior 10
Programme advertising rates: On application
Any Special Occasions during 1994/95: 75th Year

Ground Details:

Ground Address: The Woodlands Memorial Ground, Blackpool Road, Ansdell, Lytham St Annes, FY8 4EL
Ground Tel No: 0253 734733
Simple Directions to Ground: Leave M55 at Exit 4 onto A583 (Preston/Kirkham) to traffic lights, turn right into Whitehill Road to next set of traffic lights turn left onto Queensway. The ground is about 3 miles on left, opposite Blossoms Pub and R C Church.
Spectator Capacity: Total: 5,490, seated 490, standing 5,000
Ticket Prices: Adults: £5, OAP: £3, Child: £1
Training Nights: Mondays and Thursdays

Club Officials

Club President: Gordon Aplin TD
Club Chairman: Raymond Woolley
Club Secretary: Peter Makin, 5 Ribblesdale Place, Preston, Lancashire, PR1 8BZ. Tel: (H) 0253 722713 (W) 0722 259625 Fax: 0772 259628
Fixtures Secretary: David R Taylor, 18 St Georges Road, St Annes on Sea, Lancashire, FY8 2AE. Tel: (H) 0995 61322 (W) 0253 781010 Fax: 0253 780735
Press Officer: A S Brown, 179 Hardhorn Road, Poulton le Fylde, FY6 8ES. Tel: (H) 0253 883100
Registration Officer: Peter Makin
1994/ 95 1st XV Captain: B Hanavan
1994/95 Club Coach: Graham Smith

Andy Parker makes the break that led to a try for Brendan Hanavan at Coventry

FYLDE RUFC

COURAGE LEAGUE RECORDS

Biggest Home Win: 68 v Birmingham 7-11-87 CL3   **Defeat:** 5-32 v Newcastle Gosforth 27-3-93 CL2
Biggest Away Win: 38-12 v Morley 17-10-87 CL3   **Defeat:** 3-51 v Sale 19-9-92 CL2
Most Tries For in a Match: 10 v Birmingham 7-11-87 CL3, v Redruth 9-4-94 CL3
Most Tries Against in a Match: 7 v Plymouth 19-11-88 CL3
Most consecutive Wins: 6   **Defeats:** 4
No. of Matches failed to score: 1   **Clean Sheets:** 1   **Drawn Matches:** 6
Most appearances Forward: 57 Craig Burns   **Back:** 54 Brendan Hanavan
Most consecutive appearances: 34 Mike Jackson
Consecutive matches scoring Tries: 3 Mark Preston, Greg Anderton, Andy Parker
Consecutive matches scoring Points: 20 Steve Burnage

INDIVIDUAL SCORING RECORDS

IN A MATCH

Most Points: 28 Steve Burnage v Birmingham 7-11-87 Home CL3

Most Tries: 4 Brendan Hanavan v Exeter 3-1O-87 Home CL3, v Birmingham 7-11-87 Home CL3, v Redruth 9-4-94 Home CL3

Most Conversions: 9 Steve Burnage v Birmingham 7-11-87 Home CL3

Most Penalties: 4 Steve Burnage v Rugby 14-1-98 Home CL3 v Lydney 1O-3 9O CL3, Mike Jackson v Morley 13-1O-9O Home CL3, v Exeter 21-12-91 Away CL3, v Richmond 11-1-92 Home CL3

Most Drop Goals: 1 On 10 occasions by 4 men

IN A SEASON

Most Points: 121 Steve Bunage 1987-88 CL3
Most Tries: 12 Brendan Hanavan 1993-94 CL3
Most Conversions: 3O Steve Burnage 1987-88 CL3
Most Penalties: 26 Mike Jackson 1991-92 CL3
Most Drop Goals: 2 Steve Burnage 1989-9O CL3

IN A CAREER

Most Points: 318 Steve Burnage 1987-91
Most Tries: 35 Brendan Hanavan 1987-94
Most Conversions: 45 Steve Burnage 1987-91
Most Penalties: 64 Steve Burnage 1987-91
Most Drop Goals: 4 Steve Burnage 1987-91

COURAGE LEAGUE RECORD

	DIV	PLD	W	D	L	F	T	C	P	D	A	T	C	P	D
1987-88	3	11	6	0	5	269	41	30	14	1	164	26	12	11	1
1988-89	3	11	4	0	7	136	13	6	24	0	181	26	13	14	3
1989-90	3	11	5	0	6	169	19	9	23	2	222	30	15	24	0
1990-91	3	12	7	2	3	183	25	10	17	2	115	14	7	13	2
1991-92	3	12	9	1	2	198	21	12	28	2	109	11	4	16	3
1992-93	2	12	0	3	9	108	9	3	18	1	290	31	18	30	3
1993-94	3	18	13	0	5	339	46	20	21	2	219	19	11	31	3

SEASON BY SEASON LEADING SCORERS

	Most Points			Most Tries	
1987-88	121	Steve Burnage	1O	Brendan Hanavan	
1988-89	88	Steve Burnage	4	Mark Hesketh	
1989-9O	91	Steve Burnage	7	Brendan Hanavan	
1990-91	62	Mike Jackson	5	Brendan Hanavan	
1991-92	1O6	Mike Jackson	4	Anthony Ireland	
1992-93	4O	Mike Jackson	2	John Nicholson Steve Gough	
1993-94	109	Andy Parker	12	Brendan Hanavan	

LONDON SCOTTISH FC

Scots' Heroic Escape

The high hopes with which the season started were soon dashed when a continuing series of injuries dogged us all through the season culminating in a fixture against Waterloo in which we had nine first team regulars missing including all our International players. Forty two players were used to complete our league programme.

In order to survive in the second division we had to win our last two games, home to West Hartlepool and away to Saracens. No one gave us much of a chance but two magnificent victories assured our survival and showed what might have been without the recurring injury problem.

With Paul Burnell as club captain we hope that the impetus of the end of season's victories continues as we are determined to recapture top status.

CLUB PLAYING RECORD 1993-94

National League: Two
Final League Position at end of 1993/94 Season: 8th
League Playing record: P 18, W 6, D 0, L 12, Pts For 232, Pts Against 325
Season Playing record (including league matches/Pilkington Cup): P 29, W 8, D 1, L 20, Pts F 374, Pts A 643

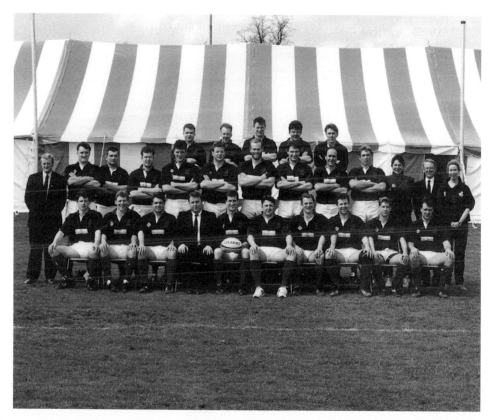

LONDON SCOTTISH FC

PLAYING SQUAD 1993-94

Full Back: M Appleson, C Russell
Wing: N Grecian, L Renwick, S Wichary, C Henderson, A Campbell
Centre: M Sly, R Eriksson, F Harrold, G Dingwall
Fly Half: M Walker, R Cramb
Scrum Half: D Millard, K Troup, S Pearson
Prop: P Burnell, B Hillicks, D Signorini, A Stewart
Hooker: L Mair, B Gilchrist, J McLellan
2nd Row: D Cronin, R Scott, D Johnston, D Orr Ewing, J Beddoe, J Johnston, T Swan
Flanker: I Morrison, I Dixon, T Gray, S Buchanan-Smith, A Walker, I Macleod, B Mackay
No 8: D Leckie, C Brown

MOST CAPPED PLAYERS

(including British Lions Appearances)
A G Hastings, 51 + 6
A F McHarg, 44
D B White, 41 + 1
A P Burnell, 37 + 1
I H P Laughland, 31
D G Cronin, 28

LEADING APPEARANCES FOR CLUB:

M Walker, 26, 1993/94
C Brown, 23, 1993/94
M Appleson, 22, 1993/94
B Hillicks, 21
N Grecian, 20

LEADING SCORERS (1993-94):

M Walker, Fly Half, 93
S Wichary, Winger/Full Back, 75
C Russell, Full Back, 47
N Grecian, Winger, 38
R Eriksson, Centre, 30
D Millard, Scrum Half, 18

LONDON SCOTTISH FC

Club Details

Club Colours: Blue
Change of Colours: White
Date Founded: 1878
Membership: Total: 1446, Playing members 231, Junior/Youth/Minis: 235, Other 980.
No. of teams: Senior 9, Youth 3, Mini 7
Programme advertising rates: Full £500

Ground Details

Ground Address: Richmond Athletic Ground, Kew Foot Road, Richmond, Surrey, TW9 2SS
Ground Tel No: 081 332 2473 Fax: 081 332 6775
Simple Directions to Ground: From Richmond Circus, 100 yds on. Right on A316 or 2 minutes walk from station (BR/Tube)
Spectator Capacity: Total: 6,200, seated 1,200, standing 5,000
Ticket Prices: Adults: £5, OAP/Child: £3
Training Nights: Tuesdays and Thursdays

Club Officials

Club President: A C W Boyle
Club Secretary: John J Smith, London Scottish FC, Richmond Athletic Ground, Kew Foot Road, Richmond, Surrey, TW9 2SS. Tel: (H) 0784 459463 (W) 081 332 2473 Fax: 081 332 6775
Fixtures Secretary: A I Rhodes, 19 St Peter Street, Winchester, Hants, SO23 8BU. Tel: (W) 0962 844440
Press Officer: John J Smith
Registration Officer: John J Smith
1994/ 95 1st XV Captain: Paul Burnell
1994/95 Club Coach: Tony Lewis

London Scottish Football Club

Founded 1878

Saturday, 23rd April, 94
London Scottish v West Hartlepool

THE FAMOUS GROUSE FINEST SCOTCH WHISKY
OFFICIAL CLUB SPONSOR

137

LONDON SCOTTISH FC

COURAGE LEAGUE RECORDS

HIGHEST SCORE : 5O v Northampton (5O-3) 3-1O-87 Home CL2
LARGEST WINNING MARGIN : 47 As above
HIGHEST SCORE AGAINST : 41 v Saracens (17-41) 13-3-93 Away CL1
LARGEST LOSING MARGIN : 36 v Bath (6-4O) 3-4-93 Away CL1
DRAWN MATCHES : 3
CLEAN SHEETS : 3
FAILED TO SCORE : 1

INDIVIDUAL SCORING RECORDS

IN A MATCH

Most Points: 26 Andy Mitchell v Northampton 3-1O-87 Home CL2
Most Tries: 3 Jerry Macklin v Northampton 3-1O-87 Home CL2
Most Conversions: 5 Andy Mitchell v Northampton 3-1O-87 Home CL2, Gavin Hastings v Vale of Lune 23-9-89 Home CL3, Mark Appleson v Rugby 31-1O-92 Away CL1
Most Penalties: 4 Gavin Hastings v Sale 12-11-88 Home CL2, v Coventry 22-4-89 Home CL2, Cameron Glasgow v London Iris 14-1-89 Home CL2, Nick Grecian v Blackheath 16-11-91 Home CL2, C Russell v Saracens 11-12-93 Home CL2, Murray Walker v Moseley 12-3-94 Away CL2
Most Drop Goals: 3 Murray Walker v W Hartlepool 23-4-94 Home CL2

IN A SEASON

Most Points: 124 Nick Grecian 1991-92 CL2
Most Tries: 11 Nick Grecian 1991-92 CL2
Most Conversions: 16 Nick Grecian 199O-91 CL2
Most Penalties: 18 Nick Grecian 1991-92 CL2
Most Drop Goals: 5 Murray Walker 1993-94 CL2

IN A CAREER

Most Points: 335 Nick Grecian 1988-94
Most Tries: 23 Lindsey Renwick 1987-94, Nick Grecian 1988-94
Most Conversions: 41 Nick Grecian 1988-94
Most Penalties: 52 Nick Grecian 1988-94
Most Drop Goals: 8 Richard Cramb 1989-93

SEASON BY SEASON LEADING SCORERS

	Most Points			Most Tries	
1987-88	38	Andy Mitchell	4	Lindsay Renwick	
1988-89	49	Gavin Hastings	3	Nick Grecian	
1989-9O	64	Gavin Hsastings	4	Tim Exeter	
1990-91	89	Nick Grecian	9	Lindsey Renwick	
1991-92	124	Nick Grecian	11	Nick Grecian	
1992-93	4O	Nick Gecian	4	Derek White	
1993-94	81	Murray Walker	3	Ronnie Eriksson	

MOSELEY FC

Mose's Second Near Miss

For their second successive season, Moseley were left with the feeling of what might have been. The club must wish the season started in January as their post Christmas form reflected championship material in the making.

In the end a fifth place in the league and an outstanding quarter final performance against Leicester ending in a narrow 12-6 defeat reflected a creditable season and the promise of greater things to come.

Exciting young talents in Garry Becconsall (England U21's), Eral Anderson, Nathan Webber, Robin Poll, Matt Whiteley, Matt Birch (All Midland U21's) and Justin Redrup (Wales U21's), Jan Bonney (England U21's), Charlie Mulraine (England Schools), Mark Chudleigh (England Colts), Dean Ball (Midlands B), allied to the experienced and venerable talents of England Internationals, Mark Linnett and Simon Hodgkinson, and Divisional players Steve Lloyd and Peter Shillingord and Richard Moon give Moseley a firm base on which to continue their redevelopment programme.

Alex Keay their Director of Rugby has had his contract extended for a further three years and adds, "The club have a fine tradition but have been somewhat shaken up by the demands of National League rugby. By building a broad base at youth level, and attracting and keeping quality players the club are well placed to challenge the top echelons of the game.

"Attitudes have had to change on and off the field - strategic planning has given the club a vision and opportunity for the future. We have a good squad of players, and definite plans to improve facilities and resources at the Reddings. With the continued playing improvement and commitment to creating a centre of excellence we can provide a platform for the club and players to re-establish their place in the 1st Division and ultimately place themselves in the elite top four. We have still got a long way to go, but everyone is positive in the way forward and the challenges ahead. Consistency on and off the field will only enhance that challenge".

Club Playing Record 1993-94

National League: Two
Final League Position at end of 1993/94 Season: 5th
League Playing record: P 18, W 9, D 1, L 8, Pts For 266, Pts Against 220
Season Playing record (including league matches/Pilkington Cup): P 47, W 26, D 1, L 20, Pts F 898, Pts A 716

MOSELEY FC

ACHIEVEMENTS/COMPETITIONS WON DURING 93/94 SEASON:
Kettering 7's Winners

PLAYING SQUAD 1993-94
Full Back: L Corbett, C Dossett, S Purdy
Wing: E Anderson, G Bartlett, D Hanson, L McKenzie, L Sherriffe, D Wilkinson
Centre: T Ballance, I Bancroft, J Bonney, R Bruce-Payne, A Houston, A Kerr, R Massey
Fly Half: M Hamlin, S Hodgkinson
Scrum Half: G Becconsall, M Chudleigh, R Moon, C Mulraine
Prop: L Baker, M Linnett, G Smith, R Wareham, N Webber, M Whiteley
Hooker: D Ball, R Hampton
2nd Row: M Bright, S Lloyd, C Raymond, G Watson
Flanker: R Barr, R Harknett, J Morris, M Ord
No 8: W Hart, R Poll, P Shillingford, M Teague

MOST CAPPED PLAYERS
(including British Lions Appearances)
M Teague, 34
N Horton, 20
P Robbins, 19
P Crammer, 16
N Jeavons, 14
J Finlan, 13

LEADING SCORERS (1993-94)
S Hodgkinson, Fly Half, 166
A Kerr, Centre, 124
M Hamlin, Fly Half, 50
M Linnett, Prop, 35
J Bonney, Centre, 25
A Houston, Centre, 25

MOSELEY FC

Club Details

Club Colours: Red & black hoops
Change of Colours: White
Date Founded: 1873
Membership: Total: 1650, Playing members, 120, Junior/Youth/Minis 400
No. of teams: Senior 3, U21's 1, Colts 1, Junior 10
Programme advertising rates: From £150

Ground Details:

Ground Address: The Reddings, Reddings Road, Moseley, Birmingham, B13 8LU
Ground Tel No: 021 449 2149/442 2095 Fax: 021 442 4147
Simple Directions to Ground: South Birmingham A38 Take Priory Road Traffic lights, county cricket ground on left, at island right into Moorcroft Road then left into Reddings Road.
Spectator Capacity: Total: 9,999, seated 2,000, standing 7,999
Ticket Prices: Adults: £5, OAP?Child: £2
Training Nights: Tuesdays and Thursdays

Club Officials

Club President: D A E Evans
Club Chairman: K P Birrell
Club Secretary: P Veitch, c/o Moseley FC (RU), The Reddings, Reddings Road, Moseley, Birmingham, B13 8LW. Tel: (W) 021 449 2149 Fax: 021 442 4147
Fixtures Secretary: A Keay, c/o Moseley FC (RU)
Press Officer: A Keay, c/o Moseley FC (RU)
Registration Officer: A Keay, c/o Moseley FC (RU)
1994/ 95 1st XV Captain: N Shillingford
1994/95 Club Coach: D Nutt
Director of Rugby: A Keay
Commercial Manager: G Edwards
Bar & Functions Manager: J Lewis

COURAGE RECORDS

New man Simon Hodgkinson broke Carl Arntzens record for points in a season in courage rugby. Hodgkinsons 83 points beat the previous best of 68 dating back to 1990-91.

	PTS	T	C	P	D	APPS	AVE
Simon Hodgkinson	83	—	7	23	—	13	6.38
Carl Arntzen	68	2	6	15	1	11	6.18

Hodgkinson's 5 penalties and 15 points inthe match v Saracens both equaled Simon Penningtons club records.

No. 8 Peter Shillingford extended his career try scoring record to 16. While prop Mark Linnet tops the seasons try scoring list and moves to joint second on the all time list with Simon Robinson.

MOSELEY FC

COURAGE LEAGUE RECORDS

Biggest Home Win: 47-15 v Sale 4-4-92 CL2   **Defeat:** 19-43 v Leicester 27-4-91 CL1
Biggest Away Win: 26-20 v Newcastle Gosforth 25-4-92 CL2   **Defeat:** 10-39 v Wasps 19-11-88 CL2
Most Tries For in a Match: 9 v Sale 4-4-92 CL2
Most Tries Against in a Match: 8 v Bath 12-11-88 Home CL1, v Wasps 18-11-89 Home CL1
Most consecutive Wins: 3   **Defeats:** 7
No. of Matches failed to score: 5   **Clean Sheets:** 2   **Drawn Matches:** 4
Most appearances Forward: 77 Mark Linnett   **Back:** 36 Simon Purdy
Most consecutive appearances: 21 A James
Consecutive matches scoring Tries: 3 Peter Shillingford, Simon Purdy
Consecutive matches scoring Points: 11 Carl Arntzen

INDIVIDUAL SCORING RECORDS

IN A MATCH

Most Points: 15 Simon Pennington v Morley 16-11-91 Home CL2, Simon Hodgkinson v Saracens 8-1-94 Home CL2

Most Tries: 3 Peter Shillingford v Wasps 5-2-88 Home CL1, Dave Spillar v Sale 4-4-92

Most Conversions: 4 Alistair Kerr v Sale 4-4-92 Home CL2

Most Penalties: 5 Simon Pennington v Morley 16-11-91 Home CL2, Simon Hodgkinson v Saracens 8-1-94 Home CL2

Most Drop Goals: 2 Alistair Kerr v Plymouth 21-12-92 Home CL2

IN A SEASON

Most Points: 83 Simon Hodgkinson 1993-94 CL2
Most Tries: 8 Peter Shillingford 1987-88 CL1
Most Conversions: 13 Alistair Kerr 1991-92 CL2
Most Penalties: 23 Simon Hodgkinson 1993-94 CL2
Most Drop Goals: 2 Paul Roblin 1991-92 CL1

IN A CAREER

Most Points: 176 Carl Arntzen 1987-91
Most Tries: 16 Peter Shillingford 1987-94
Most Conversions: 23 Alistair Kerr 1991-94
Most Penalties: 41 Carl Arntzen 1987-91
Most Drop Goals: 3 Alistair Kerr 1991-94

COURAGE LEAGUE RECORDS

	DIV	PLD	W	D	L	F	T	C	P	D	A	T	C	P	D
1987-88	1	11	5	0	6	167	25	8	17	0	170	22	14	17	1
1988-89	1	11	3	0	8	113	13	8	14	1	242	34	20	20	2
1989-90	1	11	2	0	9	138	20	8	14	0	258	37	28	17	1
1990-91	1	12	1	1	10	113	12	7	15	2	244	34	18	21	3
1991-92	2	12	6	0	6	215	31	14	18	3	196	25	9	25	1
1992-93	2	12	6	2	4	184	19	7	22	3	150	10	8	23	5
1993-94	2	18	9	1	8	266	23	14	38	1	220	21	10	32	1

SEASON BY SEASON LEADING SCORERS

	Most Points			Most Tries	
1987-88	48	John Goodwin	8		Peter Shillingford
1988-89	46	Carl Arntzen	4		Peter Shillingford
1989-90	52	Carl Arntzen	6		Simon Robson
1990-91	68	Carl Arntzen	3		Carl Arntzen
1991-92	62	Alistair Kerr	2		Dave Spillar
1992-93	40	Bob Massey	3		Nick Parry Bob Massey
1993-94	83	Simon Hodgkinson	5		Mark Linnett

NEWCASTLE GOSFORTH RFC

Season to forget quickly

For Newcastle Gosforth the season could not end quickly enough as disaster followed disaster and the first season of home and away matches saw them finish at the foot of the League One table with only two wins and a draw to show for their efforts and two of those successes came when all was lost in any case. A points situation of 190 scored and a massive 483 conceded tells its own story.

In such situations a good cup run can be a consolation and thanks to a huge 53-10 victory over gallant Bridgwater and Albion in Round Four of the Pilkington Cup they did at least progress to the last 16, where visitors Orrell won a tight game (12-7).

It would be best not to dwell in the past and the club will hope that there will be no hangover from the 1993-94 disasters and that they can pick themselves up immediately. Even though they will not now attract the very best players in England there should be a talented team on show, particularly if some big names from Scotland join them as has been rumoured.

Newcastle Gosforth deep in thought

NEWCASTLE GOSFORTH RFC

COURAGE CLUBS CHAMPIONSHIP
NATIONAL DIVISION ONE 1993-94

No	Date	Opponents	Venue	Result	Point Scorers
1	11/9	Orrell	A	L12-42	Johnson (3P) Wilcox (DG)
2	18/9	Gloucester	H	D12-12	Johnson (4P)
3	25/9	Wasps	A	L21-38	Vanzandvliet (T) Wilkinson (T) Johnson (C)(3P)
4	2/10	Quins	H	L3-22	Johnson (P)
5	9/10	Leicester	H	L13-22	Arnold (T) Wilcox (C)(2P)
6	13/11	Bath	A	L3-46	Willcox (P)
7	20/11	L. Irish	H	L9-13	Willcox (2P)(DG)
8	4/12	Bristol	A	L0-26	
9	11/12	Northampton	H	L8-28	Douglas (T) Willcox (DG)
10	8/1	Orrell	H	W13-12	Frankland (T) Johnson (C)(2P)
11	15/1	Gloucester	A	L9-15	Johnson (3P)
12	29/1	Wasps	H	L16-18	Douglas (T) Corry (T) Johnson (P)(DG)
13	12/2	Quins	A	L6-12	Johnson (2P)
14	12/3	Leicester	A	L5-66	Wilkinson (T)
15	26/3	Bath	H	L5-29	Corry (T)
16	9/4	L Irish	A	W19-17	Wilkinson (T) Douglas (T) Vanzandulier(T) Johnson (2C)
17	23/4	Bristol	H	L13-22	Wilkinson (T) Penn (T) Johnson (P)
18	30/4	Northampton	A	L23-43	Corry (T) Casado (T) Penn (T) Johnson (C)(2P)

Club Details

Club Colours: Green/White/Black hoops
Change of Colours: N/A
Date Founded: 1877
Membership: Total: 2,990

Ground Details:

Ground Address: Newcastle Gosforth RFC, Kingston Park, Brunton Road, Kenton Bank Foot, Newcastle Upon Tyne, NE13 8AF
Ground Tel No: 091 2140422
Simple Directions to Ground:
Spectator Capacity: Total: 8,365, Seated 365, Standing 8,000
Ticket Prices: Adults:
Training Nights: Tuesdays & Thursdays

Club Officials

Club President: Godfrey Clark
Club Chairman: Geoff Brown
Club Secretary: Gordon McMurchie, Newcastle Gosforth RFC, Kingston Park, Brunton Road, Kenton Bank Foot, Newcastle Upon Tyne, NE13 8AF. Tel: (W) 091 2140422 Fax: 091 214088
Fixtures Secretary: Tom Hall, 10 Elmfield Grove, Gosforth, Newcastle upon Tyne, NE3 4XA
Press Officer: Kingsley Hyland, c/o Newcastle Gosforth RFC
Registration Officer: Gordon McMurchie, c/o Newcastle Gosforth RFC
1994/ 95 1st XV Captain:
1994/95 Club Coach: Alan Old

NEWCASTLE GOSFORTH RFC

MATCH BY MATCH PLAYERS BY POSITION

Bennett	Penn	Wilkinson	Wilcox	Winham	Johnson	Douglas	Fuller	Frankland	Archer	Arnold	Chandler	White	Davidson	Vanzandvliet	Gibbs	Chick	Clark	Murray	Fowler	Merritt	Nicholson	Casado	Hetherington
15	14	13	12	11	10	9	1	2	5	6													
15	14	13	R		10	9	1	2	4	6	12	11	R	3	5	7	8						
15	14	13			10	9	1	2	4	7		11		3		6	8	12	5				
15	14	13			10	9	1	2	4	8	12	11		3		6		5	R	7			
15	14	13	10						4	8	12	11		1		6		5	9	7	R	2	
15	14				10	9		2	4	7		11		3		6		5	12	8			
15	14				10	9		2	4	8		11		3		6		5	13	7			
15					10	9			5	7		11		3		6		4	13	8	14	2	
15			10	11		9		R	8					3		6		4	12	7	14	2	
15	11	12			10	9		7	R			13		3			8	4			10	2	
15					10			7				11		1			8	4			14	2	
	14				10	9			8			11		3				4	12		15	2	
15	14				10	9		2	8		13	11		1				4					
	11	13			10	9			6		15			3							14	2	
15	11				10	9			8		13			3			R				14	2	
15	11	12			10	9			8		13			3			R	5			14	2	
	11	13			10			7			12			3			8		5				14
	11	13			10			7	4		12			3			8		5		14	2	

Match 5 Curry 3, Match 6 Beattie 13, Fraser 1, Match 7 Beattie 12, Fraser 1, Match 8 Beattie R156, Whisker 12, Mitchell R11, Fraser 1, Match 9 Whisker 13, Fraser 1, Mitchell 5, Corrie R7, Match 11 Tetlow 13, Beattie 12, Clarkson 9, Fraser 3, Mitchell 5, Corry 6, Match 12 Tetlow 13, Beattie R13, Fraser 1, Mitchell 5, Corrie 6, Hoole 7, Match 13, Teslow 12, Fraser 3

COURAGE LEAGUE RECORDS

David Johnsons 79 points see him extend his Newcastle career record to 484 points.

	PTS	T	C	P	D	APPS	AVE
David Johnson	484	2	65	105	10	56	8.64

Ross Wilkinson passed David Walkers career try scoring record. Wilkinson ended the season with 15 spread over 7 seasons and 60+ appearances.

NEWCASTLE GOSFORTH RFC

COURAGE LEAGUE RECORDS

Biggest Home Win: 76-4 v Liverpool St Helens 29-2-92 CL2 **Defeat:** 9-47 v Saracens 22-4-89 CL2
Biggest Away Win: 36-13 V Morley 21-11-92 CL2 **Defeat:** 5-66 v Leicester 12-3-94 CL1
Most Tries For in a Match: 13 v Liverpool St Helens 29-2-92 CL2
Most Tries Against in a Match: 10 v Leicester 12-3-94 CL1
Most consecutive Wins: 6 **Defeats:** 12
No. of Matches failed to score: 2 **Clean Sheets:** 1 **Drawn Matches:** 3
Most appearances Forward: 66+ Neil Frankland **Back:** 62+ Ross Wilkinson
Most consecutive appearances: 44 Neil Frankland 13-1-90 thru 2-10-93
Consecutive matches scoring Tries: 3 P Walton (twice), Mike White, Ross Wilkinson, Ian Chandler
Consecutive matches scoring Points: 17 David Johnson

INDIVIDUAL SCORING RECORDS

IN A MATCH

Most points: 28 David Johnson v Morley 11-1-92 Home CL2, v Liverpool St Helens 24-2-92 Home CL2
Most tries: 3 Peter Walton v Blackheath 14-12-91 Home CL2, Graham CLark v Liverpool St Helens 29-2-92 Home CL2, Richard, Arnold v Liverpool St Helens 29-2-92 Home CL2
Most conversions: 9 David Johnson v Liverpool St Helens 29-2-92 Home CL2
Most penalities: 6 David Johnson v Morley 11-1-92 Home CL2, v Nottingham 10-10-92 Home CL2
Most drop goals: 2 David Johnson v Bedford 5-12-87 AwayCL2

IN A SEASON

Most points: 147 David Jonson 1991-92 CL2
Most tries: 10 Peter Walton 1991-92 CL2
Most conversions: 31 David Johnson 1991-92 CL2
Most penalties: 30 David Johnson 1992-93 CL2
Most drop goals: 4 David Johnson 1987-88

IN A CAREER

Most points: 484 David Johnson 1987-94
Most tries: 15 Ross Wilkinson 1987-94
Most conversions: 65 David Johnson 1987-94
Most penalties: 105 David Johnson 1987-94
Most drop goals: 10 David Johnson 1987-94

COURAGE LEAGUE RECORDS

	DIV	PLD	W	D	L	F	T	C	P	D	A	T	C	P	D
1987-88	2	10	2	1	7	124	14	4	16	4	145	21	5	16	1
1988-89	2	11	4	0	7	176	21	13	21	1	248	41	14	12	6
1989-90	2	11	1	1	9	108	11	5	17	1	266	39	25	20	0
1990-91	2	12	6	0	6	169	20	10	21	2	140	16	8	15	5
1991-92	2	12	7	0	5	371	57	31	26	1	140	16	8	15	5
1992-93	2	12	10	0	2	241	22	16	30	3	106	7	4	20	1
1993-94	1	18	2	1	15	190	17	6	27	4	483	54	27	51	2
		86	32	3	51	1379	162	85	158	16	1528	194	88	154	17

SEASON BY SEASON LEADING SCORES

	Most Points			Most Tries	
1987-88	57	David Johnson	4	David Walker	
1988-89	57	Peter Clark	3	David Walker	
1989-90	62	Graham Spearman	1	by 11 players	
1990-91	66	David Johnson	5	Steve Douglas	
1991-92	147	David Johnson	10	Peter Walton	
1992-93	136	David Johnson	6	Ross Wilkinson	
1993-94	79	David Johnson	4	Ross Wilkinson	

NOTTINGHAM RFC

Late rally gives hope for future

There was a time, a long time, during the season when the once high flying Nottingham team looked like taking a further drop in status, as an early poor start consigned them to the lower reaches of League Two, but to the relief of their loyal support there was a late rally with eight of the last ten matches being won and a safe sixth place was achieved when all seemed lost.

If this form were to be transferred into the new season promotion would be a real possibility, but they need to work with the team they now have and cannot expect too many exciting new signings. England prospects must always be looking at the top league clubs - and if they are not they are soon approached in any case.

The cups produced no consolation in a dour season as their first hurdle in the Pilkington Cup was a visit from Gloucester, themselves struggling in the top flight. The 'Cherry and Whites' did not arrive in a charitable mood and ended the home challenge comfortably - 29-9.

However, that was all during the days of depression and the late rally should be viewed by the club as the best guide to their potential and exploited accordingly.

Club Playing Record 1993-94

National League: Two
Final League Position at end of 1993/94 Season: 6th
League Playing record: P 18, W 8, D 1, L 9, Pts F 254, Pts A 326
Season Playing record (including league matches/Pilkington Cup):
P 34, W 15, D 1, L 18, Pts F 571, Pts A 794

Achievements/competitions won during 93/94 season:
Survival in League 2 after Played 8 Won 0 start to season!

COURAGE RECORDS

Guy Gregory continues to re-write the Nottingham scoring records. His 171 points for the season beats his own Nottingham record set last season and the division two record of David Johnson set in 1991-92.

	PTS	T	C	P	D	APPS	AVE
Guy Gregory	171	1	11	43	5	18	9.50
David Johnson	147	1	31	26	1	12	12.25

His 43 penalties broke Saracens Andy Kennedys record of 30 set in the 1988-89 second division season. It also beat Simon Hodgkinsons club record of 22.
Gregory now has 331 career points and should pass Simon Hodgkinsons Nottingham career record next season.

	PTS	T	C	P	D	APPS	AVE
Simon Hodgkinson	416	4	35	100	10	48	8.66
Guy Gregory	331	2	27	70	19	48	6.90

Andy Smallwood in his debut season equals the club record for tries in a season, 5, jointly held by Clifton Jones and Gary Hartley.

NOTTINGHAM RFC

COURAGE CLUBS CHAMPIONSHIP
NATIONAL DIVISION ONE 1993-94

No	Date	Opponents	Venue	Result	Point Scorers
1	11/9	Otley	H	L25-30	Gregory (T)(C)(5P)(DG)
2	18/9	Rugby	A	L14-16	Brackenbury (T) Gregory (3P)
3	25/9	Moseley	H	L6-25	Gregory (2P)
4	2/10	Wakefield	A	D6-6	Gregory (2P)
5	9/10	Saracens	A	L3-13	Gallagher (P)
6	13/11	W Hartlepool	H	L9-17	Gregory (2P)(DG)
7	20/11	L Scottish	A	L14-21	Smallwood (T) Gregory (3P)
8	4/12	Sale	H	L9-30	Gregory (3P)
9	11/12	Waterloo	A	W19-8	Bradley (T) Gregory (C)(3P)(DG)
10	8/1	Otley	A	W 18-12	Bradley (T) Furley (T) Gregory (P)(DG)(C)
11	15/1	Rugby	H	W17-16	West (T) Jackson (T) Gregory (2C)(P)
12	29/1	Moseley	A	L0-17	
13	12/2	Wakefield	H	W16-13	West (T) Bradley (T) Gregory (2P)
14	12/3	Saracens	H	W18-9	Gregory (6P)
15	26/3	W Hartlepool	A	W23-13	Bradley (T) Smallwood (T) Gregory (2C)(2P)(DG)
16	9/4	L Scottish	H	W23-18	West (T) Smallwood (T) Gregory (2C)(3P)
17	23/4	Sale	A	L7-41	Smallwood (T) Gregory (C)
18	30/4	Waterloo	H	W27-21	Smallwood (T) Royer (T) Gregory (C)(5P)

Club Details

Club Colours: Green & White
Change of Colours: Yellow shirt, green shorts
Date Founded: 1876
Membership: Total: 1,100, Playing members 100, Junior/Youth/Minis 200
No. of teams: Senior 4, Junior 5, Mini 6
Programme advertising rates: Negotiable

Ground Details:

Ground Address: Ireland Avenue, Dovedote Lane, Beeston, Nottingham, NG9 1JD
Ground Tel No: 0602 254238
Simple Directions to Ground: Off Queen's Road (main Long Eaton to Nottingham Road), Beeston
Spectator Capacity: Total: 5,000, Seated 750, Standing 4,250
Ticket Prices: Adults: £5, OAP/Child: £2.50
Training Nights: Mondays & Thursdays

Club Officials

Club President: John Drapkin
Club Chairman: Alan Bragg
Club Secretary: Gordon Wallis, 3 Norfolk Park, Mapperley Plains, Nottingham, NG5 6PN. Tel: (H) 0602 263013 (W) 0602 500055 Fax: 0602 475246
Fixtures Secretary: George Reay, 43 Mapperley Orchard, Arnold, Nottingham. Tel: (H) 0602 262612
Press Officer: Andi Starr, 7 Cavendish Court, Woodborough Road, Mapperley, Nottingham, NG3 5RA. Tel: (H) 0602 609411
Registration Officer: Neil Hannah, 62 Beeston Fields Drive, Beeston, Nottingham, BJ9 3DD. Tel: (H) 0602 254798 (W) 0602 243243
1994/ 95 1st XV Captain: Chris Gray
1994/95 Club Coach: Paul Stone
Treasurer: John Hughes
Marketing Committee Chairman: Tony Walker
1st XV Coach: Gary Rees

NOTTINGHAM RFC

MATCH BY MATCH PLAYERS BY POSITION

Wills	Croft	Jones	Furley	Byron	Gregory	Roberts	Freer	West	Jackson	Gray	Hindmarch	Davies	Bradley	Brackenbury	Morris	Robinson	Gallagher	Ryan	Smallwood	Royer	Malik	Bygrave	Musto
15	14	13	12	11	10	9	1	2	3	4	5	6	7	8									
15	14	12	13	11	10	9	1	2	3	4	5	6	8	7									
15	14	12	13		10	9	1	2	3	4		6	7	8	5								
F	R	E	E	F	R	E	E	F	R	E	E	F	R	E	E								
	14	12	13		10			2	3	5	4		8				15	R	11	9	6		
	14				10			2	3	5			8	7			15		11	9		13	12
				11	10	R		2	3	4		7	8	5			15	14		9	6	13	12
	14	13			10	9	1		3	4	5		8	7			15		11				12
	14		12		10		1		3	4	5		8	7			15		11	9		13	
	14		12		10		1		3	4			8	7			15		11	9		13	
	14		12		10		1		3	4			8	7			15		11	9		13	
	14		12		10		1		3	4			8	7			15		11	9		13	
	14	13			10		1	2		4	5		8				15		11	9			12
		13			10		1	2	3	4	5		8				15	14	11	9	7		12
	14	13			10		1	2	3	5	4			7			15		11	9			12
	14	13			10		1	2	3	4	5		8				15		11	9			12
		13			10		1	2	3	5	4		8	R			15	14	11	9	7		12
	14	13			10		1	2	3	4		6	8				15		11	9			12

Match 6 Skrypeck 4, Rees 6, Match 7 Rees R9, Match 8 Drury 2, Rees 6, Match 9 Drury 2, Rees 6, Match 10 Drury 2, Skrypeck 5, Rees 6, Match 11 Drury 2, Langley 5, Rees 6, Match 12 Drury 2, Langley 5, Rees 6, Match 13 Downey 3, Berry 6, Rees 7, Drury R7

PLAYING SQUAD 1993-94

Full Back: Matt Gallagher, Steve Wills, Ben Ryan

Wing: Richard Byrom, Andy Smallwood, Richard Croft, Spence Summons

Centre: Andy Furley, Buster Musto, Richard Bygrave, Clifton Jones

Fly Half: Guy Gregory

Scrum Half: Alan Royer, Dave Roberts

Prop: Andy Jackson, Martin Freer, Martin Downey, Mark Ireland, Myle Hallam

Hooker: Dorian West, Steve Drury

Lock: Chris Gray, David Hindmarch, George Robinson, Brandon Langley, Mark Skrypec

Flanker: Gary Rees, Nick Berry, Nigel Malik, Andy Morris, Ali Metcalfe, Nick Davies

No 8: Mark Bradley, Russ Brackenbury

MOST CAPPED PLAYERS (including British Lions Appearances)	LEADING APPEARANCES FOR CLUB	LEADING SCORERS (1993-94)
B C Moore, 25 (E) 2 BL, 1987/8-1989/90	R Matson, 369, 1969/70-1980/1	Guy Gregory, No 10, 275
G W Rees, 23 (E), 1983/4-1991/2	P W Cook, 355, 1980/1-1992/3	Andy Smallwood, No 11, 40
C A Gray, 22 (SCOT), 1988/9-1991/2	M Northard, 334, 1977/8-1987/8	Mark Bradley, No 8, 30
V H Cartwright, 14 (E), 1903/4-1906/7	J T Pearce, 307, 1967/8-1978/9	Dorian West, No 2, 30
S D Hodgkinson, 14 (E), 1988/9-1991/92	I Clayton, 292, 1970/1-1979/80	Matt Gallagher, No 15, 25
C R Andrew, 9 (E), 1984/5-1985/6	S D Hodgkinson, 288, 1981/2-1992/3	Russell Brackenbury, No6/8, 15
	G W Rees, 282, 1981/2-date	

NOTTINGHAM RFC

COURAGE LEAGUE RECORDS

Biggest Home Win: 78-0 v Morley 24-10-92 CL1   **Defeat:** 0-32 v Bristol 16-11-91 CL1
Biggest Away Win: 46-5 v Blackheath 26-9-92 CL2   **Defeat:** 7-41 v Sale 23-4-94 CL2
Most Tries For in a Match: 12 v Morley 24-10-92 CL1
Most Tries Against in a Match: 6 v Sale 23-4-94 CL2
Most consecutive Wins: 5   **Defeats:** 6
No. of Matches failed to score: 2   **Clean Sheets:** 3   **Drawn Matches:** 4
Most appearances Forward: 70 Chris Gray   **Back:** 72 Richard Byrum
Most consecutive appearances: 41 Guy Gregory 23-11-91 to date
Consecutive matches scoring Tries: 4 Andy Smallwood
Consecutive matches scoring Points: 20 Guy Gregory

INDIVIDUAL SCORING RECORDS

IN A MATCH

Most Points: 25 Guy Gregory v Utley 11-9-93 CL2
Most Tries: 4 Gary Hartley v Bedford 18-11-9O Home CL1
Most Conversions: 9 Guy Gregory v Morley 24-1O-92 Home CL2
Most Penalties: 6 Guy Gregory v Saracens 12-3-94 CL2
Most Drop Goals: 2 Andy Sutton v Harlequins 31-3-9O Away CL1, Guy Gregory v Rosslyn Park 4-4-92 Home CL1, v Rosslyn Park 21-11-92 Away CL2, v Fylde 9-1-93 Home CL2, v Bedford 13-2-93 Away CL2

IN A SEASON

Most Points: 171 Guy Gregory 1993-94 CL2
Most Tries: 5 Clifton Jones 1987-88 CL1, Gary Hartley 1989-9O CL1, Andy Smallwood 1993-94 CL2
Most Conversions: 13 Simon Hodgkinson 1989-9O CL1
Most Penalties: 43 Guy Gregory 1993-94 CL2
Most Drop Goals: 9 Guy Gregory 1992-93 CL2

IN A CAREER

Most Points: 416 Simon Hodgkinson 1987-93
Most Tries: 11 Richard Byrom 1987-94
Most Conversions: 35 Simon Hodgkinson 1987-93
Most Penalties: 1OO Simon Hodgkinson 1987-93
Most Drop Goals: 19 Guy Gregory 1991-94

COURAGE LEAGUE RECORD

	DIV	PLD	W	D	L	F	T	C	P	D	A	T	C	P	D
1987-88	1	11	4	1	6	146	14	6	22	4	170	22	11	18	2
1988-89	1	11	6	1	4	142	10	6	24	6	122	7	5	26	2
1989-90	1	11	6	0	5	187	22	15	19	4	148	21	8	15	1
1990-91	1	12	6	0	6	138	12	9	22	2	194	24	13	22	2
1991-92	1	12	2	1	9	133	11	7	22	3	204	24	12	27	1
1992-93	2	12	8	0	4	249	22	14	28	9	145	13	4	21	3
1993-94	2	18	8	1	9	254	17	11	44	5	326	31	18	38	7

SEASON BY SEASON LEADING SCORERS

	Most Points			**Most Tries**	
1987-88	86	Simon Hodgkinson	5	Clifton Jones	
1988-89	98	Simon Hodgkinson	2	Lee Johnson	
1989-9O	82	Simon Hodgkinson	5	Gary Hartley	
1990-91	80	Simon Hodgkinson	3	Richard Byrom	
1991-92	48	Guy Gregory	4	Martin Pepper	
1992-93	106	Guy Gregory	3	Richard Byrom	
1993-94	171	Guy Gregory	5	Andy Smallwood	

LONDON IRISH RFC

Relegation a hiccup?

The 1993/94 season proved to be a frustrating experience for the Irish. Looking to consolidate their position in the Courage First Division, injuries and loss of key players cost them dearly. Six matches were lost in the last five minutes and the club has been relegated to League Division Two. However, London Irish has a strong base on which to re-build. The Second XV, U21s and U19s all had impressive seasons and in the junior section the club won every county championship from U8 through to U17. The club is confident that their relegation is only a hiccup in their determination to remain a top-ranking club.

Club Playing Record 1993-94

National League: One
Final League Position at end of 1993/94 Season: 9th
League Playing record: P 18, W 4, D 0, L 14, Pts F 217, Pts A 401
Season Playing record (including league matches/Pilkington Cup): P 35, W 11, D 2, L 22, Pts F 672, Pts A 745

London Irish wing Mike Nolan vs Bath

LONDON IRISH RFC

COURAGE CLUBS CHAMPIONSHIP
NATIONAL DIVISION ONE 1993-94

No	Date	Opponents	Venue	Result	Point Scorers
1	11/9	Harlequins	A	L15-30	Geoghegan (T) Halpin (T) Corcoran (T)
2	18/9	Bristol	H	L0-16	
3	25/9	Northampton	A	L12-23	Burke (3P)(DG)
4	2/10	Orrell	H	W19-6	Geoghegan (T) Burke (C)(4P)
5	9/10	Gloucester	A	W10-9	Dooley (T) Burke (C)(P)
6	13/11	Wasps	H	L14-29	Geoghegan (T) Corcoran (3P)
7	20/11	Newcastle G	A	W13-9	Hennesey (T) Corcoran (C) Burke (2P)
8	4/12	Leicester	H	L10-22	Geoghegan (T) Corcoran (C) Cobbe (DG)
9	11/12	Bath	A	L8-28	Collins (T) Corcoran (P)
10	8/1	Quins	H	L7-33	Domoni (T) Cobbe(C)
11	15/1	Bristol	A	L8-21	Corcoran (T)(P)
12	29/1	Northampton	H	L13-16	Henderson (T) Jenkins (T) Corcoran (P)
13	12/2	Orrell	A	L3-24	Corcoran (P)
14	12/3	Gloucester	H	L12-15	Corcoran (4P)
15	26/3	Wasps	A	W22-21	Corcoran (T)(C)(5P)
16	9/4	Newcastle G	H	L17-19	Hennessey (T) Corcoran (2P) Cathcart (2P)
17	23/4	Leicester	A	L3-38	Cathcart (P)
18	30/4	Bath	H	L31-32	Cathcart (T) Henderson (T) Higgins (T) Donovan (T) Cathcart (C)(3P)

Club Details

Club Colours: Green jerseys, white shorts, green socks
Change of Colours: White jerseys with green trim, white shorts, green socks
Date Founded: 1898
Membership: Total: 2,500, Playing members 360, Junior/Youth/Minis 500, Social 100
No. of teams: Senior 12, Junior 15
Programme advertising rates: Contact General Manager

Ground Details:

Ground Address: The Avenue, Sunbury on Thames, Middlesex, TW16 5EQ
Ground Tel No: 0932 783034 Fax: 0932 784462
Simple Directions to Ground: The Avenue is off the A308 Kingston Road
Spectator Capacity: Total: 6,000, seated 1,400, standing 4,600
Ticket Prices: Adults: £7 (including programme), OAP/Child: £2.50
Training Nights: Senior teams Tuesdays and Thursdays, Junior teams Mondays and Wednesdays

Club Officials

Club President: Brian Little
Club Chairman: Duncan Leopold
Club Secretary: Kieran McCarthy, c/o London Irish RFC, The Avenue, Sunbury on Thames, Middlesex, TW16 5EQ. Tel: (H/W) 081 940 4999 Fax: 0932 784462
Fixtures Secretary: Bill Gingles, Flat 609, Keyes House, Dolphin Square, London SW1V 3LX. Tel: (W) 071 480 5516 Fax: 071 480 5830
Press Officer: Michael Flatley, c/o London Irish RFC, The Avenue, Sunbury on Thames, Middlesex, TW16 5EQ. Tel: (H) 081 398 3878 (W) 081 746 3334
Registration Officer: Kieran McCarthy
1994/ 95 1st XV Captain: Paul Bell
1994/95 Club Coach: Clive Woodward
General Manager: David Coleman
Playing Coordinator: Michael Gibson

LONDON IRISH RFC

MATCH BY MATCH PLAYERS BY POSITION

Staples	Geoghegan	Hennessy	Dooley	Corcoran	Burke	Briers	Halpin	Kellam	Donovan	Higgins	Keenan	Lamb	Pegler	Collins	Hall	Cobbe	Henderson	Burns	Jenkins	Verling	Saunders	Domoni	Rolandi
15	14	13	12	11	10	9	1	2	3	4	5	6	8	R	R								
	11	15	12		10	9	3	2	1		5	6		4			14	13	7	8			
		11	12		10	9	3	2	1	5	4	6			15		14	13	7	8			
	14		12		10		3	2	1	4	5	6			15	11	13		7	8	9		
		15	12	11	10		3	2	1	4	5	6					14	13	7	8	9		
15	11			14	10		3	2	1	4			8	6			13		7	9	5	12	
	11	15	12	14	10		3	2	1	4	5	6					13		7	8	9		
	14	15	12	1			3	2	1	4			8	6		10	13		7	9	5		
13	14	15		11			3	2	1	4			8	6		10	12		7	9	5		
15		13			10		3	2	1	4	R	6			12	11			7	8	9	5	
				14	15		3			5	2	7		4			13	11		9		12	
15	11			14	10		3	2	1			6		4			13		7	8	9	5	
15	11			14		9	3	2	1			6		5	10		13		7	8		4	
15	14			11	10		3	2	1				8	5			13	R	7	9		12	4
15	11			14			3	2					8	5			13			9		12	4
	15			14				2	3	4			8				13	11	7	9		12	5
15						9	3		1		5		8	4			13	11	7			12	
						9			1		5		8				13		7			12	4

Match 14 Bird 6, Match 15 Cathcart 10, McCormack 1, Sharkey 6, Bird 7, Match 11 Cathcard 10, McCormack 1, Nary 6, Bird 8, Match 16 Sharkey R15* Street R14* Cathcart 10, McCormack 1, Bird 6, Match 17 O'Sullivan 14, Cathcart 10, Bird 6, Match 18 Walsh 15, Dalton 11, Cathcart 10, McCormick 3, Bird 6

PLAYING SQUAD 1993-94

Full Back: Jim Staples, Ray Hennessy
Wing: Ray Hennessy, Michael Corcoran, Ritchie Hunter
Centre: Sean Burns, Ritchie Hunter, Rob Henderson, Pete McAlister, Dan Dooley
Fly Half: Paul Burke, Owen Cobbe
Scrum Half: Johanthan Byrne, Nick Briers
Prop: Neil Donovan, Liam Mooney, Mike McCormack, Conor McGauley
Hooker: John McFarland, Rob Kellam, Adrian Norris
Flanker: Ciaran Bird, David Pegler, Lee Thomas, Rory Jenkins, Paul Collins, Adrian Norris, Sam Domoni, Howard Lamb
Second Row: Mat Keenan, Colin Hall, Aidan Higgins, Sam Domoni
No 8: Paul Collins

MOST CAPPED PLAYERS

(including British Lions Appearances)
Ken Kennedy, 45 + 5 Lions, 1965-75
George Stephenson, 42, 1920-30
Leading Scorers:
Michael Corcoran, Wing, 110

153

LONDON IRISH RFC

COURAGE LEAGUE RECORDS

Biggest Home Win: 39-0 v Waterloo 27-10-89 CL2   **Defeat:** 3-39 v Harlequins 21-12-91 CL1
Biggest Away Win: 27-6 v Gosforth 18-11-90 CL2   **Defeat:** 27-19 v Sale 25-11-90 CL2
Most Tries For in a Match: 6 v Gosforth 19-11-88 Home CL2, v Waterloo 27-10-89 Home CL2
Most Tries Against in a Match: 7 v Headingley 12-11-88
Most consecutive Wins: 4   **Defeats:** 7
No. of Matches failed to score: 2   **Clean Sheets:** 2   **Drawn Matches:** 7
Most appearances Forward: 57+ Paul Collins   **Back:** 53+ Jim Staples
Most consecutive appearances: 25 N Donovan
Consecutive matches scoring Tries: 4 Rob Saunders
Consecutive matches scoring Points: 16 Michael Corcoran

INDIVIDUAL SCORING RECORDS
IN A MATCH

Most points: 22 Michael Corcoran v Wasps 26-3-94 Away CL1
Most tries: 3 Rob Saunders v Rugby 13-10-90 Home CL2
Most conversions: 4 Brian Mullen v Gosforth 19-11-88 Home CL2
Most penalities: 6 Michael Corcoran v London Scottish 27-3-93 Away CL1
Most drop goals: 2 Ralph Kuhn v London Scottish 14-1-89 Away CL2, Brian Mullen v Richmond 8-4-89 Away CL2, Ian Aitchison v Plymouth 13-1-90 Home CL2, Paul Burke v Bristol 24-1-92 Home CL2

IN A SEASON

Most points: 117 Brian Mullen 1990-91 CL2
Most tries: 6 Shaun Brown 1989-90 CL2, Rob Saunders 1990-91 CL2
Most conversions: 16 Ian Aitchison 1989-90 CL2, Brian Mullen 1990-91 CL2
Most penalties: 31 Michael Corcoran 1992-93 CL1
Most drop goals: 6 Paul Burke 1992-93 CL1

IN A CAREER

Most points: 265 Michael Corcoran 1989-94
Most tries: 16 Simon Geoghegan 1988-94
Most conversions: 27 Brian Mullen 1988-92
Most penalties: 64 Michael Curcoran 1989-94
Most drop goals: 10 Brian Mullen 1988-92

COURAGE LEAGUE RECORDS

	DIV	PLD	W	D	L	F	T	C	P	D	A	T	C	P	D
1987-88	2	11	4	1	6	120	15	6	14	2	177	22	10	20	3
1988-89	2	11	5	2	4	194	20	9	26	6	222	25	13	29	3
1989-90	2	11	6	0	5	228	25	19	27	3	247	33	20	21	4
1990-91	2	12	9	1	2	239	30	16	22	7	192	21	12	26	2
1991-92	1	12	3	3	6	147	11	8	25	4	237	31	13	26	3
1992-93	1	12	6	0	6	175	9	5	33	7	223	25	16	20	2
1993-94	1	18	4	0	14	217	19	7	34	2	391	40	22	43	6
		87	37	7	43	1320	129	70	181	31	1619	197	106	185	23

SEASON BY SEASON LEADING SCORES

	Most Points			Most Tries	
1987-88	27	Paul Bell		4	Harry Harbison
1988-89	100	Brian Mullen		5	Simon Geoghegan
1989-90	107	Ian Aitchison		6	Shaun Brown
1990-91	117	Brian Mullen		6	Rob Saunders
1991-92	71	Michael Corcoran		4	Michael Corcoran
1992-93	111	Michael Corcoran		3	Simon Geoghegan

SARACENS FC

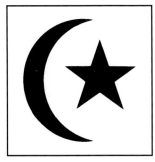

Sarries Just Miss Out

Relegation and then an exodus of several of their best players were bitter pills for Saracens to swallow, but they bounced back with a vengeance and so easily could have gained promotion at the first attempt.

It took time for the side to gel, and we then saw a new and impressive back row emerge. Anthony Diprose became the latest No 8 to roll off the Saracens production line, winning caps at England 'A', Emerging England and Under 21 levels and he won the Young Player of the Year Award. Alongside him were blindside John Green who arrived from Bridgend and Richard Hill from Salisbury whose pace won many plaudits and a place in the England Under 21 side.

Another to play a key role and win a place in the Emerging England squad was full back Andy Tunningley.

Saracens were narrowly defeated at home by both West Hartlepool and Sale and there was a similar result away to 'West'. Those matches could so easily have gone Saracens' way and then promotion would have been theirs.

With all personnel staying for next season, plus the arrival of centre Dan Dooley returning from London Irish and several outstanding youngsters, prospects can only be good for Saracens in Season 1994/95.

Club Playing Record 1993-94

National League: Two
Final League Position at end of 1993/94 Season: 3rd
League Playing record: P 18, W 11, D 1, L 6, Pts For 299, Pts Against 238
Season Playing record (including league matches/Pilkington Cup): P 32, W 21, D 1, L 10, Pts F 625, Pts A 422

Saracens 1st Team Squad 19934-95
Back row (L to R) — Steve Ravenscroft, David Choules, Gregg Botterman, John Green, Mark Burrow, Mark Langley, Anthony Diprose, Richard Hill, Gary Clark, Alan Clark
Front row (L to R) — Andy Lee, Paul Hughes, Brian Davies (capt), Richard Andrews, Andy Tunningley, John Buckton, Stuart Wilson
Above — Barry Crawley, Peter Harries, Malcolm Kemp, Gareth Hughes

SARACENS FC

ACHIEVEMENTS/COMPETITIONS WON DURING 93/94 SEASON:
Kept all our players!

PLAYING SQUAD 1993-94
Full Back: A Tunningley, D Willett
Wing: M Kemp, P Harries, P Butler, P Hughes
Centre: J Buckton, S Ravenscroft, A Atkinson
Fly Half: A Lee, G Hughes, L Evans
Scrum Half: B Davies, D Choules, P Friel
Prop: R Andrews, S Wilson, J Cooke, R James
Hooker: G Botterman, A Clark, C Olney
Second Row: M Burrow, M Langley
Flanker: R Hill, J Green, G Clark, A MacPherson
No 8: A Diprose, B Crawley

MOST CAPPED PLAYERS
(including British Lions Appearances)
V S J Harding, 6
J H Steeds, 5
G A Sherriff, 3
J Buckton, 3
J Leonard, 2

LEADING APPEARANCES FOR CLUB:
Green, 29, 1993/94
Ravenscroft, 29, 1993/94
Buckton, 26, 1993/94
Wilson, 26, 1993/94
Burrow, 26, 1993/94
Tunningley, 23, 1993/94
Andrews, 23, 1993/94
Langley, 23, 1993/94

LEADING SCORERS:
Tunningley, 224, 1993/94
Lee, 57, 1993/94
Harries, 35, 1993/94
Hughes, 26, 1993/94
Butler, 25, 1993/94
Ravenscroft, 25, 1993/94

SARACENS FC

Club Details

Club Colours: Black, red star and crescent, black shorts, red socks
Change of Colours: Red, black collar, white & black hoops on sleeve
Date Founded: 1876
Membership: Total: 1500, Playing members 150, Junior/Youth/Minis 300
No. of teams: Senior 6, Junior 11
Programme advertising rates: Full £400, half £250, Quarter £150

Ground Details:

Ground Address: Bramley Road Sports Ground, Chase Side, Southgate, London, N14 4AB
Ground Tel No: 081 449 3770
Simple Directions to Ground: M25 Exit 24 (Potters Bar) Follow A111 to Cockfosters towards Southgate. Ground on left over roundabout after Cockfosters.
Spectator Capacity: Total: 3,000, seated 300, standing 2,700
Ticket Prices: Cup and League: Stand all seats £7, Ground £6, OAP £4, Under 16 £3. All others: Stand £6, Ground £5, OAP £3, Under 16 £2.50
Training Nights: Mondays, Tuesdays, Wednesdays and Thursdays

Club Officials

Club President: JAD Wyness
Club Secretary: B D W Richards, 36 Stone Hall Road, Winchmore Hill, London, N21 1LP. Tel: (H) 081 360 4061 Fax: 081 449 9101
Fixtures Secretary: D H J Grammer, 75 Roundwood Lane, Harpenden, Herts, AL5 3EX. Tel: (H) 0582 762356
Press Officer: W Edwards, 15 Braemore Court, 119 Cockfosters Road, Barnet, EN4 0AE. Tel: (H) 081 449 6313 (W) 081 449 3770 Fax: 081 449 9101
Registration Officer: M Scott, 11 Burlington Road, Enfield, EN2 0GL. Tel: (H) 081 449 6313 (W) 081 449 3770 Fax: 081 449 9101
1994/ 95 1st XV Captain: Brian Davies
1994/95 Club Coach: Mark Evans

COURAGE RECORDS

Andy Tunningley breaks Andy Kennedys record for most points in a courage season for Saracens. In 1988-89 Kennedy scored 138 points, while last season Tunningley went 11 better to finish the season with 149.

	PTS	T	C	P	D	APPS	AVE
Andy Tunningley	149	5	14	31	1	17	8.76
Andy Kennedy	138	5	14	30	0	10	13.80

Tunningley broke Kennedys record for most penalties in a season whilst equalising his record for most conversions (see above).
Tunningley ends the season with a career record 203 points just 10 behind Saracens all time leader Ben Rudling.

	PTS	T	C	P	D	APPS	AVE
Ben Rudling	213	4	22	49	6	35	6.09
Andy Tunningley	203	6	24	41	1	33	6.15

Gareth Hughes equals Ben Rudling career record 6 drop goals when he dropped 2 in the final game of the season v London Scottish.

SARACENS FC

COURAGE LEAGUE RECORDS

Biggest Home Win: 50-10 v Bedford 19-11-88 CL2   **Defeat:** 6-49 v Bath 27-4-91
Biggest Away Win: 48-12 v Blackheath 23-3-88 CL2   **Defeat:** 3-52 v Sale 18-9-93 CL2
Most Tries For in a Match: 9 v Gosforth 22-4-89 CL2
Most Tries Against in a Match: 9 v Gosforth 22-4-89 CL2
Most consecutive Wins: 17   **Defeats:** 7
No. of Matches failed to score: 1   **Clean Sheets:** 2   **Drawn Matches:** 5
Most appearances Forward: 61+ R Andrews   **Back:** 67+ John Buckton
Most consecutive appearances: 53 Brian Davies 6-10-90 to date
Consecutive matches scoring Tries: 6 Dave McLagen
Consecutive matches scoring Points: 19 Andy Tunningley

INDIVIDUAL SCORING RECORDS

IN A MATCH

Most Points: 24 Andy Kennedy v Northampton 12-11-88 Away CL2
Most Tries: 3 Laurie Smith v Gosforth 22-4-89 Away CL2
Most Conversions: 5 Nick Holmes v Blackheath 23-3-88 Away CL2, v London Scot 23-4-88 Home CL2, Andy Kennedy v Bedford 19-11-88 Home CL2 v Moseley 28-1O-89 Home CL1
Most Penalties: 5 Andy Kennedy v Richmond 11-3-89 Home CL2, v London Scot 8-4-89 Home CL2
Most Drop Goals: 2 Andy Lee v Wasps 22-2-92 Away CL1, Ben Rudling v London Irish 11-4-92 Home CL1, Gareth Hughes v Bath 24-4-93 Home CL1

IN A SEASON

Most Points: 138 Andy Kennedy 1988-89 CL2
Most Tries: 1O Dave McLagen 1987-88 CL2
Most Conversions: 14 Andy Kennedy 1988-89 CL2
Most Penalties: 3O Andy Kennedy 1988-89 CL2
Most Drop Goals: 4 Ben Rudling 1991-92 CL1

IN A CAREER

Most Points: 213 Ben Rudling 1987-93
Most Tries: 17 Dave McLagen 1987-89
Most Conversions: 27 Andy Kennedy 1987-9O
Most Penalties: 45 Ben Rudling 1987-93
Most Drop Goals: 6 Ben Rudling 1987-93

COURAGE LEAGUE RECORD

	DIV	PLD	W	D	L	F	T	C	P	D	A	T	C	P	D
1987-88	2	11	7	2	2	228	38	17	13	1	86	11	6	8	2
1988-89	2	11	11	0	0	288	37	19	33	1	80	9	4	11	1
1989-90	1	11	7	1	3	168	25	16	11	1	167	26	9	14	1
1990-91	1	12	5	0	7	151	20	10	14	3	228	32	20	18	2
1991-92	1	12	7	1	4	176	18	10	22	6	165	17	8	27	0
1992-93	1	12	3	0	9	137	13	6	16	4	180	15	9	28	1
1993-94	2	18	11	1	6	299	30	16	34	5	238	16	10	41	5
		87	51	5	31	1447	181	94	143	21	1144	126	66	147	12

SEASON BY SEASON LEADING SCORERS

	Most Points			Most Tries	
1987-88	46	Nick Holmes	1O	Dave McLagen	
1988-89	138	Andy Kennedy	7	Dave McLagen	
1989-9O	5O	Andy Kennedy	4	Ben Clarke	
1990-91	36	Ben Rudling	4	Ben Clarke	
1991-92	91	Ben Rudling	4	Martin Gregory	
1992-93	43	Ben Rudling	3	Barry Crawley	
1993-94	149	Andy Tinningley	5	Richard Hill, Andy Tinningley	

WAKEFIELD RFC

Potential Not Achieved

The season started full of anticipation of success building on the position reached the year before. Most senior players had been retained and with the influx of experienced players like Mike Jackson (Fylde), Richard Szabo, Derek Falkingham and Paul White (all Morley), Simon Croft (Harrogate) and Nick Green (Leeds) along with talented youngsters Nick Miller, Andy Sleightholme, Kern Yates and Tom Holloway the scene looked rosy.

Wins in our opening friendly games together with an excellent 48-16 victory in our first league games against demoted Rugby perhaps raised expectations too high, reality returning in narrow defeat on our next two league outings. This was to prove the pattern for the season as potential safe league points were allowed to slip away along with promotion chances.

Our re-entry into the Yorkshire Cup after a three year absence saw us beat near neighbours Sandal 35-8 in the final. Exciting wins over Bath and Orrell saw us reach the semi-final of the National 10s where we were beaten by eventual tournament winners Bristol. The previous day we had reached the semi-final of the Caldy 7s.

Representative calls at various levels came thick and fast and we were delighted a the appointment of Mike Harrison as manager of the Emerging England Squad - a just accolade for this fine ambassador of rugby and scorer of TRY OF THE SEASON.

Club Playing Record 1993-94

National League: Two
Final League Position at end of 1993/94 Season: 4th
League Playing record: P 18, W 8, D 3, L 7, Pts For 347, Pts Against 240
Season Playing record (including league matches/Pilkington Cup): P 36, W 20, D 3, L 13, Pts F 772, Pts A 459

WAKEFIELD RFC

ACHIEVEMENTS/COMPETITIONS WON DURING 93/94 SEASON:
Yorkshire Cup Winners
Semi-Finalists Caldy 7's
Semi-Finalists National 10's

PLAYING SQUAD 1993-94
Full Back: Mike Jackson, Simon Cowling
Wing: Jonathon Sleightholme, Richard Thompson, Kerry Morley, Paul White, Mike Harrison, Andy Sleightholme, Tom Holloway
Centre: Diccon Edwards, Andy Metcalfe, Phil Maynard, Paul White, Andy Atkinson, Simon Cowling
Stand Off: Robert Liley, Steve Townend, Paul White, Angus Moran
Scrum Half: Dave Scully, Mike Cawthorne, Justin Morris
Prop: Richard Szabo, Roger Murman, Clive Yemm, Andy Day, Rod Latham
Hooker: Terry Garnett, Steve Cruise, Duncan Allott
2nd Row: Paul Stewart, Simon Croft, Derek Falkingham
Flanker: Jonathon Griffiths, Paul Stewart, Nick Green, Kern Yates, Phil Joyce, Martin Price, Richard Bramley, David Cooper, Clive Harris, Ian Hill
No 8: Mark Sowerby, Martin Price, Mark Rawnsley, Jonathon Ions

MOST CAPPED PLAYERS
(including British Lions Appearances)
Mike Harrison, 15, 1985-88
Bryan Barley, 7, 1984,86,88

LEADING APPEARANCES FOR CLUB
Richard Thompson, 32, 1993/94
Simon Croft, 29, 1993/94
Mark Sowerby, 29, 1993/94
Terry Garnett, 28, 1993/94
Nick Green, 25, 1993/94
Diccon Edwards, 24, 1993/94
Paul Stewart, 24, 1993/94
Johnathon Griffiths, 22, 1993/94
Phil Maynard, 22, 1993/94
Dave Scully, 22, 1993/94

LEADING SCORERS: (1993-94)
Robert Liley, 140, (1T, 31P, 21C)
Michael Jackson, 114, (1T, 11C, 29P)
Jonathon Sleightholme, 75, (14T)
Richard Bramely, 75, (15 T)
Kerry Morley, 65, (13T)
Simon Cowling, 42, (2T, 10C, 4P)
Andy Metcalfe, 25, (4T)

WAKEFIELD RFC

Club Details

Club Colours: Black and gold quarters
Change of Colours: Gold with black hoop or all red
Date Founded: 1901
Membership: Total: 420, Playing members 95, Junior/Youth/Minis 22, Other 303
No. of teams: Senior 4, Junior 1
Programme advertising rates: Full £160, Half £90

Ground Details:

Ground Address: College Grove, Eastmoor Road, Wakefield, WF1 3RR.
Ground Tel No: 0924 374801 Fax: 0924 374801
Simple Directions to Ground: From M1 (north or south) Exit 41, A650 into Wakefield (city centre sign). Turn left at Queen Elizabeth Grammar School, Westfield Road, ground in front 250 yards. From M62 (east or west) Exit 30, A642 into Wakefield. Turn right at traffic lights immediately after Pinderfields Hospital. Ground on left.
Spectator Capacity: Total: 4,000, seated 450, standing 3,550
Ticket Prices: Adults: £4 + £1 stand, OAP/Child: £2
Training Nights: Mondays and Thursdays

Club Officials

Club President: John Waind
Club Chairman: Nigel Foster
Club Secretary: Jim Coulson, 39 Melbourne Road, St Johns, Wakefield, WF1 2RL. Tel: (H) 0924 373586 (W) 0924 374801 Fax: 0924 374801
Fixtures Secretary: Bill Halstead, 84 Whitcliffe Road, Cleckheaton, BD19 3DR. Tel: (H) 0274 872710
Press Officer: Jim Coulson
Registration Officer: Jim Coulson
1994/ 95 1st XV Captain: Mike Jackson
1994/95 Club Coach: Jim Kilfoyle
Commercial Manager: Jim Boucher
Colts Secretary: Cyril Edge

COURAGE RECORDS

Robert Liley in the opening match of the season kicked 23 points to beat Andy Atkinsons record for points in a match. Atkinsons record was 22 v Mat Police back in 1988.
Jon Sleightholme scored 12 tries in the season and surpassed the previous record for tries in a season jointly held by Simon Cowling, Dave Scully and Sleightholme himself of 8.
After just 3 seasons of Courage Rugby Sleightholme is just 1 behind Dave Scullys career record 28 tries.

	TRIES	APPS	AVE
Dave Scully	28	85	0.32
Jon Sleightholme	27	38	0.71

Robert Liley is now within 9 points of Andy Atkinsons career record 223.

	PTS	T	C	P	D	APPS	AVE
Andy Atkinson	223	11	30	39	0	37	6.03
Robert Liley	214	2	23	51	2	23	9.30

WAKEFIELD RFC

COURAGE LEAGUE RECORDS

Biggest Home Win: 70-0 v Metropolitan Police 24-9-88 CL3   **Defeat:** 19-28 v Sale 9-4-94 CL2
Biggest Away Win: 50-3 v Birmingham 31-10-87 CL3   **Defeat:** 3-37 v Sale 7-12-91 CL2
Most Tries For in a Match: 14 v Metropolitan Police 24-9-88 CL3
Most Tries Against in a Match: 6 v Sale 7-12-91 CL2
Most consecutive Wins: 10   **Defeats:** 3
No. of Matches failed to score: 1   **Clean Sheets:** 5   **Drawn Matches:** 5
Most appearances Forward: 65 Terry Garnett   **Back:** 85 Dave Sculley
Most consecutive appearances: 49 Dave Scully
Consecutive matches scoring Tries: 4 S Cowling, A Holloway, M Murtagh, D Scully, J Sleightholme
Consecutive matches scoring Points: 21 Robert Liley

INDIVIDUAL SCORING RECORDS

IN A MATCH

Most Points: 23 Robert Liley v Rugby 11-9-93 H CL2
Most Tries: 3 Simon Cowling v Birmingham 31-10-87 Away CL3, v Nuneaton 5-12-87 Home CL3, Andy Holloway v Morley 12-3-88 Away CL3, Mike Harrison v Met Police 24-9-88 Home CL3, v London Irish 28-4-90 Home CL3, Andy Atkinson v Met Police 24-9-88 Home CL3, Mike Murtagh v Askeans 11-11-89 Home CL3, Jon Sleightholme v Blackheath 4-1-92 Home CL2
Most Conversions: 7 Ray Adamson v Birmingham 31-10-87 Away CL3
Most Penalties: 6 Ray Adamson v Vale of Lune 27-2-88 CL2
Most Drop Goals: 1 Steve Townend v Nuneaton 18-11-89 Away CL3, v Rugby 6-10-90 Away CL3, Robert Liley v Bedford 26-9-92 Home CL2, v Rosslyn Park 3-4-93 Home CL2

IN A SEASON

Most Points: 105 Ray Adamson 1987-88 CL3
Most Tries: 12 Jon Sleightholme 1993-94 CL2
Most Conversions: 19 Ray Adamson 1987-88 CL2
Most Penalties: 24 Robert Liley 1992-93 CL2
Most Drop Goals: 2 Robert Liley 1992-93 CL2

IN A CAREER

Most Points: 223 Andy Atkinson 1987-93
Most Tries: 25 David Scully 1987-93
Most Conversions: 36 Ray Adamson 1987-90
Most Penalties: 39 Andy Atkinson 1987-93
Most Drop Goals: 2 Steve Townend 1987-93, Robert Liley 1991-93

COURAGE LEAGUE RECORD

	DIV	PLD	W	D	L	F	T	C	P	D	A	T	C	P	D
1987-88	3	11	10	0	1	308	45	25	26	0	90	8	5	13	3
1988-89	3	11	9	0	2	282	46	25	16	0	114	12	6	15	3
1989-90	3	11	7	1	3	210	34	16	13	1	126	15	6	16	2
1990-91	2	12	8	0	4	188	25	11	21	1	109	8	4	21	2
1991-92	2	12	7	0	5	187	30	14	13	0	194	27	16	14	4
1992-93	2	12	8	1	3	186	17	10	24	3	123	10	5	15	6
1993-94	2	18	8	3	7	347	34	18	47	0	240	21	9	35	4

SEASON BY SEASON LEADING SCORERS

	Most Points			Most Tries	
1987-88	105	Ray Adamson	8	Simon Cowling	
1988-89	69	Andy Atkinson	8	David Scully	
1989-90	31	Ray Adamson	7	Mike Murtagh Mike Harrison	
1990-91	89	Andy Atkinson	4	Raz Bowers David Scully	
1991-92	32	Robert Liley Jon Sleightholme	8	Jon Sleigholme	
1992-93	101	Robert Liley	7	Jon Sleightholme	
1993-94	90	Mike Jackson	12	Jon Sleightholme	

WATERLOO FC

Injuries ruin high hopes

After only just losing out on promotion into the First Division and a good run in the Cup with wins over Bath and Orrell in 1992/93, pre-season expectations were high. However, with 50 per cent of the squad unavailable at the start of the league season owing to injuries picked up in warm up games, Waterloo struggled early on and sustained three consecutive losses before the first point was obtained from a drawn match against Saracens in October. The first win was against Otley at home followed by a particularly hard fought victory in atrocious weather conditions at Rugby. The winning run continued against Moseley the next week despite losing two players in the game. Injury gremlins persisted to be in attendance so that by Christmas there had been four captains of the team. Post Christmas away victories against London Scottish and Otley and a further win against Rugby at home ensured mid table safety and the retention of Second Division status for the 1994/95 season.

Club Playing Record 1993-94

National League: Two
Final League Position at end of 1993/94 Season: 7th
League Playing record: P 18, W 6, D 2, L 10, Pts F 231, Pts A 346
Season Playing record (including league matches/Pilkington Cup): P 37, W 20, D 2, L 15, Pts F 686, Pts A 584

Achievements/competitions won during 93/94 season

Won the Lancashire Cup for the second consecutive season

COURAGE RECORDS

Steve Swindells breaks Paul Grayson's record for points in a season. Swindells ends the season on 137, 11 better than Grayson managed the previous season.

	PTS	T	C	P	D	APPS	AVE
Steve Swindells	137	2	5	39	0	17	8.06
Paul Grayson	126	1	8	29	6	10	12.60

Swindells kicks 39 penalties to beat Grayson's record of 29. He also equals Ian Aitchison's record of 6 penalties in a match in the away fixture at Otley.

WATERLOO RFC

COURAGE CLUBS CHAMPIONSHIP
NATIONAL DIVISION ONE 1993-94

No	Date	Opponents	Venue	Result	Point Scorers
1	11/9	W Hartlepool	A	L11-30	Greenwood (T) Swindells (2P)
2	18/9	Sale	A	L6-15	Handley (2P)
3	25/9	L. Scottish	H	L13-17	Meredith (T) Handley (C)(2P)
4	2/10	Saracens	H	D12-12	Swindells (4P)
5	9/10	Otley	H	W39-16	Ashcroft (2T) Saverimutto (T) Aitchison (T) Meredith (T) Emmett (2C)(P) Swindells (2C)(P)
6	13/11	Rugby	A	W8-3	Fletcher (T) Swindells (P)
7	20/11	Moseley	H	W12-5	Swindells (4P)
8	4/12	Wakefield	A	L6-47	Swindells (P) Emmett (P)
9	11/12	Nottingham	H	L8-19	Craig (T) Swindells (P)
10	8/1	W Hartlepool	H	L15-25	Swindells (5P)
11	15/1	L Scottish	A	W18-9	Swindells (5P) Craig (DG)
12	29/1	Sale	H	L10-28	Hill (T) Swindells (C) Ryan (DG)
13	12/2	Saracens	A	L0-37	
14	12/3	Otley	A	W21-15	Swindells (6P) Aitchison (DG)
15	26/3	Rugby	A	W19-17	Greenhalgh (T) Swindells (C) (4P)
16	9/4	Moseley	A	D6-6	Swindells (2P)
17	23/4	Wakefield	H	L6-18	Handley (2P)
18	30/4	Nottingham	A	L21-27	Swindells (2T)(C)(3P)

Club Details

Club Colours: Myrtle/Scarlet/white hoops
Change of Colours: White with thin myrtle/scarlet V
Date Founded: 1882
Membership: Total: 900, Playing members 100,
Junior/Youth/Minis 150
No. of teams: Senior 4, Junior 6
Programme advertising rates: Full £500, Half £250

Ground Details:

Ground Address: The Pavilion, St Anthony's Road,
Blundellsands, Liverpool, L23 8JW
Ground Tel No: 051 924 4552
Simple Directions to Ground: End of M57, follow
signs for Crosby, Waterloo FC signposted to ground.
Spectator Capacity: Total: 9,000, seated 900,
standing 8,100
Ticket Prices: Adults: £4, OAP/Child: £2
Training Nights: Mondays and Thursdays, Juniors &
Colts Tuesdays

Club Officials

Club President: Colin Brennand
Club Chairman: Ray Wilson
Club Secretary: Keith Alderson, 66 St Michaels
Road, Blundellsands, Liverpool, L23 7UW. Tel: (H)
051 924 1168 (W) 0925 634283 Fax: 0925 638844.
Fixtures Secretary: John Rimmer, 2 Chapel
Meadow, Longton, Preston, Pr4 5NR. Tel: (H) 0772
614277 (W) 0722 885000 Fax: 0722 203702
Press Officer: Ian Fazey, 8 Beach Lawn, Waterloo,
Liverpool, L22 8QA. Tel: (H) 051 928 3441 (W) 051
834 9381
Registration Officer: Ian Fazey
1994/ 95 1st XV Captain: Peter Buckton
1994/95 Club Coach: Dick Greenwood (Rugby
Advisor)
Chairman of Finance: Tony Cooper
Chairman of Football: Chris Delaney

WATERLOO RFC

MATCH BY MATCH PLAYERS BY POSITION

Swindells	Healey	Hill	Fraser	Aitchison	Saverimutto	Beckett	Hayton	Peters	Wilkinson	Allott	Cooper	Ashcroft	Beeley	Meredith	Handley	Hackett	White	Fletcher	Craig	Emmett	Ashcroft P	Turner	Buckton
15	14	12	11	10	9	1	2	3	4	5	6	7	8										
15	13	12	14		9	1		3	5	4			8	11	10	2	6				7		
15	12	13	11		9	1		3	5				8	14	10	2	6	4			7		
F	R	E	E			F	R	E	E		F	R	E	E	F	R	E	E					
15	12	11		R	9	1		3	4	5			8	14		2	6		13	10	7		
15	11	12			9	1	2		4				8	14	10			5	13		6	3	7
15	11	12	R		9	1	2		4				8	14	10			5	13		6	3	7
15	14	12	11		9	1	2		4				8	13				5	10		6	3	7
15	11	12	14		9	1	2		4	5			8		10		6		13			3	7
15	12	11			9			3	4	5					10	2	6		13		1		7
15	13	11			9			3	4				8	14		2		5	12		1		7
15	R	14			9	1			4				8	11	12	2		5	13			3	7
15	13	11			9								8	14		2	4	5				3	7
15	11	10				1			4	5	6		8	14	12	2			13				7
15		10				1		3		5	6		8	14	13	2	4			12			7
15								3	4				8	14	13	2		5		12			7
	14									5			8	15		2	4			12		3	7
15		12											8	13		2	4	5		14		3	7

Match 1 Greenwood 13. Match 10 Greenhalgh 14, Blyth 8, Match 11 Ryan 10, Blyth 6, Math 12, Ryan 10, Blyth 6, Match 13 Greenhalgh 12, Ryan10, Mitchell 1, Blyth 6* Match 14 Wright 9, Mitchell 3, Match 5 Greenhalgh 11, Wright 9, Match 16 Greenhalgh 11, Ryan 10, Wright 9, Match 17 Roberts 13, Greenhalgh 11, Ryan 10, Wright 9, Blyth 6, Match 18 Greenhalgh 11, Ryan 10, Wright 9, Blyth 6

MOST CAPPED PLAYERS
(including British Lions Appearances)
Joe Periton, 14
H (Bert) Toft
Jack Heaton
Gordon Rimmer
Alan Ashcroft
Watcyn Thomas

LEADING APPEARANCES FOR CLUB
Laurie Connor, 550
David Carfoot, 473
Jeff Tickle, 465
Nigel Wilkinson, 419
Steve Christopherson, 379
Shaun Gallagher, 322

LEADING SCORERS (1993-94)
Steve Swindells, Full Back, 293
Tony Handley, Stand Off, 37
Ian Aitchison, Stand Off, 33
Simon Greenhalgh, Wing, 25
Chris Saverimutto, Scrum Half, 20
Gary Meredith, Wing, 20

WATERLOO FC

COURAGE LEAGUE RECORDS

Biggest Home Win: 40-12 v Liverpool St Helens 21-12-91 CL2   **Defeat:** 22-34 v Leicester 12-11-88 CL1
Biggest Away Win: 34-6 v Blackheath 25-4-92 CL2   **Defeat:** 6-47 v Wakefield 4-12-93 CL2
Most Tries For in a Match: 5 v Liverpool St Helens 21-12-91 CL2
Most Tries Against in a Match: 8 v Bath 8-4-89 Away CL1
Most consecutive Wins: 7   **Defeats:** 11
No. of Matches failed to score: 3   **Clean Sheets:** 0   **Drawn Matches:** 3
Most appearances Forward: 71 Peter Hackett   **Back:** 46 Jeff Tickle
Most consecutive appearances: 39 Shaun Gallagher 17-10-87 to 17-11-90
Consecutive matches scoring Tries: 4 Steve Bracegirdle
Consecutive matches scoring Points: 10 Paul Grayson

INDIVIDUAL SCORING RECORDS

IN A MATCH

Most Points: 22 Ian Aitchison v Blackheath 25-4-92 Away CL2

Most Tries: 2 on 7 occasions by 6 players, Steve Bracegirdle only man twice

Most Conversions: 4 Ian Aitchison v Liverpool SH 21-12-91 Home CL2

Most Penalties: 6 Ian Aitchison v Blackheath 25-4-92 Away CL2, Steve Swindell v Otley 12-3-94 Away CL2

Most Drop Goals: 2 Ian Aitchison v Gloucester 31-10-87 Home CL1, v Sale 2-1-88 Home CL1, Ian Cropper v Sale 9-3-91 Home CL2, Paul Grayson v 13-3-93 Home CL2

IN A SEASON

Most Points: 137 Steve Swindells 1993-94 CL2
Most Tries: 8 Steve Bracegirdle 1990-91 CL2
Most Conversions: 1O Ian Aitchison 1991-92 CL2
Most Penalties: 39 Steve Swindells 1993-94 CL2
Most Drop Goals: 6 Paul Grayson 1992-93 CL2

IN A CAREER

Most Points: 3O1 Ian Aitchison 1987-93
Most Tries: 14 Steve Bracegirdle 199O-93
Most Conversions: 22 Ian Aitchison 1987-93
Most Penalties: 76 Ian Aitchison 1987-93
Most Drop Goals: 8 Ian Aitchison 1987-94

COURAGE LEAGUE RECORD

	DIV	PLD	W	D	L	F	T	C	P	D	A	T	C	P	D
1987-88	1	10	4	0	6	123	13	4	14	7	208	23	13	27	3
1988-89	1	11	1	1	9	120	8	5	25	1	235	31	15	23	4
1989-90	2	11	3	0	8	147	16	7	21	2	193	29	16	15	0
1990-91	2	12	4	0	8	154	15	8	24	2	206	30	13	16	4
1991-92	2	12	8	0	4	206	21	13	31	1	184	27	14	15	1
1992-93	2	12	10	0	2	228	17	10	33	8	138	7	2	32	1
1993-94	2	18	6	2	10	231	13	8	47	3	346	35	24	40	1
		86	36	4	47	1209	103	55	195	24	1510	182	97	168	14

SEASON BY SEASON LEADING SCORERS

	Most Points			Most Tries
1987-88	66	Ian Aitchison	4	Peter Cooley
1988-89	77	Ian Aitchison	4	Peter Cooley
1989-9O	43	Richard Angell	5	Peter Cooley
199O-91	57	Ian Aitchison	8	Steve Bracegirdle
1991-92	92	Ian Aitchison	4	Gary Meredith
1992-93	126	Paul Grayson	3	Austin Healey
1993-94	137	Steve Swindells	2	

NATIONAL LEAGUE THREE

RESULTS AND LEAGUE TABLES
1987-1994
Pages 168-171

MEMBER CLUBS
1994-95

NATIONAL LEAGUE THREE RESULTS

1987-88

		1	2	3	4	5	6	7	8	9	10	11	12
1	Birmingham					3-22		3-3	3-46	,15-42	3-50	6-43	
2	Exeter	32-0				4-3			9-18	12-12		19-29	6-18
3	Fylde	68-7	48-13								12-14	3-23	12-17
4	Maldston	18-3	23-9	16-18		15-0	9-3				14-16		
5	Metropolitan Police		9-23	9-6		26-12			25-18			6-7	6-22
6	Morley	23-3	10-10	12-38						7-12		7-38	
7	Nuneaton		9-11	13-18		7-12	21-6		9-7				
8	Plymouth Albion			33-17	45-11		24-0			43-7		16- 12	
9	Sheffield	34-0		13-12	10-3	13-6		15-9			8-3		
10	Vale of Lune		27-3			13-6	25-19	6-3	13-16				12-21
11	Wakefield				27-9			33-3		41-0	32-12		16-12
12	West Hartlepool				12-10		23-3	37-14	19-10	25-10			

1988-89

		1	2	3	4	5	6	7	8	9	10	11	12
1	Askeans		6-20			21-10		12-28				10-23	10-10
2	Exeter					14-6	12-25	6-21		19-12	12-26		
3	Fylde	13-6	16-14		34-7				12-17	9-24			18-13
4	Maidstone	12-15	0-21			10-27	11-28					6-23	
5	Metropolitan Police		17-15				32-13		6-36		13-7		10-25
6	Nuneaton	12-19	24-10					3-21	15-18		16-6		22-18
7	Plymouth Albion			43-6	20-6	57-3				34-13		21-12	20-12
8	Rugby	41-3	23-3		44-3			10-26			28-9	14-13	
9	Sheffield	17-27			28-3	10-6	25-16		6-22		9-9		
10	Vale of Lune	29-12		6-0	12-7			6-20				4-19	
11	Wakefield		29-18	10-6		70-0	42-4			25-22			
12	West Hartleypool		16-3		37-9				3-15	12-4	9-6	9- 16	

1989-90

		1	2	3	4	5	6	7	8	9	10	11	12
1	Askeans		19-11			29-28		12-19	20-9	16-26	25-21		
2	Exeter	30-3		22-17		15-7			9-7			18-13	15-15
3	Fylde				12-26		18-13	17-14			19-18	15-11	
4	London	31-6	16-7			18-14		36-0			34-3		
5	London Welsh			29-9				3-22	9-10		20-0		17-15
6	Lydney	7-10	16-6		16-0				18-13	7-9		7-9	
7	Nuneaton		27-14						19-15	11-18	16-14	7-9	
8	Roundbay			27-21	3-30				22-10	20-0			12-15
9	Sheffield		7-3	33-18	24-28							12-27	13- 10
10	Vale of Lune		25-10			9-0	21-20	24-10		7-28			6-16
11	Wakefield	40-14			4-10	24-10		,26-3		37-20		10-10	
12	West Hartlepool	25-6		10-12	3-9		28-6	28-4					

1990-91

	1	2	3	4	5	6	7	8	9	10	11	12	13
1 Askeans		29-6	9-10		19-7			9-9	22-10		9-9		
2 Broughton Park				10-4		9-12	3-0	11-15		13-11		6-7	
3 Clifton		25-6		28-3			9-4	9-15	17-22		18-16		
4 Exeter	13-7					9-3	28-3			13-3		14-12	18- 18
5 Fylde		6-14	25-6	11-11				16-6	20-3		29-12		
6 Lydney	31-6		10-10		4-20					12-10		9-14	3-19
7 Metropolitan Police	3-21				6-20	13-15				17- 12		24-18	8-12
8 Morley			22-6			19-7	11-17			30-3		33-3	10- 9
9 Nuneaton		16-6		6-13		35-3	23-12	10-17			14-23		
10 Roundhay	23-4		34-7		7-7				10-6			22-13	9-21
11 Sheffield		13-21		16-28		24-16	16-23	18-23		23- 3			
12 Vale of Lune	16-6		14-7		9-18				18-27		9- 13		0-32
13 West Hartleypool	w/o	47-4	36-16		18-4				39-8		29-10		

1991-92

	1	2	3	4	5	6	7	8	9	10	11	12	13
1 Askeans				3-12			36-0		12-8	10-8	6-17	9-6	
2 Broughton Park	42-15		20-15		9-10			27-3		3-20			22-7
3 Clifton	48-7			21-3		42-3		26-9	16-10		29-9		
4 Exeter		13-0	16-10		9-16	26-13		25-18					15-15
5 Fylde	34-4						17-0		16-13	9-9	12-13	29-12	
6 Headingley	0-25	19-13	11-38		6-12			10-9					18-3
7 Lydney		3-17		21-15		9-16		22-4			7-18		13-19
8 Nuneaton	16-16		12-15		9-18				33-8	9-15		25-25	
9 Otley		23-16		3-9		19-12	34-4			119-9	15-10		
10 Redruth				10-16		13-6	15-6		21-16		6-9	13- 3	
11 Richmond		20-18	16-15	16-16		28-13		43-6					57-3
12 Roundhay		9-9		13-31		25-12	28-3				3-50		18-5
13 Sheffield	12-6		16-23		4-22			13-9	22-10	17-15			

1992-93

	1	2	3	4	5	6	7	8	9	10	11	12
1 Askeans		23-16	6-18	6-24				8-6				8-45
2 Aspatria			24-8		16-21	13-12	10			42-20		15-32
3 Broughton Park					19-33	3-22	10-30		10-21	31-3		
4 Clifton	10-10		35-24		13-13					24-8		35-6
5 Exeter	P					21-18	28-33		16-11	15-8	20-9	
6 Havant	10-3			17-6			35-11	9-6	20-16		3-3	
7 Leeds	24-23	34-15		43-32				16-10	0-16		10-17	
8 Liverpool St. Helens		77-5	21-3	21-8	19-26							13-3
9 Otley	61-6	47-8		14-9				20-7			19-19	21-7
10 Plymouth Albion	20-23					3-35	22-27	6-12	16-28	13-20		
11 Redruth	23-13	24-6	10-5	13-5				26-11				11-20
12 Sheffield			12-5		15-6	8-9	12-0			48-11		

NATIONAL LEAGUE THREE TABLES

1987-88

	P	W	D	L	F	A	Pts
Wakefield	11	10	0	1	308	90	20
West Hartlepool	11	10	0	1	249	105	20
Plymouth A.	11	8	0	3	276	125	16
Sheffield	11	7	1	3	134	161	15
Vale of Lune	11	7	0	4	183	149	14
Fylde	11	6	0	5	269	170	142
Met. Police	11	5	0	6	130	128	10
Maidstone	11	4	0	7	134	162	8
Exeter	11	3	2	6	128	197	8
Nuneaton	11	2	1	8	94	157	5
Morley	11	1	1	9	109	235	3
Birmingham	11	0	1	10	46	381	1

1990-91

	P	W	D	L	F	A	Pts
West Hartlepool	12	10	1	1	282	90	21
Morley	12	9	1	2	210	118	19
Fylde	12	7	2	3	183	115	16
Exeter	12	7	2	3	160	139	16
Clifton	12	6	1	5	172	186	13
Askeans	12	4	2	6	141	137	10
Nuneaton	12	5	0	7	180	200	10
Broughton Park	12	5	0	7	109	185	10
Roundhay	12	4	1	7	147	166	9
Sheffield	12	4	1	7	193	222	9
Lydney	12	4	1	7	125	188	9
Met. Police	12	4	0	8	130	188	8
Vale of Lune	12	3	0	9	123	221	6

1998-89

	P	W	D	L	F	A	Pts
Plymouth A.	11	11	0	0	311	89	22
Rugby	11	10	0	1	268	99	20
Wakefield	11	9	0	2	282	114	18
West Hartlepool	11	5	1	5	164	133	11
Nuneaton	11	5	0	6	178	214	10
Sheffield	11	4	1	6	170	182	9
Vale of Lune	11	4	1	6	120	145	9
Askeans	11	4	1	6	141	215	9
Exeter	11	4	0	7	142	180	8
Fylde	11	4	0	7	136	181	8
Met. Police	11	4	0	7	130	275	8
Maidstone	11	0	0	11	74	289	0

1991-92

	P	W	D	L	F	A	PD	Pts
Richmond	12	10	1	1	296	124	172	21
Fylde	12	9	1	2	198	109	89	19
Clifton	12	9	0	3	298	132	166	18
Exeter	12	8	2	2	203	138	65	18
Redruth	12	6	1	5	155	123	32	13
Broughton Park	12	5	1	69	196	157	39	11
Askeans	12	5	1	6	149	203	-54	11
Sheffield	12	5	1	6	146	228	-82	11
Otley	12	5	0	7	177	190	-13	10
Roundhay	12	3	2	7	161	240	-79	8
Headingley	12	4	0	8	139	220	-81	8
Nuneaton	12	1	2	9	153	237	-84	4
Lydney	12	2	0	10	91	261	-170	4

1989-90

	P	W	D	L	F	A	Pts
Lon. Scottish	11	11	0	0	258	92	22
Wakefield	11	7	1	3	310	126	15
West Hartlepool	11	5	2	4	175	110	12
Sheffield	11	6	0	5	176	174	12
Askeans	11	6	0	5	170	235	12
Exeter	11	5	1	5	149	153	11
Roundhay	11	5	0	6	156	166	10
Fylde	11	5	0	6	169	222	10
Vale of Lune	11	4	0	7	154	219	8
Nuneaton	11	4	0	7	127	196	8
Lydney	11	3	0	8	153	166	6
Lon. Welsh	11	3	0	8	141	179	6

1992-93

	P	W	D	L	F	A	PD	Pts
Otley	11	8	1	2	274	118	156	17
Havant	11	8	1	2	185	93	92	17
Exeter	11	8	1	2	247	169	78	17
Redruth	11	7	2	2	175	125	50	16
Sheffield	11	7	0	4	208	134	74	14
Leeds	11	7	0	4	228	220	8	14
Liverpool St. H.	11	5	0	6	203	130	73	10
Clifton	11	4	2	5	206	175	31	10
Aspatria	11	3	1	7	170	308	-138	7
Askeans	11	3	0	8	132	300	-168	6
Broughton Park	11	2	0	9	136	217	-81	4
Plymouth Albion	11	0	0	11	130	305	-175	0

NATIONAL LEAGUE THREE STATISTICS 1993/94

RESULTS

		1	2	3	4	5	6	7	8	9	10
1	Bedford		6-0	21-15	18-14	23-12	27-12	25-10	22-3	18-6	28-13
2	Blackheath	34-9		13-14	22-5	11-17	30-14	29-9	31-13	18-6	16-7
3	Coventry	17-10	23-19		39-12	24-18	22-3	35-5	60-13	23-20	22-25
4	Exeter	13-12	16-3	32-27		27-3	25-20	14-15	19-12	21-16	13-13
5	Fylde	20-6	20-8	15-9	15-6		11-3	24-18	54-6	23-10	24-6
6	Havant	14-20	19-27	16-21	0-41	10-22		20-7	36-19	17-16	5-22
7	Morley	18-17	12-13	9-12	10-9	9-11	25-0		35-6	13-27	8-33
8	Redruth	14-33	7-16	3-19	9-20	11-10	15-3	12-14		9-27	9-39
9	Richmond	20-26	22-0	15-22	16-12	29-27	36-3	23-10	20-9		6-19
10	Rosslyn Park	12-17	3-15	10-12	21-9	3-13	46-8	34-18	30-8	36-9	

WEEK BY WEEK POSITIONS

	13/11	20/11	4/12	11/12	18/12	8/1	15/1	22/1	29/1	12/2	26/2	12/3	26/3	9/4	23/4	30/4
Bedford	1	2	1	3	3	6	6	7	7	7	4	3	4	3	3	3
Backheath	5	7	7	7	7	4	5	2	4	3	2	6	3	4	4	4
Coventry	3	3	2	1	1	1	1	1	1	1	1	1	1	1	1	1
Exeter	7	6	6	6	4	7	7	5	5	6	5	4	6	6	7	6
Fylde	4	4	4	4	5	5	2	3	2	4	3	2	2	2	2	2
Havant	9	9	9	9	9	9	9	9	9	9	9	9	9	9	9	9
Morley	8	8	8	8	8	8	8	8	8	8	8	8	8	8	8	8
Redruth	10	10	10	10	10	10	10	10	10	10	10	10	10	10	10	10
Richmond	2	1	3	2	2	3	4	6	6	2	6	5	7	7	6	7
Rosslyn Park	6	5	5	5	6	2	3	4	3	5	7	7	5	5	5	5

PLAYING RECORD AND POINTS BREAKDOWN

									HOME						AWAY				
	P	W	D	L	F	A	Pts	P	W	D	L	F	A	P	W	D	L	F	A
Coventry	18	14	0	4	406	259	28	9	8	0	1	255	125	9	6	0	3	151	134
Fylde	18	13	0	5	339	219	26	9	9	0	0	206	72	9	4	0	5	133	147
Bedford	18	12	0	6	332	260	24	9	8	0	1	182	98	9	4	0	5	150	162
Blackheath	18	11	0	7	305	222	22	9	7	0	2	204	94	9	4	0	5	101	128
Rosslyn P	18	10	1	7	372	240	21	9	5	0	4	195	109	9	5	1	3	177	131
Exeter	18	9	1	8	308	271	19	9	7	1	1	180	121	9	2	0	7	128	150
Richmond	18	9	0	9	337	300	18	9	6	0	3	187	128	9	3	0	6	150	172
Morley	18	6	0	12	245	334	12	9	4	0	5	139	128	9	2	0	7	106	206
Havant	18	3	0	15	203	432	6	9	3	0	6	137	195	9	0	0	9	66	237
Redruth	18	2	0	16	178	488	4	9	2	0	7	89	181	9	0	0	9	89	307

RUGBY SPECIALISTS Bourne Sports

COURAGE

CRT7.

CRT2.

CRT8.

CRT1.

CRT5.

COURAGE
RUGBY TACKLE   RANGE

CRT1 Rugby Jersey - 100% cotton, long sleeves rugby jersey, embroidered badge, unisex, generous sizes, all our usual quality features, taped inside collar, reinforced seams and snug stretch cuffs, sizes S, M, L, XL.
CRT1. Usual £29.95 **League price £25.00**

CRT6.   CRT3.

CRT2 Rugby Jersey - 100% cotton, long sleeves with all features of CRT1 in alternative design, sizes S, M, L, XL.
CRT2. Usual £29.95 **League price £25.00**

CRT3 Polo Shirt - Fashionable Polo Shirt, comfortable 50/50 poly-cotton fabric with embroidered badge, sizes S, M, L, XL.
CRT3. Usual £13.99 **League price £12.50**

CRT4 Training Jacket - Two Colour Jacket in hard wearing 100% cotton drill with embroidered badge, sizes S, M, L, XL, XXL, not illustrated
CRT4. Usual £24.95 **League price £21.00**

CRT5 Sweatshirt - Heavy fleece sweatshirt, 50/50 poly-cotton in navy with embroidered logo, sizes S, M, L, XL, Usual £17.99 **League price £15.**

CRT6 Hooded Top - Fashionable garment, 50/50 poly-cotton with embroidered badge, sizes S, M, L, XL. **CRT6.** Usual £26.95 **League price £24.**

CRT7 Cap - Pro style cap adjustable to any size, embroidered badge, **£9.95**
CRT7. Usual £9.95 **League price £8.95**

CRT8 T-Shirt - Printed T-Shirt, 50/50 poly-cotton, sizes available S, M, L, XL, XXL, **£10.95**
CRT8. Usual £10.95 **League price £8.00**

BOURNE SPORTS

Bourne Sports, Church Street Stoke-on-Trent, ST4 1DJ   **Tel: 0782 410411. Fax: 0782 411072**

All orders value £40 and over post free. Other orders plus £3 postage and packing. Send cheque/postal order or telephone your order quoting Access, Visa, American Express, Diners Card, or Switchcard.

Special Prices for Courage League Players

BEDFORD RUFC

Club Details

Club Colours: Oxford & Cambridge blue hoops
Date Founded: 1886
Membership: Total: 3,500, Playing members 120, Junior/Youth/Minis 300, Other 3,000
No. of teams: Senior 3, Under 21, Colts

Ground Details:

Ground Address: Goldington Road, Bedford.
Ground Tel No: 0234 347511/354619
Simple Directions to Ground: Near Jcn A428 Bedford-Cambridge & B660 Bedford-Bimbolton
Spectator Capacity: Total: 7,500, seated 800, standing 6,700
Ticket Prices: Adults: £6 Stand £4 Ground, OAP/Child £2/Free
Training Nights: Mondays and Thursdays

Club Officials

Club President: G B Willey
Club Chairman: I M Bullerwell
Club Secretary: A D Mills, 1 Newbury House, Kimbolton Road, Bedford, MK40 2PD. Tel: (H) 0234 212524 (W) 0234 364351
Fixtures Secretary: J Saunders, College Farm, Oakley, Bedfordshire. Tel: (H) 0234 822328 (W) 0234 822328
Press Officer: J Travis, c/o Bedford RUFC, Goldington Road, Bedford. Tel: 0234 213808
Registration Officer: I M Bullerwell, Duncombe Heights, Avenue Farm Lane, Wilden, Bedfordshire, MK44 2PY. Tel: (H) 0234 771419 (W) 0234 268818 Fax: 0234 268843
1994/ 95 1st XV Captain: Paul Alston
1994/95 Club Coach: Mike Rafter

CLUB PLAYING RECORD 1993-94

National League: Three
Final League Position at end of 1993/94 Season: 3rd
League Playing record: P 18, W 12, D 0, L 6, Pts F 330, Pts A 260
Season Playing record (including league matches/Pilkington Cup):
P 37, W 21, D 0, L 16, Pts For 868, Pts Against 640

BEDFORD RUFC

MOST CAPPED PLAYERS
(including British Lions Appearances)
D P (Budge) Rogers, 36, 1961-69
D G Perry, 15, 1963-66
W C C Steele (Scotland), 15, 1971-73
J P A Janion, 9, 1971-73
J Orwin, 7, 1988
R D Hearn, 6, 1966-67
R M Wilkinson, 6, 1975-76

LEADING APPEARANCES FOR CLUB
D P Rogers, 485, 1956-75
M Howe, 460, 1976-present
R Eidsforth, 374, 1924-49
R Willsher, 354, 1928-49
F N Barker, 347, 1966-77
J Smith, 343, 1953-68

LEADING SCORERS (1993-94)
Andy Finnie, Stand Off, 292
Paul Alston, Back Row, 62
Vince Turner, Wing, 60
Ashley Tapper, Stand Off/Centre, 47
Ben Whetstone, Centre, 45
Matt Deans, Back Row, 40

COURAGE RECORDS

Andy Finnie finishes leading scorer for the 6th season out of 7 for Bedford and in the process smashes the Bedford and division three record for most points in a season. He also smashed both club and division record for penalties in a season, 45.

	PTS	T	C	P	D	APPS	AVE
Andy Finnie	172	0	14	45	3	15	11.47

Finnie extended all Bedfords career points records, points to 554, conversions to 47, penalties to 133 and drop goals to 16.

Vince Turner breaks Mark Rennells record of 5 tries in a season. Turner ends the season with 8 tries. In doing so, he equals Rennels career record of 10 tries.

Turner also becomes the second Bedford player to score 2 tries in a match after Brian Gabriel.

BEDFORD RUFC

COURAGE LEAGUE RECORDS

Biggest Home Win: 52-10 v Blackheath 14-3-92 CL2   **Defeat:** 8-71 v Harlequins 14-10-89 CL1
Biggest Away Win: 33-14 v Redruth 26-2-94 CL3   **Defeat:** 0-76 v Bath 13-1-90 CL1
Most Tries For in a Match: 9 v Blackheath 14-3-92
Most Tries Against in a Match: 14 v Bath 13-1-90 CL1
Most consecutive Wins: 5   **Defeats:** 14
No. of Matches failed to Score: 4   **Clean Sheets:** 2   **Drawn Matches:** 8
Most appearances Forward: 64 Mark Howe   **Back:** 66 Andy Finnie
Most consecutive appearances: 30 Paul Alston 19-9-92 to date
Consecutive Matches scoring Tries: 5 Vince Turner   **Points:** 17 Andy Finnie

INDIVIDUAL SCORING RECORDS

IN A MATCH

Most Points: 25 Andy Finnie v Coventry 27-3-93 Home CL2
Most Tries: 2 On 11 occasions by 8 players, Most B Gabriel & V Turner twice
Most Conversions: 5 Steve Batty v Liverpool SH 3O-4-88 Home CL2, Andy Finnie v Blackheath 14.3.92 Home CL2
Most Penalties: 7 Andy Finnie v Coventry 23-4-94 Home CL3
Most Drop Goals: 2 Andy Finnie v Coventry 27-3-93 Home CL2

IN A SEASON

Most Points: 172 Andy Finnie 1993-94 CL3
Most Tries: 8 Vince Turner 1993-94 CL3
Most Conversions:: 14 Andy Finnie 1991-92 CL2
Most Penalties: 45 Andy Finnie 1987-88 CL2 & 1991-92 CL2
Most Drop Goals: 4 Andy Finnie 199O-91 CL2

IN A CAREER

Most Points: 554 Andy Finnie 1987-94
Most Tries: 10 Mark Rennell 1990-93, Vince Turner 1991-94
Most Conversions: 47 Andy Finnie 1987-94
Most Penalties: 133 Andy Finnie 1987-94
Most Drop Goals: 16 Andy Finnie 1987-94

COURAGE LEAGUE RECORD

	DIV	PLD	W	D	L	F	T	C	P	D	A	T	C	P	D
1987-88	2	11	6	2	3	168	18	12	22	2	164	17	9	23	3
1988-89	2	11	6	2	3	141	13	7	21	4	187	23	13	20	3
1989-90	1	11	0	0	11	70	9	5	7	1	467	83	42	15	2
1990-91	2	12	4	2	6	138	16	7	16	4	203	27	10	22	3
1991-92	2	12	4	0	8	168	20	11	19	3	204	24	15	25	1
1992-93	2	12	6	2	4	186	13	8	32	3	183	15	9	24	6
1993-94	3	18	12	0	6	332	29	14	50	3	260	27	13	32	1
		87	38	8	41	1203	118	64	167	20	1668	216	111	161	19

SEASON BY SEASON LEADING SCORERS

	Most Points			Most Tries
1987-88	75	Andy Finnie	3	Steve Harris Brian Gabriel Steve Batty
1988-89	56	Andy Finnie	2	Steve Harris Garry Colleran
1989-9O	13	Richard Greed	3	Mark Howe
199O-91	78	Andy Finnie	3	Tim Young
1991-92	92	Andy Fnnie	5	Mark Rennell
1992-93	75	Andy Finnie	3	Mark Rennell
1993-94	172	Andy Finnie	8	Vince Turner

LEAGUE THREE PROGRAMMES

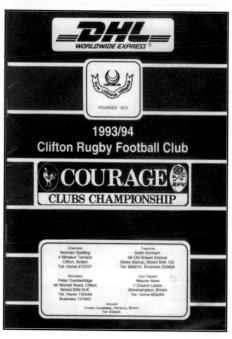

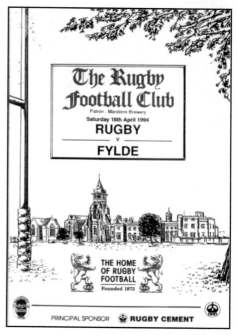

BLACKHEATH FC

"Club" On The Way Up?

A Superb pre-season tour of South Africa with fixtures in Cape Town, Port Elizabeth and Durban saw the squad, under new coach Danny Vaughan, well prepared for the new season but the inability to put more than three consecutive wins together was a problem throughout the season. Inconsistent goal kicking turned four possible victories into defeat. The end of the season was tinged with disappointment. Promotion was a possibility right up to the penultimate fixture when Fylde won a close game, winger Anderton scoring two second-half break-away tries.

In the Pilkington Cup Blackheath progressed to the fourth round. The largest home crowd for many seasons saw a nervous Leicester side finally win 16-10 courtesy of two Neil Black tries.

Young loose-head prop Matt Stewart was picked for Scotland Under 21 and only a fractured hand denied him a Scotland 'A' cap in April; he has since made the initial Scotland World Cup training squad. Three further Colts gained international representative honours. The great Mick Skinner has finally retired to assist in recruitment and the promotion of the club.

Prospects for the future are rosy with the squad averaging 22 years. Toby Booth takes over the captaincy and last season's experience, 13 members of the squad playing their first full season in the Courage National Leagues, should enable them to challenge strongly for promotion in the coming season.

CLUB PLAYING RECORD 1993-94

National League: Three
Final League Position at end of 1993/94 Season: 4th
League Playing record: P 18, W 11, D 0, L 7, Pts F 305, Pts A 222
Season Playing record (including league matches/Pilkington Cup): P 34, W 21, D 0, L 13, Pts F 638, Pts A 509

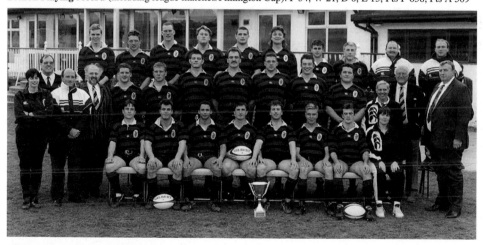

Blackheath Football Club 1993-94

Back row: Paul Mitchell, Toby Booth, Mick Harris, Josh Taylor, Dominic Walton, Mick Skinner, Steve Douglas, Jon Tierney, Pete Danckert (coach), Danny Vaughan (head coach)

Middle row: Sue Julians(physio), John Legge (chair of playing), Iain Exeter (coach), Alan Davies (director of rugby), Colin Ridgway, Matt Stewart, Matt Begley, Doug Hersey, Garry Furneaux, Jeremy Sampson, Neil Cousins, Ron Bailey (ast XV manager), Martin Turner (president), Frank McCarthy (chairman)

Front row: Mike Friday, Pat Jones, Matt Griffiths, Owen Coyne (captain), Paul Mycroft, Sam Howard, Stuart Burns, Laura Hanna (physio)

BLACKHEATH FC

ACHIEVEMENTS/COMPETITIONS WON DURING 93/94 SEASON:
Highest League position since Courage Leagues began

PLAYING SQUAD 1993-94
15 Burns, Mycroft
14 Aldridge, Douglas, Griffiths
13 Neil-Dwyer, MacIntyre
12 Coyne, Groves, P Smith
11 Jones, Mitchell
10 Howard
9 Friday, Greenway, Springhall
8 Harris, Slack
7 Booth, T Smith
6 Barham, Skinner, D Walton
5 Begley, Hursey, Kidman, Lloyd
4 Furneaux, Sampson
3 Cousins, Tierney
2 Howe, Nicholson, Ridgway
1 Stewart, Taylor

MOST CAPPED PLAYERS
(including British Lions Appearances)
N S Bruce, 31
C N Lowe, 25
M G Skinner, 21
C H Pilman, 18
L G Brown, 18
H T Gamlin, 15
B H Black, 15

LEADING APPEARANCES FOR CLUB
D Hursey, 250
B Howe, 180
P Jones, 150
M Skinner, 130

LEADING SCORERS (1993-94)
Stuart Burns, Full Back, 78 (17P, 6C, 3T)
Mike Friday, Scrum Half, 50 (10T)
Paul Mycroft, Full Back, 46 (7P, 5C, 2T)
Mick Harris, No 8, 25 (7P, 2C)
Steve Douglas, Wing, 20 (4T)
Paul Mitchel, 20 (4T)

COURAGE RECORDS
Mike Fridy, in his debut season breaks Joe McIntyres record of 5 tries in a season for Blackheath, Friday ends the season with 9 including the first ever hat-trick for the club in a league match.
Pat Jones, the only man to play in all 7 seasons for Blackheath, extends his career tries total to 11.

BLACKHEATH FC

Club Details

Club Colours: Black & red hoops
Change of Colours: Black
Date Founded: 1858
Membership: Total: 1,200, Playing members 200, Junior/Youth/Minis 600, Other 3
No. of teams: Senior 7, Junior 4
Programme advertising rates: Full £500, Half £300, Quarter £175

Ground Details:

Ground Address: Rectory Field, Charlton Road, Blackheath, SE3 8SR
Ground Tel No:081 858 1578
Simple Directions to Ground: Charlton Road is B210 off A2 500 yards from Royal Standard Public House in Stratheden Road, SE3.
Spectator Capacity: Total: 3,500, seated 500
Ticket Prices: Adults: £5
Training Nights: Tuesdays and Thursdays

Club Officials

Club President: Martin Turner
Club Secretary: Barry Shaw, 86 Crown Woods Way, Eltham, SE9 2NN. Tel: (H) 081 850 7976 (W) 071 439 3111 Fax: 081 850 7421
Fixtures Secretary: Jim Collett, 8 Vanbrush Fields, Blackheath, London SE3 7TZ. Tel: (H) 081 858 7751 (W) 081 539 3348
Press Officer: c/o John Legge, Blackheath FC, The Rectory Field, London SE3 8SR. Tel: (H) 0622 738177 (W) 081 850 1578 Fax: 0622 738177
Registration Officer: Ron Bailey, 11 Meadowlands, Seal, Sevenoaks, Kent. Tel: (H) 0732 762428
1994/ 95 1st XV Captain: Toby Booth
1994/95 Club Coach: Danny Vaughan

Skinner "champ...ing" at the bit "Nobody attacks my blindside"

BLACKHEATH FC

COURAGE LEAGUE RECORDS

Biggest Home Win: 31-10 v Gosforth 24-9-88 CL2   **Defeat:** 5-46 v Nottingham 26-9-92 CL2
Biggest Away Win: 27-19 v Havant 30-4-94 CL3   **Defeat:** 10-52 v Bedford 14-4-94 CL3
Most Tries For in a Match: 6 v Gosforth 24-9-88, v Havant 8-1-94 Home CL3
Most Tries Against in a Match: 9 v Bedford 14-3-92 CL2
Most consecutive Wins: 3   **Defeats:** 6
No. of Matches failed to Score: 2   **Clean Sheets:** 4   **Drawn Matches:** 5
Most appearances Forward: 49 Mike Harris   **Back:** 55 Pat Jones
Most consecutive appearances: 23 Pat Jones 22-9-90 thru 11-4-92
Consecutive Matches scoring Tries: 3 Peter Mitchell   **Points:** 9 Grant Eagle

INDIVIDUAL SCORING RECORDS

IN A MATCH

Most Points: 2O Grant Eagle v Moseley 28-3-92 Home CL2
Most Tries: 3 Mike Friday v Morley 6-11-93 Home CL3
Most Conversions: 3 Colin Parker v Richmond 12-11-88 Home CL2, v London Irish 28-4-9O Home CL2, Paul Mycroft v Morley 6-11-93 Home CL3
Most Penalties: 6 Grant Eagle v Moseley 28-3-92 Home CL2, v Rosslyn Park 9-1-93 Home CL2
Most Drop Goals: 2 Jon King v Coventry 19-11-88 Away CL2, v London Irish 22-4-89 Away CL2, v London Irish 28-4-9O Home CL2

IN A SEASON

Most Points: 97 Grant Eagle 1992-93 CL3
Most Tries: 9 Mike Friday 1993-94 CL3
Most Conversions: 1O Colin Parker 1987-88 CL2 & 1989-9O CL2
Most Penalties: 26 Grant Eagle 1992-93 CL2
Most Drop Goals: 8 Jon King 1988-89 CL2

IN A CAREER

Most Points: 175 Colin Parker 1987-91
Most Tries: 11 Pat Jones 1987-94
Most Conversions: 23 Colin Parker 1987-91
Most Penalties: 38 Colin Parker 1987-91
Most Drop Goals: 16 Jon King 1987-91

COURAGE LEAGUE RECORD

	DIV	PLD	W	D	L	F	T	C	P	D	A	T	C	P	D
1987-88	2	11	2	0	9	102	14	5	11	1	187	27	11	17	2
1988-89	2	11	4	1	6	181	19	12	19	8	144	17	5	22	0
1989-90	2	11	3	2	6	141	15	12	15	4	205	25	12	27	0
1990-91	2	12	4	0	8	134	12	4	22	4	169	18	8	25	0
1991-92	2	12	4	0	8	140	12	4	25	3	266	37	20	26	0
1992-93	2	12	4	2	6	142	9	5	27	2	231	23	13	26	4
1993-94	3	18	11	0	7	305	36	13	30	3	222	18	12	34	2
		87	32	5	50	1145	117	55	149	25	1424	165	81	177	10

SEASON BY SEASON LEADING SCORERS

	Most Points			Most Tries	
1987-88	30	Nick Colyer	2	Pat Jones Giles Marshall Martin Holcombe
1988-89	70	Colin Parker	3	Peter Vaughan Mickey Scott
1989-90	57	Colin Parker	3	Jon King
1990-91	48	Colin Parker	3	Pat Jones
1991-92	61	Neil Munn	2	Andy Mercer
1992-93	97	Grant Eagle	5	Joe McIntyre
1993-94	78	Stuart Burns	9	Mike Friday

CLIFTON RFC

Clifton — Leagues' Only Unbeaten Club

The introduction of the 18 game home and away league programme was a challenge to new coach Peter Polledri. Promotion was his target but to complete the campaign unbeaten was at the start beyond his wildest dreams but with promotion already guaranteed this became a reality on April 30.

Polledri with several new faces in his squad opted for a fluid style of play, although when conditions dictated his side could revert with ease to a forward orientated game. This adaptability along with his attention to pre match preparation was a vital key to the final success.

The inability to win away from home had proved Clifton's downfall in the previous season. Victory away to Exeter in the Pilkington Cup followed by a draw at Harrogate in the opening league fixture instilled in the side the belief that they could perform on opposition territory and with this their confidence grew. This confidence enabled games which in previous seasons would have been lost to be won.

Another key element to the success was the ability to field a settled side in league games with only 25 players starting games of which seven played in every game and another seven in 12 or more. The injury list was minimal with the only significant casualty being prop Andy Ellis who missed the second half of the season with a back injury.

The scoring contributions of fly half Simon Hogg with 222 points in league games and speedy winger John Phillips was immense but the achievement was built around an all round team performance. The move of back row man Andy Heywood to the second row was a gamble which worked. Newcomers Ellis, prop Andy Fisher, flanker Simon Swales and winger Trevor Davis all played their part with Swales proving a more than useful addition to a mobile back row.

The future looks bright with several younger players impressing in senior appearances towards the end of the season and the prospect of Division 3 rugby also attracting several young and promising players to the club.

CLUB PLAYING RECORD 1993-94

National League: Three
Final League Position at end of 1993/94 Season: 1st
League Playing record: P 18, W 16, D 2, L 0, Pts For 477, Pts Against 205
Season Playing record (including league matches/Pilkington Cup): P 40, W 28, D 3, L 9, Pts F 955, Pts A 552

Back row: Mike Anderson (Vice President), Sheridan Smith (Team Sec), Mike Skinner (Team Manager), Derek Farley (Vice President), Simon Swales, Andy Heywood, Mark Wyatt, Chris Blake, Andy Fisher, Peter Naivalurua, Grant Watson (President), Fred Cannon (Vice President), Norman Golding (Chairman), Bob Miller (Assistant Coach), Brian Jordan (Fixture Sec)
Middle row: Charles Newyh, Paul Cox, Paul Jeffery, Wayne Hone (Captain), Kerry Lock, Richard John, Mark Beresford, Peter Polledri (Coach)
Front row: Phil Cue (Assistant Coach), John Phillips, Trevor Davis, Mike Cotton, Simon Hogg　　　　　　　*Photo: Keith Fowler*

CLIFTON RFC

ACHIEVEMENTS/COMPETITIONS WON DURING 93/94 SEASON

Champions National League Four (unbeaten)
2nd XV known as Wanderers - Champions West of England 2nd Team Merit Table
Runners up Gloucester Under 18s Cup
5 members of Ladies XV played at World Cup

MOST CAPPED PLAYERS (including British Lions appearances)	LEADING APPEARANCES FOR CLUB	LEADING SCORERS (1993-94)
R J McEwen, 15, 1953-58	Dave Mason, 278, 1983-94	Simon Hogg, Fly Half, 431 (8T, 59C, 75P, 16DG)
P D Young, 9, 1953-55	Steve Jucken, 222, 1982-94	John Phillips, Wing, 160 (32T)
J A Bush, 5, 1872-76	Mark Wyatt, 147, 1989-94	Trevor Davis, Wing, 65 (13T)
A Budd, 5, 1878-81	Paul Cox, 126, 1990-94	Mark Wyatt, No 8, 45 (9T)
	Chris Blake, 110, 1991-94	Kerry Lock, Centre, 35 (7T)
	Simon Hogg, 105, 1992-94	Peter Naivalurua, Centre, 30 (6T)

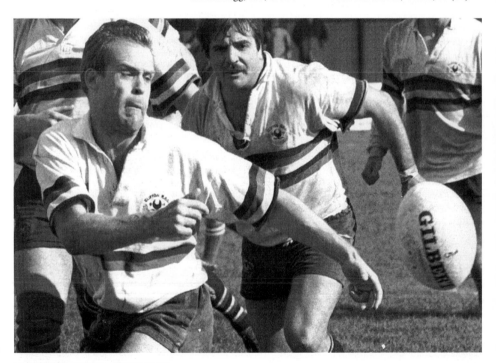

PLAYER OF THE YEAR — KERRY LOCK

Many would have anticipated Clifton choosing as their player of the year either the countries leading point scorer Simon Hogg or leading try scorer John Phillips, but instead the mantle fell on the shoulders of 25 year old centre Kerry Lock.

He is not a flamboyant player but gains the admiration of all around him for the work he performs on the field. Renowned for his strong tackling his greatest asset in his ability to tidy and secure the ball when things go wrong in midfield. Phillip and fellow winger Trevor Davis can vouch for his ability to make a half break and time his pass as many of their tries resulted from the initial work of Kerry. Not a prolific scorer he twice surprised Sudbury with his pace when he scorched over from a distance to score.

Kerry, a product of Clifton's successful and prolific junior section, is in his second spell with the club. After gaining County representative honours at both Colts and Under 21 level he moved to neighbours Bristol in 1989 and after limited opportunities returned to Clifton in September 1992. Since then he has established himself as a first choice centre and this season formed a strong pairing with Peter Naivalurua.   *Photo: Keith Fowler*

CLIFTON RFC

Ground Details:

Ground Address: Station Road, Cribbs Causeway, Henbury, Bristol, BS10 7TT
Ground Tel No: 0272 500445 Fax: 0272 500445
Simple Directions to Ground: Leave M5 at Junction 17 and take A4018 (signposted Bristol West) down duel carriageway. Proceed to the third roundabout (Old Crow Public House) and return down the opposite side of the dual carriageway. Turn left just after the BP petrol station and before the second roundabout down lane signposted to Clifton RFC. Turn right at end of the lane and entrance is through gate 100 metres on left. You will pass the ground on the left as you pass the second roundabout but vehicular access is not possible from here due to a small one way system.
Spectator Capacity: Total: 2,250, seated 250
Ticket Prices: Adults: £4, OAP/Child: £2/free
Training Nights: Mondays and Wednesdays

Club Details

Club Colours: Lavender & black hoops
Change of Colours: white, thin lavender & black hoops
Date Founded: 1872
Membership: Total: 900, Playing members 250, Junior/Youth/Minis 300, Other 350
No. of teams: Senior 8, Junior 11, Ladies 3
Programme advertising rates: Full £200, Half £100 (1993/94)

Club Officials

Club President: Grant Watson
Club Chairman: Norman Golding
Club Secretary: Peter Cumberlidge, 48 Worrall Road, Clifton, Bristol BS8 4LU. Tel: (H) 0272 735048 (W) 0272 737993 Fax: 0272 733167
Fixtures Secretary: Brian "Ben" Jordan, 17 Royal Close, Henbury, Bristol, BS10 7XF. Tel: (H) 0272 504723 (W) 0272 506723 Fax: 0272 500445
Registration Officer: Sheridan Smith, Garden Flat, 11 West Field Park, Redland, Bristol, BS6 6LT. Tel: (H) 0272 739910 (W) 0272 994531 Fax: 0272 215419
1994/ 95 1st XV Captain: Wayne Hone
1994/95 Club Coach: Peter Polledri
Clubhouse Manager: Dick Lemon

Centre Peter Naivalurua gets his pass in to flanker Simon Swales despite the tackle from Sheffield's No 8 Dave Watson. The supporting players are prop Paul Cox and locks Andy Heywood and Chris Blake   *Photo: Keith Fowler*

CLIFTON RFC

COURAGE LEAGUE RECORDS

Highest score: 64 v Bournemouth (64-7) 19-9-87 Home SW1
Largest winning margin: 57 as above
Highest score against: 43 v Leeds (32-43) 24-4-93 Away CL3
Largest losing margin: 27 v Roundhay (7-34) 27-4-91 Away CL3
Drawn Matches: 3
Clean Sheets: 2
Failed to score: 2

INDIVIDUAL SCORING RECORDS
IN A MATCH

Most points: 24 Roger Gilbert v Bournemouth 19-9-87 Home SW1
Most tries: 4 Dave Cottrell v Askeans 4-1-92 Home CL3
Most conversions: 9 Roger Gilbert v Bournemouth 19-9-87 SW1
Most penalities: 5 Simon harvey v Metropolitan Police 23-9-89 Home D4S, Mark Beresford v Sheffield 22-9-90 Home CL3
Most drop goals: 2 Simon Harvey v Sudbury 14-10-89 Home D4S, Phil Cue v Lydney 23-3-90 Away CL3

IN A SEASON

Most points: 322 Simon Hogg 1993-94 CL4
Most tries: 16 John Phillips 1993-94 CL4
Most conversions: 16 Roger Gilbert 1987-88 SW1, Simon Hogg 1991- 92 CL3
Most penalties: 19 Simon Hogg 1991-92 CL3
Most drop goals: 6 Simon Harvey 1989-90 SW1

IN A CAREER

Most points: 604 Simon Hogg 1991-94
Most tries: 25 Mark Wyatt 1988-93
Most conversions: 25 Simon Hogg 1991-93
Most penalties: 34 Simon Hogg 1991-93
Most drop goals: 11 Simon Harvey 1987-91

SEASON BY SEASON LEADING SCORERS

	Most Points			Most Tries	
1987-88	60	Roger Gilbert	7	Mike Speakman	
1988-89	49	Roger Gilbert	4	Mark Trott	
1989-90	83	Simon Harvey	6	Mark Trott Mark Wyatt	
1990-91	32	Phil Cue	6	Dave Cottrell Mark Wyatt	
1991-92	100	Simon Hogg	8	M Brain	
1992-93	71	Simon Hogg	5	Mark Wyatt, Doug Woodman	
1993-94	222	Simon Hogg	16	John Phillips	

EXETER FC

Exeter's Happy Hundred

This was the first season of home and away matches in the Courage League; the leagues being restructured in order to accommodate them.

Exeter's league season began in October; however, in September, as part of the celebrations to mark 100 years of rugby at the County Ground the club entertained Devon and the Barbarians. Later in the season Cornwall were our guests. Both Devon and Cornwall were beaten 15-12 and 27-17 respectively, while the Barbarians playing in front of 7,000 spectators recorded a victory of 59-14.

On the 23rd October the league began in earnest and saw Exeter suffer a defeat of 39-12 at Coventry. After this inauspicious start we went on to record nine wins and one draw finishing in sixth place and ensuring another season in National League Three (our eighth).

The Bass Devon Cup was won for the sixth consecutive time equalling Plymouth's record; fittingly, the final was against Plymouth and the score 22-12 to Exeter.

During the season injuries were sustained by Jeff Tutchings and Andy Green. Jeff was soon back in action while Andy's knee injury sustained in a Devon Cup game against Bideford in early March ruled him out for the remainder of the season. Andy Baker made a welcome return from injury in January.

On the representative front Robert Pugsley played for the English Fire Brigade, Paul Westgate captained Devon and in the team were Trevor Harris, Phil Sluman and Harry Langley. Sean Doyle played for South West U21s.

Club Playing Record 1993-94

National League: Three
Final League Position at end of 1993/94 Season: 6th
League Playing record: P 18, W 9, D 1, L 8, Pts F 308, Pts A 271
Season Playing record (including league matches/Pilkington Cup): P 38, W 33, D 1, L 14, Pts F 791, Pts A 534

Photo: Chas Williamson

EXETER FC

ACHIEVEMENTS/COMPETITIONS WON DURING 93/94 SEASON:
Devon Cup Winners

PLAYING SQUAD 1993-94
Full Back: I Steward, P Miles
Wing: S Dovell, S Boatfield, M Chatterton, S Doyle
Centre: J Tutchings, R Lambert, A Turner, A Baker
Fly Half: A Green, J Dance
Scrum Half: A Maunder, D Oxland
Prop: R Gibbins, P Sluman, T Harris, S Byrne, J Sussex
Hooker: R Pugsley, P Sitch, S Kelly, S Western
Lock: R Langley, R Bess, P Hodge, J Batchlor
Wing Forwards: P Westgate, N Southern, R Hutchinson, M Reeve, L Stratton
No 8: M Cathery, R Walker

LEADING APPEARANCES FOR CLUB
A Maunder, 35, 1993/94
I Steward, 34, 1993/94
J Tutchings, 33, 1993/94
A Turner, 33, 1993/94

LEADING SCORERS (1993-94)
Andy Green, Fly Half, 265
Mark Chatterton, Wing, 11 tries
Andy Maunder, Scrum Half, 10 tries

MOST CAPPED PLAYERS
(including British Lions Appearances)
J Buchanan, 16, 1924-25
M Underwood, 5, 1962-64
R Madge, 4, 1948
D Manley, 4, 1963
P Nicholas, 3, 1902

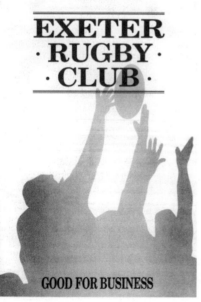

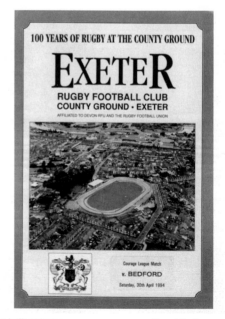

All sponsorship details concerning the club

A brilliant history cum programme — quality publication

EXETER FC

Club Details

Club Colours: Black with white collars
Change of Colours: White
Date Founded: 1872
Membership: Total: 650, Playing members, 110, Junior/Youth/Minis 120, Other 18
No. of teams: Senior 6, Junior 9
Programme advertising rates: Full £450, Half £250, Quarter £140, Eighth £90
Any Special Occasions during 1994/95: Opening of Club House extension

Ground Details:

Ground Address: County Ground, Church Road, St Thomas, Exeter, EX2 9BQ
Ground Tel No: 0392 78759
Simple Directions to Ground: Jcn 30 M5 Head on A377 to town centre. Sainsbury Store turn left (Cowick Street) under railway bridge turn left at traffic lights, then turn right - ground approx 100 yards.
Spectator Capacity: Total: 6,500, seated 1,750
Ticket Prices: Adults: £5, OAP/Child: £2.50
Training Nights: Tuesdays and Thursdays

Club Officials

Club President: R J Roach
Club Chairman: J Baxter
Club Secretary: B P (Tug) Wilson, 11 Washbrook View, Ottery St Mary, Devon, EX11 1EP. Tel: (H) 0404 813316 (W) 0884 243200 Fax: 0884 257303
Fixtures Secretary: T Turner, April House, Sandford, Crediton, Devon, EX17 4NH. Tel: (H) 0363 772044
Registration Officer: B P (Tug) Wilson
1994/ 95 1st XV Captain: A Maunder
1994/95 Club Coach: D Wiggins
Other Club Officers:
M Dalton, Commercial Manger
R Staddon, Director of Coaching
R Huxtable, Hon Match Secretary

Simon Dovell beating Coventry winger to score winning try   *Photo: Nigel Chanter*

EXETER FC

COURAGE LEAGUE RECORDS

Biggest Home Win: 48-13 v Askeans 10-10-92 CL3   **Defeat:** 28-33 v Leeds 13-3-93 CL3
Biggest Away Win: 41-0 v Havant 26-2-94 CL3   **Defeat:** 13-48 v Fylde 3-10-87 CL3
Most Tries For in a Match: 6 v Gosforth 24-9-88, v Havant 8-1-94 Home CL3
Most Tries Against in a Match:7 v Birmingham 21-3-88 CL3, v Havant 26-2-94 CL3
Most consecutive Wins: 6   **Defeats:** 6
No. of Matches failed to Score: 0   **Clean Sheets:** 4   **Drawn Matches:** 9
Most appearances Forward: **Back:**
Most consecutive appearances:
Consecutive Matches scoring Tries: 3 Andy Maunder, John Davies   **Points:** 32 Andy Green

INDIVIDUAL SCORING RECORDS
IN A MATCH

Most Points: 2O Andy Green v Met Pol 1O-11-9O Home CL3
Most Tries: 3 Mike Cathery v Birmingham 26-3-88 Home CL3 Andy Green v Met Pol*
Most Conversions: 3 Andy Green on 6 occasions
Most Penalties: 5 Andy Green v W Hartlepool 28-1O-89 Home CL3, v Sheffield 28-3-92 Home CL3, v Plymouth 14.11.92 Home CL3.
Most Drop Goals: 2 Andy Green v Sheffield 23-4-88 Home CL3.

IN A SEASON

Most Points: 125 Andy Green 1993-94 CL3
Most Tries: 5 Andy Maunder 1993-94 CL3
Most Conversions: 16 Andy Green 1993-94 CL3
Most Penalties: 31 Andy Green 1992-93 CL3
Most Drop Goals: 4 Andy Green 1987-88 CL3

IN A CAREER

Most Points: 563 Andy Green 1987-94
Most Tries: 21 Andy Maunder 1987-94
Most Conversions: 52 Andy Green 1992-94
Most Penalties: 122 Andy Green 1992-94
Most Drop Goals: 12 Andy Green 1992-94

COURAGE LEAGUE RECORDS

	DIV	PLD	W	D	L	F	T	C	P	D	A	T	C	P	D
1987-88	3	11	3	2	6	128	15	4	16	4	197	27	16	19	0
1988-89	3	11	4	0	7	142	17	7	14	6	180	22	10	20	4
1989-90	3	11	5	1	5	149	15	7	25	0	153	17	5	19	6
1990-91	3	12	7	2	3	160	20	7	22	0	139	16	6	21	0
1991-92	3	12	8	2	2	203	29	12	19	2	138	14	5	22	2
1992-93	3	11	8	1	2	247	25	10	31	3	169	16	7	24	1
1993-94	3	18	9	1	8	308	32	20	34	2	271	23	15	38	4
		86	44	9	33	1337	153	67	161	17	1247	135	64	163	17

SEASON BY SEASON LEADING SCORERS

	Most Points			Most Tries
1987-88	42	Andy Green	3	Andy Green
1988-89	65	Malcolm Collins	4	Andy Maunder
1989-9O	99	Andy Green	2	Andy Green
199O-91	92	Andy Green	4	Jeff Tutchings
1991-92	77	Andy Green	4	Mark Chatterton, Jon Davis
1992-93	122	Andy Green	5	Andy Maunder
1993-94	125	Andy Green	5	Andy Maunder

*1O-11-9O Home CL3, M Chatterton v Headingley 23-11-91 Home CL3, Harry Langley 24-4-93 v Broughton Park Away CL3

HARROGATE RUFC

Harrogate Keep on Climbing

The season fulfilled the highest hopes of the supporters with the team continuing from where they left off the previous season to win promotion for the second year running as runners up to clear champions Clifton. For the team and supporters alike a feature of the season was playing so many clubs for the first time and visiting their grounds.

A good set of results in September and early October came to an abrupt end in the Pilkington Cup at Birmingham and Solihull where the home team playing with flair and commitment won a close game 7-3.

There was no respite with the first league game following immediately when Clifton made their first visit to Harrogate. Clifton built up a 15-0 half time lead but Harrogate put in a tremendous second half display eventually to draw 15 all. This gave the team confidence and they remained unbeaten until the visit to Liverpool St Helens where the home side won comfortably 24-10.

As Clifton continued to win it became a race with Liverpool to see who would get the second spot and it remained like this until the teams met again in April when a 21-7 home win and victory at Broughton Park the following week ensured promotion.

In the meantime progress in the Yorkshire Cup halted in the semi-final at ultimate winners Wakefield with a 15-0 defeat.

Guy Easterby, Richard Whyley and Peter Clegg and that of Roger Shackleton with the second team and skipper Jeremy Hopkinson's leadership on the field made a major contribution to the club's success.

The junior section expanded further to 213 members (8-16 years) and the Mini Tournament attracted teams with a total of 450 players.

Club Playing Record 1993-94

National League: Four
Final League Position at end of 1993/94 Season: 2nd
League Playing record: P 18, W 14, D 2, L 2, Pts F 479, Pts A 219
Season Playing record (including league matches/Pilkington Cup): P 33, W 23, D 2, L 8, Pts F 658, Pts A 386

Back row: R Zoing, E Atkins, A Simpson
Middle row: P Clegg (coach), W Carswell (physio), R Bell, I Hassall, S Baker, R Whyley, R Marcroft, W Lowe (touch judge)
Front row: D Hall, S Towse, P Taylor, J Hopkinson (capt), G Easterby, D Wheat, C Reed

189

HARROGATE RUFC

ACHIEVEMENTS/COMPETITIONS WON DURING 93/94 SEASON:
Promotion from Division Four to Three
2nd Team won York R1 Floodlit Competition

PLAYING SQUAD 1993-94
Full Back: Ian Hassall, Matthew Yates
Wing: Ericson Atkins, Rob Bell, James Riley, Jon-Paul Wong, Peter Woolley
Centre: Craig Reed, Ralph Zoing, Adam Pearson, Andy Taylor, Dominic Magee
Stand Off Steve Towse
Scrum Half: Guy Easterby
Loose Head: Andy Simpson
Hooker: Richard Whyley, James Wade
Tight Head: David Hall, Stuart Cameron, Glyn Harland
Lock: Peter Taylor, Richard Castleton, Simon Brown, Mike Ruthen
Flanker: David Wheat, Steve Baker, Mark Heap, Richard Marcroft, A Pride
No 8: J Hopkinson

MOST CAPPED PLAYERS
(including British Lions Appearances)
P J Squires, 30, 1973-79
J Young, 24, 1968-73
T O Grant, 6, 1960-64
R I Shackleton, 4, 1970
I King, 3, 1954
A Pickering, 1, 1907

LEADING APPEARANCES FOR CLUB
Steve Fawcett, 563, 1978-94

LEADING SCORERS:
R Zoing, Centre, 170
J Hopkinson, No 8, 80
M Yates, SO/FB, 47
E Atkins, Wing, 45
I Hassall, Full Back, 45
S Towse, Stand Off, 37

HARROGATE
RUGBY UNION FOOTBALL CLUB
COURAGE NATIONAL LEAGUE 4 1993-94

H. R. U. F. C.

(FOUNDED 1871)
DIVISION 4 NORTH CHAMPIONS 1992-93
YORKSHIRE CUP WINNERS 1991 AND 1992

Official Programme
COUNTY GROUND, CLARO ROAD, HARROGATE

HARROGATE RUFC

Club Details

Club Colours: Red, amber & black, white shorts, red socks
Change of Colours: Red
Date Founded: 1871
Membership: Total: 648, Playing members 128, Junior/Youth/Minis 213, Other 307
No. of teams: Senior 6, Junior 9, Colts 1

Ground Details:

Ground Address: County Ground, Claro Road, Harrogate, North Yorkshire, HG1 4AG.
Ground Tel No: 0423 566966 Fax: 0423 562776
Simple Directions to Ground: Claro Road is on the North side of the A59 York-Skipton road between the Granby & County Hotel.
Spectator Capacity: Total: 5,000, seated 499
Ticket Prices: Adults: £3, OAP/Child TBA
Training Nights: Mondays and Thursdays

Club Officials

Club President: W Glyn Smith
Club Chairman: Allen T Tattersfield
Club Secretary: B Rodney Spragg, Pear Tree Cottage, Nidd, Harrogate, HG3 3BJ. Tel: (H) 0423 770126 (W) 0423 562634 Fax: 0423 562776
Fixtures Secretary: Graham E Siswick, 22A Hillway, Tranmere Park, Guiseley, Nr Leeds. Tel: (H) 0943 845620 (W) 0532 570413
Press Officer: Rodney Spragg
Registration Officer: Rodney Spragg
1994/ 95 1st XV Captain: Jeremy T Hopkinson
1994/95 Club Coach: Peter J Clegg
Other Club Officers:
Roy Guy, Vice Chairman
W Alun Jones, Rugby Chairman
Bob Thompson, Commercial Chairman
Peter Bell, Junior Chairman
Mike Hymas, Ground Chairman

Harrogate v Sudbury

HARROGATE RUFC

COURAGE LEAGUE RECORDS

Biggest Home Win: 78-12 v Aspatria 30-4-94 CL4   **Defeat:** 21-56 v Otley 22-9-90 D4N
Biggest Away Win: 34-6 v West Park 22-10-88 N1, v Kendall 3-10-92 D4N
Biggest Away Defeat: 8-32 v Stourbridge 11-4-92 CL4
Most Tries For in a Match: 14 v Aspatria 30-4-94 CL4
Most Tries Against in a Match: 9v Otley 22-9-90 D4N
Most consecutive Wins: 5   **Defeats:** 3
No. of Matches failed to Score: 0   **Clean Sheets:** 4   **Drawn Matches:** 5
Most appearances Forward: **Back:**
Most consecutive appearances:
Consecutive Matches scoring Tries: 6 Clive Ware   **Points:** 13 Ralph Zoing

INDIVIDUAL SCORING RECORDS

IN A MATCH

Most points: 25 Steve Baker v Lichfield 14-11-92 Home D4N

Most tries: 5 Steve Baker v Lichfield 14-11-92 Home D4n

Most conversions: 9 Ralph Zoing v Towcestrians 13-3-93 Home D4N

Most penalities: 7 Ralph Zoing v Halifax 18-11-89 Home N1

Most drop goals: 2 Ralph Zoing v Askeans 20-11-93 Home D4

IN A SEASON

Most points: 130 Ralph Zoing 1992-93 D4N
Most tries: 13 Jeremy Hopkinson 1993-94 D4
Most conversions: 29 Ralph Zoing 1992-93D4N
Most penalties: 22 Ralph Zoing 1989-90 N1
Most drop goals: 3 Ralph Zoing 1993-94 D4

IN A CAREER

Most points: 551 Ralph Zoing 1987-94
Most tries: 27 Jeremy Hopkinson 1990-94
Most conversions: 91 Ralph Zoing 1987-94
Most penalties: 95 Ralph Zoing 1987-93
Most drop goals: 6 Ralph Zoing 1987-94

COURAGE LEAGUE RECORD

	DIV	PLD	W	D	L	F	T	C	P	D	A	T	C	P	D
1987-88	N1	10	5	0	5	147					113				
1988-89	N1	10	7	1	2	204					120				
1989-90	N1	10	8	0	2	188					82				
1990-91	D4N	12	6	1	5	220					204				
1991-92	D4N	12	6	0	6	170					175				
1992-93	D4N	12	10	1	1	363					115				
1993-94	4	18	14	2	2	479	60	31	30	9	219	20	15	26	1
		84	56	5	23										

SEASON BY SEASON LEADING SCORERS

	Most Points			Most Tries	
1987-88	28	Ralph Zoing	2	Andy Caldwell Dave Bowe	
1988-89	64	Ralph Zoing	8	Clive Ware	
1989-90	91	Ralph Zoing	4	Clive Ware	
1990-91	47	Ralph Zoing	9	Jeremy Hopkinson	
1991-92	45	Ralph Zoing	3	Steve Baker	
1992-93	130	Ralph Zoing	9	Steve Baker, Guy Easterby	
1993-94	106	Ralph Zoing	13	Jeremy Hopkinson	

MORLEY RFC

Bill Mitchell Got Us Wrong!

We had three main objectives last September - to stay in Division 3, to construct a new weight training area with modern physio treatment room and install improved lighting on a training pitch. All were achieved and also standards maintained in other areas. Morley now has a weights room comparable with any and new lights for training, resulting from generous benefactors and good administration.

Despite losing a dozen or more first XV players in the summer of 1993, the "maroons" with young squad regained Division 3 status under the guidance of Rugby Chairman Chris Leathley and coaches Robin Kay and Alan Price. Several Colts, who were brought into the side perhaps earlier than normal, played with courage, determination and improving skills.

After an emphatic victory at home over Redruth, a narrow one followed against Exeter then remarkable wins against them away. Again at home Havant were decisively beaten and Bedford by one point. There were pulsating home defeats by Coventry and Blackheath and Fylde squeezed promotion by two points in the last game of the season. Satisfactorily for Morley, Bill Mitchell's forecasts in the Directory for 1993-94 proved wrong - Morley were not relegated (touché - BM!)

Our young players continue to be recognised. Scrum half Scott Benton and flanker Ben Wade played for England Colts, we had representatives in Yorkshire's U15's and U17's, three County Colts, four players in the County's U21's, Bruce Rowland turned out for England Students and Gordon Throup and Jamie Grayshon helped Yorkshire win the Championship.

Club Playing Record 1993-94

National League: Three
Final League Position at end of 1993/94 Season: 8th
League Playing record: P 18, W 6, D 0, L 12, Pts F 245, Pts A 334
Season Playing record (including league matches/Pilkington Cup): P 33, W 10, D 0, L 23, Pts F 473, Pts A 646

Morley v Blackheath at Morley — Dan McFarland in possession supported by Jon Moore and Andy Crussley

MORLEY RFC

ACHIEVEMENTS/COMPETITIONS WON DURING 93/94 SEASON:
Northern 7s Winners
West Park Bramhope 7s Winners
Yorkshire Colts Merit Table Winners

PLAYING SQUAD 1993-94
15 A Sales, P Massey, J Cross
14 S Wray, A Crossley, B Rowland, M Lang
13 A Crossley, G Jenkins, C Barnes, J Fieldhouse
12 G Jenkins, C Liptrot, C Barnes, C Johnson
11 T Clark, B Rowland, C Barnes, M Lang, C Liptrot
10 J Grayshon, J Greenslade, E Falshaw, C Johnson
9 S Cayzer, S Benton, J Chard
1 D McFarland, M Oxley
2 G Throup, D Irish, S Kneale, D Grice
3 D McSwiney, M Oxley, D Cusworth, D Irish, D Grice
4 S Enright, N Kenyon, C Taylor, D Sonia, T Throssell, P Fountain, I Hill, M McMahon
5 J Stow, C Taylor
6 M McSwiney, I Spence, T Acland, I Hill, J Stow, B Wade, J Moore, I Anderson, M Terry
7 A Yule, J Moore, B Wade, M Ramus, M Currie, I Anderson, J Bethel, A Murray
8 S Enright, I Hill, T Acland, W McSwiney, I Spence, B Wade, J Stow, N Smart

MOST CAPPED PLAYERS
(including British Lions Appearances)
J P Shooter
H Bedford
G H Marsden

LEADING APPEARANCES FOR CLUB
Richard D Binks, 728, 1962-1989

LEADING SCORERS (1993-94)
J Grayshon, Fly Half, 192
A Clarke, Wing, 40
E Flashaw, Fly Half, 23
G Jenkins, Centre, 21
P Massey, Full Back, 20
B Rowland, Wing, 20
S Wray, Wing, 20

MORLEY RFC

Club Details

Club Colours: Maroon and white
Change of Colours: Black
Date Founded: 1871
Membership: Total: 981, Full members 598, Junior/Youth/Minis 177, Social Members 206
No. of teams: Senior 5, Junior and Colts 12
Programme advertising rates: Full £280, Half £150, Quarter £80

Ground Details:

Ground Address: Scatcherd Lane, Morley, Leeds, LS27 0JJ
Ground Tel No: 0532 533487
Simple Directions to Ground: From West: Leave M62 at Junction 27. Follow A650 towards Wakefield for 1.2 miles. Turn left into St Andrew's Avenue. Club 0.3 miles on left. From East: Leave M62 at Junction 28. Follow A650 towards Bradford for 1.7 miles. Turn right into St Andrew's Avenue. Club 0.3 miles on left.
Spectator Capacity: Total: 5,826, Seated 826
Ticket Prices: Adults: £4, OAP/Child: £2
Training Nights: Mondays and Thursdays

Club Officials

Club President: Jim Woodhead
Club Chairman: Trevor Richmond
Club Secretary: David Vinegrad, 5 Elmfield Court, Morley, Leeds, LS27 0EP. Tel: (H) 0532 529306 (Car) 0836 663601 Fax: 0532 534144
Fixtures Secretary: Brian F Falshaw, 17 Rein Road, Morley, Leeds, LS27 0HZ. Tel: (H) 0532 539507 (Car) 0860 383628 Fax: 0532 539507
Press Officer: Fred Pickstone, Westbourne, St Andrew's Avenue, Morley, Leeds, LS27 0JT. Tel: (H) 0532 533508 Fax: 0532 531411
Registration Officer: Tony Tonge, 30 Cardigan Avenue, Morley, Leeds, LS27 0DP. Tel: (H) 0532 531250 Fax: 0532 534144
1994/ 95 1st XV Captain: TBA
1994/95 Club Coach: Alan Price
Director of Coaching: Chris Leathley

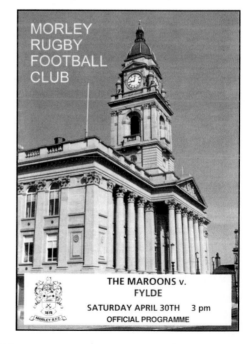

195

MORLEY RFC

COURAGE LEAGUE RECORDS

Biggest Home Win: 35-6 v Redruth 30-10-93 CL3   **Defeat:** 7-38 v Wakefield 12-3-88 CL3
Biggest Away Win: 49-6 v Liverpool St Helens 14-3-92 CL2   **Defeat:** 0-78 v Nottingham 24-10-92 CL2
Most Tries For in a Match: 9 v Liverpool St Helens 14-3-92 CL2
Most Tries Against in a Match: 12 v Nottingham 24-10-92 CL2
Most consecutive Wins: 8   **Defeats:** 11
No. of Matches failed to Score: 4   **Clean Sheets:** 3   **Drawn Matches:** 3
Most appearances Forward: Back:
Most consecutive appearances:
Consecutive Matches scoring Tries: 3 Jon Clarke (2), Faulkner   **Points:** 13 Jamie Grayshon

INDIVIDUAL SCORING RECORDS

IN A MATCH

Most Points: 17 Jamie Grayshon v Birmingham
24-9-88 Away ALN
Most Tries: 3 Paul White v Winnington Park 28-4-9O
Home ALN
Most Conversions: 5 Jamie Grayshon v Liverpool SH
14-3-92 Away CL2
Most Penalties: 4 Jamie Grayshon v Waterloo 1O-1O-
92 Away CL2 , v Blackheath 12-2-90 Home CL3
Most Drop Goals: 2 Jamie Grayshon v Wakefield 13-2-
93 Away CL2, v Richmond 13-11-93 Home CL3

IN A SEASON

Most Points: 117 Jamie Grayshon 1993-94 CL3
Most Tries: 8 Tony Clark 1993-94 CL3
Most Conversions: 12 Jamie Grayshon 1993-94 CL3
Most Penalties: 28 Jamie Grayshon 1993-94 CL3
Most Drop Goals: 3 Jamie Grayshon 1992-93 CL2,
1993-94 CL3

IN A CAREER

Most Points: 490 Jamie Grayshon 1987-94
Most Tries: 28 Tony Clark 1987-94
Most Conversions: 51 Jamie Grayshon 1987-94
Most Penalties: 111 Jamie Grayshon 1987-94
Most Drop Goals: 13 Jamie Grayshon 1987-94

COURAGE LEAGUE RECORD

	DIV	PLD	W	D	L	F	T	C	P	D
1987-88	3	11	1	1	9		14	8	8	1
1988-89	ALN	10	5	0	5		12	6	23	2
1989-90	ALN	10	8	0	2		21	9	19	2
1990-91	3	12	9	1	2		30	15	19	1
1991-92	2	12	4	0	8		20	11	20	3
1992-93	2	12	0	1	11					
1993-94	3	18	6	0	12					
		85	33	3	49					

SEASON BY SEASON LEADING SCORERS

	Most Points			Most Tries	
1987-88	31	Jamie Grayshon	3	Tony Clark	
1988-89	91	Jamie Grayshon	6	Tony Clark	
1989-9O	78	Jamie Grayshon	5	Paul White	
199O-91	5O	Jamie Grayshon	5	Mark Faulkner	
1991-92	57	Jamie Grayshon	4	Tony Clark, Martin Collins	
1992-93	66	Jamie Grayshon	2	Tony Clark	
1993-94	117	Jamie Grayshon	8	Tony Clark	

OTLEY RUFC

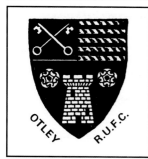

Otley's Rise Halted

After promotion in four seasons out of five and the record breaking 1992/93 season, 1993/94 was an anti-climax and it is indicative of the importance of league rugby that the failure to avoid relegation to National Division Three overshadowed the overall success of the club. After gaining promotion to National Division Two at the eleventh hour the previous season and making a reasonable start the 1st XV found it heavy going against sides the majority of whom had first division experience, but to their credit they were in with a chance right up to the penultimate fixture. An ever lengthening injury list meant that 37 players appeared for the 1st XV and this did not help.

Overall the five senior XVs played 134 games winning 81 and drawing four plus scoring over 3,000 points. On the representative front Ian Carroll played for Yorkshire in the county Championship winning side at Twickenham and the successful Youth and Junior Section continued to produce talented players who gained honours. Chris Baldwin played for Yorkshire and North Under 21's, England Students; James Overend and Alex Bennett for England Colts; Robert Gill, Ian Spence and Steve Rush for Yorkshire Colts; Mark Dodds for Yorkshire Schools and North; Nick Clark Yorkshire Schools; William Darby, Sam Gardner and Alan Moffatt for Yorkshire Under 17s.

Club Playing Record 1993-94

National League: Two
Final League Position at end of 1993/94 Season: 10th
League Playing record: P 18, W 4, D 1, L 13, Pts F 235, Pts A 449
Season Playing record (including league matches/Pilkington Cup): P 31, W 12, D 1, L 18, Pts F 612, Pts A 731

Otley's Pete Rutledge gets the ball away in the game at Cross Green

OTLEY RUFC

ACHIEVEMENTS/COMPETITIONS WON DURING 93/94 SEASON:

1st XV runners up Leeds & West Park Sevens. Semi finalists Yorkshire Cup
Colts Winners Sandal & Skipton Sevens. Semi finalists Yorkshire Cup
Under 17s Yorkshire U17s Cup Winners and Ilkley Tournament

PLAYING SQUAD 1993-94

Full Back: P Rutledge, I Colquhoun
Wing: G Melville, S Atikinson, G Balmer, M Waddington, M Hoskins, AD Scott
Centre: AD Scott, AN Scott, J Flint, S Atkinson, J Overend
Stand Off: R Petyt, J Flint
Scrum Half: M Farrar, M Waddington
Prop: S Rice, C Baldwin, G Demaine, J Chappell, N Marklew
Hooker: M Barnett, A Munro, M Peel, G Demaine
Lock: I Carroll, S Wilson, S Henry, G Scott
Blind Side: S Tipping, R Midgeley, I Spence, J Hall
Open Side: M Winterbottom, J Chapman, A Hargreaves, R Midgeley
No 8: A Hargreaves, J Chapman, R Midgeley, J Hall, S Henry

MOST CAPPED PLAYERS

(including British Lions Appearances)
N D Melville, 11, 1984-88
A H Bateson, 4, 1930
F W S Malir, 3, 1930
A Gray, 3, 1947
L Manfield, 2, 1948
G E Hughes, 1, 1896
W Mocelutu, 1, 1968

LEADING APPEARANCES FOR CLUB

A Hargreaves, 410, 1981/82-1993/94
M Barnett, 330, 1981/82-1993/94
N Marklew, 266, 1983/84 - 1993/94
D Lester, 231, 1981/82-1992/93
I Carroll, 229, 1982/83-1993/94
S Rice, 211, 1986/87-1993/94
G Melville, 208, 1983/84-1993/94

LEADING SCORERS (1993-94)

P Rutledge, Full Back, 244
S Atkinson, Wing, 60
R Petyt, Fly Half, 41
M Farrar, Scrum Half, 35

OTLEY RUFC

Club Details

Club Colours: Black & white hoops
Change of Colours: Red & white hoops
Date Founded: 1865
Membership: Total: 760, Playing members 120, Junior/Youth/Minis 200, Colts 25
No. of teams: Senior 5 + colts, Junior 10
Programme advertising rates: Full £200

Ground Details:

Ground Address: Cross Green, Otley, West Yorkshire, LS21 1HE.
Ground Tel No: 0943 461180
Simple Directions to Ground: Take Harrogate Road from Centre of Otley. Ground about 3/4 mile on left.
Spectator Capacity: Total: 7,000, Seated 850
Ticket Prices: Adults: £4, OAP/Child: £2
Training Nights: Tuesdays and Thursdays

Club Officials

Club President: G Hinchliffe
Club Chairman: M H E Dracup
Club Secretary: G Hinchliffe, 22 Cyprus Drive, Thackley, Bradford, West Yorkshire, BD10 0AJ. Tel: (H) 0274 615543 (W) 0274 724282
Fixtures Secretary: R Franks, 38 Ings Lane, Guiseley, Leeds, LS20 8DA. Tel: (H) 0943 877086
Press Officer: J C Finch, 9 Glen Mount, Henston, Ilkley, LS29 6DJ. Tel: (H) 0943 872491
Registration Officer: D W S Malir, 7 London Street, Little London, Rawdon, Leeds. Tel: (H) 532 391027 (W) 0274 575861
1994/ 95 1st XV Captain: Ian Carroll
1994/95 Director of Rugby: Nigel Melville

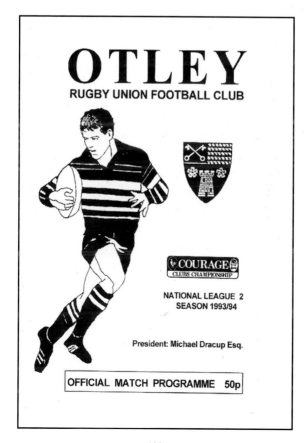

OTLEY
RUGBY UNION FOOTBALL CLUB

COURAGE
CLUBS CHAMPIONSHIP

NATIONAL LEAGUE 2
SEASON 1993/94

President: Michael Dracup Esq.

OFFICIAL MATCH PROGRAMME 50p

OTLEY RUFC

COURAGE LEAGUE RECORDS

HIGHEST SCORE : 61 v Askeans (61-O) 27-3-93 Home CL3
LARGEST WINNING MARGIN : 61 As above
HIGHEST SCORE AGAINST : 33 v Nuneaton (8-33) 7-3-93 Away CL3
LARGEST LOSING MARGIN : 25 As above
DRAWN MATCHES : 2
CLEAN SHEETS : 6
FAILED TO SCORE : O

INDIVIDUAL SCORING RECORDS
IN A MATCH

Most Points: 25 Jon Howarth v Lichfield 13-1O-9O Away D4N
Most Tries: 4 Glyn Melville v Wigton 12-3-88 Home ND1, John Walker v Harrogate 22-9-9O Away D4N, Mark Farrar v Askeans 27-3- 93 Home CL3
Most Conversions: 7 Ian Colquhuon v Birmingham 27-4-91 Home CL3
Most Penalties: 5 Jon Howarth v Lichfield 13-1O-9O Away D4N
Most Drop Goals: 1 David Lester v Middlesborough 28-4-9O Away N1, v Harrogate 22-9-9O Away D4N, v Walsall 1O-11-9O Home D4N, Richard Petyt v Clifton 23-11-91 Away CL3, v Redruth 29-2-92 Away CL3

IN A SEASON

Most Points: 121 Peter Rutledge 1992-93 CL3
Most Tries: 16 John Walker 199O-91 D4N
Most Conversions: 17 Jon Howarth 199O-91 D4N
Most Penalties: 26 Peter Rutledge 1992-93 CL3
Most Drop Goals: 2 David Lester 199O-91 D4N & Richard Petyt 1991- 92

IN A CAREER

Most Points: 146 Glyn Melville 1987-93
Most Tries: 35 Glyn Melville 1987-93
Most Conversions: 22 Robert Sharp 1987-92
Most Penalties: 26 Peter Rutledge 1992-93
Most Drop Goals: 3 David Lester 1987-93

SEASON BY SEASON LEADING SCORERS

	Most Points			**Most Tries**
1987-88	34	Ian Colquhuon	8	Glyn Merlville
1988-89	59	Robert Sharp	3	Robert Sharp
1989-9O	31	David Lester	3	John Walker
1990-91	73	David Lester	16	John Walker, Jon Howarth
1991-92	62	Richard Petyt	4	Mark Farrar
1992-93	121	Peter Rutledge	6	Glyn Melville

RICHMOND FC

"Rich" Can Do Better

The end of term report reads "Could have done better". Under new coach John Kingston, the club embarked on playing a style of rugby that the players were not used to and, although the team were riding high in the league up until Christmas, they fell away in the second half of the season, and particularly in the last six weeks. However, the talent is there, the ability to adapt to different tactics in a match is improving, and the demands to league rugby are being met by a predominantly young side. A number of last year's unbeaten Under 21 side made regular 1st team appearances, and it is hoped that the benefit of a year's experience of league rugby, allied to the more experienced squad members, should bear fruit in the coming eight months. The excuses of a young developing squad and inexperience should not apply this year with a squad that has been strengthened in the close season.

Club Playing Record 1993-94

National League: Three
Final League Position at end of 1993/94 Season: 7th
League Playing record: P 18, W 9, D 0, L 9, Pts F 337, Pts A 300
Season Playing record (including league matches/Pilkington Cup): P 32, W 15, D 0, L 17, Pts F 693, Pts A 582

RICHMOND FC

PLAYING SQUAD 1993-94

Full Back: J Clarke, R Banks, P Gregory
Wing: P Greenwood, N Dontoh, J Reynolds, S Brown, R Stubbs
Centre: M Hutton, D Elliott, C Goodburn, J Tiffin, J Makin
Fly Half: J Hoad, D Clift, M Livesey, J Barker
Scrum Half: C Hornung, E Rouse, C Kys
Prop: J Foster, D Sinclair, D Goodwin, M Yeldham
Hooker: A Cuthbert, D Jeffrey, S Miller
2nd Row: M Fitzgerald, R Sherry, P Carr, J Lewis, D Cooper, G Sage
Back Row: P Della-Savina, L Jones, A Fox, D Hawkes, G Taylor, J Bower
No 8: T Benson, D Thompson

MOST CAPPED PLAYERS	LEADING APPEARANCES FOR CLUB	LEADING SCORERS (1993-94)
(including British Lions Appearances)	Paul Greenwood, 31, 1993/94	Jason Hoad, Fly half/Full back, 184
A S Gould, 27	Mike Hutton, 31, 1993/94	Martin Livesey, Fly Half, 153
T P Reynolds, 25	Paul Carr, 30, 1993/94	Paul Greenwood, Wing, 65
P W Kininmouth, 21	Chris Hornung, 27, 1993/94	Mike Hutton, Centre, 35
C W Ralson, 21	Phil Della-Savina, 26, 1993/94	Phil Della-Savina, Wing Forward, 30
N M Hall, 17	Matt Yeldham, 25, 1993/94	Giles Goodburn, Centre/Wing, 30
E T Gurdon, 16		

Richmond scrum half Ed Rowe

RICHMOND FC

Club Details

Club Colours: Old gold, red & black
Change of Colours: Black with gold collar
Date Founded: 1861
Membership: Total: 1,200. Paying members 200, Junior/Youth/Minis 175, Other 100
No. of teams: Senior 5, Junior 12
Programme advertising rates: Full £500, Half £300
Any Special Occasions during 1994/95: Centenary of sharing ground with London Scottish FC

Ground Details:

Ground Address: The Athletic Ground, Kew Foot Road, Richmond, Surrey, TW9 2SS
Ground Tel No:081 940 0397 Fax 081 332 6775
Spectator Capacity: Total: 2,840, seated 840
Ticket Prices: Adults: £5, OAP/Child: £2.50
Training Nights: Mondays and Wednesdays

Club Officials

Club President: S J B James
Club Chairman: Captain A P Hallett
Club Secretary: J Wright, Richmond FC, The Athletic Ground, Kew Foot Road, Richmond, TW9 2SS. Tel:081 392 9671 (W) 071 225 1881 Fax: 081 332 6775
Fixtures Secretary: V Balchin, 11 Troutbeck Close, Twyford, Berks, RG10 9DA. Tel: (H) 0734 345765
Press Officer: V Codrington, The Athletic Ground, Kew Foot Road, Richmond, TW9 2SS. Tel: (H) 071 385 2371 (W) 081 332 7112 Fax: 081 332 6775
Registration Officer: A Reynolds, 23 Bridge Gardens, East Moseley, Surrey, KT8 9HU. Tel: (H) 081 224 1094 (W) 081 224 1124 Fax: 081 876 0824
1994/ 95 1st XV Captain: Chris Hornung
1994/95 Club Coach: John Kingston
Other Club Officers:
Vinny Codrington, Director of Rugby

RICHMOND FC

COURAGE LEAGUE RECORDS

Biggest Home Win: 86-8 v Headingley 28-4-90 CL2 **Defeat:** 15-40 v Londos Scottish 17-11-90 CL2
Biggest Away Win: 50-3 v Roundhay 11-4-92 **Defeat:** 9-50 v Sale 10-9-88 CL2
Most Tries For in a Match: 16 v Headingley 28-4-90 CL2
Most Tries Against in a Match: 8 v Sale 10-9-88 CL2
Most consecutive Wins: 7 **Defeats:** 4
No. of Matches failed to Score: 1 **Clean Sheets:** 1 **Drawn Matches:** 4
Most appearances Forward: **Back:**
Most consecutive appearances:
Consecutive Matches scoring Tries: 3 Jim Fallow, Rick Forde, Mike Hutton
Consecutive Matches scoring Points: 19 Martin LIvesey

INDIVIDUAL SCORING RECORDS

IN A MATCH

Most Points: 22 Martin Livesey v Blackheath 13-11-93 Home CL3
Most Tries: 3 Phil Della-Savina v Nuneaton 28-3-92 Home CL3
Most Conversions: 7 Martin Livesey v Sheffield 25-4-92 Home CL3
Most Penalties: 6 Nick Preston v Bedford 27-3-88 Home CL2,
Martin Livesey v London Irish 8-4-89 Home CL2, Jon Clark v Lydney 14-3- 92 Home CL3
Most Drop Goals: 3 Martin Livesey v Northampton 19-11-88 CL2

IN A SEASON

Most Points: 12O Martin Livesey 1989-9O CL2
Most Tries: 7 Jim Fallon 1989-9O CL2
Most Conversions: 24 Martin Livesey 1989-9O CL2
Most Penalties: 2O Martin Livesey 1989-9O CL2 & 1992-93 CL2, Jason Hoad 1993-94 CL3
Most Drop Goals: 6 Martin Livesey 1991-92 CL3

IN A CAREER

Most Points: 512 Martin Livesey 1988-94
Most Tries: 13 Mike Hutton 1988-94
Most Conversions: 74 Martin Livesey 1988-94
Most Penalties: 100 Martin Livesey 1988-94
Most Drop Goals: 14 Martin Livesey 1988-94

COURAGE LEAGUE RECORD

	DIV	PLD	W	D	L	F	T	C	P	D	A	T	C	P	D
1987-88	2	11	6	0	5	140	14	6	20	4	156	22	7	16	2
1988-89	2	11	4	1	6	112	8	4	21	3	216	24	18	25	3
1989-90	2	11	7	1	3	282	41	29	20	0	135	16	4	19	2
1990-91	2	12	3	1	8	134	17	9	14	2	245	25	14	31	8
1991-92	3	12	10	1	1	296	39	22	26	6	124	13	9	17	1
1992-93	2	12	5	0	7	204	19	4	25	2	196	15	8	33	2
1993-94	3	18	9	0	9	337	30	26	40	5	300	30	18	37	1
		87	44	4	39		168	110	166	22		145	78	178	19

SEASON BY SEASON LEADING SCORERS

	Most Points			Most Tries	
1987-88	6O	Simon Smith	5	Simon Pennock
1988-89	74	Martin Livesey	3	Paul Seccombe
1989-9O	12O	Martin Livesey	7	Jim Fallonon
199O-91	38	Martin Livesey	6	Mike Hutton
1991-92	95	Martin Livesey	6	Phil Della-Savina
1992-93	95	Martin Livesey	3	David Sole
1993-94	22	Martin Livesey	6	Paul Greenwood

ROSSLYN PARK FC

Park's Firm Basis For Recovery

At the start of the season hopes were high based on the youthful side that had developed over the past year. These hopes were dashed in the first home League game of the season against Bedford. Within the space of 30 minutes major injuries to Holder (damaged knee ligaments), Abrahams (fractured collar bone), and Essenheigh (broken forearm) spelt disaster not only for the match which Bedford eventually won 17-12, but for the next ten weeks of the season. Losing one senior player is bad enough, but three in one match was hard to say the least.

Putting this disaster behind them they had a resounding win away against Coventry, Shane Raiser scoring "the try of the season" with his 75 yard run which brought praise from Coventry's Peter Jackson.

In the Pilkington Cup Park had a good away win at Redruth, followed by home wins against Plymouth Albion and Coventry. However, in the fifth round, although with a home draw, Park eventually lost to the much stronger Saracens pack.

Clearly the experience gained over the season by the young players, the average age of the backs was under 21, has been of great value and coupled with the influx of some more experienced players should provide a firm basis for next season.

CLUB PLAYING RECORD 1993-94

National League: Three
Final League Position at end of 1993/94 Season: 5th
League Playing record: P 18, W 10, D 1, L 7, Pts F 372, Pts A 240
Season Playing record (including league matches/Pilkington Cup): P 35, W 23, D 1, L 11, Pts F 857, Pts A 511

ROSSLYN PARK FC

INDIVIDUAL PLAYER INFORMATION
Most Capped Players (including British Lions Appearances)
J Scott, 34
M Colclough, 25
A Ripley, 24
C Winn, 8
P Warfield, 8
C Kent, 5

LEADING APPEARANCES FOR CLUB
I Pickup, 30, 1993/94
I Campbell-Lamerton, 28, 1993/94
T Ashworth, 27, 1993/94
R Dewney, 27, 1993/94
S Roiser, 27, 1993/94
A Milward, 25, 1993/94

LEADING SCORERS (1993-94)
P Roblin, Fly Half, 121
G Abraham, Fly Half, 100
A Holder, Centre, 88
M Giffen, Winger, 63
S Roiser, Winger, 60

COURAGE RECORDS
No 8 Tony Brooks becomes the first Rosslyn Park player
to score a hat-trick of tries in a Courage League match,
v Havant at home on 12th March 1994.
Sean Rosier breaks Tony Brooks' record of 6 tries in a season.
While Tony Brooks extends his career tries total to 14.

ROSSLYN PARK FC

Club Details

Club Colours: Red & white hoops
Change of Colours: Dark blue
Date Founded: 1879
Membership: Total: 900, Playing members 200, Junior/Youth/Minis 150
No. of teams: Senior 4, Junior 5
Programme advertising rates: Full £280

Ground Details:

Ground Address: Priory Lane, Roehampton, London SW15 5JH
Ground Tel No:081 876 1879 Fax: 081 878 7527
Simple Directions to Ground: Ground situated at the Junction of the Upper Richmond Road (South Circular) and Roehampton Lane SW15.
Spectator Capacity: Total: 4,630, Seated 630
Ticket Prices: Adults: £5, OAP/Child: £2.50
Training Nights: Tuesdays and Thursdays

Club Officials

Club President: Dick Malthouse
Club Chairman: Roy Reynolds
Club Secretary: David J Whittam FRCS, 37 Queen's Road, Kingston upon Thames, Surrey, KT2 7SL. Tel: (H) 081 549 4209 (W) 081 725 2052 Fax: 081 944 8059
Fixtures Secretary: Don Bell, 148 Trentham Street, London SW18 5DJ. Tel: (H) 081 870 5285 Fax: 081 878 7527
Press Officer: Bernard Wiggins, 2 Beardsfolly Cottages, New Way Lane, Hurstpierpoint, West Sussex, BN6 9BD. Tel: (H) 0273 844028 (W) 0273 323434 Fax: 0273 202627
Registration Officer: Peter Berryman, 52, Crescent Road, Kingston upon Thames, Surrey, KT2 7RF. Tel: (H) 081 546 1228 (W) 081 949 6171 Fax: 081 949 5604
1994/ 95 1st XV Captain: David Barnett
1994/95 Club Coach: Simon Henderson
Director of Rugby: Peter Berryman

Alex Milward winning the ball against "Cov" Courage League match

207

ROSSLYN PARK FC

COURAGE LEAGUE RECORDS

Biggest Home Win: 48-0 v Northampton 27-4-91 CL1 **Defeat:** 8-26 v Gloucester 12-11-88 CL1
Biggest Away Win: 39-9 v Redruth 26-3-94 CL3 **Defeat:** 14-64 v Orrell 28-4-90 CL1
Most Tries For in a Match: 9 v Northampton
Most Tries Against in a Match: 11 v Orrell 28-4-90 CL1
Most consecutive Wins: 5 **Defeats:** 8
No. of Matches failed to Score: 0 **Clean Sheets:** 2 **Drawn Matches:** 4
Most appearances Forward: 66 Paul Essenhich **Back:** 61 John Graves
Most consecutive appearances: 45 John Graves 19-9-87 to 27-4-91
Consecutive Matches scoring Tries: 3 Sean Rosier
Consecutive Matches scoring Points: 25 John Graves

INDIVIDUAL SCORING RECORDS

IN A MATCH

Most Points: 22 John Graves v Coventry 13-2-93 Home CL2
Most Tries: 3 Tony Brooks v Havant 12-3-94 Home CL3
Most Conversions: 4 John Graves v Bedford 31-3-90 Home CL1, v Liverpool SH 23-3-91 Home CL2, Gary Abraham v Havant 12-3-94 Home CL3
Most Penalties: 6 Gary Abraham v Morley 27-3-93 Home CL2
Most Drop Goals: 2 Paul Roblin v Goucester 4-1-92 CL1

IN A SEASON

Most Points: 92 John Graves 1990-91 CL1
Most Tries: 7 Sean Rosier 1993-94 CL3
Most Conversions: 13 John Graves 1993-94 CL3
Most Penalties: 21 John Graves 1989-90 CL1
Most Drop Goals: 2 Paul Roblin 1991-92 CL1

IN A CAREER

Most Points: 455 John Graves 1987-94
Most Tries: 14 Tony Brooks 1987-94
Most Conversions: 44 John Graves 1987-94
Most Penalties: 114 John Graves 1987-94
Most Drop Goals: 4 Mark Jermyn 1987-93

COURAGE LEAGUE RECORD

SEASON BY SEASON LEADING SCORERS

		Most Points		Most Tries
1987-88	73	John Graves	6	Tony Brooks
1988-89	89	John Graves	3	Simon Hunter, Richard Crawford, Rob Nelson-Williams
1989-90	87	John Graves	4	Mark Jermyn
1990-91	92	John Graves	3	Peter Taylor, Guy Leleu, Kelvin Wyles
1991-92	53	John Graves	2	Mark Thomas
1992-93	61	John Graves, Gary Abraham	3	Paul Essenhigh
1993-94	59	Paul Roblin	7	Sean Rosier

RUGBY FC

Lions Determined to Halt Slide

The 1993/94 season was again extremely disappointing as the Lions were again relegated, this time into Division 3. Too many times the Lions did not turn obvious territorial advantage into points and were narrowly beaten by the final whistle.

The Lions' usual excellent away form deserted them completely in the season, not recording a single victory in the league programme. Of 12 league defeats the Lions were to lose by five or less points on six occasions. Such is the fickle game of rugby football.

An early exit from the Pilkington Cup, losing 17-13 to Sale, added to the disappointment of this season.

However, the players responded to these adversities, and their efforts against Moseley in the last league match where a win would have avoided relegation were nothing short of Herculean.

The Lions now believe that last season will prove to be a watershed for the club. Plans are already well established for an immediate return to Division 2, spurred and fuelled with real determination to return to top flight rugby in the shortest possible time.

CLUB PLAYING RECORD 1993-94

National League: Two
Final League Position at end of 1993/94 Season: 9th
League Playing record: P 18, W 5, D L 12, Pts F 186, Pts A 302
Season Playing record (including league matches/Pilkington Cup): P 36, W 16, D 1, L 19, Pts F 712, Pts A 574

RUGBY FC

ACHIEVEMENTS/COMPETITIONS WON DURING 93/94 SEASON:
Ralli Cup Winners
County Semi Finalists - Colts

PLAYING SQUAD 1993-94
Full Back: Mark Mapletoft, Paul Mason
Wing: Kevin Mills, Dean Watson, Spencer Bromley, Eddie Saunders, Sam Rush
Centre: Jim Quantrill, Richard Tomlinson, Luke Turnell, Stuart Glover, John Cockerill, John Coombe-Lilley
Fly Half: Richard Pell, John MacLeod
Scrum Half: David Bishop, Mark Broomhall, Richard Cox, Peter Dewey, Nick Morris
Prop: Trevor Revan, Neil Riley, Richard Mee, Steve Hotton, Gavin Wright
Hooker: Rob Burdett, Rob Milner, David Fry
Lock: Steve Smith, Phil Bowman, Neil Underhill, Ian Russell, Andy Scott, Phil Laing
Flanker: Dave Oram, John Jenkins, Chris Gubbins, Mark J Ellis, John Gardner
No 8: Mark Rennell, Jim Darragh

MOST CAPPED PLAYERS
(including British Lions Appearances)
S E Brain, 13, 1984-86
G S Conway, 11, 1922-24
S J Purdy, 1, 1962
L J Percival, 1, 1893

LEADING APPEARANCES FOR CLUB
Trevor Revan, 31, 1993/94
Mark Rennell, 30, 1993/94
Mark Mapletoft, 29, 1993/94
Jim Quantrill, 28, 1993/94
Steve Smith, 28, 1993/94
David Bishop, 25, 1993/94

LEADING SCORERS (1993-94)
Mark Mapletoft, Full Back, 249
Paul Mason, Fly Half/Full Back, 51
David Bishop, Scrum Half, 35
Kevin Mills, Wing, 35
Eddie Saunders, Wing, 35
Richard Pell, Fly Half, 31

COURAGE RECORDS
Eddie Saunders extends his record of most Courage League tries for Rugby in a a career from 31 to 33 in 70 appearances.
Mark Mapletoft ends his Rugby playing days with 201 Courage League points second only to Chris Howard.

	PLD	T	C	P	D	APPS	AVE
C Howard	31	10	52	52	1	306	9.87
M Mapletoft	41	6	14	45	3	201	4.90

RUGBY FC

Club Details

Club Colours: Orange, black & white shirts, black shorts
Change of Colours: White shirts, navy shorts
Date Founded: 1873
Membership: Total: 480, Playing members 78, Junior/Youth/Minis 140
No. of teams: Senior 3, Junior 2

Ground Details:

Ground Address: 9 Webb Ellis Road, Rugby, CV22 7AN
Ground Tel No: 0788 542254
Simple Directions to Ground: Second turning right, half mile South West of Town Centre on A4071, Bilton Road. Access to A4071 (using motorway): From NW - M6 Exit 1/A426. From NE - M1 Exit 20/A426. From SW - M5 Exit 4A/M42 Exit 6/A45. From SE - M1 Exit 17/M45.
Spectator Capacity: Total: 4,200, Seated 200, Standing 4,000
Ticket Prices: Adults: Club Games £4, League & Cup £4.50, OAP/Child £2, Programme £1, Parking £1
Training Nights: Tuesdays and Thursdays

Club Officials

Club President: J W Llenwellyn
Club Chairman: D Rees
Club Secretary: Ivan Cawood, Stanford House, Stanford-on-Avon, Northants, NN6 7JR. Tel: (H) 0788 860409 (W) 0788 373444 Fax: 0788 537149
Fixtures Secretary: Richard Stocking, 5 Cunningham Way, Rugby, CV22 7JD. Tel: (H) 0788 816598 Fax: 0788 568711
Press Officer: Roger Large, 58 Bawnmore Road, Rugby, CV22 7QW. Tel: (H) 0788 816363 (W) 0788 544508 Fax: 0788 568711
Registration Officer: Neal Mapletoft, 14 Oberon Close, Rugby, CV22 6LZ. Tel: (H) 0788 810763 (W) 0788 522022 Fax: 1788 522260
1994/ 95 1st XV Captain: TBA
1994/95 Club Coach: TBA
Other Club Officers:
Mrs Terri Short, Commercial Manager
Roger Large, Playing Committee Chairman
Neal Mapletoft, Playing Administrator

Trevor Revan with ball — Rigby v Wakefield

RUGBY FC

COURAGE LEAGUE RECORDS

Biggest Home Win: 49-9 v Gosforth 11-11-89 CL2 **Defeat:** 20-45 v London Scottish 31-10-92 CL1
Biggest Away Win: 36-6 v Mat Police 19-11-88 CL3 **Defeat:** 0-66 v Orrell 13-3-93 CL1
Most Tries For in a Match: 8 v Askeans 8-10-88 CL3
Most Tries Against in a Match: 11 v Orrell 13-3-93 CL1
Most consecutive Wins: 8 **Defeats:** 9
No. of Matches failed to Score: 4 **Clean Sheets:** 2 **Drawn Matches:** 4
Most appearances Forward: 64 Trevor Revan, Phil Bowman **Back:** 73 David Bishop
Most consecutive appearances: 33 Mark Fleetwood
Consecutive Matches scoring Tries: 5 Eddie Saunders
Consecutive Matches scoring Points: 19 Chris Howard

INDIVIDUAL SCORING RECORDS

IN A MATCH

Most Points: 25 Chris Howard v Gosforth 11-11-89 Home CL2
Most Tries: 3 Chris Howard v Vale of lune 1O-9-88 Home CL3
Most Conversions: 6 Chris Howard v Gosforth 11-11-89 Home CL2
Most Penalties: 6 Chris Howard v Nneaton 22-1O-88 Away CL3, Russell Hensley v Leicester 25-4-92 Away CL1
Most Drop Goals: 1 On 22 occasions R Pell 13, S Vaudin 3, C Howard 1, M Maplestoft 2, J McLeod 2

IN A SEASON

Most Points: 123 Chris Howard 1988-89 CL3
Most Tries: 9 David Bishop 1990-91 CL2
Most Conversions: 19 Chris Howard 1988-89 CL3
Most Penalties: 22 Mark Maplestoft 1993-94 CL2
Most Drop Goals: 4 Richard Pell 1987-88

IN A CAREER

Most Points: 306 Chris Howard 1987-91
Most Tries: 33 Eddie Saunders 1987-94
Most Conversions: 52 Chris Howard 1987-91
Most Penalties: 52 Chris Howard 1987-91
Most Drop Goals: 13 Richard Pell 1987-94

COURAGE LEAGUE RECORD

	DIV	PLD	W	D	L	F	T	C	P	D	A	T	C	P	D
1987-88	4N	10	9	0	1	184	25	15	17	1	100	9	2	18	2
1988-89	3	11	10	0	1	268	41	19	19	3	99	8	5	19	0
1989-90	2	11	5	0	6	238	34	21	18	2	172	24	11	17	1
1990-91	2	12	10	0	2	252	39	18	16	6	146	20	9	13	3
1991-92	1	12	2	3	7	124	11	4	23	1	252	36	15	26	0
1992-93	1	12	1	0	11	104	10	6	11	3	368	50	26	19	3
1993-94	2	18	5	1	12	186	15	9	25	6	302	29	17	39	2
		86	42	4	40	1356	175	92	127	22	1439	176	85	151	11

SEASON BY SEASON LEADING SCORERS

Season	Most Points		Most Tries	
1987-88	69	Chris Howard	7	Eddie Saunders
1988-89	123	Chris Howard	3	Chris Howard
1989-90	1OO	Chris Howard	7	Eddie Saunders
1990-91	68	Stuart Vaudin	9	David Bishop
1991-92	60	Mark Mapletoft	2	Eddie Saunders, David Bishop
1992-93	26	Mark Mapletoft	3	Eddie Saunders
1993-94	115	Mark Mapletoft	5	Mark Mapletoft

NATIONAL LEAGUE FOUR

RESULTS AND LEAGUE TABLES
1987-1993
LEAGUE 4 NORTH — Pages 214-216
LEAGUE 4 SOUTH — Pages 217-219

RESULTS AND LEAGUE TABLES
1994
Page 220

MEMBER CLUBS
1994-95

NATIONAL LEAGUE FOUR NORTH RESULTS

1987-88

		1	2	3	4	5	6	7	8	9	10	11
1	Birkenhead Park		7-6		9-26		10-21		16-28		28-3	
2	Broughton Park			19-6		34-9		24-12		16-20		20- 6
3	Derby	11-16			33-13		9-14		6-12		34-8	
4	Durham City		4-0			23-18		12-10		9-12		30-12
5	Lichfield	27-0		11-7			27-9		10-27		13-13	
6	Northern		15-13		3-12			6-22		17-27		14-14
7	Preston Grasshoppers	24-17		22-10		19-15			6-5		31-9	
8	Roundhay		20-6		6-12		0-0			4-8		16-3
9	Rugby	20-0		28-16		24-12		21-3				
10	Solihull		7-14		0-24		7-16		0-12			9-21
11	Stourbridge	13-14		21-4		9-6		86-15		11-0		

1988-89

		1	2	3	4	5	6	7	8	9	10	11
1	Birmingham				12-33	0-29		7-20		0-10	0-31	
2	Broughton Park			45-9			14-9		10-0			23-9
3	Durham City	34-0				9-16	20-13		16-24			22-10
4	Lichfield		12-3	15-9				6-15		17-6	6-10	
5	Morley		10-34		13-3			12-10		15-13	6-15	
6	Northern	52-7			19-10	21-9		6-10				16-9
7	Preston Grasshoppers		13-30	31-12			15-25			25-7	11-4	
8	Rounday	79-0			10-10	13-9		22-9				48-12
9	Stoke		12-17	3-9			9-6		9-19		13-3	
10	Stourbridge		18-3	0-12			28-15		0-10			9-3
11	Winnington Park	63-3			16-0	23-16		16-12		27-6		

1989-90

		1	2	3	4	5	6	7	8	9	10	11
1	Broughton Park				16-10	13-17		9-7	67-3			
2	Durham City	24-22			13-3			22-13		21-22		
3	Kendall	6-33	22-21				18-6				18-13	18-10
4	Lichfield			0-10		12-7	9-3					15-9
5	Morley		12-6	19-13			16-12					25-19
6	Northern	17-4	18-21						22-16	9-15		
7	Preston Grasshoppers			16-3	10-7	3-10					9-12	12-9
8	Stoke			7-15	6-12	0-25		6-15				18-25
9	Stourbridge			10-6	22-15	13-15		17-7	20-6			
10	Walsall	9-20	14-20				9-18		10-3	12-15		
11	Winnington Park	9-15	19-6				15-19			13-4	27-20	

1990-91

	1	2	3	4	5	6	7	8	9	10	11	12	13
1 Birmingham		3-16		9-9	6-42		15-9				13-17	15- 22	
2 Durham			23-2	6-3	15-15		6-12				3-16	10-11	
3 Harrogate	30-12					14-14		21-50	25-15	48-12	6- 16		
4 Hereford			29-6		10-34	3-12			13-9	21-9	15-24		
5 Kendal			7-13			6-13		3-16	12-6	19-0	7-4		
6 Lichfield	18-13	25-8						7-37	11-16	27-17	24-7		
7 Northern			4-18	18-3	16-16	6-9						17-10	18-12
8 Otley	51-15	29-3		50-0			43-6					36-0	36- 0
9 Preston Grasshoppers	21-12	13-0					14-19	16-4		36-3	23-0		
10 Stoke	12-3	25-3					13-13	11-40			6-10	9-23	
11 Stourbridge	18-0	12-16					10-10	7-32				20-13	6-9
12 Walsall			0-12	22-7	12-13	12-13			9-20				15-13
13 Winnington			22-6	9-9	21-17	13-4			0-3	35-9			

1991-92

	1	2	3	4	5	6	7	8	9	10	11	12	13
1 Aspatria			21-12			2-15		16-0	3-0	23-0	24-9		
2 Durham City	15-26					13-9		24-15	3-22	12-18	9-21		
3 Harrogate		9-6		12-19	13-22	18-0						26-14	13-7
4 Hereford	21-18	31-0				33-4				33-10		9-6	4-3
5 Kendal	3-13	18-6		9-9		14-4					10-4		18-10
6 Litchfield			25-24	13-23	6-38		9-16					21- 14	19-12
7 Northern	13-41	10-11						10-24	6-26	13-6	7-9		
8 Preston G'hoppers			16-13	42-14	13-14	0-10						13-6	28-3
9 Stourbridge			32-8	10-12	21-3	9-17		3-24		10-23			
10 Towcestrians			3-7	6-15	18-6	0-21		4-9					22-10
11 Vale of Lune			10-15		6-12	9-9		6-11	8-15	15- 13			
12 Walsall	9-26	6-16					19-15		10-14	12-10	18-6		
13 Winnington Park	3-13	29-18					22-7		20-0		19-10	21-21	

1992-93

	1	2	3	4	5	6	7	8	9	10	11	12	13
1 Durham		7-33	31-10	19-6				10-28				6-7	35- 17
2 Harrrogate					54-6	25-16	36-3		19-13	20-5	71-7		
3 Hereford			12-29	11-7	14-15		0-8			19-19	38-10		
4 Kendal			6-34		6-20		19-12		36-17	6-9	25-13		
5 Lichfield	54-11					42-6	15-12		12-16	14-12	13- 13		
6 Nuneaton	18-17		22-13	13-36				10-28				16- 9	5-36
7 Preston Grasshoppers	8-10					13-3		10-6	9-7	17- 16	28-7		
8 Rotherham			6-6	20-7	30-16	34-12						36-11	16-5
9 Stoke	20-11		14-5			15-14	13-15					32-6	20-9
10 Stourbridge	10-12					17-16		12-14	14-6			27-0	9-11
11 Towcestrians	27-17					11-6		11-26	19-32	9-12		10-12	
12 Walsall		14-21	29-6	3-10	2-10		12-14						26-8
13 Winnington Park		20-15	12-12	8-9		17-8	9-10			15-0			

NATIONAL LEAGUE 4 NORTH TABLES

1987-88

	P	W	D	L	F	A	Pts
Rugby	10	9	0	1	184	100	18
Durham	10	8	0	2	165	100	16
Roundhay	10	6	2	2	131	67	14
Preston G'hprs	10	5	1	4	178	149	11
Northern	10	5	1	4	121	137	11
Broughton Park	10	5	0	5	152	106	10
Stourbridge	10	5	0	9	132	134	10
Lichfield	10	4	0	6	150	165	8
Birkenhead Park	10	4	0	6	117	179	8
Derby	10	2	0	8	136	197	4
Solihull	10	0	0	10	59	219	0

1990-91

	P	W	D	L	F	A	Pts
Otley	12	11	0	1	424	89	22
Lichfield	12	8	1	3	177	152	17
Preston G'hprs	12	8	0	4	192	109	16
Winnington Park	12	7	1	4	167	148	15
Kendal	12	6	2	4	191	132	14
Harrogate	12	6	1	5	220	204	13
Northern	12	5	3	4	148	169	13
Stourbridge	12	5	1	6	134	161	11
Walsall	12	5	0	7	149	176	10
Durham City	12	4	1	7	109	185	9
Hereford	12	3	2	7	122	208	8
Stoke	12	2	1	9	126	278	5
Birm. Solihull	12	1	1	10	116	265	3

1988-89

	P	W	D	L	F	A	Pts
Roundhay	10	8	1	1	235	81	17
Broughton Park	10	8	0	2	179	92	16
Stourbridge	10	6	0	4	118	79	12
Northern	10	5	0	5	188	155	10
Winnington Park	10	5	0	5	188	155	10
Preston G'hprs	10	5	0	5	161	141	10
Durham City	10	5	0	5	172	157	10
Morley	10	5	0	5	135	141	10
Lichfield	10	4	1	5	112	113	9
Stoke on Trent	10	3	0	7	88	138	9
Birmingham	10	0	0	10	29	171	0

1991-92

	P	W	D	L	F	A	PD	Pts
Aspatria	12	11	0	1	253	100	153	22
Hereford	12	10	1	1	223	133	90	21
Kendal	12	8	1	3	157	123	34	17
Preston G'Hprs	12	8	0	4	195	123	72	16
Lichfield	12	6	1	5	174	177	-3	13
Stourbridge	12	6	0	6	163	137	26	12
Harrogate	12	6	0	6	170	175	-5	12
Winnington Park	12	4	1	7	159	173	-14	9
Towcestrians	12	4	0	8	123	153	-30	8
Durham City	12	4	0	8	133	215	-82	8
Walsall	12	3	1	8	139	187	-48	7
Vale of Lune	12	3	1	8	119	185	-66	7
Northern	12	2	0	10	105	232	-127	4

1989-90

	P	W	D	L	F	A	Pts
Broughton Park	10	8	0	2	246	111	16
Morley	10	8	0	2	169	115	16
Stourbridge	10	7	0	3	146	133	14
Durham City	10	6	0	4	195	169	12
Kendal	10	6	0	4	130	136	12
Preston G'hprs	10	5	0	5	122	109	10
Lichfield	10	5	0	5	110	121	10
Northern	10	4	0	6	139	144	8
Winnington Park	10	4	0	6	142	152	8
Walsall	10	2	0	8	143	183	4
Stoke	10	0	0	10	88	257	0

1992-93

	P	W	D	L	F	A	PD	Pts
Harrogate	12	10	1	1	363	115	248	21
Rotherham	12	10	1	1	259	123	136	21
Preston G'hprs	12	8	0	4	144	140	4	16
Stoke on Trent	12	7	0	5	193	168	25	14
Lichfield	12	6	1	5	221	224	-3	13
Kendal	12	6	0	6	182	189	-7	12
Walsall	12	6	0	6	165	179	-14	12
Durham City	12	6	0	6	179	219	-40	12
Stourbridge	12	5	1	6	161	144	17	11
Winnington Park	12	5	1	6	167	165	2	11
Hereford	12	2	2	8	147	216	-69	6
Nuneaton	12	2	0	10	138	269	-131	4
Towcestrians	12	1	1	10	118	286	-168	3

NATIONAL LEAGUE 4 SOUTH TABLES

1987-88

	P	W	D	L	F	A	Pts
Askeans	10	8	1	1	141	83	17
Sidcup	10	7	2	1	130	72	16
Lydney	10	7	0	3	173	99	14
Camborne	10	5	2	3	113	119	12
Havant	10	5	0	5	116	102	10
Stroud	10	5	0	5	112	114	10
Southend	10	5	0	5	63	108	10
Sudbury	10	3	2	5	125	106	8
Salisbury	10	3	1	6	84	94	7
Cheltenham	10	3	0	7	95	152	6
Streatham/Croydon	10	0	0	10	70	173	0

1990-91

	P	W	D	L	F	A	Pts
Redruth	12	12	0	0	225	79	24
Basingstoke	12	9	0	3	187	104	18
Lon. Welsh	12	7	0	5	235	165	14
Camborne	12	6	0	6	204	179	12
Weston S-Mare	12	6	0	6	192	182	12
North Walsham	12	5	2	5	170	180	12
Sudbury	12	6	0	6	160	172	12
Havant	12	5	0	7	157	173	10
Southend	12	5	0	7	152	194	10
Ealing	12	5	0	7	174	218	10
Maidstone	12	4	1	7	122	164	9
Maidenhead	12	4	1	7	130	208	9
Cheltenham	12	2	0	10	150	240	4

1988-89

	P	W	D	L	F	A	Pts
Lydney	10	8	1	1	240	98	17
Havant	10	8	1	1	177	92	17
Camborn	10	6	1	3	198	126	13
Redruth	10	6	1	3	136	81	13
Sudbury	10	5	1	4	141	89	11
Cheltenham	10	4	2	4	122	151	10
Salisbury	10	4	1	5	113	139	9
Southend	10	4	0	6	116	168	8
Ealing	10	3	0	7	144	188	6
Stroud	10	3	0	7	119	180	6
Sidcup	10	0	0	10	74	168	0

1991-92

	P	W	D	L	F	A	PD	Pts
Havant	12	11	0	1	301	91	210	22
Basingstoke	12	11	0	1	218	88	130	22
Lon. Welsh	12	9	0	3	292	160	132	18
Sudbury	12	8	0	4	235	150	85	16
High Wycombe	12	8	0	4	196	139	57	16
Camborne	12	7	0	5	166	195	-29	14
North Walsham	12	5	0	7	153	152	1	10
Maidstone	12	5	0	7	147	180	-33	10
Weston S-Mare	12	4	0	8	175	215	-40	8
Met. Police	12	3	0	9	149	195	-46	6
Southend	12	3	0	9	134	240	-106	6
Sidcup	12	3	0	9	103	290	-187	6
Ealing	12	0	1	11	112	286	-174	2

1989-90

	P	W	D	L	F	A	Pts
Met. Police	10	9	0	1	255	74	18
Clifton	10	8	1	1	240	122	17
Redruth	10	7	0	3	151	84	14
Camborne	10	6	1	3	164	113	13
Havant	10	5	1	4	132	126	11
Sudbury	10	5	0	5	162	138	10
Southend	10	4	2	4	124	125	10
Basingstoke	10	3	1	6	138	144	7
Cheltenham	10	2	0	8	107	201	4
Maidstone	10	2	0	8	64	237	4
Salisbury	10	1	0	9	74	247	2

1992-93

	P	W	D	L	F	A	PD	Pts
Sudbury	12	11	1	0	337	130	207	23
London Welsh	10	10	0	2	353	170	183	20
Lydney	12	8	0	4	187	170	17	16
Cambourne	12	7	1	4	180	168	12	15
Basingstoke	12	7	0	5	192	145	47	14
Southend	12	6	1	5	196	189	7	13
Berry Hill	12	4	3	5	187	216	-29	11
High Wycombe	12	5	0	7	196	160	36	10
Met Police	12	4	1	7	201	207	-6	9
Weston-S-Mare	12	4	1	7	154	226	-72	9
North Walsham	12	4	0	8	125	209	-84	8
Maidstone	12	2	0	10	122	306	-184	4
Thurrock	12	2	0	10	147	295	-148	2

NATIONAL LEAGUE FOUR SOUTH RESULTS

1987-88

	1	2	3	4	5	6	7	8	9	10	11
1 Askeans		14-0		14-3		17-12		13-4		23-9	
2 Camborne			17-6		23-13		9-7		10-8		10-10
3 Cheltenham	3-20			11-15		16-12		15-0		4-16	
4 Havant		6-7			19-11		6-10		25-15		14-10
5 Lydney	25-3		26-12			10-0		21-0		24-3	
6 Salisbury		6-6		3-17			9-15		28-4		10-0
7 Sidcup	3-3		17-9		6-9			20-3		12-8	
8 Southend		6-18		12-4		9-4			3-0		10-3
9 Streatham Croydon	9-18		6-19		10-20		6-16			9-13	
10 Stroud		31-9		9-7		19-10		10-16			11-10
11 Sudbury	15-16		23-6		23-14		12-12		19-3		

1988-89

	1	2	3	4	5	6	7	8	9	10	11
1 Camborne			45-12	21-18			18-0		6-19	33-13	
2 Cheltenham	10-34				3-35	16-6		20-4			15-15
3 Ealing		12-6			17-21	3-15		53-12			13-10
4 HAvant		23-4	29-4				6-3		15-6	29-7	
5 Lydney	27-12			16-16		14-9		47-0			17-7
6 Redruth	9-9			15-6			11-0		14-4		15-0
7 Salisbury		9-9	13-10		9-32				22-15	13-6	
8 Sidcup	9-20			16-19		4-26	9-37				4-11
9 Southend		13-19	18-17		16-15			15-10		3-25	
10 Stroud		0-20	18-3		9-16	15-16		20-6			
11 Sudbury	9-0			0-6			23-7		25-6	41-6	

1989-90

	1	2	3	4	5	6	7	8	9	10	11
1 Basingstoke		12-12			3-13		6-12		28-7	34-10	
2 Camborne			24-21	13-11		29-3		10-16			
3 Cheltenham	24-13				12-17				10-15	0-10	
4 Clipton	24-3		19-10				33-24		44-7		
5 Havant		3-13		18-26		22-6					21-7
6 Maidstone	6-20		22-7	6-22			3-36			6-24	
7 Metropolitan Police		20-11			25-0				46-0	15-9	14-9
8 Redruth	14-9		14-10	3-12		35-0	3-6				
9 Salisbury		8-26			9-16			6-39			6-17
10 Southend		13-7			13-13			0-3	12-10		12-16
11 Sudbury	22-10		10-13	17-28		36-3		22-12			

1990-91

	1	2	3	4	5	6	7	8	9	10	11	12	13
1 Basingstoke			10-0	32-10				15-6		0-4		10- 12	27-19
2 Camborne	12-5				17-12	18-25	30-12		26-6		19-6		
3 Cheltenham		25-18		12-25				6-15		3-7		25-10	18-35
4 Ealing	12-6		29-9		9-17	22-6		13-14			12-16		
5 London Welsh	12-13		31-7	18-26			6-16		32-10		26-12		
6 Maidenhead		6-20			22-6	6-28				9-18		9-8	10-9
7 North Walsham	8-12		23-17	39-11				16-16		6-16		13-7	
8 Redruth		24-6			26-7	18-16					20-6	25-0	23-4
9 Southend	3-27		19-12	0-7			27-12	16-12	9-17				
10 Sudburm		11-6			20-9	12-17	16-19				24-20		22-9
11 Weston-S-Mare		24-10			7-12	18-7	21-8		21-18		6- 18		

1991-92

	1	2	3	4	5	6	7	8	9	10	11	12	13
1 Basingstoke		22-13		16-7		9-7			18-6	38-6	11-3		
2 Camborne			18-15		10-8		19-9	21-14				3-17	14-11
3 Ealing	8-28				12-8	12-15			10-28	10-13	10-12		
4 Havant		34-9	42-3				42-12	19-6				16-9	25-10
5 High Wycombe	13-7			7-10		23-14			25-12	33-9	25-22		
6 London Welsh		35-15		6-9			18-15	29-18				34-12	36-19
7 Maidstone	0-7		21-18		9-12				12-10	20-10	31- 17		
8 Met. Police	0-15		40-7		3-14		7-3		3-13	10-15			
9 North Walsham		6-17		7-9		3-21				30-3	6-0		23-9
10 Sidcup		9-17		3-32		6-49			10-3		4-27	15-21	
11 Southend			12-10	3-56	13-26		19-15					7- 21	15-20
12 Sudbury	6-22		25-0		25-12	13-15	30-13	25-9					
13 Weston-S-Mare	19-25		28-7		6-16		7-0	10-17			15-22		

1992-93

	1	2	3	4	5	6	7	8	9	10	11	12	13
1 Basingstoke		25-16		12-5			19-8	10-6			9-16		37-6
2 Berry Hill			16-16			14-22	18-6	18-7			9-9		18-18
3 Camborne	12-8				6-32	13-8			17-12	11-5	34- 11		
4 High Wycombe		7-10	8-10				22-5	29-17			20-22		27-5
5 London Welsh	36-16	44-3		13-8					42-12	46-21	45-14		
6 Lydney	20-18			19-18	6-5				11-3	20-26	15-14		
7 Maidstone			11-10		23-35	8-28		5-38	,5-36		16-13		
8 Metropolitan Police			19-3		27-32		7-13		16- 16	10-49			14-16
9 North Walsham	3-16	8-29		10-8			14-11	10-13			8-20		
10 Southend	11-6	31-25		12-6			37-10		15-16		11-6		
11 Sudbury			22-10		18-6	20-17				24-11		58- 11	41-14
12 Thurock	6-16	23-6		25-28			34-14	6-27	11-18				
13 Weston-S-Mare			16-38		10-17	24-8			6-10	3-0	23-0		

NATIONAL LEAGUE FOUR STATISTICS 1993/94

RESULTS

		1	2	3	4	5	6	7	8	9	10
1	Askeans		26-12	11-19	3-40	12-16	11-3	5-20	28-16	9-6	28-15
2	Aspatria	23-20		16-18	12-21	9-20	11-8	16-10	46-21	19- 9	28-0
3	Broughton Park	27-16	8-3		12-15	0-31	27-7	5-31	9-15	17-16	16-26
4	Clifton ▲	37-13	33-11	18-8		6-6	33-6	35-21	47-10	33-11	41-10
5	Harrogate	22-7	78-29	33-6	15-15		28-10	21-7	53-22	12- 6	20-6
6	Leeds	9-19	35-15		13-22	29-20		17-9	3-1	24-3	14-3
7	L'pool St Helens	30-23	19-12	33-21	16-20	24-10	33-10		38-8	18-8	27-12
8	Plymouth Albion	13-10	9-13	39-13	13-17	15-29	30-17	13- 12		11-9	28-21
9	Sheffield	32-9	20-22	16-11	9-18	9-28	27-10		45-3		17-19
10	Sudbury	18-18	18-6	20-18	16-26	7-27	8-14	16-20	6-13	19-22	

WEEK BY WEEK POSITIONS

	13/11	20/11	4/12	11/12	8/1	22/1	29/1	12/2	26/2	12/3	26/3	9/4	23/4	30/4
Askeans	5	7	4	6	5	7	8	9	9	9	8	7	7	7
Aspatria	10	10	10	10	8	6	6	8	5	5	4	5	5	5
Broughton	7	8	8	8	9	9	7	5	7	7	7	8	9	8
Clifton	1	1	1	1	1	1	1	1	1	1	1	1	1	1
Harrogate	3	2	2	2	2	2	2	2	2	2	2	2	2	2
Leeds	6	4	5	7	7	8	9	7	6	6	6	6	6	6
L'pool St Helens	2	3	3	3	3	3	3	3	3	3	3	3	3	3
Plymouth	8	5	6	4	4	4	4	4	4	4	5	4	4	4
Sheffield	4	6	7	5	6	5	5	6	8	8	9	9	8	9
Sudbury	9	9	9	9	10	10	10	10	10	10	10	10	10	10

PLAYING RECORD AND POINTS BREAKDOWN

	P	W	D	L	F	A	Pts	HOME						AWAY					
								P	W	D	L	F	A	P	W	D	L	F	A
Clifton	18	16	2	0	477	205	34	9	8	1	0	283	96	9	8	1	0	194	109
Harrogate	18	14	2	2	479	211	30	9	8	1	0	292	100	9	6	1	2	187	111
Liverpool St Helens	18	11	1	6	396	275	23	9	7	1	1	238	134	9	4	0	5	158	141
Plymouth	18	9	0	9	286	416	18	9	6	0	3	167	141	9	3	0	6	119	275
Aspatria	18	8	0	10	295	372	16	9	6	0	3	180	126	9	2	0	7	115	246
Leeds	18	7	0	11	243	318	14	9	6	0	3	158	110	9	1	0	8	85	208
Askeans	18	6	1	11	268	358	13	9	5	0	4	133	147	9	1	1	7	135	211
Broughton P	18	6	0	12	243	356	12	9	4	0	5	121	160	9	2	0	7	122	196
Sheffield	18	5	1	12	287	310	11	9	4	0	5	188	148	9	1	1	7	99	162
Sudbury	18	4	1	13	240	393	9	9	2	1	6	128	164	9	2	0	7	112	229

ASKEAN RFC

CLUB PLAYING RECORD 1993-94

National League: Four
Final League Position at end of 1993/94 Season: 8th
Season Playing record (including league matches/Pilkington Cup):
P 29, W 13, D 1, L 15, Pts F 516, Pts A 502

LEADING SCORERS

Richard Larking, Fly Half, 185
Jamie Graham, Centre, 64
C Johns, Wing, 42
Leon White, Flanker, 40
Steve Hill, No 8, 25
Harold Evans, Scrum Half, 15

Club Details

Club Colours: Blue, black & white
Change of Colours: Red & white
Date Founded: 1929
Membership: Total 950, Playing members 150, Junior/Youth/Minis 150, Other 650
No. of teams: Senior 5, Junior 5
Programme advertising rates: Full £250, Half £150, Quarter £75

Ground Details:

Ground Address: 60A Broadwalk, Kidbrooke, London, SE3 8NB
Ground Tel No: 081 856 1025
Simple Directions to Ground: A2 from Blackwall Tunnel off the Rochester Way
Spectator Capacity: Total: 1,000, Seated 250, Standing 750
Ticket Prices: Adults: £4, OAP/Child £2
Training Nights: Tuesdays and Thursdays

Club Officials

Club President: Alex Noble
Club Chairman: Bill Ruston
Club Secretary: Graham Terry, End Waye, Brookhurst Gardens, Southborough, Tunbridge Wells, Kent, TN4 0Ua. Tel: (H) 0892 528996 (W) 071 387 9366 Fax: 0892 528996
Fixtures Secretary: Mick Sidgwick, 53 Borkwood Way, Orpington, Kent, BR6 9PB. Tel: (H) 0689 867436
Press Officer: John Ratcliffe, Broughtons, Leafy Grove, Keston, Kent. Tel: (H) 0322 59366
Registration Officer: Alan Eastick, 97 Heathlee Road, Blackheath, London, SE3 9HS. Tel: (H) 081 852 8596
1994/ 95 1st XV Captain: Richard Hennah
1994/95 Club Coach: Steve Hill
Club Coach: Barry Pinder
Commercial Manager: David Wickerson

ASKEAN RFC

COURAGE RECORDS

Richard Larkin re-wrote a number of Askeans Courage League scoring records. His 117 points for the season easily eclipsed John Fields 78 points from 1988-89.

	PLD	T	C	P	D	PTS	AVE
R Larkin	14	0	9	29	4	117	
J Field	11	1	10	18	0	78	

Larkin broke Colin Taylors record of 18 points in a match with his 21 points aganist Aspatria in April. In that match , he kicked 5 penalties which bettered the previous record of 4 held by Aled Hughes since 1989. His 2 drop goals in that match equalled Rob Gilden record of 2 in a match set in April 90.
Chris John equalled Jon Satterleys record of 6 tries in a Courage League season for Askeans. Satterleys 6 tries came in 8 matches while johns 6 came in 16 matches.
Jaime Graham extended his record of 13 Courage League tries for Askeans to 15 in 58 matches.
Larkin with 29 broke John Fields record of 18 penalties in a Courage League season for Askeans.

ASKEAN RFC

COURAGE LEAGUE RECORDS

Biggest Home Win: 36-0 v Lydney 11-1-92 CL3   **Defeat:** 3-40 v Clifton 18-12-93 CL4
Biggest Away Win: 27-17 v Sheffield 26-11-88 CL3   **Defeat:** 6-61 v Otley 27-3-93 CL3
Most Tries For in a Match: 7 v Lydney 11-1-92 CL3   **Against:** 8 v Otley 27-3-93 CL3
Most consecutive Wins: 5   **Defeats:** 5
No. of matches failed to Score: 0   **Clean Sheets:** 3   **Drawn Matches:** 6
Most appearance Forward: 58 Dylan Davies   **Back:** 58 Jaime Grahame
Consecutive matches scoring Tries: 3 Jon Satterley, Jaime Grahame
Consecutive matches scoring Points: 13 John Field

INDIVIDUAL SCORING RECORDS

IN A MATCH

Most points: 21 Richard Larkin v Aspatria 9-4-94 Home CL4

Most tries: 2 Jon Satterley v London Welsh 14-10-89 Home CL3, Chris Johns v Lydney 30-3-90 Away CL3, Steve Francis v Lydney 11- 1-92 Home CL3, David Osbourne v lydney 11-1-92 Home CL3, Chris John v Plymouth 13-11-93 Home CL4, Pat Richardson v Leeds 26-3-94 Away CL4, Leon White v Sudbury 30-4-94 Home CL4

Most conversions: 4 Gareth Hughes v Lydney 11-1-92 Home CL3

Most penalities: 5 Richard Larkin v Aspatria 9-4-94 Home CL4

Most drop goals: Rob Gilden v Roundhay 28-4-90 Home CL3

IN A SEASON

Most points: 117 Richard Larkin 1993-94 CL4
Most tries: 6 Jon Satterley 1989-90 CL3, Chris Johns 1993-94 CL4
Most conversions: 10 John Field 1988-89 CL3
Most penalties: 29 Richard Larkin 1993-94 CL4
Most drop goals: 5 Rob Gilden 1989-90 CL3

IN A CAREER

Most points: 212 John Field 1987-92
Most tries: 15 Jaime Grahame 1989-94
Most conversions: 26 John Field 1987-92
Most penalties: 47 John Field 1987-92
Most drop goals: 6 Rob Gilden 1989-91

COURAGE LEAGUE RECORD

	DIV	PLD	W	D	L	F	T	C	P	D	A	T	C	P	D
1987-88	ALS	10	8	1	1	141	21	9	13	0	83				
1988-89	3	11	4	1	6	141	14	11	20	1	215	29	12	24	1
1989-90	3	11	6	0	5	170	20	9	18	6	235	33	14	23	2
1990-91	3	12	4	2	6	141	14	8	21	2	137	15	4	21	2
1991-92	3	12	5	1	6	149	22	11	12	1	203	31	11	15	4
1992-93	3	11	3	0	8	132	12	6	18	2	300	36	18	26	2
1993-94	4	18	6	1	11	268	25	10	37	4	358	38	18	36	8

SEASON BY SEASON LEADING SCORERS

	Most Points			Most Tries	
1987-88	69	John Field	5		H Corliss
1988-89	78	John Field	2		G Jaques, H Coirliss, G Francis
1989-90	36	Aled Hughes	6		Jon Satterley
1990-91	65	John Field	3		Jaime Graham
1991-92	62	Gareth Hughes	4		Jaime Grahame
1992-93	68	Colin Taylor	3		Jamie Grahame
1993-94	117	Richard Larkin	6		Chris Johns

LEAGUE FOUR PROGRAMMES

LEEDS RUFC

HARROGATE
Saturday 23rd April 1994
Sponsored by
Read Hind Stewart

PROGRAMME

ASPATRIA RUFC

Aspatria overcome wretched luck

The season started very slowly with the first five League games ending in defeat. A major blow was suffered when our key scrum half George Doggart broke his ankle in August and missed the full season. Experienced forwards Fred Story and Malcolm Brown returned in November and eventually the 1st XV settled down to a more consistent pattern. An eventual win at Plymouth just before Christmas gave us our first away victory.

Perhaps the most vital win was against Liverpool St Helens in March; not only did we pick up two points but the manner in which we won gave the best show of the season. Another key factor was the goal kicking of Mike Scott who kept many games alive, notably away at Sheffield. With further home victories against Sudbury and Plymouth we eventually move our way into the League's mid table.

With both our 2nd and 3rd XV's both having a very successful year, the club ended in good spirits.

CLUB PLAYING RECORD 1993-94

National League: Four
Final League Position at end of 1993/94 Season: Fifth
League Playing record: P 18, W 8, D 0, L 10, Pts F 303, Pts A 367
Season Playing record (including league matches/Pilkington Cup): P 30, W 14, D 0, L 16, Pts F 543, Pts A 610

Aspatria RUFC 1993-94

225

ASPATRIA RUFC

LEADING APPEARANCES FOR CLUB
M Richardson, 29, 1993/94

LEADING SCORER 1993-94
Mike Scott, Fly-half, 185

PLAYING SQUAD 1993-94
Full Back: J Miller
Wing: D Murray, C Marriott, W Davidson, W Tinnion, S Davidson
Centre: M Southward, B Stephenson, P Cusack, K Hetherington, B Kyffin
Fly Half: M Scott
Scrum Half: G Campbell, A Guthrie
Prop: S Irving, J McCune, I Sewell, A Day
Hooker: N Brown, M Barton
Lock: T Clementson, B Atkinson, F Story
Flanker: N Wedgewood, S Urquhart, M Tinnion, M Maughan, D Benson, J Barbour
No 8: M Richardson, M Brown

ASPATRIA RUFC

Club Details

Club Colours: Black with red hoops
Change of Colours: Red
Date Founded: 1875
Membership: Total: 500, Playing members 75, Junior/Youth/Minis 70, Other 250
No. of teams: Senior 3, Junior 3
Programme advertising rates: Full £120, Half £60
Any Special Occasions during 1994/95: Opening of new Sponsors Bar and Function Room

Ground Details:

Ground Address: Bower Park, Station Road, Aspatria, Cumbria, CA5 2AJ
Ground Tel No: 06973 20420
Simple Directions to Ground: Leave M6 at Junction
Spectator Capacity: Total: unlimited, seated 250
Ticket Prices: Adults £3, OAP/Child £1
Training Nights: Tuesdays and Thursdays

Club Officials

Club President: N Lazonby
Club Chairman: D Miller
Club Secretary: M Hanley, 7 King Street, Aspatria, Cumbria, CA5 3AD. Tel: (H) 06973 20328 (W) 0946 815111 Fax: 0946 815082
Fixtures Secretary: P Gray, Ingledene, 4 Queen Street, Aspatria, Cumbria, CA5 3AP. Tel: (H) 06973 21760 (W) 06973 31234
Press Officer: As secretary
Registration Officer: T Borthwick, Smithy Cottage, Scales, Aspatria, Cumbria. Tel: (W) 0900 870625
1994/ 95 1st XV Captain: M Richardson
1994/95 Club Coach: T Borthwick/D Robinson
Other Club Officers: Tom Borthwick, Director of Coaching

WELCOME TO
BOWER PARK
Season 1993/94

MAIN SPONSOR

ASPATRIA
RUGBY UNION
FOOTBALL CLUB
v. HARROGATE

BROUGHTON PARK FC

Main aim achieved

After a poor previous season, maintaining League status was the chief aim for 1993-94. The squad was strengthened by returning and new players and well prepared in fitness by Kevin Knowles. High expectations were based on the all county front row of J Russell, A Yates and M Lloyd. Unfortunately injury and self inflicted absence meant this solid base never played together in League games. The coaches, Barry Jackson, a former England international, and Stan Mousdale, instilled a good spirit and direction into the squad and Park's open style resulted in the three main wings showing over thirty tries during the season. Meanwhile avoidable home losses were balanced by good away wins at Aspatria and Askeans. Park then stick on 10 points which saw them slide into the relegation zone. Former international Kevin O'Brien was recalled from guiding the 2nd XV and his experience did the trick for a while.

Everything was to hang on the last game of the season. Park were not found wanting. Captain Chris Allen forcefully led a concerted and direct team effort to overcome a strong Leeds XV. Results elsewhere meant Park maintained their place in the top forty clubs. A feature of the game was the outstanding contribution of outside half Andy Rimmer absent from the side since Christmas through illness and injury.

Next season Park (free from merger doubts) hope for a good season under new Captain, Graham Higginbotham, a hard tackling centre who has been with the club from mini-rugby. New coach Ian MacLure will find strong commitment from the nine former Park Colts in the 1st XV squad.

CLUB PLAYING RECORD 1993-94

National League: Four
Final League Position at end of 1993/94 Season: 8th
League Playing record: P 18, W 6, D 0, L 12, Pts F 243, Pts A 356
Season Playing record (including league matches/Pilkington Cup): P 35, W 15, D 0, L 20, Pts F 521, Pts A 673

Broughton Park FC

229

BROUGHTON PARK FC

ACHIEVEMENTS/COMPETITIONS WON DURING 93/94 SEASON:
U13s won Lancashire Cup. Coached by K O'Brien

PLAYING SQUAD 1993-94
15 K Knowles, M Fleet, C Elliot
14 M Kelly P Bloomfield
13 G Higginbotham, K Richardson
12 A Murison, M Watkinson, S Evans
11 A Speakman, S Brown
10 A Rimmer, K O'Brien
9 R Goodwin, M Llewellyn
1 J Russell, B Crawford, B Middlehurst
2 O Brabbins, A Yates, S Unsworth
3 J Bennett, M Lloyd, P Wright
4 P Kirk, M Sever, D Beckler
5 A Floss, A Whittle, P Moore
6 C Allen (Capt), J Clifford, I McClure
7 C Tatton, R Glover, S Parsons
8 J Idehen, C Allen, N Royle

MOST CAPPED PLAYERS
(including British Lions Appearances)
A Neary, England 43, British lions 1
K O'Brien, Ireland 3
B Jackson, England 2
M Leadbetter, England 2

LEADING APPEARANCES FOR CLUB
K O'Brien, 556, 21 seasons

LEADING SCORERS (1993-94)
A Rimmer, Stand Off, 144
K O'Brien, Stand Off/Full Back, 84
M Kelly, Right Wing, 50
A Speakman, Left Wing, 50

Above: Broughton Park v Leeds, 30-4-94 — Andy Rimmer on his way to scoring a try Photo: *John Fryer*

Below: Broughton Park v Liverpool St Helens, 23-10-94 — John Russell passing the ball, Paul Kirk in background

Photo: *John Fryer*

BROUGHTON PARK FC

Club Details

Club Colours: Black & white
Change of Colours: Red
Date Founded: 1882
Membership: Total: 410, Playing members 80,
Junior/Youth/Minis 145
No. of teams: Senior 4, Junior 9
Programme advertising rates: TBA

Ground Details:

Ground Address: Chelsfield Grove, Mauldeth Road,
West Chorlton, Manchester, M21 5SU
Ground Tel No: 061 881 2481
Simple Directions to Ground: From end of M56
follow signs to city centre Manchester. At the fitfth set
of traffic lights turn left into Mauldeth Road West and
follow road for 3/4 mile.
Spectator Capacity: Total: 2,000, Seated 400,
Standing 1,600
Ticket Prices: Adults: £2, Student/Junior/U16/OAP £1
Training Nights: Tuesdays and Thursdays

Club Officials

Club President: J L Rimmer
Club Chairman: W R Seddon
Club Secretary: Ron Greenall, 260 Barlow Moor
Road, Chorlton, Manchester, M21 2HA. Tel: (H) 061
861 0457
Fixtures Secretary: David B Ramsbottom, 9 Yew Tree Grove, Heald Green, Cheadle, Cheshire, SK8 8TJ.
Tel: (H) 061 437 3017
Press Officer: Don Evans, 71 Claude Road, Chorltonville, Manchester, M21 1DE. Tel: (H) 061 881 6705
Registration Officer: Ron Greenall
1994/ 95 1st XV Captain: Graham Higginbotham
1994/95 Club Coach: Ian McClure

BROUGHTON PARK
FOOTBALL CLUB
Founded 1882
Chelsfield Grove, off Mauldeth Road West, Manchester 21

PARK
v
LEEDS
Saturday, 30th April 1994

COURAGE
CLUBS CHAMPIONSHIP

HAVANT RFC

Down with a bump

After six magnificent seasons in the championship during which they gained promotion once and were twice runners up in their respective divisions, the Hampshire club came down to earth with a resounding crash.

Their short life in what was an entirely new-look and awesomely powerful national Division Three will be regarded by all at Hooks Lane as a period best forgotten.

A massive injury list, constant team changes, a new game plan the players were never comfortable with, a new coach who resigned with a month of the season still remaining all combined to make the 1993-94 campaign a constant struggle.

The player statistics showed just what a struggle it was. In their 18 championship matches that produced only three wins, Havant used no less than 43 players with only prop Dave Rees and flanker Nick Roach having a 100 per cent record for appearances in the league programme.

But it was not all gloom and doom. The club opened their new stand at the start of the season and extended and completely renovated their large clubhouse to meet the demands of national league rugby and the challenge that awaits them this season in their quest to bounce straight back into division three.

CLUB PLAYING RECORD 1993-94

League 1993-94: National League Three
Final League Position at end of 1993-94 season: 9th
League playing record: P 18, W 3, D 0, L 15, Pts F 203, Pts A 432
Season playing record (including league matches/Pilkington Cup etc):
P 35, W 13, D 0, L 22, Pts F 522, Pts A 745

HAVANT RFC

PLAYING SQUAD 1993-94

Full Back: R Ashworth, R Davey, D Jones
Wing 3/4: J Bates, J Clarke, J Fenn, T Hames, A Jewitt, A White, A Wilson
Centre: A Balls, S Boydell, N Burt, P Jenkins, S Lippiett, R Packer, S Parry, S Powley, D Sibson
Stand Off: A Goodwin, T Gummer, A Perry, P Russell
Scrum 1/2: B Gray, J Shepherd, I Torpey
No. 8: W Knight, D White
Flanker: M Baldwin, M Loveday, K Middleton, G Powell, P Redden, N Roach, M Sheldon
2nd Row: G Curtis, S Morgan B Pearce, B Rouse, I Ward
Prop: K Jewitt, J McEriean, D Rees, M Rees, S Walsh
Hooker: D Howard, M Vickers, R Whitehead

LEADING APPEARANCE FOR CLUB

Dave Rees, Leag 18, Ttl 25, 1993-94
Nick Roach, Leag 18, Ttl 23, 1993-94
Will Knight, Leag 17, Ttl 25, 1993-94
Davy Jones, Leag 17, Ttl 25, 1993-94
Jimmy Bates, Leag 15, Ttl 19, 1993-94
Mike Baldwin, Leag 15, Ttl 23, 1993-94

LEADING SCORERS (1993-94 SEASON)

Pete Russell, Stand Off, Leag 32, Ttl 111
Davy Jones, Scrum Half, Leag 25, Ttl 45
Rob Ashworth, Full Back, Leag 31, Ttl 40
Nick Roach, Flanker, Leag 20, Ttl 35
Greg Powley, Centre, Leag 0, Ttl 32
Tony White, Wing, Leag 15, Ttl 30

HAVANT RUGBY FOOTBALL CLUB

GROUND: HOOKS LANE, FRASER ROAD, BEDHAMPTON, HAVANT, HANTS. PO9 3EJ
Telephone: 0705-477843

SEASON 1993 - 1994

OFFICIAL PROGRAMME

£

HAVANT RFC

Club Officials

President: Philip West
Chairman: Dave Platt
Club Secretary: Colin Sewell, 6 Font Close, Titchfield Common, Fareham, Hants, PO14 4QH. Tel: (H) 0489 583417 (W) 0705 563904
Fixtures Secretary: Mick Chalk, 16 Highclere Avenue, Havant, Hants, PO9 4RB. Tel: (H)0705 472239 (W) 0705 822351 x 23155
Press Officer: Ray Quinn, c/o W W Fischer, Unit 6, Stratfield Park, Elletra Ave, Waterlooville, Hants, PO7 7XN. Tel: (W) 0705 241122 (Fax) 0705 257596
Registration Officer: Colin Sewell, Hon. Sec. As above
1994-95 Captain: David Rees
Club Coach: Owen Jarrett
Chairman of Rugby: Peter Price

Club Details

Club Colours: Navy blue & white hoops, blue shorts
Change of Colours: Red shirts
Date Founded: 1951
Membership: Total 350, Playing members 200, Junior/Youth/Minis 200, Other 200
No. of teams: Senior 10, Junior 15
Programme advertising rates: Page £250, 1/2 page £150, 1/4 page £85

Ground Details

Ground Address: Hooks Lane, Fraser Road, Bedhampton, Havant, Hants, PO9 3EJ
Ground Tel No: 0705 477843
Directions to Ground: From the A3(M) take B2177 to roundabout. Follow road signs to Bedhampton; straight over mini-roundabout. Straight across traffic lights then bear left at level crossing. Take second left (James Road) then left into Fraser Road at T- junction. Clubhouse is 200 yards on the right hand side.
Capacity: 2,000, seated 200, standing 1,800
Ticket prices: Adults league £3 other £2
Training nights: Monday/Thursday

LEEDS RUFC

Leeds still a sleeping giant

New clubs like the merged Leeds need time to establish a special identity and until they do so they must inevitably achieve only modest results and a final league position in the new fourth flight of sixth would suggest that this is the case. They never looked likely to descend any further, but promotion was always out of reach even though they took part in some exciting matches and had good wins over Aspatria, Liverpool St. Helens and promoted Harrogate in the penultimate game of the season, which left them with their place secured.

The Pilkington Cup produced a result they would like to forget - a 12-6 loss to junior club Kettering. This along with a poor overall record would suggest that the club can only improve, but greater consistency is needed all round plus a regular goalkicker, who takes on all the kicks. Dave Breakwell and Dan Eddie shared last season's duties and both did well enough, but sharing does not make for consistency. On a similar note there is also a need for a consistent try scoring wing - or, even better, a pair of wings. Good sides usually have at least one player who finishes a season well into double figures in terms of try scoring.

But these are still early days for the new club and it will only need a successful season for all criticisms to be put on hold and their coaches are undoubtably aware of this.

CLUB PLAYING RECORD 1993-94

National League: Four
Final League Position at end of 1993/94 Season: 6th
League Playing record: P 18, W 7, D 0, L 11, Pts F 240, Pts Against 318
Season Playing record (including league matches/Pilkington Cup): P 32, W 12, D 0, L 20, Pts F 461, Pts A 634

Scrum half Gary Cassidy gets the ball away watched by No 8 Ian Moule and flanker Neil Hargreaves against Wakefield, 15-2-94
Photo: Gordon Bunney

237

LEEDS RUFC

ACHIEVEMENTS/COMPETITIONS WON DURING 93/94 SEASON
Bridlington, Yarnbury and Leeds Sevens

PLAYING SQUAD 1993-94
Full Back: David Breakwell, David Riley, David Lowther
Wing: Jon Eagle, Chris Thornton, Gary Cassidy
Centre: Tom Whitford, Kevin Bowling, Wayne Hartley, Lee Douglas, Chris Chudleigh, Richard Andrew
Fly Half: Dan Eddie, Alex Barkhouse, Jon Rees
Scrum Half: Dave Andrew, John Swarbrigg, John Singleton, Toby Powell
Prop: Richard Broderick, Mike Cutter, Adam Machell, John Wright, Chris Head, David Hayle, Perry Hardy, Paddy McCarthy
Hooker: Neil Lineham, Richard Wollaston, Ian Salkeld
Second Row: Jim Davies, Nick Wilde, Paul Burkenshaw, Andy Fraser, Trevor Thomas
Flanker: Phil Griffin, Neil Hargreaves, Stuart Lancaster, Stuart Brotherton, Gareth Vernon-James, Damian Carr
No 8: Gary Thomas, Mark Cooper, Ian Moule, Steve Murray

MOST CAPPED PLAYERS
(including British Lions Appearances)
Ian McGeechan (Scotland), 32 + 2, 1973-79
Peter Winterbottom, 29 + 1, 1982-88
Peter Thompson, 17, 1956-59
John Spencer, 14 + 1, 1969-71
Dennis Wilkins, 13, 1951-53
Colin Aarvold, 11 + 2, 1928-31

LEADING APPEARANCES FOR CLUB
David Breakwell, 58, 1992-94
Chris Thornton, 56, 1992-94
Neil Hargreaves, 48, 1992-94
Wayne Hartley, 47, 1992-94
Jon Eagle, 43, 1992-94
Kevin Bowling, 40, 1992-94

LEADING SCORERS 1993-94
David Breakwell, Full Back, 128
Dan Eddie, Fly Half, 105
Jon Eagle, Wing, 35
Gary Cassidy, Wing, 25
Phil Griffin, Blind Side, 20
Neil Hargreaves, Open Side, 15

LEEDS RUFC

COURAGE LEAGUE RECORDS

Highest score: 43 v Clifton (43-32) 24-4-93 Home CL3
Largest winning margin: 20 v Broughton Park (30-10) 14-11-92 Away CL3
Highest score against: 35 v Havant (11-35) 26-9-92 Away CL3
Largest losing margin: 24 as above
Drawn Matches: 0
Clean Sheets: 0
Failed to score: 2

INDIVIDUAL SCORING RECORDS

IN A MATCH

Most points: 20 David Breakwell v Aspatria 27-10-93 Home CL4
Most tries: 3 Chris Thornton v Exeter 13-3-93 Away CL3
Most conversions: 4 Dan Eddie v Clifton 24-4-93 Home CL3
Most penalities: 4 Bob Lloyd v Askeans 13-2-93 Home CL3
Most drop goals: 2 Dan Eddie v Broughton park 19-2-94 Home CL4

IN A SEASON

Most points: 97 David Breakwell 1993-94 CL4
Most tries: 7 Chris Thornton 1992-93 CL3
Most conversions: 12 David Breakwell 1993-94 CL4
Most penalties: 20 David Breakwell 1993-94 CL4
Most drop goals: 4 Dan Eddie 1993-94 CL4

IN A CAREER

Most points: 144 David Breakwell 1992-94
Most tries: 9 Chris Thornton1992-94
Most conversions: 19 David Breakwell 1992-94
Most penalties: 26 David Breakwell 1993-94
Most drop goals: 7 Dan Eddie 1992-94, Bob Lloyd 1992-93

SEASON BY SEASON LEADING SCORERS

		Most Points		Most Tries
1992-93	45	Bob Lloyd	7	Chris Thornton
1993-94	97	David Breakwell	3	Penalty Try

LEEDS RUFC

Club Details

Club Colours: Royal blue, old gold and white
Change of Colours: red
Date Founded: June 1991
Membership: Total: 1142, Playing members 140, Junior/Youth/Minis 168, Other 834
No. of teams: Senior 7, Junior 6
Programme advertising rates: Full A5 page in monochrome £175

Ground Details:

Ground Address: Clarence Field, Bridge Road, Kirkstal, Leeds, LS5 3BN
Ground Tel No: 0532 755029
Spectator Capacity: Total: 7,850, seated 850, standing 7,000
Ticket Prices: Adults: £3, OAP/Child: £1.50
Training Nights: Tuesdays and Thursdays

Club Officials

Club President: F S C Browning
Club Chairman: M Palmer-Jones
Club Secretary: Mike Bidgood, 4 West Hill Avenue, Leeds, LS7 3QH. Tel: (H) 0532 682784 (W) 0532 625382 Fax: 0532 621251
Fixtures Secretary: Les Jackson, 4 Glendhow Wood Avenue, Leeds, LS8 1NY. Tel: (H) 0532 665544 (W) 0532 665544 Fax: 0532 665544
Press Officer: Alan Pearson, 2 Chandos Garth, Leeds, LS8 1QY. Tel: (H) 0532 662541 (W) 0532 662541
Fax: 0532 662541
Registration Officer: Les Jackson
1994/ 95 1st XV Captain: Neil Hargreaves
1994/95 Club Coach: Chris Spowatt
Director of Rugby: Alan Pearson

County winger Chris Thornton about to take a pass against Sheffield, March 5th 1994   *Photo: Gordon Bunney*

LIVERPOOL ST HELENS FC

Fine start not maintained

The club got off to an excellent start scoring a total of 66 points in their first two fixtures. A new member, Simon Mason, was responsible for quite a number of these points in that he kicked 15 goals from 15 attempts. This was Simon's first season in senior rugby and he later went on to play for Ireland Under 21's.

Many players gained representative honours; David Dahinton, Second Row, played for the Army and Kevin Simms again captained the Northern Division including playing for them against the All Blacks at Anfield, home of Liverpool Association Football Club. Prior to this match the All Blacks squad had been guests of L.S.H., training at Moss Lane during the week before the fixture. On the day of the game some one hundred plus visitors were entertained to luncheon at Moss Lane and afterwards travelled to Anfield by luxury coach returning to Moss Lane after the game for light refreshments.

The club were in with a very real chance of promotion until late in the season when they failed to cope with the very heavy grounds during March, losing three League matches in succession. The very young pack have gained in experience and this, added to the arrival of some new recruits, means that prospects for the next season look good.

The junior sides have given very good accounts of themselves the colts, under 16's and under 14's all playing in the finals of the Lancashire Cup. Losing in the final was the Under 16's first defeat in two years.

CLUB PLAYING RECORD 1993-94

National League: Four
Final League Position at end of 1993/94 Season: Third
League Playing record: P 18, W 11, D 1, L 6, Pts F 397, Pts A 275
Season Playing record (including league matches/Pilkington Cup): P 32, W 19, D 2, L 11, Pts F 756, Pts A 506

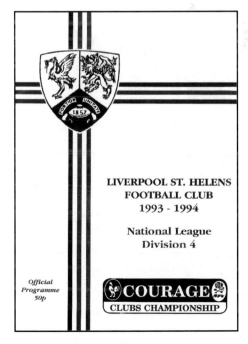

LIVERPOOL ST. HELENS
FOOTBALL CLUB
1993 - 1994

National League
Division 4

Official
Programme
50p

COURAGE
CLUBS CHAMPIONSHIP

241

LIVERPOOL ST HELENS FC

PLAYING SQUAD 1993-94

Full Back: Simon Mason, S Bettinson
Wing: J McLinchy, M Sephton, D Crompton, N Walker, S Bettinson
Centre: S Bettinson, K Davies, K Tyrer, K Simms, N Simms, B Wellens
Fly Half: A Higgin, B Wellens
Scrum Half: G Eldoy
Back Row: N Hughes, T Wood, D Lupton, D Hendry, D Gaskell
Prop: R Hudson, T Allen, S Gill, R Allen, I Harrison
Hooker: J Grigg, R Whittle, T Melia
Lock: S Hughes, D Dahinton, M Nugent, D Hodson

MOST CAPPED PLAYERS

(including British Lions Appearances)
M Slemen (Lions), 31, 1976
M Regan, 1953-54
R Higgins (Lions), 1953-54
K Bearne (Scotland), 1960-61
R French, 1960-61
T Brophy, 1964-65
T Rudd, 1964-65
F Cotton (Lions), 1971
M Beese, 1972-78
D Roughley, 1972-78
J Horton, 1972-78
K Simms, 1985
D Morris, 1990

LEADING APPEARANCES FOR CLUB

T Morris, 334, 1970-82
W Murphy, 339
N Coleclough, 337
D Boult, 309
J Crellin, 305
J Hennigan, 300

LEADING SCORERS (1993-94)

Simon Mason, Full back, 216 (32c, 43p, 1dg, 4t)
Mark Sephton, Wing 3Q, 90 (18t)
Andy Higgin, Fly half/full back, 76 (4t, 7c, 13p 1dg)
Graham Eldoy, Scrum Half, 50 (10t)
Dean Crompton, Wing 3Q, 35 (7t)
Nick Walker, Centre, 30 (6t)
D Gaskell, Flank, 30 (6t)
D Lopton, Flank, 30 (6t)

PLAYER OF THE SEASON

Graham Eldoy, Scrum Half

LIVERPOOL ST HELENS FC

COURAGE LEAGUE RECORDS

Biggest Home Win: 77-5 v Aspatria 13-3-94 CL3   **Defeat:** 6-49 v Morley 14-3-92 CL2
Biggest Away Win: 31-5 v Broughton Park 23-10-93 CL4   **Defeat:** 4-76 v Newcastle Gosforth 29-2-92 CL2
Most Tries For in a Match: 12 v Aspatria 13-3-94 CL3   **Against:**
No. of matches failed to Score: 3   **Clean Sheets:** 2   **Drawn Matches:** 4
Most appearance Forward: **Back:**
Consecutive matches scoring Tries: 3 N Walker
Consecutive matches scoring Points: 14 Andy Higgin

INDIVIDUAL SCORING RECORDS

IN A MATCH

Most points: 20 Mark Sephton v Aspatria 13-3-93 Home CL3, Dean Crompton v Aspatrai 13-3-93 Home CL3

Most tries: 4 Mark Sephton v Aspatria 13-3-93 Home CL3, Dean Crompton v Aspatria 13-3-93 Home CL3

Most conversions: 7 Andy Higgin v Aspatria 13-3-93 Home CL3

Most penalities: 5 Tosh Askew v Bedford 30-4-88 Away, v Moseley 26-11-88 Away CL1, Simon Mason v Sudbury 18-12-93 Home CL4

Most drop goals: 2 Nick Simms v Blackheath 9-1-88 Home CL2, Tosh Askew v Headingley 14-10-89 Home CL2

IN A SEASON

Most points: 183 Simon Mason 1993-94 CL4
Most tries: 9 Mark Sephton 1993-94 CL4
Most conversions: 16 Simon Mason 1993-94 CL4
Most penalties: 30 Simon Mason 1993-94 CL4
Most drop goals: 4 Andy Higgin 1992-93 CL3

IN A CAREER

Most points: 183 Andy Higgin 1990-94
Most tries: 28 Mark Sephton 1989-94
Most conversions: 19 Andy Higgin 1990-94
Most penalties: 43 Tosh Askew 1987-90
Most drop goals: 4 Andy Higgin 1990-94

COURAGE LEAGUE RECORD

	DIV	PLD	W	D	L	F	T	C	P	D	A	T	C	P	D
1987-88	2	11	8	1	2	154	18	8	19	3	97	10	6	13	2
1988-89	1	11	1	0	10	116	9	4	22	2	254	37	20	22	0
1889-90	2	11	8	2	1	154	20	7	18	2	106	12	5	14	2
1990-91	1	12	0	0	12	88	9	5	13	1	349	57	35	16	1
1991-92	2	12	0	0	12	87	14	5	7	0	418	65	37	27	1
1992-93	3	11	5	0	6	203	22	12	19	4	130	13	4	18	1
1993-94	4	18	11	1	6	396	44	22	43	1	275	25	12	37	5
		86	33	4	49										

SEASON BY SEASON LEADING SCORERS

	Most Points			Most Tries	
1987-88	34	Tosh Askew	3	Ian Gibbons, John Shinwell	
1988-89	55	Tosh Askew	3	Brendan Hanavan	
1989-90	66	Tosh Askew	6	Mark Sephton	
1990-91	31	Andy Higgin	2	Mark Sephton, Paul Buckton	
1991-92	26	Paul Ramsden	4	Mark Elliott	
1992-93	96	Andy Higgin	8	Mark Sephton	
1993-94	140	Simon Mason	9	Mark Sephton	

LIVERPOOL ST HELENS FC

Club Details

Club Colours: Red, white, black and blue hoops, black shorts
Change of Colours: White - red edging
Date Founded: 1857
Membership: Total 450, Junior/Youth/Minis 150
No. of teams: Senior 5, Junior 3 plus Colts & Minis
Programme advertising rates: Full £300 plus VAT for season
Any Special Occasions during 1993-94: Hosted All Blacks for training prior to game v Northern Division at Anfield

Ground Details:

Ground Address: Moss Lane, Windle, St Helens, WA11 7PL
Ground Tel No:0744 25708
Simple Directions to Ground: M6 Junction 23. A580 (Liverpool) 5 miles A570 (Southport) 100 yards, small lane on left to ground.
Spectator Capacity: Total: 2,000, seated 300
Ticket Prices: Adults £3.50 including programme, OAP/Child £1
Training Nights: Tuesdays and Thursdays

Club Officials

Club President: John Tandy
Club Chairman: W S Magowan
Club Secretary: E C Hyland, 22 Salisbury Road, Cressington Park, Liverpool, L19 0PJ. Tel: (H) 051 427 8831
Fixtures Secretary: John Robertson, 36 Beryl Road, Nocotum, Wirral, Merseyside. Tel: () 051 677 5611 (W) 051 427 7535
Press Officer: Christopher Brown, 47 Cowley Hill Lane, St Helens, WA10 2AR. Tel: (H) 0744 590785
Registration Officer: Ian Clark, 5 Rowan Close, Laffak, St Helens, WA11 9ED. Tel: (H) 0744 56632 (W) 051 777 4029
1994/ 95 1st XV Captain: Kevin Simms
1994/95 Club Coach: David Buttery
Other Club Officers:
J A Walker, Chariman of Rugby
J Freeman, Sponsorship
Dennis Larsen, Steward

COURAGE RECORDS

Andy Higgins became Liverpools most prolific scorer in Courage League Rugby, he finishes the season with 183 points from 40 matches. The previous record was 155 by Tosh Askew.

	PLD	T	C	P	D	PTS	AVE
Andy Higgin	40	2	19	41	4	183	
Tosh Askew	33	0	10	43	2	155	

Higgin also extends his career conversions record to 19 and is only 2 behind Askew's career record of 43 penalties for Liverpool in Courage Rugby.

Mark Sephton breaks his own record of most tries in a season with 9 beating the 8 he scored last season, he also extends his career record to 29 set over 6 seasons.

Simon Mason breaks a number of Liverpools Courage records his 140 points for the season easily beat the previous record of 96 set the previous season.

	SEASON	PLD	T	C	P	D	PTS	AVE
Simon Mason	1993-94	15	2	16	30	1	140	
Andy Higgin	1992-93	11	1	11	19	4	96	

His 16 conversions and 30 penalties were both seasonal records beating the 11 and 19 of Andy Higgin set the previous season.

He also becomes the 2nd Liverpool player after Tosh Askew, to kick 5 penalties in a Courage League match.

PLYMOUTH ALBION RFC

Albion arrest plunge

Having tumbled from National Division Two in consecutive seasons the priority was to consolidate a position in National Division Four. During this period we lost, either to retirement or for other reasons, the majority of our experienced players.

We commenced the season with a young and inexperienced squad and although hopes were high they knew that a battle for survival had begun and losing our opening four friendly matches sent the warning bells ringing.

The loss of influential Vice Captain and No 8 Ian Gregory, Matt Trott (scrum half) and Kevin Courtney (hooker) through injury placed considerable pressure on the squad and on Captain Mark Slade.

The squad carefully nurtured by coach Ray Westlake and the panel of coaches gradually regained its confidence and with it came success and a creditable fourth place in Division Four.

Half way through the season saw the full emergence of two of the season's outstanding players Rob Daniels (forward) and Steve Pooley (hooker), also other young players were gaining in confidence and Lee Thomas had made the scrum half berth his own.

We also saw the renaissance of veteran prop Iain Davies who provided experience and stability whilst Roger Bailey brought confidence to the back row, especially in the absence of Ian Gregory.

They look forward to 1994/94 with cautious optimism. A young squad supplemented by new players, including players from our successful colts squad, will be hungry for success, led by Captain Roger Bailey and Vice Captain Martin Tompson and guided by Ray Westlake our strong team of coaches will, I believe, bring attractive and successful rugby to Beacon Park.

Roger Bailey scores in the 35-13 win at Beacon Park over Broughton Park

PLYMOUTH ALBION RFC

CLUB PLAYING RECORD 1993-94

National League: Four
Final League Position at end of 1993/94 Season: 4th
League Playing record: P 18, W 9, D 0, L 9, Pts F 286, Pts A 416
Season Playing record (including league matches/Pilkington Cup): P 35, W 18, D 0, L 17, Pts F 640, Pts A 710

ACHIEVEMENTS/COMPETITIONS WON DURING 93/94 SEASON:

Finalists Devon Cup

PLYMOUTH ALBION RFC

Club Details

Club Colours: Cherry, green, white
Change of Colours: Green
Date Founded: 1876
Membership: Total: 650, Playing members 90,
Junior/Youth/minis 220, Other 340
No. of teams: Senior 5, Junior 8
Programme advertising rates: Full £175, Half £120,
Quarter £60
Any Special Occasions during 1994/95: Players
supper 2nd week May VP Lunches October &
February

Ground Details:

Ground Address: Beacon Park, Beacon Park Road,
Peverell, Plymouth, PL2 3JP
Ground Tel No: 0752 772924 Fax: 0752 777454
Simple Directions to Ground: On approaching
Plymouth follow the Plymouth Argyle FC signs, 200
yds past Safeway Superstore at 3rd set of traffic lights
turn right.
Spectator Capacity: Full: 2,500, seated 500
Ticket Prices: Adults £3.50 stand £2.50 ground,
OAP/Child £1.25
Training Nights: Mondays and Wednesdays

Club Officials

Club President: Robert Hicks MP
Club Chairman: Clive Cross
Club Secretary: Roger Bowden, 7 Winnow Close,
Staddiscombe, Plymouth, PL9 9RZ. Tel: (H) 0752
491642 Fax: 0752 777454
Fixtures Secretary: Andy Watts, 52 Brook Road,
Ivybridge. Tel: (H) 0752 896293 Fax: 0752 777454
Press Officer: Paddy Marsh, 8 Frensham Gardens,
Glenholt, Plymouth. Tel: (H) 0752 794981 Fax: 0752
777454
Registration Officer: Paddy Marsh
1994/ 95 1st XV Captain: Roger Bailey
1994/95 Club Coach: Ray Westlake
Other Club Officers:
Bob Evans, Rugby Manager
Terry Brown, Sponsorship Manager

COURAGE RECORDS

Mark Slade extends his club record 115 points to 165. The 165 pts have come in 39 full appearances and 9 as
replacement and is made up of 6T 18C 34P.
Steve Walklin after a 2 year absence comes back and extends his club record 17 Courage League tries to 19 in 32
matches.
Mark Slade is the only Plymouth player to have played in all 7 Courage League seasons for the club.

PLYMOUTH ALBION RFC

COURAGE LEAGUE RECORDS

Biggest Home Win: 57-3 v Met Police 26-11-88 CL3 **Defeat:** 3-35 v Havant 13-3-93 CL3
Biggest Away Win: 46-3 v Birmingham 17-10-87 CL3 **Defeat:** 21-54 v Newcastle Gosforth 28-3-92 CL2
Most Tries For in a Match: 9 v Birmingham 17-10-87 CL3 **Against:**
Most consecutive Wins: 11 **Defeats:** 16
No. of matches failed to Score: 1 **Clean Sheets:** 1 **Drawn Matches:** 0
Most appearance Forward: 53 Ian Russell **Back:** 45 Nick Leonard
Most consecutive appearances: 43 Kevin Turton 12-9-87 to 23-3-91
Consecutive matches scoring Tries: 3 S Walkin, S Hughes, N Leonard, C Hocking, K Turton, J Martin
Consecutive matches scoring Points: 9 Martin Thompson

INDIVIDUAL SCORING RECORDS

IN A MATCH

Most points: 25 Dominic Cundy v Metropolitan Police 26-11-88 Home CL3
Most tries: 4 Steve Walkin v Birmingham 17-10-87 Away CL3, Ian Russell v Fyl;de 31-10-87 Away CL3
Most conversions: 8 Dominic Cundy v Metropolitan Police 26-11-88 Home CL3
Most penalities: 6 Mark Slade v Bedford 14-12-91 Home CL2
Most drop goals: 2 Dominic Cundy v Wakefield 10-9-88 Home CL2

IN A SEASON

Most points: 108 Martin Livesey 1987-88 CL3
Most tries: 8 Kevin Norris 1987-88 CL3 & Steve Walklin 1988-89 CL3
Most conversions: 23 Martin Livesey 1987-88 CL3
Most penalties: 17 Martin Livesey 1987-88 CL3, Martin Thompson 1993-94 CL4
Most drop goals: 3 Dominic Cundy 1988-89 CL3, Martin Thompson 1993-94 CL4

IN A CAREER

Most points: 165 Mark Slade 1990-94
Most tries: 19 Steve Walklin 1987-94
Most conversions: 23 Martin Livesey 1987-88
Most penalties: 34 Mark Slade 1990-94
Most drop goals: 3 Dominic Cundy 1988-89, Martin Thompson 1993-94

COURAGE LEAGUE RECORD

	DIV	PLD	W	D	L	F	T	C	P	D	A	T	C	P	D
1987-88	3	11	8	0	3	276	41	23	21	1	125	11	3	22	3
1988-89	3	11	11	0	0	311	47	27	19	4	89	5	3	18	3
1989-90	2	11	5	0	6	206	32	15	16	0	164	17	12	21	3
1990-91	2	12	4	0	8	129	9	6	23	4	210	30	15	18	2
1991-92	2	12	3	0	9	153	16	7	25	0	209	23	12	27	4
1992-93	3	11	0	0	11	130	16	4	13	1	305	38	20	22	3
1993-94	4	18	9	0	9	286	31	13	31	4	416	47	26	41	2
		86	40	0	46	1491	192	95	148	14	1518	171	91	169	20

SEASON BY SEASON LEADING SCORERS

	Most Points			Most Tries	
1987-88	111	Martin Livesey	8	Kevin Norris
1988-89	101	Dominic Cundy	8	Steve Walkin
1989-90	36	Charlie Gibbitas	4	Ian Russell, Steve Walklin
1990-91	44	Kevin Thomas	2	Charlie Gabbitas
1991-92	62	Mark Slade	2	By 5 players
1992-93	26	Martin Thompson	3	Mark Haimes
1993-94	90	Martin Thompson	5	R Bailey

READING RFC

Reading roll on

Reading Rugby Football Club was founded in 1898 under the name of Berkshire Wanderers. The name change came about in 1956.

Last season's winning of the National Division Five South League Championship to gain promotion to National Division Four was the second season in a row that they have won promotion. They gained the South West Division Title in 1992/93.

On top of these two achievements was the club's retention of the Price Waterhouse (Windsor) Berkshire Cup. They have now won the County Cup seven times in the past nine seasons. They also retained the Bisley Office Equipment Southern Merit Table to win that competition for a new record fifth time. Only one other club has won the merit championship twice since its inauguration in the 82/83 season.

Reading won 27 of their 34 games last season, drawing two, scoring 1031 points in the process while conceding 289. They have been unbeaten at home since October 1992. Full back Phil Bershaw scored 407 points and finished second highest senior clubs scorer in England. One of Reading's outstanding victories was in a club friendly at home over Clifton by 23-18. The visitors won the National Division Four title with a 100 per cent record.

Reading coach Mike Tewkesbury, who has been with the club for three seasons, has inspired the players to new heights of fitness and confidence. Tewkesbury's tactical awareness will prepare his squad well for the challenges ahead.

CLUB PLAYING RECORD 1993-94

National League: Five South
Final League Position at end of 1993/94 Season: 1st
League Playing record: P 12, W 10, D 1, L 1, Pts F 248, Pts A 61
Season Playing record (including league matches/Pilkington Cup): P 34, W 27, D 2, L 5, Pts F 1032, Pts A 291

ACHIEVEMENTS/COMPETITIONS WON DURING 93/94 SEASON:

National League Division Five South Winners
Berkshire Cup Winners
Bisley Office Equipment Southern Merit Table Winners

READING RFC

Club Details

Club Colours: Myrtle & white hoops, Navy blue shorts
Change of Colours: navy blue
Date Founded: 1898
Membership: Total: 400, Playing members 120, Junior/Youth/Minis 150, Other 130
No. of teams: Senior 5, Junior 7
Programme advertising rates: Full £250

Ground Details:

Ground Address: Holme Park, Sonning Lane, Near Reading, Berks RG4 0SJ
Ground Tel No: 0734 696592
Simple Directions to Ground: Signposted left from the A4 about 2 miles east of Reading
Spectator Capacity: Total: 2,500, Seated 500
Ticket Prices: Adults £3 (£2 members), OAP/Children Free
Training Nights: Tuesdays and Thursdays

Club Officials

Club President: John Lucas
Club Chairman: Peter Walker
Club Secretary: Mike Wickson, 21 Lunds Farm Road, Woodley, Reading, Berkshire, RG5 4PZ. Tel: (H) 0734 695999 (W) 0734 475002 Fax: 0734 463761
Fixtures Secretary: Sefton Hewitt, 21 Purfield Drive, Wargrave, Berkshire, RF10 8AP. Tel: (H) 0734 402909
Press Officer: Lorcan Mullally, 35 Western Elms Avenue, Reading, Berkshire, RG3 2AL. Tel: (H) 0734 572357
Registration Officer: Mike Wickson
1994/ 95 1st XV Captain: John Dixon
1994/95 Director of Rugby: M M Tewkesbury
Other Club Officers: Craig Hunter, Publicity Secretary

R U G B Y

FOOTBALL

C L U B

R E A D I N G

SEASON 1993/94

FANZINES

Following the pattern of other national sports, several high profile rugby clubs have inspired supporters to produce fanzines and a notable example of this is "EVERYTIME REF, EVERYTIME", which is produced in honour of Bath and is on the whole light hearted and humorous, although as a life long Queen of 'The South' supporter I resented the suggestion in last last season's No. 12 that they are Britains worst soccer team; their ultimate results show that statement to be totally untrue!!

Properly and responsibly edited such publication, which are usually economically and neatly produced, do have a place in the game.

They are fun to produce, usually fun to read and providing they avoid the uneducated vitriol from which some soccer clubs have suffered, we will be looking forward to seeing many more.

REDRUTH RFC

Injuries dump reds

A crop of late summer injuries to key players set the tone for a frustrating time for the Reds. The biggest blow was the loss of skipper Kevin Thomas with a shattered heel. He was out for the whole season.

With league restructuring bringing seven ex 2nd Division clubs down to League 3 it was never going to be an easy season. Despite 100 per cent commitment from players the team was never quite on pace with the opponents. Matches fell into a pattern of massive Redruth effort in the first two thirds keeping them within a score of the lead. Then in the last 20 minutes the opposition's superior pace and fitness would take them through, often with a scoreline which never reflected the game as a whole.

Defeat by Rosslyn Park in the Pilkington Cup set the pattern for a run of early season defeats. Victory against Fylde just before Christmas lifted spirits for a while but the new year saw a return to disappointment.

However there were positive sides to the year and good pointers for the future. Injuries gave an opportunity for younger players, including some colts, to move up to the first team. In games against sides such as Coventry, Bedford and Richmond, the youngsters gained valuable experience.

The club is determined to push forward and consolidate in League 4. Under new Coaching Administrator Peter Johnson the Reds will be looking to climb back into the top flight of league rugby.

CLUB PLAYING RECORD 1993-94

National League: Four
Final League Position at end of 1993/94 Season: Bottom
League Playing record: P 18, W 2, D 0, L 16, Pts F 178, Pts A488
Season Playing record (including league matches/Pilkington Cup): P 36, W 11, D 1, L 24, Pts F 491, Pts A 768

Redruth RFC 1993-94

253

REDRUTH RFC

PLAYING SQUAD 1993-94

Full Back: John Wyatt
Wing: Guy Shore, Simon Blake, Andy Knowles, Marcel Gomez, Rick Bigland, David Williams, Ben Stafford
Centre: Scott Wilkins, Chris Sidwell, Tony Mead, Ian Bramley, Gary Wills
Stand Off: Steward Whitworth, Jeremy Stephens
Scrum Half: Chris Whitworth, Dean Hussey
Prop: Adam Ellery, Richard Tonkin, John May, Euan Cowie
Hooker: Mike Phillips, Brian Andrew
Second Row: Tony Cook, Simon O'Sullivan, Mark Wesson
Flanker: John Wedlake, Matt Stearn, Glynn Williams, Adrian Curtis, Shaun Roberts
No 8: Andy Hawken, Paul Thomason

MOST CAPPED PLAYERS

(including British Lions Appearances)
R Sharp, 17
E Scott, 5
J Davey, 2
D Prout, 1
W Grylls, 1
B Solomon, 1

LEADING APPEARANCES FOR CLUB

Andy Hawken, 29, 1993/94
Tony Cook, 27, 1993/94
Chris Whitworth, 24, 1993/94

LEADING SCORERS 1993-94

Simon Blake, Full back, 178 (5t, 18c, 39p)
Stuart Whitworth, Fly half, 43 (1t, 1c, 10p, 2dg)
Marcel Gomez, Wing, 29

REDRUTH RFC

Club Details

Club Colours: Red shirt, white shorts
Change of Colours: Black shirt
Date Founded: 1875
Membership: Total: 1075, Playing members 175, Junior/Youth/Minis 120
No. of teams: Senior 4, Junior 8
Programme advertising rates: Full £225

Ground Details:

Ground Address: Recreation Ground, North Street, Redruth, Cornwall, TR15 1SY
Ground Tel No: 0209 215520
Simple Directions to Ground: A30 West through Cornwall, leave at Redruth exit over twin roundabout, past Avers Garage - Ground signposted on left
Spectator Capacity: Total: 15,000 Seated 670
Ticket Prices: Adults £3, OAP/Child £1.50
Training Nights: Mondays and Wednesdays

Club Officials

Club President: W J Bishop OBE JP
Club Chairman: S W Curtis
Club Secretary: Ivor Horscorft, Silver Fields, Chapel Street, Redruth, Cornwall, TR15 2DT. Tel: (H) 0209 612244 (W) 0209 215941 Fax: 0209 214019
Fixtures Secretary: Jerry Penna, Chy Avalon, North Country, Redruth, Cornwall, TR16 4BZ. Tel: (H) 0209 211520 (W) 0872 74282 Ext 3221
Press Officer: Nick Serpell, 68 Falmouth Road, Redruth, Cornwall, TR15 2QP. Tel: (H) 0209 212611 (W) 0209 314400
Registration Officer: Peter Johnson, Recreation Ground, Redruth, TR15 1SY. Tel: (W) 0209 215520 Fax: 0209 314438
1994/ 95 1st XV Captain: Kevin Thomas
1994/95 Club Coach: Phil Angove
Other Club Officers: Bryan Prouse, Commercial Manager
Peter Johnson, Director of Coaching

REDRUTH RFC

COURAGE LEAGUE RECORDS

Biggest Home Win: 42-6 v St Ives 19-9-87 ALS   **Defeat:** 9-39 v Rosslyn Park 26-3-94 CL3
Biggest Away Win: 39-6 v Salisbury 23-9-89 ALS   **Defeat:** 13-60 v Coventry 30-4-94 CL3
Most Tries For in a Match: **Against:** 10 v Fylde 9-4-94 Away CL3
Most consecutive Wins: 16   **Defeats:** 9
No. of matches failed to Score: 0   **Clean Sheets:** 5   **Drawn Matches:** 5
Most appearance Forward: 53 Tony Cook   **Back:**
Most consecutive appearances: 53 Tony Cook 22-9-90 to date
Consecutive matches scoring Tries: 3 Andy Knowles, Marcel Gomez, Paul Thomason
Consecutive matches scoring Points: 11 Kevin Thomas

INDIVIDUAL SCORING RECORDS

IN A MATCH

Most points: 15 Kevin Thomas v Lydney 21-12-91 H CL3, Simon Blake v Havant 23-4-94 H CL3
Most tries: 3 J Wills v Clifton 2-1-88 H ALS
Most cons: 3 Simon Blake v Havant 23-3-91 H D4S
Most penalities: 5 Kevin Thomas v Lydney 21-12-91 H CL3, Simon Blake v Havant 23-3-91 H D4S
Most drop goals: 2 Grant Champion v Headingley 11-4-92 H CL3

IN A SEASON

Most points: 89 Simon Blake 1990-91 D4S, Kevin Thomas 1992-93 CL3
Most tries: 6 Andy Knowles 1990-91 D4S, 1992-93 CL3
Most conversions: 13 Simon Blake 1990-91 D4S
Most penalties: 24 Kevin Thomas 1992-93 CL3
Most drop goals: 2 Grant Champion 1991-92 CL3

IN A CAREER

Most points: 169 Kevin Thomas 1991-93
Most tries: 14 Andy Knowles 1990-94
Most conversions: 14 Simon Blake 1990-94
Most penalties: 46 Kevin Thomas 1991-93
Most drop goals: 3 Grant Champion 1991-93

COURAGE LEAGUE RECORD

	DIV	PLD	W	D	L	F	T	C	P	D	A	T	C	P	D
1987-88	SW1	10	7	1	2	222					107				
1988-89	ALS	10	6	1	3	136					81				
1989-90	ALS	10	7	0	3	151					84				
1990-91	D4S	12	12	0	0	225	34	16	19	0	79				
1991-92	3	12	6	1	5	155	14	3	28	3	123	10	1	23	4
1993-93	3	11	7	2	2	175	17	9	23	1	125	13	3	18	0
1993-94	3	18	2	0	16	178	9	2	41	2	488	63	34	33	2
		83	17	5	31										

SEASON BY SEASON LEADING SCORERS

	Most Points			Most Tries	
1990-91	89	Simon Blake	6	Andy Knowles	
1991-92	80	Kevin Thomas	2	Simon Blake, Marcel Gomez, Andy Knowles, Jeff Berryman	
1992-93	89	Kevin Thomas	6	Andy Knowles	
1993-94	71	Simon Blake	2	Chris Whitworth, Rose	

ROTHERHAM RUFC

"Catch Up" Lands Spoils

After just losing out to Harrogate on points difference for the promotion spot to National Four last season Rotherham surged through with a run of nine successive victories to take the newly designated National Five North title.

By the standards of recent seasons Rotherham had a poor start, losing at Winnington Park in the first round of the Pilkington Cup and suffering a heavy defeat at Morley. Injuries and county calls meant that they could rarely turn out a settled side and the results showed this clearly.

In the league Rotherham started badly with their heaviest ever defeat at Winnington Park but the same side trounced Stowbridge the following week. The next away game at Hereford was drawn 3-3 on a quagmire and with only three points out of six Rotherham were always playing "catch up". To their credit the side improved and victories at Kendal and Lichfield plus home wins against Stoke and Nuneaton set up a final run of five league games in six weeks. Victory at Birmingham and Solihull was followed by the all important victory in a tense game at home to Preston Grasshoppers. Durham were buried at Rotherham and Walsall defeated away. The final game at home to Bradford saw Rotherham fall 13-0 behind in the first ten minutes but a superb display in front of a big crowd saw the home side triumph 54-19 to clinch the title.

CLUB PLAYING RECORD 1993-94

National League: Five North
Final League Position at end of 1993/94 Season: First
League Playing record: P 12, W 10, D 1, L 1, Pts F 335, Pts A142
Season Playing record (including league matches/Pilkington Cup): P 28, W 20, D 1, L 7, Pts F 714, Pts A 448

Rotherham celebrate promotion after last league fixture   Photo: *Rotherham Advertiser*

ROTHERHAM RUFC

ACHIEVEMENTS/COMPETITIONS WON DURING 93/94 SEASON
National Division Four North Champions

PLAYING SQUAD 1993-94
Full Back: Dave Pullan, Danny Walker, Terry Khoo
Wing: Paul Scott, Russ Askwith, Gary Adams, Scott Allott, Rob Harrison, Pip Reeves
Centre: Steve Hough, Jason Sorby, Grant Treece, Jimmy Rodgers, Joe Bowman, Richard Wood
Stand Off: Kevin Plant, Danny Walker, John Harrison
Scrum Half: Steve Worrall, Jimmy Rodgers, Dave Schudler
Prop: Simon Bunting, Sam Coy, Lee Rick, Ben Hebden, Scott Wilson
Hooker: Tom Bayston, Andy Hucknall
Second Row: John Dudley, Brian Richardson, Ian Gresser, Julian Brooksbant
Back Row: Richard Selkirk, Craig West, Andy Challinor, Mark Pinder, Ieuan Evans, Steve Hanson

LEADING APPEARANCES FOR CLUB
Dudley, 25, 1993/94
Hough, 25, 1993/94
Pullan, 25, 1993/94
Scott, 25, 1993/94
Selkirk, 25, 1993/94
Coy, 24, 1993/94
Bayston, 24, 1993/94
Worrall, 23, 1993/94
Bunting, 22, 1993/94
West, 20, 1993/94

LEADING SCORERS: 1993/94
Kevin Plant, Stand Off, 165
John Dudley, 2nd Row, 110
Steve Worrall, Scrum Half, 57
Richard Selkirk, No 8, 55
Paul Scott, Wing, 55
Danny Walker, Stand Off/Centre, 51

ROTHERHAM RUFC

Club Details

Club Colours: Maroon & Sky blue hoops
Change of Colours: Maroon
Date Founded: 1923
Membership: Total: 900, Playing members 100, Juniors/Youth/Minis 100
No. of teams: Senior 4 + U21s, Junior 8
Programme advertising rates: Full £300

Ground Details:

Ground Address: Clifton Lane, Rotherham
Ground Tel No: 0709 370763
Simple Directions to Ground: (a) Leave M1 at Junction 33. Follow Rotherway for half a mile to roundabout. Take second exit signposted Bawtry 3/4 miles. Traffic lights, straight on up hill to roundabout. Exit first left. Follow road into centre of town. Ground approx. 1 mile on right. (b) Leave M18 at Junction 1. Follow signs to Rotherham. After 2 miles approx at second roundabout (Breeks Hotel) fork right. At next roundabout (Stag Inn) second exit. Follow road into centre of town. Ground approx 1 mile on right.
Spectator Capacity: Total: 1,500, seated 270
Ticket Prices: Adults £3 (league) OAP/Child £1
Training Nights: Mondays and Thursdays

Club Officials

Club President: Allan Williams
Club Chairman:
Club Secretary: Keith Oxley, 119 Broom Lane, Rotherham, S60 3NN. Tel: (H) 0709 542887 (W) 0742 523389
Fixtures Secretary: Andy Fraser, 10 Birch Close, Killamarsh, Sheffield. Tel: (H) 0742 482051 (W) 0742 7690245
Press Officer: Allan Williams, 116 Grange Road, Rotherham, S60 3LL. Tel: (H) 0709 364190
Registration Officer: Steve Cousins, c/o Yorkshire Window Company, Hellaby Ind. Est., Rotherham. Tel: (W) 0709 540982
1994/95 1st XV Captain: Kevin Plant
1994/95 Club Coach: Jon Curry
Director of Coaching: Jon Curry

Kevin Plant scores final try in last league game against Bradford   *Photo: Rotherham Advertiser*

ROTHERHAM RUFC

COURAGE LEAGUE RECORDS

Biggest Home Win: 76-3 v Durham 19-3-94 D5N   **Defeat:** 10-18 v Huddersfield 7-4-90 N2
Biggest Away Win: 34-3 v Blaydon 14-1-89 NE1   **Defeat:** 3-26 v Winnington Park 23-10-93 D5N
Most consecutive Wins: 17   **Defeats:** 2
Most Tries For in a Match: 11 v Durham 19-3-94 D5N   **Against:**
No. of matches failed to Score: 1   **Clean Sheets:** 5   **Drawn Matches:** 3
Most appearance Forward: 74 Richard Selkirk   **Back:**
Most consecutive appearances: 74 Richard Selkirk
Consecutive matches scoring Tries: 4 T Reece
Consecutive matches scoring Points: 14 Kevin Plant

INDIVIDUAL SCORING RECORDS

IN A MATCH

Most points: 24 Paul Scott v Westoe
Most tries: 6 Paul Scott v Westoe 8-4-89 NE1
Most cons: 9 Kevin Plant v Durham 19-3-94 H D5N
Most penalities: 6 David Francis v Keighley 8-4-89 H NE1
Most drop goals: 1 on 13 occasions, Kevin Plant 11, Steve Worrell 1, John Harrison 1

IN A SEASON

Most points: 118 Kevin Plant 1993-94 D5N
Most tries: 12 Paul Scott 1988-90 NE1
Most conversions: 22 Kevin Plant 1993-94 D5N
Most penalties: 21 Kevin Plant 1988-89 NE1, 1989-90 N2, 1993-94 D5N
Most drop goals: 3 Kevin Plant 1990-91 N1

IN A CAREER

Most points: 564 Kevin Plant 1987-94
Most tries: 35 Paul Scott 1987-94
Most conversions: 90 Kevin Plant 1987-94
Most penalties: 107 Kevin Plant 1987-94
Most drop goals: 11 Kevin Plant 1987-94

COURAGE LEAGUE RECORD

	DIV	PLD	W	D	L	F	T	C	P	D	A	T	C	P	D
1987-88	NE1	10	8	0	2	175	22	9	21	2	52				
1988-89	NE1	10	10	0	0	273	40	22	21	2	54				
1989-90	N2	10	9	0	1	214	26	16	24	2	134				
1990-91	N1	10	6	1	3	198	28	13	17	3	107				
1991-92	N1	10	10	0	0	245	36	19	21	0	123				
1992-93	D4N	12	10	1	1	259	32	15	21	2	123				
1993-94	D5N	12	10	1	1	335	42	25	23	2	142				

SEASON BY SEASON LEADING SCORERS

	Most Points			Most Tries	
1987-88	55	Kevin Plant	6	Richard Selkirk	
1988-89	111	Kevin Plant	12	Paul Scott	
1989-90	98	Kevin Plant	6	Paul Scott	
1990-91	81	Kevin Plant	4	Richard Selkirk, J Dudley, Walker	
1991-92	60	Steve Worrell	7	Richard Selkirk	
1992-93	50	Steve Worrell	8	Andy Challinor	
1993-94	118	Kevin Plant	8	J Dudley	

LEAGUE 5 NORTH

LEAGUE 5 SOUTH

RESULTS AND LEAGUE TABLES
1993-94
Pages 262-263

MEMBER CLUBS
1994-95

League 5 North & 5 South Official:
L C K Angel
1 Rochford Road
Basingstoke
Hampshire RG21 1TQ
Tel: (H) 0256 27935
(B) 0256 844844 x 4584

League 5 North & 5 South Registrar:
M J Wilson
Michael Humphreys & Partners Ltd
68 South Lambeth Road
Vauxhall
London SW8 1RL
Tel: (B) 071-820 9911

NATIONAL LEAGUE FIVE NORTH STATISTICS 1993/94

RESULTS

		1	2	3	4	5	6	7	8	9	10	11	12	13
1	B'ham & S'hull			16-11	14-3	20-15	6-7			8-15			10-17	12-9
2	Bradford & B	26-5			16-0	22-34			11-14					27-26
3	Durham		19-11				21-13		3-13		27-15	14-16		
4	Hereford			17-12					10-25	3-3	16-9		20-10	15-15
5	Kendal			3-3	11-6			16-6		8-16			6-14	6-3
6	Lichfield	12-5			12-22	16-8				10-13			7-18	5-0
7	Nuneaton	9-8	6-20				9-3		11-23		8-8	19-18		
8	P Grasshoppers	17-16				11-3	20-15	21-12					25-7	18-10
9	Rotherham		54-19	76-3				26-6	11-10		37-8	54-18		
10	Stoke on Trent	9-11	18-13			11-5	17-5		19-3			10-12		
11	Stourbridge	19-3	11-3		15-11	34-15	0-16		10-6					
12	Walsall		16-15	22-16				17-0		23-27	6-13	12-0		
13	Winnington Park			66-3				24-12		26-3	24-16	15-9	9-6	

WEEK BY WEEK POSITIONS

	13/11	11/12	29/1	26/2	12/3	26/3	30/4
Birmingham & S	4	5	8	11	9	11	9
Bradford & B	12	8	7	6	7	9	13
Durham	6	11	11	9	6	8	12
Hereford	2	3	4	5	5	6	8
Kendal	7	12	12	12	11	13	10
Lichfield	10	6	9	10	12	10	7
Nuneaton	11	10	13	13	13	12	11
P Grasshoppers	1	1	1	1	1	2	2
Rotherham	5	2	2	3	2	1	1
Stoke on Trent	8	7	5	7	8	5	6
Stourbridge	13	13	10	8	10	7	5
Walsall	9	9	3	2	3	3	3
Winnington Park	3	4	6	4	4	4	4

PLAYING RECORD

	PLD	W	D	L	F	A	PD	Pts
Rotherham	12	10	1	1	335	142	193	21
Preston Grasshoppers	12	10	0	2	191	128	63	20
Walsall	12	7	0	5	166	148	18	14
Winnington Park	12	6	1	5	227	132	95	13
Stourbridge	12	6	0	6	162	188	-26	12
Stoke on Trent	12	5	1	6	153	167	-14	11
Lichfield	12	5	0	7	118	138	-20	10
Hereford	12	4	2	6	126	153	-27	10
Birmingham & Solihull	12	5	0	7	128	162	-34	10
Kendal	12	4	1	7	142	171	-29	9
Nuneaton	12	4	1	7	122	200	-78	9
Durham City	12	4	1	7	159	279	-120	9
Bradford & Bingley	12	4	0	8	189	210	-21	8

NATIONAL LEAGUE FIVE SOUTH STATISTICS 1993/94

RESULTS

		1	2	3	4	5	6	7	8	9	10	11	12	13
1	Basingstoke			20-9		12-9	10-16			10-26		13-17	12-9	
2	Berry Hill	14-7			13-6	24-34				3-3		16-12	15-6	
3	Camvorne		17-16		38-13			23-3	2-25		3-3			32-17
4	High Wycombe	13-11				16-13	6-6			0-23		23-14	7-14	
5	London Welsh			17-17			3-3	56-3	12-8		0-12			39-7
6	Lydney		8-13	23-3				33-7	16-7		6-13			15-3
7	Maidstone	19-58	6-14		6-20					14-26		3-50	9-23	
8	Met. Police	28-13	19-9		15-6		3-10			16-3			13-31	
9	North Walsham			8-13		13-6	11-13					15-9	6-6	11- 14
10	Reading	32-3	21-6		17-0			41-0	26-0	32-3				
11	Southend		17-3	10-18		13-15	18-26		29-28		11-14			14-18
12	Tabard		25-9			12-12	17-16				13-22	19-6		8-9
13	W Super Mare	18-22	15-3		5-10		29-6		12-5		16-15			

WEEK BY WEEK POSITIONS

	13/11	4/12	11/12	8/1	29/1	26/2	12/3	26/3	9/4	23/4	30/4
Basingstoke	7	6	4	8	6	9	11	11	11	11	11
Berry Hill	12	10	8	6	9	7	5	7	6	7	7
Camborne	6	7	7	3	5	6	7	4	4	4	4
H Wycombe	4	5	9	7	3	4	6	8	9	9	9
L. Welsh	11	9	10	10	8	11	9	6	5	6	6
Lydney	2	2	2	2	2	2	2	2	2	2	2
Maidstone	10	12	13	13	13	13	13	13	13	13	13
Met. Police	13	13	12	12	11	8	10	9	10	10	10
North Walsham	5	4	6	9	10	10	8	10	7	8	8
Reading	1	1	1	1	1	1	1	1	1	1	1
Southend	9	11	11	11	12	12	12	12	12	12	12
Tabard	3	3	3	4	7	5	3	3	3	3	3
Weston-Super-Mare	8	8	5	5	4	3	4	5	8	5	5

PLAYING RECORD

	PLD	W	D	L	F	A	PD	Pts
Reading	12	10	1	1	248	61	187	21
Lydney	12	7	2	3	181	111	70	16
Tabard	12	6	2	4	183	136	47	14
Camborne	12	6	2	4	197	180	17	14
Weston-Super-Mare	12	7	0	5	163	180	-17	14
London Welsh	12	5	3	4	216	140	76	13
Berry Hill	12	6	1	5	146	154	-8	13
North Walsham	12	5	2	5	148	136	12	12
High Wycombe	12	5	1	6	120	173	-53	11
Metropolitan Police	12	5	0	7	167	174	-7	10
Basingstoke	12	5	0	7	191	210	-19	10
Southend	12	3	0	9	203	208	-5	6
Maidstone	12	1	0	11	86	386	-300	2

COURAGE LEAGUE FIXTURES

**1994-95
NATIONAL LEAGUE
FIVE NORTH**

January 7 (Week 17)
Lichfield v Sheffield
Wharfedale v Birmingham Solihull
Preston Grasshoppers v Nuneaton
Walsall v Kendal
Barkers Butts v Stoke-on-Trent
Winnington Park v Hereford

September 17 (Week 3)
Nuneaton v Kendal
Birmingham Solihull v Stoke-on-Trent
Sheffield v Hereford
Litchfield v Stourbridge
Wharfedale v Winnington Park
Preston Grasshoppers v Barkers Butts

January 14 (Week 18)
Kendal v Barkers Butts
Nuneaton v Walsall
Birmingham Solihull v Preston Grasshoppers
Sheffield v Wharfedale
Hereford v Stourbridge
Stoke-on-Trent v Winnington Park

September 24 (Week 4)
Kendal v Birmingham Solihull
Barkers Butts v Walsall
Winnington Park v Preston Grasshoppers
Stourbridge v Wharfedale
Hereford v Lichfield
Stoke-on-Trent v Sheffield

February 11 (Week 22)
Wharfedale v Lichfield
Preston Grasshoppers v Sheffield
Walsall v Birmingham Solihull
Barkers Butts v Nuneaton
Winnington Park v Kendal
Stourbridge v Stoke-on-Trent

October 1 (Week 5)
Birmingham Solihull v Nuneaton
Sheffield v Kendal
Lichfield v Stoke-on-Trent
Wharfedale v Hereford
Preston Grasshoppers v Stourbridge
Walsall v Winnington Park

February 25 (Week 24)
Kendal v Stourbridge
Nuneaton v Winnington Park
Birmingham Solihull v Barkers Butts
Sheffield v Walsall
Lichfield v Preston Grasshoppers
Stoke-on-Trent v Hereford

October 15 (Week 7)
Kendal v Lichfield
Nuneaton v Sheffield
Winnington Park v Barkers Butts
Stourbridge v Walsall
Hereford v Preston Grasshoppers
Stoke-on-Trent v Wharfedale

March 4 (Week 25)
Preston Grasshoppers v Wharfedale
Walsall v Lichfield
Barkers Butts v Sheffield
Winnington Park v Birmingham Solihull
Stourbridge v Nuneaton
Hereford v Kendal

October 22 (Week 8)
Sheffield v Birmingham Solihull
Lichfield v Nuneaton
Wharfedale v Kendal
Preston Grasshoppers v Stoke-on-Trent
Walsall v Hereford
Barkers Butts v Stourbridge

March 25 (Week 28)
Kendal v Stoke-on-Trent
Nuneaton v Hereford
Birmingham Solihull v Stourbridge
Sheffield v Winnington Park
Lichfield v Barkers Butts
Wharfedale v Walsall

October 29 (Week X2)
Kendal v Preston Grasshoppers
Nuneaton v Wharfedale
Birmingham Solihull v Lichfield
Stourbridge v Winnington Park
Hereford v Barkers Butts
Stone-on-Trent v Walsall

April 8 (Week 30)
Walsall v Preston Grasshoppers
Barkers Butts v Wharfedale
Winnington Park v Lichfield
Stourbridge v Sheffield
Hereford v Birmingham Solihull
Stoke-on-Trent v Nuneaton

264

COURAGE LEAGUE FIXTURES

1994-95
NATIONAL LEAGUE
FIVE SOUTH

September 17 (Week 3)
Camborne v Basingstoke
High Wycombe v Weston-Super-Mare
Lydney v North Walsham
Berry Hill v Henley
London Welsh v Tabard
Barking v Metropolitan Police

September 24 (Week 4)
Basingstoke v High Wycombe
Metropolitan Police v Sudbury
Tabard v Barking
Henley v London Welsh
North Walsham v Berry Hill
Weston-Super-Mare v Lydney

October 1 (Week 5)
High Wycombe v Camborne
Lydney v Basingstoke
Berry Hill v Weston-Super-Mare
London Welsh v North Walsham
Barking v Henley
Sudbury v Tabard

October 15 (Week 7)
Basingstoke v Berry Hill
Camborne v Lydney
Tabard v Metropolitan Police
Henley v Sudbury
North Walsham v Barking
Weston-Super-Mare v London Welsh

October 22 (Week 8)
Lydney v High Wycombe
Berry Hill v Camborne
London Welsh v Basingstoke
Barking v Weston-Super-Mare
Sudbury v North Walsham
Metropolitan Police v Henley

October 29 (Week X2)
Basingstoke v Barking
Camborne v London Welsh
High Wycombe v Berry Hill
Henley v Tabard
North Walsham v Metropolitan Police
Weston-Super-Mare v Sudbury

January 7 (Week 17)
Berry Hill v Lydney
London Welsh v High Wycombe
Barking v Camborne
Sudbury v Basingstoke
Metropolitan Police v Weston-Super-Mare
Tabard v North Walsham

January 14 (Week 18)
Basingstoke v Metropolitan Police
Camborne v Sudbury
High Wycombe v Barking
Lydney v London Welsh
North Walsham v Henley
Weston-Super-Mare v Tabard

February 11 (Week 22)
London Welsh v Berry Hill
Barking v Lydney
Sudbury v High Wycombe
Metropolitan Police v Camborne
Tabard v Basingstoke
Henley v Weston-Super-Mare

February 25 (Week 24)
Basingstoke v Henley
Camborne v Tabard
High Wycombe v Metropolitan Police
Lydney v Sudbury
Berry Hill v Barking
Weston-Super-Mare v North Walsham

March 4 (Week 25)
Barking v London Welsh
Sudbury v Berry Hill
Metropolitan Police v Lydney
Tabard v High Wycombe
Henley v Camborne
North Walsham v Basingstoke

March 25 (Week 28)
Basingstoke v Weston-Super-Mare
Camborne v North Walsham
High Wycombe v Henley
Lydney v Tabard
Berry Hill v Metropolitan Police
London Welsh v Sudbury

April 8 (Week 30)
Sudbury v Barking
Metropolitan Police v London Welsh
Tabard v Berry Hill
Henley v Lydney
North Walsham v High Wycombe
Weston-Super-Mare v Camborne

BARKERS' BUTTS RFC

CLUB PLAYING RECORD 1993-94
National League: Midlands Div 1
Final League Position at end of 1993/94 Season: 1st

ACHIEVEMENTS/COMPETITIONS WON DURING 93/94 SEASON
Champions — Midlands Division One
Winners — Warwickshire Cup

Club Details
Club Colours: Blue and gold hoops
Change of Colours: Red
Date Founded: 1946
Membership: Total: 450, Playing members 180, Junior/Youth/Minis 8
No. of teams: Senior 5, Junior 2
Programme advertising rates: Full £100, then pro rata
Any Special Occasions during 1994/95: First Season National League

Ground Details:
Ground Address: Pickford Grange Lane, Allesley, Coventry, CV5 9AR
Ground Tel No: 0607 22192 Fax: 0676 23633
Simple Directions to Ground: Off A45 at Meriden outskirts of Coventry towards Birmingham Airport.
Spectator Capacity: Total: 250 standing
Ticket Prices: Adults: £2.00, OAP/Child Free
Training Nights: Tuesdays and Thursdays

Club Officials
Club President: K J Aldridge
Club Chairman: A A Fairchild
Club Secretary: J I Evans, 70 Norman Place Road, Coventry, CV6. Tel: (H) 0203 335780 Fax: 0676 23633
Fixtures Secretary: R Baty, 59 Sutton Avenue, Eastern Green, Coventry, CV5 7EG. Tel: (H) 0203 471236 Fax: 0676 23633
Press Officer: P J Jackson, 87 Gretna Road, Green Lane South, Coventry, CV3 6DT. Tel: (H) 0203 419595 Fax: 0676 23633
Registration Officer: G C Chuter, 1 Fairbourne Way, Coundon, Coventry, CV6 2NF. Tel: (H) 0203 336709 Fax: 0676 23633
1994/ 95 1st XV Captain: A Wood
1994/95 Club Coach: P Carter
Chairman - Playing Committee: A R Gibbs

LEAGUE 5 NORTH PROGRAMMES

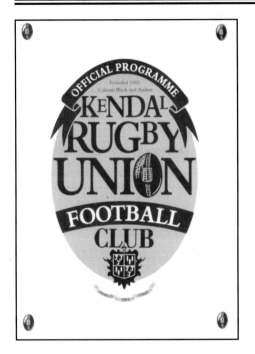

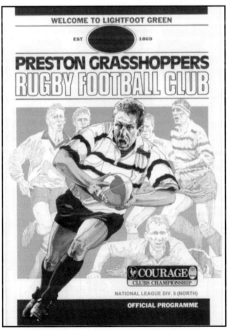

BIRMINGHAM & SOLIHULL RFC

Half a loaf better than no bread

The 1993-94 season was one of consolidation for Birmingham and Solihull RFC. Their final playing record was played 34 won 17 lost 17.

The began the Courage League season with great promise with early season victories over Stoke, Kendal and Durham. However, they found it difficult to recapture this form after the Christmas break and they had to win their final two games of the season against Winnington Park and Hereford to ensure their Courage League status. Undoubtedly the highlight of the season was their successful run in the Pilkington Cup in which they reached the fourth round where they were beaten by Saracens.

The team was captained by prop Max Reeve who took over from fellow front row forward Rob Hetherington who tore knee ligaments in only the second game of the season. The season also saw the emergence of several youngsters from the club's flourishing junior section. David Cox, Stuart Legg Simon Adams and Andy Wilshaw all played significant parts in the final league games of the season. Finally, the 1993-94 season was the last for stalwart hooker Chris Barbour who after many years of loyal service announced his retirement.

CLUB PLAYING RECORD 1993-94

National Division: Five North
Final League Position at end of 1993/94 season: Mid Table
Season Playing Record: P 34, W 17, D 0, L 17

Club Details

Colours: Black, red, yellow & white quarters
Change of Colours:
Date Founded: 1989
Membership: Total 165
Number of Teams: Senior 6, Junior 10

Ground Details

Ground Address: Searmans Cross Road, Solihull
Telephone: 021 705 7993
Directions: M42 Jcn 5 (A3400) towards B'ham, right at 4th traffic lights, 2 miles on right

Club Officials

President: C Gifford
Chairman: R Sutton
Club Secretary: A Henderson, 9 Grey Mine Close, Monkspath, Solihull, BG0 4ME. Tel: (H) 021 745 4198 (W) 021 749 2240 (Fax) 021 748 3838
Fixtures Secretary: A Morden, Station Farm, 40 Station Road, Hampton-in-Arden, Solihull. Tel: (H) 0675 442462 (W) 643 021 2736
Press Officer: R Montegue, 9 Coppice Drive, Acorns Green, Birmingham. Tel: (H) 021 604 1663 (W) 021 785 2000
Registration Officer: A Morden — As Fix. Sec.
1993/94 1XV Captain: Gareth Smith
1993/94 1XV Coach: Malcolm Swan

LEAGUE 5 NORTH PROGRAMMES

WHARFEDALE R.U.F.C.
OFFICIAL PROGRAMME

WHARFESIDE AVENUE, THRESHFIELD
Tel. GRASSINGTON 752547

STOURBRIDGE
RUGBY FOOTBALL CLUB

1993 / 94 SEASON

ST UR VIEW

OFFICIAL MATCH PROGRAMME
Bridgnorth Road, Stourton,
Stourbridge, West Midlands, DY7 6QZ
Telephone: Stourbridge (0384) 393889

STOKE ON TRENT

RUGBY UNION FOOTBALL CLUB
Hartwell Lane, Barlaston, Stoke-on-Trent, Telephone 0782 372807

National
League
Division V
North

SEASON
1993/94

COURAGE
CLUBS CHAMPIONSHIP

Mark Coupe Homes

OFFICIAL MATCH PROGRAMME

SHEFFIELD RUGBY UNION FOOTBALL CLUB

Founded 1902, Abbeydale Park, Sheffield

SEASON 1993 - 94

SUPPORTED BY & TAYLOR EMMET SOLICITORS

COURAGE
CLUBS CHAMPIONSHIP

HEREFORD RUFC

CLUB PLAYING RECORD 1993-94

National League: Five North
Final League Position at end of 1993/94 Season: 8th
League Playing record: P 12, W 4, D 2, L 6, Pts F 126, Pts A 153
Season Playing record (including league matches/Pilkington Cup):
P 38, W 18, D 3, L 17, Pts F 494, Pts A 563

ACHIEVEMENTS/COMPETITIONS WON DURING 93/94 SEASON
Semi-final North Midlands Cup
2nd Round Pilkington Cup

Club Details

Club Colours: Red, black, white
Change of Colours: White
Date Founded: 1870
Membership: Total: 490, Playing members 120, Junior/Youth/Minis 150
No. of teams: Senior: 4 + Vets
Programme advertising rates: Full £100
Any Special Occasions during 1994/95: 125th Year

Ground Details:

Ground Address: Wyeside, Belvedere Lane, Hereford, NR4 9UT
Ground Tel No: 0432 273410
Simple Directions to Ground: A49 North side of river bridge - West, 2nd on left, turn left into Belvedere Lane
Spectator Capacity: Total: 1,300, seated 300, standing 1,000
Ticket Prices: Adults: £2, OAP/Child: £1
Training Nights: Tuesdays and Thursdays

Club Officials

Club President: Rory Davis
Club Chairman: N W Jarvis
Club Secretary: M H V Littlefield, The Rides, 13 Burwood Close, Hereford, HR1 1DQ. Tel: (H) 0432 275468 (W) 0432 356310 Fax: 0432 356310
Fixtures Secretary: D Beech, Melbourne, Blackmoor Park Road, Malvern, Worcestershire, WR1 6NN. Tel: (H) 0684 310292
Press Officer: Miss M Miles, 31 Quarry Road, Tupsley, Hereford. Tel: (H) 0432 277129 (W) 0432 355353
Registration Officer: M H V Littlefield
1994/ 95 1st XV Captain: Neil Coulson
1994/95 Club Coach: Andy Douthwaite
Captain of Rugby: M Lewis

LEADING APPEARANCES FOR CLUB
Rory Davis
Gus Grishan
John Watkins
Dave Rogers

LEADING SCORERS 1993-94
Simon Williams, Wing, 90
John Watkins, Lock, 120
Rory Davis, Scrum half, 85

Top Left: Mr Consistency, fly half Chris Mann, kicks one of his six penalties for Stourbridge v Nuneaton. Photo: Ceri Davies
Top Right: Top try scorer Richard Trigg in typically aggressive mood for Stourbridge v Nuneaton, October 1993. Photo: Ceri Davies

Bottom Left: Mark Rogers, Sheffield's leading points scorer 1993-94
Bottom Right: Preston Grasshoppers skipper Phil Crayston on a typical charge against Waterloo with scrum half John Bleasdale, lock Michael Bailey and hooker Peter Carter in support. Photo: Lancashire Evening Post.

KENDAL RUFC

Kendal's Last Gasp Escape

1993/94 was a rather disappointing season with a below par performance in the League. By beating Bradford & Bingley 34-22 in the last game of the season we avoided relegation. The two points saw us move from bottom to 10th in what must be the closest finish since leagues were introduced.

Our brief run in the Pilkington Cup ended in the first round when we lost at York. We did better in domestic competitions with the runners-up spot in the Cumbria Cup and success in the Westmorland Cup.

Peter Kremer, No 8 and former Captain, dislocated his shoulder in the Cumbria Cup final and may be forced to retire. The silver lining to the cloud is that he has been appointed Director of Coaching.

Last season four players - Steve Healey, Shaun Pratt, Jason Slater and Ian Thompson - won their club badge for 20 first team appearances. Jonathon Nicholson, a former first team hooker, returned to the squad after two seasons out through injury, and will be captaining the side for the 94/95 season. With only two transfer outs and two new signings, the squad is looking quite healthy.

Having demonstrated what they are capable of at Bradford & Bingley, we are looking forward to the 1994/95 season with anticipation.

CLUB PLAYING RECORD 1993-94

National League: Five North
Final League Position at end of 1993/94 Season: 10th
League Playing record: P 12, W 4, D 1, L 7, Pts Fo142, Pts A 171
Season Playing record (including league matches/Pilkington Cup): P 31, W 16, D 1, L 14, Pts F 537, Pts A 434

ACHIEVEMENTS/COMPETITIONS WON DURING 93/94 SEASON

Runners up — Cumbria Cup
Westmorland Cup — Winners

Kendal RUFC, 1993-94

KENDAL RUFC

Club Details

Club Colours: Amber & black
Change of Colours: Amber, black & white
Date Founded: 1905
Membership: Total: 420, Playing Members 75, Junior/Youth/Minis 95
No. of teams: Senior 3, Junior 10
Programme advertising rates: Full £150

Ground Details:

Ground Address: Mint Bridge, Shap Road, Kendal, Cumbria, LA9 6DL
Ground Tel No: 0539 734039 & 724239
Simple Directions to Ground: From South Follow A6 signs for Penrith (One Way System) to Duke of Cumberland. Keep left, club on left half a mile.
Spectator Capacity: Total: 1,000+, 250 seated
Ticket Prices: Adults £2.50, OAP 50p
Training Nights: Tuesdays & Thursdays

Club Officials

Club President: R A Short
Club Chairman: I W Hutton
Club Secretary: P A Ruiz, 29 Mint Street, Kendal, LA9 6DS. Tel: (H) 0539 720686 (W) 0539 734039
Fixtures Secretary: A Quarry, 14 Collinfield, Kendal, LA9 5JD. Tel: (H) 0539 731640 (W) 0539 720391 Fax: 0539 720645
Press Officer: John Hutton, 168 Vicarage Drive, Kendal, LA9 5BX. Tel: (H) 0539 733152 (W) 0539 722112
Registration Officer: P Ruiz, Hon Secretary
1994/ 95 1st XV Captain: J Nicholson
1994/95 Club Coach: P Kremer
Other Club Officers: R Wilson, Match Secretary

PLAYING SQUAD 1993-94

Full Back: P Dodds, M Mace, G Slater
Wing: J Bill, P Dalzell, G Fisher, S Morris, I Murray, M Wood
Centre: M Healey, S Healey, J Slater
O/Half: D Bell, A Dolan, M Fell,
Scrum Half: M Airey, R Morris, D Sharpe
Prop: J Bracken, B Coxon, S Hulme, N Pearson, S Pratt
Hooker: J Nicholson, I Thompson
Lock: M Capstick, H Nicholson, K Robinson, R Stewart
Back Row: I Downham, A Nutter, G Rigg, R Stowe, M Thomas, S Whitehead
No 8: P Kremer

LEADING APPEARANCES FOR CLUB

S Healey, 30, 1993/94
S Hulme, 28, 1993/94
J Slater, 28, 1993/94
R Stewart, 27, 1993/94
P Kremer, 27, 1993/94

LEADING SCORERS:

M Mace, Full Back, 103
J Bill, Wing, 85
S Healey, Centre, 38
D Bell, O/Half, 35

LICHFIELD RUFC

FOUNDED 1874

Lichfield Finish Strongly

It was hoped that 1993/94 would be a season of progress after the many changes of the previous year. A lack of stability in team selection - mainly due to injuries - and the consequential loss of confidence meant that too many games were lost by narrow margins, when victory was achievable.

Following Christmas, the missing ingredients above were discovered and much improved form ensued enabling Lichfield to have a good finish to the season, ending with more victories than losses. More importantly, relative safety in Division Five North was achieved in the final two games, in what turned out to be a very competitive league with no overall pattern to results.

The club's lower sides all had very decent seasons and hopes are high for the 1994/95 season for the colts side, in particular. The development of the Under 21 team was severely hindered by a lack of appropriate opposition.

The minis and junior section continue to flourish at all levels with many age groups having two sides. National Power held two coaching days for younger players during the season.

CLUB PLAYING RECORD 1993-94

National League: Five North
Final League Position at end of 1993/94 Season: 7th
League Playing record: P 12, W 5, D 0, L 7, Pts F 11, Pts A 138
Season Playing record (including league matches/Pilkington Cup): P 31, W 16, D 1, L 15, Pts F 596, Pts A 427

Achievements/competitions won during 93/94 season
Won various Mini & Junior tournaments

Lichfield RUFC   *Photo: Lichfield Mercury*

LICHFIELD RUFC

Club Details

Club Colours: Myrtle Green shirts, navy shorts, red socks
Change of Colours: Yellow shirts with V on green
Date Founded: 1874
Membership: Total: 550, Playing Members 130, Junior/Youth/Minis 250, Other 150
No. of teams: Senior 6 + U21s & Colts, Junior 10
Programme advertising rates: Full £400
Any Special Occasions during 1994/95: Staffs 7s Competition, National Prison Officers Tournament, Fire Service National 7s.

Ground Details:

Ground Address: Cooke Fields, Tamworth Road, Lichfield, Staffs
Ground Tel No: 0543 263020
Simple Directions to Ground: From South & NE - A38 towards Lichfield, take the A51 (towards Tamworth) out of Lichfield for 2 miles. From NW, M6 then A51 south to Lichfield, then as above.
Spectator Capacity: Total: 5,500, seated 500
Ticket Prices: Adult £2.50 League, £2 other, OAP/Child £1
Training Nights: Tuesdays and Thursdays

Club Officials

Club President: Wilf Linney
Club Chairman: Jim Greenhorn
Club Secretary: Shaun D Godfrey, 1 Old College, House, Dam Street, Lichfield, Staffs, WS13 6AA. Tel: (H) 0543 268539 (W) 021 454 7033 Fax: 0543 419958
Fixtures Secretary: Tony Young, 5 Covey Close, Lichfield, Staffordshire, WS13. Tel: (H & W) 0543 262832
Press Officer: Mrs Emma Ridgway, 33 Church Street, Whittington, Lichfield, WS14 9LE Tel: (H) 1543 432972 (W) 021 230 5035 Fax: 021 233 3579 or 0543 432972
Registration Officer: David Lewis, 52 Stafford Road, Lichfield, Staffs, WS13 7BZ. Tel: (H) 0543 254985 (W) 01509 670777 Fax:01509 670011
1994/95 1st XV Captain: Danny Bourne
1994/95 Club Coach: Barry Broad
Other Club Officers:
Dave Lewis, Director of Playing
Jim Ashpole, Commercial Manager
Maurice Keenan, Hon Treasurer
Mark Davis, 1st XV Manager/Assistant Coach
Ian Cobden, Assistant Coach

LEADING APPEARANCES FOR CLUB

Mark Moysey, 29, 1993/94
Danny Bourne, 27, 1993/94
Ian Grant, 26, 1993/94
Jim Ridgway, 24, 1993/94
Sam Henstock, 22, 1993/94
Trevor Cartwright, 22, 1993/94

LEADING SCORERS

Dave Richards, Fly/Scrum Half, 173
Sam Henstock, Centre, 88
Neil Law, Centre, 31
Dorrington Vaughan, Lock Forward, 30
Tony Bartlett, Fly Half, 26
Ian Grant, Lock Forward, 25
Mike Prince, Scrum Half, 25

NUNEATON RFC

Nuneaton's Shaky Survival

The campaign for 1993/94 despite the pre season training got off badly due to a complete new team being formed after a massive recruitment drive. Although many had played rugby for seasons they were inexperienced. As the season progressed, improvements were ongoing particularly when Steve Redfern joined us in early October 1993, the club only winning five games up to Christmas 93 of which two were league games (Birmingham & Solihull 9-8 and Lichfield 9-3).

After Christmas Dave Lyons joined us from Leicester as a backs coach, and, where lack of confidence had been the order of the day, it was restored vigorously, producing some five wins in the latter part of the season notably obtaining five points out of six in the best three league games of the season.

Nuneaton survived the relegation battle and now, as only one member has left (job move), further recruitment along with most of last year's players being available means that we can consolidate and improve on this season's performance.

CLUB PLAYING RECORD 1993-94

National League: Five North
Final League Position at end of 1993/94 Season: 11th
League Playing record: P 12, W 4, D 1, L 7
Season Playing record (including league matches/Pilkington Cup): P 39, W 12, D 2, L 25, Pts F 538, Pts A 926

ACHIEVEMENTS/COMPETITIONS WON DURING 93/94 SEASON
TNT Floodlit Trophy

Nuneaton RFC 1993-94. Back row: K Howells (President), S Redfern (Coach), G Humford, I Croft, A Brown, C Court, M Mitchell, S Newman, A Kearns, A Lascelles, D Cake (Chairman), E Ballard (Sec), J Wright (P/Administrator).
Front row: S Gibson, P Clayton, S Reid, P Flowers (Capt), J Brain, M Green, C Taylor, A Moore, K Howie.

NUNEATON RFC

Club Details

Club Colours: Red, white & black hoops
Change of Colours: Black
Date Founded: 1879
Membership: Total: 400 — Playing members 100, Junior/Youth/Minis 300, Junior Colts 20
No. of teams: Senior 3 + Colts, Junior 11
Programme advertising rates: Full £220, Half £110, Quarter £55 (all + VAT)
Any Special Occasions during 1994/95: Ground re-location (May- September 1995)

Ground Details:

Ground Address: Harry Cleaver Ground, Attleborough Road, Nuneaton, CV11 4JR
Ground Tel No: 0203 383925/383206 Fax: 0203 383925
Spectator Capacity: Total: 5,000, seated 650
Ticket Prices: Adults £3, OAP/Child £1
Training Nights: Mondays & Thursdays

Club Officials

Club President: K J Howells
Club Chairman: D N Cake
Club Secretary: Mrs Marion Gunn, 151 Windermere Avenue, Nuneaton, CV11 6HN. Tel: (H) 0203 387515 Fax: 0203 371852
Fixtures Secretary: John Davies, 3, Saints Way, Nuneaton, CV10 0UU. Tel: (H) 0203 370011 (W) 0203 344800 Fax: 0203 371852
Registration Officer: Mrs M Gunn
1994/ 95 1st XV Captain: Mark Mitchell
1994/95 Club Coach: Dave Lyons & Steve Redfern

PLAYING SQUAD 1993/94

15 S Reid, S Newman, S May
14 W Boffey, A Webb, J Button
13 S Jervis, D Masser, A Kearns, S Finney
12 C Medford, D Cottrill
11 C Bent, P Jones, P Clayton, D Barry
10 C Taylor, W Masser
9 A Savage, K Howie, P Mitchell, M Elvidge, M Scanlon
1 A Moore, N Johnson, J Claridge
2 S Gibson, B Masser, M Barkes
3 P Flowers, C Court
4 A Roberts, G Mumford
5 A Brown, M Mears, I Croft
6 M Mitchell, A Taylor, M Hutton
7 T Simms, A Jones, H Green, S Elkin
8 J Brain, D Burke

LEADING APPEARANCES FOR CLUB

Mark Mitchell, 36, 1993/94
Andy Moore, 34, 1993/94
Simon Reid, 31, 1993/94
Paul Flowers, 31, 1993/94
Clive Medford, 30, 1993/94
Clive Bent, 29, 1993/94

LEADING SCORERS

Colin Taylor, Fly Half, 137
Warwick Hasser, Fly Half, 103
Simon Reid, Full back, 87
Clive Bent, Right Wing, 30
Simon Jervis, Outside Centre, 25
Mark Mitchell, Back Row, 25

PRESTON GRASSHOPPERS RFC

Hoppers disappointed but watch them go!

Second place in the League (after finishing 3rd and 4th in the previous two seasons), a best ever Pilkington Cup run, and in excess of 20 victories for the fourth year in succession may appear to add up to a fine season. However, having lead Division Five North for a long period the one point defeat at Rotherham was a major disappointment but the crucial points were probably lost in an early under par performance at Stoke.

Wade Dooley has retired but will be involved in the club particularly assisting coach John Morgan who has extended his duties to encompass all rugby matters within the club. Dooley apart, all last season's squad will be available again next term with some interesting additions to the strength. Phil Crayston will again lead the side which is still young and has basically been together for three seasons.

Crayston, Jim Moore and Jeff Laker have all played for Lancashire, John Bleasdale for British Fire Services and Neil Ashton has been in the British Police squad. Another member of the Mini/Junior/Colts production line, Patrick Sanderson, has played for England at 16 group level.

Preparations for next season include a major Summer Tour to Canada where matches will be played at 1st XV and a more junior level. A major sponsorship deal has brought a Sportsmatch Grant to enable further expansion of the club's facilities - ie a weights room and gymnasium.

CLUB PLAYING RECORD 1993-94

National League: Five North
Final League Position at end of 1993/94 Season: 2nd
League Playing record: P 12, W 10, D 0, L 2, Pts F 191, Pts A 128
Season Playing record (including league matches/Pilkington Cup): P 36, W 21, D 1, L 14, Pts F 606, Pts A 531

Preston Grasshoppers RFC 1993-94. Back row: Bill Johnston (Coach), John Morgan (Coach), Glyn Dewhurst, Jeff Laker, Richard Crayston, Wade Dooley, Joe Hindle, Michael Bailey, Jim Musson, Steve Holden, John Crayston (Team Manager), Helen Thompson (Physio). Front row: Barry Greenwood, John Chesworth, Peter Carter, Neil Ashton, Phil Crayston (Capt), Andy Taylorson, Jim Moore, Mike Kirby, John Bleasdale, Gordon Humphreys.　　　　*Photo: Lancashire Evening Post*

PRESTON GRASSHOPPERS RFC

Club Details

Club Colours: Navy blue & white
Change of Colours: Emerald Green
Date Founded: 1869
Membership: Total: 1316, Playing members 156, Junior/Youth/Minis 290, VP 110-Full 481-Social 279
No. of teams: Senior 8, Junior/Mini 9, Youth 2
Programme advertising rates: From £45 + VAT to £200 + VAT according to position and size
Any Special Occasions during 1994/95: Canadian Tour July 1994. 125th Anniversary Dinner 28th September 1994.

Ground Details:

Ground Address: Lightfoot Green, Fulwood, Preston PR4 0AP
Ground Tel No:0722 863546/863027 and 861605 (press box)
Simple Directions to Ground: M6 junction 32. Follow Garstang Sign. Turn left towards Preston - in 50 yards turn left again. Follow signs to INGOL. Ground 1 mile from motorway.
Spectator Capacity: Total: 2750, seated 250
Ticket Prices: Adults £4 League £3 other (members £2.50)
Training Nights: Mondays, Wednesdays & Thursdays

Club Officials

Club President: Richard C H Eastwood JP
Club Chairman: George E Thompson
Club Secretary: Leslie Anson, Oak Tree, 110 Whittingham Lane, Broughton, Preston PR3 5DD. Tel: (H) 0772 862050
Fixtures Secretary: John M Powell, 121 Bare Lane, Bare, Morecambe, LA4 4RD
Press Officer: As secretary
Registration Officer: As secretary
1994/ 95 1st XV Captain: Philip J Crayston
1994/95 Club Coach: John Morgan
Other Club Officers:
Ken Moore, Administration Officer
Bob Bailey, Chairman of Rugby
John Hetherington, Programme Editor & Sponsorship
Robbie Jarvis, Bar Chairman
Jim Powdrell, Hon Treasurer
John Muirhead, Finance Chairman

PLAYING SQUAD 1993-94

Full Back: J Chesworth, E Dean
Wing: J C Hindle, B Greenwood, R Stainer, P Cornall
Centre: J Moore, D Whittingham, A D Taylorson, J Erdozain, A Christopherson
Stand Off: M Kirby, I Jackson, J Lamb, J Musson, T S K Aitchison
Scrum Half: J Bleasdale, W Mould, A Davies, S Wiggins
Prop: L Bell, R Crayston, J Holden, R Spicer, N Leeming, D Woolley, J Nixon, G Humphreys, J Williams
Hooker: P Carter, M Maddox, M Sutcliffe
Lock: P Crayston, W A Dooley, N Battersby, K Temmen, M Slater, R Anthony, M Kenny
Flanker: N Ashton, S Holden, G Dewhurst, R Dransfield, D Grant, T Edwards
No 8: J Laker, M Bailey, W Shumba

MOST CAPPED PLAYERS (including British Lions Appearances)	LEADING APPEARANCES FOR CLUB	LEADING SCORERS 1993-94
Wade A Dooley, 58 (3), 1985-93	Roy Dransfield, 493, 1975-94	Mike Kirby, Fly Half, 147
A N Hornby, 9, 1877-82	Dave Percy, 421, 1978-93	John Chesworth, Full back, 65
R Hunt, 4, 1881-78	Graham Cox, 421, 1973-88	Joe Hindle, Wing, 60
W H Hunt, 4, 1876-78	Stan Sherlock, 326, 1974-86	Barry Greenwood, Wing, 45
J T Hunt, 3, 1882-84	Alan Wyllie, 285, 1978-91	Julian Lamb, Fly Half, 29
J A Schofield, 1, 1911	Joe Hindle, 279, 1981-93	Ian Jackson, Fly Half/Centre, 26
	Mick Parker, 273, 1978-93	

SHEFFIELD RUFC

Sheffield will return after shock drop

Having lost a number of 1st XV squad players in the previous 12 months, the club's lack of depth led to relegation to the Divisional Section for the first time. This despite a points record which was only just negative as the victories were decisive and the great majority of the losses by narrow margins.

Long term injury absences during the season of Dave Watson, Alistair Challoner and Ian Wright did not help the cause and there were also two suspensions at important times.

There was little sign of the trouble to come in the early part of the season but a run of seven defeats in February and March, culminating in a last minute home defeat by Sudbury, proved conclusive. The team showed its fighting qualities to the end, beating fellow strugglers Broughton Park and drawing at Liverpool St. Helens on the last day. However, results elsewhere nevertheless meant relegation.

David Kaye was an excellent captain under difficult circumstances throughout and his deputy Mark Rodgers provided the bulk of the points with 240 for the season. Martin Kirk, Matthew Howard, Nick Crapper and Paul Oldridge were others to do consistently well and Shaun McMain represented Yorkshire in the County Cup final at Twickenham and the North in the Divisional Championship and against the All Blacks at Anfield.

CLUB PLAYING RECORD 1993-94

National League: Five North
Final League Position at end of 1993/94 Season: 9th (of 10) Relegated
League Playing record: P 18, W 5, D 1, L 12, Pts F 287, Pts A 310
Season Playing record (including league matches/Pilkington Cup): P 29, W 10, D 1, L 18, Pts F480, Pts A 555

David Kaye, Sheffield's Club Captain 1993-94

SHEFFIELD RUFC

Club Details

Club Colours: Royal blue, white hoops, red socks, navy blue shorts
Change of Colours: Red shirts
Date Founded: 1902
Membership: Total: 600, Playing members 120, Junior/Youth/Minis 150
No. of teams: Senior 5, Junior 1

Ground Details:

Ground Address: Abbeydale Park, Abbeydale Road South, Sheffield, S17 3LJ
Ground Tel No: 0742 367011 Fax: 0742 621054
Spectator Capacity: Total: 1,000, Seated 250
Ticket Prices: Adults £3
Training Nights: Tuesdays & Thursdays

Club Officials

Club President: Q R (Robert) Dean
Chairman: Mike Howarth
Club Secretary: J (Jim) Goulding, 34 Whinfell Court, Whirlow, Sheffield, S11 9QA. Tel: (H) 0742 620543 (W) 0742 751776 Fax: 0742 759242
Fixtures Secretary: Q R Dean, 94 Riverdale Road, Sheffield, S10 3FD. Tel: (H) 0742 301021 (W) 0742 377036 Fax: 0742 839947
Press Officer: Ian Harris, 109 Totley Brook Road, Sheffield, S17 3DQ. Tel: (H) 0742 351491
Registration Officer: William (Bill) Oliver, "Rosehill", 49 Chelsea Road, Sheffield, S11 9BQ. Tel: (H) 0742 556817
1994/ 95 1st XV Captain: David Kaye
1994/95 Chairman of Playing Administration: Graham Solley

PLAYING SQUAD 1993-94

Full Back: Mark Allatt
Wing: Mark Rodgers, Jamie Morley, Tim Nicholson, Martin Dawson
Centre: Chris Saul, Martin Kirk, Jos Baxendell
Fly Half: Dave Hill, Bill Reichwald
Scrum Half: Ian Wright, Neal Pearson
Prop: Dave Bosworth, Shaun McMain, Mel Jones, Allen Broomhead, Fred Heaton, Andy Downes
Hooker: Matthew Howard, Alistair Challoner, Alistair Gilfillan
Lock: David Kaye, Tim Meadley, Adam Doran, John Dale
Flanker: Ian Kearney, Harold Barrett, Nick Crapper
No 8: Dave Watson, Paul Oldridge

MOST CAPPED PLAYER

(including British Lions Appearances)
A G B Old, 1, 1977-78

LEADING APPEARANCES FOR CLUB

W Reichwald, 502, 1974-94
H Johnson, 340, 1955-74
R Goodliffe, 326, 1979-90
D Watson, 310, 1979-94
A Reichwald, 302, 1975-90
M Pierce, 301, 1973-91

LEADING SCORERS 1993-94

Mark Rodgers, Wing, 240
Chris Saul, Centre, 32
Dave Hill, Fly Half, 22

STOKE-ON-TRENT RUFC

Ambitious Stoke's strong finish

Overall the 1993/94 season was very much one of two halves. The 1st XV started the season badly losing disappointingly to Preston Grasshoppers in the first round of the Pilkington Cup. Their progress over the next couple of months was not what was expected caused in the main by heavy commitments to County rugby coupled with a string of injuries to key players, as can be witnessed by the use of 58 players in the 1st XV.

However the season turned around towards the end of November with excellent Courage League wins against Lichfield, Walsall, Bradford & Bingley and Preston. Progress was also maintained in the County Cup resulting in a fourth consecutive appearance in the final. A further league win against Kendal and a draw against Nuneaton meant we again finished in the top half of the table.

Pluses for the season were the emergence of several young players, notably Simeon Lloyd (wing), Andrew Cheetham (centre), Steve Currie (prop) and Mick Wynne (2nd row), as well as the form of the club's Under 17 side which won the County Cup.

With Tosh Askew taking a break from club coaching duties having steered the club through three excellent years, last year's club captain and England 'B' International Simon Robson takes over and will be looking to push the club into the National Divisions next season.

CLUB PLAYING RECORD 1993-94

National League: Five North
Final League Position at end of 1993/94 Season: 6th
League Playing record: P 12, W 5, D 1, L 6, Pts F 153, Pts A 162
Season Playing record (including league matches/Pilkington Cup): P 32, W 16, D 1, L 15, Pts F 513, Pts A 485

ACHIEVEMENTS/COMPETITIONS WON DURING 93/94 SEASON

Runners up Staffordshire Cup
U17 County Champions

Stoke-on-Trent RUFC 1993-94   *Photo: Staffordshire Sentinel*

STOKE-ON-TRENT RUFC

Club Details

Club Colours: Dark blue & light blue stripes
Change of Colours: Red
Date Founded: 1884
Membership: Total: 400, Playing members 100, Junior/Youth/Minis 120, Other 180
No. of teams: Senior 4, Junior 7
Programme advertising rates: Full £50, Half £30

Ground Details:

Ground Address: Hartwell Lane, Nr Barlaston, Stoke-on-Trent, ST3 7NG
Ground Tel No:0782 372807
Simple Directions to Ground: From the north use either the M6 or M1. From the M1, follow the A38 then A50. Turn left at first set of traffic lights on the outskirts of the city (A520). After approximately 3 miles, take the road to Barlaston. The Club is 1 mile on the left. From the M6 leave at Junction 15, follow the A34 south, then follow the sign for Barlaston. The Club is through the village, 1 mile on the right. From the south, leave the M6 at Junction 14, follow the A34 north, directions are then as above.

Spectator Capacity: Total: 2,000, Seated 250
Ticket Prices: Adults £2, OAP/Child free
Training Nights: Mondays and Thursdays

Club Officials

Club President: Fhil Tarakaniec
Club Chairman: Les Hart
Club Secretary: Stephen Beck, 10 Hillside Close, Fulford, Stoke- on-Trent, ST11 9RU. Tel: (H) 0782 398090 (W) 021 631 3555 Fax: 021 633 0068
Fixtures Secretary: Eric Hardisty, 8 Maple Gardens, Stone, Staffs, ST15 0EJ. Tel: (H) 0785 813641
Press Officer: Tom Maskrey, 225 Weston Road, Meir, Stoke-on-Trent, ST3 6EF. Tel: (H) 0782 313346
Registration Officer: Keith Roberts, 44 Caverswall Road, Blythe Bridge, Stoke-on-Trent, ST11 9UG. Tel: (H) 0782 396387 (W) 0782 402233
1994/ 95 1st XV Captain: Nigel Binns
1994/95 Club Coach: Simon Robson
Chairman of Selection: Tony Brindley

PLAYING SQUAD 1993-94

15 S Teasdale, M Lamplugh, J Titley
14 D Potts, A Marsh, M Hardie
13 A Buckley, M Foster, M Smith
12 A Cheetham, M Elliot, J Edge, J Forster, A Berresford
11 S Lloyd, M Lucas, P Lucasawicz, A Jones, P Horton
10 S Ashcroft, A Askew, K Sketcher, K Hodgson
9 S Robson (Captain), P Millington, C Hobbs, B Davies
1 S Currie, V Russell, S Groves
2 J Cheadle, J Furnival
3 R Bradley, G Barker, M Hill
4 N Phillips, M Wynne, P Shaw
5 T Bainbridge, N Scott, G Cornwall, K Howell, K Lennon
6 N Binns, I Brassington, J Ryan
7 I Gittens, S Boote, M Hill, N McPherson
8 S Maskrey, S Williams, M Caine, M Cockerill

LEADING APPEARANCES FOR CLUB

Jim Cheadle, 30, 1993/94
Dave Putts, 28, 1993/94
Nigel Binns, 26, 1993/94
Adrian Buckley, 24, 1993/94
Tim Bainbridge, 24, 1993/94
Simon Ashcroft, 24, 1993/94
Richard Bradley, 24, 1993/94

LEADING SCORERS 1993-94

Simon Ashcroft, Stand Off, 156
Steve Teasdale, Full Back, 53
Dave Potts, Winger, 50
Tim Bainbridge, 2nd Row, 30
Kevin Sketcher, Stand Off, 27

STOURBRIDGE RFC

Cup success sparks Stour revival

Stourbridge have traditionally struggled in cup competitions, regularly under-performing at North Midlands Cup level and only winning one tie in the National Knock Out Cup Competition in its first twenty two years, yet it was a magnificent run in the Pilkington Cup which led Stour to recovery from imminent relegation. Knocked out of the North Midlands Cup in the first round they were firmly entrenched at the foot of Division Five North as a second round Pilkington Cup tie took them to Aspatria.

An injury time interception try by winger Richard Trigg - leading try scorer again - saw Stour through and the confidence gained by this victory was the catalyst for a season which finished with them in their highest league position for four seasons. Having won only once in the first six league games they recovered to lose only one of the next six as they climbed eight places from late February.

Newcomer Chris Mannat fly half led the points scorers, notching over ten points a game after joining from London French. His 186 points from 18 games even included five tries, with winger Richard Trigg top try scorer for the third successive season. Former captain, second row Nick Perry, set a modern day club record of 369 appearances before taking over as 1st XV manager for 1994/95. The club basked in the reflected glory of former Captain and President John Jeavons-Fellows' appointment to the IRB, one of the top administrative jobs in the sport.

CLUB PLAYING RECORD 1993-94

National League: Five North
Final League Position at end of 1993/94 Season: 5th
League Playing record: P 12, W 6, D 0, L 6, Pts F 162, Pts A 188
Season Playing record (including league matches/Pilkington Cup): P 36, W 19, D 1, L 16, Pts F 633, Pts A 610

ACHIEVEMENTS/COMPETITIONS WON DURING 93/94 SEASON
Kidderminster 1TC 2nd XV Cup

Stourbridge RFC 1st XV Squad 1993-94

Photo: Ceri Davies

STOURBRIDGE RFC

PLAYING SQUAD 1993-94

Full Back: Steve Baker, Adrian Taft, Jim Reed-Daunter
Wing: Jim Thompson, Richard Trigg, Peter Bate, Simon Pennington, Adrian James
Centre: Mark Wilson, Alun Tapper, Pete Bate, Brian Edwards, Scott Badcock
Fly Half: Tim Grenfell, Chris Mann, Simon Pennington
Scrum Half: Jason Williams, Chris Parsons, Trigger Dawson
Prop: Phil Farrar, Steve Phillips, Harry Jeavons-Fellows, Rob Merritt
Hooker: Tom Jeavons-Fellows
Second Row: Nick Perry, John Taylor, Clive Bishop, Phil Ralph
Flanker: Nick Tibbets, Phil Ralph, Simon Barnes, Simon Hill, Howard Baldwin, Dale Smallman
No 8: John Taylor

Club Details

Club Colours: Navy blue shirts with narrow white hoops, navy blue shorts
Change of Colours: Green & blue hoops, blue shorts
Date Founded: 1876
Membership: Total 700, Full 500, Junior/Youth/Minis 200
No. of teams: Senior 6, Junior 10

Ground Details:

Ground Address: Bridgnorth Road, Stourton, Stourbridge, West Midlands, DY7 6QZ
Ground Tel No: 0384 393889
Simple Directions to Ground: A458 (Bridgnorth Road) from Stourbridge, Ground on left, 1 1/2 miles from Stourbridge
Spectator Capacity: Total: 3,000 standing
Ticket Prices: Adults: £2.50, OAP/Child: Free
Training Nights: Tuesdays and Thursdays 7.00pm

Club Officials

Club President: Lynne Jenkins
Club Secretary: Bob Browne, 41 Western Road, W Hagley, Nr Stourbridge, W Midlands, DV9 0JY. Tel: (H) 0562 882020 (W) 021 423 2345 Fax: 021 423 1907
Fixtures Secretary: Alan Macreadie, 24 Lea Vale Road, Norton, Stourbridge, W Midlands. Tel: (H) 0384 373904 (W) 0384 373904
Press Officer: Ceri Davies, 3 Eggington Road, Stourbridge, W Midlands DY8 4QJ. Tel: (H) 0384 376201 (W) 0905 748404 Fax: 0905 748430
Registration Officer: Nick Perry, Tel: (H) 0384 375337 (W) 0789 400193
1994/ 95 1st XV Captain: Tom Jeavons-Fellows
1994/95 Club Coach: Dave Fourness

MOST CAPPED PLAYER

(including British Lions Appearances)
Huw Davies, 21, 1981-86

LEADING APPEARANCES FOR CLUB 1993/94

Richard Trigg, 27
Tom Jeavons-Fellow, 26
Clive Bishop, 26
John Taylor, 25
Nick Perry, 25
Mark Wilson, 24
Alun Tapper, 24
Harry Jeavons-Fellows, 24
Simon Hill, 23
Nick Tibbetts, 20

LEADING APPEARANCES FOR CLUB 1977-1994

Nick Perry, 369, 1997-94
John Wainwright, 356, 1977-93
Nigel Price, 329, 1980-92
Ceri Davies, 327, 1977-92
Robin Edwards, 298, 1977-94
John Shaw, 268, 1982-93
Andy Dickens, 264, 1978-89
Paul Dodge, 260, 1977-88

LEADING SCORERS 1993-94

Chris Mann, Fly Half, 186 (5T 16C 43P)
Steve Baker, Full Back, 85 (2T 12C 17P)
Richard Trigg, Wing, 65 (13T)
John Taylor, No 8/Second Row, 30 (6T)
Alun Tapper, Centre, 28 (4T 4C)
Simon Pennington, Fly half/Wing, 27 (3C 7P)

WALSALL RUFC

Good season but Walsall can do better

Walsall recovered from a disappointing Autumn and some indifferent displays in friendly club fixtures to complete their most successful season in terms of competitive football since the advent of cups and the courage Leagues.

Third in League 5 North is their highest finish on the Courage League ladder. They regained the Staffordshire Cup, champions for the sixth time after a gap of 11 years, retained the Burton Floodlit Sevens Shield, and were runners-up to the host club, Wolverhampton, in the Staffordshire Sevens Tournament.

Before Christmas there was the frustration of turning a 14-3 lead with 20 minutes to go into a 17-22 home defeat by Wharfedale in the 2nd round of the Pilkington Cup and suffering three League losses — to Winnington Park, Hereford and Stoke - despite dominating for much of those matches.

A gritty win in the Kendal mud proved the turning point and Walsall increasingly added considerable panache and style to their undoubted fine team spirit, skills and effort.

Their flair was never better shown than in a flowing 24-6 County Cup Final win over Stoke, a superb 16-3 victory at Clifton, the ultimate League 3 champions and only unbeaten club in National League games, and a splendid performance in 23-27 defeat by League 5 North champions Rotherham.

Leading scorer Richard Mills topped 200 points for the fourth successive season, gathering those points in fewer than 20 of his appearances and breaking the club's individual record when scoring all of Walsall's 26 points against Burton in Staffordshire Cup Round Two. Full back Mike Friar, with 33 outings, and lock Rob Harding, whose 32 appearances leave him needing four more to break the club record of 336, played the most matches. That may well be a rarity anywhere for senior club officers — Friar is Walsall's Fixture Secretary and Harding the Club Chairman!

CLUB PLAYING RECORD 1993-94

National League: Five North
Final League Position at end of 1993/94 Season: 3rd
League Playing record: P 12, W 7, D 0, L 5, Pts F 166, Pts A 148
Season Playing record (including league matches/Pilkington Cup): P 34, W 18, D 1, L 15, Pts F 641, Pts A 456

ACHIEVEMENTS/COMPETITIONS WON DURING 93/94 SEASON

Staffordshire Cup Winners
Burton Floodlight 7's

WALSALL RUFC

Club Details

Club Colours: Scarlet jerseys, black shorts, scarlet stockings
Change of Colours: Black shirts (red collar & cuffs), black shorts
Date Founded: 1922
Membership: Total: 500, Playing Members 150, Junior/Youth/Minis 150, Other 200
No. of teams: Senior 6, Junior 10
Programme advertising rates: Full £75

Ground Details:

Ground Address: Delves Road, Walsall, West Midland, WS1 3JY
Ground Tel No:0922 26818
Simple Directions to Ground: (From the North) Exit M6 at Junction 9, turn left to Walsall, fork right on ring road, 4 sets of traffic lights, club 2nd road on left.
Spectator Capacity: Total 800
Ticket Prices: Adults £2
Training Nights: Tuesdays and Thursdays

Club Officials

Club President: D H Peacock
Club Chairman: R M Harding
Club Secretary: S C E Tillott, 6 Lichfield Road, Sandhills, Walsall Wood, West Midlands.
Tel: (H) 0543 372667 (W) 021 770 4431
Fixtures Secretary: M I Friar, 8a Beacon Street, Walsall, West Midlands. Tel: (H) 0922 36243 (W) 0788 541222
Press Officer: K H W Clews, 4 Binbrook Road, Short Heath, Willenhall, West Midlands, WV12 4TW.
Tel: (H) 0902 631947
1994/ 95 1st XV Captain: Gary Taylor
1994/95 Club Coach: Colin Jarvis

PLAYING SQUAD 1993-94

15 M Friar   **14** D Marshall, D Wild, J Rowe
13 S Watson, D Rose   **12** J Flynn
11 M Walker, R Bateman   **10** R Mills
9 A Steward, J Harper
1 G Taylor   **2** D Haley
3 M Johnson, K Jones   **4** R Harding
5 M Ellis, R Coleman   **6** P Till, G Tillott
7 G Till   **8** P Till, R Coleman

MOST CAPPED PLAYERS (including British Lions Appearances)	LEADING APPEARANCES FOR CLUB	LEADING SCORERS 1993-94
T J Cobner (Wales & Lions), 22, 1974-78	A O Evans, 336, 1970-88	R Mills, Fly Half, 212 (2T, 26C, 48P, 2DG)
J G Webster (England), 12, 1972-75	N J Archer, 335, 1973-90	J Flynn, Centre, 76 (4T, 7C, 14P)
P Ringer (Wales), 8, 1978-80	R M Harding, 333, 1981-94	R Coleman, No 8/2nd Row, 35 (7T)
R H St J B Moon (Wales), 12, 1993-94		D Marshall, Wing, 35 (7T)
		G Till, Wing Forward, 35 (7T)
		R Edmonds, Fly-Half, 34 (1T, 1C, 9P)

WHARFEDALE RUFC

Wharfedale's superb treble

Season 1993/94 was comfortably the most successful in the club's history. It was a season in which Wharfedale gained its third promotion, this time winning the highly competitive North Division One.

A pre-season tour to Toronto, which saw a 50-point victory over the Ontario Development XV, set the spirit for the season, which ended with an equally successful short trip to Dublin.

The league programme produced 12 wins from 12 matches, in the course of which the team scored 327 points and conceded 77, of which only 30 were conceded away from home. In all, the season yielded over 1,000 points in total, and included defeats by only two clubs. In its first entry into the Pilkington Cup, Wharfedale reached the fourth round after three away victories at Scunthorpe, Walsall and Sheffield, only to fall in yet another away tie at Otley.

A new individual scoring record was set by winger Alex Howarth, whose 409 beat the previous record by more than 100 points. Three players received recognition at county level, and one - Charles Vyvyan - was selected for North Division and the Barbarians.

CLUB PLAYING RECORD 1993-94

National League: North 1
Final League Position at end of 1993/94 Season: 1st
League Playing record: P 12, W 12, D 0, L 0, Pts F 327, Pts A 77
Season Playing record (including league matches/Pilkington Cup): P 33, W 29, D 0, L 4, Pts F 1008, Pts A 339

ACHIEVEMENTS/COMPETITIONS WON DURING 93/94 SEASON

Champions, North Division One
Winners, Yorkshire Referees Society Trophy
Reached Pilkington Cup Fourth Round

Wharfedale RUFC 1993-94

WHARFEDALE RUFC

Club Details
Club Colours: Emerald Green
Change of Colours: Dark Blue
Date Founded: 1923
Membership: Total: 570, Playing members 210, Junior/Youth/Minis 146, Other 212
No. of teams: Senior 6, Junior 8
Programme advertising rates: Full £120, Half £60

Ground Details:
Ground Address: Wharfeside Avenue, Threshfield, Skipton, North Yorkshire, BD23 5BS
Ground Tel No: 0756 752547
Simple Directions to Ground: From Skipton by-pass take B6265 for 8 miles to Threshfield, turn right towards Grassington & look for sign
Spectator Capacity: Total: 2,000, seated 120
Ticket Prices: Adults £2
Training Nights: Mondays and Wednesdays

Club Officials
Club President: John S Spencer
Club Chairman: Frank W House
Club Secretary: Gordon H Brown, Wharfemead, Wood Lane, Grassington, Skipton, North Yorkshire, BD23 5ND. Tel: (H) 0756 752410 (W) 0756 752410 Fax: 0756 752123
Fixtures Secretary: J Michael Harrison, Old Hall Farm, Threshfield, Skipton, North Yorkshire, BD23 5ND. Tel: (H) 0756 752777 (W) 0756 752777
Press Officer: Keith Lewis, Willow Bank, Bank Road, Cross Hills, Keighley, West Yorkshire, BD20 8AA. Tel: (H) 0535 634318
Registration Officer: J M Harrison, Old Hall Farm, Threshfield, Skipton, North Yorkshire, BD23 5PL. Tel: (H) 0756 752777
1994/ 95 1st XV Captain: Stuart Hird
1994/95 Club Coach: J Michael Harrison
Commercial Manager: David Procter
Director of Coaching Michael Harrison

LEADING APPEARANCES FOR CLUB
Dennis Wood, 32, 1993/94
Alex Howarth, 31, 1993/94
Neil Heseltine, 30, 1993/94
John Lawn, 30, 1993/94
Simon Slater, 28, 1993/94
Gary Rogers, 28, 1993/94

LEADING SCORERS 1993-94
Alex Howarth, Wing, 409
Glenn Harrison, Centre, 90
Simon Slater, Centre/Wing, 81
Steven Howarth, Wing, 80
Neil Heseltine, Full Back, 72
Daniel Harrison, Scrum Half, 45

WINNINGTON PARK RFC

FOUNDED 1907

Promotion must come soon for Park

We had an excellent year finishing fourth in Division 5 North, together with reaching the 4th round of the Pilkington Cup, our best ever, and winning the Cheshire Cup for the second successive season.

In the League only away form let us down and it is somewhat ironic that we beat eventual Champions Rotherham both in the League and the Pilkington Cup. We enjoyed the cup run in the Pilkington losing eventually to Moseley in the 4th round. However, we did achieve the goal of the Cheshire Cup beating New Brighton for the second successive season 30-12.

On the playing side we again were well represented in the Cheshire side which went on to gain promotion. The Junior teams grow from strength to strength and we had outstanding successes at U11, U12 and U17 levels as well as Colts.

For the coming year the objective is to play as well away from home as we do at home and look to promotion to Division 4 and another long run in the Pilkington Cup.

CLUB PLAYING RECORD 1993-94

National League: Five North
Final League Position at end of 1993/94 Season: 4th
League Playing record: P 12, W 6, D 1, L 5, Pts F 227, Pts A 132
Season Playing record (including league matches/Pilkington Cup): P 29, W 20, D 1, L 8, Pts F 606, Pts A 132

ACHIEVEMENTS/COMPETITIONS WON DURING 93/94 SEASON
Cheshire Cup Winners
4th Round Pilkington Cup

Club Details

Club Colours: White with light and dark blue circlet
Change of Colours: Light and dark blue hoops
Date Founded: 1907
Membership: Total 500, Playing members 250, Junior/Youth/Minis 220, Colts 25
No. of teams: Senior 6, Junior 9, Youth 2
Programme advertising rates: Full £120, Half £65
Any Special Occasions during 1994/95: Super 10's May

Ground Details:

Ground Address: Burrows Hill, Hartford, Northwich, Cheshire, CW8 3AA
Ground Tel No: 0606 74242
Simple Directions to Ground: One mile from Hartford turn off A556, turn left by traffic lights at Hartford Church into Bradburns Lane, then right into Beach Road B5152. Burrows Hill is first left and ground is on right.
Spectator Capacity: Total: 5,000 standing
Ticket Prices: Adults: £1 (£2 Cup), OAP/Child: Free
Training Nights: Mondays and Thursdays 7.00pm

Club Officials

Club President: T R Palin
Club Chairman: W G Scragg
Club Secretary: Alex Simpson, 14 Applefield, Hart Ford, Northwich, Cheshire, CW8 4TE. Tel: (H) 0606 782943 (W) 0270 759759 Fax: 0270 759166
Fixtures Secretary: P N Worrall, 7 Limewood Crescent, Barnton, Northwich, Cheshire. Tel: (H) 0606 76455 (W) Runcorn 511290
Press Officer: R Dean, 24 East Avenue, Rudheath, Northwich. Tel: (H) 0606 43084
Registration Officer: Alex Simpson
1994/95 1st XV Captain: David Nicholls
1994/95 Club Coach: Vince Murphy

WINNINGTON PARK RFC

PLAYING SQUAD 1993-94
Full Back: Hall, Swann, Taylor
Wing: Bird, Owens, Gibson, Oliver R, Edwards D
Centre: Lloyd, Sutton C, Woods, Nicholl J, Higson, Critchley
Fly Half: Bebbington S, Bebbington M, Yardley, Staley, Sproston, Jones T
Stand Off: Forster
Scrum Half: Green
Prop: Allcock D, Cundick, Davies I, Blenkinsop N, Cartman
Hooker: Allcock R
Lock: Rees, Nicholl D
No 8: McGarrigle, Davies J

MOST CAPPED PLAYERS
(including British Lions Appearances)
Dewi Morris, 18 + British Lions
David Wrench, 3

LEADING APPEARANCES FOR CLUB
D Nicholl, 28, 1993/94
Green, 26, 1993/94
Lloyd, 25, 1993/94
D Allcock, 25, 1993/94
R Allcock, 25, 1993/94
Rees, 24, 1993/94
C Sutton, 22, 1993/94
Forster, 21, 1993/94
Cundick, 21,1993/94
Hall, 20, 1993/94
Bird, 20, 1993/94
Owens, 20, 1993/94

LEADING SCORERS 1993-94
Hall, Full back, 176
Gibson, Wing, 80
Owens, Wing, 45
Lloyd, Centre, 35
Gibson, Wing, 25
McGarrigle, No 8, 25
Allcock R, Hooker, 20
Staley, Wing, 20

RUGBY SPECIALISTS Bourne Sports

COURAGE

CRT7.

CRT2.

CRT8.

CRT1.

CRT5.

COURAGE
RUGBY TACKLE RANGE

CRT1 Rugby Jersey - 100% cotton, long sleeves rugby jersey, embroidered badge, unisex, generous sizes, all our usual quality features, taped inside collar, reinforced seams and snug stretch cuffs, sizes S, M, L, XL.
CRT1. Usual £29.95 **League price £25.00**

CRT2 Rugby Jersey - 100% cotton, long sleeves with all features of CRT1 in alternative design, sizes S, M, L, XL,
CRT2. Usual £29.95 **League price £25.00**

CRT3 Polo Shirt - Fashionable Polo Shirt, comfortable 50/50 poly-cotton fabric with embroidered badge, sizes S, M, L, XL.
CRT3. Usual £13.99 **League price £12.50**

CRT4 Training Jacket - Two Colour Jacket in hard wearing 100% cotton drill with embroidered badge, sizes S, M, L, XL, XXL, not illustrated
CRT4. Usual £24.95 **League price £21.00**

CRT5 Sweatshirt - Heavy fleece sweatshirt, 50/50 poly-cotton in navy with embroidered logo, sizes S, M, L, XL. Usual £17.99 **League price £15.**

CRT6 Hooded Top - Fashionable garment, 50/50 poly-cotton with embroidered badge, sizes S, M, L, XL, **CRT6.** Usual £26.95 **League price £24.**

CRT7 Cap - Pro style cap adjustable to any size, embroidered logo, **£9.95**
CRT7. Usual £9.95 **League price £8.95**

CRT8 T-Shirt - Printed T-Shirt, 50/50 poly-cotton, sizes available S, M, L, XL, XXL, **£10.95**
CRT8. Usual £10.95 **League price £8.00**

CRT6.

CRT3.

BOURNE SPORTS

**Bourne Sports, Church Street
Stoke-on-Trent, ST4 1DJ**

**Tel: 0782 410411.
Fax: 0782 411072**

All orders value £40 and over post free. Other orders plus £3 postage and packing. Send cheque/postal order or telephone your order quoting Access, Visa, American Express, Diners Card, or Switchcard.

Special Prices for Courage League Players

THE
RUGBY PROGRAMME CLUB

The development of the Rugby Programme Club is certainly a sign that competition within the Courage Leagues is creating much more progressive attitudes within clubs.

League matches are well advertised, entrance fees are often raised compared with 'friendly' matches, the presentation of the match over the loudspeaker is important and the club's image can be greatly enhanced by its programme.

A well complied and edited publication on quality paper and including good features, statistics and photos will be a great public relations vehicle for the club.

Indeed a smart programme will attract many local advertisers and can actually make money for the club. The editor can also highlight forthcoming club events and fixtures plus encourage participation in many fund raising schemes.

Soccer clubs at all levels have produced splendid programmes for many years and programme surveys, clubs and fairs have sprung up as thousands of collectors have enjoyed their hobby.

So it is great to see that David Fox's Rugby Programme Club has enjoyed a successful season and last year's awards went to:

CLUB PROGRAMME OF THE YEAR
1st — Llanelli RFC
2nd — Bristol RFC
3rd — Bath RFC

THE MOST IMPROVED PROGRAMME
Bath RFC
Bridgend RFC
Newbridge RFC

OVERSEAS PROGRAMME OF THE YEAR
Otago RFC in New Zealand for the 1993 Bledisloe Cup

Programmes are judged on thirty different aspects from the front cover to the value for money and type of paper and should any clubs wish to enter their 1994-95 survey please send at least two copies of their programme to

David Fox, Rugby Programme Club, 9 Pine Close, Bristol BS12 1AS.

Details of membership of the club can be obtained from David and the fee for joining at present stands at five pounds. We wish him well and we are sure his club will bring great pleasure to many enthusiasts

Tony Williams

BARKING RUFC

Home grown Barking reach big time

1993/94 was Barking's most successful season since its inception 64 years ago. Winning London Division One after only two years in this league, they have now gone from London Division Two to National League Five in three years, making them the premier side in Essex.

The club has gone from strength to strength since the arrival of Mike Lovett and Lance Hayworth as coaches, with Dean Cutting at scrum half controlling operations on the pitch, with 195 points in the League. Kristian Chesney has made a big impact on the team in the three years he's been playing rugby, scoring 10 tries this season.

Barking once again won the Essex Cup making it five wins in seven years, beating Thurrock in the closing minutes 20-11 after a hard fought match.

In the Pilkington Cup Barking drew two long away matches beating Weston Super Mare 39-10 and losing to Plymouth in the 2nd round 11-22. The aim this year is to go beyond the 2nd round.

Since its arrival at the clubhouse at Goresbrook six years ago Barking have been building from within, with five senior sides and seven junior and mini teams.

Club Playing Record 1993-94

National League: London Division 1
Final League Position at end of 1993/94 Season: 1st
League Playing record: P 12, W 10, D 1, L 1, Pts F 290, Pts A 149
Season Playing record (including league matches/Pilkington Cup): P 31, W 23, D 1, L 7, Pts F 704, Pts A 413

Barking RUFC 1993-94

BARKING RUFC

Club Details

Club Colours: Cardinal & Grey hoops
Change of Colours: Orange
Date Founded: 1930
Membership: Total: 350, Playing members: 105, Junior/Youth/Minis: 130, Colts: 24
No. of teams: Senior: 5, Junior: 7
Programme advertising rates: £200 per season

Ground Details:

Ground Address: Goresbrook, Gale Street, Dagenham, Essex, RM9 4TY
Ground Tel No: 081 595 7324
Simple Directions to Ground: A13 from London over Ripple Road. Flyover 1st turning on left at 400 yds. Gale Street.
Spectator Capacity: Total: 1,000 standing
Ticket Prices: Adults £2.50
Training Nights: Mondays & Wednesdays

Club Officials

Club President: W Marshall
Club Chairman: G Mansfield
Club Secretary: G Darley, 12 Glenton Way, Romford, Essex, RM1 4AF. Tel: (H) 0708 764828
Fixtures Secretary: G Comley, 26 Beltinge Road, Harold Wood, Essex, RM3 0UJ. Tel: (H) 0708 709609 (W) 071 956 2464
Press Officer: J Caney, 13 Madeira Grove, Woodford Green, Essex. Tel: (H) 081 505 1192
Registration Officer: M Lovett, 650 Rainham Road South, Dagenham, Essex, RM9 6DA. Tel: (H) 081 595 1082 (W) 071 921 5000
1994/ 95 1st XV Captain: D Cutting
1994/95 Club Coach: M Lovett
Other Club Officers: M Lovett, Chief Coach

LEADING SCORERS (1993-94)
Garry Cutting, Full Back, 195
Christian Chesney, 2nd Row, 10 tries

ACHIEVEMENTS/COMPETITIONS WON DURING 93/94 SEASON
Essex Cup Winners
London Division 1 League Champions

BASINGSTOKE RFC

CLUB PLAYING RECORD 1993-94

National League: Five South
Final League Position at end of 1993/94 Season:
League Playing record: P 12, W 5, D 0, L 7, Pts F 191, Pts A 210
Season Playing record (including league matches/Pilkington Cup):
P 31, W 21, D 0, L 10, Pts F 686, Pts A 476

ACHIEVEMENTS/COMPETITIONS WON DURING 93/94 SEASON
Pilkington Cup 4th Round
Hampshire Cup Winners

LEADING SCORERS

Richard Rowledge, Full back, 220 (6T 37P 38C 1DG)
Hamish Rushin, Fly Half/Full Back, 73 (1T 16P 10C)
Simon Denning, Left Wing, 50 (10T)

Club Details

Club Colours: Amber & blue
Change of Colours: Blue
Date Founded: 1948
Membership: Total: 600, Playing members 120, Junior/Youth,Minis 150, Other 330
No. of teams: Senior 5, Junior 8
Programme advertising rates: TBA

Ground Details:

Ground Address: Down Grange, Pack Lane, Basingstoke, Hants, RG22 5HH
Ground Tel No: 0256 23308
Simple Directions to Ground: From Jct 6 M3 follow Ringway South signs to Winchester. At Brighton Hill roundabout follow signs for Down Grange Playing Field
Spectator Capacity: Total: 4,250, seated 250, standing 4,000
Ticket Prices: Adults: £5 (League/Pilkington) £1.50 (Hants Cup/New League), OAP/Child: Free
Training Nights: Mondays and Wednesdays, 7.30pm

Club Officers for 1994/95 Season:

Club President: J G Evans CBE TD
Club Chairman: D A Williams
Club Secretary: Paul Bailey, "The Wolery", 20 Basingstoke Road, Ramsdell, Basingstoke, Hants, RG26 5RB. Tel: (H) 0256 851042 (W) 0256 473400 Fax: 0256 844557
Fixtures Secretary: Alan Paynter, 152 Pack Lane, Kempshott, Basingstoke, Hants, RG22 5HR. Tel: (H) 0256 27857 (W) 0256 843191
Press Officer: Paul Bailey
Registration Officer: J Byett, 42 Byfleet Avenue, Old Basing, Basingstoke, Hants. Tel: (H) 0256 23313 (W) 071 283 3000
1994/ 95 1st XV Captain: P Hawkins
1994/95 Club Coach: L Johnson

LEAGUE 5 SOUTH PROGRAMMES

Official Programme

BARKING RUGBY UNION FOOTBALL CLUB

Courage Clubs Championship
LONDON DIVISION ONE

BARKING

v

DORKING

Saturday, 9th April 1994
Kick-Off 3.00 p.m.

OFFICIAL
PROGRAMME

ROYAL FOREST OF DEAN

SEASON 1993 / 1994

Berry Hill Rugby Football Club

KINGSMEAD ROAD
HIGH WYCOMBE

BERRY HILL RFC

Berry Hill perform well with small resources

As far as one could make out Berry Hill are still in the unique position of being the only village-based rugby club playing in National League rugby.

Last season was very hard with games being played against good class Welsh opposition such as Abertillery, Penarth and Newbridge as well as League and Cup matches. The Pilkington Cup interest ended quickly with a First Round defeat by Henley by a four point margin.

The league programme was one of joy and despair, which contained some first-rate victories negated by some unnecessary defeats. This resulted in a mid-table placing at the end of the season, and proved to the players and supporters alike that every year it becomes harder for a club like ours with limited resources.

The general playing record was good, with victories doubling up on defeats. A lot of players were used in 'friendly' matches, which appears to be becoming accepted practice throughout rugby nowadays.

Outside-half Lee Osborne distinguished himself with his points scoring, mainly with his kicking skills showing up well in the National list of individual scorers.

Skipper Nick Harris led from the front with confidence, and new coach Paul Greenway often doubled up as a replacement player, with club chairman John Evans still playing 1st XV rugby. For some games Berry Hill had the club chairman, captain and coach all on the field of play at the same time. Is this a record?

Club Playing Record 1993-94

National League: Five South
Final League Position at end of 1993/94 Season: 7th
League Playing record: P 12, W 6, D 1, L 5, Pts F 146, Pts A 154
Season Playing record (including league matches/Pilkington Cup): P 35, W 21, D 2, L 12, Pts F 563, Pts A 583

ACHIEVEMENTS/COMPETITIONS WON DURING 93/94 SEASON
Dave Harris Memorial Cup

Berry Hill RFC. Back Row: B Hale, D Powell, I Seymour, A Powles, M Wells, C Boyd, D Edwards, G Jones, J Evans, J Powell, T Ruck, P Greenway. Front Row: P Baldwin, Nick Tippins, L Osborne, A Jones, N Harris (Capt), Nigel Tippins, J Bennett, I Hoare.

BERRY HILL RFC

Club Details

Club Colours: Black and Amber
Change of Colours: Red
Date Founded: 1893
Membership: Total: 225, Playing members: 85, Junior/Youth/Minis: 100, Vice Presidents: 115
No. of teams: Senior: 4 plus 1 under 19s, 1 under 21s, Junior: 5
Programme advertising rates: Full £100, Half £55, Quarter £35

Ground Details:

Ground Address: Lakers Road, Berry Hill, Coleford, Glos, GL16 7LY
Ground Tel No: 0594 833295
Simple Directions to Ground: A4136 Monmouth to Gloucester Road near Coleford. Turn to Berry Hill at crossroads at Five Acres Garage. Ground 200 yds on right hand side.
Spectator Capacity: Total: 600 standing
Ticket Prices: Adults: £2, OAP/Child: 50p
Training Nights: Mondays and Wednesdays, Seniors & Under 19s & 21s. Sunday mornings, minis & Juniors

Club Officials

Club President: R W Jenkins JP
Club Chairman: John Evans
Club Secretary: T J Baldwin, 'Hill Brink', Joyford Hill, Coleford, Glos, GL16 7AH. Tel: (H) 0594 832539 (W) 0594 562631 Fax: 0594 563662
Fixtures Secretary: G Goddard, 71A Cheltenham Road, Glos, GL2 0JG. Tel: (H)0452 306749
Press Officer: John Belcher, 'Spion Kop', Joyford Hill, Coleford, Glos, GL16 7AH. Tel: (H) 0594 832249
Registration Officer: John Cole, No 2 The Close, Broadwell, Coleford, Glos, GL16 7DJ. Tel: (H) 0594 835351 (W) 0594 542421.
1994/ 95 1st XV Captain: Nicky Harris
1994/95 Club Coach: Ian Seymour
Other Club Officers: Ian Seymour, Director of Coaching
Derek Symonds, Vice-Chairman
John Cole, Chairman of Selectors

PLAYING SQUAD 1993-94

Full Back: N Tippins, J Powell, M Wells, T Price
Wing: Nigel Tippins, P Tingle, S Powell, J Elsmore, K Mapps, I Kear, D Cole
Centre: G Jones, D Edwards, P Greenway, P Hunt
Fly Half: L Osborne, J Powell
Scrum Half: J Bennett, N Young, P Jones
Prop: A Jones, A Powles, A Ruck, J Hoare, P Chandler
Hooker: P Baldwin, M Gunter, C Revill, P Aston
Lock: J Evans, N Harris, I Jenkins, D Kear, P Kear
Flanker: T Ruck, C Boyd, I Bell, W Jones, R Powles, G Alexander, F Hobbs
No 8: I Seymour, M Smith

LEADING APPEARANCES FOR CLUB:

Jeff Powell, 33, 1993/94
John Evans, 32, 1993/94
T Ruck. 32, 1993/94
J Bennett, 32, 1993/94

LEADING SCORERS:

Lee Osborne, Outside Half
Jeremy Bennett, Scrum Half

CAMBORNE RFC

Fourth place achieved

Although we had a mixed start to the season, by the end of January it looked as though we might be able to press for promotion, but unfortunately two defeats in succession by Metropolitan Police and Tabard put paid to our hopes. A draw against Reading and wins against North Walsham and Weston-super-Mare meant we were able to secure fourth place.

The club was well represented at county level by Tommy Adams, Darran Chapman, Paul Gadston, Ian Pollard, Simon Pinnegar and David Weeks all playing for Cornwall in the County Championship. Our Colts won the County Knock Out Cup for the second year running and the Mini and Junior Sections continue to prosper.

CLUB PLAYING RECORD 1993-94

National League: Five South   **Final League Position at end of 1993/94 Season:** 4th
League Playing record: P 12, W 6, D 2, L 4, Pts F 197, Pts A 161
Season Playing record (including league matches/Pilkington Cup): P 36, W 23, D 2, L 11, Pts F 795, Pts A 478

ACHIEVEMENTS/COMPETITIONS WON DURING 93/94 SEASON
Camborne Colts won the county Knock-Out Cup

Club Details
Club Colours: Cherry & White
Change of Colours: Blue
Date Founded: 1878
Membership: Total: 450, Playing Members 75, Junior/Youth/Minis 160, Colts 30
No. of teams: Senior 3, Junior 9
Programme advertising rates: TBA

Ground Details:
Ground Address: The Recreation Ground, Camborne, Cornwall
Ground Tel No: 0209 713227
Simple Directions to Ground: Leave A30 Camborne/Redruth by-pass at Junction Camborne West and follow signs to recreation ground.
Spectator Capacity: Total: 9,200, Seated 777
Ticket Prices: Adults TBA, OAP/Child TBA
Training Nights: Mondays & Wednesdays

Club Officials
Club President: David Roberts
Club Chairman: Roger Harris
Club Secretary: W J C Dunstan, The Retreat, 11 Station Hill, Praze-an-Beeble, Camborne, Cornwall, TR14 0JT. Tel: (H) 0209 831373 (W) 0736 795456 Fax: 0736 797075
Fixtures Secretary: E T Pascoe, 51 St Meriadoc Road, Camborne, Cornwall, TR14 7HL. Tel: (H) 0209 718158
Press Officer: W J C Dunstan
Registration Officer: W J C Dunstan
1994/ 95 1st XV Captain: David Weeks
1994/95 Club Coach: Nigel Pellowe
Other Club Officers:
Ewart White, Team Secretary
Mike Trott, Sponsorship Secretary
Nigel Davey, Assistant General Secretary

LEADING APPEARANCES FOR CLUB
Nigel Pellowe, 1003, 1969-1993
Bobby Tonkin, 710, 1967-1985
Frank Butler, 530, 1968-1988
David Kingston, 520, 1967-1982
Ivor Moyle, 508, 1955-1970
John Rockett, 507, 1956-1974

MOST CAPPED PLAYERS
(including British Lions Appearances)
John Collins, 3, 1952 A F Reed, 8

LEADING SCORERS
Darren Chapman, Fullback, 193
Ian Pollard, Wing, 105
David Weeks, Wing, 70
Simon Moyle, Fly Half, 59
Kelvin Smitham, Wing, 55
Tommy Adams (Capt), Lock, 30

Gavin Sharp, Henley's leading Try Scorer, wrong foots the North Walsham defence in a 3rd round Pilkington Cup match at Henley   Photo: John Batt

Henley come out for their game against St Ives at Henley   Photo: John Batty

HENLEY RFC

Henley's annus mirabilis brings senior status

The last season proved to be the most successful in the club's 64 year history. Promotion from South-West One was gained without a single league point being conceded. By scoring an average of nearly four tries a game Henley demonstrated their commitment to a 15-man style of rugby.

Henley's much publicised "flat ball" game was the major contributing factor to the success. However, it is as important a learning process for the forwards as the backs. Some defences found the game Henley played very difficult to predict.

A strong squad of some 30 players assured the league success and a remarkable Pilkington Cup run which saw victories over Berry Hill, St Ives, by a record margin, and North Walsham. Eventually the South-West One side succumbed at the Memorial Ground Bristol in front of some 1,500 of their own supporters. Henley were one of three Junior Clubs throughout the country to reach the Fourth Round of the competition. With the Pilkington Cup out of the way by Christmas, Henley's attention turned to the League Programme and their efforts to retain the Oxfordshire Cup which was realised at Iffley Road in March. The final league game against St Ives at Dry Leas drew a record crowd and ensured Henley's progression into National League 5 (South).

CLUB PLAYING RECORD 1993-94

National League: Five South
Final League Position at end of 1993/94 Season: Champions
League Playing record: P 12, W 12, D 0, L 0, Pts F 328, Pts A125
Season Playing record (including league matches/Pilkington Cup): P 30, W 25, D 0, L 5, Pts F 921, Pts A 426

ACHIEVEMENTS/COMPETITIONS WON DURING 93/94 SEASON
Champions SW1
County Cup Winners - Oxfordshire (4th year in succession)
4th round Pilkington Cup

Henley 1st Team Squad

HENLEY RFC

Club Details

Club Colours: Navy/Bottle Green/Gold Hoops
Change of Colours: Gold
Date Founded: 1930
Membership: Total: 600, Playing members 200, Junior/Youth/Minis 200, Other 200.
No. of teams: Senior 5, Junior 6
Programme advertising rates: £250 per page per season

Ground Details:

Ground Address: Dry Leas, Marlow Road, Henley-on-Thames, Oxon, RG9 2JA
Ground Tel No: 0491 574499/576561
Simple Directions to Ground: Leave Henley by the Oxford Road (A4155). Fork right at the Marlow Road (A4130). Dry Leas on left about 150 yards from junction of Oxford/Marlow roads
Spectator Capacity: Total: 2,000 standing
Ticket Prices: Adults £2 + £1 programme
Training Nights: Mondays and Thursdays

Club Officials

Club President: Tony Hobbs
Club Chairman: Graham Horner
Club Secretary: Peter J Allen, 81 St Katherines Road, Henley-on- Thames, Oxfordshire, RG9 1PJ. Tel: (H) 0491 575154 (W) 081 788 7272 Fax: 081 565 6680
Fixtures Secretary: Paul Emerson, 16 St Mary's Close, Henley-on- Thames, Oxfordshire. Tel: (H) 0491 578606 (W) 1734 402455
Press Officer: Noel Armstead, Harlequin House, 15 Brampton Chase, Shiplake, Henley-on-Thames, Oxfordshire, RG9 8BX. Tel: (H) 0734 401094
Registration Officer: Gordon Pike, 16 Merlewood Close, High Wycombe, Bucks. Tel: (H) 0494 443528 (W) 0753 549550
1994/ 95 1st XV Captain: Rob Heginbotham
1994/95 Club Coach: Nigel Dudding/Clive Woodward
Other Club Officers: Adrian Lewington, Treasurer Phil Woodall, Commercial Manager Alan Hudson, Clubhouse Manager

PLAYING SQUAD 1993-94

Full Back: Danny Batty, Paul Beard, Steve Mann
Wing: Rob McCulloch, Ben Tubb, Gavin Sharp, Simon Henderson, Gary McGregor, Adam Horler, John Hottot, John Griffiths, Nick Blofeld, Alan Cotton, Simon Littler
Centre: Simon Hearn, Tim Dawes, Derek Oswald, Jonty French
Fly Half: Mike Oulson, Ollie Tubb, Gavin Alpe
Scrum Half: Bill Davidson, Giles Harper, Dan Naylor
Prop: Simon Matthews, Phil New, Rob Heginbotham, Richard Elson, Dave Gavins
Hooker: Nick Bradbury
Lock: Seb Wylder, Sean Fleming, Jason Hollis, Nigel Spiers, Tim Matthews
No 8: Steve Berryman, Willy Phillips, Mike Crook, Ron Westdorp

LEADING APPEARANCES FOR CLUB

Nigel Dudding (now head of coaching), 360
Nick Bradbury, 28
Simon Hearn, 27
Mike Poulson, 26
Seb Wylder, 25
Bill Davidson, 24
Sean Fleming, 24

LEADING SCORERS 1993-94

Mike Poulson, Fly-Half, 319, 133
Gavin Sharp, Wing, 100, 50 (20 tries)
Simon Hearn, Centre, 60, 30
Bill Davidson, Scrum-half, 55, 15
Ben Tubb, Winger, 43, 20
Rod McCulloch, Flanker, 40, 10

HIGH WYCOMBE RUFC

Wycs urgently seek stability

There were mixed fortunes for the club last season. Consistency was difficult to maintain, due to injury and unavailability. Forty three players were used in the First XV and also saw a departure, to a large extent, from the fluid running game of previous seasons to a more forward oriented game, which many of our spectators found alien to their expectations.

In a very competitive League, after the high hopes at the beginning of the season, we finished a disappointing ninth. The post Christmas surge of previous years failed to materialise this time.

Overall, better results were achieved outside the League.

In the Pilkington Cup we defeated Cheshunt in the First Round before going out to Preston Grasshoppers at home in an enjoyable and close fought game.

In the Bucks Cup campaign we comfortable defeated Buckingham and Chesham in the earlier rounds and after winning a tight game against Bletchley with their big experienced pack defeated our old rivals Aylesbury in the Final. Aylesbury gained their revenge in an end of season friendly when both sides fielded weakened teams.

The Bisley Office Equipment Merit table gave us the opportunity to renew acquaintances with old friends on the playing field and we finished a respectable second to Reading.

We look forward to a more stable side next season and an improvement in our playing performance especially in the League.

CLUB PLAYING RECORD 1993-94

National League: Five South
Final League Position at end of 1993/94 Season: Ninth
League Playing record: P 12, W 5, D 1, L 6, Pts F 120, Pts A 173
Season Playing record (including league matches/Pilkington Cup): P 32, W 21, D 1, L 10, Pts F 648, Pts A 375

ACHIEVEMENTS/COMPETITIONS WON DURING 93/94 SEASON

Buckinghamshire County Cup
Boduers (VETS) XV won Slough Veterans Tournament
BXV won Beaconsfield Twelves Tournament

High Wycombe RUFC 1993-94   *Photo: Marcus Kinch, Bucks Free Press*

HIGH WYCOMBE RUFC

Club Details

Club Colours: Black, Green & White hoops
Change of Colours: Black
Date Founded: 1929 (present form) Originally 1891
Membership: Total: 749, Playing members 187, Junior/Youth/Minis 246, Other 316.
No. of teams: Senior 8, Colts 1, Junior 4
Programme advertising rates: Full £125

Ground Details:

Ground Address: Kingsmead Road, High Wycombe, Bucks, HP11 1JB
Ground Tel No: 0494 524407
Simple Directions to Ground: From East - M40 off Junction 3 (Wycombe East) to roundabout. First left to mini roundabout. Turn right. 800 yards road takes sharp right hand bend. Kingsmead Road straight on. Club 1 mile on right. From South & West - Junction 4 on M40. Follow A404 into Wycombe. Turn right on A40 (Beacons Field). Follow 1 1/2 miles. Immediately past Red Lion Pub on left turn right into Abbey Barn Road. 800 yards road takes sharp left hand bend into Kingsmead Road. Club 1 mile on left.

Spectator Capacity: Total: Unlimited
Ticket Prices: Admission by programme £2
Training Nights: Tuesdays and Thursdays

Club Officials

Club President: John Brine
Club Chairman: Dr Eric Wilsuer
Club Secretary: Don Dickerson, 3 Talbot Avenue, High Wycombe, Bucks, HP13 5HL. Tel: (H) 0494 532024 (W) 0494 441211
Fixtures Secretary: Terry Baker, 5 Orchard Way, Homer Green, High Wycombe, Bucks, HP15 6RF.
Press Officer: Dudley Scott, 82 Kings Ride, Penn, Bucks, HP10 8BP. Tel: (H) 0494 813399 (W) 0494 813399
Registration Officer: Don Dickerson
1994/ 95 1st XV Captain: Eliot Forster
1994/95 Club Coach: Simon Edwards
Other Club Officers:
John Reid (35th season), Treasurer
Mike Band (34th season), Team Secretary

PLAYING SQUAD 1993-94

Full Back: L Tebb, P Smith, M Alnutt
Wing: R Chuter, M Watters, P Smith, J Hewes, T Hoggon, G Carter
Centre: S Gaster, S Sutton, R Hawkins, J Urie, S Cutler, R Wyatt, C Roddick, C Preston, C Smith, P Nisbet
Fly Half: J Owen, R Hawkins, C Preston
Scrum Half: M Saltmarsh, S Shaw, J Openshaw, M Jordan
Prop: C Mahoney, R Turner, W Jeans, M Hinch, N Ball
Lock: J Abbott, N Kidby, M Dudley, N Dinsdale, A Stone, M Ruinett, J R Bartlett, A Stanners
Flanker: J Sedman, S Barnes, F Walton, M Stockdale, S Molloy
No 8: M Cussell, E Forster

LEADING APPEARANCES FOR CLUB

Mike Cussell, 324
Chris Roddick, 273
Chris Preston, 269
Jerome Bartlett, 249
John Openshaw, 161
Jeff Abbott, 148

LEADING SCORERS 1993-94

Peter Smith, Full Back/Wing, 115
Liam Tebb, Full Back, 108
Richard Chuter, Wing, 65
John Hewes, Wing, 45
Simon Gaster, Centre, 40
Eliot Forster, No 8, 35

LONDON WELSH RFC

Welsh to go up at last?

The Welsh were a very much better side than their final record of sixth place might indicate. The departure of former Playing Controller John Dawes and coach Bill Calcraft did cause initial problems, but the club recovered its poise, were unbeaten in the second half of the league campaign, and would have challenged for promotion but for early difficulties. The side again reached the third round of the Pilkington Cup.

Outside the league, the Welsh played some magnificent rugby in beating Pontypridd, who were fielding all their internationals, Newport and Treorchy - all now in the premier division of the Heineken League. There were also excellent victories against Nottingham, Richmond, Havant and Llanharan.

Graeme Peacock was an outstanding leader at No 8 or lock, and was given fine support from Colin Charvis, whose storming displays in the loose won him a Wales Under-21 cap, and Andy Newcombe. Charvis was also the top try-scorer with 12 touchdowns, three ahead of winger Peter Walters, while Rhodri Phillips amassed 158 points, with some splendid place-kicking in the closing months of the season. Long serving centre Guy Leleu recorded his 200th career appearance. Graeme Peacock has decided to stay with the Welsh this season and will be joined by two other former captains who have returned to the club - Andy Tucker and Lee Thomas.

CLUB PLAYING RECORD 1993-94

National League: Five South
Final League Position at end of 1993/94 Season: 6th
League Playing record: P 12, W 5, D 3, L 4, Pts F 216, Pts A 140
Season Playing record (including league matches/Pilkington Cup): P 35, W 16, D 3, L 16, Pts F 673, Pts A 729

ACHIEVEMENTS/COMPETITIONS WON DURING 93/94 SEASON
Colin Charvis won Wales U21 Cap

London Welsh RFC, 1993-94

LONDON WELSH RFC

Club Details

Club Colours: Scarlet
Change of Colours: Green
Date Founded: 1885
Membership: Total: 1,200, Playing members 100, Junior/Youth/Minis 220, Ladies 20
No. of teams: Senior 6, Junior 12
Programme advertising rates: Full page £400

Ground Details:

Ground Address: Old Deer Park, Kew Road, Richmond, Surrey, TW9 2AZ
Ground Tel No: 081 940 1604 Fax: 081 940 2368
Simple Directions to Ground: Half mile north of Richmond Station, adjacent Kew Gardens
Spectator Capacity: Total: 7,200, seated 1,200
Ticket Prices: Adults: £4, OAP/Child £1.50
Training Nights: Tuesdays and Thursdays

Club Officials

Club President: Kelvin Bryan
Club Chairman: Ernie Williams
Club Secretary: Pete Taylor, 16 Monks Road, Virginia Water, Surrey, GU25 4RR Tel: (H) 0344 842070 (W) 0932 857433 Fax: 0932 852377
Fixtures Secretary: Colin Bosley, 21 Ellesmere Avenue, London, NW7 3EX. Tel: (H) 081 906 0799
Press Officer: Dr Allan Price, 26 Limewood Close, St Johns, Woking, Surrey, GU21 1XA. Tel: (H) 0483 472944 (W) 071 815 7924
Registration Officer: Pete Taylor
1994/ 95 1st XV Captain: Andy Newcombe
1994/95 Club Coach: Mike Gosling

PLAYING SQUAD 1993-94

Full Back: Richard Jones, Richard Walters
Wing: Peter Walters, Alistair Sandilands, Time Pike, Micky Bell
Centre: Guy Leleu, Steve Thomas, Michael Dawes, Nick Cedarwell
Fly Half: Rhodri Phillips, David Shufflebotham
Scrum Half: Gerallt Phillips, Andy Tucker
Prop: Mark Herbert, Martin Pritchard, Alan Andrews, Barry Beeken
Hooker: Robbie Jones, Andy Tucker
Lock: Owen Davies, James Fletcher, Dai Harries, Neil Thomas
Flanker: Rowan Westlake, Colin Charvis, Andy Newcombe, Ceri Davies
No 8: Graeme Peacock, David Parry-Jones

MOST CAPPED PLAYER
(including British Lions Appearances)
M Douglas, 3, 1984

LEADING APPEARANCES FOR CLUB 1993/94
G Peacock, 32
R Phillips, 30
G Leleu, 29
R Westlake, 28
O Davies, 26
M Herbert, 26
T Pike, 26

LEADING SCORERS 1993-94
R Phillips, Stand Off, 158 (4T 15C 30P 6DG)
R Walters, Full Back, 73 (2T 9C 15P)
C Charvis, Flanker, 60 (12T)
D Shufflebotham, Stand Off, 53 (1T 3C 14P)
P Walters, Wing, 45 (9T)
R Jones, Full Back, 40 (3T 5C 5P)

LYDNEY RFC

Lydney's season of consolidation

Lydney consolidated their position in National League Division Five South last season and had ambitions to achieve promotion to Division Four. Unfortunately this was not to be, as league games were lost to Berry Hill, Tabard and Reading which resulted in the club finishing second.

Although disappointed in missing out on promotion the club can look back upon some pleasing results and performances. A tremendous start was made to the season under Nick Nelmes's direction in his second season as captain. The first eight games were won including wins over Gloucester, Plymouth, Coventry and a Wasps XV.

A total of 54 players represented the 1st XV and 899 points were scored with 29 wins. Overall this has been the club's most successful season since 1983/84 when 980 points were scored with 32 wins.

Andy Halford was once again the top points scorer with 207 points and Mike Stubbs was the top try scorer joining in with the scrums from the wing to pinch push over tries from the forwards.

CLUB PLAYING RECORD 1993-94

National League: Five South
Final League Position at end of 1993/94 Season: 2nd
League Playing record: P 12, W 7, D 2, L 3, Pts F 181, Pts A 111
Season Playing record (including league matches/Pilkington Cup): P 42, W 29, D 2, L 11, Pts F 899, Pts A 405

Lydney on the attack against Stroud

LYDNEY RFC

Club Details

Club Colours: Black & white hoops
Change of Colours: Red
Date Founded: 1887
Membership: Total: 550, Playing members 80, Junior/Youth/Minis 80
No. of teams: Senior 4, Junior 3
Programme advertising rates: Full £60, Quarter £25 (Plus VAT)

Ground Details:

Ground Address: Regentsholme, Regent Street, Lydney, Glos, GL15 5RN
Ground Tel No: 0594 841479 Fax: 0594 844604
Simple Directions to Ground: Turn into Swan Lane at Swan Hotel on A48. 1st turn left then 2nd turn right into ground
Spectator Capacity: Total 3,000 plus. Seated 340, Standing 2,500 plus
Ticket Prices: Adults £3 League & Cup £2 other, OAP/Child £1.50 & £1
Training Nights: Tuesdays and Thursdays

Club Officials

Club President: T C Bailey
Club Chairman: Dr P Catlin
Club Secretary: A John Jones, 5 Kimberley Close, Lydney, Glos, GL15 5AE. Tel: (H) 0594 842709 (W) 0594 841470 Fax: 0594 844604
Fixtures Secretary: Richard Powell, 'Skaint Mesto', Park Hill, Whitecroft, Lydneym, Glos, GL15 4PL. Tel: (H) 0594 562820 (W) Mobile 0860 497301
Press Officer: Gordon Sargent, 'Woodfalls', Forest Road, Bream, Lydney, Glos, GL15 6LZ. Tel: (H) 0594 562822 (W) 0594 841470 Fax: 0594 844604
Registration Officer: A John Jones
1994/ 95 1st XV Captain: Nicholas D Nelmes
1994/95 Club Coaches: Brian J Vine, Rod Sealy, Andy Wyman
Other Club Officers:
Mrs Ann Sargent, Sponsorship Secretary
Mrs Diane Emery, Club Manageress

LEADING SCORERS 1993-94

Andy Halford, O/S Half, 207
Robert Mills, Centre, 105
Gerry Price, O/S Half, 100
Mike Stubbs, Winger, 85
Johnny Edwards, Scrum Half, 60
Mark Bonser, Fullback, 43

METROPOLITAN POLICE RFC

Settled Met stay put

There is not too much to reflect on last season. Suffice to say we survived in Area 5 South having lost five of our first six league matches in what was generally regarded as the easier part of the season - what a foolish notion! What followed was a complete transformation with excellent wins against Camborne (in Cornwall), High Wycombe, Basingstoke and Berry Hill; only over-elaboration and perhaps doubt in our own ability resulted in defeats against Lydney and London Welsh. In that early season lethargy the club also lost at North Walsham in the first round of the Pilkington Cup.

That we survived owed much to the drive and enthusiasm of Rowly Williams who took on the mantle of club coach and the emerging captaincy skills of Kevin Walsh. Our change in fortune also coincided with the ability to select the same backs for each of these games and, only through injury, needed to make two or three adjustments to the forwards. Having a settled side was the greatest bonus and a luxury we are seldom able to experience.

CLUB PLAYING RECORD 1993-94

National League: Five South
Final League Position at end of 1993/94 Season: Tenth
League Playing record: P 13, W 5, D 0, L 7, Pts F 167, Pts A 173
Season Playing record (including league matches/Pilkington Cup): P 32, W 12, D 2, L 18, Pts F 525, Pts A 681

ACHIEVEMENTS/COMPETITIONS WON DURING 93/94 SEASON

Lothian & Boarders Police 7s winners

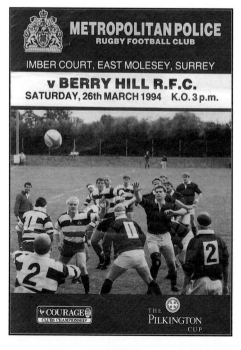

METROPOLITAN POLICE RFC

Club Details

Club Colours: Blue & White hoops, blue shorts
Change of Colours: All blue
Date Founded: 1923
Membership: Total: 260, Playing members 135
No. of teams: Senior 3

Ground Details:

Ground Address: Imber Court Sports Club, Ember Lane, East Molesey, Surrey, KT8 0BT
Ground Tel No: 081 398 1267 Fax No: 081 398 9755
Simple Directions to Ground: M25 Junction 12, M3 to London Junction 1, A308 to Hampton Court, Turn Left at next roundabout. Turn right to Ember Court Road, Club end of road.
Spectator Capacity: Total: Total: 4,000, seated 750, standing
Ticket Prices: Adults £3, OAP/Child £1.50
Training Nights: Mondays and Thursdays

Club Officials

Club President: Sir Paul Condon OPM MA(Oxon)
Club Chairman: David Veness QPM
Club Secretary: David Barham, Room G11, Wellington House, Buckingham Gate, London, SW1E 6BE. Tel: (H) 081 422 4966 (W) 071 230 7109 Fax: 071 230 7215
Fixtures Secretary: Simon Gill, 10 Prestbury Crescent, Woodmansterne, Surrey. Tel: (H) 0737 353184
Press Officer: Phil Judge, 16 William Street, Bushey, Herts, WD2 2HU. Tel: (H) 0923 234348
Registration Officer: David Barham
1994/ 95 1st XV Captain: Kevin Walsh
1994/95 Club Coach: Rowly Williams
Other Club Officers: Frank Armstrong, First Team Manager

PLAYING SQUAD 1993-94

15 J Lunn, G Chesterton, I Dobson, R Cox, S Gill
14 A Carter, P Switzer, P Softley, A Fairweather
13 K Walsh, R Plant, P Daly, B Sweeney
12 R Ferry, F Armstrong, M Slevin
11 P Wakeford, L Davies, S Stockton
10 S Welch, M Sinclair, R Williams, C Lakey, R Kensey
9 R Jenkins, G Fryer, R Lees, N Bibby, E Jones
1 D Barham, B Marsay, A Stewart
2 D Bennett, A Kearns, H Monk, R Kirby, C Adams, J Harris
3 M Kerslake, I Warlow, R McGregor, M Booth
4 N Hanchett, J Moon, R Bannister, D Musker, D Hay, B Barrow
5 J Tunn, P Thompson, D Rinzivillo, P Tanner, R Lambert
6 P Galvin, R Galvin, R Jones, C Welsh, P Judge
7 g tovey, S Drew, R Dowling, S Williams
8 G Raybould, P Totham, P Turner

MOST CAPPED PLAYERS (including British Lions Appearances)	LEADING APPEARANCES FOR CLUB	LEADING SCORERS 1993-94
J C Wright, England 4, 1934	A Carter, 25, 1993/94	A Carter, Wing, 167
D S Wilson, England 5, 1953/54	S Barham, 24, 1993/94	J Lunn, Full Back, 44
A M Bees, Wales 8, 1934-1938	K Walsh, 21, 1993/94	M Sinclair, Outside Half, 32
	M Kerslake, 20, 1993/94	R Jones, Blindside, 30
	G Raybould, 20, 1993/94	L Davies, Wing, 25
	G Tovey, 20, 1993/94	K Walsh, Centre, 25
	P Wakeford, 20, 1993/94	P Wakeford, Wing, 25

NORTH WALSHAM RFC

Away successes bring survival

During the early part of the season the club was rather unsettled following one or two quite serious injuries necessitating experiments with playing positions. During this phase, however, we were quite competitive in the league but scored only five points before Christmas. It was noted and emphasised that one more successful penalty kick per match would have altered three league results in our favour, indicating, amongst other things, the intensity of the competition and highlighting how well and closely matched the teams are at all levels of Courage National Leagues.

We also progressed to the third round of the Pilkington Cup, going down eventually away to a strong Henley side, now, of course, promoted to our Courage League.

By far the most satisfying aspect of our season was the spirit and determination within the Club to retain our league status throughout the closing stages of the competition when, it will be remembered, all the teams threatened with relegation put in sterling performances against higher placed teams.

North Walsham were extremely proud of their team's performance in winning their last three away matches, an achievement which was necessary to ensure our survival, irrespective of other teams' results. The style, commitment and character of their approach left no doubt of their ability to survive and progress at national level.

CLUB PLAYING RECORD 1993-94

National League: Five South
Final League Position at end of 1993/94 Season: 8th
League Playing record: P 12, W 5, D 2, L 5, Pts F 148, Pts A 136
Season Playing record (including league matches/Pilkington Cup): P 29, W 15, D 3, L 11, Pts F 471, Pts A 251

North Walsham RFC 1993-94. Back Row: Richard Flatters (Club Coach), Rob Hawkins (prop), Richard Hannant (hooker), Matthew Scott (prop), Rex Hargrave (lock), Ian Baker (no 8), Dean Lythgoe (lock), Charles Hartley (no 8), Martin Browne (flanker), John Jones (centre), Tony Ridley (hooker), Nick Youngs (Leics & England) (1st Team Coach). Front Row: Ian Woodcock (Player Manager), Pat Dye (President), Ben Yaxley (flanker), Tony Kingsmill (outside half), Chris Greenhall (full back), Ian Fox (centre, Captain), Nick Greenhall (centre), Nick Sherman (wing), David Tanner (wing), David Moore (scrum half), Keith Jarvis (Chairman)

NORTH WALSHAM RFC

Club Details

Club Colours: Green with black band, black shorts
Change of Colours: All white
Date Founded: 1962
Membership: Total: 500, Playing members 100
No. of teams: Senior 5, Junior 6 + minis
Programme advertising rates: Contact Mr P Dye
Any Special Occasions during 1994/95: Opening of new Junior Playing Field

Ground Details:

Ground Address: Norwich Road, Scotton, Norfolk
Ground Tel No: 0692 538461
Simple Directions to Ground: Leave Norwich on B1150 (North Walsham Rd), Pass village of Coltishall.
Ground approx. 4 miles further on left.
Ticket Prices: Adults £2 (1st XV only)
Training Nights: Tuesdays & Thursdays

Club Officials

Club President: Cyril Durrant
Club Chairman: Keith Jarvis
Club Secretary: B A Egerton, 144 Cromer Road, Norwich, Norfolk, NR6 6XN. Tel: (H) 0603 789851
Fixtures Secretary: Keith Jarvis, The Chilterns, 2D Millfield Road, North Walsham, Norfolk, NR28 0EB. Tel:
(H) 0692 406429 (W) 0263 732341 Fax: 0263 734843
Press Officer: Tony Marcantonio, The White House, Southwood Road, Brighton, Great Yarmouth, Norfolk.
Tel: (H) 0493 751837 (W) 0692 407017
Registration Officer: Joe Hodges, Church View, Town Street, Highline, Norwich, Norfolk. Tel: (H) 0692
598318
1994/ 95 1st XV Captain: Nick Greenhall
1994/95 Club Coach: Richard Flatters (Director of Coaching)
Other Club Officers:
Mr P Dye, Marketing Manager

PLAYING SQUAD 1993-94

Full Back: Chris Greenhall
Wing: Nick Sherman, David Tanner
Centre: John Jones, Ian Fox (Captain), Nick Greenhall
Outside Half: Tony Kingsmill
Scrum Half: David Moore
Prop: Rob Hawkins, Matthew Scott
Hooker: Richard Hannant, Tony Ridley
Lock: Rex Hargrave, Dean Lythgoe
Flanker: Martin Browne, Ben Yaxley
No 8: Ian Baker, Charles Hartley

LEADING SCORERS

Tony Kingsmill, Fullback/Outside Half, Points
Chris Greenhall, Fullback/Wing, Tries

*Above: Weston-Super-Mare v High Wycombe at Weston
Photo: Weston Mercury*

Centre: Jerome Bartlett, High Wycombe. Photo: Matt Fowler

Below: Tabard 1st XV receiving Herts Cup

SUDBURY RUFC

CLUB PLAYING RECORD 1993-94
National League: Four
Final Position in League: 10th

ACHIEVEMENTS/COMPETITIONS WON DURING 1993-94 SEASON
Easter Counties Cup: Winners
Suffolk Cup Finalist (2nd XV)

Club Details
Colours: Navy blue with wide white hoop
Change of Colours: Maroon with white stripes
Date Founded: 1925
Membership: Total 330, Playing Members 75, Junior/Youth/Minis 100, Ladies 20
Number of Teams: Senior 5, Junior 7

Ground Details
Ground Address: Moors Field, Rugby Road, Gt Cornard, Sudbury
Telephone: 0787 377547
Directions: Take A133 road to Bures, 1 1/2 miles from Sudbury town centre turn left at Kings Head (PH) and 300 yards first right into Rugby Road
Capacity: Total 300, Standing 300
Ticket Prices: Adults £3.00
Training Nights: Tuesday, Thursday (Youths Wednesdays)

Club Officials
President: T F Mcneill
Chairman: R G Newton
Club Secretary: D Clarke, Bakersfield, School Road, Little Maplestead, Halstead, Essex, CO9 2RY. Tel: (H) 0787 475551 (W) 0933 442287 (Fax) 0787 478977
Fixtures Secretary: G Underwood, Mill Cottages, 11 Bures Rd, Sudbury, Suffolk, CO10 0EJ. Tel: (H) 0787 373045
Press Officer: A Haythornthwaite, 21 Stone Street, Boxford, Sudbury, Suffolk, CO10 5NR. Tel: (H) 0787 211173 (W) 0473 823262 (Mobile) 0374 480200 (Fax) 0473 823868
Registration Officer: T Atherton, 23 The Malthouse, Long Melford, Sudbury, Suffolk, CO10 9TP. Tel: (H) 0787 379026
1993/94 1XV Captain: G Atherton
1993/94 1XV Coach: D Thompson

TABARD RFC

Tabard's excellent senior start

Last season was Tabard's first in the National Leagues and they ended up a highly creditable third in the table behind Reading and Lydney. There were some memorable league performances, notably a 15 minute spell that brought 28 points against Metropolitan Police, an impressive start against Camborne with 18 points in the first quarter and a powerful performance against High Wycombe who were looking for revenge for the previous year's Pilkington Cup defeat. The injury time drop goal against Lydney by stand off Nick Churchman provided the narrowest margin of victory, one point and, on the debit side, Reading handed them their biggest league defeat by 22-13.

Churchman also kicked an injury time penalty to give Tabard victory over Bishop's Stortford on their way to a record breaking sixth Honda Herts President's Cup win, defeating local rivals Old Albanians 34-13 in the final. Tabard also won the Herts Merit table for the sixth consecutive time.

Although defeating Ruislip in the Pilkington Cup, Tabard then suffered their largest defeat of the season at the hands of Sudbury in the next round.

Centre Dave Robjohns, in his first full season at Tabard, notched up the highest number of tries with 12, just one ahead of winger Adam Gilbert, and Churchman again topped the points scored with 167.

CLUB PLAYING RECORD 1993-94

National League: Five South
Final League Position at end of 1993/94 Season: third
League Playing record: P 12, W 6, D 2, L 4, Pts F 209, Pts A 137
Season Playing record (including league matches/Pilkington Cup): P 32, W 25, D 2, L 5, Pts F 828, Pts A 330

ACHIEVEMENTS/COMPETITIONS WON DURING 93/94 SEASON

Herts "Honda" Presidents Cup
Herts "Fullers" Merit Table

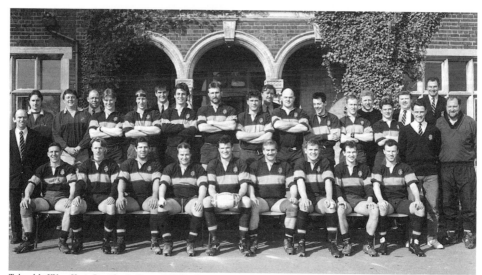

Tabard 1stXV — Herts President's Cup at Old Merchant Taylor's Ground.   *Photo: Reflections*

TABARD RFC

Club Details

Club Colours: Navy, broad yellow band edged with red
Change of Colours: Red/yellow quarters
Date Founded: 1951
Membership: Total: 450, Playing members 200
No. of teams: Senior 5 (+ 1 vets)

Ground Details:

Ground Address: Cobden Hill, Radlett, WD7 7LN
Ground Tel No: 0923 855561
Simple Directions to Ground: On A5183 Watling Street from Elstree turn right after entry into Radlett, blind entrance by high brick wall (Cat & Fiddle Pub is 100m past entry on left).
Spectator Capacity: Total: 2,000 standing
Ticket Prices: Adults £2, OAP/Child £1
Training Nights: Tuesdays and Thursdays

Club Officials

Club President: D Burrows
Club Chairman: B Brennan
Club Secretary: Piers S R Wood, 67A Falcon Road, Battersea, London SW11 2PG. Tel: (H) 071 924 1520 (W) 071 246 3753 Fax: 071 246 3924
Fixtures Secretary: K Carmichael, 10 Chandos Road, Borehamwood, Herts, WD6 1UU. Tel: (H) 081 953 9006 (W) 081 492 4997 Fax: 081 953 9246
Press Officer: P Cook, 32 Pinewood Close, Borehamwood, Herts, WD6 5NW. Tel: (H) 081 207 5564 (W) 071 492 4997 Fax: 071 492 4981
Registration Officer: G Bird, 1 Kendals Close, Radlett, Herts, WD7 9NQ. Tel: (H) 0923 852465 (W) 0923 856711
1994/ 95 1st XV Captain: R Malone
1994/95 Club Coach: I Jones

PLAYING SQUAD 1993-94

Full Back: R Lloyd, S Tansley, H Herts, J Allen
Wing: A Gilbert, G West, P Wood, M Evans, G Hedge, E Moss, O Gardener, P Lincoln
Centre: M Lemon, D Robjohns, S Lloyd, D Niven, R Sant
Half Backs: N Churchman, R Long, R Hardy, C Jackson, S Andrews, R Beadle
Prop: D Warner, R Welsh, J Bambra, N Gouch, M Byrne, C Collinson
Hooker: M Trippick, R Botterman, D Dearsly
Second Rows: R Malone, G Sjollema, L Stokes, J Woodhead, C Reynolds
Back Row: G Pratt, S Reynolds, M Richards, S Armstrong, N Finch, M Hanson, D Haylen, E Browne, A Douglas, P Dillon

LEADING SCORERS 1993-94

Nick Churchman, Stand-off, 167
Simon Tansley, Fullback, 115
Bob Lloyd, Fullback, 71
Dave Robjohns, Centre, 60
Adam Gilbert, Wing, 55
Martin Richards, No 8, 50

WESTON-SUPER-MARE RFC

Weston can do it in 1994-95

The season has seen significant improvements, both on and off the field. The new club coach, Chris Williams, has started the rebuilding process with a pleasing degree of success. New players to the club — Matt Ford, Tony Cottle and Matt Richmond — made valuable contributions, as indeed did the returning Mark Venner. However, it was Dave Williams who made his presence felt in the back-row of the side. He had an outstanding season, was voted 'Player of the Year' and selected for the R.A.F. for their friendlies and inter-service matches.

Next season, with the promise of more new players to the club, we should see further improvements in the playing strength, and quite possibly keen competition for a number of positions.

This season also started with the opening of the new weight training gymnasium, fully equipped to meet the needs of players and non-playing members of the club. This venture is being run, most ably and successfully, by Nigel Penny, one of our senior ex- players.

A new gas central heating system was installed, together with a new gas boiler system, supplying hot water to all the shower areas. In addition to this, the clubhouse was re-decorated and all the furniture was refurbished.

One of our playing highlights of the season was to be the only League side to defeat Reading RFC.

Another memorable day, was our second flight to Norwich to play North Walsham and this was followed by a two page colour spread in the April edition of Rugby World.

Next season, our Mini/Junior section will be celebrating 25 years of organised rugby in the club. Their Committee are working hard with special events to commemorate the occasion.

It is our intention to improve our League position next season and challenge for promotion while also developing all aspects of the club.

CLUB PLAYING RECORD 1993-94

National League: Five South
Final League Position at end of 1993/94 Season: 5th
League Playing record: P 12, W 7, D 0, L 5, Pts F 163, Pts A 180
Season Playing record (including league matches/Pilkington Cup): P 37, W 20, D 0, L 17, Pts F 683, Pts A 626

Weston-Super-Mare RFC, August 1993   *Photo: Barry Richardson*

318

WESTON-SUPER-MARE RFC

Club Details

Club Colours: Royal blue, red, white hoops
Change of Colours: Red or blue
Date Founded: 1875
Membership: Total: 720, Playing members 65+, Junior/Youth/Minis 140, Other 510.
No. of teams: Senior 3, Junior 9
Programme advertising rates: TBA
Any Special Occasions during 1994/95: Celebrating 25 years of mini/junior rugby in club. Special tournaments being arranged

Ground Details:

Ground Address: Recreation Ground, Drove Road, Weston-Super-Mare, BS23 3PA
Ground Tel No: 0934 623118 (Office - 625643)
Simple Directions to Ground: M5 Junction 21. Follow A320 into New Bristol Road, then Locking Road. Into Weston-Super-Mare approx 2.5 miles. 3rd set of traffic lights left over railway bridge. 4th exit off roundabout to ground.
Spectator Capacity: Total: 6,499, Seated 499, Standing 6,000
Ticket Prices: Adults £2.50, OAP/Child £1
Training Nights: Mondays and Wednesdays

Club Officials

Club President: Dr George Papworth
Club Chairman: John Brentnall
Club Secretary: Clayton Hope, 25 Feniton, Clovelly Road, Worle, Weston-Super-Mare, Avon, BS22 0LN. Tel: (H) 0934 511834 (W) 0934 625643
Fixtures Secretary: Roy Main, 142 Quantock Road, Weston-Super- Mare, Avon, BS23 4DP. Tel: (H) 0934 417864 (W) 0934 625643
Press Officer: Bernard Pauncefort OBE, 10 New Church Road, Uphill, Weston-Super-Mare. Tel: (H) 0934 626174
Registration Officer: Clayton Hope
1994/ 95 1st XV Captain: Andy Croker
1994/95 Club Coach: Chris Williams
Other Club Officers:
Alan Knight, Treasurer
Bill Caddick, Chairman of Marketing Committee
Bill Poole, Chairman of Rugby Committee
John Fry, Chairman of Ground Committee

PLAYING SQUAD 1993-94

Full Back: P Thatcher, J Collard, A Baskerville, P Newbury, P McCormack
Wing: M Richmond, C Larkin, D Steele, C Heath, C Brown, P Whatley
Centre: M Longden, M Mousdale, J Robinson, P Forde
Fly Half: P Tincknell, J Ritchie, C Sheryn
Scrum Half: R Chamberlain, N Coleman, A Gaulton
Prop: Andy Croker, B Popham, J Board, M Philp, R Hedges, S Turvey, N Garbutt
Hooker: I Mitchell, G Hill, J Press
Lock: J Cornish, A Cottle, J Pitt, R Main, R Harris
Flanker: D Williams, M Venner, R Fear, S Knight, N Beaver, B Sparks
No 8: M Ford, L Walsh, P Sloman, P Redman

LEADING APPEARANCES FOR CLUB

Jon Cornish, 35, 1993/94
Barry Popham, 29, 1993/94
Martin Longden, 28, 1993/94
Paul Thatcher, 27, 1993/94
Andy Croker, 27, 1993/94
Tony Cottle, 26, 1993/94

LEADING SCORERS 1993-94

Paul Thatcher, Fullback/OH, 191
Jarryd Collard, Fullback/Centre, 106
Mark Venner, Wing Forward, 50
Matt Richmond, Wing, 45
Dave Steele, Wing, 30
Mike Mousdale, Centre, 25

LEAGUE 5 SOUTH PROGRAMMES

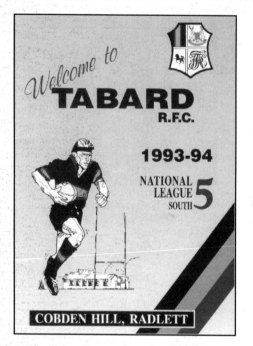

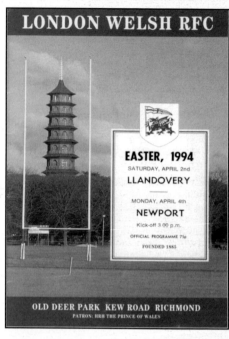

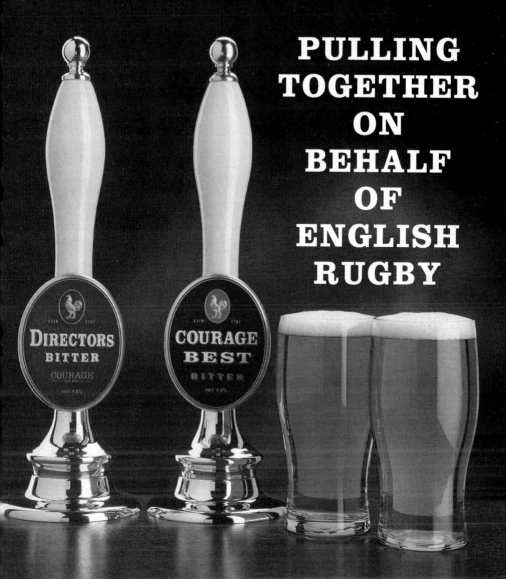

PULLING TOGETHER ON BEHALF OF ENGLISH RUGBY

Proud Sponsors of The Courage Clubs Championship and the England Squad

RUGBY SPECIALISTS Bourne Sports

CRT7.

CRT2.

CRT8.

CRT1.

CRT5.

COURAGE

COURAGE
RUGBY TACKLE RANGE

CRT1 Rugby Jersey - 100% cotton, long sleeves rugby jersey, embroidered badge, unisex, generous sizes, all our usual quality features, taped inside collar, reinforced seams and snug stretch cuffs, sizes S, M, L, XL.
CRT1. Usual £29.95 **League price £25.00**

CRT2 Rugby Jersey - 100% cotton, long sleeves with all features of CRT1 in alternative design, sizes S, M, L, XL,
CRT2. Usual £29.95 **League price £25.00**

CRT3 Polo Shirt - Fashionable Polo Shirt, comfortable 50/50 poly-cotton fabric with embroidered badge, sizes S, M, L, XL,
CRT3. Usual £13.99 **League price £12.50**

CRT4 Training Jacket - Two Colour Jacket in hard wearing 100% cotton drill with embroidered badge, sizes S, M, L, XL, XXL, not illustrated
CRT4. Usual £24.95 **League price £21.00**

CRT5 Sweatshirt - Heavy fleece sweatshirt, 50/50 poly-cotton in navy with embroidered logo, sizes S, M, L, XL. Usual £17.99 **League price £15.**

CRT6 Hooded Top - Fashionable garment, 50/50 poly-cotton with embroidered badge, sizes S, M, L, XL, **CRT6.** Usual £26.95 **League price £24.**

CRT7 Cap - Pro style cap adjustable to any size, embroidered logo, **£9.95**
CRT7. Usual £9.95 **League price £8.95**

CRT8 T-Shirt - Printed T-Shirt, 50/50 poly-cotton, sizes available S, M, L, XL, XXL, **£10.95**
CRT8. Usual £10.95 **League price £8.00**

CRT6.

CRT3.

BOURNE SPORTS

Bourne Sports, Church Street
Stoke-on-Trent, ST4 1DJ

Tel: 0782 410411.
Fax: 0782 411072

All orders value £40 and over post free. Other orders plus £3 postage and packing. Send cheque/postal order or telephone your order quoting Access, Visa, American Express, Diners Card, or Switchcard.

Special Prices for Courage League Players

THE REGIONAL DIVISIONS

NORTHERN
PAGE 324

MIDLAND
PAGE 371

LONDON & SOUTH EAST
PAGE 417

SOUTH WEST
PAGE 485

NORTHERN DIVISION

OFFICIALS 1994-95

CHAIRMAN, League Sub-Committee
Bob Archer, Brookfield House, Scotland Head, Winlaton, Tyne & Wear NE21 6PL (H) 091 414 3532

N.E. CO-ORDINATOR AND YORKSHIRE REPRESENTATIVE
Les Bentley, 32 Moorhead Terrace, Shipley, W. Yorkshire BD18 4LB (H) 0274 585460

N.W. CO-ORDINATOR AND LANCASHIRE REPRESENTATIVE
Bill Chappell, Seawood House, Carter Road, Kents Bank, Grange-over-Sands, Cumbria LA11 7AS (H) 0539 533456

DURHAM REPRESENTATIVE
Ray Thoburn, 70 Theresa Street, Blaydon, Tyne & Wear (H) 091 414 2669

NORTHUMBERLAND REPRESENTATIVE
Ian Rae, 196 Broadway, Tynemouth, Tyne & Wear NE30 3RY (H) 091 259 2136

CHESHIRE REPRESENTATIVE
Mike Lord, 68 Hoole Road, Chester, Cheshire CH2 3NL (H) 0244 312702 (B) 051 356 6241

CUMBRIA REPRESENTATIVE
Jack Hamer, 55 Rush Green Road, Lymm, Cheshire WA13 9PS (H) 0925 755584 (W) 051 548 6756

LEAGUE SECRETARIES
North One R. Holmes, 7 Ashdene Crescent, Crofton, Wakefield, W. Yorks WF4 1PL (H) 0924 863151 (B) 0226 205571

North Two Mike Smith, The Lowe, Wainstalls, Halifax, W Yorks HX2 7TR. (H) 0422 882879 (Mobile) 0850 233019

North East One I. Clark, 109 Dryden Road, Low Fell, Gateshead, Tyne and Wear NE9 5TS (H) 091 487 5480 (B) 091 232 5091 x 4087

North East Two J. Scott, 8 Main Street, Cherry Burton, Beverley, East Yorks HU17 7RF (H) 0964 551340 (B) 0612 237981

Durham/North One S. Harrison, 9 Gillside Grove, Roker, Sunderland, Tyne & Wear SR6 9PQ (H) 091 548 4272

Durham/North Two Mrs Joyce Baty, 5 Brooklands, Ponteland, Northumberland NE20 9LZ (H) 0661 823527

Durham/North Three Anthony Brown, 22 Mill Crescent, Hebburn, Tyne & Wear NE31 1UQ (H) 091 469 3716

Yorkshire One P J Lee, 64 Station Road, Burley-in-Wharfedale, Ilkley, W Yorks LS28 7NG (H) 0904 551340 (B) 0612 237981

Yorkshire Two Ron Lewis, 33 Swift Way, Sandal, Wakefield, W. Yorkshire WF2 6SQ (H) 0924 253049

Yorkshire Three Terry McCreedy, 42 Fearnville Place, Leeds, W. Yorks LS8 3DY. (H) 0532 655065 (B) 0274 727524

Yorkshire Four P Hazledine, 90 Fairburn Drive, Garforth, Leeds LS25 2JD (H) 0532 866035 (B) 0532 869091

Yorkshire Five A.S. McNally, 28 Cherry Tree Road, Armthorpe, Doncaster, S Yorks (H) 0302 834252

North West One Alan Johnson, 6 Rugby Drive, Titherton, Macclesfield, Cheshire (H) 0625 614697

North West Two Ivon Hodgeson, Kimberley End, 22 Capesthorn Close, Holmes Chapel, Cheshire CW4 7EW(H) 0477 533406

Cumbria/North Lancs Roger Bott, 123 Albert Road West, Heaton, Bolton, Lancs BL1 5ED (H) 0204 841376

Cumbria Bill Hopkinson, Far Hey Farm, Littleborough, Rochdale, Lancs OL15 9NS (H) 0706 379879 (B) 0706 47474 x 4531

North Lancs One Colin Barton, 4 Oulderhill Drive, Rochdale, Lancs OL11 5LB (H) 0706 350312

North Lancs Two Ian Scott Brown, Brumsholme, Pendleview, Grindleton, Nr. Clitheroe, Lancs BB7 4QU (H) 0200 40102 (B) 0254 582749 / 57846

Cheshire/South Lancs Mike Massey, Fieldside, Grange Road, Bowden, Cheshire WA14 3EE (H) 061 928 2997

Cheshire Ken Punshon, 24 Newcombe Road, Holcombe Brook, Nr. Bury, Lancs (H) 0204 884886

South Lancs Vic Thomas, 5 Portree Close, Winton, Eccles, Manchester M30 8LX (H) 061 788 7274

NORTHERN DIVISION

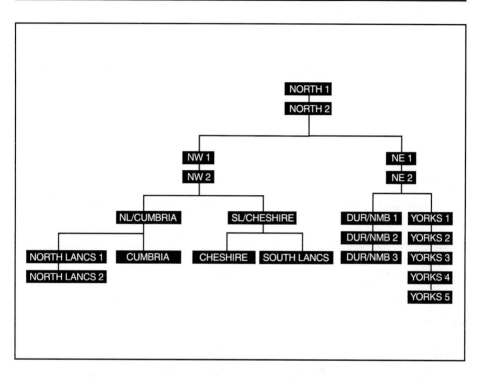

ADMINISTRATIVE RULES

On League Saturdays, both Clubs will telephone the match result through to their League Secretary. Both clubs will also confirm within 48 hours the result and score in writing together with the list of players and replacements featuring in the match to the League Secretary on a card signed by the referee.

a.   In the case of Northern Division Leagues 1 and 2, North West Leagues 1 and 2 and North East Leagues 1 and 2, such telephone calls shall be made not later than 5.30pm on the evening of the game and the League Secretary shall report the results to Snowdon Sports Editorial, PO Box 154, Sheffield S10 4BW. Tel: Sheffield 0742 303093/4 (24 hour answering copy line).

b.   The remaining League Secretaries will telephone the results as soon as possible, but in any case not later than 3.00pm on the Sunday following the games to Snowdon Sports Editorial at the above numbers.

c.   In Northern Division Leagues 1 and 2 the League Secretaries will remit to the Chairman the scores and

results in writing within 48 hours. The remaining League Secretaries will remit the results and the scores in writing to their North East or North West co-ordinator within 48 hours.

d.   In the case of an abandoned match the Secretary of the League must be supplied by the home Club with a certificate signed by the Referee indicating the point at which the match was abandoned, and the score.

e.   These arrangements do not prohibit local publicity and Clubs are advised to maintain and improve local publicity by informing their local press as usual.

f.   Any Club failing to notify the result in accordance with this Rule shall on the first occasion during a season be fined £10, on the second occasion be fined £25 and on the third occasion there will be a recommendation to the RFU that the Club be suspended or expelled from the League. Should payment of fines not be honoured within 28 days of the date of the invoice, the offending club will lose 2 league points.

NORTHERN CHAMPIONS ROLL OF HONOUR 1993/94

North 1
Wharfedale RUFC

North 2
York RUFC

North West 1
New Brighton FC

North West 2
Wilmslow RUFC

North East 1
Doncaster RUFC

North East 2
Horden Colliery Welfare RFC

Durham & Northumberland 1
Darlington Mowden Park RFC

Durham & Northumberland 2
Ponteland RFC

Durham & Northumberland 3
Billingham RUFC

Yorkshire 1
North Ribblesdale RUFC

Yorkshire 2
Barnsley RUFC

Yorkshire 3
Aireborough RUFC

Yorkshire 4
Phoenix Park RUFC

Yorkshire 5
Garforth RUFC

Cumbria/Lancashire North
Fleetwood RUFC

Cumbria
Keswick RUFC

North Lancashire 1
De La Salle (Salford) RUFC

North Lancashire 2
Heaton Moor RUFC

Cheshire & Lancashire South
Leigh RUFC

Cheshire
Port Sunlight RUFC

South Lancashire
Vulcan RUFC

Doncaster RUFC 1st XV — Season 1993/94

326

NORTHERN DIVISION FEATURED CLUBS

DONCASTER

Doncaster is best known as the place with its famous racecourse, where the St Leger has been run for centuries and now the Lincolnshire Handicap also has its home there. The soccer club is also well known although it is currently going through a moderate patch.

But rugby? Yes, they do have a club and in the latest season they went through their North East One programme with only one defeat from a dozen fixtures for a most impressive 232-70 for and against situation and inevitable promotion to the North's big time.

This has been achieved through an aggressive playing and marketing policy. The former has produced a first team which includes 12 ex-colts in its ranks aided by inspiring captaincy from Drew Noble and excellent coaching by former captains Paul Morris and John Lowe. Club President Tony De Mulder aided efficiently by Roger Linsley has encouraged an energetic supporters' section and successfully sought additional sponsorship. Their facilities are superb and as good as any in most senior clubs.

Neighbours Rotherham are now very much in the National swim from humble origins. Doncaster must be fully capable of following suit. After all, in 1991 they gave themselves five seasons to rise from Yorkshire One to the top of North East One — and they have already achieved that target!

DARLINGTON MOWDEN PARK

Darlington Mowden Park is a club which has been knocking at the door to better things for many seasons, but in the latest campaign they have surpassed themselves by winning Durham and Northumberland's top league with a perfect record from their 12 matches and a points difference of 256 scored and 76 conceded.

In a season when only three games were lost overall the team reached the semi-final of the Durham County Cup, losing to eventual winners Hartlepool Rovers, and also won the Newcastle Journal Merit Table ahead of second placed West Hartlepool, who will operate in the National top league this coming campaign!

The club has been revolutionised by coach Eddie Bell, a former England and North prop, and New Zealander Steve Hall, who has also been the club's top tries scorer. On current form it looks as if promotion to North East Two is just a start and the famous old Quaker town may just be another sleeping giant waiting to take game of rugby by storm.

Darlingto Mowden Park RFC

NORTHERN DIVISION

NORTH ONE
1994-95
FIXTURES

January 7 (Week 17)
Durham City v West Park Bramhope
Tynedale v Manchester
Middlesbrough v Stockton
Wigton v Hull Ionians
Bradford & Bingley v Huddersfield
Sandal v York

September 17 (Week 3)
Manchester v West Park Bramhope
Tynedale v Sandal
Middlesbrough v Bradford & Bingley
Wigton v Widnes
Hull Ionians v Huddersfield
Stockton v York

January 14 (Week 18)
Hull Ionians v Middlesbrough
Stockton v Tynedale
Manchester v Durham City
West Park Bramhope v Sandal
York v Bradford & Bingley
Huddersfield v Widnes

September 24 (Week 4)
West Park Bramhope v Stockton
York v Hull Ionians
Huddersfield v Wigton
Widnes v Middlesbrough
Bradford & Bingley v Tynedale
Wigton v Durham City

February 11 (Week 22)
Bradford & Bingley v West Park Bramhope
Sandal v Manchester
Durham City v Stockton
Tynedale v Hull Ionians
Middlesbrough v Wigton
Widnes v York

October 1 (Week 5)
Hull Ionians v West Park Bramhope
Stockton v Manchester
Durham City v Bradford & Bingley
Tynedale v Widnes
Middlesbrough v Huddersfield
Wigton v York

February 25 (Week 24)
Wigton v Tynedale
Hull Ionians v Durham City
Stockton v Sandal
Manchester v Bradford & Bingley
West Park Bramhope v Widnes
York v Huddersfield

October 15 (Week 7)
Manchester v Hull Ionians
West Park Bramhope v Wigton
York v Middlesbrough
Huddersfield v Tynedale
Widnes v Durham City
Bradford & Bingley v Sandal

March 4 (Week 25)
Huddersfield v West Park Bramhope
Widnes v Manchester
Bradford & Bingley v Stockton
Sandal v Hull Ionians
Durham City v Wigton
Tynedale v MIddlesbrough

October 22 (Week 8)
Middlesbrough v West Park Bramhope
Wigton v Manchester
Hull Ionians v Stockton
Sandal v Widnes
Durham City v Huddersfield
Tynedale v York

March 25 (Week 28)
Middlesbrough v Durham City
Wigton v Sandal
Hull Ionians v Bradford & Bingley
Stockton v Widnes
Manchester v Huddersfield
West Park Bramhope v York

October 29 (Week X2)
Stockton v Wigton
Manchester v Middlesbrough
West Park Bramhope v Tynedale
York v Durham City
Huddersfield v Sandal
Widnes v Bradford & Bingley

April 8 (Week 30)
York v Manchester
Huddersfield v Stockton
Widnes v Hull Ionians
Bradford & Bingley v Wigton
Sandal v Middlesbrough
Durham City v Tynedale

NORTH ONE

BRADFORD & BINGLEY RFC
Ground Address:Wagon Lane, Bingley, West Yorkshire.
Tel: 0274 775443
Club Secretary: Mr JS Oddy, The Coach House, Warren
Farm, Slate Quarry Lane, Eldwick, Bingley, Yorkshire
BD16 3NP. Tel: (H) 0274 563254 Tel: (W) 0274 729792
Fixtures Secretary: Mr WK Wilkinson, Green Acres,
Station Lane, Birkenshaw, Bradford, West Yorkshire. Tel:
(H) 0274 681231
Club Colours: Red, amber & black hoops, black shorts.
DURHAM CITY RFC
Ground Address:Hollow Drift, Green Lane, Durham City
DH1 3JU. Tel: 091 3861172
Club Secretary: Mr R Elston, 18 Mayorswell Field,
Claypath, Durham City DH1 1JW. Tel: (H) 091 3863245
Tel: (W) 0207 507001
Fixtures Secretary: Mr J Thompson, Cherry Tree House,
West End, Wolsingham, Co Durham. Tel: (H) 0388 528071
Tel (W) 0388 762522
Club Colours: Gold & blue hooped shirt, white shorts..
HUDDERSFIELD RUFC
Ground Address:Tandem Ground, Waterloo, Huddersfield
HD5 0AN. Tel: 0484 423864 & 517569
Club Secretary: AR Field, 54 Quarry Lane, Lascelles Hall,
Huddersfield HD5 0AR. Tel: (H) 0484 534318 Tel: (W)
0484 424055
Fixtures Secretary: B Starbuck, 2 The Cottages,
Upperthong, Holmfirth, Huddersfield HD7 2UX. Tel: (H)
0484 686059 Tel (W) 061 445 8141
Club Colours: White, claret & gold.
HULL IONIANS RUFC
Ground Address:Brantingham Road, Elloughton, Brough,
North Humberside HU15 1HX. Tel: 0482 667342
Club Secretary: Peter Sharp, 38 Corby Park, North
Ferriby, North Humberside HU14 3AY. Tel: (H) 0482
631819 Tel: (W) 0482 803933
Fixtures Secretary: John Clayton, 60 Annandale Road,
Kirkella, Hull HU10 7UP. Tel: (H) 0482 659784
Club Colours: Red, white, blue, green quarters.
MANCHESTER FC
Ground Address:Grove Park, Grove Lane, Cheadle
Hulme, Cheadle, Cheshire, SK8 7NB. Tel: 061 485 1115
Club Secretary: Norman R Thomas, 94 Kitts Moss Lane,
Bramhall, Cheshire, SK7 2BQ. Tel: (H) 061 439 3385 Tel:
(W) 061 367 9000
Fixtures Secretary: Derek W Partington, 28 Crossfield Drive,
Worsley, Greater Manchester, M28 4GP. Tel: (H) 061 790 6742
Club Colours: Red and White hooped jersey, white shorts,
red socks.
MIDDLESBROUGH RUFC
Ground Address:Acklam Park, Green Lane, Acklam,
Cleveland, Middlesbrough TS5 7SL. Tel: 0642 919567
Club Secretary: Don Brydon, 20 Westwood Avenue,
Linthorpe, Middlesbrough, Cleveland TS5 5PY. Tel: (H)
0642 819954 Tel: (W) 0642 264047
Fixtures Secretary: John D Cunningham, 2 Bush Street,
Linthorpe, Middlesbrough. Tel: (H) 0642 818192 Tel (W)
0429 275453
Club Colours: Maroon shirts, white shorts.
SANDAL RUFC
Ground Address:Milnthorpe Green, Sandal, Wakefield,
West Yorkshire WF2 0BH. Tel: 0924 250661
Club Secretary: Len Bedford, 14 Lindale Mount, Batley
Road, Wakefield, West Yorkshire WF2 0BH. Tel: (H) 0924
379263 Fax: 0924 379263 Tel: (W) 0924 379263
Fixtures Secretary: Colin Critchett, 48 Sinclair Garth,
Sandal, Wakefield WF2 6RE. Tel: (H) 0924 254329
Club Colours: Maroon, gold & white.
STOCKTON RFC
Ground Address:c/o Norton Cricket Field, Station Road,
Norton, Stockton, Cleveland TS20 1PE. Tel: 0642 554031

FINAL TABLE

	P	W	D	L	F	A	PD	Pts
Wharfedale	12	12	0	0	327	77	250	24
Sandal	12	9	0	3	219	131	88	18
Hull Ionians	12	9	0	3	185	137	48	18
Manchester	12	8	0	4	208	159	49	16
Tynedale	12	7	0	5	255	168	87	14
Middlesbrough	12	7	0	5	161	141	20	14
Widnes	12	5	0	7	172	180	-8	10
Huddersfield	12	5	0	7	164	148	16	8
Stockton	12	4	0	8	132	245	-133	8
Wigton	12	3	1	8	184	271	-87	7
Hartlepool Rovers	12	3	0	9	135	248	-113	6
Vale of Lune	12	3	0	9	90	265	-175	6
Northern	12	2	1	9	166	228	-62	5

Club Secretary: John Robinson, 17 Rook Lane, Norton,
Stockton, Cleveland TS20 1SB. Tel: (H) 0642 557288 Tel:
(W) 0642 433069
Fixtures Secretary: Brendon Thornton, 23 Loweswater
Crescent, Stockton, Cleveland. Tel: (H) 0642 613745
Club Colours: Red shirts, white shorts.
TYNEDALE RFC
Ground Address:Tynedale Park, Corbridge,
Northumberland NE45 5AY. Tel: 0434 632996/7
Club Secretary: A Smith, West Fell, Corbridge,
Northumberland NE45 5RZ. Tel: (H) 0434 632044 Tel:
(W) 091 477 1412
Fixtures Secretary: JA Suddes, Glendalough, West
Hextol, Hexham, Northumberland. Tel: (H) 0434 603989
Club Colours: Royal blue & white horizontal stripes,
white shorts, blue & white stockings.
WEST PARK BRAMHOPE RUFC
Ground Address:The Sycamores, Bramhope, Leeds LS16
9JR. Tel: 0532 671437
Club Secretary: Andrew Oddy, 89 The Birches,
Bramhope, Leeds LS16 9DP. Tel: (H) 0532 673316 Tel:
(W) 0943 858071
Fixtures Secretary: Mr Mike Openshaw, 5 Victoria
Grove, Horsforth, Leeds LS18 4ST. Tel: (H) 0532 587338
Club Colours: Black, gold hoops round chest.
WIDNES RUFC
Ground Address:Heath Road, Widnes, Cheshire WA8
7NU. Tel: 051 424 2575
Club Secretary: Ian Barker, 14 Amelia Close, Widnes, Cheshire
WA8 9FR. Tel: (H) 051 423 4128 Tel: (W) 061 721 2326
Fixtures Secretary: R Heapey, 108 Coroners Lane,
Widnes, Cheshire. Tel: (H) 051 424 6565
Club Colours: Red & black.
WIGTON RUFC
Ground Address:Lowmoor Road, Wigton, Cumbria CA7
9QT. Tel: 06973 42206
Club Secretary: Malcolm Sunter, Alpha, Lowmoor Road,
Wigton, Cumbria CA7 9QR. Tel: (H) 06973 42917 Tel:
(W) 0228 519271
Fixtures Secretary: Alan Robson, 2 Station Hill, Wigton,
Cumbria. Tel: (H) 06973 42310 Tel (W) 0228 45810
Club Colours: Green shirts, white shorts, green socks,
white tops.
YORK RUFC
Ground Address:Clifton Park, Shipton Road, York YO3
6RE. Tel: 0904 623602
Club Secretary: Brian McClure, 15 Stubden Grove, York
YO3 4UY. Tel: (H) 0904 691026 Tel: (W) 0532 431888
Fixtures Secretary: Peter Ayers, 1 Clifton Dale, York
YO3 6LJ. Tel: (H) 0904 622360
Club Colours: Green, black & white hoops.

NORTHERN DIVISION

NORTH TWO
1994-95
FIXTURES

January 7 (Week 17)
Halifax v Northern
Old Crossleyans v Vale of Lune
Hartlepool Rovers v Macclesfield
Bridlington v Alnwick
Birkenhead Park v Northwich
West Park (St Helens) v Doncaster

September 17 (Week 3)
Vale of Lune v Northern
Old Crossleyans v West Park (St Helens)
Hartlepool Rovers v Birkenhead Park
Bridlington v New Brighton
Alnwick v Northwich
Macclesfield v Doncaster

January 14 (Week 18)
Alnwick v Hartlepool Rovers
Macclesfield v Old Crossleyans
Vale of Lune v Halifax
Northern v West Park (St Helens)
Doncaster v Birkenhead Park
Northwich v New Brighton

September 24 (Week 4)
Northern v Macclesfield
Doncaster v Alnwick
Northwich v Bridlington
New Brighton v Hartlepool Rovers
Birkenhead Park v Old Crossleyans
West Park (St Helens) v Halifax

February 11 (Week 22)
Birkenhead Park v Northern
West Oark (St Helens) v Vale of Lune
Halifax v Macclesfield
Old Crossleyans v Alnwick
Hartlepool Rovers v Bridlington
New Brighton v Doncaster

October 1 (Week 5)
Alnwick v Northern
Macclesfield v Vale of Lune
Halifax v Birkenhead Park
Old Crossleyans v New Brighton
Hartlepool Rovers v Northwich
Bridlington v Doncaster

February 25 (Week 24)
Bridlington v Old Crossleyans
Alnwick v Halifax
Macclesfield v West Park (St Helens)
Vale of Lune v Birkenhead Park
Northern v New Brighton
Doncaster v Northwich

October 15 (Week 7)
Vale of Lune v Alnwick
Northern v Bridlington
Doncaster v Hartlepool Rovers
Northwich v Old Crossleyans
New Brighton v Halifax
Brikenhead Park v West Park (St Helens)

March 4 (Week 25)
Northwich v Northern
New Brighton v Vale of Lune
Birkenhead Park v Macclesfield
West Park v Alnwick
Halifax v Bridlington
Old Crossleyans v Hartlepool Rovers

October 22 (Week 8)
Hartlepool Rovers v Northern
Bridlington v Vale of Lune
Alnwick v Macclesfield
West Park (St Helens) v New Brighton
Halifax v Northwich
Old Crossleyans v Doncaster

March 25 (Week 28)
Hartlepool Rovers v Halifax
Bridlington v West Park (St Helens)
Alnwick v Birkenhead Park
Macclesfield v New Brighton
Vale of Lune v Northwich
Northern v Doncaster

October 29 (Week X2)
Macclesfield v Bridlington
Vale of Lune v Hartlepool Rovers
Northern v Old Crossleyans
Doncaster v Halifax
Northwich v West Park (St Helens)
New Brighton v Birkenhead Park

April 8 (Week 30)
Doncaster v Vale of Lune
Northwich v Macclesfield
New Brighton v Alnwick
Birkenhead v Bridlington
West Park (St Helens) v Hartlepool Rovers
Halifax v Old Crossleyans

330

NORTH TWO

ALNWICK RFC
Ground Address: Greensfield, St James, Alnwick, Northumberland. Tel: 0665 602342
Club Secretary: Tim Flood, Witton Shield House, Netherwitton, Marthern, Nr Morpeth, Northumberland. Tel: (H) Hartburn 327
Fixtures Secretary: D Reavely, Tilesheds, North Ancroft, Nr Berwick. Tel: (H) Berwick 87371 Tel (W) Berwick 87371
Club Colours: Royal blue shirts, white shorts, blue socks with gold tops.

BIRKENHEAD PARK FC
Ground Address: Upper Park, Park Road North, Birkenhead L41 8AA. Tel: 051 652 4646
Club Secretary: RS Thomas, 80 Upton Road, Moreton, Wirral, Merseyside L43 0SF. Tel: (H) 051 677 3877 Tel: (W) 051 236 1226
Fixtures Secretary: R Hardman, 32 Shamrock Road, Claughton, Birkenhead L41 0EQ. Tel: (H) 051 652 5204
Club Colours: Red, white, navy blue hoops, white shorts, red socks.

BRIDLINGTON RUFC
Ground Address: Dukes Park, Queensgate, Bridlington, East Yorkshire. Tel: 0262 676405
Club Secretary: Phil Preston, 16 West Street, Flamborough, Nr Bridlington YO16 1PH. Tel: (H) 0262 850071 Tel: (W) 0262 603979
Fixtures Secretary: J Waller, 25 Airedale Drive, Bridlington. Tel: (H) 0262 603476 Tel (W) 0262 676198
Club Colours: Blue with amber hoops.

DONCASTER RUFC
Ground Address: Sandal Beat Lane, off Armthorpe Road, Doncaster. Tel: 0302 831388
Club Secretary: John Lowe, 57 Wroot Road, Finningley Village, Doncaster, South Yorkshire DN9 3DR. Tel: (H) 0302 770275
Fixtures Secretary: Roger Linsley, The Barn House, Wilsic, Doncaster DN11 9AG. Tel: (H) 0302 851847 Tel (W) 0302 866906
Club Colours: Blue with two red & white hoops.

HALIFAX RUFC
Ground Address: Standeven Memorial Ground, Ovenden Park, Keighley Road, Halifax, West Yorkshire HX2 8AR. Tel: 0422 365926
Club Secretary: A V Edwards, 6 Heath Street, Savile Park, Halifax, West Yorkshire HX3 0DJ. Tel: (H) 0422 356314 Tel: (W) 0422 360272
Fixtures Secretary: RA Childs, 718 Horton Place, Bradshaw, Halifax, West Yorkshire HX2 9UY. Tel: (H) 0422 244608 Tel (W) 0836 376497
Club Colours: Dark blue, light blue & white hoops.

HARTLEPOOL ROVERS FC
Ground Address: The New Friarage, West View Road, Hartlepool, Cleveland TS24 0BP. Tel: 0424 267741
Club Secretary: Mr Bill Dale, 21 Knapton Avenue, Wolviston Court, Billingham, Cleveland. Tel: (H) 0642 556314
Fixtures Secretary: Mr Michael Ainslie, 18 Clavering Road, Hartlepool, Cleveland. Tel: (H) 0429 276570
Club Colours: White shirts, black shorts, red socks.

MACCLESFIELD RUFC
Ground Address: Priory Park, Priory Lane, Macclesfield SK10 4AE. Tel: 0625 827899
Club Secretary: T McCreery, 20 Carnovstie Drive, Macclesfield SK10 2TB. Tel: (H) 0625 615488
Fixtures Secretary: A Johnson, 6 Rugby Drive, Macclesfield SK10 2JD. Tel: (H) 0625 614697
Club Colours: Blue with white hoops.

NEW BRIGHTON FC
Ground Address: Reeds Lane, Moreton, Wirral L46 3RH. Tel: 051 677 1873
Club Secretary: Mrs Beryl Bowes, 4 Murrayfield Drive, Moreton, Wirral L46 3RS. Tel: (H) 051 678 2654 Tel: (W)

FINAL TABLE

	P	W	D	L	F	A	PD	Pts
York	12	10	0	2	217	138	79	20
West Pk Bramhope	12	9	1	2	269	93	176	19
Bridlington	12	9	1	2	250	99	151	19
Macclesfield	12	9	1	2	250	104	146	19
Alnwick	12	7	2	3	200	93	107	16
O Crossleyans	12	7	0	5	170	153	17	14
West Pk St Helens	12	5	0	7	172	184	-12	8
Birkenhead Park	12	4	0	8	138	190	-52	8
Northwich	12	4	0	8	131	214	-83	8
Halifax	12	4	0	8	153	241	-88	8
Lymm	12	3	1	8	142	233	-91	7
Wigan	12	2	0	10	103	255	-152	4
Carlisle	12	2	0	10	62	260	-198	4

051 224 3409
Fixtures Secretary: Mr Bernard Murphy, 43 Brookfield Gardens, West Kirby, Wirral. Tel: (H) 051 625 8835 Tel (W) 051 647 7969
Club Colours: Dark blue, light blue & white.

NORTHERN FC
Ground Address: McCracken Park, Great North Road, Gosforth, Newcastle upon Tyne NE3 3DG. Tel: 091 236 3369
Club Secretary: Mrs PM Spong, c/o Northern FC, McCracken Park, Great North Road, Gosforth, Newcastle upon Tyne NE3 3DG. Tel: (W) 091 236 3369
Fixtures Secretary: Chairman of Rugby: WJ Davidson, 43 Woolsington Gardens, Woolsington, Newcastle upon Tyne NE13 8AP. Tel: (H) 091 286 5734
Club Colours: White shirts, navy shorts, red socks.

NORTHWICH RUFC
Ground Address: Moss Farm Leisure Centre, Moss Road, Winnington, Northwich, Cheshire. Tel: 0606 79987
Club Secretary: Ron McLaverty, 7 Pear Tree Drive, Wincham, Northwich, Cheshire CW9 6EZ. Tel: (H) 0565 733997 Tel: (W) 0606 74481
Fixtures Secretary: Keith Naylor, 8 Granville Road, Northwich, Cheshire CW9 8ET. Tel: (H) 0606 46107 Tel (W) 0270 255155
Club Colours: Black shirts, black shorts.

OLD CROSSLEYANS RUFC
Ground Address: Standeven House, Broomfield Avenue, Halifax, West Yorkshire HX3 0JF. Tel: 0422 363000
Club Secretary: Mr RA Davies, 4 Warley Dene, Warley Road, Warley, Halifax, West Yorkshire. Tel: (H) 0422 832218
Fixtures Secretary: Keith Davies, 23 School Close, Ripponden, Sowerby Bridge, West Yorkshire HX6 4HP. Tel: (H) 0422 823662 Tel (W) 051 604 2315/0831 804523
Club Colours: Blue, white & amber.

VALE OF LUNE RUFC
Ground Address: Powder House Lane, Lancaster LA1 2TT. Tel: 0524 64029
Club Secretary: Peter Fell, 55 Stanhope Avenue, Morecombe, Lancashire. Tel: (H) 0524 416519
Fixtures Secretary: Brian Garside, 57 Torrisholme Road, Lancashire. Tel: (H) 0524 66834
Club Colours: Cherry & white hooped jersey, navy shorts, red socks. Change Blue & white hoops.

WEST PARK (ST HELENS) RFC
Ground Address: Eccleston Hill, Prescot Road, St Helens, Merseyside. Tel: 0744 26138
Club Secretary: William Bold, 76 Greenfield Road, St Helens, Merseyside. Tel: (W) 0744 26138
Fixtures Secretary: JE Briers, 51 Daresbury Road, Eccleston, St Helens, Merseyside. Tel: (H) 0744 734665
Club Colours: Green & gold.

NORTHERN DIVISION

NORTH WEST ONE
1994-95
FIXTURES

September 17 (Week 3)
Netherhall   v   Blackburn
Davenport   v   Wilmslow
Sandbach   v   Carlisle
Chester   v   Sedgley Park
Oldershaw   v   Cockermouth
Wigan   v   Lymm

September 24 (Week 4)
Blackburn   v   Wigan
Lymm   v   Oldershaw
Cockermouth   v   Chester
Sedgley Park   v   Sandbach
Carlisle   v   Davenport
Wilmslow   v   Ashton-on-Mersey

October 1 (Week 5)
Oldershaw   v   Blackburn
Wigan   v   Netherhall
Ashton-on-Mersey v Davenport
Sandbach   v   Cockermouth
Chester   v   Lymm

October 15 (Week 7)
Lymm   v   Oldershaw
Blackburn   v   Chester
Lymm   v   Sandbach
Cockermouth   v   Davenport
Sedgley Park   v   Ashton-on-Mersey

October 22 (Week 8)
Sandbach   v   Blackburn
Chester   v   Netherhall
Oldershaw   v   Wigan
Wilmslow   v   Sedgley Park
Ashton-on-Mersey v Cockermouth
Davenport   v   Lymm

October 29 (Week X2)
Wigan   v   Chester
Netherhall   v   Sandbach
Blackburn   v   Davenport
Lymm   v   Ashton-on-Mersey
Cockermouth   v   Wilmslow
Sedgley Park   v   Carlisle

January 7 (Week 17)
Ashton-on-Mersey v Blackburn
Davenport   v   Netherhall
Sandbach   v   Wigan
Chester   v   Oldershaw
Carlisle   v   Cockermouth
Wilmslow   v   Lymm

January 14 (Week 18)
Oldershaw   v   Sandbach
Wigan   v   Davenport
Netherhall   v   Ashton-on-Mersey
Blackburn   v   Wilmslow
Lymm   v   Carlisle
Cockermouth   v   Sedgley Park

February 11 (Week 22)
Carlisle   v   Blackburn
Wilmslow   v   Netherhall
Ashton-on-Mersey v Wigan
Davenport   v   Oldershaw
Sandbach   v   Chester
Sedgley Park   v   Lymm

February 25 (Week 24)
Chester   v   Davenport
Oldershaw   v   Ashton-on-Mersey
Wigan   v   Wilmslow
Netherhall   v   Carlisle
Balckburn   v   Sedgley Park
Lymm   v   Cockermouth

March 4 (Week 25)
Cockermouth   v   Blackburn
Sedgley Park   v   Netherhall
Carlisle   v   Wigan
Wilmslow   v   Oldershaw
Ashton-on-Mersey v Chester
Davenport   v   Sandbach

March 25 (Week 28)
Sandbach   v   Ashton-on-Mersey
Chester   v   Wilmslow
Oldershaw   v   Carlisle
Wigan   v   Sedgley Park
Netherhall   v   Cockermouth
Balckburn   v   Lymm

April 8 (Week 30)
Lymm   v   Netherhall
Cockermouth   v   Wigan
Sedgley Park   v   Oldershaw
Carlisle   v   Chester
Wilmslow   v   Sandbach
Ashton-on-Mersey v Davenport

NORTH WEST ONE

ASHTON-ON-MERSEY RUFC
Ground Address: Banky Lane, off Carrington Lane, Ashton-on-Mersey, Sale, Cheshire M33 5NP. Tel: 061 973 6637
Club Secretary: Max Nobbs, 116 Mercer Street, Newton-le-Willows, Merseyside WA12 9TL. Tel: (H) 0925 220350
Fixtures Secretary: Mr Pat Stokes, 109 Buxton Crescent, Sale Cheshire M33 3LG. Tel: (H) 061 976 2284
Club Colours: Maroon shirts, navy shorts, maroon socks with white tops.
BLACKBURN RUFC
Ground Address: Ramsgreave Drive, Blackburn BB! 8NB. Tel: 0254 247669
Club Secretary: MJ Walker, 6 Westview Place, Revidge, Blackburn BB2 6JG. Tel: (H) 0254 681172 Tel: (W) 0204 308431
Fixtures Secretary: G Bancroft, 3 Higher House Close, Livesey, Blackburn BB2 4RN.
Club Colours: Royal blue shirts, white shorts, red & white socks.
CARLISLE RFC
Ground Address: Warwick Road, Carlisle, Cumbria CA1. Tel: 0228 21300
Club Secretary: NJ Laycock, 90 Greystone Road, Carlisle, Cumbria CA1 2DD. Tel: (H) 0228 22895 (not after 10pm) Tel: (W) 0228 20277
Fixtures Secretary: R Lawson, 35 Carlisle Road, Dalston, Carlisle, Cumbria. Tel: (H) 0228 710559
Club Colours: Irregular navy blue, white & red hoops.
CHESTER RUFC
Ground Address: Hare Lane, Vicars Cross, Chester CH3 7BD. Tel: 0244 336017
Club Secretary: P Rhodes, The Hollies, off Carriage Drive, Frodsham, via Warrington WA6 6EF. Tel: (H) 0928 731485 Tel: (W) 051 225 2404
Fixtures Secretary: C Cawthorn, 21 Oaklands Avenue, Tattenhall, Nr Chester. Tel: (H) 0829 70498 Tel (W) 0244 603420
Club Colours: Red shirts, white shorts.
COCKERMOUTH RUFC
Ground Address: Laithwaite, Low Road, Cockermouth, Cumbria. Tel: 0900 824884
Club Secretary: Bill McDowell, 10 The Green, Cockermouth, Cumbria CA13 9AS. Tel: (H) 0900 824274 Tel: (W) 0697 320234
Club Colours: Black & amber.
DAVENPORT RUFC
Ground Address: Bridge Lane Memorial Grounds, Headlands Road, Bramhill, Stockport, Cheshire, Tel: 061 439 2150
Club Secretary: M Hargreaves, 80 Ladybridge Road, Cheadle Hume, Cheshire SK8 5NZ. Tel: 061 485 8450.
Club Colours: Red, green and white.
LYMM RFC
Ground Address: Beechwood, Crouchley Lane, Lymm, Warrington, Cheshire WA13 0AT. Tel: 0925 753212
Club Secretary: Varun Maharaj, 5 Farrell Road, Stockton Heath, Warrington WA4 6LR. Tel: (H) 0925 264566 Tel: (W) 0204 32611
Fixtures Secretary: C Monks, 8 Newlands Road, Stockton Heath, Warrington, Cheshire WA4 2DS. Tel: (H) 0925 262904 Tel (W) 0925 573511
Club Colours: Green, black & white hoops, black shorts.
NETHERHALL RFC
Ground Address: Netherhall Park, Netherhall Road, Maryport, W Cumbria. Tel: 0900 815833
Club Secretary: P Bartlett, 66 Garborough Close, Vrosby, Nr Maryport, W Cumbria, CA15 6RZ. Tel: (H) 0900 818420 Tel: (W) 0946 692261
Fixtures Secretary: L Rumney, 4 Orchard Cose, Seaton, Workington, W Cumbria. Tel: (H) 0900 871440
Club Colours: Claret and gold.

FINAL TABLE

	P	W	D	L	F	A	PD	Pts
New Brighton	12	10	1	1	310	87	223	21
Oldershaw	12	9	2	1	242	83	159	20
Chester	12	8	2	2	185	116	69	18
Sandbach	12	6	3	3	172	163	9	15
Sedgley Park	12	5	2	5	201	134	67	12
Cockermouth	11	5	1	5	81	125	-44	11
Stockport	11	5	0	6	140	153	-13	10
Ashton on Mersey	11	5	0	6	128	143	-15	10
Blackburn	12	5	0	7	127	169	-42	10
Caldy	12	4	0	8	121	203	-82	8
St Edwards OB	12	3	1	8	119	230	-111	7
Merseyside Police	11	3	0	8	106	191	-85	6
Kirkby Lonsdale	12	2	0	10	108	243	-135	2

OLDERSHAW RUFC
Ground Address: Beledevere Playing Fields, Beledevere Road, Liscard, Wallasey, Wirral. Tel: 051 638 4379
Club Secretary: David Cooley, 17 Shrewsbury Road, Wallasey, Wirral. Tel: (H) 051 630 4957
Fixtures Secretary: Peter Purland, 63 Croxteth Road, Liverpool 8. Tel: (H) 051 733 4854
Club Colours: Navy blue and gold.
SANDBACH RUFC
Ground Address: Bradwell Road, Sandbach, CW11 9AP. Tel: 0270 762457
Club Secretary: John Gater, 7 Colley Lane, Sandbach, Cheshire CW11 0HE. Tel: (H) 0270 764035 Tel: (W) 0260 283815
Club Colours: Green with red band.
SEDGLEY PARK RUFC
Ground Address: The Clubhouse, Park Lane, Whitefield, Manchester M45 7DZ. Tel: 061 766 5050
Club Secretary: Mark G Mold, 32 Vicarage Avenue, Cheadle Hulme, Cheadle, Cheshire SK8 7JW. Tel: (H) 061 486 0496 Tel: (W) 06# 794 4755
Fixtures Secretary: George Hinds, 104 Nuttall Avenue, Whitefield, Manchester M45 6QA. Tel: (H) 061 766 8925
Club Colours: Claret & gold hooped jerseys, white shorts, maroon socks.
WIGAN RUFC
Ground Address: Douglas Valley, Wingates Road, off Leyland Mill Lane, Wigan, Lancashire. Tel: 0924 42556
Club Secretary: Graham Heeley, 30 Darley Road, Hawkley Hall, Wigan WN3 5PG. Tel: (H) 0924 201360 Tel: (W) 061 486 6211
Fixtures Secretary: Dave Clarke, 224 Billinge Road, Pemberton, Wigan, Lancashire WN5 9HX. Tel: (H) 0942 207771
Club Colours: Black & white irregular hoops.
WILMSLOW RUFC
Ground Address: Memorial Ground, Pownall Park, Kings Road, Wilmslow SK9 5PZ. Tel: 0625 522274
Club Secretary: David Pike, 12 Fairbourne Drive, Wilmslow SK9 6JF. Tel: (H) 0625 525616
Fixtures Secretary: Geoff Mitchell, Green Bank Farm, Brookhouse Green, Smallwood, Sandbach, Cheshire. Tel: (H) 0477 500329 Tel (W) 0455 251683
Club Colours: Sky blue, maroon & white jerseys, white shorts, maroon stockings.

NORTHERN DIVISION

NORTH WEST TWO
1994-95
FIXTURES

September 17 (Week 3)
Rossendale v Vagabonds
Ruskin Park v Kirkby Lonsdale
Fleetwood v Egremont
St Edwards OB v Old Salians
Merseyside Police v Old Aldwinians
Leigh v Caldy

September 24 (Week 4)
Vagabound v Leigh
Caldy v Merseyside Police
Old Aldwinians v St Edwards OB
Old Salians v Fleetwood
Ergemont v Ruskin Park
Kirkby Lonsdale v Penrith

October 1 (Week 5)
Merseyside Police v Vagabonds
Leigh v Rossendale
Penrith v Ergemont
Ruskin Park v Old Salians
Fleetwood v Old Aldwinians
St Edwards OB v Caldy

October 15 (Week 7)
Rossendale v Merseyside Police
Vagabonds v St Edwards OB
Caldy v Fleetwood
Old Aldwinians v Ruskin Park
Old Salians v Penrith
Ergemont v Kirkby Lonsdale

October 22 (Week 8)
Fleetwood v Vagabonds
St Edwards OB v Rossendale
Merseyside Police v Leigh
Kirkby Lonsdale v Old Salians
Penrith v Old Aldwinians
Ruskin Park v Caldy

October 29 (Week X2)
Leigh v St Edwards OB
Rossendale v Fleetwood
Vagabonds v Ruskin Park
Caldy v Penrith
Old Aldwinians v Kirkby Lonsdale
Old Salians v Egremont

January 7 (Week 17)
Penrith v Vagabonds
Ruskin Park v Rossendale
Fleetwood v Leigh
St Edwards OB v Merseyside Police
Ergemont v Old Aldwinians
Kirkby Lonsdale v Caldy

January 14 (Week 18)
Merseyside Police v Fleetwood
Leigh v Ruskin Park
Rossendale v Penrith
Vagabonds v Kirkby Lonsdale
Caldy v Egremont
Old Aldwinians v Old Salians

February 11 (Week 22)
Egremont v Vagabonds
Kirkby Lonsdale v Rossendale
Penrith v Leigh
Ruskin Park v Merseyside Police
Fleetwood v St Edwards OB
Old Salians v Caldy

February 25 (Week 24)
St Edwards OB v Ruskin Park
Merseyside Police v Penrith
Leigh v Kirkby Lonsdale
Rossendale v Ergemont
Vagabonds v Old Salians
Caldy v Old Aldwinians

March 4 (Week 25)
Old Aldwinians v Vagabonds
Old Salians v Rossendale
Egremont v Leigh
Kirkby Lonsdale v Merseyside Police
Penrith v St Edwards OB
Ruskin Park v Fleetwood

March 25 (Week 28)
Fleetwood v Penrith
St Edwards OB v Kirkby Lonsdale
Merseyside Police v Egremont
Leigh v Old Salians
Rossendale v Old Aldwinians
Vagabonds v Caldy

April 8 (Week 30)
Caldy v Rossendale
Old Aldwinians v Leigh
Old Salians v Merseyside Police
Egremont v St Edwards OB
Kirkby Lonsdale v Fleetwood
Penrith v Ruskin Park

NORTH WEST TWO

CALDY RFC
Ground Address: Paton Field, Thurstaston Road, Caldy, Wirral. Tel: 051 625 8043
Club Secretary: RB Flashman, 26 Milton Cresent, Heswall, Wirral. Tel: (H) 051 342 5300 Tel: (W) 051 653 0566
Fixtures Secretary: K Doolan, 37 Peartree Close, Great Sutton Street, Wirral. Tel: (H) 051 348 0119
Club Colours: Sable, claret, silver & gold hoops.

EGREMONT RUFC
Ground Address: Bleach Green, Egremont, Cumbria. Tel: 0946 820645
Club Secretary: WHF Moran, 58 Dent View, Egremont, Cumbria CA22 2ET. Tel: (H) 0946 822119 Tel: (W) 09467 72443 Fax: 09467 72446
Fixtures Secretary: JWA Crichton, 25 Springfield Gardens, Bigrigg, Egremont, Cumbria. Tel: (H) 0946 811933 Tel (W) 0946 811933
Club Colours: Black & gold.

FLEETWOOD RUFC
Ground Address: Melbourne Avenue, Fleetwood, Lancashire. Tel: 0253 874774
Club Secretary: Trevor Michael Jones, 'The Cottage', Derby Road, Poulton le Fylde, Lancashire, FY6 7AF. Tel: (H) 0253 899352 Tel: (W) 0253 873030
Fixtures Secretary: Brian Olsen, 32 Huntingdon Road, Anchorsholme, Cleveleys, Lancashire, FY5 1SR. Tel: (H) 0253 854758 Tel (W) 0253 866336
Club Colours: Green and gold hoops, blue shorts.

KIRKBY LONSDALE RUFC
Ground Address: The Club House, Underley Park, Kirkby Lonsdale, via Carnforth, Lancs. Tel: 05242 71780
Club Secretary: Richard Harkness, Meadowgarth, Fairbank, Kirkby Lonsdale. Tel: (H) 05242 71137 Tel: (W) 0524 843160
Club Colours: Red, black, amber hoops & socks, black shorts.

LEIGH RUFC
Ground Address: Round Ash Park, Hand Lane, Leigh, Lancashire WN7 3NA. Tel: 0942 673526
Club Secretary: Mark Downs, 3 Melling Close, Leigh, Lancashire. Tel: (H) 0942 676704
Fixtures Secretary: Tom Hughes, 2 Launceston Road, Hindley Green, Wigan, Lancashire. Tel: (H) 0942 57427 Tel (W) 0695 33061
Club Colours: Black & amber hoops.

MERSEYSIDE POLICE RUFC
Ground Address: Police Sports Ground, Riversdale Road, Aigborth, Liverpool 19, Mersyside. Tel: 051 427 2208
Club Secretary: D/Sgt Andy Ward, 229 Pensby Road, Heswall, Wirral L61 5Ua. Tel: (H) 051 342 8825 Tel: (W) 0244 533500
Fixtures Secretary: Constable Fred Evans, 42 Greenheys Road, Wavertree, Liverpool L44 5UO. Tel: (H) 051 638 1448 Tel (W) 051 709 6010 x5206
Club Colours: Blue shirts, black shorts.

OLD ALDWINIANS RUFC
Ground Address: Audenshaw Park, Droylsden Road, Audenshaw, Manchester M34 5SN. Tel: 061 301 1001
Club Secretary: Colin S Ingham, 441 Manchester Road, Denton, Manchester M34 3GN. Tel: (H) 061 337 9903 Tel: (W) 061 330 3332
Fixtures Secretary: Alan Whalley, 190 Greenside Lane, Droylsden, Manchester M35 6RA. Tel: (H) 061 370 0921 Tel (W) 061 223 1353 x246
Club Colours: Red & white hoops.

OLD SALIANS RUFC
Ground Address: Rookwood, Clarendon Crescent, off Dane Road, Sale, Cheshire. Tel: 061 973 7250
Club Secretary: Paul Robinson, 9 Amberley Road, Sale, Cheshire M33 6QP. Tel: (H) 061 973 2706 Tel: (W) 0282

FINAL TABLE

	P	W	D	L	F	A	PD	Pts
Wilmslow	12	11	0	1	312	95	217	22
Netherhall	12	9	0	3	250	90	160	18
Old Aldwinians	12	9	0	3	186	131	55	18
Ruskin Park	12	7	1	4	185	131	54	15
Rossendale	12	6	2	4	171	124	47	14
Egremont	12	6	0	6	173	165	8	12
Vagabonds	12	6	0	6	106	120	-14	12
O Salians	12	4	1	7	85	116	-31	9
Penrith	12	4	1	7	119	187	-68	9
Ormskirk	12	6	0	6	192	250	-58	8
Warrington	12	2	1	9	108	197	-89	5
Rochdale	12	3	0	9	109	197	-88	4
Wirral	12	2	0	10	104	297	-193	4

415323
Fixtures Secretary: Andrew Parkinson, Alexandra Road, Sale, Cheshire. Tel: (H) 061 976 3904
Club Colours: Navy blue shirts with white chest band, navy shorts & socks.

PENRITH RUFC
Ground Address: Winters Park, Penrith, Cumbria CA11 8RG. Tel: 0768 63151
Club Secretary: Keith Davis, Ivybank, Lowther Street, Penrith, Cumbria CA11 7UQ. Tel: (H) 0768 66089 Tel: (W) 0768 217339
Fixtures Secretary: William F Mounsey, The Luham, Edenhall, Penrith CA11 8TA. Tel: (H) 0768 881202
Club Colours: Myrtle green & white hoops, white shorts.

ROSSENDALE RUFC
Ground Address: Marl Pits Sports Centre, Newchurch Road, Rawtenstall, Rossendale, Lancs BB4 7SW. Tel: 0706 229152
Club Secretary: Peter Brotherton, 47 Poulton Avenue, Accrington, Lancs BB5 5EP. Tel: (H) 0254 234310 Tel: (W) 0282 772511
Fixtures Secretary: Terence Kelly, 111 Pinkington Terrace, Broadway, Haslingden, Rossendale, Lancs. Tel: (H) 0706 217361
Club Colours: Maroon.

RUSKIN PARK RFC
Ground Address: Ruskin Drive, St Helens, Merseyside WA10 6RP. Tel: 0774 22893
Club Secretary: SP Smith, 23 Stuart Road, Windle, St Helens, Merseyside WA10 6HU. Tel: (H) 0744 27394 Tel: (W) 0744 696804
Fixtures Secretary: G White, 25 Dodd Avenus, Eccleston, St Helens. Tel: (H) 0744 56478 Tel (W) 0744 696575
Club Colours: Royal blue, white & black hoops.

ST EDWARDS OLD BOYS RUFC
Ground Address: St Edwards College, Sandfield Park, West Derby, Liverpool, Merseyside. Tel: 051 228 1414
Club Secretary: David Phoenix, 11 Linden Drive, Huyton, Merseyside, L36 5TT. Tel: (H) 051 489 1221
Club Colours: Royal blue, broad horizontal blue band.

VAGABONDS (IOM) RUFC
Ground Address: Glencrutchery Road, Douglas, Isle of Man. Tel: 0624 661996
Club Secretary: Ian Forrest, Arkadia, Alexander Drive, Douglas, Isle of Man. Tel: (H) 0624 676106 Tel: (W) 0624 623991
Fixtures Secretary: Steve Wilson, 49 St Catherines Close, Douglas, Isle of Man. Tel: (H) 0624 673029 Tel (W) 0624 673029 (answerphone)
Club Colours: White with black & yellow chest band, black shorts, black & yellow hooped socks.

NORTHERN DIVISION

CUMBRIA & LANCASHIRE NORTH 1994-95 FIXTURES

September 17 (Week 3)
St Benedicts v De la Salle
Windermere v Rochdale
Keswick v Furness
Workington v Moresby
Vickers v Upper Eden
Ormskirk v Caldervale

September 24 (Week 4)
De la Salle v Ormskirk
Caldervale v Vickers
Upper Eden v Workington
Moresby v Keswick
Furness v Windermere
Rochdale v Tyldesley

October 1 (Week 5)
Vickers v De la Salle
Ormskirk v St Bendicts
Tyldesley v Furness
Windermere v Moresby
Keswick v Upper Eden
Workington v Caldervale

October 15 (Week 7)
St Benedicts v Vickers
De la Salle v Workington
Caldervale v Keswick
Upper Eden v Windermere
Moresby v Tyldesley
Furness v Rochdale

October 22 (Week 8)
Keswick v Da la Salle
Workington v St Benedicts
Vickers v Ormskirk
Rochdale v Moresby
Tyldesley v Upper Eden
Windermere v Caldervale

October 29 (Week X2)
Ormskirk v Workington
St Benedicts v Keswick
De La Salle v Windermere
Caldervale v Tyldesley
Upper Eden v Rochdale
Moresby v Furness

January 7 (Week 17)
Tyldesley v De la Salle
Windermere v St Benedicts
Keswick v Ormskirk
Workington v Vickers
Furness v Upper Eden
Rochdale v Caldervale

January 14 (Week 18)
Vickers v Keswick
Ormskirk v Windermere
St Benedicts v Tyldesley
De la Salle v Rochdale
Caldervale v Furness
Upper Eden v Moresby

February 11 (Week 22)
Furness v De la Salle
Rochdale v St Benedicts
Tyldesley v Ormskirk
Windermere v Vickers
Keswick v Workington
Moresby v Caldervale

February 25 (Week 24)
Workington v Windermere
Vickers v Tyldesley
Ormskirk v Rochdale
St Benedicts v Furness
De la Salle v Moresby
Caldervale v Upper Eden

March 4 (Week 25)
Upper Eden v De la Salle
Moresby v St Benedicts
Furness v Ormskirk
Rochdale v Vickers
Tyldesley v Workington
Windermere v Keswick

March 25 (Week 28)
Keswick v Tyldesley
Workington v Rochdale
Vickers v Furness
Ormskirk v Moresby
St Benedicts v Upper Eden
De la Salle v Caldervale

April 8 (Week 30)
Caldervale v St Benedicts
Upper Eden v Ormskirk
Moresby v Vickers
Furness v Workington
Rochdale v Keswick
Tyldesley v Windermere

CUMBRIA & LANCASHIRE NORTH

DE-LA-SALLE (SALFORD) RUFC
Ground Address:Lancaster Road, Playing Fields, Slaford, 6 Greater Manchester. Tel: 061 789 2261
Club Secretary: Mr John Malone, 57 Hayfield Road, Salford 6, M6. Tel: (H) 061 736 9953
Fixtures Secretary: Mr Roy Waddington, 8 Carver Avenue, Prestwich, M25 5QA. Tel: (H) 061 798 8374 Tel (W) 061 736 9448
Club Colours: Scarlet ad old gold hoops, black shorts, red socks.
FURNESS RUFC
Ground Address: Strawberry Grounds: Abbey Road, Barrow-in-Furness Cumbria. Tel: 0229 825226
Club Secretary: J H Malkinson, 64 Hawcoat Lane, Barrow-in-Furness, Cumbria LA14 4HQ Tel: (H) 0229 824938 (W) 0229 63064
Club Colours: Blue and white.
KESWICK RUFC
Ground Address:Davidson Park, Keswick, Cumbria. Tel: 07687 72823
Club Secretary: ME Bowman, 3 Briar Rigg, Keswick, Cumbria CA12 4NW. Tel: (H) 07687 74878
Fixtures Secretary: AJ Branthwaite, 15 St Herberts Street, Keswick, Cumbria. Tel: (H) 07687 74234
Club Colours: Navy, green, gold hoops, white shorts.
MORESBY RUFC
Ground Address:Walk Mill Park, Moresby Parks, Whitehaven, Cumbria. Tel: 0946 695984
Club Secretary: Mr Jeff Peet, Middle Croft, Tallentire, Nr Cockermouth, Cumbria. Tel: (H) 0900 823069 Tel: (W) 09467 73141
Fixtures Secretary: Mr Syd Bray, 75 Lowther St, Whitehaven, Cumbria. Tel: (H) 695561 Tel (W) 695561 Ext 236
Club Colours: Red shirt, white shorts.
ORMSKIRK RUFC
Ground Address:Green Lane, Ormskirk, Lancs. Tel: 0695 572523
Club Secretary: Mr LA Bumford, 28 Gores Lane, Formby, Mersyside. Tel: (H) 0704 878702 Tel: (W) 051 934 4428
Fixtures Secretary: AA Worthington, 21 Sefton Gardens, Aughton, Ormskirk, Lancs L39 6RY. Tel: (H) 0695 423762 Tel (W) 0695 572405
Club Colours: Dark blue, light blue & green hoops.
ROCHDALE RUFC
Ground Address:Moorgate Avenue, Bamford, Rochdale, Gtr Manchester, OL11 5LU. Tel: 0706 46863
Club Secretary: JBL McManus, 27 Hunstanton Drive, Brandlesholme, Bury, Lancs, BL8 1EG. Tel: (H) 061 761 4371 Tel: (W) 061 740 4993
Fixtures Secretary: MP Deasey, 17 Honeysuckle Way, Rochdale, Gtr Manchester, OL12 6XL. Tel: (H) 0706 356094 Tel (W) 0706 353208
Club Colours: Maroon & white hoops.
ST BENEDICTS RUFC
Ground Address:Newlands Avenue, Mirehouse, Whitehaven, Cumbria.
Club Secretary: MJ Morgan, 264 Meadow Road, Mirehouse, Whitehaven, Cumbria. Tel: (H) 0946 64076
Fixtures Secretary: A Relph, 145 Balmoral Road, Whitehaven, Cumbria. Tel: (H) 0946 62490
Club Colours: Amber & black, emerald green & black.
TYLDESLEY RUFC
Ground Address:Well Street, Tyldesley. Tel: 0942 882967
Club Secretary: Fred Eckersley, 48 Hough Lane, Tyldesley M29 8NW. Tel: (H) 0942 876074 Tel: (W) 061 794 6215
Fixtures Secretary: Alf Yates, 65 Parkfield Close, Astley, Tyldesley, Manchester M29 7GM. Tel: (H) 0942 874651
Club Colours: Blue shirts, white shorts.

FINAL TABLE

	P	W	D	L	F	A	PD	Pts
Fleetwood	12	9	1	2	327	94	233	19
Tyldsley	12	8	0	4	221	150	71	16
U Eden	12	8	0	4	190	137	53	16
Windermere	12	7	1	4	180	161	19	13
Calder Vale	12	6	1	5	167	155	12	13
Workington	12	6	0	6	175	189	-14	12
St Benedicts	12	5	1	6	122	127	-5	11
Vickers	12	6	0	6	163	172	-9	10
Morseby	12	5	0	7	145	214	-69	10
Furness	12	4	1	7	120	154	-34	9
Oldham	12	4	1	7	97	152	-55	9
Metrovick	12	5	0	7	131	151	-20	8
Smith Bros	12	2	0	10	97	279	-182	4

UPPER EDEN RUFC
Ground Address:Pennine Park, Westgarth, Kirkby Stephen, Cumbria CA17 4TD. Tel: 07683 71585
Club Secretary: Stuart Reed, 87 High Street, Kirkby Stephen, Cumbria CA17 4JH. Tel: (H) 07683 72197
Fixtures Secretary: G Todd, Melbecks House, Melbecks, Kirkby Stephen, Cumbria. Tel: (H) 07683 71562
Club Colours: Black & white hoops.
VICKERS
Ground Address:Hawcoat Park, Hawcoat Lane, Barrow in Furness, Cumbria. Tel: 0229 825296
Club Secretary: Mr T Mason, 48 Croslands Park, Barrow in Furness, Cumbria LA13 9NH. Tel: (H) 0229 821624 Tel: (W) 0229 820628
Fixtures Secretary: Mr C High, 19 Cowlarns Road, Barrow in Furness, Cumbria LA14 4HJ. Tel: (H) 0229 826886
Club Colours: Maroon & white.
WINDERMERE RUFC
Ground Address:Dawes Meadow, Longlands, Bowness on Windermere, Cumbria LA23 3AS. Tel: 05394 43066
Club Secretary: R Nigel Rimmer, Langrigge Close, Langrigge Drive, Bowness on Windermere, Cumbria LA23 3AF. Tel: (H) 05394 45540 Tel: (W) 05394 72002
Fixtures Secretary: Guy W Aspinwall, c/o Brayrigg, Craig Walk, Windermere, Cumbria LA23 2HB. Tel: (H) 05394 42708 or 05394 88019
Club Colours: Amber shirts, black shorts.
WORKINGTON RUFC
Ground Address:Ellis Sports Ground, Mossbay Road, Workington CA14 3XZ. Tel: 0900 602625
Club Secretary: M Heaslip, 32 Elizabeth Street, Workington CA14 4DB. Tel: (H) 0900 66339 Tel: (W) 0900 65656
Fixtures Secretary: J Heaslip, 3 St Michael's Road, Workington CA14 3EZ. Tel: (H) 0900 603449
Club Colours: Black & white hoops.

NORTHERN DIVISION

CUMBRIA
1994-95
FIXTURES

September 17 (Week 3)
Greengarth v Whitehaven
Carnforth v Millom
Smith Bros v British Steel

September 24 (Week 4)
British Steel v Carnforth
Millom v Greengarth
Whitehaven v Silloth

October 1 (Week 5)
Silloth v Millom
Greengarth v British Steel

October 15 (Week 7)
British Steel v Silloth
Millom v Whitehaven

October 22 (Week 8)
Creighton v Ambleside
Whitehaven v British Steel

October 29 (Week X2)
Ambleside v Smith Bros
British Steel v Millom

January 7 (week 17)
Carnforth v Ambleside
Smith Bros v Creighton

January 14 (Week 18)
Creighton v Carnforth
Ambleside v Greengarth

February 11 (Week 22)
Silloth v Ambleside
Greengarth v Creighton
Carnforth v Smith Bros

February 25 (Week 24)
Smith Bros v Greengarth
Creighton v Silloth
Ambleside v Whitehaven

March 4 (Week 25)
Millom v Ambleside
Whitehaven v Creighton
Silloth v Smith Bros
Greengarth v Carnforth

March 25 (Week 28)
Carnforth v Silloth
Smith Bros v Whitehaven
Creighton v Millom
Ambleside v British Steel

April 8 (Week 30)
British Steel v Creighton
Millom v Smith Bros
Whitehaven v Carnforth
Silloth v Greengarth

CUMBRIA

AMBLESIDE RUFC
Ground Address:Galava Park, Borrans Road, Ambleside, Cumbria LA22 0UL. Tel: 05394 32536
Club Secretary: Mrs Jeanette Irwin, No. 1 Hodge Howe Cottages, Windermere, Cumbria. Tel: (H) 05394 42025
Fixtures Secretary: Mr Nick Felitt, Hart Head Farm, Rydal, Ambleside, Cumbria. Tel: (H) 05394 33772 Tel (W) 05394 32296
Club Colours: 1st XV Black & amber hoops, 2nd XV All black.

BRITISH STEEL RUFC
Ground Address:Moss Bay Works, Moss Bay, Workington, Cumbria. Tel: 0900 603570
Club Secretary: B Rumney, 70 Church Road, Harrington, Workington, Cumbria. Tel: (H) 0946 830413
Club Colours: Red, white & blue hoops, black shorts.

CARNFORTH RFC
Ground Address:Carnforth High School, Kellet Road, Carnforth, Lancashire. Tel: 0524 732723
Club Secretary: John Marsden, Whinfell, Eden Mount Way, Carnforth LA5 9XN. Tel: (H) 0524 734832 Tel: (W) 0860 848151 Fax: 0524 736639
Fixtures Secretary: Bob Coulton, 28 The Drive, Crag Bank, Carnforth, Lancashire. Tel: (H) 0524 733306
Club Colours: Green & black 4' hoops.

CREIGHTON RUFC
Ground Address:Carrs Field, Caxton Road, off Newton Road, Carlisle. Tel: 0228 21169
Club Secretary: David Thomlinson, 146 Moorhouse Road, Belle Vue, Carlisle CA2 7QR. Tel: (H) 0228 35111 Tel: (W) 0228 24379
Fixtures Secretary: John Graham, 117 Pinecroft, Newfield, Carlisle CA3 0DB. Tel: (H) 0228 26705
Club Colours: Navy blue, red collars/cuffs, white shorts, red socks.

GREENGARTH RUFC
Ground Address:Greengarth Hall, Holmbrook, Cumbria. Tel: 09467 24202
Club Secretary: Ian Sharp, 1 Pelham Drive, Calderbridge, Seascale, Cumbria. Tel: (H) 0946 841744 Tel: (W) 0946 820206
Fixtures Secretary: Mr Steven Hall, 57 Coniston Avenue, Seascale, Cumbria. Tel: (H) 09467 28663
Club Colours: Maroon & gold.

MILLOM RUFC
Ground Address:Wilson Park, The Dunes, Haverigg, Millom, Cumbria. Tel: 0229 770401
Club Secretary: Pauline Hartley, 50 Palmers Lane, Millom, Cumbria LA18 5EE. Tel: (H) 0229 774407 Tel: (W) 0229 772300
Fixtures Secretary: JAP Davies, 21 Town Head, Haverigg, Millom. Tel: (H) 0229 772650
Club Colours: Blue & white.

SILLOTH RUFC
Ground Address:Old Marshalling Yard, Eden Street, Silloth, Carlisle, Cumbria. Tel: 0697 331492
Club Secretary: R Edwards, Mayfair, Beckfoot, Silloth, Cumbria. Tel: (H) 06973 31382
Club Colours: Green & black hoops.

SMITH BROS RUFC
Ground Address:Seven Fields, Brantley, Whitehaven. Tel: 0946 65905
Club Secretary: G Ryan, 17 Mirehouse Road, Witehaven, Cumbria CA28 9RW. Tel: (H) 0946 693754 Tel: (W) 0946 68176
Club Colours: Blue & white.

FINAL TABLE

	P	W	D	L	F	A	PD	Pts
Keswick	8	7	0	1	245	62	183	14
Creighton	8	6	1	1	140	60	80	13
Carnforth	8	4	1	3	146	108	38	9
Millom	8	4	1	3	115	82	33	9
British Steel	8	3	1	4	128	107	21	7
Greengarth	8	2	2	4	110	140	-30	6
Whitehaven	8	2	1	5	97	113	-16	5
Ambleside	7	2	1	4	69	171	-102	5
Silloth	7	1	0	6	23	230	-207	2

WHITEHAVEN RUFC
Ground Address:The Playground, Richmond Terrace, Whitehaven, Cumbria. Tel: 0946 695253
Club Secretary: Mr E McConnell, 38 Loop Road South, Whitehaven, Cumbria CA28 7SE. Tel: (H) 0946 692225
Fixtures Secretary: Mr WG Anderson, 18 Hensingham Road, Whitehaven, Cumbria. Tel: (H) 0946 692822
Club Colours: Maroon & white hoops, white shorts.

NORTHERN DIVISION

NORTH LANCS ONE
1994-95
FIXTURES

September 17 (Week 3)
Burnage v Trafford M V
Heaton Moor v Oldham
Chorley v Bury
Ashton-under-Lyne v Bolton
Colne & Nelson v Thornton Cleveley
Blackpool v North Manchester

September 24 (Week 4)
Trafford M V v Blackpool
North Manchester v Colne & Nelson
Thornton Cleveley v Ashton-under-Lyne
Bolton v Chorley
Bury v Heaton Moor
Oldham v Dunkenfield

October 1 (Week 5)
Colne & Nelson v Trafford M V
Blackpool v Burnage
Dukenfield v Bury
Heaton Moor v Bolton
Chorley v Thornton Cleveley
Ashton-under-Lyne v North Manchester

October 15 (Week 7)
Burnage v Colne & Nelson
Trafford M V v Ashton-under-Lyne
North Manchester v Chorley
Thornton Cleveley v Heaton Moor
Bolton v Dunkenfield
Bury v Oldham

October 22 (Week 8)
Chorley v Trafford M V
Ashton-under-Lyne v Burnage
Colne & Nelson v Blackpool
Oldham v Bolton
Dunkenfield v Thornton Cleveley
Heaton Moor v North Manchester

October 29 (Week X2)
Blackpool v Ashton-under-Lyne
Burnage v Chorley
Trafford M V v Heaton Moor
North Manchester v Dukenfield
Thornton Cleveley v Oldham
Bolton v Bury

January 7 (Week 17)
Dukenfield v Trafford M V
Heaton Moor v Burnage
Chorley v Blackpool
Ashton-under-Lyne v Colne & Nelson
Bury v Thornton Cleveley
Oldham v North Manchester

January 14 (Week 18)
Colne & Nelson v Chorley
Blackpool v Heaton Manor
Burnage v Dukenfield
Trafford M V v Oldham
North Manchester v Bury
Thornton Cleveley v Bolton

February 11 (Week 22)
Bury v Trafford M V
Oldham v Burnage
Dukenfield v Blackpool
Heaton Manor v Colne & Nelson
Chorley v Ashton-under-Lyne
Bolton v North Manchester

January 25 (Week 24)
Ashton-under-Lyne v Heaton Moor
Colne & Nelson v Dukenfield
Blackpool v Oldham
Burnage v Bury
Trafford M V v Bolton
North Manchester v Thornton Cleveley

March 4 (Week 25)
Thornton Cleveley v Trafford M V
Bolton v Burnage
Bury v Blackpool
Oldham v Colne & Nelson
Dukenfield v Ashton-under-Lyne
Heaton Moor v Chorley

March 25 (Week 28)
Chorley v Dukenfield
Ashton-under-Lyne v Oldham
Colne & Nelson v Bury
Blackpool v Bolton
Burnage v Thornton Cleveley
Trafford M V v North Manchester

April 8 (Week 30)
North Manchester v Burnage
Thornton Cleveley v Blackpool
Bolton v Colne & Nelson
Bury v Ashton-under-Lyne
Oldham v Chorley
Dukenfield v Heaton Moor

NORTH LANCS ONE

TRAFFORD M.V. RFC
Ground Address:MacPherson Park, Finney Bank Road, Sale, Manchester, M33 1LR. Tel: 061 976 7061
Club Secretary: Peter Coppock, 65 Central Road, West Didsbury, Manchester, M20 9YD. Tel: (H) 061 445 2335 Tel: (W) 061 834 3224
Fixtures Secretary: Bryn Maddick, 1 Pollen Close, Sale, M33 3LS. Tel: (H) 061 962 9948 Tel (W) 061 480 9629
Club Colours: Black & white hoops.

ASHTON-UNDER-LYME RC
Ground Address:Gambrel Bank, St Albans Avenue, Ashton-under-Lyme. Tel: 061 330 1361
Club Secretary: Dennis Gee, 26 Burnedge Lane, Grasscroft, Oldham, Lancs OL4 4EA. Tel: (H) 0457 872823 Tel: (W) 061 303 9482
Fixtures Secretary: Alan Bradley, 4 Whernside Avenue, Ashton-under-Lyme OL6 8UY. Tel: (H) 061 330 0561
Club Colours: Red, amber & black hoops.

BLACKPOOL RUFC
Ground Address:Fleetwood Road, Norbreck, Blackpool, Lancashire FY5 1RN. Tel: 0253 853308
Club Secretary: Cliff Wainscott, 15 Stafford Avenue, Poulton-le-Fylde, Lancs FY6 8BJ. Tel: (H) 0253 885151
Fixtures Secretary: Ian Taylor, Vine Cottage, 3 Gosforth Road, Blackpool, Lancs FY2 9UB. Tel: (H) 0253 358183
Club Colours: Red & blue hooped shirts & socks, navy shorts. Change: yellow & black shirts.

BOLTON
Ground Address:Mortfield Pavilion, Avenue St, off Chorley Old Road, Bolton BL1 3AW. Tel: 0204 363710
Club Secretary: RD Pemberton, Grasmere House, 23 Wilkinson St, Leigh, Lancs WN7 4DQ. Tel: (H) 0942 678257
Fixtures Secretary: DA Patchett, Badger Cottage, 2 Richmill Terrace, Ramsbottom BL0 9EW. Tel: (H) 0706 826298
Club Colours: Red & white hoops, black shorts, red socks.

BURNAGE FC
Ground Address:Varley Park, Battersea Road, Heaston, Mersey, Stockport. Tel: 061 432 2150
Club Secretary: P Higgins, 434 Didsbury Road, Heaton, Mersey, Stockport, Cheshire SK4 3BY. Tel: (H) 061 431 4090 Tel: (W) 0565 653015
Club Colours: Black & white.

BURY RUFC
Ground Address:Radcliffe Road, Bury. Tel: 061 764 1528
Club Secretary: GJ Hilton, 66 Twiss Green Lane, Culcheth, Warrington. Tel: 0925 762119 Tel: (W) 0925 762975
Fixtures Secretary: M Freschini, 15 Watling Street, Elton, Bury. Tel: (H) 061 764 9051
Club Colours: Red, gold & blue hooped jersey, navy blue shorts, red stockings.

CHORLEY RUFC
Ground Address:Brookfields, Chancery Road, Astley Village, Chorley, Lancashire PR7 1XP. Tel: 0257 268806
Club Secretary: Ken Potter, 97 The Farthings, Astley Park, Chorley PR7 1SH. Tel: (H) 0257 267411 Tel: (W) 0695 53485
Fixtures Secretary: Tim Holland, 45 Stump Lane, Chorley PR6 0AL. Tel: (H) 0257 266147 Tel (W) 0257 242344
Club Colours: Black & white hoops.

COLNE & NELSON RUFC
Ground Address:Holt House, Harrison Drive, Colne, Lancs. Tel: 0282 863339
Club Secretary: Keith Ian Thornton, 12 Camden Street, Nelson, Lancashire BB9 0BL. Tel: (H) 0282 613612
Fixtures Secretary: Duncan Bolton, 21 Tennyson Road, Colne, Lancashire BB8 9SD. Tel: (H) 0282 869321 Tel (W) 0282 818883
Club Colours: All black.

FINAL TABLE

	P	W	D	L	F	A	PD	Pts
De La Salle Salford	13	13	0	0	197	51	146	26
Bolton	13	11	0	2	327	122	205	22
Bury	13	9	0	4	182	109	73	18
Blackpool	12	8	1	3	123	90	33	17
Colne & Nelson	12	8	0	4	216	88	128	16
Thornton Cleveleys	13	7	0	6	232	122	110	14
Chorley	13	6	1	6	166	153	13	13
Burnage	12	5	1	6	81	145	-64	11
Ashton-under-Lyne	12	5	1	6	90	155	-65	11
Dukinfield	12	4	0	8	106	138	-32	8
O Bedians	12	3	1	8	91	147	-56	7
Eccles	13	3	0	10	97	185	-88	6
Broughton	12	1	1	10	88	232	-144	3
Clitheroe	10	0	0	10	42	301	-259	0

DUKINFIELD RUFC
Ground Address:Blocksages Playing Fields, Birch Lane, Dukinfield, Cheshire. Tel: 061 343 2592
Club Secretary: Ernie Taylor, 52 Gower Road, Hyde, Cheshire SK14 5AD. Tel: (H) 061 366 9541 Tel: (W) 0706 47422
Fixtures Secretary: AE Hilton, Old St Georges Vicarage, Pennine View, Heyrod, Stalybridge. Tel: (H) 061 338 3410
Club Colours: Blue & gold hoops.

HEATON MOOR RUFC
Ground Address:Green Lane, Heaton Moor, Stockport SK4 2NF. Tel: 061 432 3407
Club Secretary: Peter Jackson, 35 Stanley Road, Heaton Moor, Stockport SK4 4HW. Tel: (H) 061 442 9061 Tel: (W) 0928 717070
Fixtures Secretary: Peter Shaw, 20 Lowerfold Drive, Offerton, Stockport. Tel: (H) 061 456 9758 Tel (W) 061 499 9900
Club Colours: Red, black & amber.

NORTH MANCHESTER & OLDHAM COLLEGES RUFC
Ground Address:Tudor Lodge, Victoria Avenue, Moston, Manchester M10 9SH (No mail to ground address). Tel: 061 682 9234
Club Secretary: BH Stott, 8 Barlea Avenue, New Moston, Manchester M40 3WL. Tel: (H) 061 682 0541
Fixtures Secretary: P McCabe, 6 Millpool Walk, Harpurney, Manchester M9 4DX. Tel: (H) 061 202 3038
Club Colours: Green, black & white hoops or purple.

OLDHAM RUFC
Ground Address:Manor Park, Bryth Road, Bardsley, Oldham, Lancs. Tel: 061 624 6383
Club Secretary: TJ Brown, 12 Tilton St, Oldham, Lancs OL1 4JA. Tel: (H) 061 620 1878 Tel: (W) 0254 57149
Fixtures Secretary: T Park Esq, Flat 71, Imogen Court, Regent Park, Ordsall, Salford. Tel: (H) 061 832 4551
Club Colours: Red & white hoops, blue shorts, red stockings.

THORNTON CLEVELEYS RUFC
Ground Address:Fleetwood Road, Thornton Cleveleys, Lancashire. Tel: 0253 854104
Club Secretary: M Boardman, 41 Roylyn Avenue, Carleton, Poulton-le-Fylde, Lancashire FY6 7PH. Tel: (H) 0253 890099 Tel: (W) 0253 332487
Fixtures Secretary: M Johnson, 15 Beryl Avenue, Cleveleys, Lancashire. Tel: (H) 0253 822857
Club Colours: Red, black & amber, black shorts.

NORTHERN DIVISION

NORTH LANCS TWO
1994-95
FIXTURES

September 17 (Week 3)
Agecroft v Marple
Clitheroe v Eccles
Littleborough v Shell Carrington

September 24 (Week 4)
Shell Carrington v Clitheroe
Eccles v Agecroft
Marple v Broughton

October 1 (Week 5)
Lostock v Old Bedians
Broughton v Eccles
Agecroft v Shell Carrington

October 15 (Week 7)
Old Bedians v British Aerospace
Shell Carrington v Broughton
Eccles v Marple

October 22 (Week 8)
Littleborough v Old Bedians
British Aerospace v Lostock
Marple v Shell Carrington

October 29 (Week X2)
Lostock v Littleborough
Old Bedians v Clitheroe
Shell Carrington v Eccles

January 7 (Week 17)
Agecroft v Old Bedians
Clitheroe v Lostock
Littleborough v British Aerospace

January 14 (Week 18)
British Aerospace v Clitheroe
Lostock v Agecroft
Old Bedians v Broughton

February 11 (Week 22)
Marple v Old Bedians
Broughton v Lostock
Agecroft v British Aerospace
Clitheroe v Littleborough

February 25 (Week 24)
Littleborough v Agecroft
British Aerospace v Broughton
Lostock v Marple
Old Bedians v Eccles

March 4 (Week 25)
Shell Carrington v Old Bedians
Eccles v Lostock
Marple v British Aerospace
Broughton v Littleborough
Agecroft v Clitheroe

March 25 (Week 28)
Clitheroe v Broughton
Littleborough v Marple
British Aerospace v Eccles
Lostock v Shell Carrington

April 8 (Week 30)
Shell Carrington v British Aerospace
Eccles v Littleborough
Marple v Clitheroe
Broughton v Agecroft

NORTH LANCS TWO

AGECROFT RUFC
Ground Address:Ordsall Sports Centre, Craven Drive,
Ordsall, Salford M6 6QW. Tel: 061 848 0646
Club Secretary: Mr MJ Whitby, 28 Grange Street, Salford
M6 5PR. Tel: (H) 061 743 1060 Tel: (W) 061 228 4618
Fixtures Secretary: H Getz, 11 Rockley Gardens, Salford
M6 6QW. Tel: (H) 061 737 6035 Tel (W) 061 205 2333
x2339
Club Colours: Red & black hoops, black shorts.
BAE WARTON RFC
Ground Address:Bank Lane Playing Fields, BAE Warton
Sports & Social, Warton Aerodrome, Warton, Preston,
Lancs. Tel: 0772 852788/0772 856354
Club Secretary: Gavin Rowlandson, 32 Preston Road,
Lytham St Annes, Lancs FY8 5AA. Tel: (H) 0253 738912
Tel: (W) 0772 855422
Fixtures Secretary: Matt Jagger, 53 Caton Green Road,
Brookhouse, Lancaster LA2 9JJ. Tel: (H) 0524 771068 Tel
(W) 0772 853244
Club Colours: Blue & white quarters, white shorts, blue
socks.
BROUGHTON RUFC
Ground Address:Yew St, Lower Broughton, Salford M7
9HL. Tel: 061 792 2920
Club Secretary: Paul Walsh, 6 Grassfield Avenue, Lower
Broughton, Salford M7 9HW. Tel: (H) 061 792 1571
Fixtures Secretary: John Barrow, 111 Derby Road,
Salford M5 2LE. Tel: (H) 061 736 5827
Club Colours: Claret, gold & blue hoops.
CLITHEROE RUFC
Ground Address:Littlemoor Park, Littlemoor Road,
Clitheroe, Lancs. Tel: 0200 22261
Club Secretary: John Hyde, Moorhey Cottage, Knowle
Green, Longridge, Preston PR3 2XE. Tel: (H) 0254 878402
Tel: (W) 0282 415543
Fixtures Secretary: Phil Isherwood, 160 Chatburn Road,
Clitheroe BB7 2AZ. Tel: (H) 0200 23781 Tel (W) 0254
824033
Club Colours: Maroon & amber.
ECCLES RFC
Ground Address:Gorton Street, Peel Green, Eccles,
Manchester M30 8LX. Tel: 061 789 2613
Club Secretary: M Dutton, Ashley Drive, Swinton,
Manchester M27 3AX. Tel: (H) 061 794 2904
Club Colours: Navy blue & white hoop shirts and
stockings, white shorts.
LITTLEBOROUGH RUFC
Ground Address:Rakewood, Hollingworth Lake,
Littleborough, Lancs OL15 0AP. Tel: 0706 370220
Club Secretary: John Dawson, 11 Coleridge Drive,
Smithy Bridge, Littleborough, Lancs OL15 0RA. Tel: (H)
0706 373707 Tel: (W) 061 872 2141
Fixtures Secretary: Mr Harry Hanson, 639 Oldham Road,
Royton, Lancs. Tel: (H) 061 624 7880
Club Colours: Green, black & amber.
LOSTOCK RFC
Ground Address:Lostock RFC, Lostock Lane, Lostock,
Bolton.
Club Secretary: R Fletcher, 19 Shaftesbvury Avenue,
Lostock, Bolton, Lancs BL6 4AP. Tel: (H) 0204 698362
Fixtures Secretary: D Ball, 18 Lenora Street, Bolton,
Lancs. Tel: (H) 0204 63629
Club Colours: All black.
MARPLE RUFC
Ground Address:Wood Lane, Marple, Stockport,
Cheshire.
Club Secretary: Mr MJ Cleverly, 16 Lyme Grove, Marple,
Stockport, Cheshire SK6 7NW. Tel: (H) 061 449 8393 Tel:
(W) 061 419 2520
Fixtures Secretary: Mr N Hawkley, Bottomlock Cottage,
Marple Bridge, Stockport, Cheshire SK6 5LB. Tel: (H) 061

FINAL TABLE

	P	W	D	L	F	A	PD	Pts
Heaton Moor	7	7	0	0	187	22	165	14
N Manchester	7	6	0	1	163	40	123	12
Littleborough	7	4	0	3	140	53	87	8
Shell Carrington	7	4	0	3	57	46	11	8
Marple	7	4	0	3	115	51	64	6
Lostock	7	2	0	5	52	141	-89	4
Agecroft	7	1	0	6	42	145	-103	2
British Aerospace	7	0	0	7	25	283	-258	-2

449 9985 Tel (W) 061 273 3322
Club Colours: Red & black shirts, black shorts.
OLD BEDIANS RUFC
Ground Address:Underbank Farm, Millgate Lane, East
Didsbury, Manchester. Tel: 061 445 8862
Club Secretary: Ms Lynn Connor, 17 Brixton Avenue,
Withington, Manchester M20 1JF. Tel: (H) 061 434 0559
Tel: (W) 061 832 6637
Fixtures Secretary: Roger Davies, 3 Beaminster Avenue,
Heaton Mersey, Stockport. Tel: (H) 061 432 8587
Club Colours: Blue shirts, white shorts.
SHELL (CARRINGTON) RUFC
Ground Address:Shell Chemicals UK Ltd, Carrington
Works, Urmston, Manchester. Tel: (H) 061 776 3000
Club Secretary: J B Bush, 249 Woodsend Road, Urmston,
Manchester, M41 8QG. Tel: (H) 061 748 9066 Tel: (W)
061 776 3103
Fixtures Secretary: A Kelly, 332 Liverpool Rd, Irlam,
Manchester, M30 6AN. Tel: (H) 061 775 7743 Tel (W) 061
792 2578
Club Colours: Red & yellow.

NORTHERN DIVISION

CHESHIRE & LANCASHIRE SOUTH 1994-95 FIXTURES

January 7 (Week 17)
Wirral v Crewe & Nantwich
Old Anselmians v Kersal
Vulcan v Warrington
Parkonians v Southport
South Liverpool v Aspull
Sefton v Eagle

September 17 (Week 3)
Kersal v Crewe & Nantwich
Old Ansemians v Sefton
Vulcan v South Liverpool
Parkonians v Port Sunlight
Southport v Aspull
Warrington v Eagle

January 14 (Week 18)
Southport v Vulcan
Warrington v Old Anselmians
Kersal v Wirral
Crewe & Nantwich v Sefton
Eagle v South Liverpool
Aspull v Port Sunlight

September 24 (Week 4)
Crewe & Nantwich v Warrington
Eagle v Southport
Aspull v Parkonians
Port Sunlight v Vulcan
South Liverpool v Old Anselmians
Sefton v Wirral

February 11 (Week 22)
South Liverpool v Crewe & Nantwich
Sefton v Kersal
Wirral v Warrington
Old Anselmians v Southport
Vulcan v Parkonians
Port Sunlight v Eagle

October 1 (Week 5)
Southport v Crewe & Nantwich
Warrington v Kersal
Wirral v South Liverpool
Old Anselmians v Port Sunlight
Vulcan v Aspull
Parkonians v Eagle

February 25 (Week 24)
Parkonians v Old Anselmians
Southport v Wirral
Warrington v Sefton
Kersal v South Liverpool
Crewe & Nantwich v Port Sunlight
Eagle v Aspull

October 15 (Week 7)
Kersal v Southport
Crewe & Nantwich v Parkonians
Eagle v Vulcan
Aspull v Old Anselmians
Port Sunlight v Wirral
South Liverpool v Sefton

March 4 (Week 25)
Aspull v Crewe & Nantwich
Port Sunlight v Kersal
South Liverpool v Warrington
Sefton v Southport
Wirral v Parkonians
Old Anselmians v Vulcan

October 22 (Week 8)
Vulcan v Crewe & Nantwich
Parkonians v Kersal
Southport v Warrington
Sefton v Port Sunlight
Wirral v Aspull
Old Anselmians v Eagle

March 25 (Week 28)
Vulcan v Wirral
Parkonians v Sefton
Southport v South Liverpool
Warrington v Port Sunlight
Kersal v Aspull
Crewe & Nantwich v Eagle

October 29 (Week X2)
Warrington v Parkonians
Kersal v Vulcan
Crewe & Nantwich v Old Anselmians
Eagle v Wirral
Aspull v Sefton
Port Sunlight v South Liverpool

April 8 (Week 30)
Eagle v Kersal
Aspull v Warrington
Port Sunlight v Southport
South Liverpool v Parkonians
Sefton v Vulcan
Wirral v Old Anselmians

CHESHIRE & LANCASHIRE SOUTH

ALTRINCHAM (KERSAL) RFC
Ground Address:Kersal Drive, Stelfox Avenue,
Timperley, Altrincham, Cheshire. Tel: 061 973 9157
Club Secretary: Dominic Leach, 19 Dawson Road,
Altrincham, Cheshire WA14 5JP. Tel: (H) 061 941 3085
Tel: (W) 061 929 1851
Fixtures Secretary: PRL Blakeman, 32 Glebelands Road,
Knutsford, Cheshire. Tel: (H) 0565 634276
Club Colours: Black, red & white hoops, blue shorts.

ASPULL RFC
Ground Address:Woodshaw Park, Woods Road, Aspull,
Wigan, Lancs. Tel: 0942 831611
Club Secretary: Geoff Gregson, 26 Lyndon Avenue,
Shellington, Wigan, Lancashire WN6 8BT. Tel: (H) 0257
421421 Tel: (W) 0942 492221
Fixtures Secretary: Geoff Gregson, 26 Lyndon Avenue,
Shellington, Wigan, Lancashire WN6 8BT. Tel: (H) 0257
421421 Tel (W) 0942 492221
Club Colours: Sky & navy blue hoops.

CREWE AND NANTWICH RUFC
Ground Address:King George V Playing Fields, West St,
Crewe. Tel: 0270 213437
Club Secretary: AG Jones, 9 Gingerbread Lane,
Nantwich, Cheshire CW5 6NH. Tel: (H) 0270 625737 Tel:
(W) 0270 213261
Fixtures Secretary: RL Christie, 127A Welsh Row,
Nantwich, Cheshire CW5 5ET. Tel: (H) 0270 629637 (after
8pm) Tel (W) 0270 624160
Club Colours: White with single black circuit.

EAGLE RUFC
Ground Address:Thornton Road, Great Sankey,
Warrington, Cheshire. Tel: 0925 632926
Club Secretary: Vince Sandwell, 23 Watercourse Lane,
Winwich, Warrington WA2 8LH. Tel: (H) 0925 650367
Tel: (W) 0925 830007
Fixtures Secretary: Alan Knight, 7 Trefoil Close,
Birchwood, Warrington. Tel: (H) 0925 831490
Club Colours: Black & white hoops.

OLD ANSELMIANS RUFC
Ground Address:Malone Field, Eastham Village Road,
Eastham, Wirral. Tel: 051 327 1613
Club Secretary: Tony Neville, 33 Stapleton Avenue,
Greasby, Wirral L49 2QT. Tel: (H) 051 678 4154 Tel: (W)
051 350 1696
Fixtures Secretary: Tony McArdle, 18 Greenbank Drive,
Heswall, Wirral L61 5UF. Tel: (H) 051 342 1470
Club Colours: Blue, gold & white.

PARKONIANS RUFC
Ground Address:HM Curphey Memorial Ground, Holm
Lane, Birkenhead, Merseyside L43 2HD. Tel: 051 652 3105
Club Secretary: Mr PL Mullen, 8 Deerwood Crescent,
Little Sutton, South Wirral L66 1BE. Tel: (H) 051 339
1270 Tel: (W) 051 448 6280
Fixtures Secretary: Mr EJ Flynn, 471 Woodchurch Road,
Prenton, Birkenhead, Merseyside. Tel: (H) 051 608 3408
Club Colours: Maroon, blue & white hooped jerseys &
stockings, white shorts.

PORT SUNLIGHT RUFC
Ground Address:Green Lane Sports Field, Bromborough,
Wirral, Merseyside. Tel: 051 334 3677
Club Secretary: Alan Haigh, 13 Charlottes Meadow,
Bebington, Wirral, Merseyside L63 3JH. Tel: (H) 051 334
1304
Fixtures Secretary: Chris Dodd, 16 Thornton Road,
Bebington, Wirral, Merseyside L63 5PS. Tel: (H) 051 608
7022 Tel (W) 051 653 4400 x330
Club Colours: Black & white hoops.

SEFTON RUFC
Ground Address:Thornhead Lane, Leyfield Road, West
Derby, Liverpool L12. Tel: 051 228 9092
Club Secretary: Graham Price, 5 Avalon Road, Liverpool

FINAL TABLE

	P	W	D	L	F	A	PD	Pts
Leigh	12	10	1	1	214	117	97	21
Aspull	11	9	0	2	265	90	175	18
Southport	12	8	1	3	201	124	77	17
Altrincham Kersal	10	7	1	2	135	86	49	15
Old Anselmians	11	6	2	3	161	159	2	14
Sefton	12	5	1	6	170	130	40	11
Old Parkonians	12	5	1	6	122	139	-17	11
Eagle	12	5	1	6	152	171	-19	11
South Liverpool	11	5	0	6	159	129	30	10
Crewe & Nantwich	12	3	2	7	122	163	-41	8
Liverpool Coll	12	4	0	8	83	149	-66	8
St Marys OB	12	2	2	8	146	234	-88	6
Newton-Le-Willows	11	0	0	11	47	286	-239	0

L12 9ER. Tel: (H) 051 220 1043 Tel: (W) 051 487 0606
Fixtures Secretary: B Houghton, 14 Gateacre Vale Road,
Liverpool L25 5NP. Tel: (H) 051 428 3740
Club Colours: Red & white hooped shirts/socks, blue
shorts.

SOUTH LIVERPOOL RUFC
Ground Address:Bridgefield Forum Leisure Centre,
Halewood, Knowsley, Liverpool L26. Tel: 051 443 2123
Club Secretary: Mr Lawrence Sherrington, 14 Brook
Way, Great Sankey, Warrington, Cheshire. Tel: (H) 0925
726768
Fixtures Secretary: Mr Dave Edge, 93 Millwood road,
Speke, Liverpool L24 2HR. Tel: (H) 051 425 4018 Tel (W)
051 486 2930
Club Colours: Amber & black quarters. Change royal blue.

SOUTHPORT RUFC
Ground Address:Waterloo Road, Hillside, Southport PR8
4QW. Tel: 0704 569906
Club Secretary: Mr AR Coakley, 26 Brocklebank Road,
Hesketh Park, Southport PR9 9LP. Tel: (H) 0704 538341
Fixtures Secretary: Mrs M Jackson, 43 Kenilworth Road,
Ainsdale, Southport. Tel: (H) 0704 578362
Club Colours: Red, black & amber.

VULCAN RUFC
Ground Address:Off Wargrave Road,
Newton-le-Willows, Lancashire. Tel: 0925 224180
Club Secretary: Mr D W Lodge, 19 Pipit Avenue,
Newton-le-Willows, Lancashire, Wa12 9RG. Tel: (H) 0925
225108 Tel: (W) 0925 225171
Fixtures Secretary: Mr John Bajer, 5 Heylock Close,
Newton-le-Willows, Lancashire, Wa12 8SU. Tel: (H) 0925
226653
Club Colours: Black with amber hoops on chest.

WARRINGTON RUFC
Ground Address:Bridge Lane, Appleton, Warrington,
Cheshire. Tel: 0925 264591
Club Secretary: Mr GP Robinson, 8 Bellhouse Lane,
Grappenhall, Warrington WA4 2SD. Tel: (H) 0925 261644
Fixtures Secretary: Mr K Wilkinson, 5 Osborne Road,
Lower Walton, Warrington WA4 6JD. Tel: (H) 0925
267964
Club Colours: Red, white & green.

WIRRAL RFC
Ground Address:Memorial Ground, Thornton Common
Road, Clatterbridge, Wirral, Mersyside. Tel: 051 334 1309
Club Secretary: Mr P Darch, 19 Tamar Close, Spital,
Bedington, Wirral, Merseyside L63 9AN. Tel: (H) 051 346
1299 Tel: (W) 051 639 8181
Fixtures Secretary: Mr ICT Ritchie, 49 Meadow Lane,
Willaston, Wirral, Merseyside. Tel: (H) 051 327 5695
Club Colours: Maroon & white.

NORTHERN DIVISION

CHESHIRE
1994-95
FIXTURES

September 17 (Week 3)
Shell Stanlow v Helsby
Holmes Chapel v Congleton
Bowden v Whitehouse Park

September 24 (Week 4)
Helsby v Hoylake
Whitehouse Park v Holmes Chapel
Congleton v Wallasey

October 1 (Week 5)
Prenton v Helsby
Hoylake v Shell Stanlow
Wallasey v Whitehouse Park

October 15 (Week 7)
Shell Stanlow v Prenton
Helsby v Moore
Whitehouse Park v Congleton

October 22 (Week 8)
Bowden v Helsby
Moore v Shell Stanlow
Prenton v Hoylake

October 29 (Week X2)
Hoylake v Moore
Shell Stanlow v Bowden
Helsby v Holmes Chapel

January 7 (Week 17)
Wallasey v Helsby
Holmes Chapel v Shell Stanlow
Bowden v Hoylake
Moore v Prenton

January 14 (Week 18)
Prenton v Bowden
Hoylake v Holmes Chapel
Shell Stanlow v Wallasey
Helsby v Congleton

February 11 (Week 22)
Whitehouse Park v Helsby
Congleton v Shell Stanlow
Wallasey v Hoylake
Holmes Chapel v Prenton
Bowden v Moore

February 25 (Week 24)
Moore v Holmes Chapel
Prenton v Wallasey
Hoylake v Congleton
Shell Stanlow v Whitehouse Park

March 4 (Week 25)
Whitehouse Park v Hoylake
Congleton v Prenton
Wallasey v Moore
Holmes Chapel v Bowden

March 25 (Week 28)
Bowden v Wallasey
Moore v Congleton
Prenton v Whitehouse Park

April 8 (Week 30)
Whitehouse Park v Moore
Congleton v Bowden
Wallasey v Holmes Chapel

CHESHIRE

BOWDON RUFC
Ground Address: Clay Lane, Timperley, Cheshire. Tel: 061 980 8321
Club Secretary: Tom St John Sloan, 7 Leigh Road, Hale, Altrincham. Tel: (H) 061 941 5865 Tel: (W) 061 491 5343
Fixtures Secretary: Frank Norton, 36 Greenwalk, Timperley, Altrincham. Tel: (H) 061 980 8195 Tel (W) 0925 834639
Club Colours: Black, white, burgundy hoops.

CONGLETON RUFC
Ground Address: Clubhouse: 78 Park Street, Congleton, Cheshire. Ground: Hankinson's Field. Tel: 0260 273338
Club Secretary: Dennis Thorley, 46 Bladon Crescent, Alsager, via Stoke-on-Trent, Cheshire ST7 2BG. Tel: (H) 0270 878293 Tel: (W) 061 223 1301 x3066
Fixtures Secretary: Ken Williams, 2 Sprink Lane, Buglawton, Congleton, Cheshire. Tel: (H) 0260 279202
Club Colours: Red, white, red, black broad hoops.

HELSBY RUFC
Ground Address: Helsby Sports & Social Club, Chester Road, Helsby. Tel: 0928 722267
Club Secretary: Eric Lamb, 5 Firbank Road, Elton, Nr Chester, Cheshire CH2 4LY. Tel: (H) 0928 724039 Tel: (W) 051 350 4392
Fixtures Secretary: T Ryder, 64 Chester Road, Helsby. Tel: (H) 0928 723733
Club Colours: Black & amber hoops.

HOLMES CHAPEL RUFC
Ground Address:c/o Holmes Chapel Leisure Centre, Holmes Chapel, Cheshire. Tel: 0477 534401
Club Secretary: Mark Finch, 54 Primrose Chase, Goostrey, Cheshire CW4 8LJ. Tel: (H) 0477 535368
Club Colours: Shirts: Blue & gold hoops. Shorts: Black. Socks: Royal blue.

HOYLAKE RUFC
Ground Address: Melrose Avenue, Hoylake, Wirral, Merseyside L47 3AU. Tel: 051 632 2538
Club Secretary: Mrs Susan Kurton, 7 Meadowcroft Road, Meols, Wirral, Merseyside L47 6BG. Tel: (H) 051 632 5540 Tel: (W) 051 678 3434
Fixtures Secretary: Mr K Ellesmore, 5 Woodland Avenue, Meols, Wirral, Merseyside. Tel: (H) 051 632 2862
Club Colours: Red, green & white.

MOORE RUFC
Ground Address: Moss Lane, Moore, Warrington, Cheshire WA4 6UP. Tel: 0925 740473
Club Secretary: DA Dean, 39 Pheasant Walk, High Legh, Knutsford, Cheshire WA16 6QA. Tel: (H) 0925 755498 Tel: (W) 0204 383756
Fixtures Secretary: PJ Woollacott , 6 Woodlands Drive, Thelwall, Warrington, Cheshire WA4 2EU. Tel: (H) 0925 266576
Club Colours: Black with gold band.

PRENTON RUFC
Ground Address: The Club House, Prenton Dell, Prenton Dell Road, Prenton, Wirral, Merseyside L43 3BS. Tel: 051 608 1501
Club Secretary: Paul Foster, 8 Rake Close, Upton, Wirral, Merseyside L49 0XD. Tel: (H) 051 678 6634
Fixtures Secretary: Chas Cheary, 23 Kings Road, Bebington, Wirral L63 5QQ. Tel: (H) 051 608 0111 Tel (W) 051 229 5378
Club Colours: Maroon, gold & black.

FINAL TABLE

	P	W	D	L	F	A	PD	Pts
PT Sunlight	9	9	0	0	213	22	191	18
Congleton	9	8	0	1	159	45	114	16
Prenton	9	6	0	3	168	90	78	12
Wallasey	8	6	0	2	127	61	66	12
Shell Stanlow	8	5	0	3	99	71	28	10
Bowdon	9	3	0	6	134	135	-1	6
Holmes Chapel	9	2	0	7	85	164	-79	4
Helsby	9	2	0	7	67	224	-157	4
Hoylake	9	2	0	7	93	163	-70	2
Moore	9	1	0	8	55	225	-170	0

SHELL (STANLOW)
Ground Address: The Shell Club, Chester Road, Whitby, Ellesmere Port, Cheshire. Tel: 051 355 2364 Fax: 051 357 4175
Club Secretary: Mrs ARJ Dale, 12 Archers Way, Great Sutton, South Wirral, Cheshire L66 2RY. Tel: (H) 051 339 7823 Tel: (W) 051 355 2157 x207 Fax: 051 355 7263
Fixtures Secretary: Mr G Fennion, 19 Belgrave Drive, Ellesmere Port L65. Tel: (H) 051 356 1952 Tel (W) 0244 281281 x213 Fax: 0244 287287
Club Colours: Amber shirts, white shorts, red socks.

WALLASEY RUFC
Ground Address: Cross Lane, Leasowe Road, Wallasey, Wirral, Merseyside. Tel: 051 638 1486
Club Secretary: Mr JA Burton, 14 Seaview Lane, Irby, Wirral, Merseyside L61 3UL. Tel: (H) 051 648 4341 Tel: (W) 061 236 3707
Fixtures Secretary: Mr A Rae, 8 Inchcape Road, Wallasey, Wirral, Merseyside. Tel: (H) 051 638 6903 Tel (W) 051 933 6446
Club Colours: Red, black, white hoops.

WHITEHOUSE PARK RUFC
Ground Address: Halton Sports, Murdishaw, Runcorn, Cheshire.
Club Secretary: AC Howat, 29 Barncroft, Norton Cross, Runcorn, Cheshire WA7 6RJ. Tel: (H) 0928 712531
Fixtures Secretary: F Williams, 20 Rawdon Close, Palace Fields, Runcorn, Cheshire. Tel: (H) 0928 718 738
Club Colours: Blue & white hoops.

NORTHERN DIVISION

LANCASHIRE SOUTH 1994-95 FIXTURES

September 17 (Week 3)
St Marys OB v Birchfield
Manchester YMCA v Douglas
Mossley Hill v Halton
Hightown v Lucas

September 24)
Lucas v Mossley Hill
Halton v Manchester YMCA
Douglas v St Marys OB
Birchfield v Liverpool College

October 1 (Week 5)
Newton le Willows v Didsbury Toc H
Liverpool College v Douglas
St Marys OB v Halton
Manchester YMCA v Lucas

October 15 (Week 7)
Didsbury Toc H v Hightown
Lucas v St Marys OB
Halton v Liverpool College
Douglas v Birchfield

October 22 (Week 8)
Mossley Hill v Didsbury Toc H
Hightown v Newton le Willows
Birchfield v Halton
Liverpool College v Lucas

October 29 (Week X2)
Newton le Willows v Mossley Hill
Didsbury Toc H v Manchester YMCA
Lucas v Birchfield
Halton v Douglas

January 7 (Week 17)
St Marys OB v Didsbury Toc H
Manchester YMCA v Newton le Willows
Mossley Hill v Hightown
Douglas v Lucas

January 14 (Week 18)
Hightown v Manchester YMCA
Newton le Willows v St Marys OB
Didsbury Toc H v Liverpool College
Lucas v Halton

February 11 (Week 22)
Birchfirld v Didsbury Toc H
Liverpool College v Newton le Willows
St Marys OB v Hightown
Manchester YMCA v Mossley Hill

January 25 (Week 24)
Mossley Hill v St Marys OB
Hightown v Liverpool College
Newton la Willows v Birchfield
Didsbury Toc H v Douglas

March 4 (Week 25)
Halton v Didsbury Toc H
Douglas v Newton le Willows
Birchfield v Hightown
Liverpool College v Mossley Hill
St Marys OB v Manchester YMCA

March 25 (Week 28)
Manchester YMCA v Liverpool College
Mossley Hill v Birchfield
Hightown v Douglas
Newton le Willows v Halton
Didsbury Toc H v Lucas

April 8 (Week 30)
Lucas v Newton le Willows
Halton v Hightown
Douglas v Mossley Hill
Birchfield v Manchester YMCA
Liverpool College v St Marys OB

LANCASHIRE SOUTH

BIRCHFIELD RUFC
Ground Address: Albright & Wilson Recreational Club, Bircvhfield Road, Widnes, Cheshire WA8 9ES. Tel: 051 424 3222
Club Secretary: David Rowlands, 30 Kirkham Road, Widnes, Cheshire WA8 6RG. Tel: (H) 051 420 6054
Fixtures Secretary: Kevin McDonnel, 102 Hurst Street, Widnes, Cheshire WA8 0AL. Tel: (H) 051 424 4259 Tel (W) 051 424 6739
Club Colours: Blue & yellow.
DIDSBURY TOC H RFC
Ground Address: Ford Lane, Didsbury, Manchester. Tel: 061 446 2146
Club Secretary: Peter JM Bradley, 8 Barnard Avenue, Heaton Moor, Stockport SK4 4EP. Tel: (H) 061 432 0496 Tel: (W) 061 788 9611
Fixtures Secretary: Rudolph F Speed, 9 Moorfield Road, West Didsbury, Manchester M20 8UZ. Tel: (H) 061 446 2972
Club Colours: Black jerseys with broad amber chest band, black shorts.
DOUGLAS (IOM) RUFC
Ground Address: Port-E-Chee, Poraddan, Isle of Man. Tel: 0624 676493
Club Secretary: P E Garrett, 3 Ridgeway, St Douglas, Isle of Man. Tel: (H) 0624 629037 Tel: (W) 0624 624535
Club Colours: Maroon & gold band.
HALTON RUFC
Ground Address:ICI Recreation Ground, Liverpool Road, Widnes, Cheshire. Tel: 051 424 2355
Club Secretary: SG Dennett, 267 Lunts Heath Road, Widnes, Cheshire WA8 9BB. Tel: (H) 051 424 3978
Fixtures Secretary: D Dyer, 6 Parlington Close, Widnes, Cheshire WA8 8YF. Tel: (H) 051 495 2402
Club Colours: Blue & white hoops, navy shorts.
HIGHTOWN RUFC
Ground Address: Sandy Lane, Hightown, Merseyside, L38. Tel: 051 929 2330
Club Secretary: John Houghton, APT, 63 East Waterloo Dock, Liverpool, L3 7BE. Tel: (H) 051 258 1315 Tel: (W) 0860 827225
Club Colours: Navy, chocolate & white hoops.
LIVERPOOL COLLEGIATE OLD BOYS RUFC
Ground Address: Peter Lloyd Leisure Centre, Millbank, West Derby, Liverpool. Tel: 051 228 7132
Club Secretary: R Smith, 4 Staveley Road, Garston, Liverpool L19 9AS. Tel: (H) 051 427 6534 Tel: (W) 051 258 1825
Fixtures Secretary: I Johnson, 30 Woolhope Road, Liverpool L4 6TA. Tel: (H) 051 523 2365 Tel (W) 061 904 8989
Club Colours: Dark blue & light blue hoops.
LUCAS MERSEYSIDE RUFC
Ground Address: Walton Sports Cenbtre, Walton Hall Avenue, Liverpool L4 9XP. Tel: 051 523 3472
Club Secretary: I Whitehead, 14 Aylton Road, Liverpool L36 2LU. Tel: (H) 051 449 2137 Tel: (W) 051 524 6555
Fixtures Secretary: R Chesworth, 27 Moss Side, Dovecot, Liverpool L14 0SS. Tel: (H) 051 489 1352
Club Colours: Royal blue.
MANCHESTER YMCA RUFC
Ground Address: The Hollies, Mersey Road, West Didsbury, Manchester 20. Tel: 061 445 2315
Club Secretary: M Kennedy, 14 Beeston Close, Bolton, Lancs BL1 7RT. Tel: (H) 0204 597891 Tel: (W) 0254 55211 x45296
Fixtures Secretary: P Watson, 7 Vicker Close, Clifton, Manchester M27 2QD. Tel: (H) 061 793 9212
Club Colours: Red, black & white hoops.

FINAL TABLE

	P	W	D	L	F	A	PD	Pts
Vulcan	8	7	0	1	175	71	104	14
Didsbury TOC H	8	6	0	2	183	70	113	12
Douglas (IoM)	7	5	1	1	119	71	48	11
Manchester YMCA	8	4	2	2	149	90	59	10
Birchfield	7	4	0	3	158	124	34	6
Mossley Hill	8	2	2	4	71	127	-56	6
Hightown	8	2	1	5	75	123	-48	3
Lucas	8	1	1	6	97	226	-129	3
Halton	8	0	1	7	82	207	-125	1

MOSSLEY HILL RUFC
Ground Address: Mossley Hill Road, Liverpool L18. Tel: 051 724 3411
Club Secretary: Andy Pealing, 5 Fieldfare Clkose, Liverpool L25 4YB. Tel: (H) 051 428 4177 Tel: (W) 051 228 3565
Fixtures Secretary: John Parr, 98 Hunts Cross Avenue, Liverpool 25. Tel: (H) 051 428 7277
Club Colours: Maroon & gold hoops or quarters.
NEWTON-LE-WILLOWS RUFC
Ground Address: Newton-le-Willows Sports Club, Crow Lane East, Newton0le-Willows, Merseyside. Tel: 0925 224591
Club Secretary: Mr David Hughes, 127 Birley Street, Newton-le-Willows, Merseyside WA12 9UN. Tel: (H) 0925 221304 Tel: (W) 0942 57171 x3532
Fixtures Secretary: Mr LR Gannon, 48 Ashfield Crescent, Billinge, Wigan, Lancashire WN5 7TE. Tel: (H) 0744 895875 Tel (W) 0860 337647 (Mobile)
Club Colours: Amber & royal blue.
ST MARY'S OB RUFC
Ground Address: St Mary's OB Playing Field, Gorsey Lane, Hightown, Merseyside. Tel: 051 924 1774
Club Secretary: Mark Cunningham, 48 Cambridge Ave, Crosby, Liverpool, L23 7XW. Tel: (H) 051 924 5201
Fixtures Secretary: Peter Moore, 77 Freshfield Road, Formby, Merseyside. Tel: (H) 07048 78537 Tel (W) 051 924 4210
Club Colours: Maroon, yellow, blue hoops.

NORTHERN DIVISION

NORTH EAST ONE
1994-95
FIXTURES

September 17 (Week 3)
Redcar v Thornensians
Roundhegians v Old Brodleians
Driffield v Pontefract
Gateshead Fell v Horden
Blaydon v Cleckheaton
Selby v Keighley

September 24 (Week 4)
Thornensians v Selby
Keighley v Blaydon
Cleckheaton v Gateshead Fell
Horden v Driffield
Pontefract v Roundhegians
Old Brodleians v Morpeth

October 1 (Week 5)
Blaydon v Thornensians
Selby v Redcar
Morpeth v Pontefract
Roundhegians v Horden
Driffield v Cleckheaton
Gateshead Fell v Keighley

October 15 (Week 7)
Redcar v Blaydon
Thornensians v Gateshead Fell
Keighley v Driffield
Cleckheaton v Roundhegians
Horden v Morpeth
Pontefract v Old Brodleians

October 22 (Week 8)
Driffield v Thornensians
Gateshead Fell v Redcar
Blaydon v Selby
Old Brodleians v Horden
Morpeth v Cleckheaton
Roundhegians v Keighley

October 29 (Week X2)
Selby v Gateshead Fell
Redcar v Driffield
Thornensians v Roundhegians
Keighley v Morpeth
Cleckheaton v Old Brodleians
Horden v Pontefract

January 7 (Week 17)
Morpeth v Thornensians
Roundhegians v Redcar
Driffield v Selby
Gateshead Fell v Blaydon
Pontefract v Cleckheaton
Old Brodleians v Keighley

January 14 (Week 18)
Blaydon v Driffield
Selby v Roundhegians
Redcar v Morpeth
Thornensians v Old Brodleians
Keighley v Pontefract
Cleckheaton v Horden

Fabruary 11 (Week 22)
Pontefract v Thornensians
Old Brodleians v Redcar
Morpeth v Selby
Roundhegians v Blaydon
Driffield v Gateshead Fell
Horden v Keighley

February 25 (Week 24)
Gateshead Fell v Roundhegians
Blaydon v Morpeth
Selby v Old Brodleians
Redcar v Pontefract
Thornensians v Horden
Keighley v Cleckheaton

March 4 (Week 25)
Cleckheaton v Thornensians
Horden v Redcar
Pontefract v Selby
Old Brodleians v Blaydon
Morpeth v Gateshead Fell
Roundhegians v Driffield

March 25 (Week 28)
Driffield v Morpeth
Gateshead Fell v Old Bordleians
Blaydon v Pontefract
Selby v Horden
Redcar v Cleckheaton
Thornensians v Keighley

April 8 (Week 30)
Keighley v Redcar
Cleckheaton v Selby
Horden v Blaydon
Pontefract v Gateshead Fell
Old Brodleians v Driffield
Morpeth v Roundhegians

NORTH EAST ONE

BLAYDON RUFC
Ground Address: Crow Trees Ground, Hexham Road, Swalwell, Newcastle-upon-Tyne NE16 3BN. Tel: 091 414 2528
Club Secretary: GH March, Twickers, 48A Spen Burn, Ashtree Court, High Spen, Rowlands Gill, Tyne & Wear NE39 2DN. Tel: (H) 0207 545397
Fixtures Secretary: JM Huxley, The Mount, 59 Sunniside Road, Sunniside, Newcastle-upon-tyne NE16 5NF. Tel: (H) 091 488 7280
Club Colours: Scarlet jerseys, white collar, white shorts.

CLECKHEATON RUFC
Ground Address: Moorend, Cleckheaton, West Yorkshire BD19 3UD. Tel: 0274 873410
Club Secretary: Mr Ian Worley, 342 Whitehall Road, Westfield, Wyke, Bradford, West Yorkshire BD12 9DP. Tel: (H) 0274 677526
Fixtures Secretary: Mr Jack Wood, Tranquair, 705 Halifax Road, Cleckheaton, West Yorkshire. Tel: (H) 0274 873532 Tel (W) 0274 872423
Club Colours: Red & white hoops, black shorts, red socks.

DRIFFIELD RUFC
Ground Address: Keleythorpe, Driffield, East Yorkshire YO25 9DN. Tel: 0377 256598
Club Secretary: Stephen Edwards, Cedar Cottage, St John's Road, Driffield YO25 7RS. Tel: (H) 0377 253757 Tel: (W) 0482 864101
Fixtures Secretary: J Harrison, 9 Parsonage Close, Nafferton, Driffield YO25 0LH. Tel: (H) 0377 253032
Club Colours: Blue, black & white irregular hoops, blue shorts & socks. Change: Red.

GATESHEAD FELL RFC
Ground Address: Hedley Lawson Park, Eastwood Gardens, Gateshead. Tel: 091 487 5739
Club Secretary: MA Nunn, 30 Limetrees Gardens, Low Fell, Gateshead NE9 5BE. Tel: (H) 091 420 3089
Fixtures Secretary: N Wood, 18 Lyndhurst Grove, Low Fell, Gateshead NE9 5AU. Tel: (H) 091 487 6477
Club Colours: Dark blue & light blue (narrow rings), white shorts, red stockings.

HORDEN COLLIERY WELFARE RFC
Ground Address: Welfare Park, Horden. Tel: 091 586 3501
Club Secretary: L Applegarth, 10 Almond Terrace, Horden, Co. Durham SR8 4EZ. Tel: (H) 091 586 2477
Fixtures Secretary: J Fenwick, 1 Leyburn Place, Peterlee, Co. Durham. Tel: (H) 091 586 6540
Club Colours: Maroon & sky blue.

KEIGHLEY RUFC
Ground Address: Skipton Road, Utley, Keighley BD20 6DT. Tel: 0535 602174
Club Secretary: MT Greaves, Holmlea, Summerhill Lane, Steeton, Keighley BD20 6RX. Tel: (H) 0535 653192 Tel: (W) 0535 605646
Fixtures Secretary: J Midgley, 21 Woodville Road, Keighley BD20 6JA. Tel: (H) 0535 602414 Tel (W) 0535 605311
Club Colours: Emerald, scarlet & white equal hoops.

MORPETH RUFC
Ground Address: Grange House Field, Mitford Road, Morpeth, Northumberland NE61 1RJ. Tel: 0670 512508
Club Secretary: Ken Fraser, Solway House, De Merley Road, Morpeth, Northumberland NE61 1HZ. Tel: (H) 0670 511208 Tel: (W) 0670 822625 x201 Fax: 0670 829378
Fixtures Secretary: Bill Hewitt, The Birches, Lane End Farm, Felton, Northumberland. Tel: (H) 0670 787757
Club Colours: Scarlet & white hooped shirts, white shorts, scarlet & white socks.

OLD BRODLEIANS RUFC
Ground Address: Denholme Gate Road, Hipperholme, Nr Halifax, West Yorkshire HX3 8JU. Tel: 0422 202708
Club Secretary: Simon Heaton, Sutcliffe Wood Farm, Hove Edge, Brighouse, West Yorkshire. Tel: (H) 0484 721628 Tel: (W) 0274 687719

FINAL TABLE

	P	W	D	L	F	A	PD	Pts
Doncaster	12	11	0	1	232	70	162	22
Driffield	12	8	1	3	173	109	64	17
Pontefract	12	8	1	3	215	147	68	15
Blaydon	12	6	1	5	171	106	65	13
Thornensians	12	6	1	5	127	141	-14	13
Keighley	12	6	1	5	121	170	-49	13
Selby	12	6	0	6	124	175	-51	12
O Brodleians	12	4	3	5	147	117	30	11
Roundhegians	12	6	1	5	140	152	-12	11
Gateshead Fell	12	2	3	7	121	167	-46	7
Morpeth	12	3	1	8	75	126	-51	7
Redcar	12	3	0	9	98	210	-112	6
Novocastrians	12	2	1	9	84	138	-54	5

Fixtures Secretary: M Hey, 2 Sunnybank Crescent, Sowerby Bridge, West Yorkshire HX6 2PL. Tel: (H) 0422 839614 Tel (W) 0924 490803
Club Colours: Black, red & white.

PONTEFRACT RUFC
Ground Address: Moor Lane, Carleton, Pontefract, West Yorkshire WF8 3RX. Tel: 0977 702650
Club Secretary: R Peacock, 12 Fair View, Carleton, Pontefract, West Yorkshire WF8 3NT. Tel: (H) 0977 702284 Tel: (W) 0977 677421
Fixtures Secretary: M Higgitt, The Chimes, Common Lane, Upton, Pontefract, West Yorkshire WF9 1DF. Tel: (H) 0977 643605
Club Colours: Blue shirts with white V, white shorts.

REDCAR RUFC
Ground Address: Mackinlay Park, Green Lane, Redcar, Cleveland TS10 3RW. Tel: Redcar 482733
Club Secretary: Dr David R Palmer, c/o Redcar Rugby Union Football Club, Mackinlay Park, Green Lane, Redcar, Cleveland TS10 3RW. Tel: (W) Redcar 482733
Fixtures Secretary: Terry Baxter, 12 The Crescent, Redcar, Cleveland. Tel: (H) 0642 483900
Club Colours: Red, white & black.

ROUNDHEGIANS RUFC
Ground Address: The Memorial Ground, Chelwood Drive, Leeds 8. Tel: 0532 667377
Club Secretary: AJ Rowell, 16 The Moorlands, Shadwell Lane, Leeds L17 8AB. Tel: (H) 0532 669278 Tel: (W) 0532 610022
Fixtures Secretary: G English, 109 Swithenbank Avenue, Gawthorpe, Ossett, West Yorkshire WF5 9RS. Tel: (H) 0924 265858
Club Colours: Green, black & white hoops.

SELBY RUFC
Ground Address: Sandhill Lane, Leeds Road, Selby, West Yorkshire. Tel: 0757 703608
Club Secretary: MWM Blackwell, c/o Blackwell Grain Ltd, Market Weighton Road, Selby, North Yorkshire YO8 7LD. Tel: (H) 0904 633517 Tel: (W) 0757 289111
Fixtures Secretary: MJP Sharp, 7 The Causeway, Thorpe Willoughby, Selby, North Yorkshire. Tel: (H) 0757 702737 Tel (W) 0904 646651
Club Colours: Red, green & gold hoops.

THORNENSIANS RUFC
Ground Address: The Clubhouse, Coulman Road, Thorne, Doncaster, South Yorkshire. Tel: 0405 812746
Club Secretary: Ian Robson, Windyridge Cottage, Fieldside, Thorne, Dopncaster, South Yorkshire DN8 4BD. Tel: (H) 0405 812360 Tel: (W) 0405 812200
Fixtures Secretary: Colin Thompson, 2 Orchard Croft, Bawtry, Doncaster, South Yorkshire. Tel: (H) 0302 719956
Club Colours: Blue, white & black hoops.

NORTHERN DIVISION

NORTH EAST TWO
1994-95
FIXTURES

September 17 (Week 3)
North Ribblesdale v Goole
Rockliff v Hull
Mowden Park v Whitby
Beverley v Bramley
Novocastrians v Ashington
Westoe v Blyth

September 24 (Week 4)
Goole v Westoe
Blyth v Novocastrians
Ashington v Beverley
Bramley v Mowden Park
Whitby v Rockliff
Hull v Ripon

October 1 (Week 5)
Novocastrians v Goole
Westoe v North Ribblesdale
Ripon v Whitby
Rockliff v Bramley
Mowden Park v Ashington
Beverley v Blyth

October 15 (Week 7)
North Ribblesdale v Novocastrians
Goole v Beverley
Blyth v Mowden Park
Ashington v Rockliff
Bramley v Ripon
Whitby v Hull

October 22 (Week 8)
Mowden Park v Goole
Beverley v North Ribblesdale
Novocastrians v Westoe
Hull v Bramley
Ripon v Ashington
Rockliff v Blyth

October 29 (Week X2)
Westoe v Beverley
North Ribblesdale v Mowden Park
Goole v Rockliff
Blyth v Ripon
Ashington v Hull
Bramley v Whitby

January 7 (Week 17)
Ripon v Goole
Rockliff v North Ribblesdale
Mowden Park v Westoe
Beverley v Novocastrians
Whitby v Ashington
Hull v Blyth

January 14 (Week 18)
Novocastrians v Mowden Park
Westoe v Rockliff
North Ribblesdale v Ripon
Goole v Hull
Blyth v Whitby
Ashington v Bramley

February 11 (Week 22)
Whitby v Goole
Hull v North Ribblesdale
Ripon v Westoe
Rockliff v Novocastrians
Mowden Park v Beverley
Bramley v Blyth

February 25 (Week 24)
Beverley v Rockliff
Novocastrians v Ripon
Westoe v Hull
North Ribblesdale v Whitby
Goole v Bramley
Blyth v Ashington

March 4 (Week 25)
Ashington v Goole
Bramley v North Ribblesdale
Whitby v Westoe
Hull v Novocastrians
Ripon v Beverley
Rockliff v Mowden Park

March 25 (Week 28)
Mowden Park v Ripon
Beverley v Hull
Novocastrians v Whitby
Westcoe v Bramley
North Ribblesdale v Ashington
Goole v Blyth

April 8 (Week 30)
Blyth v North Ribblesdale
Ashington v Westoe
Bramley v Novocastrians
Whitby v Beverley
Hull v Mowden Park
Ripon v Rockliff

NORTH EAST TWO

ASHINGTON RFC
Ground Address: Recreation Ground, High Market, Ashington, Northumberland. Tel: 0670 814123
Club Secretary: J Nicholson, 13 Avebury Avenue, Sherbourne Park, Stakeford, Northumberland NE62 5HE. Tel: (H) 0670 828458
Fixtures Secretary: A Armstrong, 17 Highfield Drive, North Seaton, Ashington, Northumberland. Tel: (H) 0670 812649 Tel (W) 0670 512120
Club Colours: Royal blue & amber, white shorts.

BEVERLEY RUFC
Ground Address: Beaver Park, Norwood, Beverley, North Humberside. Tel: 0480 870306
Club Secretary: Andrew Winter, 4 The Vineyards, Leven, Beverley, North Humberside HU17 5LD. Tel: (H) 0964 543981 Tel: (W) 0482 885027
Fixtures Secretary: Rob Jenner, 3 Spark Mill Terrace, Beverley, North Humberside. Tel: (H) 0482 868944
Club Colours: Green, brown & white.

BLYTH RFC
Ground Address: Plessey Road, Blyth, Northumberland. Tel: 0620 352063
Club Secretary: J Jackson, 22 Winchester Avenue, Blyth, Northumberland. Tel: (H) 0670 369258 Tel: (W) 0670 813248
Fixtures Secretary: J Norris, 10 Dene View Drive, Blyth, Northumberland NE24 5PU. Tel: (H) 0670 369177 Tel (W) 091 273 8866 x2326
Club Colours: Emerald green & black.

BRAMLEY RUFC
Ground Address: The Warrels, Grosmount Terrace, Warrels Road, Bramley, Leeds LS13 3NY. Tel: 0532 577787
Club Secretary: AN Hurdley, Hall Farm, Hall Road, Little Preston, Leeds LS26 8UT. Tel: (H) 0532 860131 Tel: (W) 0274 741433
Fixtures Secretary: Brian Parkin, 4 Westroyd Crescent, Pudsey, Leeds LS28 8JD. Tel: (H) 0532 563127 Tel (W) 0532 536199
Club Colours: Green with black & gold chest band.

DARLINGTON MOWDEN PARK RFC
Ground Address:22 Yiewsley Drive, Darlington, Co Durham DL3 9XS. Tel: 0325 465932
Club Secretary: GF Nevill, 44 Leith Road, Darlington, Co Durham DL3 8BG. Tel: (H) 0325 469001 Tel: (W) 0325 480891/0677 423737
Fixtures Secretary: M Charlton, 14 Kettle End, Barton, Richmond, North Yorkshire. Tel: (H) 0325 377292 Tel (W) 0325 368568
Club Colours: Royal blue & white.

GOOLE RUFC
Ground Address: The Clubhouse, Murham Avenue, Goole DN14 6PA. Tel: 0405 762018
Club Secretary: IR Higgins, 14 The Meadows, Howden, Goole, North Humberside DN14 7DX. Tel: (H) 0430 430037 Tel: (W) 0405 768621
Fixtures Secretary: P Shand, Hallgarth, 22 Ledgate Lane, Burton Salmon, Leeds LS25 5JY. Tel: (H) 0977 677660 Tel (W) 0977 703357
Club Colours: Navy blue & gold quarters.

HULL RUFC
Ground Address: Haworth Park, Emmott Road, Beverley Road, Hull HU6 7AB. Tel: 0482 802119
Club Secretary: DJ Ward, 78 St Margaret's Avenue, Cottingham, Hull HU16 5NB. Tel: (H) 0482 842292 Tel: (W) 0482 35242
Fixtures Secretary: Robin Mason, 223 Beverley Road, Kirkella. Tel: (H) 0482 657495 Tel (W) 0482 652528
Club Colours: Black with red & orange hoops.

NORTH RIBBLESDALE RUFC
Ground Address: Grove Park, Greenfoot, Settle, North

FINAL TABLE

	P	W	D	L	F	A	PD	Pts
Horden	12	10	1	1	262	123	139	21
Cleckheaton	12	10	0	2	310	133	177	20
Goole	12	8	1	3	189	109	80	17
Ashington	12	8	1	3	173	134	39	17
Blyth	12	6	1	5	173	129	44	13
Whitby	12	5	1	6	110	177	-67	11
Hull	12	6	0	6	170	147	23	10
Beverley	12	5	0	7	138	223	-85	10
Ripon	12	4	0	8	94	194	-100	8
Bramley	12	3	1	8	152	243	-91	7
Rockliff	12	3	0	9	127	184	-57	6
Acklam	12	1	1	10	89	235	-146	3

Yorkshire. Tel: 0729 822755
Club Secretary: RT Graveson, Attermire House, Castle Hill, Settle, North Yorkshire. Tel: (H) 0729 823559 Tel: (W) 0729 825252
Fixtures Secretary: AM Davidson, Gasker, Lawkland, Austwick, Lancaster. Tel: (H) 0729 825595 Tel (W) 0524 66215
Club Colours: Blue & white. Change: Maroon.

NOVOCASTRIANS RFC
Ground Address: Sunderland Park, The Drive, High Heaton, Newcastle upon Tyne, NE7 7SY. Tel: 091 266 1247
Club Secretary: R B Pollock, 101 Marine Avenue, Whitley Bay, Tyne & Wear, NE26 3LN. Tel: (H) 091 2511562 Tel: (W) 091 2960303
Club Colours: Shirts/socks — red, black and white hoops — white shorts.

RIPON RUFC
Ground Address: Mallorie Park, Ripon, North Yorkshire HG4 2QD. Tel: 0765 604675
Club Secretary: MP Viner, 20 Church Close, Tollerton, York YO6 2ES. Tel: (H) 0347 838180 Tel: (W) 0609 780780 x2915
Fixtures Secretary: Andy Proud, 1 Ure Bank Terrace, Ripon, North Yorkshire HG4 1JG. Tel: (H) 0765 605474 Tel (W) 0423 500066
Club Colours: Blue, black & white hoops.

WESTOE
Ground Address: Dean Road, South Shields, Tyne & Wear. Tel: 091 456 1506
Club Secretary: J R Wells, 240 <owbray Road, South Shields, Tyne & Wear, NE33 3NW. Tel: (H) 091 455 2260 Tel: (W) 091 456 0403
Fixtures Secretary: D Aller, 7 Wood Tee, South Shields. Tel: (H) 091 456 9531 Tel (W) 091 456 1115
Club Colours: Red, Sky and dark blue hoops.

WHITBY RUFC
Ground Address: Whiteleys Road, Whitby, North Yorkshire. Tel: 0947 602008
Club Secretary: F Howarth, 18 Lime Grove, Whitby, North Yorkshire YO21 1LP. Tel: (H) 0947 600692
Fixtures Secretary: J Wardel, 23 Asile Road, Redcar, Cleveland TS10 2BB.
Club Colours: Maroon shirts, black shorts.

WHITLEY BAY ROCKCLIFF RFC
Ground Address: Hillheads, Lovaine Avenue, Whitley Bay, Northumberland NE25 8RW. Tel: 091 251 3704
Club Secretary: Graham Shepherd, Bank Chambers, 31 Station Road, Wallsend NE28 6SZ. Tel: (H) 091 276 2067 Tel: (W) 091 262 3952
Fixtures Secretary: Mike Hopper, 19 Briarsyde, Benton, Newcastle-upon-Tyne M2 9SL. Tel: (H) 091 270 2098
Club Colours: Cardinal red with gold trimmings, white shorts.

NORTHERN DIVISION

DURHAM & NORTHUMBERLAND ONE 1994-95 FIXTURES

January 7 (Week 17)
Percy Park   v   Wallsend
Darlington   v   Hartlepool TDSOB
Darlington R.A.   v   Ponteland
Ryton   v   Guisborough
Acklam   v   North Shields
Sunderland   v   North Durham

September 17 (Week 3)
Hartlepool TDSOB   v   Wallsend
Darlington   v   Sunderland
Darlington R.A.   v   Acklam
Ryton   v   Bishop Auckland
Guisborough   v   North Shields
Ponteland   v   North Durham

January 14 (Week 18)
Guisborough   v   Darlington R.A.
Ponteland   v   Darlington
Hartlepool TDSOB   v   Percy Park
Wallsend   v   Sunderland
North Durham   v   Acklam
North Shields   v   Bishop Auckland

September 24 (Week 4)
Wallsend   v   Ponteland
North Durham   v   Guisborough
North Shields   v   Ryton
Bishop Auckland   v   Darlington R.A.
Acklam   v   Darlington
Sunderland   v   Percy Park

February 11 (Week 22)
Acklam   v   Wallsend
Sunderland   v   Hartlepool TDSOB
Percy Park   v   Ponteland
Darlington   v   Guisborough
Darlington R.A.   v   Ryton
Bishop Auckland   v   North Durham

October 1 (Week 5)
Guisborough   v   Wallsend
Ponteland   v   Hartlepool TDSOB
Percy Park   v   Acklam
Darlington   v   Bishop Auckland
Darlington R.A.   v   North Shields
Ryton   v   North Durham

February 25 (Week 24)
Ryton   v   Darlington
Guisborough   v   Percy Park
Ponteland   v   Sunderland
Hartlepool TDSOB   v   Acklam
Wallsend   v   Bishop Auckland
North Durham   v   North Shields

October 15 (Week 7)
Hartlepool TDSOB   v   Guisborough
Wallsend   v   Ryton
North Durham   v   Darlington R.A.
North Shields   v   Darlington
Bishop Auckland   v   Percy Park
Acklam   v   Sunderland

March 4 (Week 25)
North Shields   v   Wallsend
Bishop Auckland   v   Hartlepool TDSOB
Acklam   v   Ponteland
Sunderland   v   Guisborough
Percy Park   v   Ryton
Darlington   v   Darlington R.A.

October 22 (Week 8)
Darlington R.A.   v   Wallsend
Ryton   v   Hartlepool TDSOB
Guisborough   v   Ponteland
Sunderland   v   Bishop Auckland
Percy Park   v   North Shields
Darlington   v   North Durham

March 25 (Week 28)
Darlington R.A.   v   Percy Park
Ryton   v   Sunderland
Guisborough   v   Acklam
Ponteland   v   Bishop Auckland
Hartlepool TDSOB   v   North Shields
Wallsend   v   North Durham

October 29 (Week X2)
Ponteland   v   Ryton
Hartlepool TDSOB   v   Darlington R.A.
Wallsend   v   Darlington
North Durham   v   Percy Park
North Shields   v   Sunderland
Bishops Auckland   v   Acklam

April 8 (Week 30)
North Durham   v   Hartlepool TDSOB
North Shields   v   Ponteland
Bishop Auckland   v   Guisborough
Acklam   v   Ryton
Sunderland   v   Darlington R.A.
Percy Park   v   Darlington

DURHAM & NORTHUMBERLAND ONE

ACKLAM RUFC
Ground Address: Talbot park, Saltersgill Avenue,
Middlesborough, Cleveland, TS4 3PR. Tel: 0642 321397
Club Secretary: Paul Pearson, Blackhall, Sands, Acklam,
Middlesborough. Tel: (H) 0642 596433 Tel: (W) 0325
461231
Club Colours: Green/black.
BISHOP AUCKLAND RUFC
Ground Address: West Mills Playing Fields, Bridge Road,
Bishop Auckland, Co Durham DL14 7PA. Tel: 0388
602922
Club Secretary: Mr KA Wilkinson, 7 Victoria Avenue,
Bishop Auckland, Co Durham DL14 7JH. Tel: (H) 0388
605768 Tel: (W) 0388 603388
Fixtures Secretary: Mr E Farrer, 35 Windermere Drive,
West Auckland, Co Durham DL14 9LF. Tel: (H) 0388
832810
Club Colours: Navy & sky blue.
DARLINGTON RA RUFC
Ground Address: Brinkburn Road, Darlington, Co
Durham.
Club Secretary: Andrew Thompson, 23 Westgate
Crescent, Darlington, Co Durham DL3 0SY. Tel: (H) 0325
284354 Tel: (W) 0325 300770
Fixtures Secretary: M Thompson. Tel: (H) 0325 480547
Club Colours: Black & amber.
DARLINGTON RFC
Ground Address: Blackwell Meadows, Grange Road,
Darlington, Co Durham, DL1 5NR. Tel: 0325 363888
Club Secretary: A P F Foster, 45 artford Road, Darlington,
Co Durham, DL3 8HF. Tel: (H) 0325 466501 Tel: (W)
0325 381818
Fixtures Secretary: D E Gardner, Balder View,
Cothorstone, Barnard Castle. Tel: (H) 0833 650543 Tel
(W) 0833 690305
Club Colours: Black and white hoops, black shorts, red
socks.
GUISBOROUGH RUFC
Ground Address: Belmangate, Guisborough, Cleveland
TS14 7BB. Tel: 0287 632966
Club Secretary: Dennis Childs, 32 Boston Drive, Marton,
Cleveland TS7 8LZ. Tel: (H) 0642 314081
Fixtures Secretary: Graham Crooks, 51 Farndale Drive,
Pinehills, Guisborough, Cleveland TS14 8JJ. Tel: (H) 0287
633244
Club Colours: Black & amber.
NORTH DURHAM RFC
Ground Address: Prince Consort Road, Gateshead NE8
1WS. Tel: 091 478 3072
Club Secretary: R Thompson, 3 Ancroft Place, Fenham,
Newcastle upon Tyne NE5 2HN. Tel: (H) 091 274 6041
Fixtures Secretary: T Tate, 14 Alverstone Avenue, Low
Fell, Gateshead, Tyne & Wear NE9 6EU. Tel: (H) 091 491
3083
Club Colours: Broad red & white hoops.
NORTH SHIELDS RFC
Ground Address: Preston Playing Fields, Preston Village,
North Shields, Tyne & Wear. Tel: 091 257 7352
Club Secretary: David Daniels, 1 Highcross Road, North
Shields, Tyne & Wear NE30 3JG. Tel: (H) 091 252 6395
Tel: (W) 091 271 6777
Fixtures Secretary: Alistair Shield, 9 Cresswell Avenue,
North Shields, Tyne & Wear. Tel: (H) 091 259 0402
Club Colours: Royal blue & white hoops, white shorts.
PERCY PARK RFC
Ground Address: The Clubhouse, Preston Avenue, North
Shields, Tyne & Wear. Tel: 091 257 5710
Club Secretary: AC Baker, 30 The Garth, Winlaton, Tyne
& Wear NE21 6DD. Tel: (H) 091 257 7007 Tel: (W) 091
4144869
Fixtures Secretary: J Elliott, 13 Brundon Avenue, Whitley

FINAL TABLE

	P	W	D	L	F	A	PD	Pts
Mowden Park	12	12	0	0	256	76	180	24
W Hart TDSOB	12	10	1	1	286	115	171	21
Ryton	12	7	1	4	224	166	58	15
Percy Park	12	6	2	4	234	111	123	14
Sunderland	12	6	0	6	176	137	39	12
Darlington	12	6	0	6	195	162	33	12
N Shields	12	5	1	6	193	161	32	11
Bishop Auckland	12	6	1	5	168	193	-25	11
Guisborough	12	5	1	6	117	158	-41	11
N Durham	12	5	0	7	156	203	-47	10
Darlington RA	12	3	0	9	114	239	-125	6
Seaham	12	2	1	9	134	305	-171	5
Consett	12	1	0	11	104	331	-227	2

Bay, Tyne & Wear. Tel: (H) 091 252 6109
Club Colours: Black & white hoops, black shorts.
PONTELAND RUFC
Ground Address: Ponteland Leisure Centre, Callerton
Lane, Ponteland NE20 9EG.
Club Secretary: Adrian S Jackson, 34 Collingwood
Crescent, Darras Hall, Ponteland NE20 9DZ. Tel: (H) 0661
871832 Tel: (W) 091 385 3131
Fixtures Secretary: Joyce Baty, 5 Brooklands, Ponteland
NE20. Tel: (H) 0661 823527
Club Colours: Maroon shirts, black & white hoops, white
shorts.
RYTON RUFC
Ground Address: Main Road, Ryton, Tyne & Wear NE40
3AG. Tel: 091 413 3820
Club Secretary: JA Trodden, 63 Horsley Avenue, Ryton,
Tyne & Wear NE40 4XQ. Tel: (H) 091 413 2700 Tel: (W)
0670 713451
Fixtures Secretary: RT Thoburn, 70 Theroba Street,
Blaydon, Tyne & Wear. Tel: (H) 091 414 2669
Club Colours: Royal blue & white.
SUNDERLAND RFC
Ground Address: Ashbrooke, West Lawn, Sunderland,
Tyne & Wear SR2 7HH. Tel: 091 528 4536
Club Secretary: J Martin, 11 Roker Park Terrace,
Sunderland. Tel: (H) 091 567 7045
Fixtures Secretary: A Scott-Gray, 37 Glenesk Road,
Sunderland. Tel: (H) 091 522 6188
Club Colours: Red, black, gold hoops, white shorts.
WALLSEND RFC
Ground Address: Sam Smith's Pavilion, Benfield School
Campus, Benfield Road, Walkergate,
Newcastle-Upon-Tyne. Tel: 091 265 9357
Club Secretary: Brian J Thirlaway, 25 Blanchard Close,
Battle Hill Estate, Wallsend, Tyne & Wear, NE28 9DU.
Tel: (H) 091 234 4877
Fixtures Secretary: Frank McDonald, 88 Appletree
Gardens, Walkerville, Newcastle. Tel: (H) 091 262 2759
Club Colours: Myrtle green jerseys with gold trim, white
shorts, green socks.
WEST HARTLEPOOL TECHNICAL DAY SCHOOL
OLD BOYS RUFC
Ground Address: Wiltshire Way, Hartlepool, Cleveland.
Tel: 0429 233548
Club Secretary: D Bramley, 63 Hutton Avenue,
Hartlepool, Cleveland TS26 9PP. Tel: (H) 0429 263157
Tel: (W) 0642 433363
Fixtures Secretary: A Cheshire, 22 Loyalty Road,
Hartlepool, Cleveland. Tel: (H) 0429 234659
Club Colours: Royal blue.

NORTHERN DIVISION

DURHAM & NORTHUMBERLAND TWO 1994-95 FIXTURES

September 17 (Week 3)
Wensleydale v Richmondshire
Hartlepool BBOB v Medicals
Seaham v Chester-le-Street
Hartlepool v Seghill
Consett v Seaton Carew
Billingham v Houghton

September 24 (Week 4)
Richmondshire v Billingham
Houghton v Consett
Seaton Carew v Hartlepool
Seghill v Seaham
Chester-le-Street v Hartlepool BBOB
Medicals v Winlaton Vulcans

October 1 (Week 5)
Consett v Richmonshire
Billingham v Wensleydale
Winlaton Vulcans v Chester-le-Street
Hartlepool BBOB v Seghill
Seaham v Seaton Carew
Hartlepool v Houghton

October 15 (Week 7)
Wensleydale v Consett
Richmondshire v Hartlepool
Houghton v Seaham
Seaton Carew v Hartlepool BBOB
Seghill v Winlaton Vulcans
Chester-le-Street v Medicals

October 22 (Week 8)
Seaham v Richmondshire
Hartlepool v Wensleydale
Consett v Billingham
Medicals v Seghill
Winlaton Vulcans v Seaton Carew
Hartlepool BBOB v Houghton

October 29 (Week X2)
Billingham v Hartlepool
Wensleydale v Seaham
Richmondshire v Hartlepool BBOB
Houghton v Winlaton Vulcans
Seaton Carew v Medicals
Seghill v Chester-le-Street

January 7 (Week 17)
Winlaton Vulcans v Richmondshire
Hartlepool BBOB v Wensleydale
Seaham v Billingham
Hartlepool v Consett
Chester-le-Street v Seaton Carew
Medicals v Houghton

January 14 (Week 18)
Consett v Seaham
Billingham v Hartlepool BBOB
Wensleydale v Winlaton Vulcans
Richmondshire v Medicals
Houghton v Chester-le-Street
Seaton Carew v Seghill

February 11 (Week 22)
Chester-le-Street v Richmondshire
Medicals v Wensleydale
Winlaton Vulcans v Billingham
Hartlepool BBOB v Consett
Seaham v Hartlepool
Seghill v Houghton

February 25 (Week 24)
Hartlepool v Hartlepool BBOB
Consett v Winlaton Vulcans
Billingham v Medicals
Wensleydale v Chester-le-Street
Richmondshire v Seghill
Houghton v Seaton Carew

March 4 (Week 25)
Seaton Carew v Richmondshire
Seghill v Wensleydale
Chester-le-Street v Billingham
Medicals v Consett
Winlaton Vulcans v Hartlepool
Hartlepool BBOB v Seaham

March 25 (Week 28)
Seaham v Winlaton Vulcans
Hartlepool v Medicals
Consett v Chester-le-Street
Billingham v Seghill
Wensleydale v Seaton Carew
Richomndshire v Houghton

April 8 (Week 30)
Houghton v Wensleydale
Seaton Carew v Billingham
Seghill v Consett
Chester-le-Street v Hartlepool
Medicals v Seaham
Winlaton Vulcans v Hartlepool BBOB

DURHAM & NORTHUMBERLAND TWO

BILLINGHAM RUFC
Ground Address:c/o Billingham Synthonia Recreation Ciub, Belasis Lane, Billingham.
Club Secretary: John Ker, 4 Anlaby Close, Billingham, Cleveland TS23 3RA. Tel: (H) 0642 560536 Tel: (W) 0642 560692
Fixtures Secretary: Colin Wakenshaw, 30 Grampian Road, Billingham, Cleveland TS23 2PH. Tel: (H) 0642 535374
Club Colours: Green & white hoops.

CHESTER-LE-STREET RFC
Ground Address:Rowing Club Building, Riverside Park, Chester-le-Street, Co Durham. Tel: 091 388 4121
Club Secretary: Paul Langley, 58 Rydal Road, Chester-le-Street, Co Durham DH2 3DT. Tel: (H) 091 388 5989 Tel: (W) 091 383 3443
Fixtures Secretary: G Rodger, 3 Fife Avenue, Chester-le-Street, Co Durham. Tel: (H) 091 389 1713
Club Colours: Navy blue shirts & shorts, red socks.

CONSETT & DISTRICT RFC
Ground Address:Belle Vue Park, Medomsley Road, Consett, Co Durham. Tel: 0207 504261
Club Secretary: Mr Tony Clarke, 18 Third Street, Crookhall, Consett, Co Durham DH8 7LT. Tel: (W) 0207 503477 x200
Fixtures Secretary: Mr David Herdman, 10 Park Avenue, Consett, Co Durham. Tel: (H) 0207 581385
Club Colours: Black & amber quarters.

HARTLEPOOL BOYS BRIGADE OLD BOYS RFC
Ground Address:Old Friarage, Headland, Hartlepool.
Club Secretary: GK Faint, 11 Nesbyt Road, Hartlepool, Cleveland TS24 9NB. Tel: (H) 0429 265674 Tel: (W) 091 477 0288 x7963
Fixtures Secretary: I Mulrooney, 65 Percy Street, Hartlepool, Cleveland TS26 0HT. Tel: (H) 0429 278082 Tel (W) 0429 260471
Club Colours: White with broad black band, black shorts.

HARTLEPOOL RFC
Ground Address:Mayfield Park, Easington Road, Hartlepool, Cleveland TS24 9BA. Tel: 0429 266445
Club Secretary: Keith Dobson, 15 Sandbanks Drive, Hart Station, Hartlepool, Cleveland TS24 9RP. Tel: (H) 0429 261236 Tel: (W) 0429 266522 x2263
Fixtures Secretary: Gary Mayes, 62 Whitrout Road, Hartlepool, Cleveland TS24 9PW. Tel: (H) 0429 262984 Tel (W) 0429 279837
Club Colours: Black.

HOUGHTON RUFC
Ground Address:Dairy Lane, Houghton le Spring, Tyne & Wear DH7 0DZ. Tel: 091 584 1460
Club Secretary: David Winthrop, Hillcroft, 14 North Road, Hetton le Hole, Tyne & Wear. Tel: (H) 091 526 2163 Tel: (W) 091 567 0094
Fixtures Secretary: John Felton, 37 Larchwood, Harraton Wood, Washington, Tyne & Wear. Tel: (H) 091 416 1467 Tel (W) 091 487 7171
Club Colours: Black shirts, white hoop, black shorts, black socks, white tops.

MEDICALS RFC
Ground Address:Cartington Terrace, Newcastle-upon-Tyne. Tel: 091 276 1473
Club Secretary: Dr AR Greenwood, 45 Church Road, Gosforth, Newcastle-upon-Tyne NE3 1UE. Tel: (H) 091 285 0686 Tel: (W) 091 491 5600
Fixtures Secretary: Dr AR Greenwood, 45 Church Road, Gosforth, Newcastle-upon-Tyne NE3 1UE. Tel: (H) 091 285 0680 Tel (W) 091 491 5600
Club Colours: Maroon & white.

RICHMONDSHIRE RUFC
Ground Address:The Playing Fields, Theakston Lane, Richmond, North Yorkshire. Tel: 0748 850515
Club Secretary: Mr S Speakman, 36 Victoria Road, Richmond, North Yorkshire DL10 4AU. Tel: (H) 0748 825579 Tel: (W) 0748 850111
Fixtures Secretary: Mr B Dixon, 3 St Nicholas Drive, Richmond, North Yorkshire. Tel: (H) 0748 825360
Club Colours: Red, gold & white hoops.

FINAL TABLE

	P	W	D	L	F	A	PD	Pts
Ponteland	11	9	1	1	220	75	145	19
Wallsend	11	8	2	1	324	84	237	18
Winlaton Vulcans	11	7	2	2	154	69	85	16
Hartlepool	11	7	0	4	203	87	116	14
Wensleydale	11	7	0	4	184	84	100	14
Medicals	11	6	1	4	147	104	43	13
Chester-Le-Street	11	5	1	5	111	112	-1	11
Seghill	11	4	0	7	146	277	-131	8
Hartlepool BBOB	11	3	0	8	101	321	-220	6
Houghton	11	3	0	8	148	218	-70	4
Seaton Carew	11	1	2	8	59	207	-148	4
Newton Aycliffe	11	1	1	9	86	242	-156	-1

SEAHAM RUFC
Ground Address:New Drive Playing Fields. Club: 27 Cornelia Terrace, Seaham, Co Durham. Tel: 091 581 2331
Club Secretary: Mrs C Pinder, 27 Cornelia Terrace, Seaham, Co Durham. Tel: (W) 091 581 2331
Fixtures Secretary: Mr Alan Mason, 1 Membury Close, Sunderland, Tyne & Wear. Tel: (H) 091 520 0282
Club Colours: Red shirts. Change: Black shirts.

SEATON CAREW RUFC
Ground Address:Hornby Park, Elizabeth Way, Seaton Carew, Cleveland TS25 2AZ. Tel: 0429 260945
Club Secretary: Paul McManus, 9 Ruswarp Grove, Seaton Carew, Hartlepool, Cleveland TS25 2BA. Tel: (W) 0429 268821 Fax: 0429 860700
Fixtures Secretary: Colin P Chappell, 19 Endeavour Close, Seaton Carew, Hartlepool, Cleveland TS25 1EY. Tel: (H) 0429 868058 Tel (W) 0325 460606
Club Colours: Maroon & amber hooped shirts & socks, black shorts.

SEGHILL RUFC
Ground Address:Welfare Park, Seghill, Cramlington, Northumberland NE23 7ER. Tel: 091 237 0414
Club Secretary: Stewart Grainger, 16 Carrick Drive, Parklands, Blyth NE24 3SX. Tel: (H) 0670 355 909
Club Colours: Red & black.

WENSLEYDALE RUFC
Ground Address:Cawkhill Park, Wensley Road, Leyburn, North Yorkshire. Tel: 0969 23067
Club Secretary: David Ward, 3 Kelbordale Terrace, Leyburn, North Yorkshire DL8 5AR. Tel: (H) 0969 24462 Tel: (W) 0969 22046
Fixtures Secretary: Ian Burdon, Lane House Farm, Jervaulx, Ripon, North Yorkshire. Tel: (H) 0677 460226
Club Colours: Black & amber hoops.

WINATON VULCANS RUFC
Ground Address:Axwell View Playing Fields, Winlaton, Tyne & Wear. Tel: 091 414 2502
Club Secretary: M Roddam, 70 Silverdale Drive, Winlaton, Tyne & Wear, Tyneside, T1. Tel: (H) 091 414 2901 Tel: (W) 0207 542935
Club Colours: Black with white collar.

WINLATON VULCANS RFC
Ground Address:Axwell View Playing Fields, Winlaton, Blaydon-on-Tyne, NE21 6NF. Tel: 091 4142502
Club Secretary: Timothy Williams, 29 Huntley Cres, Winlaton, Blaydon-on-Tyne, NE21 6EU. Tel: (H) 091 4144636 Tel: (W) 091 4887943
Fixtures Secretary: Ian Bilclough, 8 Holly Ave, Winlaton Mill, Blaydon-on-Tyne, NE21 6SL. Tel: (H) 091 4148560
Club Colours: Black shirts, white collar, black shorts, black socks.

NORTHERN DIVISION

DURHAM & NORTHUMBERLAND THREE 1994-95 FIXTURES

September 17 (Week 3)
Newton Ayecliffe v Benton
Barnard Castle v Belmont
Washington v Sedgefield

September 24 (Week 4)
Benton v Prudhoe Hospital
Sedgefield v Barnard castle
Belmont v Wearside

October 1 (Week 5)
Hartlepool Athletic v Benton
Prudhoe Hospital v Newton Ayecliffe
Wearside v Sedgefield

October 15 (Week 7)
Newton Ayecliffe v Hartlepool Athletic
Benton v Jarrovians
Sedgefield v Belmont

October 22 (Week 8)
Washington v Benton
Jarrovians v Newton Ayecliffe
Hartlepool Athletic v Prudhoe Hospital

October 29 (Week X2)
Prudhoe Hospital v Jarrovians
Newton Ayecliffe v Washington
Benton v Barnard Castle

January 7 (Week 17)
Wearside v Benton
Branard Castle v Newton Ayecliffe
Washington v Prudhoe Hospital
Jarrovians v Hartlepool Athletic

January 14 (Week 18)
Hartlepool Athletic v Washington
Prudhoe Hospital v Barnard Castle
Newton Ayecliffe v Wearside
Benton v Belmont

February 11 (Week 22)
Sedgefield v Benton
Belmont v Newton Ayecliffe
Wearside v Prudhoe Hospital
Barnard Castle v Hartlepool Athletic
Washington v Jarrovians

February 25 (Week 24)
Jarrovians v Barnard Castle
Hartlepool Athletic v Wearside
Prudhoe Hospital v Belmont
Newton Ayecliffe v Sedgefield

March 4 (Week 25)
Sedgefield v Prudhoe Hospital
Belmont v Hartlepool Athletic
Wearside v Jarrovians
Barnard Castle v Washington

March 25 (Week 28)
Washington v Wearside
Jarrovians v Belmont
Hartlepool Athletic v Sedgefield

April 8 (Week 30)
Sedgefield v Jarrovians
Belmont v Washington
Wearside v Barnard Castle

DURHAM & NORTHUMBERLAND THREE

BARNARD CASTLE RUFC
Ground Address: Clubhouse, Birch Road, Barnard Castle, Co Durham DL12 8JP. Tel: 0833 31766
Club Secretary: Tim Worley, 17 Newgate, Barnard Castle, Co Durham DL12 8NQ. Tel: (H) 0833 37608 Tel: (W) 0833 690305
Fixtures Secretary: John Stead, Tutta Beck Farmhouse, Rokeby, Nr Barnard Castle, Co Durham. Tel: (H) 0833 690214
Club Colours: All black.
BELMONT RUFC
Ground Address: Gilesgate Moor Sports & Social Club, Belmont, Durham. Tel: 091 386 4615
Club Secretary: James MG Nangle, 5 Winchester Road, Newton Hall, Durham DH1 5QU. Tel: (H) 091 386 0827 Tel: (W) 091 386 2621
Fixtures Secretary: Mike Weetman, 10 Willowbank Crescent, Gilesgate, Durham. Tel: (H) 091 384 7513
Club Colours: Dark blue, light blue quarters.
BENTON RFC
Ground Address: Civil Service Sports Ground, Darsley Park, Old Whitley Road, Newcastle-upon-Tyne. Tel: 091 266 2726
Club Secretary: C Reid, 114 Northumberland Street, Wallsend, Tyne & Wear NE28 7PX. Tel: (H) 091 262 4913
Fixtures Secretary: G Parker, 9 Wilson Terrace, Forrest Hall, Newcastle 12, Tyne & Wear. Tel: (H) 091 268 5821
Club Colours: White shirt with broad blue hoop, white shorts, red socks. Change: Black shirt, white shorts, red socks.
HARTLEPOOL ATHLETIC RFC
Ground Address: Oakesway Estate, Hartlepool, Cleveland TS24 0RE. Tel: 0429 274715
Club Secretary: Jim Ainslie, Archway Cottage, 10 Regent Street, Hartlepool, Cleveland TS24 0QN. Tel: (H) 0429 260003 Tel: (W) 0836 258317
Fixtures Secretary: John Bentham, 22 Tempest Road, Hartlepool, Cleveland. Tel: (H) 0429 222239
Club Colours: Sky blue.
JARROVIANS RUFC
Ground Address: Lukes Lane Estate, Hebburn, Tyne & Wear. Tel: 091 489 3291
Club Secretary: Steve Softley, 20 Gladstone Street, Hebburn, Tyne & Wear NE31 2XJ. Tel: (H) 091 489 0789 Tel: (W) 091 477 2271 x250
Fixtures Secretary: Dave King, 46 Lichfield Way, Hedworth, Jarrow, Tyne & Wear NE32 4UW. Tel: (H) 091 489 1611 Tel (W) 091 427 1717 x5071
Club Colours: Black & amber hoops, black shorts & socks.
NEWTON AYCLIFFE RUFC
Ground Address: Newton Aycliffe, Co Durham, DL5 5AG. Tel: 0325 312768
Club Secretary: Mr Shaun Pettit, 2 Zetland Hunt, Newton Aycliffe. Tel: (H) 0325 311569
Fixtures Secretary: Mr Brian Parsonage, 253 Rowan Place, Newton Aycliffe. Tel: (H) 0325 310515
Club Colours: Maroon, green, old gold.
PRUDHOE HOSPITAL RUFC
Ground Address: Prudhoe Hospital, Prudhoe, Northumberland. Tel: 0661 33068
Club Secretary: Mr G Bridgwater, 3 Hillcrest Court, Prudhoe, Northumberland, NE42 5PQ. Tel: (H) 0661 832772
Fixtures Secretary: J Haslem, 12 Cowan Close, Stella Park Estate, Blaydon, NE21 4LQ.
Club Colours: Shirt red, blue quarters, white shorts, red socks.

FINAL TABLE

	P	W	D	L	F	A	PD	Pts
Billingham	9	8	0	1	266	59	207	16
Richmondshire	9	8	0	1	209	27	182	16
Barnard Castle	9	8	0	1	150	62	88	16
Sedgefield	9	5	0	4	166	117	49	10
Jarrovians	9	5	0	4	120	152	-32	10
Wearside	9	3	1	5	102	116	-14	7
Belmont	9	3	0	6	84	180	-96	6
Prudhoe	9	3	0	6	94	194	-100	6
Hartlepool Athletic	9	0	2	7	36	148	-112	2
Washington	9	0	1	8	41	213	-172	-1

SEDGEFIELD RUFC
Ground Address: Sedgefield Community College, Sedgefield, Stockton-on-Tees, Cleveland. Tel: 0740 621097
Club Secretary: Mr N Hetherington, 1 The Meadows, Sedgefield, Stockton-on-Tees, Cleveland TS21 2DL. Tel: (H) 0740 621179 Tel: (W) 0836 292665
Fixtures Secretary: Mr M Price, 61 West End, Sedgefield, Stockton-on-Tees, Cleveland. Tel: (H) 0740 622792
Club Colours: Red & black quarters.
WASHINGTON RUFC
Ground Address: Northumbria Centre, Northern Area Playing Fields, Stephenson Industrial Estate, Washington, Tyne & Wear
Club Secretary: Ian Cruickshank, 20 Martin Court, Ayton Village, Washington, Tyne & Wear NE38 0AD. Tel 415 4655
Club Colours: Blue & gold stripes.
WEARSIDE RUFC
Ground Address: Fulwell Quarry Reclamation Site, Newcastle Road, Sunderland, Tyne & Wear.
Club Secretary: Mervyn Ironside, 41 Hylton Street, Millfield, Sunderland, Tyne & Wear. Tel: (H) 091 567 9711 Tel: (W) 091 565 6256 x49722
Fixtures Secretary: Jeff Fowler, 8 Kirkwood Avenue, Hastings Hill, Sunderland, Tybe & Wear. Tel: (H) 091 534 5191
Club Colours: Red & blue hoops, white shorts, red socks.

NORTHERN DIVISION

YORKSHIRE ONE
1994-95
FIXTURES

September 17 (Week 3)
Sheffield Oaks   v   Yarnbury
Wheatley Hills   v   Ilkley
Wath   v   Hemsworth
Pocklington   v   Old Otliensians
Leodiensians   v   Castleford
Malton & Norton   v   Barnsley

September 24 (Week 4)
Yarnbury   v   Malton & Norton
Barnsley   v   Leodiensians
Castleford   v   Pocklington
Old Otliensians   v   Wath
Hemsworth   v   Wheatley Hills
Ilkley   v   Bradford Salem

October 1 (Week 5)
Leodiensians   v   Yarnbury
Malton & Norton   v   Sheffield Oaks
Bradford Salem   v   Hemsworth
Wheatley Hills   v   Old Otliensians
Wath   v   castleford
Pocklington   v   Barnsley

October 15 (Week 7)
Sheffield Oaks   v   Leodiensians
Yarnbury   v   Pocklington
Barnsley   v   Wath
Castleford   v   Wheatley ills
Old Otliensians   v   Bradford Salem
Hemsowrth   v   Ilkley

October 22 (Week 8)
Wath   v   Yarnbury
Pocklington   v   Sheffield Oaks
Leodiensians   v   Malton & Norton
Ilkley   v   Old Otliensians
Bradford Salem   v   Castleford
Wheatley Hills   v   Barnsley

October 29 (Week X2)
Malton & Norton   v   Pocklington
Sheffield Oaks   v   Wath
Yarnbury   v   Wheatley Hills
Barnsley   v   Bradford Salem
Castleford   v   Ilkley
Old Otliensians   v   Hemsworth

January 7 (Week 17)
Bradford Salem   v   Yarnbury
Wheatley Hills   v   Sheffield Oaks
Wath   v   Malton & Norton
Pocklington   v   Leodiensians
Hemsworth   v   Castleford
Ilkley   v   Barnsley

January 14 (Week 18)
Leodiensians   v   Wath
Malton & Norton   v   Wheatley Hills
Sheffield Oaks   v   Bradford Salem
Yarnbury   v   Ilkley
Barnsley   v   Hemsworth
Castleford   v   Old Otliensians

February 11 (Week 22)
Hemsworth   v   Yarnbury
Ilkley   v   Sheffield Oaks
Bradford Salem   v   Malton & Norton
Wheatley Hills   v   Leodiensians
Wath   v   Pocklington
Old Otliensians   v   Barnsley

February 25 (Week 24)
Pocklington   v   Wheatley Hills
Leodiensians   v   Bradford Salem
Malton & Norton   v   Ilkley
Sheffield Oaks   v   Hemsworth
Yarnbury   v   Old Otliensians
Barnsley   v   Castleford

March 4 (Week 25)
Castleford   v   Yarnbury
Old Otliensians   v   Sheffield Oaks
Hemsworth   v   Malton & Norton
Ilkley   v   Leodiensians
Bradford Salem   v   Pocklington
Wheatley Hills   v   Wath

March 25 (Week 28)
Wath   v   Bradford Salem
Pocklington   v   Ilkley
Leodiensians   v   Hemsworth
Malton & Norton   v   Old Otliensians
Sheffield Oaks   v   Castleford
Yarnbury   v   Barnsley

April 8 (Week 30)
Barnsley   v   Sheffield Oaks
Castleford   v   Malton & Norton
Old Otliensians   v   Leodiensians
Hemsworth   v   Pocklington
Ilkley   v   Wath
Bradford Salem   v   Wheatley Hills

YORKSHIRE ONE

BARNSLEY RUFC
Ground Address: Wombwell Lane, Stairfoot, Barnsley, South Yorshire S70 3NS. Tel: 0226 284344
Club Secretary: M Marshall, 4 Westbourne Grove, Barnsley, South Yorkshire S75 1AE. Tel: (H) 0226 204614
Fixtures Secretary: S Roper, 20 Loxley Road, Burton Grange, Barnsley, South Yorkshire S71 5NR. Tel: (H) 0226 285687 Tel (W) 0484 429696 x273
Club Colours: Red, white, navy blue hoops.

BRADFORD SALEM RFC
Ground Address: Shay Lane, Heaton, Bradford BD9 6SL. Tel: 0274 496430
Club Secretary: Steve Dunn, 205 Highgate, Heaton, Bradford BD9 5PU. Tel: (H) 0274 826442 Tel: (W) 0937 844515
Fixtures Secretary: John Dobson, 2 Highfield Drive, Heaton, Bradford BD9 6MN. Tel: (H) 0274 487587 Tel (W) 0422 330022
Club Colours: Royal, gold, black hoops, black shorts, royal socks. Change: Green or red.

CASTLEFORD RUFC
Ground Address: Willow Bridge Lane, Whitwood, Castleford, West Yorkshire. Tel: 0977 554762
Club Secretary: Dale M Botham, 11 Poundfields Close, Kippax, Leeds LS25 7HN. Tel: (H) 0532 869591 Tel: (W) 0532 579001 x51
Fixtures Secretary: Mr G E Hills, 1a Pinfold Lane, Hethley, Leeds LS26 9AU. Tel: (H) 0977 515784 Tel (W) 0532 414056
Club Colours: Red, white & blue hoops.

HEMSWORTH RUFC
Ground Address: Moxon Fields, Lowfield Road, Hemsworth, Pontefract, West Yorkshire WF9 4JT. Tel: 0977 610078
Club Secretary: Mark Roberts. 'The Elms', Stockinggate/South Kirby/Pontefract WF9 3QX. Tel: (H) 0977 644379 Tel: (W) same
Club Colours: Navy blue shirts, shorts and socks.

ILKLEY RUFC
Ground Address: Stacks Field, Denton Road, Ilkley, West Yorkshire LS29 0BZ. Tel: 0943 607037
Club Secretary: Mr G Whiteley, Springs End House, 44 Springs Lane, Ilkley, West Yorkshire LS29 8TH. Tel: (H) 0943 609792 Tel: (W) 0532 343397
Fixtures Secretary: Mr K Bernard, 36 Dale View, Ilkley, West Yorkshire LS29 9BP. Tel: (H) 0943 602945 Tel (W) 0532 451000
Club Colours: Red, white & black.

LEODIENSIAN RUFC
Ground Address: Cragg Lane, Alwoodley, Leeds 17. Tel: 0532 673409
Club Secretary: Hugh Doring, 17 Newlaithes Gardens, Horsforth, Leeds, LS18 4JW. Tel: (H) 0532 590607 Tel: (W) 0532 444421
Club Colours: Navy blue and gold.

MALTON & NORTON RUFC
Ground Address: Pasture Lane, Peasey Hill, Malton, North Yorkshire. Tel: 0653 694657
Club Secretary: CO Wincup, Arboretum, Keld Head Hall, Middleton Road, Pickering, North Yorkshire YO18 8NR. Tel: (H) 0751 477170 Tel: (W) 0723 584141
Fixtures Secretary: Mr JQ Knock, 36 St Peter's Street, Norton, Malton. Tel: (H) 0653 696302 Tel (W) 0653 696302
Club Colours: Red, white & black hoops.

OLD OTLIENSIANS RUFC
Ground Address: Chaffers Field, Pool Road, Otley, West Yorkshire. Tel: 0943 461476
Club Secretary: D Taylor, 39 The Whartons, Otley, West Yorkshire. Tel: (H) 0943 850913 Tel: (W) 0274 733671 x270

FINAL TABLE

	P	W	D	L	F	A	PD	Pts
N Ribblesdale	12	10	0	2	221	114	107	20
Wheatley Hills	12	8	2	2	206	98	108	18
Bradford Salem	12	8	0	4	145	150	-5	16
Wath	12	7	1	4	192	143	49	15
Old Otliensians	12	7	1	4	172	126	46	15
Ilkley	12	7	0	5	237	82	155	14
Leodiensians	12	7	0	5	210	165	45	14
Sheffield Oaks	12	6	0	6	152	152	0	12
Hemsworth	12	6	0	6	137	185	-48	12
Malton & Norton	12	5	0	7	140	203	-63	10
Pocklington	12	4	0	8	130	225	-95	8
Yarnbury	12	1	0	11	94	197	-103	2
York RI	12	0	0	12	93	289	-196	0

Fixtures Secretary: AS Normanton, 26 Roseberry Crescent, Great Ayton, Middlesbrough, Cleveland. Tel: (H) 0642 723199 Tel (W) 0642 467144
Club Colours: Navy blue, royal blue & white.

POCKLINGTON RUFC
Ground Address: Percy Road, Pocklington, York. Tel: 0759 303358
Club Secretary: MB Herring, 34 Hill Rise Drive, Market Weighton, York YO4 3JZ. Tel: (H) 0430 872156 Tel: (W) 0482 666198
Fixtures Secretary: JB Rudsdale, 3 Beckside, Wilberfoss, York YO4 5NS. Tel: (H) 0759 380312
Club Colours: Navy & white hoops.

SHEFFIELD OAKS RUFC
Club Secretary: Mr KJW Mallinson, 8 Ashurst Drive, Stannington, Sheffield, South Yorkshire S6 5LL. Tel: (H) 0742 333078 Tel: (W) 0742 303937
Fixtures Secretary: Mr G Davies, Griffs Lodge, Stopes Road, Stannington, Sheffield S6 6BW. Tel: (H) 0742 335829 Tel (W) 0742 630222 x6386
Club Colours: Royal blue & gold hoops.

WATH RUFC
Ground Address: Moor Road, Wath Upon Deane, Rotherham, S Yorkshire. Tel: 0709 872399
Club Secretary: M Criddle, 45 Sandbeck Road, Bennethorpe, Doncaster, S Yorkshire. Tel: (H) 0302 368518 Tel: (W) 0302 320444
Club Colours: Blue with maroon gold bands.

WHEATLEY HILLS RUFC
Ground Address: Wheatley Hills Sports Ground, Brunel Road, York Road Industrial Estate, Doncaster, Yorkshire DN5 8PT. Tel: 0302 781472
Club Secretary: AR Dunkerley, 1 Mayfields, Scawthorne, Doncaster, Yorkshire DN5 7UA. Tel: (H) 0302 7822c14 Tel: (W) 0709 522292
Fixtures Secretary: I Blessed, 75 Chestnut Avenue, Wheatley, Doncaster DN2 5SR. Tel: (H) 0302 341614 Tel (W) 0302 341614
Club Colours: Maroon & gold quartered shirts, maroon shorts.

YARNBURY (HORSFORTH) RUFC
Ground Address: Brownberrie Lane, Horsforth, Leeds LS18 5HB. Tel: 0532 581346
Club Secretary: Paul Trigg, 16 Moorland Grove, Moortown, Leeds LS17 6HS. Tel: (H) 0532 664680
Fixtures Secretary: J Riley, 65 Broadgate Lane, Leeds 18. Tel: (H) 0532 589131 Tel (W) 0924 441818
Club Colours: Blue, black & white uneven hoops.

NORTHERN DIVISION

YORKSHIRE TWO
1994-95
FIXTURES

September 17 (Week 3)
Sheffield Tigers v Aireborough
West Leeds v Huddersfield YMCA
Halifax Vandals v Northallerton
Hessle v Scarborough
Old Modernians v York R.I.
Dinnington v Wibsey

September 24 (Week 4)
Aireborough v Dinnington
Wibsey v Old Modernians
York R.I. v Hessle
Scarborough v Halifax Vandals
Northallerton v West Leeds
Huddersfield YMCA v Moortown

October 1 (Week 5)
Old Modernians v Aireborough
Dinnington v Sheffield Tigers
Moortown v Northallerton
West Leeds v Scraborough
Halifax Vandals v York R.I.
Hessle v Wibsey

October 15 (Week 7)
Sheffield Tigers v Old Modernians
Aireborough v Hessle
Wibsey v Halifax Vandals
York R.I. v West Leeds
Scarborough v Moortown
Northallerton v Huddersfield YMCA

October 22 (Week 8)
Halifax Vandals v Aireborough
Hessle v Sheffield Tigers
Old Modernians v Dinnington
Huddersfield YMCA v Scarborough
Moortown v York R.I.
West Leeds v Wibsey

October 29 (Week X2)
Dinnington v Hessle
Seffield Tigers v Halifax Vandals
Aireborough v West Leeds
Wibsey v Moortown
York R.I. v Huddersfield YMCA
Scarborough v Northallerton

January 7 (Week 17)
Moortown v Aireborough
West Leeds v Sheffield Tigers
Halifax Vandals v Dinnington
Hessle v Old Modernians
Northallerton v York R.I.
Huddersfield YMCA v Wibsey

January 14 (Week 18)
Old Modernians v Halifax Vandals
Dinnington v West Leeds
Sheffield Tigers v Moortown
Aireborough v Huddersfield YMCA
Wibsey v Northallerton
York R.I. v Scarborough

February 11 (Week 22)
Northallerton v Aireborough
Huddersfield YMCA v Sheffield Tigers
Moortown v Dinnington
West Leeds v Old Modernians
Halifax Vandals v Hessle
Scarborough v Wibsey

February 25 (Week 24)
Hessle v West Leeds
Old Modernians v Moortown
Dinnington v Huddersfield YMCA
Sheffield Tigers v Northallerton
Aireborough v Scarborough
Wibsey v York R.I.

March 4 (Week 25)
York R.I. v Aireborough
Scarborough v Sheffield Tigers
Northallerton v Dinnington
Huddersfield YMCA v Old Modernians
Moortown v Hessle
West Leeds v Halifax Vandals

March 25 (Week 28)
Halifax Vandals v Moortown
Hessle v Huddersfield
Old Modernians v Northallerton
Dinnington v Scarborough
Sheffield Tigers v York R.I.
Aireborough v Wibsey

April 8 (Week 30)
Wibsey v Sheffield Tigers
York R.I. v Dinnington
Scarborough v Old Modernians
Northallerton v Hessle
Huddersfield YMCA v Halifax Vandals
Moortown v West Leeds

YORKSHIRE TWO

AIREBOROUGH RUFC
Ground Address:Green Lane Cricket Club, Nunroyd Park,
Yeadon, Nr Leeds, West Yorkshire L19. Tel: 0943 878299
Club Secretary: AM Tullie, 55 Warren Lane, Eldwick,
Bingley, West Yorkshire BD16 3BS. Tel: (H) 0274 569631
Tel: (W) 0532 436671
Fixtures Secretary: C Clarke, 55 Coppice View, Idle, Nr
Bradford, West Yorkshire BD10 8UF. Tel: (H) 0274
610896 Tel (W) 0274 544466
Club Colours: Maroon & white.
DINNINGTON RUFC
Ground Address:Lodge Lane, Dinnington, Sheffield,
South Yorkshire, S31 7PB. Tel: 0909 562044
Club Secretary: M Burke, 5 Room Walk, Dinnington,
Sheffield, South Yorkshire S31 7AQ. Tel: (H) 0909 564712
Club Colours: Blue, white & gold hoops.
HALIFAX VANDALS RUFC
Tel: 0422 831703
Club Secretary: A Ward, 124 Ravenstone Drive, Greetland,
Halifax. Tel: (H) 0422 371999 Tel: (W) 0422 824186
Fixtures Secretary: C Clegg, 28 Vicar Park Drive, Norton
Tower, Halifax. Tel: (H) 0422 359813
Club Colours: Royal blue & white narrow stripes, blue shorts.
HESSLE RUFC
Ground Address:Livingstone Road, Hessle, North
Humberside HU13 0ES. Tel: 0482 643430
Club Secretary: DP Sewell, 67 Barrow Lane, Hessle,
North Humberside HU13 0QB. Tel: (H) 0482 645191 Tel:
(W) 0482 869286
Fixtures Secretary: P Denton, 7 Maplewood Avenue, Hull
HU5 5YE. Tel: (H) 0482 561338
Club Colours: Green, black & white irregular hoops, white
shorts, black socks.
HUDDERSFIELD YMCA RFC
Ground Address:Laund Hill Sports Ground, Salendine
Nook, Huddersfield, West Yorkshire. Tel: 0484 654052
Club Secretary: Ian Leask, 3 Cheviot Way, Mirfield, West
Yorkshire WF14 8HW. Tel: (H) 0924 496448 Tel: (W)
0706 32512
Fixtures Secretary: Gary Schofield, 7 Stonefield Avenue,
Crosland Moor, Huddersfield HD4 5QF. Tel: (H) 0484 651738
Club Colours: Black & red hoops, black shorts.
MOORTOWN RUFC
Ground Address:Moss Valley, (off The Avenue),
Alwoodley Park, Leeds, West Yorkshire. Tel: 0532 678243
Club Secretary: Mr GP Spark, 7 Hall Cliffe Grove,
Horbury, Wakefield, West Yorkshire WF4 6DE. Tel: (H)
0924 271808 Tel: (W) 0924 273442
Fixtures Secretary: Mr C Forbes, 19 The Mount, Alwoodley,
Leeds, West Yorkshire LS17 7RH. Tel: (H) 0532 675974
Club Colours: Maroon, white & green hoops.
NORTHALLERTON RUFC
Ground Address:Brompton Lodge, Northallerton Road,
Brompton, Northallerton, North Yorkshire DL6 2PZ. Tel:
0609 773496
Club Secretary: Mr NH Kendrew, 18 Brompton Road,
Northallerton, North Yorkshire DL6 1EA. Tel: (H) 0609
774007 Tel: (W) 0677 422661 x274
Fixtures Secretary: Mr NH Kendrew, 18 Brompton Road,
Northallerton, North Yorkshire DL6 1EA. Tel: (H) 0609
774007 Tel (W) 0677 422661 x274
Club Colours: Green, yellow & amber.
OLD MODERNIANS RUFC
Ground Address:Cookridge Lane, Cookridge, Leeds,
West Yorkshire LS16 7ND. Tel: 0532 671075
Club Secretary: Kevin R Shotton, 11 Adwalton Close,
Drighlinton, Bradford, West Yorkshire BD11 1DG. Tel:
(H) 0532 854896 Tel: (W) 0422 343111
Fixtures Secretary: David Carter, 81 Green Lane,
Cookridge, Leeds, West Yorkshire. Tel: (H) 0532 674718
Tel (W) 0532 432519

FINAL TABLE

	P	W	D	L	F	A	PD	Pts
Barnsley	12	11	0	1	245	91	154	22
Castleford	12	10	0	2	270	73	197	20
Old Modernians	12	10	0	2	221	78	143	20
Northallerton	12	8	0	4	211	110	101	16
Halifax Vandals	12	7	0	5	157	128	29	14
Sheffield Tigers	12	6	0	6	167	169	-2	12
West Leeds	12	5	0	7	225	221	4	10
Scarborough	12	5	0	7	126	183	-57	10
Hessle	12	4	0	8	117	141	-24	8
Dinnington	12	4	0	8	165	220	-55	8
Huddersfield YMCA	12	3	0	9	106	175	-69	6
Moortown	12	4	0	8	97	183	-86	4
Leeds CSSA	12	1	0	11	79	414	-335	2

Club Colours: Red & black hooped shirts, black shorts,
red & black socks.
SCARBOROUGH RUFC
Ground Address:The Club House, Scalby Road,
Scarborough, North Yorkshire YO12 6EE. Tel: 0723
363039
Club Secretary: Mrs S E Hanson, c/o Scarborough RUFC,
The Club House, Scalby Road, Scarborugh, North
Yorkshire YO12 6EE. Tel: (W) 0723 363039
Fixtures Secretary: Mr D Prince, 15 Newlands Park
Drive, Scarborough YO12 6DW. Tel: (H) 0723 377419
Club Colours: Navy, maroon & white.
SHEFFIELD TIGERS RUFC
Ground Address:Hathersage Road, Dore Moor, Sheffield
S17 3AB. Tel: 0742 360075
Club Secretary: Martin Caine, 20 Sandy Acres Drive,
Waterthorpe, Sheffield S19 6LS. Tel: (H) 0742 489052 Tel:
(W) 0602 620532
Fixtures Secretary: Ron Lewis, 33 Swift Way, Sandal,
Wakefield WF2 6SQ. Tel: (H) 0924 253049 Tel (W) 0532
435301
Club Colours: Maroon & white hoops, black shorts.
WEST LEEDS RUFC
Ground Address:Blue Hill Lane, Wortley, Leeds LS12
4NZ. Tel: 0532 639869
Club Secretary: Gordon W Falding, 20 Walkers Lane,
Wortley, Leeds LS12 4AP. Tel: (H) 0532 639989
Fixtures Secretary: John MacAndrew, 27 Rooms Fold,
Morley, Leeds LS27 9PS. Tel: (H) 0532 520369
Club Colours: Navy, old gold & white.
WIBSEY RUFC
Ground Address:Northfield Road, Wibsey, Bradford,
West Yorkshire BD6. Tel: 0274 671643
Club Secretary: Martin Spencer, 188 St Enoch's Road,
Wibsey, Bradford, West Yorkshire. Tel: (H) 0274 605566
Tel: (W) 0274 390400
Fixtures Secretary: 18 Overton Drive, Horton Bank Top,
Bradford. Tel: (H) 0274 574905
Club Colours: Red & green hoops.
YORK RI RUFC
Ground Address:Railway Institute Sports Ground, New
Lane, Acomb, York YO2 4NU. Tel: 0904 798930
Club Secretary: J Cooper, 8 Otterwood Bank, Foxwood
Hill, Acomb, York YO2 3JS. Tel: (H) 0904 797858 Tel:
(W) 0904 628982 x2773
Fixtures Secretary: WF Cooper, Moorcrodt, Lucy Hall
Drive, Baildon, Shipley, West Yorkshire BD17 5BG. Tel:
(H) 0274 584355
Club Colours: Royal blue & white hooped shirts, black
shorts, royal blue socks. Change: red shirts.

NORTHERN DIVISION

YORKSHIRE THREE
1994-95
FIXTURES

January 7 (Week 17)
Lawnswood v Burley
Knottingley v Heath
Leeds Corinthians v Wetherby
Phoenix Park v Hullensians
Marist v Rodillians
Old Rishworthians v Ossett

September 17 (Week 3)
Heath v Burley
Knottingley v Old Rishworthians
Leeds Corinthians v Marist
Phoenix Park v Skipton
Hullensians v Rodillians
Wetherby v Ossett

January 14 (Week 18)
Hullensians v Leeds Corinthians
Wetherby v Knottingley
Heath v Lawnswood
Burley v Old Rishworthians
Ossett v Marist
Rodillians v Skipton

September 24 (Week 4)
Burley v Wetherby
Ossett v Hullensians
Rodillians v Phoenix Park
Skipton v Leeds Corinthians
Marist v Knottingley
Old Rishworthians v Lawnswood

February 11 (Week 22)
Marist v Burley
Old Rishworthians v Heath
Lawnswood v Wetherby
Knottingley v Hullensians
Leeds Corinthians v Phoenix Park
Skipton Park v Ossett

October 1 (Week 5)
Hullensians v Burley
Wetherby v Heath
Lawnswood v Marist
Knottingley v Skipton
Leeds Corinthians v Rodillians
Phoenix Park v Ossett

February 25 (Week 24)
Phoenix Park v Knottingley
Hullensians v Lawnswood
Wetherby v Old Rishworthians
Heath v Marist
Burley v Skipton
Ossett v Rodillians

October 15 (Week 7)
Heath v Hullensians
Burley v Phoenix Park
Ossett v Leeds Corinthians
Rodillians v Knottingley
Skipton v Lawnswood
Marist v Old Rishworthians

March 4 (Week 25)
Rodillians v Burley
Skipton v Heath
Marist v Wetherby
Old Rishworthians v Hullensians
Lawnswood v Phoenix Park
Knottingley v Leeds Corinthians

October 22 (Week 8)
Leeds Corinthians v Burley
Phoenix Park v Heath
Hullensians v Wetherby
Old Rishworhtians v Skipton
Lawnswood v Rodillians
Knottingley v Ossett

March 25 (Week 28)
Leeds Corinthians v Lawnswood
Phoenix Park v Old Rishworthians
Hullensians v Marist
Wetherby v Skipton
Heath v Rodillians
Burley v Ossett

October 29 (Week X2)
Wetherby v Phoenix Park
Heath v Leeds Corinthians
Burley v Knottingley
Ossett v Lawnswood
Rodillians v Old Rishworthians
Skipton v Marist

April 8 (Week 30)
Osett v Heath
Rodillians v Wetherby
Skipton v Hullensians
Marist v Phoenix Park
Old Rishworthians v Leeds Corinthians
Lawnswood v Knottingley

YORKSHIRE THREE

BURLEY RUFC
Ground Address:Clubhouse, Abbey Road, Leeds LS5 3NG. Tel: 0532 757400
Club Secretary: Terry McCreedy, 42 Fearnville Place, Leeds LS8 3DY. Tel: (H) 0532 655065 Tel: (W) 0274 727524
Fixtures Secretary: John Sanderson, 5 Southolme Close, Leeds LS5 3LP. Tel: (H) 0532 787772
Club Colours: Maroon & white.

HEATH RUFC
Ground Address:North Dean, Stainland Road, Greetland, Nr Halifax, West Yorkshire HX4 8LS. Tel: 0422 372920
Club Secretary: Craig Bedford, 58 Hollins Lane, Sowerby Bridge, Halifax HX6 2RP. Tel: (H) 0422 834473 Tel: (W) 0422 373462
Fixtures Secretary: Gary Mason, 16 Scar Bottom Road, Halifax, West Yorkshire. Tel: (H) 0422 349271 Tel (W) 0422 371909
Club Colours: Claret, gold, emerald.

HULLENSIANS RUFC
Ground Address:Springhead Lane, Anlaby, Hull. Tel: 0482 505656
Club Secretary: Mark Bayston, 4 Park Lane West, Anlaby Park, Hull HU4 6TU. Tel: (H) 0482 54222 Tel: (W) 0482 830367 Fax: 0482 830369
Fixtures Secretary: Tim Robinson, 79 Huntley Drive, Chanterlands Avenue, Hull HU5 4DP. Tel: (H) 0482 48181 Tel (W) 0482 23631
Club Colours: Red & black.

KNOTTINGLEY RUFC
Ground Address:Howards Field, Marsh Lane, Knottingley, West Yorkshire. Tel: 0977 672438
Club Secretary: Glen McCusker LL.B, ACI Arb, 9A Manor Garth, Riccall, York YO4 6QZ. Tel: (H) 0757 248548
Fixtures Secretary: Mick Leach, 73 The Poplars, Knottingley, West Yorkshire. Tel: (H) 0977 676701
Club Colours: Blue & white regular hoops, navy shorts.

LAWNSWOOD RUFC
Ground Address:Lawnswood Sports Ground, Otley Road, Leeds LS16 6HQ. Tel: 0532 678168
Club Secretary: David G Smith, 46 Highfield Avenue, Wortley, Leeds LS12 4BY. Tel: (H) 0532 790365 Tel: (W) 0532 380002
Fixtures Secretary: Dr RW Marshall, 38 Barthorpe Crescent, Leeds LS17 5PE. Tel: (H) 0532 685755 Tel (W) 0532 332599
Club Colours: Green & black wide hoops.

LEEDS CORINTHIANS RFC
Ground Address:Middleton District Centre, Leeds 10. Tel: 0532 711574
Club Secretary: Mr Malcolm Naylor, 9 Staithe Gardens, Leeds LS10 3NA. Tel: (H) 0532 705919
Fixtures Secretary: Mr Graham Mapplebeck, 33 Oakley Street, Thorpe, Wakefield WF3 3DX. Tel: (H) 0924 828809 Tel (W) 0532 457205
Club Colours: Black with gold trim. Change: Red.

MARIST RUFC
Ground Address:Cranbrook Avenue, Hull. Tel: 0482 859216
Club Secretary: Kevin Johnson, 11 Roborough Close, Hull HU7 4RN. Tel: (H) 0482 828973 Tel: (W) 0482 781202
Fixtures Secretary: Ralph Ayre, 92 Auckland Avenue, Cottingham Road, Hull. Tel: (H) 0482 804166
Club Colours: Royal blue & white.

OLD RISHWORTHIAN RUFC
Ground Address:The Clubhouse, Copley, Halifax, West Yorkshire. Tel: 0422 353919
Club Secretary: Dave Butler, Keepers, Shaw Lane, Holywell Green, Halifax, West Yorkshire HX4 9DW. Tel: (H) 0422 371672 Tel: (W) 0484 721223
Fixtures Secretary: Ray Wadsworth, 7 Newstead Terrace, Newstead, Halifax, West Yorkshire HX1 4TA. Tel: (H) 0422 323172 Tel (W) 0482 845740

FINAL TABLE

	P	W	D	L	F	A	PD	Pts
Aireborough	12	12	0	0	291	54	237	24
Wibsey	12	10	1	1	362	124	238	21
Hullensians	12	9	0	3	189	106	83	18
Wetherby	12	8	1	3	184	130	54	17
Heath	12	7	1	4	136	134	2	15
Knottingley	12	7	0	5	152	107	45	14
O Rishworthians	12	5	1	6	175	126	49	11
Marist	12	4	1	7	140	179	-39	9
Burley	12	3	1	8	114	213	-99	7
Ossett	12	3	0	9	126	189	-63	6
Leeds Corinthians	12	4	0	8	86	177	-91	6
Stanley Rodillians	12	3	0	9	117	228	-111	6
Leeds YMCA	12	0	0	12	56	361	-305	0

Club Colours: Maroon, white & black hoops.

OSSETT RUFC
Ground Address:Spring Mill, off Queens Drive, Ossett, West Yorkshire. Tel: 0924 273618
Club Secretary: Jeremy A Slack, 1 Spa Croft Road, Ossett, West Yorkshire WF5 0EU. Tel: (H) 0924 273952 Tel: (W) 0924 273952
Fixtures Secretary: David Dearnley, 4 Crown Point Close, Kingsway, Ossett WF5 8RH. Tel: (H) 0924 278991 Tel (W) 0274 671267 x8358
Club Colours: Black & red quarters, black shorts. Change: Black & white quarters, black shorts.

PHOENIX PARK RUFC
Ground Address:Oval Ball, Stont Royd, Farsley, Leeds. Tel: 0532 553439
Club Secretary: Michael Ryan, 280 Whitehall Road, Wyke, Bradford BD12 9DX. Tel: (W) 0274 727886
Fixtures Secretary: John Duckworth, 29 Peterborough Terrace, Bradford. Tel: (H) 0274 640154
Club Colours: Royal blue & gold.

SKIPTON RUFC
Ground Address:Cowthorpe Memorial Grounds, Sandylands, Carleton New Road, Skipton, Yorkshire. Tel: 0756 793148
Club Secretary: Andrew Clark, 200 Moorview Way, Skipton, North Yorkshire BD23 2TN. Tel: (H) 0756 798137 Tel: (W) 0836 560140
Fixtures Secretary: Peter Shearer, 128 Moorview Way, Skipton, North Yorkshire. Tel: (H) 0756 799364 Tel (W) 0535 636116
Club Colours: Cardinal red shirts, white shorts, red socks.

STANLEY RODILLIANS RUFC
Ground Address:Manley Park, Lee Moor Road, Stanley, Wakefield, West Yorkshire. Tel: 0924 823619
Club Secretary: RJ Matthews, 27 Newlands Walk, Stanley, Wakefield, West Yorkshire WF3 4DT. Tel: (H) 0924 828727 Tel: (W) 0924 823135
Fixtures Secretary: IR Young, 21 Eastfield Drive, Woodlesford, Leeds LS26 8SO. Tel: (H) 0532 826743 Tel (W) 0742 671131
Club Colours: Green, black & white hoops, black shorts.

WETHERBY RUFC
Ground Address:Grange Park, Wetherby, West Yorkshire. Tel: 0937 582461
Club Secretary: Mr Chris Nussey, 62 Wighill Lane, Tadcaster, North Yorkshire LS24 8EX. Tel: (H) 0937 833494 Tel: (W) 0532 760730
Fixtures Secretary: K Astbury, 2 Fir Tree Avenue, Garforth, Leeds LS25 2JN. Tel: (H) 0532 862347
Club Colours: Red & white hooped jerseys, white shorts, red socks.

NORTHERN DIVISION

YORKSHIRE FOUR
1994-95
FIXTURES

January 7 (Week 17)
Adwick le Street v Knaresborough
Yorkshire Main v Garforth
Stocksbridge v B.P. Chemicals
Withersea v Danum Phoenix
Mosborough v Baildon
Rowntrees v Hornsea

September 17 (Week 3)
Garforth v Knarsborough
Yorkshire Main v Rowntrees
Stocksbridge v Mosborough
Withersea v De la Salle (Sheffield)
Danum Phoenix v Baildon
B.P. Chemicals v Hornsea

Janaury 14 (Week 18)
Danum Phoenix v Stocksbridge
B.P. Chemicals v Yorkshire Main
Garforth v Adwick le Street
Knaresborough v Rowntrees
Hornsea v Mosborough
Baildon v De la Salle (Sheffield)

September 24 (Week 4)
Knaresborough v B.P. Chemicals
Hornsea v Danum Phoenix
Baildon v Withersea
De la Salle (Sheffield) v Stocksbridge
Mosborough v Yorksire Main
Rowntrees v Adwick le Street

February 11 (Week 22)
Mosborough v Knaresborough
Rowntrees v Garforth
Adwick le Street v B.P. Chemicals
Yorkshire Main v Danum Phoenix
Stocksbridge v Withersea
De la Salle (Sheffield) v Hornsea

October 1 (Week 5)
Danum Phoenix v Knaresborough
B.P. Chemicals v Garforth
Adwick le Street v Mosborough
Yorkshire Main v De la Salle (Sheffield)
Stocksbridge v Baildon
Withersea v Hornsea

February 25 (Week 24)
Withersea v Yorkshire Main
Danum Phoenix v Adwick le Street
B.P. Chemicals v Rowntrees
Garforth v Mosborough
Knaresborough v De la Salle (Sheffield)
Hornsea v Baildon

October 15 (Week 7)
Garforth v Danum Phoenix
Knaresborough v Withersea
Hornsea v Stocksbridge
Baildon v Yorkshire Main
De la Salle (Sheffield) v Adwick le Street
Mosborough v Rowntrees

March 4 (Week 25)
Baildon v Knaresborough
De la Salle (Sheffield) v Garforth
Mosborough v B.P. Chemicals
Rowntrees v Danum Phoenix
Adwick le Street v Withersea
Yorkshire Main v Stocksbridge

October 22 (Week 8)
Stocksbridge v Knaresborough
Withersea v Garforth
Danum Phoenix v B.P. Chemicals
Rowntrees v De la Salle (Sheffield)
Adwick le Street v Baildon
Yorkshire Main v Hornsea

March 25 (Week 28)
Stocksbridge v Adwick le Street
Withersea v Rowntrees
Danum Phoenix v Mosborough
B.P. Chemcials v De la Salle (Sheffield)
Garforth v Baildon
Knaresborough v Hornsea

October 29 (Week X2)
B.P. Chemicals v Withersea
Garforth v Stocksbridge
Knaresborough v Yorkshire Main
Hornsea v Adwick le Street
Baildon v Rowntrees
De la Salle (Sheffield) v Mosborough

April 8 (Week 29)
Hornsea v Garforth
Baildon v B.P. Chemicals
De la Salle (Sheffield) v Danum Phoenix
Mosborough v Withersea
Rowntrees v Stocksbridge
Adwick le Street v Yorkshire Main

YORKSHIRE FOUR

ADWICK-LE-STREET RUFC
Ground Address: Church Lane Playing Fields, Adwick-le-Street, Doncaster, South Yorkshire. Tel: c/o Tally Ho! 0302 722372
Club Secretary: Robert Terry, 7 Cranfield Drive, Skellow, Doncaster, South Yorkshire DN6 8RS. Tel: (H) 0302 727580 Tel: (W) 0977 517517
Fixtures Secretary: Michael Flanagan, 31 Alexandra Road, Bentley, Doncaster, South Yorkshire. Tel: (H) 0302 872429
Club Colours: Light blue & dark blue hoops, black shorts, red hose.

B P CHEMICALS RUFC
Ground Address:B P Sports & Social Club, Salt End, Hedon Road, Hull HU12 8DS. Tel: 0482 896251
Club Secretary: Ian Batty, 349 Ings Road, Sutton-on-Hull, Hull HU7 4UY. Tel: (H) 0482 77574 Tel: (W) 0482 853235
Fixtures Secretary: Steve West, 2 Manor Road, Preston, Nr Hull HU12 8SQ. Tel: (H) 0482 891371 Tel (W) 0482 896251 x2844
Club Colours: Maroon & gold.

BAILDON RUFC
Ground Address: Jenny Lane, Baildon, Shipley, West Yorkshire BD17 6RS. Tel: 0274 582644
Club Secretary: RB Hawkins, 30 Moorfield Drive, Baildon, Shipley, West Yorkshire BD17 6LQ. Tel: (H) 0274 580292
Fixtures Secretary: Mr R Jennings, 15 Moorfield Drive, Baildon, Shipley, West Yorkshire BD17 6LQ. Tel: (H) 0274 593632 Tel (W) 0943 608765
Club Colours: Red, black & white hooped jerseys.

DANUM PHOENIX RUFC
Ground Address: Du Pont Sports & Social Club, Wheatley Hall Road, Doncaster. Tel: 0302 364307
Club Secretary: Mohan O'Hara, The Townhouse, 27 Bennetthorpe, Donaster DN2 6AA. Tel: (H) 0302 349753
Fixtures Secretary: Michael Tollerfield, 75 Appleton Way, Scawthorpe, Doncaster DN5 9NE. Tel: (H) 0302 875700
Club Colours: All black with red & yellow band on shirts.

DE LA SALLE (SHEFFIELD) RUFC
Ground Address: De La Salle Association Club, behind Beauchief Hall, off Abbey Lane, Sheffield. Tel: 0742 367756
Club Secretary: Maureen Buckley, 93 Ingram Road, Sheffield S2 2SB. Tel: (H) 0742 720246
Fixtures Secretary: Tony Buckley, 93 Ingram Road, Sheffield S2 2SB. Tel: (H) 0742 720246
Club Colours: Green & gold hoops.

GARFORTH RUFC
Ground Address: Garforth Community College, Lidgett Lane, Garforth LS25 1LJ.
Club Secretary: Richard Severn, 10 East View, Kippax, Leeds LS25 7HB. Tel: (H) 0532 872075
Fixtures Secretary: Peter Hazledine, 90 Fairburn Drive, Garforth, Leeds LS25 2JD. Tel: (H) 0532 866035 Tel (W) 0532 869091
Club Colours: Royal blue, gold & black bands, scarlet collar & cuffs.

HORNSEA RUFC
Ground Address: Hollis Recreational Ground, Atwick Road, Hornsea HU18 1ET. Tel: 0964 534181
Club Secretary: Dr Ian Sibley-Calder, Westfield, Westwood Avenue, Hornsea, North Humberside HU18 1ET. Tel: (H) 0964 534925 Tel: (W) 0964 532212
Fixtures Secretary: Mrs Lesley Wood, 15 Cheyne Garth, Hornsea HU18 1BF. Tel: (H) 0964 534050
Club Colours: Black with green & white hoops across chest.

KNARESBOROUGH RUFC
Ground Address: Hay 'A' Park, Knaresborough, North

FINAL TABLE

	P	W	D	L	F	A	PD	Pts
Phoenix Park	12	11	1	0	258	69	189	23
Skipton	12	11	1	0	150	63	87	23
Mosborough	12	8	0	4	227	102	125	16
Baildon	12	8	0	4	146	84	62	16
Hornsea	12	7	0	5	153	121	32	14
De La Salle Sheffld	12	7	1	4	145	117	28	13
Withernsea	12	4	0	8	92	213	-121	8
Knaresborough	12	4	1	7	121	136	-15	7
Castle Coll	12	3	3	8	77	141	-64	7
Yorks Main	12	4	0	8	105	169	-64	6
Danum Phoenix	12	3	0	9	99	184	-85	6
Rowntrees	12	3	0	9	91	195	-104	6
BP Chemicals	12	2	1	9	67	137	-70	5

No relegation as Castle College withdrawn from League

Yorkshire. Tel: 0423 868976/866868
Club Secretary: R C Stevenson, 48 Halfpenny Lane, Knaresborough, North Yorks HG5 0NS. Tel: (H) 0423 868976 Tel: (W) 0423 866868
Fixtures Secretary: A Buens, 4 Park Road, Knaresborough, North Yorks. Tel: (H) 866703
Club Colours: Navy blue and gold.

MOSBOROUGH RUFC
Ground Address: Mosborough Miners Sport Club, Station Road, Mosborough, Sheffield. Tel: 0724 485546
Club Secretary: Lawrence S Hannon, 12 Stonegravels Croft, Halfway, Sheffield S19 5HP. Tel: (H) 0742 488425 Tel: (W) 0246 854650 Fax: 0246 950096
Fixtures Secretary: Peter J Bishop, 18 Shaldon Grove, Aston, Sheffield S31 0DH. Tel: (H) 0742 876257 Tel (W) 0909 550520
Club Colours: Black & white hoops. Change: Red.

ROWNTREE RUFC
Ground Address: Nestlé UK, Mille Crux Playing Fields, Haxby Road, York YO1 1XY. Tel: 0904 623933
Club Secretary: AM Walters, 32 Chelker Way, Clifton, York YO3 6ZH. Tel: (H) 0904 690066 Tel: (W) 0904 603325
Fixtures Secretary: I Jackson, 65 Melton Avenue, York YO3 6PT. Tel: (H) 0904 638884
Club Colours: Red, black & white hoops.

STOCKSBRIDGE RUFC
Ground Address: Stone Moor Road, Bolstone, Sheffield.
Club Secretary: Julian McGowan, 12 Weats Grove, Penistone, Sheffield S30 6GU. Tel: 0226 765814 Tel: (W) 0532 380093
Fixtures Secretary: Chris Lambert, 616 Manchester Road, Stocksbridge, Sheffield S30 5DY. Tel: (H) 0742 885223 Tel (W) 0831 141432
Club Colours: Royal blue & white hoops, blue shorts.

WITHERNSEA RUFC
Ground Address: Plough Inn, Holymn, North Humberside HU19 2DL. Tel: 0964 612049
Club Secretary: Mr AC Ellis, 11-17 Seaside Road, Withernsea HU19 2DL. Tel: (H) 0964 613278 Tel: (W) 0964 613278
Fixtures Secretary: Mr P Vickerman, 216 Queen Street, Withernsea. Tel: (H) 0964 614654
Club Colours: White & blue hoops.

YORKSHIRE MAIN RUFC
Ground Address: Miners Welfare, Edlington Lane, Edlington, Doncaster. Tel: 0709 864075
Club Secretary: Stuart Kalne, 73 Fernleigh Court, Wakefield, W. Yorkshire. Tel: (H) 0924 384561
Club Colours: Green, black, red & white hoops.

NORTHERN DIVISION

YORKSHIRE FIVE
1994-95
FIXTURES

September 17 (Week 3)
St James v Menwith Hill

September 24 (Week 4)
New Earswick v St James
Menwith Hill v Rawmarsh

October 1 (Week 5)
Rawmarsh v New Earswick
St James v Yorkshire C.W.

October 15 (Week 7)
Armthorpe Markham v St James
Yorkshire C.W. v Rawmarsh
New Earswick v Menwith Hill

October 22 (Week 8)
Menwith Hill v Yorkshire C.W.
Rawmarsh v Armthorpe Markham
St James v Harlow Nomads

October 29 (Week X2)
Harlow Nomads v Rawmarsh
Armthorpe Markham v Menwith Hill
Yorkshire C.W. v New Earswick

January 7 (Week 17)
New Earswick v Armthorpe Markham
Menwith Hill v Harlow Nomads

January 14 (Week 18)
Harlow Nomads v New Earswick
Armthorpe Markham v Yorkshire C.W.

February 11 (Week 22)
Yorkshire C.W. v Harlow Nomads

February 25 (Week 24)
Harlow Nomads v Armthorpe Markham

April 8 (Week 30)
Rawmarsh v St James

YORKSHIRE FIVE

ARMTHORPE MARKHAM RUFC
Ground Address:Church Street, Cricket Ground,
Armthorpe, Doncaster.
Club Secretary: Barry Jones, 98 Laburnum Drive,
Armthorpe, Doncaster, DN3 3HL. Tel: (H) 0302 832804
Fixtures Secretary: Tony & Kathleen McNally, 28 Cherry
Tree Rd, Armthorpe, Doncaster, DN3 2HP. Tel: (H) 0302
834252 Tel (W) 0585 262961
Club Colours: Red, black, white, blue quarters, black
shorts, red socks.

HARLOW NOMADS RUFC
Ground Address:Harrogate Grammar School, Arthurs
Avenue, Harrogate, North Yorkshire HG2 0DZ.
Club Secretary: Mel Hill, Flat 1, 13 Dragon Avenue,
Harrogate, North Yorkshire HG1 5DS. Tel: (H) 0423
508041 Tel: (W) 0532 464681
Fixtures Secretary: Tony Rogerson, 13 Grosvenor Road,
Harrogate, North Yorkshire HG1 4EG. Tel: (H) 0423
564481 Tel (W) 0532 447623
Club Colours: Royal blue & yellow hoops.

MENWITH HILL RUFC
Ground Address:Menwith Hill Station, Harrogate, North
Yorkshire HG3 2RF. Tel: 0423 777781
Club Secretary: Athletic staff: R Bent, M Kirkbride, J
Swenson. Tel: (W) 0423 777731
Club Colours: Green with amber collar.

NEW EARSWICK RFC
Ground Address:White Rose Avenue, New Earswick,
York. Tel: 0904 750103
Club Secretary: Howard Elders, 26 Priory Wood Way,
Huntington, York YO3 9JG. Tel: (H) 0904 652471
Fixtures Secretary: David Harrap, 3 Aberford House,
Lowther Street, York. Tel: (H) 0904 637149 Tel (W) 0904
670222
Club Colours: Black & white hoops.

RAWMARSH RUFC
Ground Address:Rawmarsh Leisure Centre, Barbers
Avenue, Rawmarsh, Rotherham. Tel: c/o Earl Grey 0709
522191
Club Secretary: Alan Parker, 3 McManus Avenue,
Rawmarsh, Rotherham, S Yorkshire, S62 7RD. Tel: (H)
0709 522795
Fixtures Secretary: Eric Perkins, 21 Harding Avenue,
Rawmarsh, Rotherham, S Yorkshire, S62 7ED. Tel: (H)
0709 526786
Club Colours: Black & amber trim. Change Maroon,
yellow, Black hoops.

ST JAMES'S UNIVERSITY HOSPITAL RUFC
Ground Address:Soldiers Field, Roundhay Park,
Roundhay, Leeds, LS8. Tel: 0532 493650
Club Secretary: Peter A Billsberry, 74 Compton Crescent,
Leeds, LS9 6DQ. Tel: (H) 0532 493650 Tel: (W) 0860
492562
Fixtures Secretary: Alistair Morris, 7 North Grove Close,
Oakwood, Leeds, LS8 2NH. Tel: (H) 0532 738878
Club Colours: Dark blue shirts, black shorts, dark blue
socks.

YORKSHIRE COPPERWORKS RUFC
Ground Address:Haigh Park Road, Stourton, Leeds LS19.
Tel: 0532 701715
Club Secretary: K Bedford, PO Box 166, Leeds LS1 1RD.
Fixtures Secretary: Richard Garnham, PO Box 166, Leeds
LS1 1RD. Tel: (H) 0532 823774 Tel (W) 0532 701107
Club Colours: Blue & gold. Change: Dark green.

FINAL TABLE

	P	W	D	L	F	A	PD	Pts
Garforth	9	7	1	1	228	57	171	15
Stocksbridge	9	8	0	1	159	41	118	14
Andwick-Le-Str	9	7	0	2	178	82	96	14
Rawmarsh	9	6	1	2	163	78	85	11
New Earswick	9	4	0	5	143	112	31	8
Menwith Hill Quakrs	9	3,0		6	98	169	-71	6
Harlow Nomads	9	4	0	5	82	141	-59	4
Armthorpe Markhm	9	3	0	6	66	170	-104	4
St James	9	2	0	7	47	122	-75	2
Yorks CW	9	0	0	9	40	232	-192	0

MIDLAND DIVISION

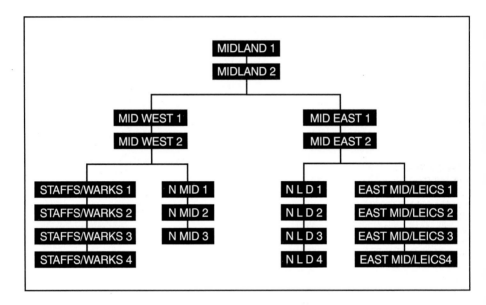

ADMINISTRATIVE RULES

NOTIFICATION OF RESULTS

Club Secretaries are responsible for their club's compliance with the rules of notification of results.

The home club shall notify the appropriate party the result of a league match by telephone by the time stated in the Administrative Instructions.

Both clubs in confirmation of the match played shall return by FIRST CLASS MAIL, the official Match Result Card, completed in all respects to the appropriate officer of the league in accordance with the Administrative Instructions.

Failure to telephone and card in the match results within the time limits laid down shall incur an immediate fine of £15. A second offence a fine of £25 and a third and subsequent offence £25 and a deduction of two league points.

Offending clubs will be notified of fines imposed. Failure to pay within 28 days will result in the offending club being deducted two league points.

There is no right of appeal.

A club with any fines outstanding after its final league game has been played will incur a recommendation to the R.F.U. that the club be suspended or expelled from the league for the following season.

ADMINISTRATIVE INSTRUCTIONS

a. League results to be telephoned to Russells by 5.00pm on the Saturday of the game. Telephone: 0533 872991, Fax: 0533 320064.

b. Match result card to be posted by first class mail on the Monday following the Saturday game.

c. Notification and collection of fines will be administered by the appropriate League Secretary.

COMPUTER PRINTOUTS FOR PLAYERS' REGISTRATIONS

If Clubs require updated printouts for new players a **stamped addressed envelope must be enclosed** with the relevant registration forms and forwarded to the Registrar, PO Box 183, Leicester LE3 8BZ. Otherwise it will be assumed that an updated printout is not required. It is essential that all Clubs appoint an officer to be responsible for all registration matters.

POSTPONED GAMES

The home club shall notify the appropriate party and the League Secretary of a postponed fixture.

Postponed games must be played on the first available non league/non cup weekend unless the club has been informed by the League Secretary of an alternative formula before the start of the season.

MIDLAND DIVISION

OFFICIALS 1994-95

CHAIRMAN
David Robins, Rugby House, Upper Chase Road, Malvern WR14 2BU (H) 0684 564826 (B) 0684 560247 (Fax) 0684 893125

HON. SECRETARY
Michael Wilson, 6 New Road, Easton-on-the-Hill, Stamford, Lincs. PE9 3NN

LEAGUE SECRETARIES
Midland One David Coe, 11 Little Meadow, Great Oakley, Corby NN18 8JN (H) 0536 460052 (B) 0536 402551 x 3112 (Fax) 0536 402680
Midland Two Geoff Goodall, 38 Presthills Road, Hinckley, Leics LE10 1AJ (H) 0455 238742 (B) 0203 562650 (Fax) 0203 563816
Midland East One Mike Bracy, Inglenook, East Street, Lilley, Nr Luton, Beds LU2 8LW (H) 0462 768447
Midland West One Pat Dalley, 153 Masshouse Lane, Kings Norton, Birmingham B38 9AD (H) 021 459 3930 / 021 680 7237 (B) 021 451 1535 (Fax) 021 433 3737
Midland East Two Brian Johnston, 9 Nursery Close, Atworth, Melksham, Wilts SN12 8HX (H) 0225 790658 (B) 0249 442771 (Fax) 0249 442865
Midland West Two Simon Peace, 12 Alfreda Avenue, Holywood, Worcs B47 5BP (H) 021 474 4142 (B) 021 744 4505
Staffs/Warks One Keith Dale, 14 St Anthony's Drive, Newcastle, Staffs ST5 2JE (H) 0782 615770
Staffs/Warks Two Bruce Braithwaite, 4 Badgers Croft, Eccleshall, Staffs ST21 6DS (H) 0785 851114 (B) 0785 277330
Staffs/Warks Three & Four Ray Roberts, 261 Alwyn Road, Bilton, Rugby, Warks CV22 7RP (H) 0788 810276
North Midland One Chris Parsons, 15 Silverbirch Drive, Wythall, Worcs B47 5RB (H) 021 474 4785
North Midland Two John McNally, St Bernadette's R.C. School, Hob Moor Road, Yardley, Birmingham B25 8QL (H) 021 604 6180 (B) 021 783 7232 (Fax) 021 789 8306
North Midland Three Nigel Banwell, 16 Riverside Close, Upton upon Severn, Worcs WR8 0JN (H) 0684 592046
Notts/Lincs & Derby One Kevin Price, 10 Seagrave Road, Thrussington, Leicestershire. LE7 4UG(H) 0664 424388
Notts/Lincs & Derby Two Paul Raymont, 18 Longhill Rise, Kirkby-in-Ashfield, Nottinghamshire NG19 9FL (H) 0623 750990
Notts/Lincs & Derby Three David H Murphy, The Old Carpenters Arms, 32 High Street, Little Bytham, Grantham, Lincolnshire NG33 4QX (H) 0780 410692
Notts/Lincs & Derby Four Andrew Woodall, 3 Brough Cottages, Brough, Bradwell, Derbyshire S30 2HG (H) 0433 620298
East Midland/Leicestershire One & Four Paul Adams, 323a Bedford Road, Kempston, Beds. MK42 8QB. (H) 0234 853390 (Fax) 0234 857552
East Midland/Leicestershire Two Michael King, 53 Kettering Road, Market Harborough, Leics. (H) 0858 467267
East Midland/Leicestershire Three Bob Ingledew, 15 Martin Close, Bedford MK41 7JY. (H) 0234 268482

MIDLANDS CHAMPIONS ROLL OF HONOUR 1993/94

Midland 1
Barkers' Butts RFC

Midland 2
Whitchurch RFC

Midland West 1
Sutton Coldfield RFC

Midland West 2
Old Laurentian RFC

Midland East 1
Hinckley RFC

Midland East 2
Long Buckby RFC

Staffs/Warwicks 1
Dunlop RFC

Staffs/Warwicks 2
Atherstone RFC

Staffs/Warwicks 3
Shipston-on-Stour RFC

Staffs/Warwicks 4
Bloxwich RFC

North Midland 1
Luctonians RFC

North Midland 2
Edwardian FC

North Midland 3
Upton-on-Severn RFC

Notts, Lincs & Derby 1
Ilkeston RUFC

Notts, Lincs & Derby 2
Leesbrook Asterdale RUFC

Notts, Lincs & Derby 3
North Kesteven RUFC

Notts, Lincs & Derby 4
Bolsover RUFC

East Midland/Leics 1
Huntingdon RUFC

East Midland/Leics 2
Old Northamptonians RFC

East Midland/Leics 3
Bedford Swifts RUFC

East Midland/Leics 4
Vauxhall Motors RUFC

Luctonians RFC

MIDLAND DIVISION
FEATURED TEAMS

MALVERN

The odds on Malvern winning the Pilkington Shield were very long until they had survived a tough semi-final against the favourites, Hucclecote Old Boys, and after that sheer grit saw them win the final at Twickenham through a try and a penalty by wing Dave Grundy.

It may have been relatively easy for them in the earlier rounds with wins at Birmingham Civil Service (30-3), at Warwickshire Police (30-14) and at home to Bournville (61-3), but they then had to fight all the way for success. Aylestone St James (Leicester) saw them emerge as successful visitors (16-3), but it was very hard at Oakham (8-5) and at home to Wibsey (20-13).

Then came a 9-9 draw after extra-time away to Edwardians and survival as the visiting team with Dave Grundy again providing all the scoring with penalties. Many had fancied the home club as ultimate winners. The rest is well known.

It is always invidious to pick out names in a winning team, but Steve Fahey at full back was a model of consistency, Dave Green a superb fly-half in partnership with Gary Henderson, Andy Ridley at No 8 was an inspiring skipper, the locks Andy McKelvie and Adrian McBurney won plenty of line-out ball and the flankers Marc Wolfe and Simon Dixon were the bane of opposing backs.

They will be too high up the league structure to defend their honour as they also recorded only two defeats in 29 games overall and were promoted to North Midlands One after winning 11 of their dozen league matches in the lower flight.

After 60 years as a club Malvern are on the march and are looking for other conquests and a rise to the highest possible status.

LUCTONIANS

Luctonians is a club, which was originally formed in 1948 for the benefit of the old boys of Lucton School in Hereford, but although the school sadly closed some years ago its name is preserved for posterity by 'Luccs', who are also doing the fine name proud by its on the field performances and thriving off field life.

The big achievement of the season was its perfect record in North Midlands Two West. In the process Luctonians scored a terrifying 438 points in their 12 matches and conceded only a mean 52, which would suggest that a further ascent cannot be ruled out.

Much of the success of the club, which runs four senior teams, a veterans' side, ladies team, colts and age group sides from 14 to 17, can be credited to secretary Huw Davies, whose enthusiasm is infectious. With him there things really tick over superbly.

Huw himself commends many aspects of the club's success story notably the scrummaging and tackling. Top scorers were scrum-half Nick Layton (130 points), full back Peter Elkington (113 points) and centre Peter Furlong (80 points), whilst the try scoring was evenly spread with fly-half Paul Woodworth to the fore (15), well aided by Nick Layton, No8 Simon Children and Chris Radbourne, a sturdy prop, who scored a dozen.

The leader on the field with a superb season was flanker Simon Hussey, but at the end of the day he and the others will all say that it was teamwork on and off the field that counted.

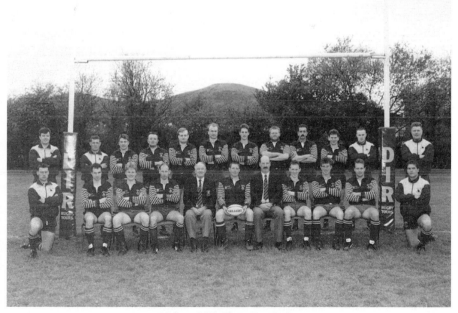

Malvern RFC. Photo: Tom Bader

MIDLAND DIVISION

<table>
<tr><td>

MIDLAND ONE
1994-95
FIXTURES

</td><td>

January 7 (Week 17)
Bedworth v Worcester
Burton v Derby
Leamington v Stafford
Mansfield v Wolverhampton
Towcestrians v Camp Hill
Westleigh v Whitchurch

</td></tr>
</table>

September 17 (Week 3)
Burton v Syston
Derby v Worcester
Leamington v Bedworth
Stafford v Wolverhampton
Westleigh v Mansfield
Whitchurch v Camp Hill

January 14 (Week 18)
Camp Hill v Mansfield
Derby v Leamington
Stafford v Westleigh
Whitchurch v Towcestrians
Wolverhampton v Bedworth
Worcester v Syston

September 24 (Week 4)
Bedworth v Westleigh
Camp Hill v Stafford
Mansfield v Towcestrians
Syston v Leamington
Wolverhampton v Derby
Worcester v Burton

February 11 (Week 22)
Bedworth v Camp Hill
Leamington v Burton
Mansfield v Whitchurch
Syston v Wolverhampton
Towcestrians v Stafford
Westleigh v Derby

October 1 (Week 5)
Burton v Wolverhampton
Derby v Camp Hill
Leamington v Worcester
Stafford v Whitchurch
Towcestrians v Bedworth
Westleigh v Syston

February 25 (Week 24)
Burton v Westleigh
Camp Hill v Syston
Derby v Towcestrians
Stafford v Mansfield
Whitchurch v Bedworth
Wolverhampton v Worcester

October 15 (Week 7)
Bedworth v Mansfield
Camp Hill v Burton
Syston v Towcestrians
Whitchurch v Derby
Wolverhampton v Leamington
Worcester v Westleigh

March 4 (Week 25)
Bedworth v Stafford
Mansfield v Derby
Syston v Whitchurch
Towcestrians v Burton
Westleigh v Leamington
Worcester v Camp Hill

October 22 (Week 8)
Burton v Whitchurch
Derby v Stafford
Leamington v Camp Hill
Mansfield v Syston
Towcestrians v Worcester
Westleigh v Wolverhampton

March 25 (Week 28)
Burton v Mansfield
Camp Hill v Wolverhampton
Derby v Bedworth
Leamington v Towcestrians
Stafford v Syston
Whitchurch v Worcester

October 29 (Week X2)
Camp Hill v Westleigh
Stafford v Burton
Syston v Bedworth
Whitchurch v Leamington
Wolverhampton v Towcestrians
Worcester v Mansfield

April 8 (Week 30)
Bedworth v Burton
Mansfield v Leamington
Syston v Derby
Towcestrians v Westleigh
Wolverhampton v Whitchurch
Worcester v Stafford

MIDLANDS ONE

BEDWORTH RFC
Ground Address: Recory Fields, Sharts Road, Bedworth, Warks CV12 0BP. Tel: 0203 312025
Club Secretary: David Hatfield, 17 New Road, Ash Green, Nr Coventry CV7 9AS. Tel: (H) 0202 365160 Tel: (W) 0203 362399
Fixtures Secretary: Keith Brown, 20 Rosemary Way, Hinckley LE10 0LH. Tel: (H) 0455 230840
Club Colours: Green jerseys, white shorts.

BURTON FC
Ground Address: Peel Croft, Lichfield Street, Burton-on-Trent, Staffs DE14 3RH. Tel: 0283 564510
Club Secretary: JD Lowe, 20 The Chevin, Stretton, Burton-on-Trent, Staffs DE13 0XU. Tel: (H) 0283 534422
Fixtures Secretary: PE Richard, 20 Olton Road, Mickleover, Derby DE5 5PL. Tel: (H) 0332 516901
Club Colours: White with black diagonal band over right shoulder, white shorts, black socks with white tops.

CAMP HILL RFC
Ground Address: Haslucks Green Road, Shirley, West Midlands. Tel: 021 744 4175
Club Secretary: Russell Homer, c/o Kidsons Impey, Bank House, 8 Cherry Street, Birmingham B2 5AD. Tel: (H) 021 631 2631 Tel: (W) 021 631 2631
Fixtures Secretary: Graham Scutt, 130 Longmore Road, Solihull, West Midlands B90 3EE. Tel: (H) 021 744 4495 Tel (W) 021 744 4495
Club Colours: Maroon & light blue.

DERBY RFC
Ground Address: Kedleston Road, Derby. Tel: 0332 344341
Club Secretary: Mrs J Newbury, 3 Denver Road, Mickleover, Derby DE3 5PS. Tel: (H) 0332 516854 Tel: (W) 0332 202404
Fixtures Secretary: Jerry Gregson, 45 West Avenue, South Chellaston, Derby. Tel: (H) 0332 701312 Tel (W) 0332 661461 x3436
Club Colours: Black & amber.

LEAMINGTON RUFC
Ground Address: Moorefields, Kenilworth Road, Blackdown, Leamington Spa, Warks CV32 6RG. Tel: 0926 425584
Club Secretary: Mr Lol Smith, 103 Telford Avenue, Leamington Spa CV32 7HG. Tel: (H) 0926 423391
Fixtures Secretary: Peter Waring, 4 Borrowell Terrace, Kenilworth CV8 1ER. Tel: (H) 0926 56865
Club Colours: Royal blue jersey with single scarlet & gold hoop, navy blue shorts, royal blue socks.

MANSFIELD RUFC
Ground Address: Eakring Road, Mansfield, Notts NG18 3EW. Tel: 0623 649834
Club Secretary: Keith Bingley, Keepers Cottage, Lamins Lane, Bestwood Park, Nottinghjam NG6 8UJ. Tel: (H) 0602 208943 Tel: (W) 0623 25821
Fixtures Secretary: Kevin Swithenbank, 40 Summercourt Drive, Ravenshead, Notts. Tel: (H) 0623 793726
Club Colours: Blue & white hoops, navy shorts.

STAFFORD RUFC
Ground Address: Country Ground, Castle Fields, Newport Road, Stafford ST16 1BG. Tel: 0785 211241
Club Secretary: PL Hill, 39 Rising Brook, Stafford ST17 9DE. Tel: (H) 0785 59583
Fixtures Secretary: AJ Cook, 52 Burton Bank Lane, Stafford ST17 9JL. Tel: (H) 0785 40295
Club Colours: Black & amber hoops, black shorts.

SYSTON RFC
Ground Address: Barkby Road, Queniborough, Leicestershire. Tel: 0533 601223
Club Secretary: JD Newton, 62 Fosse Way, Syston, Leicester LE1 1NE. Tel: (H) 0533 694647
Fixtures Secretary: B Sturgess, 28 Harwin Drive,

FINAL TABLE

	P	W	D	L	F	A	PD	Pts
Barkers Butts	12	10	0	2	180	86	94	20
Worcester	12	8	0	4	234	104	103	16
Burton	12	8	0	4	219	159	60	16
Syston	12	8	0	4	221	119	102	14
Leamington	12	7	0	5	189	150	39	14
Camp Hill	12	7	0	5	178	058	20	12
Bedworth	12	6	0	6	156	149	7	10
Mansfield	12	5	0	7	139	173	-34	10
Derby	12	5	0	7	118	177	-59	10
Westleigh	12	5	0	7	137	212	-75	10
Wolverhampton	12	4	0	8	169	221	-52	8
Towcestrians	12	3	0	9	123	218	-95	6
Leighton Buzzard	12	2	0	10	83	220	-137	4

Evington, Leicester. Tel: (H) 0533 735674 Tel (W) 0580 890275
Club Colours: Navy & saxe hoops.

TOWCESTRIANS RFC
Ground Address: Greens Norton Road, Towcester, Northamptonshire. Tel: 0327 350141
Club Secretary: Mr Richard Bodily, 36 Goodwood, Great Holm, Milton Keynes, Buckinghamshire MK8 9DZ. Tel: (H) 0908 562153 Tel: (W) 0908 510970
Fixtures Secretary: Mr Stephen Burley, 17 Hazel Crescent, Towcester, Northamptonshire NN12 6VQ. Tel: (H) 0327 353932 Tel (W) 0327 842127
Club Colours: Maroon jerseys with white edged eamber band, black shorts, maroon stockings.

WESTLEIGH RFC
Ground Address: Lutterworth Road, Blaby, Leicester. Tel: 0533 771010
Club Secretary: Mark Jordan, 16 Half Moon Crescent, Oadvy, Leicester LE2 4HD. Tel: (H) 0533 712549 Tel: (W) 0533 535328
Fixtures Secretary: Chris Barker, 66 Carisbrook Road, Leicester. Tel: (H) 0533 708676 Tel (W) 0533 881527
Club Colours: Black & white 3' hoops.

WHITCHURCH RFC
Ground Address: Edgeley Park, Whitchurch, Shropshire. Tel: 0948 663316
Club Secretary: Neil Prunier, 9 St Mary's Street, Whitchurch, AShropshire SY13 1QU. Tel: (H) 0948 663012 Tel: (W) 0948 663012
Fixtures Secretary: Paul Kaminski, Green Paddocks, Kingsway, Whitchurch, Shropshire. Tel: (H) 0948 662889
Club Colours: Red shirts, white socks.

WOLVERHAMPTON RUFC
Ground Address: Castlecroft Road, Castlecroft, Wolverhampton WV3 8NA. Tel: 0902 763900
Club Secretary: Dr DJ Rutherford, Rose Cottage, 3 Woodlands Cottages, Penn, wolverhampton WV4 4DG. Tel: (H) 0902 335926 Tel: (W) 0902 24847
Fixtures Secretary: J Hurst-Knight, 5 Westgate Villas, High Town, Bridgnorth. Tel: (H) 0746 765563
Club Colours: Black shirts with wolf's head, black shorts.

WORCESTER RFC
Ground Address: Sixways, Pershore Lane, Hindlip, Nr Worcester. Tel: 0905 454183/451173
Club Secretary: AC Harling, 6 The Grove, Claines, Worcester. Tel: (H) 0905 454900 Tel: (W) 0562 822295
Fixtures Secretary: R Paul, 139 Liverpool Road, Rontswood. Tel: (H) 0905 355565

MIDLAND DIVISION

MIDLAND TWO
1994-95
FIXTURES

January 7 (Week 17)
Hinckley v Bedford Athletic
Keresley v Newark
Leighton Buzzard v Sutton Coldfield
Matlock v Braod Street
Paviors v Belgrave
Peterborough v Willenhall

September 17 (Week 3)
Belgrave v Bedford Athletic
Broad Street v Willenhall
Keresley v Stockwood Park
Matlock v Leighton Buzzard
Newark v Sutton Coldfield
Paviors v Peterborough

January 14 (Week 18)
Bedford Athletic v Peterborough
Belgrave v Hinckley
Broad Street v Paviors
Newark v Matlock
Sutton Coldfield v Stockwood Park
Willenhall v Leighton Buzzard

September 24 (Week 4)
Bedford Athletic v Broad Street
Leighton Buzzard v Paviors
Peterborough v Hinckley
Stockwood Park v Matlock
Sutton Coldfield v Keresley
Willenhall v Newark

February 11 (Week 22)
Hinckley v Broad Street
Leighton Buzzard v Bedford Athletic
Matlock v Keresley
Paviors v Newark
Peterborough v Belgrave
Stockwood Park v Willenhall

October 1 (Week 5)
Broad Street v Belgrave
Hinckley v Leighton Buzzard
Keresley v Willenhall
Matlock v Sutton Coldfield
Newark v Bedford Athletic
Paviors v Stockwood Park

February 25 (Week 24)
Bedford Athletic v Stockwood Park
Belgrave v Leighton Buzzard
Broad Street v Peterborough
Keresley v Paviors
Newark v Hinckley
Willenhall v Sutton Coldfield

October 15 (Week 7)
Bedford Athletic v Keresley
Belgrave v Newark
Leighton Buzzard v Peterborough
Stockwood Park v Hinckley
Sutton Coldfield v Paviors
Willenhall v Matlock

March 1 (Week 25)
Hinckley v Keresley
Leighton Buzzard v Broad Street
Paviors v Matlock
Peterborough v Newark
Stockwood Park v Belgrave
Sutton Coldfield v Bedford Athletic

October 22 (Week 8)
Hinckley v Sutton Coldfield
Keresley v Belgrave
Matlock v Bedford Athletic
Newark v Broad Street
Paviors v Willenhall
Peterborough v Stockwood Park

March 25 (Week 28)
Bedford Street v Willenhall
Belgrave v Sutton Coldfield
Broad Street v Stockwood Park
Keresley v Peterborough
Matlock v Hinckley
Newark v Leighton Buzzard

October 29 (Week X2)
Bedford Athletic v Paviors
Belgrave v Matlock
Braod Street v Keresley
Stockwood Park v Leighton Buzzard
Sutton Coldfield v Peterborough
Willenhall v Hinckley

April 8 (Week 30)
Hinckley v Paviors
Leighton Buzzard v Keresley
Peterborough v Matlock
Stockwood Park v Newark
Sutton Coldfield v Broad Street
Willenhall v Belgrave

MIDLANDS TWO

BEDFORD ATHLETIC RUFC
Ground Address:Putnoe Wood, Wentworth Drive, Putnoe, Bedford. Tel: 0234 350874
Club Secretary: BM Eynon, 133 Dudley Street, Bedford MK40 3SY. Tel: (H) 0234 214929 Tel: (W) 0706 620220
Fixtures Secretary: J Ross, 63 Avon Drive, Bedford MK41 7UR. Tel: (H) 0234 343151 Tel (W) 0234 225116
Club Colours: Black & white hooped shirts, dark blue shorts, black socks.

BELGRAVE RFC
Ground Address:Belgrave Pastures, Thurcaston Road, Belgrave, Leicester. Tel: 0533 663033
Club Secretary: Michael John Goddard, Grange Court, 271a Birstall Road, Birstall, Leicester, LE4 4DJ. Tel: (H) 0533 677383 Tel: (W) 0850 334 886
Fixtures Secretary: Kevin Hick, 3 Coplow Crescent, Syston, Leicester. Tel: (H) 0533 608617
Club Colours: Shirts red & black hoops, shorts navy.

BROAD STREET RFC
Ground Address:Ivor Preece Field, Brandon Road, Coventry. Tel: 0203 453982 (club house) 0203 451706 (caretaker)
Club Secretary: Mr CJ McGinty, 60 Caludon Road, Stoke, Coventry CV2 4LP. Tel: (H) 0203 441210
Fixtures Secretary: Mr D Wilkinson, 4 Court Leet, Binley Woods, Coventry CV3 2JR. Tel: (H) 0203 543548
Club Colours: Red with white & green bands, navy shorts, green socks/Green with white & red bands, navy shorts, green socks.

HINCKLEY RFC
Ground Address:A47 Leicester Road, Hinckley. Tel: 0455 615010
Club Secretary: FJ Swift, 8 The Rills, Hinckley LE10 1NA. Tel: (H) 0455 250270
Fixtures Secretary: P Green, 10 Falmouth Close, Nuneaton. Tel: (H) 0203 345267
Club Colours: Black & amber hoops.

KERESLEY RFC
Ground Address:Burrow Hill Lane, Corley, Nr Coventry CV7 8BE. Tel: 0676 40082
Club Secretary: Paul Vuckovic, 31 Bassett Road, Coundon, Coventry, West Midlands. Tel: (H) 0203 592469 Tel: (W) 0926 430350
Fixtures Secretary: Frank Loftus, 4 Ash Grove, Ash Green, Coventry CV7 9AT. Tel: (H) 0203 367568
Club Colours: Royal blue, scarlet & white jerseys and stockings, navy blue shorts.

LEIGHTON BUZZARD
Ground Address:Wrights Meadow, Leighton Road, Stanbridge, Leighton Buzzard, Beds LU7 9HR. Tel: 0525 371322
Club Secretary: J McCormack, 15 Neptune Gardens, Leighton Buzzard, Beds LU7 8NW. Tel: (H) 0525 3781943 Tel: (W) 081 343 2133
Fixtures Secretary: A Hodey, 36 Woodman Close, Leighton Buzzard, Beds LU7 8NU. Tel: (H) 0525 379976 Tel (W) 0462 851515 x7294
Club Colours: Navy & white regular hoops.

MATLOCK RFC
Ground Address:Cromford Meadows, Cromford, Nr Matlock, Derbyshire. Tel: 0629 822821
Club Secretary: Sean Heathcote, 2 Bentley Bridge Cottages, Lumsdale Road, Matlock, Derbyshire DE4 5LB. Tel: (H) 0629 580633 Tel: (W) 0629 733291 x221
Fixtures Secretary: Neil Smedley, 5 Yokecliffe Hill, Wirksworth, Matlock, Derbyshire DE4 4PE. Tel: (H) 0629 825933 Tel (W) 0629 823948
Club Colours: Blue, silver & gold quarters.

NEWARK RUFC
Ground Address:Kelham Road, Newark, Nottinghamshire. Tel: 0636 702355
Club Secretary: Edward Hine, Flat 3, 10 Peveril Drive,

FINAL TABLE

	P	W	D	L	F	A	PD	Pts
Whitchurch	12	10	1	1	178	85	93	21
Stafford	12	9	1	2	226	75	151	19
Stockwood Park	12	8	0	4	188	145	43	16
Paviors	12	7	1	4	146	129	17	15
Bedford Athletic	12	7	0	5	207	188	19	14
Matlock	12	5	1	6	164	124	40	11
Belgrave	12	5	1	6	138	112	26	11
Broad Street	12	5	0	7	193	132	61	10
Kersley	12	5	0	7	148	192	-44	10
Newark	12	5	0	7	163	222	-59	10
Peterborough	12	4	0	8	143	187	-44	8
Willenhall	12	4	0	8	128	255	-127	8
Vipers	12	1	1	10	89	265	-176	3

The Park, Nottingham NG7 1DE. Tel: (H) 0602 475086 Tel: (W) 0602 473522
Fixtures Secretary: Hugh Daybell, The Homestead, Coddington, Newark, Nottinghamshire. Tel: (H) 0636 702197
Club Colours: Navy blue & white.

PAVIORS RFC
Ground Address:Burntstump Hill, Arnold, Nottingham NG5 8PQ. Tel: 0602 630384
Club Secretary: DI Hudson, The School House, Eakring Rd, Kneesall, Newark, Notts NG22 0AG. Tel: (H) 0623 861072
Fixtures Secretary: Len Hines, 20 Stiles Road, Arnold, Nottingham NG5 6RE. Tel: (H) 0602 269061 Tel (W) 0602 492077
Club Colours: Red & green shirts, blue shorts.

PETERBOROUGH RUFC
Ground Address:Second Drove, Fengate, Peterborough. Tel: 0733 69413
Club Secretary: B A Hedges, 85 Apsley Way, Longthorpe, Peterborough, PE3 9NZ. Tel: (H) 0733 332287
Fixtures Secretary: Mel Proud, 64 Ramsey Road, Warboys, PE17 3RW. Tel: (H) 0487 822951
Club Colours: Red, gold, silver.

STOCKWOOD PARK RFC
Ground Address:London Road, Luton, Beds LU1 4BY. Tel: 0582 28044
Club Secretary: KJ Janes, 166 Brompton Close, Luton, Beds LU3 3QU. Tel: (H) 0582 576855
Fixtures Secretary: RA Poulter Esq, St Helier, Kings Walden Road, Offley, Hitchin, Herts SG5 3DU. Tel: (H) 0462 768656 Tel (W) 0438 742366
Club Colours: Red shirts with yellow band, navy shorts, red socks.

SUTTON COLDFIELD RFC
Ground Address:Walmley Road, Walmley, Sutton Coldfield, West Midlands. Tel: 021 35#1 5323
Club Secretary: Tim Gallagher, 61 George Road, Sedgley, Dudley, West Midlands DY3 1LE. Tel: (H) 0902 887605 Tel: (W) 0902 305961
Fixtures Secretary: Roger Sholdon, Wynyate, 69 Station Road, Sutton Coldfield, West Midlands B22 5JY. Tel: (H) 021 354 7771 Tel (W) 021 422 0131
Club Colours: Emerald green & white, white shorts.

WILLENHALL RFC
Ground Address:Bognor Road, Essington, Nr Wolverhampton, South Staffordshore. Tel: 0922 405694
Club Secretary: Elfyn Pugh, 9 Five Fields Road, Willenhall, West Midlands WV12 4NZ. Tel: (H) 0902 607747 Tel: (W) 097 855 2141
Fixtures Secretary: Brian Wood, 189 Station Street, Cheslyn Hay, WS6 7EH. Tel: (H) 0922 416259
Club Colours: Maroon & black.

MIDLAND DIVISION

January 7 (Week 17)
Newbold v Kings Norton
Old Halesonians v Bromsgrove
Newcastle v Dudley
Ludlow v Leek
Longton v Old Laurentians
Old Leamingtonians v Newport

September 17 (Week 3)
Kings Norton v Newport
Dudley v Bromsgrove
Newcastle v Old Leamingtonians
Newbold v Longton
Ludlow v Aston Old Edwardians
Leek v Old Laurentians

January 14 (Week 18)
Kings Norton v Newcastle
Leek v Newbold
Dudley v Old Halesonians
Bromsgrove v Old Leamingtonians
Newport v Longton
Old Laurentians v Aston Old Edwardians

September 24 (Week 4)
Bromsgrove v Kings Norton
Newport v Leek
Old Laurentians v Ludlow
Aston Old Edwardians v Newbold
Longton v Newcastle
Old Leamingtonians v Old Halesonians

February 11 (Week 22)
Old Halesonians v Kings Norton
Longton v Bromsgrove
Old Leamingtonians v Dudley
Newcastle v Leek
Newbold v Ludlow
Aston Old Edwardians v Newport

October 1 (Week 5)
Kings Norton v Dudley
Leek v Bromsgrove
Old Halesonians v Longton
Newcastle v Aston Old Edwardians
Newbold v Old Laurentians
Ludlow v Newport

February 26 (Week 24)
Kings Norton v Old Leamingtonians
Bromsgrove v Aston Old Edwardians
Dudley v Longton
Ludlow v Newcastle
Leek v Old Halesonians
Newport v Old Laurentians

October 15 (Week 7)
Dudley v Leek
Bromsgrove v Ludlow
Newport v Newbold
Old Laurentians v Newcastle
Aston Old Edwardians v Old Halesonians
Longton v Old Leamingtonians

March 4 (Week 25)
Longton v Kings Norton
Old Laurentians v Bromsgrove
Aston Old Edwardians v Dudley
Old Leamingtonians v Leek
Old Halesonians v Ludlow
Newcastle v Newbold

October 22 (Week 8)
Leek v Kings Norton
Newbold v Bromsgrove
Ludlow v Dudley
Old Leamingtons v Aston Old Edwardians
Old Halesonians v Old Laurentians
Newcastle v Newport

March 25 (Week 28)
Kings Norton v Aston Old Edwardians
Bromsgrove v Newport
Dudley v Old Laurentians
Newbold v Old Halesonians
Ludlow v Old Leamingtonians
Leek v Longton

October 29 (Week X2)
Kings Norton v Ludlow
Dudley v Newbold
Bromsgrove v Newcastle
Newport v Old Halesonians
Old Laurentians v Old Leamingtonians
Aston Old Edwardians v Longton

April 8 (Week 30)
Old Laurentians v Kings Norton
Newport v Dudley
Aston Old Edwardians v Leek
Longton v Ludlow
Old Leamingtonians v Newbold
Old Halesonians v Newcastle

378

MIDLANDS WEST ONE

ASTON OLD EDWARDIANS FC
Ground Address:Sunnybank Avenue, Perry Common, Birmingham, West Midlands B44 0HP. Tel: 021 373 5746
Club Secretary: Malcolm A Perrott, 21 Ivy Road, Sutton Coldfield, West Midlands B73 5EB. Tel: (H) 021 355 2639 Tel: (W) 021 355 2639
Fixtures Secretary: A Stafford, 54 Station Road, Marston Green, Solihull, West Midlands B37 7BA. Tel: (H) 021 779 6288 Tel (W) 021 356 1395
Club Colours: Red, white & myrtle green hooped shirts, white shorts, green socks.

BROMSGROVE RFC
Ground Address:Finstall Park, Finstall Road, Bromsgrove, Worcs B60 3DH. Tel: 0527 874690
Club Secretary: JA Watson, 7 Bowmore Road, Harwood Park, Bromsgrove B60 2HH. Tel: (H) 0527 875467 Tel: (W) 021 458 2000 x3656
Fixtures Secretary: PR Amphlett, Birds Farm, Uphampton, Ombersley, Droitwich, Worcs WR9 0JS. Tel: (H) 0905 620514 Tel (W) 0905 620514
Club Colours: White with red, black & red hoops.

DUDLEY KINGSWINFORD RFC
Ground Address:Heathbrook, Swindon Road, Wall Heath, Kingswinford, West Midlands DY6 0AW. Tel: 0384 287006
Club Secretary: David Evans, 156 Common Road, Wombourne, West Midlands WV5 0LT. Tel: (H) 0902 894463 Tel: (W) 0902 316327
Fixtures Secretary: WR Jones, 54 Dingle View, Sedgley, West Midlands. Tel: (H) 0902 682056
Club Colours: Cambridge blue & navy hoops, black shorts, black socks.

KINGS NORTON RFC
Ground Address:Kings Norton RFC, Ash Lane, Hopwood, Birmingham, B48 7BB. Tel: 021 445 3340
Club Secretary: G S C Maciver, 11 Chapel Walk, Kings Norton, Birmingham B30 3LW. Tel: (H) 021 459 2279
Fixtures Secretary: J Williams, 44 Heaton Drive, Solihull, West Midlands. Tel: (H) 021 705 1257 Tel (W) 021 700 3018
Club Colours: Red and gold hoop jerseys, white shorts.

LEEK RUFC
Ground Address:Birchall Playing Fields, Cheddleton Road, Leek, Stoke-on-Trent, Staffordshire. Tel: 0538 383697
Club Secretary: AP Chandler, Woodside, Clay Lake, Endon, Stoke-on-Trent ST9 9DD. Tel: (H) 0782 503964
Fixtures Secretary: E Birch, 12 Sandybrook Lane, Birchall, Leek. Tel: (H) 0538 385963
Club Colours: Blue & white narrow hoops, white shorts, blue socks.

LONGTON RUFC
Ground Address:Roughcote Lane, Caverswall, Stoke on Trent. Tel: 0782 394449
Club Secretary: Mr AC Miller, 5 The Dreys, Trentham, Stoke on Trent ST4 8DU. Tel: (H) 0782 641845 Tel: (W) 0782 315188
Fixtures Secretary: Mr D Watt, 4 Whitesands Grove, Meir Park, Stoke on Trent. Tel: (H) 0782 397292 Tel (W) 0782 599052
Club Colours: Amber & black top, black shorts & socks.

LUDLOW RFC
Ground Address:The Linney Fields, Ludlow, Shropshire. Tel: 0584 875762
Club Secretary: Colin Spanner, 58 Henley Orchards, Ludlow SY8 1TN. Tel: (H) 0584 873107 Tel: (W) 0584 872333 Fax: 0584 876459
Fixtures Secretary: RA Flemons, Ford House, Orleton, Ludlow SY8 4HW. Tel: (H) 0568 780334
Club Colours: Red shirts, black shorts.

NEWBOLD-ON-AVON RFC
Ground Address:Parkfield Road, Newbold-on-Avon, Rugby. Tel: 0788 565811
Club Secretary: Arian Johnston, 46 Warren Road, Rugby CV22 5LG. Tel: (H) 0788 560804
Fixtures Secretary: KG Perks, 152 Dunchurch Road, Rugby, Warks CV22 6DR. Tel: (H) 0788 577741 Tel (W) 0788 572572
Club Colours: Red & black quarters.

FINAL TABLE

	P	W	D	L	F	A	PD	Pts
Sutton Coldfield	12	10	0	2	276	137	139	20
Bromsgrove	12	10	1	1	203	97	106	19
Newbold	12	8	0	4	172	105	67	16
Dudley	12	7	1	4	167	160	7	15
Old Longtonians	12	7	0	5	178	133	45	14
Old Haslesonians	12	6	0	6	134	149	-15	12
Newcastle (Staffs)	12	5	1	6	113	176	-63	11
Ludlow	12	4	2	6	123	137	-14	10
Kings Norton	12	5	0	7	102	121	-19	10
O Leamingtonians	12	3	2	7	119	194	-75	8
Aston O Eds	12	3	1	8	178	212	-34	5
Leek	12	3	1	8	174	212	-38	5
Nuneaton O Eds	12	2	1	9	180	286	-106	5

NEWCASTLE (STAFFS) RUFC
Ground Address:Lilleshall Road, Claxton, Newcastle-under-Lyme, Staffordshire. Tel: 0782 617042
Club Secretary: RJO Websdale, 22 Cardington Close, Seabridge, Newcastle-under-Lyme, Staffordshire ST5 3LJ. Tel: (H) 0782 633784 Tel: (W) 0782 839380
Fixtures Secretary: D Westrup, 153 Congleton Road, Sandbach, Cheshire CW11 0SR. Tel: (H) 0270 766538 Tel (W) 0352 712536
Club Colours: Maroon & white hoops, black shorts & socks.

NEWPORT (SALOP) RUFC
Ground Address:The Old Showground, Forton Road, Newport, Shropshire. Tel: 0952 810021
Club Secretary: Christopher Cann, 3 Chetwynd End, Newport, Salop. Tel: (H) 0952 810194 Tel: (W) 0952 291757
Fixtures Secretary: David Jasilionka, 53 Fisher's Lock, Newport, Salop. Tel: (H) 0952 810755
Club Colours: Maroon & white hoops.

OLD HALESONIANS RFC
Ground Address:Wassell Grove, Hagley, Stourbridge, West Midlands DY9 9JP. Tel: 0562 883036
Club Secretary: Ray Brown, 4 The Avenue, Rubery, Birmingham B45 9UE. Tel: (H) 021 453 1466 Tel: (W) 021 486 3486
Fixtures Secretary: Martin Head, 4 Apollo Road, Pedmore Hill Estate, Woolescote, West Midlands DY9 8RG. Tel: (H) 0384 8965606 Tel (W) 021 559 0011/0255
Club Colours: Royal blue shirts with amber hoop, blue shorts.

OLD LAURENTIAN RFC
Ground Address:Fenley Field, Limetree Avenue, Rugby CV22 7QT. Tel: 0788 810855
Club Secretary: AE Willis, 45 Frobisher Road, Rugby CV22 7HS. Tel: (H) 0788 813481 Tel: (W) 0203 402121 x3564
Fixtures Secretary: R Roberts, 261 Alwyn Road, Rugby CV2 7RP. Tel: (H) 0788 810855
Club Colours: Maroon, green & yellow, green shorts.

OLD LEAMINGTONIANS RFC
Ground Address:The Crofts, Bericote Road, Leamington Spa, Warks CV32 6QP. Tel: 0926 424991
Club Secretary: Barry T Ames, 11 Aintree Drive, Leamington Spa CV32 7TU. Tel: (H) 0926 338360 Tel: (W) 0926 313133
Fixtures Secretary: Mike F Russell, The Gables Bungalow, Kenilworth Road, Leamington Spa, Warks. Tel: (H) 0926 427540
Club Colours: Blue & gold hooped jerseys, blue shorts, blue stockings.

MIDLAND DIVISION

MIDLAND WEST TWO
1994-95
FIXTURES

September 17 (Week 3)
Coventry Welsh v Dunlop
Luctonians v Shrewsbury
Old Yardleians v Stratford
Kenilworth v Tamworth
Old Coventrians v Nuneaton Old Eds
Dixonians v Woodrush

September 24 (Week 4)
Dunlop v Dixonians
Woodrush v Old Coventrians
Nuneaton Old Eds v Kenilworth
Tamworth v Old Yardleians
Stratford v Luctonians
Shrewsbury v Selly Oak

October 1 (Week 5)
Old Coventrians v Dunlop
Dixonians v Coventry Welsh
Selly Oak v Stratford
Luctonians v Tamworth
Old Yardleians v Nuneaton Old Eds
Kenilworth v Woodrush

October 15 (Week 7)
Coventry Welsh v Old Coventrians
Dunlop v Kenilworth
Woodrush v Old Yardleians
Nuneaton Old Eds v Luctonians
Tamworth v Selly Oak
Stratford v Shrewsbury

October 22 (Week 8)
Old Yardleians v Dunlop
Kenilworth v Coventry Welsh
Old Coventrians v Dixonians
Shrewsbury v Tamworth
Selly Oak v Nuneaton Old Eds
Luctonians v Woodrush

October 29 (Week X2)
Dixonians v Kenilworth
Coventry Welsh v Old Yardleians
Dunlop v Luctonians
Woodrush v Selly Oak
Nuneaton Old Eds v Shrewsbury
Tamworth v Stratford

January 7 (Week 17)
Selly Oak v Dunlop
Luctonians v Coventry Welsh
Old Yardleians v Dixonians
Kenilworth v Old Coventrians
Stratford v Nuneaton Old Eds
Shrewsbury v Woodrush

January 14 (Week 18)
Old Coventrians v Old Yardleians
Dixonians v Luctonians
Coventry Welsh v Selly Oak
Dunlop v Shrewsbury
Woodrush v Stratford
Nuneaton Old Eds v Tamworth

February 11 (Week 22)
Stratford v Dunlop
Shrewsbury v Coventry Welsh
Selly Oak v Dixonians
Luctonians v Old Coventrians
Old Yardleians v Kenilworth
Tamworth v Woodrush

February 26 (Week 24)
Kenilworth v Luctonians
Old Coventrians v Selly Oak
Dixonians v Shrewsbury
Coventry Welsh v Stratford
Dunlop v Tamworth
Woodrush v Nuneaton Old Eds

March 4 (Week 25)
Nuneaton Old Eds v Dunlop
Tamworth v Coventry Welsh
Stratford v Dixonians
Shrewsbury v Old Coventrians
Selly Oak v Kenilworth
Luctonians v Old Yardleians

March 25 (Week 28)
Old Yardleians v Selly Oak
Kenilworth v Shrewsbury
Old Coventrians v Stratford
Dixonians v Tamworth
Coventry Welsh v Nuneaton Old Eds
Dunlop v Woodrush

April 8 (Week 30)
Woodrush v Coventry Welsh
Nuneaton Old Eds v Dixonians
Tamworth v Old Coventrians
Stratford v Kenilworth
Shrewsbury v Old Yardleians
Selly Oak v Luctonians

MIDLANDS WEST TWO

COVENTRY WELSH RFC
Ground Address:Burbages Lane, Longford, Coventry CV6 6AY. Tel: 0203 360303
Club Secretary: c/o JP Griffiths, 44 Woodland Avenue, Earlsdown, Coventry, West Midlands CV5 6DB. Tel: (H) 0203 674552 Tel: (W) 0203 562738
Fixtures Secretary: Mr S Morriss, 21 Cheviot Close, Stockingford, Nuneaton. Tel: (H) 0203 384312
Club Colours: Red jerseys, black shorts.

DIXONIANS RFC
Ground Address:31a Fountain Road, Edgbaston, Birmingham B17 8NJ. Tel: 021 434 3313
Club Secretary: Vivian Shingler, Timberhonger House, Timberhonger, Bromsgrove, Worcs B61 9ET. Tel: (H) 0527 861686 Tel: (W) 0564 784040
Fixtures Secretary: Dave Hall, 32 Jerrards Drive, Sutton Coldfield, West Midlands B75 7TJ.
Club Colours: Maroon, green & black jerseys, black shorts, green stockings.

DUNLOP RFC
Ground Address:Burnaby Road, Radford, Coventry. Tel: 0203 662394
Club Secretary: Seamus Harnett, 19 Stepping Stones Road, Coundon, Coventry CV5 8JJ. Tel: (H) 0203 601995 Tel: (W) 0203 416255
Fixtures Secretary: John Ormsby, 5 Postbridge Road, Stivychall, Coventry CV3 5AG. Tel: (H) 0203 410313 Tel (W) 0203 511155
Club Colours: Black & amber hoops.

KENILWORTH
Ground Address:Glasshouse Lane, Kenilworth CV8 2AJ. Tel: 0926 53945
Club Secretary: WJ Whitesmith, 4 Glasshouse Lane, Kenilworth CV8 2AJ. Tel: (H) 0926 59465 Tel: (W) 0926 851113 Fax: 0926 851394
Fixtures Secretary: Dai Davies, 33 Fishponds Road, Kenilworth CV8 1EY. Tel: (H) 0926 54824
Club Colours: Sky blue & yellow.

LUCTONIANS RFC
Ground Address:Mortimer Park, Hereford Road, Kingsland, Leominster, Herefordshire. Tel: 0568 708345
Club Secretary: Huw Davies, The Bell House, Kingsland, Leominster, Herefordshire HR6 9RU. Tel: (H) 0568 708450 Tel: (W) 0432 362130
Fixtures Secretary: David Davies, Bucknell House, Bucknell, Salop. Tel: (H) 05474 248 Tel (W) 05474 207
Club Colours: Black & white hooped jerseys, black shorts, black stockings with white ringed tops.

NUNEATON OLD EDWARDIANS RFC
Ground Address:Weddington Road, Nuneaton, Warks. Tel: 0203 386778
Club Secretary: John Jones, 168 Hinckley Road, Nuneaton CV11 6LP. Tel: (H) 0203 387719 Tel: (W) 0455 553081
Fixtures Secretary: John Sparkes, 140 Lutterworth Road, Nuneaton, Warks CV11 6PE. Tel: (H) 0203 326029 Tel (W) 0203 402121 x2750
Club Colours: Red & white hoops.

OLD COVENTRIANS RFC
Ground Address:Tile Hill Lane, Coventry CV4 9DE. Tel: 0203 715273
Club Secretary: Dr RJ Nash, 135 Farren Road, Coventry CV2 5EH. Tel: (H) 0203 614779 Tel: (W) 0533 577055 Fax: 0533 577052
Fixtures Secretary: I Knowles, 23 Meadow Road, Wolston, Coventry CV8 8HL. Tel: (H) 0203 545692
Club Colours: Old gold, black & red quarters, black shorts.

OLD YARDLEIANS RFC
Ground Address:The House Lane, Shirley, Solihull, West Midlands B90 1PW. Tel: 021 744 3380
Club Secretary: Mick Ison, 28 Quinton Close, Solihull, West Midlands B92 9BL. Tel: (H) 021 743 5311 Tel: (W) 0922 28823
Fixtures Secretary: Moss Goode, 9/34 Sherbourne Road, Acocks Green, Birmingham B27 6AE. Tel: (H) 021 707 9656
Club Colours: Green, maroon & old gold quartered shirts, navy shorts.

FINAL TABLE

	P	W	D	L	F	A	PD	Pts
Old Laurentians	12	12	0	0	259	57	202	24
Newport	12	11	0	1	448	74	374	22
Old Coventrians	12	9	0	3	244	192	52	18
Selly Oak	12	8	0	4	310	199	111	16
Old Yardleians	12	6	0	6	164	161	3	10
Dixonians	12	5	0	7	147	225	-78	10
Woodrush	12	5	0	7	157	266	-109	10
Kenilworth	12	6	0	6	213	184	29	8
West Mids Police	12	5	0	7	158	138	20	8
Tamworth	12	5	0	7	168	231	63	8
Stratford-upon-Avon	12	4	0	8	146	228	-82	8
Shrewsbury	12	2	0	10	81	280	-199	2
Coventry Welsh	12	0	0	12	86	346	-260	-2

No relegation as West Midlands Police have withdrawn from the League for '94-95 Season

SELLY OAK RFC
Ground Address:Holders Lane, Moseley, Birmingham. Tel: 021 449 7950
Club Secretary: AL Badsey, 49 Green Meadow Road, Selly Oak, Birmingham B29 4DD. Tel: (H) 021 475 5717 Tel: (W) 021 420 2623
Fixtures Secretary: B Pearce, 9 Langford Avenue, Great Barr, Birmingham B43 5NH. Tel: (H) 021 358 4442 Tel (W) 021 360 8500
Club Colours: Black & white hoops, blue shorts, red socks.

SHREWSBURY RUFC
Ground Address:Sundorne Castle, Uffington, Shrewsbury SY4 4RR. Tel: 0743 353380
Club Secretary: Graham S Jackson, 99 Highfields, Shrewsbury, Shropshire SY2 5PJ. Tel: (H) 0743 361802
Fixtures Secretary: Robbie Hunter, 58 Shelton Road, Shrewsbury. Tel: (H) 0743 241003 Tel (W) 0691 653522
Club Colours: Light blue & dark blue narrow hoops, navy shorts.

STRATFORD-UPON-AVON RFC
Ground Address:Pearcescroft, Loxley Road, Stratford-upon-Avon. Tel: 0789 297796
Club Secretary: RJ Grant, 4 St Gregory's Road, Stratford-upon-Avon, Warks CV37 6UH. Tel: (H) 0789 266722 Tel: (W) 021 502 7116
Fixtures Secretary: Mrs A Prentice, 2 Byron Road, Stratford-upon-Avon CV37 7JP. Tel: (H) 0789 269892 Tel (W) 0789 414979
Club Colours: Black & white shirts, white shorts.

TAMWORTH RUFC
Ground Address:Wiggaton Lodge, Wiggaton Park, Tamworth, Staffs B79 8ED. Tel: 0827 68794
Club Secretary: Craig Parker, 36 Ethelfleda Road, Hockley, Tamworth, Staffs B77 5HD. Tel: (H) 0827 285471 Tel: (W) 0827 310300
Fixtures Secretary: Maurice Merriman, 5 Chandlers Drive, Amington, Tamworth, Staffs B77 4AY. Tel: (H) 0827 65422
Club Colours: Maroon, black & white.

WOODRUSH RFC
Ground Address:Icknield Street, Forhill, Birmingham B38 0EL. Tel: 0564 822878
Club Secretary: SH Edwards, 6 Tanwood Close, Callow Hill, Redditch B97 5YU. Tel: (H) 0527 544281
Fixtures Secretary: Jon Harris, 7 Lime Grove, Hollywood, Nr Birmingham B47 5QQ. Tel: (H) 0564 826851 Tel (W) 0527 52815 x2254
Club Colours: Emerald green & white hoops, black shorts.

MIDLAND DIVISION

STAFFORDSHIRE & WARWICKSHIRE ONE 1994-95 FIXTURES

January 7 (Week 17)
Southam v Coventry saracens
Manor Park v Atherstone
Rugby St Andrews v Eccleshall
GEC St Leonards v GPT Coventry
Trentham v Uttoxeter
Old Wheatleyans v Stoke Old Boys

September 17 (Week 3)
Atherstone v Coventry Saracens
Manor Park v Old Wheatleyans
Rugby St Andrews v Trentham
GEC St Leonards v Trinity Guild
GPT Coventry v Uttoxeter
Eccleshall v Stoke Old Boys

January 14 (Week 18)
GPT Coventry v Rugby St Andrews
Eccleshall v Manor Park
Atherstone v Southam
Coventry Saracens v Old Wheatleyans
Stoke Old Boys v Trentham
Uttoxeter v Trinity Guild

September 24 (Week 4)
Stoke Old Boys v GPT Coventry
Uttoxeter v GEC St Leonards
Trinity Guild v Rugby St Andrews
Trentham v Manor Park
Old Wheatleyans v Southam
Coventry Saracens v Eccleshall

February 11 (Week 22)
Trentham v Coventry Saracens
Old Wheatleyans v Atherstone
Southam v Eccleshall
Manor Park v GPT Coventry
Rugby St Andrews v GEC St Leonards
Trinity Guild v Stoke Old Boys

October 1 Week 5)
GPT Coventry v Coventry Saracens
Eccleshall v Atherstone
Southam v Trentham
Manor Park v Trinity Guild
Rugby St Andrews v Uttoxeter
GEC St Leonards v Stoke Old Boys

February 25 (Week 24)
GEC St Leonards v Manor Park
GPT Coventry v Southam
Eccleshall v Old Wheatleyans
Atherstone v Trentham
Coventry Saracens v Trinity Guild
Stoke Old Boys v Uttoxeter

October 15 (Week 7)
Atherstone v GPT Coventry
Coventry Saracens v GEC St Leonards
Stoke Old Boys v Rugby St Andrews
Uttoxeter v Manor Park
Trinity Guild v Southam
Trentham v Old Wheatleyans

March 4 (Week 25)
Uttoxeter v Coventry Saracens
Trinity Guild v Atherstone
Trentham v Eccleshall
Manor Park v Rugby St Andrews
Old Wheatleyans v GPT Coventry
Southam v GEC St Leonards

October 22 (Week 8)
Rugby St Andrews v Coventry saracens
GEC St Leonards v Atherstone
GPT Coventry v Eccleshall
Old Wheatleyans v Trinity Guild
Southam v Uttoxeter
Manor Park v Stoke Old Boys

March 25 (Week 28)
GEC St Leonards v Old Wheatleyans
Rugby St Andrews v Southam
GPT Coventry v Trentham
Eccleshall v Trinity Guild
Atherstone v Uttoxeter
Coventry Saracens v Stoke Old Boys

October 29 (Week X2)
Eccleshall v GEC St Leonards
Atherstone v Rugby St Andrews
Coventry Saracens v Manor Park
Stoke Old Boys v Southam
Uttoxeter v Old Wheatleyans
Trinity Guild v Trentham

April 8 (Week 30)
Stoke Old Boys v Atherstone
Uttoxeter v Eccleshall
Trinity Guild v GPT Coventry
Trentham v GEC St Leonards
Old Wheatleyans v Rugby St Andrews
Southam v Manor Park

382

STAFFS & WARWICKS ONE

ATHERSTONE RFC
Ground Address:Ratcliffe Road, Atherstone, Warks. Tel: 0827 714934
Club Secretary: David Boal, Thurmaston House, 74 South Street, Atherstone, Warks CV9 1DZ. Tel: (H) 0827 713145
Fixtures Secretary: Keith Berry, 10 Goodacre Drive, Polesworth, Tamworth, Staffs. Tel: (H) 0827 893138 Tel (W) 0827 718092
Club Colours: All black. Change: Black & white quarters.
COVENTRY SARACENS
Ground Address:Bredon Avenue, Binley, Coventry. Tel: 0203 453557
Club Secretary: Brian Craner, 71 Westhill Road, Coundon, Coventry CV6 2AD. Tel: (H) 0203 590280 Tel: (W) 0203 832996
Fixtures Secretary: Roger Hancox, 23 Rugby Lane, Stretton on Dunsmore, Rugby LE10 3LL. Tel: (H) 0203 542252 Tel (W) 0203 687167
Club Colours: Black with red & green V.
ECCLESHALL RUFC
Ground Address:Badenhall Farm, Badenhall, Eccleshall.
Club Secretary: BJ Simpson, 35 Trinity Road, Eccleshall, Staffs ST21 6AP. Tel: (H) 0785 851997 Tel: (W) 0782 264521
Fixtures Secretary: SJ Whitcut, Woodside, Gaol Butts, Eccleshall, Staffs. Tel: (H) 0785 851846
Club Colours: Black with emerald & gold hoop.
GEC ST LEONARDS RUFC
Ground Address:GEC Alstom Protection Control, St Leonards Works, Stafford. Tel: 0785 58070
Club Secretary: J A Whibley, 32 Marlborough Avenue, Stafford, Staffordshire, ST16 3SU. Tel: (H) 0785 48932 Tel: (W) 0785 48932
Club Colours: Black with gold band.
GPT (COVENTRY) RFC
Ground Address:GPT Sports Pavilion, Allard Way, Coventry. Tel: 0203 451157
Club Secretary: RG Everitt, PP16.5 Berkley House, 245 Broad Street, Birmingham B1 2HQ. Tel: (H) 0203 456670 Tel: (W) 021 230 3564
Fixtures Secretary: GN Goodall, 38 Priesthills Road, Hinckley, Leics LE10 1AJ. Tel: (H) 0455 238742 Tel (W) 0203 562650
Club Colours: Red, blue & green hoops.
MANOR PARK RFC
Ground Address:Griff & Coton Sports Club, Heath End Road, Nuneaton, Warks. Tel: 0203 386798
Club Secretary: Nick Gajic, 65 Launceston Drive, Horeston Grange, Nuneaton, Warks CV11 6GN. Tel: (H) 0203 372847
Fixtures Secretary: Steve Atkinson, 10 East Avenue, Bedworth, Warks CV12 (EH. Tel: (H) 0203 312274
Club Colours: Red & black hooped shirts, black shorts & socks.
OLD WHEATLEYANS RFC
Ground Address:Norman Place Road, Coundon, Coventry. Tel: 0203 334888
Club Secretary: Richard Leigh, 8 Orchard Crescent, Coventry CV3 6HS. Tel: (H) 0203 501998 Tel: (W) 0203 688918
Fixtures Secretary: Dai Margetts, 2 Rochester Road, Coventry. Tel: (H) 0203 672952
Club Colours: Blue, maroon & gold.
RUGBY ST ANDREWS RFC
Ground Address:Hillmorton Grounds, Ashlawn Road, Rugby. Tel: 0788 542786
Club Secretary: Jim Corry, 3 Holme Way, Barby, Rugby CV23 8UQ. Tel: (H) 0788 891039 Tel: (W) 0455 232763
Fixtures Secretary: John Hunt, 57 Pinfold Street, Rugby. Tel: (H) 0788 574496
Club Colours: Blue & navy hoops, navy shorts.

FINAL TABLE

	P	W	D	L	F	A	PD	Pts
Dunlop	12	12	0	0	273	75	198	24
Trinity Guild	12	11	0	1	343	92	251	22
Southam	12	9	0	3	196	79	117	18
Stoke Old Boys	12	8	0	4	190	139	51	16
Manor Park	12	6	0	6	126	113	13	12
GEC Coventry	12	6	0	6	146	144	2	12
Old Wheatleans	12	7	0	5	142	127	15	10
GEC St Leonards	12	5	0	7	142	211	-69	10
Trentham	12	3	1	8	93	144	-51	7
Eccleshall	12	3	1	8	125	252	-127	7
Uttoxeter	12	2	1	9	97	317	-220	5
Coventry Saracens	12	3	1	8	123	149	-26	3
Handsworth	12	0	2	10	84	238	-154	0

SOUTHAM RUFC
Ground Address:Kineton Road, Southam, Nr Rugby, Warks. Tel: 0926 813674
Club Secretary: Mike Maville, The Tanners, Church Road, Long Itchington, Nr Rugby CV23 8PN. Tel: (H) 0426 814803 Tel: (W) 0788 570357
Fixtures Secretary: Paul Neale, 48 George Street, Stockton, Nr Rugby, Warks. Tel: (H) 0926 817402
Club Colours: Navy blue with white hoops.
STOKE OLD BOYS RFC
Ground Address:Brookvale Avenue, Binley, Coventry. Tel: 0203 453631
Club Secretary: Mr B Jose, 33 Hothorpe Close, Binley, Coventry CV3 2HX. Tel: (H) 0203 457127 Tel: (W) 0203 335121
Fixtures Secretary: Mr J Monaghan, 65 Conifer Paddock, Binley, Coventry CV3. Tel: (H) 0203 451198
Club Colours: Maroon & white, navy shorts.
TRENTHAM RUFC
Ground Address:Oaktree Road, Trentham, Stoke-on-Trent, Staffordshire. Tel: 0782 642320
Club Secretary: Mr MSM Riley, 7 Waterbeck Grove, Trentham, Stoke-on-Trent, Staffordshire ST4 8XG. Tel: (H) 0782 644874 Tel: (W) 0925 824511
Fixtures Secretary: Mr M Procter, c/o 116 Longton Road, Trentham, Stoke-on-Trent ST4 8BG. Tel: (H) 0722 623292
Club Colours: Green & white hoops, black shorts.
TRINITY GUILD RFC
Ground Address:Rowley Road, Baginton, Coventry. Tel: 0203 305928
Club Secretary: D Williams, 122 Grange Road, Longford, Coventry, Warks CV6 6DA. Tel: (H) 0203 360833 Tel: (W) 0203 666655 x2420
Fixtures Secretary: K Lightowler, 37 Oakfield Road, Coventry CV6 1ED. Tel: (H) 0203 598932
Club Colours: Maroon, old gold, dark blue hoops, navy shorts.
UTTOXETER RFC
Ground Address:Oldfields Sports Club, Springfield Road, Uttoxeter, Staffs. Tel: 0889 564347
Club Secretary: Simon Bailey, Stoneleigh Cottage, Great Cubley, Nr Ashbourne, Derbyshire DE6 2EY. Tel: (H) 0335 330306 Tel: (W) 0889 593031
Fixtures Secretary: Baz Watson, 78 Hall Road, Rolleston-on-Dove, Burnton-on-Trent, Staffordshire DE13 9BY. Tel: (H) 0283 813538 Tel (W) 0283 820426
Club Colours: Dark blue, red & gold hoops.

MIDLAND DIVISION

STAFFORDSHIRE & WARWICKSHIRE TWO 1994-95 FIXTURES

January 7 (Week 17)
Harbury v Berkswell & Balsall
Handsworth v Cannock
Pinley v Coventrians
Shipston on Stour v Earlsdon
Silhillians v Spartans
Warwickshire Police v Wednesbury

September 17 (Week 3)
Cannock v Berkswell & Balsall
Handsworth v Warwickshire Police
Pinley v Silhillians
Shipston on Stour v Linley
Earlsdon v Spartans
Coventrians v Wednesbury

January 14 (Week 18)
Earlsdon v Pinley
Coventrians v Handsworth
Cannock v Harbury
Berkswell & Balsall v Warwickshire Police
Wednesbury v Silhillians
Spartans v Linley

September 24 (Week 4)
Berkswell & Balsall v Coventrians
Wednesbury v Earlsdon
Spartans v Shipston on Stour
Linley v Pinley
Silhillians v Handsworth
Warwickshire Police v Harbury

February 11 (Week 22)
Silhillians v Berkswell & Balsall
Warwickshire Police v Cannock
Harbury v Coventrians
Handsworth v Earlsdon
Pinley v Shipston on Stour
Linley v Wednesbury

October 1 (Week 5)
Earlesdon v Berkswell & Balsall
Coventrians v Cannock
Harbury v Silhillians
Handsworth v Linley
Pinley v Spartans
Shipston on Stour v Wednesbury

February 25 (Week 24)
Shipston on Sour v Handsworth
Earlsdon v Harbury
Coventrians v Warwickshire Police
Cannock v Silhillians
Berkswell & Balsall v Linley
Wednesbury v Spartans

October 15 (Week 7)
Cannock v Earlsdon
Berkswell & Balsall v Shipston on Stour
Wednesbury v Pinley
Spartans v Handsworth
Linley v Harbury
Silhillians v Warwickshire Police

March 4 (Week 25)
Spartans v Berkswell * Balsall
Linley v Cannock
Silhillians v Coventrians
Warwickshire Police v Earlsdon
Harbury v Shipston on Stour
Handsworth v Pinley

October 22 (Week 8)
Pinley v Berkswell & Balsall
Shipston on Stour v Cannock
Earlsdon v Coventrians
Warwickshire Police v Linley
Harbury v Spartans
Handsworth v Wednesbury

March 25 (Week 28)
Pinley v Harbury
Shipston on Stour v Warwickshire Police
Earlsdon v Silhillians
Coventrians v Linley
Cannock v Spartans
Berkswell & Balsall v Wednesbury

October 29 (Week X2)
Coventrians v Shipston on Stour
Cannock v Pinley
Berkswell & Balsall v Handsworth
Wednesbury v Harbury
Spartans v Warwickshire Police
Linley v Silhillians

April 8 (Week 30)
Wednesbury v Cannock
Spartans v Coventrians
Linley v Earlsdon
Silhillians v Shipston on Stour
Warwickshire Police v Pinley
Harbury v Handsworth

STAFFS & WARWICKS TWO

BERKSWELL & BALSALL RFC
Ground Address:Meeting House Lane, Balsall Common, Nr Coventry CV7 7QE.
Club Secretary: PC Wigley, 36 Kemps Green Road, Balsall Common, Nr Coventry CV7 7QE. Tel: (H) 0676 533036 Tel: (W) 0926 464306
Fixtures Secretary: S Wake, 33 Wildcroft Road, Whoberley, Coventry. Tel: (H) 0203 711510 Tel (W) 021 500 6188 x2330
Club Colours: Red & black. Change: Black.
CANNOCK RUFC
Ground Address:The Morgan Ground, Huntingdon, Stafford Rd, Near Cannock, Staffordshire. Tel: 0543 574165
Club Secretary: Mrs N O'Sullivan, 466 Littleworth Road, Hednesford, Staffordshire, WS12 5JB. Tel: (H) 0543 422 959 Tel: (W) 0902 844 371
Fixtures Secretary: John Kidd, 171 Hednesford Road, Cannock, Staffordshire. Tel: (H) 0543 278 513 Tel (W) 0543 278513
Club Colours: Blue & gold.
COVENTRIANS RFC
Ground Address: Black Pad, Off Yelverton Road, Radford, Coventry Tel 0203 682885
Club Secretary: J H Parke 47 High Street, Ryton-on-Dunsmore, Nr Coventry CV8 3FJ. Tel: (H) 0203 304394 (W) 0203 539010 x 6952
Club Colours: Blue & white squares.
EARLSDON RFC
Ground Address:Mitchell Avenue, Canley, Coventry. Tel: 0203 464467
Club Secretary: JG Ward, 18 Wainbody Avenue, Green Lane, Coventry CV3 6BD. Tel: (H) 0203 419729
Fixtures Secretary: D Laing, 104 Torbay Road, Coventry CV5 9JL. Tel: (H) 0203 673094
Club Colours: Red & white.
HANDSWORTH RUFC
Ground Address:450 Birmingham Road, Walsall, WS5 3JP. Tel: 021 357 6427
Club Secretary: Julian P Gudz, 3 St Georges Court, Persehouse Street, Walsall, WS1 2AT. Tel: (H) 0922 645856 Tel: (W) 0384 254565
Fixtures Secretary: David Mews, 143 Birmingham Road, Wylde Green, Sutton Coldfield, B72 1LX. Tel: (H) 021 354 4518 Tel (W) 0922 614056
Club Colours: Red & white hoops, navy blue shorts.
HARBURY RFC
Ground Address:Middle Road, Harbury, Warwickshire. Tel: 0926 613462
Club Secretary: John Fry, 32 Temple End, Harbury, Warwickshire CV33 9NE. Tel: (H) 0926 613798
Fixtures Secretary: Jerry Birkbeck, 22 Campion Terrace, Leamington Spa, Warwickshire CV32 4SX. Tel: (H) 0926 424053
Club Colours: Cherry & white hoops, black shorts.
LINLEY & KIDSGROVE RUFC
Ground Address:Birchenwood Sports Ground, Birchenwood, Kidsgrove, Staffordshire.
Club Secretary: Jason Swingewood, 6 Clandon Avenue, Tunstall, Stoke-on-Trent, Staffordshire ST6 5UT. Tel: (H) 0782 837647 Tel: (W) 0836 520934
Fixtures Secretary: Rob Morrey, 1 Lordshire Place, Packmoor, Stoke-on-Trent, Staffordshire ST7 4QD. Tel: (H) 0782 771320
Club Colours: Green & gold quarters.
PINLEY RFC
Ground Address:The Croft, Wyken Croft, Coventry, West Midlands CV2 3AA. Tel: 0203 602059
Club Secretary: Mr M Brown, 75 Dennis Road, Wyken, Coventry CV2 3HS. Tel: (H) 0203 455449
Fixtures Secretary: Mr B Lester, 7 Tiverton Road, Wyken, Coventry CV2 3DN. Tel: (H) 0203 443605
Club Colours: Black with red horizontal stripe.

FINAL TABLE

	P	W	D	L	F	A	PD	Pts
Atherstone	12	11	0	1	320	36	284	22
Rugby St Andrews	12	10	0	2	296	70	226	20
Silhillians	12	10	0	2	306	87	219	20
Pinley	12	5	1	3	209	139	70	17
Earlsdon	12	8	0	4	283	96	187	16
Berkslall & Balsall	12	7	0	5	179	104	75	14
Spartans	12	7	1	4	206	125	81	16
Coventrians	12	4	1	7	71	172	-101	9
Linley	12	2	3	7	117	166	-49	7
Harbury	12	3	1	8	81	238	-157	7
Cannock	12	2	1	9	128	219	-91	5
Wednesbury	12	2	0	10	53	299	-246	4
Old Oaks	12	0	0	12	41	539	-498	0

SHIPSTON ON STOUR RUFC
Ground Address:Mayo Road, Shipston on Stour, Warks. Tel: 0608 662107
Club Secretary: Richard Slatter, Woodhills Farm, Todenham, Moreton in Marsh, Glos GL56 9PH. Tel: (H) 0608 650453 Tel: (W) 0608 650453
Fixtures Secretary: Robert Hawkins, Washbrook Place, Ilmington, Nr Shipston on Stour, Warks. Tel: (H) 0608 682216 Tel (W) 0608 682216
Club Colours: Black shirts, black shorts.
SILHILLIANS RUFC
Ground Address:Warwick Road, Copt Heath, Solihull, West Midlands B93 9LW. Tel: 0564 777680
Club Secretary: GR Loader, 4 Shackleton Drive, Perton, Wolverhampton, West MIdlands WV6 7SA. Tel: (H) 0902 742695 Tel: (W) 0902 353522
Fixtures Secretary: I Hateley, 5 Brookvale Grove, Olton, Solihull, West Midlands. Tel: (H) 021 707 1738 Tel: (W) 021 708 1830
Club Colours: Maroon, blue & white shirts, blue shorts.
SPARTANS RUFC
Ground Address: Coppice Lane, Middleton Nr Tamworth, Staffordshire Tel: 021 308 5857
Club Secretary: Sarah McGrory, 33 Alexandra Mews, Victoria Road, Tamworth, Staffs B79 7HT. Tel: (H) 0827 693132
Club Colours: Black shirts, black shorts.
WARWICKSHIRE CONSTABULARY RFC
Ground Address:Police HQ, Leek Wootton, Warwick, Warwickshire. Tel: 0926 415000
Club Secretary: AG Mumford, 11 Barton Road, Bedworth, Warwickshire CV12 8HG. Tel: (H) 0203 640109 Tel: (W) 0203 643111
Fixtures Secretary: AG Mumford, 11 Barton Road, Bedworth, Warwickshire CV12 8HG. Tel: (H) 0203 640109 Tel (W) 0203 643111
Club Colours: Maroon & navy jersey, navy shorts.
WEDNESBURY RUFC
Ground Address:Hydes Road Playing Field, Hydes Road, Wednesbury, Club: 14 Bridge Street, Wednesbury. Tel: 021 502 2477
Club Secretary: Peter Hughes, 28 Alder Road, Wednesbury, West Midlands WS10 9PX. Tel: (H) 021 556 5005 Tel: (W) 0922 721898
Fixtures Secretary: Robert F Smith, 31 Doe Bank Road, Ocker Hill, Tipton, West Midlands. Tel: (H) 021 556 6748 Tel (W) 0902 752926
Club Colours: Black & white hoops, black shorts.

MIDLAND DIVISION

STAFFORDSHIRE & WARWICKSHIRE THREE 1994-95 FIXTURES

January 14 (Week 18)
Alcester v Old Oaks
Burntwood v Coventry Technical
Claverdon v Old Warwickians
Rubery Owen v Bloxwich
Wheaton Aston v Warwick

February 11 (Week 22)
Bloxwich v Rugeley
Coventry Technical v Claverdon
Old Oars v Burntwood
Old Warwickians v Rubery Owen
Standard v Alcester

September 17 (Week 3)
Bloxwich v Standard
Burntwood v Alcester
Old Warwickians v Old Oaks
Rubery Owen v Wheaton Aston
Rugeley v Warwick

February 25 (Week 24)
Alcester v Warwick
Burntwood v Standard
Claverdon v Old Oaks
Rubery Owen v Coventry Technical
Rugeley v Old Warwickians

September 24 (Week 4)
Alcester v Claverdon
Old Oaks v Coventry Technical
Standard v Old Warwickians
Warwick v Bloxwich
Waeaton Aston v Rugeley

March 4 (Week 25)
Coventry Technical v Rugeley
Old Oaks v Rubery Owen
Old Warwickians v Bloxwich
Standard v Claverdon
Warwick v Burntwood
Wheaton Aston v Alcester

October 1 (Week 5)
Bloxwich v Wheaton Aston
Claverdon v Burntwood
Coventry Technical v Standard
Old Warwickians v Warwick
Rubery Owen v Alcester

March 25 (Week 28)
Bloxwich v Coventry Technical
Burntwood v Wheaton Aston
Claverdon v Warwick
Rubery Owen v Standard
Rugeley v Old Oaks

October 15 (Week 7)
Alcester v Rugeley
Burntwood v Rubery Owen
Standard v Old Oaks
Warwick v Coventry Technical
Wheaton Aston v Old Warwickians

April 8 (Week 30)
Coventry Technical v Old Warwickians
Old Oaks v Bloxwich
Standard v Rugeley
Warwick v Rubery Owen
Wheaton Aston v Claverdon

October 22 (Week 8)
Bloxwich v Alcester
Coventry Technical v Wheaton Aston
Old Oaks v Warwick
Rubery Owen v Claverdon
Rugeley v Burntwood

October 29 (Week X2)
Alcester v Old Warwickians
Burntwood v Bloxwich
Claverdon v Rugeley
Warwick v Standard

January 7 (Week 17)
Coventry Technical v Alcester
Bloxwich v Claverdon
Old Warwickians v Burntwood
Rugeley v Rubery Owen
Standard v Wheaton Aston

386

STAFFS & WARWICKS THREE

ALCESTER RFC
Ground Address: King's Coughton, Alcester, Warwickshire B49 5QF. Tel: 0789 764061
Club Secretary: MJ Edwards, 8 Icknield Row, Alcester, Warwicks B49 5EW. Tel: (H) 0789 764096 Tel: (W) 0789 762285
Fixtures Secretary: A John, 38 Lime Avenue, Lillington, Leamington Spa, Warks CV32 7DF. Tel: (H) 0926 452079
Club Colours: Red & black.

BLOXWICH RFC
Ground Address:TP Riley Community School, Lichfield Road, Bloxwich, Walsall. Tel: 0922 710463
Club Secretary: Jim Rudge, 5 Primrose Close, Pewall, Walsall WS3 5BT. Tel: (H) 0922 693690 Tel: (W) 0509 219990
Fixtures Secretary: Anthony Allen, 16 Sorrel Close, Featherstone, Staffs WV10 7TX. Tel: (H) 0902 739835 Tel (W) 0922 864726
Club Colours: Green shirts with black & white hoops, black shorts, green socks.

BURNTWOOD RUFC
Ground Address: Burntwood Recreation Centre, High Street, Chasetown, Nr Walsall, Staffs WS7 8XH. Tel: 0543 682911
Club Secretary: Kevin Broadhead, 12 School Walk, Chaseterrace, Mr Walsall, Staffs WS7 8NQ. Tel: (H) 0543 279038
Fixtures Secretary: Alan Wood, 62 Hunter Avenue, Burntwood, Mr Walsall, Staffordshire WS7 9AQ. Tel: (H) 0543 677513 Tel (W) 0543 673833
Club Colours: Red, green & white.

CLAVERDON RFC
Ground Address: Ymningale Common, Ossetts Hole Lane, Claverdon, Warks. Tel: 0926 843133
Club Secretary: Basil Sayer, The White House, 45 Station Road, Balsall Common, Coventry CV7 7FN. Tel: (H) 0676 532164 Tel: (W) 0933 224444
Fixtures Secretary: Chris Goldwater, Home Farm, Blackwell, Shipston on Stour, Warks. Tel: (H) 0608 82773 Tel (W) 021 454 6188 x4393
Club Colours: Red & white.

COVENTRY TECHNICAL RFC
Ground Address: Mitchell Avenue, off Charter Avenue, Canley, Coventry, West Midlands. Tel: 0203 471733
Club Secretary: N Franklin, 42 Haynestone Road, Coundon, Coventry CV6 1GJ. Tel: (H) 0203 335560
Fixtures Secretary: Tony Jones, 3 Nelson Way, Bilton, Rugby CV22 7JX. Tel: (H) 0788 811201
Club Colours: Green, gold, dark brown hoops.

OLD OAKS RUFC
Ground Address: Pelsall School, Pelsall Lane, Rushall, West Midlands. Tel: 0922 682089
Club Secretary: Mr MA Berry, 70 Charles Crescent, Pelsall, Walsall, West Midlands WS3 5BH. Tel: (H) 0922 694839
Fixtures Secretary: Mr A Raybould, 19 Bradford Road, Brownhills, West Midlands. Tel: (H) 0543 375201
Club Colours: Royal blue & scarlet quarters, navy shorts, 1 red sock, 1 blue sock.

OLD WARWICKIANS RFC
Ground Address: Hampton Road, Warwick, Warwickshire. Tel: 0926 496295
Club Secretary: Patrick Wing, 57 Broadfern Road, Knowle, Solihull B93 9OE. Tel: (H) 0564 779947 Tel: (W) 021 626 6071
Fixtures Secretary: Andrew Marshall, Far Westfields Farm House, Moreton Morrell, Leamington Spa, Warks. Tel: (H) 0926 651750
Club Colours: Maroon & white hoops.

FINAL TABLE

	P	W	D	L	F	A	PD	Pts
Shipson-on-Stour	12	10	1	1	326	87	239	21
Warwicks Police	12	9	0	3	183	66	117	18
Rubery Owen	12	8	0	4	238	111	127	16
Burntwood	12	8	0	4	190	114	76	14
Alcester	12	8	0	4	173	111	62	14
Wulfrun	12	6	0	6	172	087	-15	12
Standard	12	4	3	5	137	162	-25	11
Rugeley	12	4	1	7	165	198	-33	9
Warwick	12	4	1	7	153	231	-78	9
Wheaton Aston	12	5	0	7	190	248	-58	8
Claverdon	12	4	1	7	161	175	-14	7
Old Warwickians	12	4	1	7	121	136	-15	7
Michelin	12	0	0	12	37	420	-383	0

No relegation as Wulfrun transferred to North Midlands Three

RUBERY OWEN RFC
Ground Address: High Hill Centre, High Hill, Essington, West Midlands WV11 2DW. Tel: 0922 492795
Club Secretary: Darren Owen, 21 Osborne Drive, Victoria Mews, Darlaston, West Midlands WS10 8YQ. Tel: (H) 021 526 3431 Tel: (W) 021 557 7641
Fixtures Secretary: G Smith, 7 Oakwood Close, Essington, West Midlands. Tel: (H) 0922 400222
Club Colours: Black shirts, black shorts.

RUGELEY RUFC
Ground Address: Hagley Park, Rugeley, Staffs. Tel: 0889 582266
Club Secretary: David Ensor, 36 Anson Street, Rugeley, Staffs WS15 2BA. Tel: (H) 0889 579820
Fixtures Secretary: Steve Winter, 19 Old Eaton Road, Rugeley, Staffs WS15 2EZ. Tel: (H) 0889 586076
Club Colours: Amber jersey, black shorts.

STANDARD RFC
Ground Address: Standard Triumph Rec Club, Tile Hill Lane, Coventry. Tel: 0203 675186
Club Secretary: Alan Ferrar, 24 Roosevelt Drive, Tile Hill, Coventry CV4 9LP. Tel: (H) 0293 469935
Fixtures Secretary: H Kantor, 4 Bowfell Close, Mount Nod, Coventry CV5 7JF. Tel: (H) 0203 463855
Club Colours: Dark blue, light blue & white hoops, navy shorts.

WARWICK RFC
Ground Address: Hampton Fields, Hampton Road, Warwick. Tel: 0926 410972
Club Secretary: Mr I M Joyce, 50 Monks Road, Stoke, Coventry, CV1 2BY. Tel: (H) 0203 630250 Tel: (W) 0926 452400
Club Colours: Purple and black hoops, black shorts.

WHEATON ASTON RUFC
Ground Address: Wheaton Aston Sports & Social Club, Capley Road, Wheaton Aston, Stafford ST19 2LE. Tel: 0785 840440
Club Secretary: B Dalby, 3 Kidderminster Green, Brewood, Staffs ST19 9BQ. Tel: (H) 0902 850926
Fixtures Secretary: S Davis, 5 Kidderminster Green, Brewood, Staffs. Tel: (H) 0902 851450
Club Colours: Black shirts & shorts, gold collars.

MIDLAND DIVISION

STAFFORDSHIRE & WARWICKSHIRE FOUR 1994-95 FIXTURES

September 24 (Week 4)
Onley Park v Michelin
Ford v Stone
Jaguar v Shottery

October 1 (Week 5)
Michelin v Cheadle
Fife Street v Ford
Stone v Jaguar
Shottery v Rugby Welsh

October 15 (Week 7)
Cheadle v Onley Park
Jaguar v Fife Street
Rugby Welsh v Stone

October 22 (Week 8)
Fife Street v Rugby Welsh
Michelin v Ford
Stone v Shottery

October 29 (Week X2)
Ford v Onley Park
Jaguar v Michelin
Shottery v Fife Street

January 7 (Week 17)
Cheadle v Ford
Michelin v Rugby Welsh
Onley Park v Jaguar
Fife Street v Stone

January 14 (Week 18)
Jaguar v Cheadle
Rugby Welsh v Onley Park
Shottery v Michelin

February 11 (Week 22)
Cheadle v Rugby Welsh
Michelin v Stone
Onley Park v Shottery

February 25 (Week 24)
Fife Street v Michelin
Jaguar v Ford
Shottery v Cheadle
Stone v Onley Park

March 4 (Week 25)
Cheadle v Stone
Ford v Rugby Welsh
Onley Park v Fife Street

March 25 (Week 28)
Fife Street v Cheadle
Rugby Welsh v Jaguar
Shottery v Ford

STAFFS & WARWICKS FOUR

CHEADLE RUFC
Ground Address:Stanfields Playing Field, Tean Road,
Cheadle, Stoke-on-Trent, Staffs. Tel: 0538 751476
Club Secretary: Mrs Jo Hill, Abbot's Lea, Hall Orchard,
Cheadle, Stoke-on-trent, Staffs ST10 1HY. Tel: (H) 0538
751476
Fixtures Secretary: Mr M Cadd, K & K Cape, Tean Road,
Mobberley, Stoke-on-Trent, Staffordshire. Tel: (H) 0538
722015
Club Colours: Sky blue with whiite hoop.

FIFE STREET RFC
Ground Address:Ambleside Sports Club, Ambleside Way,
Nuneaton. Tel: 0203 371033
Club Secretary: Mrs Lynn Gillespie, 60 Bristol Road,
Earlsdon, Coventry CV5 6LH. Tel: (H) 0203 675401 Tel:
(W) 0203 831919
Fixtures Secretary: Mr A Ratcliffe, 526 Kingswood Road,
Nuneaton CV10 8QQ. Tel: (H) 0203 349456
Club Colours: Green, red & white hoops.

FORDS (LEAMINGTON) RFC
Ground Address:Newbold Comyn, Newbold Terrace,
Leamington Spa, Warks.
Club Secretary: D Guest, 22 Dudley Green, Lillington,
Leamington Spa, Warks. Tel: (H) 0926 886159
Fixtures Secretary: M McAndrew, 35 Regent Street,
Leamington Spa. Tel: (H) 0926 422543 Tel (W) 0926
425795
Club Colours: Navy blue, black & white hoops, black
shorts.

JAGUAR RFC
Ground Address:Jaguar Sports and Social Club,
Middlemarch Road, Radford, Coventry, Warks.
Club Secretary: Martin Mills, 51 Dawes Close, Stoke
Mews, Coventry, CV2 4LL. Tel: (H) 0203 459314 Tel: (W)
0203 235527
Fixtures Secretary: Martin Mills, 51 Dawes Close, Stoke
Mews, Coventry, CV2 4LL. Tel: (H) 0203 459314 Tel (W)
0203 235527
Club Colours: Dark green and yellow quarters.

MICHELIN RUFC
Ground Address:Michelin Athletic Club Sports Centre,
Rosetree Avenue, Trent Vale, Stoke-on-Trent. Tel: 0782
402899
Club Secretary: A Colclough, 35 Cookson Avenue,
Dresden, Stoke-on-Trent ST3 4NR. Tel: (H) 0782 316413
Tel: (W) 0782 402300
Fixtures Secretary: A Nicholson, 15 Richmond Street,
Penkhull, Stoke-on-Trent ST4 7EB. Tel: (H) 0782 745823
Club Colours: Yellow & blue hoops or quarters.

ONLEY PARK RFC
Ground Address:HMYOI Onley, Rugby CV23 8AP. Tel:
0788 522022
Club Secretary: N Mapletoft, 14 Oberon Close, Rugby.
Tel: (H) 0788 810763 Tel: (W) 0788 522022
Fixtures Secretary: Stu Tempest, Onley Park, Rugby. Tel:
(H) 0788 812531 Tel (W) 0788 522022
Club Colours: Black & red quarters.

RUGBY WELSH RFC
Ground Address:Clubhouse: Bakehouse Lane, Rugby
CV21 2DB. Ground: (Council pitch remote from
clubhouse) Alwyn Road, Bilton. Tel: Clubhouse: 0788
565605
Club Secretary: Roy Thompson, 1 Heather Close, Rugby
CV22 6SB. Tel: (H) 0788 577796 Tel: (W) 0788 545062
Fixtures Secretary: John Rowland, 76 Pytchley Road,
Rugby CV22 5NF. Tel: (H) 0788 574421 Tel (W) 0788
563467
Club Colours: Red shirts, white shorts, red & white socks.

FINAL TABLE

	P	W	D	L	F	A	PD	Pts
Bloxwich	8	7	1	0	184	36	148	15
Coventry Tech	8	5	1	2	104	69	35	11
Rugby Welsh	8	4	1	3	185	71	114	9
Stone	8	5	1	2	159	80	79	7
Ford	8	3	1	4	145	90	55	5
Shottery	8	2	0	6	93	172	-79	4
Cheadle	8	3	0	5	47	131	-84	4
Fife Street	8	0	0	8	38	293	-255	0

SHOTTERY RFC
Ground Address:Shottery Fields, Shottery Road,
Stratford-upon-Avon, Warwickshire.
Club Secretary: Andrew Evans, 15 Waterloo Close,
Wellesbourne, Warwickshire CV37 9JG. Tel: (H) 0789
470186
Fixtures Secretary: Steve Burford, 20 Valletta Way,
Wellesbourne, Warwickshire CV35 9TB. Tel: (H) 0789
842454 Tel (W) 0789 842454
Club Colours: Blue & white shoirts with blue shorts.

STONE RUFC
Ground Address:Alleynes School, Oulton Road, Stone,
Staffs.
Club Secretary: Len Hamilton, 43 Kingston Drive, Stone,
Staffs ST15 0JH. Tel: (H) 0785 815012 Tel: (W) 0782
57714/0831 269675
Fixtures Secretary: David Dugmore, 1 Coombe Park
Road, Walton, Stone ST15 0AY. Tel: (H) 0785 811427 Tel
(W) 0785 814930
Club Colours: Maroon & green quarters.

MIDLAND DIVISION

NORTH MIDLANDS ONE
1994-95
FIXTURES

September 17 (Week 3)
Evesham v Bridgnorth
Old Griffinians v Malvern
Old Centrals v Kidderminster Carolians
Droitwich v Telford
Edwardians v Veseyans
Five Ways Old Eds v Warley

September 24 (Week 4)
Bridgnorth v Five Ways Old Eds
Warley v Edwardians
Veseyans v Droitwich
Telford v Old Centrals
Kidderminster Carolians v Old Griffinians
Malvern v Pershore

October 1 (Week 5)
Edwardians v Bridgnorth
Five Ways Old Eds v Evesham
Pershore v Kidderminster Carolians
Old Griffinians v Telford
Old Centrals v Veseyans
Droitwich v Warley

October 15 (Week 7)
Evesham v Edwardians
Bridgnorth v Droitwich
Warley v Old Centrals
Veseyans v Old Griffinians
Telford v Pershore
Kidderminster Carolians v Malvern

October 22 (Week 8)
Old Centrals v Bridgnorth
Droitwich v Evesham
Edwardians v Five Ways Old Eds
Malvern v Telford
Pershore v Veseyans
Old Griffinians v Warley

October 29 (Week X2)
Five Ways Old Eds v Droitwich
Evesham v Old Centrals
Bridgnorth v Old Griffinians
Warley v Pershore
Veseyans v Malvern
Telford v Kidderminster Carolians

January 7 (Week 17)
Pershore v Bridgnorth
Old Griffinians v Evesham
Old Centrals v Five Ways Old Eds
Droitwich v Edwardians
Kidderminster Carolians v Veseyans
Malvern v Warley

January 14 (Week 18)
Edwardians v Old Centrals
Five Ways Old Eds v Old Griffinians
Bridgnorth v Malvern
Warley v Kidderminster Carolians
Veseyans v Telford

February 11 (Week 22)
Kidderminster Carolians v Bridgnorth
Malvern v Evesham
Pershore v Five Ways Old Eds
Old Griffinians v Edwardians
Old Centrals v Droitwich
Telford v Warley

February 25 (Week 24)
Droitwich v Old Griffinians
Edwardians v Pershore
Five Ways Old Eds v Malvern
Evesham v Kidderminster Carolians
Bridgnorth v Telford
Warley v Veseyans

March 4 (Week 25)
Veseyans v Bridgnorth
Telford v Evesham
Kidderminster Carolians v Five Ways Old Eds
Malvern v Edwardians
Pershore v Droitwich
Old Griffinians v Old Centrals

March 25 (Week 28)
Old Centrals v Pershore
Droitwich v Malvern
Edwardians v Kidderminster Carolians
Five Ways Old Eds v Telford
Evesham v Veseyans
Bridgnorth v Warley

April 8 (Week 30)
Warley v Evesham
Veseyans v Five Ways Old Eds
Telford v Edwardians
Kidderminster Carolians v Droitwich
Malvern v Old Centrals
Pershore v Old Griffinians

NORTH MIDLANDS ONE

BRIDGNORTH RFC
Ground Address:The Bull, Bridge Street, Bridgnorth,
Shropshire WV15 5AA. Tel: 0766 762796
Club Secretary: Pete Shimmin, 7 Buck Cottage, Sheinton,
Cressage, Shropshire SY5 6DJ. Tel: (H) 0952 510604 Tel:
(W) 0746 766488
Fixtures Secretary: Alun Stoll, Ty'r Ysgol, Vicarage
Road, Penn, Wolverhampton WV4 5HP. Tel: (H) 0902
332025 Tel (W) 0902 332025
Club Colours: Black shirts, shorts & socks.

DROITWICH RFC
Ground Address:The Clubhouse, Hanbury Road,
Droitwich Spa, Worcs. Tel: 0905 770384
Club Secretary: P Shelley, 2 Pelham Road, Droitwich Spa,
Worcs. Tel: (H) 0905 770438 Tel: (W) 0384 413841
Fixtures Secretary: P Smith, 21 Mayflower Road,
Droitwich Spa, Worcs. Tel: (H) 0905 779856 Tel (W) 0860
683325
Club Colours: Black & gold hooped shirts, black shorts.

EDWARDIAN FC
Ground Address:The Memorial Ground, Streetsbrook
Road, Solihull, West Midlands B90 3PE. Tel: 021 744 6831
Club Secretary: Chris Nevin, 21 Wroxhall Road, Solihull,
West Midlands B91 1DR. Tel: (H) 021 704 1870
Fixtures Secretary: Geoff Kearney, 68 Fowlmere Road,
Great Barr, Birmingham B42 2ET. Tel: (H) 021 358 1985
Tel (W) 0922 711649
Club Colours: Old gold, claret & navy irregular hoops.

EVESHAM RFC
Ground Address:Evesham Sports Club, Albert Rd,
Evesham, Worcs. Tel: 0386 446469
Club Secretary: J P Hartley, Nightingale House,
Bishampton, Pershore, Worcs, WR10 2NH. Tel: (H) 0386
46232 Tel: (W) 0527 876776
Fixtures Secretary: I Moreton, 'Frensham' Lenchwick,
Evesham, Worcs. Tel: (H) 0386 870566 Tel (W) 0386
443311
Club Colours: Navy/maroon hoops.

FIVE WAYS OLD EDWARDIANS FC
Ground Address:Masshouse, Ash Lane, Hopwood,
Worcestershire. Tel: 021 445 4909
Club Secretary: Richard Lisseter, 138 Chatsworth Road,
Halesowen, West Midlands B62 8TH. Tel: (H) 021 559
6549 Tel: (W) 021 550 1724
Fixtures Secretary: Paul Hipkiss, 37 The Crescent,
Cradley Heath, West Midlands. Tel: (H) 021 550 4280
Club Colours: Navy blue & amber.

KIDDERMINSTER CAROLIANS RFC
Ground Address:Marlpool Lane, Kidderminster, Worcs
DY11 5HP. Tel: 0562 740043
Club Secretary: Mr Wallace Boyd, 7 Belvedere Crescent,
Meadow Rise, Bewdley, Worcs DY12 1JX. Tel: (H) 0299
404171 Tel: (W) 021 233 4466 Fax: 021 233 2376
Fixtures Secretary: Mr Mike Bews, 71 Manor Avenue
South, Kidderminster DY11 8DW. Tel: (H) 0562 861678
Tel (W) 0562 861678
Club Colours: Black shirts with gold hoops, black shorts.

MALVERN RFC
Ground Address:Spring Lane, Malvern Worcs WR14
1AJ. Tel: 0684 573728
Club Secretary: MG Davies, 102 Fruitlands, Malvern, Worcs
WR14 4XB. Tel: (H) 0684 567835 Tel: (W) 0222 396131
Fixtures Secretary: D Bannister, 93 Elgar Avenue,
Malvern, Worcs WR14 2EZ. Tel: (H) 0684 569150
Club Colours: Maroon, light blue & gold.

OLD CENTRALS RFC
Ground Address:Bournevale, Little Hardwick Road,
Aldridge, West Midlands. Tel: 021 353 2856
Club Secretary: D E Smith, 14 St Andrews, Amington,
Tamworth, B77 4RA. Tel: (H) 0827 50018 Tel: (W) 021
384 7000

FINAL TABLE

	P	W	D	L	F	A	PD	Pts
Luctonians	12	12	0	0	438	52	386	24
Telford	12	8	0	4	256	131	125	16
Five Ways Old Eds	12	7	2	3	160	121	39	16
Veseyans	12	6	2	4	233	173	60	14
Old Griffinians	12	6	2	4	210	167	43	14
Pershore	12	7	0	5	203	177	26	14
Kidderminster	12	7	0	5	186	165	21	14
Old Centrals	12	5	1	6	170	179	-9	11
Evesham	12	4	1	7	162	198	-36	9
Bridgnorth	12	4	1	7	124	199	-75	9
Droitwich	12	4	0	8	127	244	-117	8
Warley	12	3	0	9	144	313	-169	6
Redditch	12	0	1	11	51	345	-294	-1

Fixtures Secretary: G Dalton, 1 Poole Meadow, Walmley,
Sutton Coldfield. Tel: (H) 021 351 079
Club Colours: Green, maroon, gold.

OLD GRIFFINIANS RFC
Ground Address:Mawdsley Hall, Walkers Heath Road,
Kings Norton, Birmingham B30. Tel: (H) 021 458 2408
Club Secretary: Rick Adie, 33 Middlemore Road,
Northfield, Birmingham B31 3UD. Tel: (H) 021 624 7504
Tel: (W) 021 453 1778
Fixtures Secretary: William Gay, 28 Garland Way,
Northfield, Birmingham B31 2BJ. Tel: (H) 021 475 6508
Club Colours: First team: All black. Second team: Red
shirts, black shorts & socks.

PERSHORE RFC
Ground Address:Mill Lane, Wyre Piddle, Pershore,
Worcs. Tel: 0386 554105
Club Secretary: Mr A K Jensinson, 12 Eltric Road,
Claines, Worcester. Tel: (H) 0905 54346
Club Colours: Black with two scarlet hoops.

TELFORD HORNETS RFC
Ground Address:Town Park, Hinkshay Road, Dawley,
Telford, Shropshire TF4 3NZ. Tel: 0952 505440
Club Secretary: Martin Dolphin, 10 Canonbie Lea,
Madeley, Telford, Shropshire TF7 5RL. Tel: (H) 0952
684904 Tel: (W) 0952 294424
Fixtures Secretary: Gareth Evans, 48 Walker Crescent,
Foxhills, St Georges, Telford, Shropshire TF2 9QB. Tel:
(H) 0952 620196 Tel (W) 0952 670010
Club Colours: Black with gold chest band.

VESEYANS RFC
Ground Address:Little Hardwick Road, Streetly, Sutton
Coldfield, West Midlands. Tel: 021 353 5388
Club Secretary: GR Humphreys, 496 Lichfield Road,
Sutton Coldfield, West Midlands. Tel: (H) 021 308 1135
Tel: (W) 021 631 3232
Fixtures Secretary: D Lake, 41 Jordan Road, Sutton
Coldfield, West Midlands. Tel: (H) 021 308 1722 Tel (W)
021 384 5874
Club Colours: Black & white hooped shirts, black shorts
& socks.

WARLEY RFC
Ground Address:Broomfield, The Uplands, Smethwick,
Warley, West Midlands B67 6BJ. Tel: 021 558 0084
Club Secretary: Keiron Ward, 72 Oak Road, Oldbury,
Warley, West Midlands B68 0BD. Tel: (H) 021 422 4639
Tel: (W) 021 200 2120
Fixtures Secretary: Peter Davies, 60 Park Road,
Smethwick, Warley, West Midlands B67 5HS. Tel: (H) 021
420 3141
Club Colours: Red & white hooped shirts, black shorts.

MIDLAND DIVISION

January 7 (Week 17)

Ross on Wye	v	Birmingham Welsh
Erdington	v	Birmingham City Off
Birmingham Civil Serv	v	Bournville
Old Saltleians	v	Bromyard
Redditch	v	Upton on Severn
Kynoch	v	Tenbury

September 17 (Week 3)

Birmingham City Off	v	Birmingham Welsh
Erdington	v	Kynoch
Birmingham Civil Serv	v	Redditch
Old Saltleians	v	Market Drayton
Bromyard	v	Upton on Severn
Bournville	v	Tenbury

January 14 (Week 18)

Birmingham Welsh	v	Kynoch
Tenbury	v	Redditch
Bromyard	v	Birmingham Civil Serv
Bournville	v	Erdington
Birmingham City Off	v	Ross on Wye
Upton on Severn	v	Market Drayton

September 24 (Week 4)

Birmingham Welsh	v	Bournville
Tenbury	v	Bromyard
Upton on Severn	v	Old Saltleians
Market Drayton	v	Birmingham Civil Serv
Redditch	v	Erdington
Kynoch	v	Ross on Wye

February 11 (Week 22)

Redditch	v	Birmingham Welsh
Ross on Wye	v	Bournville
Erdington	v	Bromyard
Birmingham Civil Serv	v	Old Saltleians
Kynoch	v	Birmingham City Off
Market Drayton	v	Tenbury

October 1 (Week 5)

Bromyard	v	Birmingham Welsh
Bournville	v	Birmingham City Off
Ross on Wye	v	Redditch
Erdington	v	Market Drayton
Birmingham Civil Serv	v	Upton on Severn
Old Saltleians	v	Tenbury

February 25 (Week 24)

Birmingham Welsh	v	Market Drayton
Old Saltleians	v	Erdington
Bromyard	v	Ross on Wye
Bournville	v	Kynoch
Birmingham City Off	v	Redditch
Tenbury	v	Upton on Severn

October 15 (Week 7)

Birmingham Welsh	v	Old Saltleians
Birmingham City Off	v	Bromyard
Tenbury	v	Birmingham Civil Serv
Upton on Severn	v	Erdington
Market Drayton	v	Ross on Wye
Redditch	v	Kynoch

March 4 (Week 25)

Upton on Severn	v	Birmingham Welsh
Market Drayton	v	Birmingham City Off
Redditch	v	Bournville
Kynoch	v	Bromyard
Ross on Wye	v	Old Saltleians
Erdington	v	Birmingham Civil Serv

October 22 (Week 8)

Birmingham Civil Serv	v	Birmingham Welsh
Old Saltleians	v	Birmingham City Off
Bromyard	v	Bournville
Kynoch	v	Market Drayton
Ross on Wye	v	Upton on Severn
Erdington	v	Tenbury

March 25 (Week 28)

Birmingham Welsh	v	Tenbury
Birmingham Civil Serv	v	Ross on Wye
Old Saltleians	v	Kynoch
Bromyard	v	Redditch
Bournville	v	Market Drayton
Birmingham City Off	v	Upton on Severn

October 29 (Week X2)

Birmingham Welsh	v	Erdington
Bournville	v	Old Saltleians
Birmingham City Off	v	Birmingham Civil Serv
Tenbury	v	Ross on Wye
Upton on Severn	v	Kynoch
Market Drayton	v	Redditch

April 8 (Week 30)

Tenbury	v	Birmingham City Off
Upton on Severn	v	Bournville
Market Drayton	v	Bromyard
Redditch	v	Old Saltleians
Kynoch	v	Birmingham Civil Serv
Ross on Wye	v	Erdington

NORTH MIDLANDS TWO

BIRMINGHAM CITY OFFICIALS RFC
Ground Address:Hand Rover Social Club, Bilsmore Green, Off Ronwood Drive, Solihull, B92 9LN. Tel: 021 742 7155
Club Secretary: Glen Owen, 11 Hunton Court, Gravelly Hill, North Birmingham, B23 6BT. Tel: (H) 021 350 1885 Tel: (W) 0902 453453
Fixtures Secretary: George Weir, 64 Jephson Drive, Sheldon, Birmingham, B26 2HW. Tel: (H) 021 743 6263
Club Colours: Navy with red and amber band.

BIRMINGHAM CIVIL SERVICE RFC
Ground Address:Old Damson Lane, Solihull, West Midlands. Tel: 021 782 0423 or 021 782 2151
Club Secretary: Dick Webb, 51 Ladbrook Road, Solihull, West Midlands B91 3RW. Tel: (H) 021 705 2812
Fixtures Secretary: Bill Pratt, 230 Alcester Road, Hollywood, Worcs B47 5HQ. Tel: (H) 0564 822401
Club Colours: Red shirts with 5' white hoop, navy blue shorts, red socks.

BIRMINGHAM WELSH RFC
Ground Address:Catherine de Barnes Lane, Bickenhill, Solihull, West Midlands. Tel: 0675 442995
Club Secretary: Martin Whateley, 19 Wimbourne Road, Sutton Coldfield, Birmingham B76 2SU. Tel: (H) 021 378 3446
Fixtures Secretary: Julian CP Griffiths, 39 School Road, Moseley, Birmingham B13 9TF. Tel: (H) 021 449 2471 Tel (W) 021 233 2838
Club Colours: Scarlet & green quarters, black shorts.

BOURNVILLE RFC
Ground Address:Rowheath, Heath Road, Bournville, Birmingham B30. Tel: 021 458 1711
Club Secretary: Mr Michael Palmer, 3 Hazelwood road, Stirchley, Birmingham B30 2PG. Tel: (H) 021 486 2433
Fixtures Secretary: Mr John Rice, Warden's Flat, MOGH, 3 College Walk, Selly Oak, Birmingham B29 6ZE. Tel: (H) 021 415 4255 Tel (W) 021 472 0163
Club Colours: Maroon with blue & yellow hoops, blue shorts.

BROMYARD RFC
Ground Address:Mintridge, Bromyard, Herefordshire. Tel: 0885 488152 (Cricket Club)
Club Secretary: M Warren, The Chestnuts, Munderfield, Bromyard, Herefordshire HR7 4JT. Tel: (H) 0885 490684 Tel: (W) 0885 490480
Fixtures Secretary: Mr GD Houghton, 3 Valley View, Bredenbury, Bromyard, Hfds HR7 4UJ. Tel: (H) 0885 488387
Club Colours: Green & gold shirts, black shorts.

ERDINGTON RFC
Ground Address:Birches Green Playing Fields, Kingsbury Road, Erdington, Birmingham. Tel: 021 373 7597
Club Secretary: Derek Owen, 129 Bradbury Road, Solihull, West Midlands B92 8AL. Tel: (H) 021 706 4699 Tel: (W) 0527 64252 x3307
Fixtures Secretary: Keith Robinson, 5 Ullenhall Road, Walmley, Sutton Coldfield, West Midlands B76 8QG. Tel: (H) 021 351 2740
Club Colours: White shirts with single blue hoop, blue shorts.

KYNOCH RFC
Ground Address:Holford Drive, Perry Barr, Birmingham B42 2TU. Tel: 021 356 4369
Club Secretary: John K Ross, 127 Leopold Avenue, Handsworth Wood, Birmingham B20 1EX. Tel: (H) 021 358 3277
Fixtures Secretary: R Jones, 17 Kenneth Grove, Erdington, Birmingham B23. Tel: (H) 021 356 9277
Club Colours: Black & white hoops.

FINAL TABLE

	P	W	D	L	F	A	PD	Pts
Edwardians	12	12	0	0	468	53	415	24
Malvern	12	11	0	1	426	104	322	20
Erdington	12	9	0	3	203	113	90	18
Birmingham City Off	12	8	0	4	266	90	176	16
Ross-on-Wye	12	6	0	6	181	229	-48	12
Tenbury	12	5	0	7	127	203	-76	10
Bournville	12	4	1	7	104	226	-122	9
Market Drayton	12	4	1	7	105	281	-176	9
Kynoch	12	5	0	7	161	181	-20	8
Bromyard	12	3	2	7	112	223	-111	8
Birmingham Welsh	12	3	0	9	131	235	-104	6
Old Saltleians	12	3	0	9	88	248	-160	6
Old Moseleians	12	3	0	9	116	302	-186	6

MARKET DRAYTON RFC
Ground Address:Greenfields, Market Drayton, Shropshire.
Club Secretary: Mr R Davies, 73 Longslow Road, Market Drayton, Shropshire TF9 3BP. Tel: (H) 0630 635069
Fixtures Secretary: Mr A Barker, Kings Arms, Shrewsbury Road, Market Drayton, Shropshire. Tel: (H) 0630 652417 Tel (W) 0630 652417
Club Colours: Black with green collars.

OLD SALTLEIANS RFC
Ground Address:Watton Lane, Water Orton, Warwicks. Tel: 021 748 3380
Club Secretary: Derek Bolton, 177 Green Lanes, Wylde Green, Sutton Coldfield B73 5LX. Tel: (H) 021 354 6439 Tel: (W) 021 766 7544
Fixtures Secretary: Kelvin Roberts, 2 Newmarsh Road, Minworth B76 8XW. Tel: (H) 021 351 1473
Club Colours: Red & gold hoops, navy shorts.

REDDITCH RFC
Ground Address: Bromsgrove Road, Redditch
Club Secretary: Bryn Richards, 29 Ladbrook Close, Oakenshaw, Redditch, Worcs. B98 7XR Tel (H) 0527 542870
Club Colours: Light/Dark Blue.

ROSS-ON-WYE RUFC
Ground Address:Sports Centre, Wilton Road, Ross-on-Wye, Herefordshire. Tel: 0989 63256
Club Secretary: John Long, Spring Farm, Hildersley, Ross-on-Wye, HHerefordshire. Tel: (H) 0989 562380
Fixtures Secretary: David Cook, 22 Brampton Svenue, Ross-on-Wye, Herefordshire. Tel: (H) 0989 564626
Club Colours: Blue & white hoops.

TENBURY RFC
Ground Address:Penlu Sports Club, Worcester Road, Tenbury Wells, Worcs. Tel: 0584 810456
Club Secretary: Roger Bowkett, c/o Bowketts (Tenbury) Ltd, Bromyard Road, Tenbury Wells, Worcs WR15 8DE. Tel: (H) 0584 810694 Tel: (W) 0584 810351
Fixtures Secretary: Nigel Hickman, Sanmere, Sinton Green, Hallow, Worcs WR2 5NW. Tel: (H) 0905 640443 Tel (W) 0886 880751
Club Colours: Emerald & green hooped jerseys.

UPTON UPON SEVERN
Ground Address:Collinghurst Meadow, Old Street, Upon-on-Severn, Worcester. Tel: 0684 594445
Club Secretary: Huw Williams, 49 The Beeches, Holly Green, Upton-on-Severn, Worcester WR8 0QQ. Tel: (H) 0684 592977
Fixtures Secretary: Nigel Banwell, 16 Riverside Close, Upton upon Severn, Worcester WR8 0JN. Tel: (H) 0684 592046
Club Colours: Black & white quarters, black shorts, black stockings.

MIDLAND DIVISION

NORTH MIDLAND THREE
1994-95
FIXTURES

September 17 (Week 3)
Bredon Star v Stourport
Birchfield v Yardley & Dist
Ledbury v Old Moseleians
Bishops Castle v Witton
Cleobury v Wulfrun

September 24 (Week 4)
Stourport v Birchfield
Yardley & Dist v Bishops Castle
Wulfrun v Ledbury
Thimblemill v Oswestry
Witton v Cleobury

October 1 (Week 5)
Bishops Castle v Stourport
Birchfield v Bredon Star
Oswestry v Old Moseleians
Ledbury v Witton
Cleobury v Yardley & Dist

October 15 (Week 7)
Bredon Star v Bishops Castle
Yardley & Dist v Ledbury
Wulfrun v Oswestry
Old Moseleians v Thimblemill
Stourport v Cleobury

October 22 (Week 8)
Ledbury v Stourport
Bishops Castle v Birchfield
Thimblemill v Wulfrun
Oswestry v Witton
Cleobury v Bredon Star

October 29 (Week X2)
Bredon Star v Ledbury
Yardley & Dist v Oswestry
Witton v Thimblemill
Wulfrun v Old Moseleians
Birchfield v Cleobury

January 7 (Week 17)
Oswestry v Stourport
Ledbury v Birchfield
Old Moseleians v Witton
Thimblemill v Yardley & Dist
Cleobury v Bishops Castle

January 14 Week 18)
Stourport v Thimblemill
Bredon Star v Oswestry
Bishops Castle v Ledbury
Yardley & Dist v Old Moseleians
Witton v Wulfrun

February 11 (Week 22)
Old Moseleians v Stourport
Thimblemill v Bredon Star
Oswestry v Birchfield
Wulfrun v Yardley & Dist
Ledbury v Cleobury

February 26 (Week 24)
Stourport v Wulfrun
Bredon Star v Old Moseleians
Bishops Castle v Oswestry
Birchfield v Thimblemill
Yardley & Dist v Witton

March 4 (Week 25)
Witton v Stourport
Wulfrun v Bredon Star
Old Moseleians v Birchfield
Thimblemill v Bishops Castle
Oswestry v Cleobury

March 25 (Week 28)
Stourport v Yardley & Dist
Bredon Star v Witton
Ledbury v Oswestry
Birchfield v Old Moseleians
Cleobury v Thimblemill

April 8 (Week 30)
Old Moseleians v Cleobury
Yardley & Dist v Bredon Star
Witton v Birchfield
Wulfrun v Bishops Castle
Thimblemill v Ledbury

BIRCHFIELD RUFC
Ground Address:Moor Lane Sports & Social Club, Moor Lane, Witton, Birmingham. Tel: 021 356 2142
Club Secretary: Mike Benton, 145 Perry Walk, Blackrock Road, Perry Common, Birmingham B23 7XL. Tel: (H) 021 384 1202 Tel: (W) 0533 588744
Fixtures Secretary: Roger Booth, 151 Chester Road, Streetly, Sutton Coldfield B74 3NE. Tel: (H) 021 353 9332 Tel (W) 021 627 6600 x3853
Club Colours: Green & black hoops.

BISHOP'S CASTLE & ONNY VALLEY RUFC
Ground Address:Love Lane, Bishop's Castle.
Club Secretary: Mr Paul Middleton, Tregaron, 7 Shrewsbury Road, Longden, Shrewsbury, SY5 8ER. Tel: (H) 0743 860141 Tel: (W) 0743 790336
Club Colours: Red & green shirts, black shorts, green socks.

BREDON STAR RFC
Ground Address:Bredon Playing Fields, Kemerton Rd, Bredon, Nr Tewks, Glos. Tel: 0684 72831
Club Secretary: Carol Julie Melpass, 33 Plantation Crescent, Bredon, Nr Tewkesbury, Glos. Tel: (H) 0684 72831
Fixtures Secretary: Neil Evans, Apple Orchard, Chapel Lane, Kinshan, Nr Tewkesbury, Glos.

CLEOBURY MORTIMER RFC
Ground Address:Collinghurst Meadow, Old St, Upton-upon-Severn. Tel: 0684 594445
Club Secretary: Peter Baker, Tiltridge Farm, Upper Hook Road, Upton-Upon-Severn, Worcs, WR8 0SA. Tel: (H) 0684 592906
Club Colours: Black and white quarters.

LEDBURY RFC
Ground Address:Ross Road Playing Field, Ross Road, Ledbury. Tel: 0531 631788
Club Secretary: Mrs Sally Rowberry, 53 Oatleys Crescent, Ledbury, Herefordshire HR8 2BY. Tel: (H) 0531 633926
Fixtures Secretary: Mr R Jones, 18 The Southend, Ledbury, Herefordshire HR8 2EY. Tel: (H) 0531 635143
Club Colours: Black & white.

OLD MOSELEIANS RFC
Ground Address:Lugtrout Lane, Solihull, West Midlands. Tel: 021 705 7847
Club Secretary: John Stefani, 6 Stand Street, Warwick CV34 6HR. Tel: (H) 0926 497275 Tel: (W) 0926 464511
Fixtures Secretary: Mick Fielding, 96 Vera Road, Yardley, Birmingham B26 1TT. Tel: (H) 021 783 6333 Tel (W) 021 707 7111
Club Colours: Black shirts with red & white chest band, black shorts.

STOURPORT RFC
Ground Address:Playing Fields, Walshes Meadow, Stourport-on-Severn, Worcestershire. Tel: 0299 822210
Club Secretary: Andy Foster, Lime-Kilns, Pensax, Abberley, Worcs WR6 6XH. Tel: (H) 0299 896631
Fixtures Secretary: Mark Shuter, 6 Park Avenue, Stourport, Worcs DY13 8XT. Tel: (H) 0299 879324 Tel (W) 021 561 5561
Club Colours: Navy blue with gold V on chest.

THIMBLEMILL RFC
Ground Address:Thimblemill Recreation Centre, Thimblemill Road, Smethwick, Warley, West Midlands. Tel: 021 429 2459
Club Secretary: David Davis, 78 Wilmington Road, Quinton, Birmingham B32 1DY. Tel: (H) 021 422 4693
Fixtures Secretary: Simon Parker, 14 Mill Gardens, Thimblemill Road, Smethwick, Warley, West Midlands. Tel: (H) 021 420 3523
Club Colours: Green & blue quarters, red & white quarters.

FINAL TABLE

	P	W	D	L	F	A	PD	Pts
Upton-on-Severn	10	10	0	0	210	73	137	20
Birmingham C Serv	10	8	0	2	212	61	151	16
Bishops Castle	10	7	1	2	139	73	66	15
Ledbury	10	6	1	3	170	77	93	13
Stourport	10	6	0	4	137	91	46	12
Birchfield	10	4	0	6	138	156	-18	8
Yardley & District	10	4	0	6	98	144	-46	8
Cleobury Mortimer	10	4	0	6	84	139	-55	8
Witton	10	3	0	7	98	139	-41	6
Oswestry	10	2	0	8	112	136	-24	4
Thimblemill	10	0	0	10	39	348	-309	0

WITTON RFC
Ground Address:Ansells Sports & Social Club, Aldridge, Road, Perry Barr, Birmingham B42 2TP. Tel: 021 356 4296/021 356 2468
Club Secretary: Mr AS Reed, 4A Rectory Road, Sutton Coldfield, West Midlands B75 7AL. Tel: (H) 021 321 2036 Tel: (W) 021 359 6436
Fixtures Secretary: Mr C Sadler, 634 Queslett Road, Great Barr, Birmingham B43 7DU. Tel: (H) 021 360 3821
Club Colours: Black shirts wiht gold V, black shorts, black socks.

WULFRUN RUFC
Ground Address:Wednesfield High School, Lakefield Road, Wednesfield, Wolverhampton, West Midlands. Tel: 0902 732470
Club Secretary: C Withers, 138 Old Park Road, Dudley, West Midlands DY1 3ND. Tel: (H) 0902 672 932 Tel: (W) 021 322 6010
Fixtures Secretary: C Turner, 148 Warstones Drive, Warstones, Wolverhampton, West Midlands WV4 6NJ. Tel: (H) 0902 653018
Club Colours: Emerald green with black V, black shorts.

YARDLEY & DISTRICT RFC
Ground Address:1 Coleham Lane, Stechford, Birmingham. Tel: 021 789 8450
Club Secretary: Joan Thornton, 45 St Gerards Road, Solihull, West Midlands B91 1UB. Tel: (H) 021 704 2973 Tel: (W) 021 212 2362
Fixtures Secretary: Mark Homans, 26 The Cedars, off Dove Close, Yardley B25 8XZ. Tel: (H) 026 624 4904 Tel (W) 021 743 8242
Club Colours: Blue & gold hoops.

MIDLAND DIVISION

MIDLAND EAST ONE
1994-95
FIXTURES

January 7 (Week 17)
Kettering v Chesterfield
Long Buckby v Biggleswade
Scunthorpe v Northampton BBOB
Spalding v Stoneygate
Vipers v Ampthill
Wellingborough v Amber Valley

September 17 (Week 3)
Ampthill v Amber Valley
Biggleswade v Northampton BBOB
Chesterfield v Stoneygate
Kettering v Stewarts & Lloyds
Long Buckby v Spalding
Vipers v Southorpe

January 14 (Week 18)
Amber Valley v Scunthorpe
Ampthill v Wellingborough
Biggleswade v Vipers
Chesterfield v Long Buckby
Northampton BBOB v Spalding
Stoneygate v Stewarts & Lloyds

September 24 Week 24)
Amber Valley v Biggleswade
Northampton BBOB v Chesterfield
Scunthorpe v Wellingborough
Spalding v Vipers
Stewarts & Lloyds v Long Buckby
Stoneygate v Kettering

February 11 (Week 22)
Long Buckby v Kettering
Scunthorpe v Ampthill
Spalding v Amber Valley
Stewarts & Lloyds v Northampton BBOB
Vipers v Chesterfield
Wellingborough v Biggleswade

October 1 (Week 5)
Biggleswade v Ampthill
Chesterfield v Amber Valley
Kettering v Northampton BBOB
Long Buckby v Stoneygate
Vipers v Stewarts & Lloyds
Wellingborough v Spalding

February 25 (Week 24)
Amber Valley v Stewarts & Lloyds
Ampthill v Spalding
Biggleswade v Scunthorpe
Chesterfield v Wellingborough
Kettering v Vipers
Northampton BBOB v Stoneygate

October 15 (Week 7)
Amber Valley v Kettering
Ampthill v Chesterfield
Northampton BBOB v Long Buckby
Spalding v Scunthorpe
Stewarts & Lloyds v Wellingborough
Stoneygate v Vipers

March 4 (Week 25)
Scunthorpe v Chesterfield
Spalding v Biggleswade
Stewarts & Lloyds v Ampthill
Stoneygate v Amber Valley
Vipers v Long Buckby
Wellingborough v Kettering

October 22 (Week 8)
Chesterfield v Biggleswade
Kettering v Ampthill
Long Buckby v Amber Valley
Vipers v Northampton BBOB
Wellingborough v Stoneygate
Scunthorpe v Stewarts & Lloyds

March 25 (Week 28)
Amber Valley v Northampton BBOB
Ampthill v Stoneygate
Biggleswade v Stewarts & Lloyds
Chesterfield v Spalding
Kettering v Scunthorpe
Long Buckby v Wellingborough

October 29 (Weel X2)
Amber Valley v Vipers
Ampthill v Long Buckby
Biggleswade v Kettering
Northampton BBOB v Wellingborough
Stewarts & Lloyds v Spalding
Stoneygate v Scunthorpe

April 8 (Week 30)
Northampton BBOB v Ampthill
Scunthorpe v Long Buckby
Spalding v Kettering
Stewarts & Lloyds v Chesterfield
Stoneygate v Biggleswade
Wellingborough v Vipers

MIDLANDS EAST ONE

AMBER VALLEY RUFC
Ground Address:Pye Bridge, Lower Somercotes, Alfreton, Derbyshire. Tel: 0773 541 368
Club Secretary: Rachel Bucknall, Twitchell House, 47 West Street, Riddings, Alfreton, Derbyshire DE55 4EW. Tel: (H) 0773 603374 Tel: (W) 0602 305522 x266
Fixtures Secretary: M Tom, 34 Beauve Way, Swanwick DE55 1DR. Tel: (H) 0773 541953
Club Colours: Amber & black.

AMPTHILL & DISTRICT RUFC
Ground Address:Dillingham Park, Woburn Road, Ampthill, Bedford MK45 2HX. Tel: 0525 403303
Club Secretary: Richard Churchill, The Bungalow, Park Gardens, Bletchley, Milton Keynes MK3 6HT. Tel: (H) 0908 379089
Fixtures Secretary: Roy Duffin, 24 Dunstable Road, Ampthill, Bedfod MK45 2RR. Tel: (H) 0525 402669 Tel (W) 0234 350389
Club Colours: Maroon & amber.

BIGGLESWADE RUFC
Ground Address:Langford Road, Biggleswade, Beds SG18 9RA. Tel: 0767 312463
Club Secretary: Mike Williams, 8 Laurel Way, Ickleford, Hitchin, Herts SG5 3UP. Tel: (H) 0462 454782 Tel: (W) 0462 424224
Fixtures Secretary: Mike Pearson, 1 Marlowes Courts, Eaton Ford, St Neots, Cambs PE19 3LG. Tel: (H) 0480 385077
Club Colours: Navy blue with red hoop.

CHESTERFIELD RUFC
Ground Address:Sheffield Road, Stonegravels, Chesterfield. Tel: 0246 232321
Club Secretary: PI Jackson, 396 Old Road, Chesterfield S40 3QF. Tel: (H) 0246 568287 Tel: (W) 0246 270112
Fixtures Secretary: M Lord, 34 Pennine Way, Loundsley Green, Chesterfield. Tel: (H) 0246 274105
Club Colours: Red & white hoops, white shorts.

KETTERING RFC
Ground Address:Waverley Road, Kettering, NN15 6NT. Tel: 0536 85589
Club Secretary: Michael Evans, 40 Brooksdale Close, Kettering, Northants, NN16 9BJ. Tel: (H) 0536 514695 Tel: (W) 0933 225445
Fixtures Secretary: Rob Bowley, Messyage Farmhouse, 10 Lower Benefield, Peterborough. Tel: (H) 0832 5382
Club Colours: Blue & white hoops, navy shorts.

LONG BUCKBY RFC
Ground Address:Station Road, Long Buckby, Northamptonshire NN6 7QA. Tel: 0327 842222
Club Secretary: P J Osborne, Ashthorne, Teeton Road, Ravensthorpe, Northamptonshire NN6 8EJ. Tel: (H) 0604 770772 Tel: (W) 0327 705785
Fixtures Secretary: S Ruddlesdin, 37 Rockhill Road, Long Buckby, Northamptonshire NN6 7QS. Tel: (H) 0327 842933
Club Colours: Emerald green.

NORTHAMPTON BOYS BRIGADE OLD BOYS RFC
Ground Address:St Andrews Hill, St Andrews Road, Northampton. Tel: 0604 32460
Club Secretary: Mrs S Jeffery, 218 Eastern Avenue, North Kingsthorpe, Northampton NN2 7AT. Tel: (H) 0604 717947
Fixtures Secretary: Mr P Johnson, 164 Gladstone Road, Northampton. Tel: (H) 0604 586421
Club Colours: Light blue, dark blue & maroon hoops, black shorts.

SCUNTHORPE RUFC
Ground Address:Heslam Park, The Queensway, Scunthorpe (Entrance from Ashby Road). Tel: 0724 843013
Club Secretary: Mr AS Bagsman, 51 Old Brumby Street, Scunthorpe, South Humberside DN16 2AJ. Tel: (H) 0724 849838 Tel: (W) 0724 280666

FINAL TABLE

	P	W	D	L	F	A	PD	Pts
Hinckley	12	10	0	2	223	97	126	20
Scunthorpe	12	9	0	3	172	109	63	18
Ampthill	12	8	1	3	198	142	56	17
Kettering	12	9	0	3	182	98	84	16
Stoneygate	12	7	0	5	121	117	4	14
Biggleswade	12	5	1	6	117	146	-29	11
Chesterfield	12	5	1	6	110	140	-30	11
Stewarts & Lloyds	12	4	1	7	128	132	-4	9
Northampton B B	12	4	0	8	111	162	-51	8
Spalding	12	5	1	6	167	138	29	7
Amber Valley	12	3	1	8	112	164	-52	7
Luton	12	2	1	9	121	184	-63	5
Moderns	12	3	1	8	119	252	-133	3

Fixtures Secretary: Nr N Cleal, 18 Cheltenham Close, Bottesford, South Humberside. Tel: (H) 0724 856801 Tel (W) 0724 843411
Club Colours: Lincoln green shirts with white collars, white shorts, green socks.

SPALDING RFC
Ground Address:Memorial Field, St Thomas Road, Spalding, Lincs PE11 2TT. Tel: 0775 725191
Club Secretary: Mr S Barber, 28 The Terrace, London Road, Spalding, Lincs PE11 2TA. Tel: (H) 0775 722073 Tel: (W) 0775 724261
Fixtures Secretary: Mr J Constable, 14 Amsterdam Gardens, Spalding, Lincs. Tel: (H) 0775 723790
Club Colours: Maroon & navy blue hoops.

STEWARTS & LLOYDS RFC
Ground Address:Occupation Road, Corby, Northants NN17 1EH. Tel: 0536 400317
Club Secretary: JM Thompson, 5 Howe Crescent, Corby, Northants NN17 2RY. Tel: (H) 0536 202433
Fixtures Secretary: D Murdoch, 12 Deene Close, Crby, Northants NN17 1HY. Tel: (H) 0536 204930 Tel (W) 0536 203381
Club Colours: Black shirts & shorts, black & white socks.

STONEYGATE FC
Ground Address:Covert Lane, Scraptoft, Leics LE7 9SP. Tel: 0533 419188
Club Secretary: Steve Morris, 203 Evington Lane, Evington, Leicester LE5 6DJ. Tel: (H) 0533 735927 Tel: (W) 0533 628596
Fixtures Secretary: Roger Foxon, 33 Buddon Lane, Quorn, Leics LE12 8AA. Tel: (H) 0509 415529 Tel (W) 0533 625564
Club Colours: Cardinal red & white hoops, navy shorts.

VIPERS RFC
Ground Address:Blaby Bypass, Whetstone, Leicester. Tel: 0533 864777
Club Secretary: Mr Paul A Hutchinson, 52 Narborough Road, South, Leicester LE3 2FN. Tel: (H) 0533 899258
Fixtures Secretary: Mr Colin Underwood, 12 Hazelbank Road, Countesthorpe, Leicester LE8 3RR. Tel: (H) 0533 776263
Club Colours: Black, green & gold jerseys, black shorts.

WELLINGBOROUGH RFC
Ground Address:Cut Throat Lane, Great Doddington, Wellingborough, Northants. Tel: 0933 222260
Club Secretary: Bob Stevenson, 12 South Street, Wollaston, Northants NN29 7RX. Tel: (H) 0933 664538 Tel: (W) 0933 226077
Fixtures Secretary: Chris Logan, 25 Lynford Way, Rushden, Northants NN10 9LZ. Tel: (H) 0933 315810
Club Colours: White shirts with red hoop, navy shorts.

MIDLAND DIVISION

MIDLAND EAST TWO
1994-95
FIXTURES

September 17 (Week 3)
Huntingdon v Coalville
Lutterworth v South Leicester
Luton v Mellish
Lincoln v West Bridgford
Grimsby v Moderns
Ilkeston v Worksop

September 24 (Week 4)
Coalville v Ilkeston
Worksop v Grimsby
Moderns v Lincoln
West Bridgford v Luton
Mellish v Lutterworth
South Leicester v Kibworth

October 1 Week 5)
Grimsby v Coalville
Ilkeston v Huntingdon
Kibworth v Mellish
Lutterworth v West Bridgford
Luton v Moderns
Lincoln v Worksop

October 15 (Week 7)
Huntingdon v Grimsby
Coalville v Lincoln
Worksop v Luton
Moderns v Lutterworth
West Bridgford v Kibworth
Mellish v South Leicester

October 22 (Week 8)
Luton v Coalville
Lincoln v Huntingdon
Grimsby v Ilkeston
South Leicester v West Bridgford
Kibworth v Moderns
Lutterworth v Worksop

October 29 (Week X2)
Ilkeston v Lincoln
Huntingdon v Luton
Coalville v Lutterworth
Worksop v Kibworth
Moderns v South Leicester
West Bridgford v Mellish

January 7 (Week 17)
Kibworth v Coalville
Lutterworth v Huntingdon
Luton v Ilkeston
Lincoln v Grimsby
Mellish v Moderns
South Leicester v Worksop

January 14 (Week 18)
Grimsby v Luton
Ilkeston v Lutterworth
Huntingdon v Kibworth
Coalville v South Leicester
Worksop v Mellish
Moderns v West Bridgford

February 11 (Week 22)
Mellish v Coalville
South Leicester v Huntingdon
Kibworth v Ilkeston
Lutterworth v Grimsby
Luton v Lincoln
West Bridgford v Worksop

February 25 (Week 24)
Lincoln v Lutterworth
Grimsby v Kibworth
Ilkeston v South Leicester
Huntingdon v Mellish
Coalville v West Bridgford
Worksop v Moderns

March 4 (Week 25)
Moderns v Coalville
West Bridgford v Huntingdon
Mellish v Ilkeston
South Leicester v Grimsby
Kibworth v Lincoln
Lutterworth v Luton

March 25 (Week 28)
Luton v Kibworth
Lincoln v South Leicester
Grimsby v Mellish
Ilkeston v West Bridgford
Huntingdon v Moderns
Coalville v Worksop

April 8 Week 30
Worksop v Huntingdon
Moderns v Ilkeston
West Bridgford v Grimsby
Mellish v Lincoln
South Leicester v Luton
Kibworth v Lutterworth

MIDLANDS EAST TWO

COALVILLE RFC
Ground Address: Memorial Ground, Broomleys Road, Coalville, Leics. Tel: 0530 812090
Club Secretary: P Smith, 50 Parkdale, Ibstock, Leics LE67 1JW. Tel: (H) 0530 262113 Tel: (W) 0530 832085
Fixtures Secretary: M Bateman, 31 Curzon Street, Ibstock, Leics. Tel: (H) 0530 262304
Club Colours: Navy shirts with amber chest band & white shorts.

GRIMSBY RUFC
Ground Address: Springfield Road, Grimsby, Sth Humberside, DN33 3JE. Tel: 0472 878594
Club Secretary: Mr D T Foulkes, 18 Amesbury Avenue, Grimsby, Sth Humberside, DN33 3HT. Tel: (H) 0472 826078 Tel: (W) 0472 887117
Fixtures Secretary: Mr R I Campodonic, 35 Bulwick Avenue, Grimsby, Sth Humberside. Tel: (H) 0472 825904
Club Colours: Royal blue shirts, white shorts.

HUNTINGDON RUFC
Ground Address: The Racecourse, Brampton, Huntingdon.
Club Secretary: John Buckingham, The Gables, Chestnut Grove, Great Stukely, Huntingdon. Tel: (H) 0480 455888 Tel: (W) 0480 414411
Fixtures Secretary: Tim Tack, 37 Egremont Road, Hardwick, Cambridge CB3 7XR. Tel: (H) 0954 211140 Tel (W) 0223 833121
Club Colours: Green shirts, blue shorts, green socks.

ILKESTON RUFC
Ground Address: Gallows Inn Fields, Nottingham Road, Ilkeston, Derbyshire. Tel: 0602 323088
Club Secretary: Ean Wykes, 8 Carman Close, Watnall, Notts NG16 1JX. Tel: (H) 0602 384307 Tel: (W) 0602 384307
Fixtures Secretary: Colin Fox, 36 Nuthall Circle, Kirk Hallam, Ilkeston, Derbyshire DE7 4GU. Tel: (H) 0602 308421
Club Colours: White, green & blue hoops.

KIBWORTH RUFC
Ground Address: Northampton Road, Market Harborough, Leicestershire. Tel: 0858 464210
Club Secretary: DR Coe, 11 Little Meadow, Great Oakley, Corby, Northamptonshire NN18 8JN. Tel: (H) 0536 402680 Tel: (W) 0536 402551 x3112
Fixtures Secretary: E Gregory, 5 Manor Road, Great Bowden, Market Harborough, Leicestershire LE16 7HE. Tel: (H) 0858 465550 Tel (W) 0858 465550
Club Colours: Black shirts, black shorts.

LINCOLN RFC
Ground Address: The Lindum, St Giles Avenue, Wragby Road, Lincoln LN2 4PE. Tel: 0522 526592
Club Secretary: J Grove, 11 Broadway Close, Broadway, Lincoln LN2 1SW. Tel: (H) 0522 525724 Tel: (W) 0522 513434
Fixtures Secretary: Mr E Coulthard, 25 Queensway, Lincoln. Tel: (H) 0522 533666 Tel (W) 0522 532191
Club Colours: Red, white & bottle green jerseys, green shorts.

LUTON RFC
Ground Address: Newlands Road, Luton, Beds LU1 4BQ. Tel: 0582 20355
Club Secretary: PJ Wilson, 17 Burghley Close, Flitwick, Bedford MK45 1TF. Tel: (H) 0525 713409 Tel: (W) 071 305 6929
Fixtures Secretary: Martin Alexander, 9 Glenfield Road, Luton, Beds LU3 2HZ. Tel: (H) 0582 598581 Tel (W) 0582 22333
Club Colours: Green with red & white hoops.

LUTTERWORTH RFC
Ground Address: Ashby Lane, Bitteswell, Nr Lutterworth, Leics. Tel: 0455 557329
Club Secretary: Colin Hudson, Mason & Bowns cottage,

FINAL TABLE

	P	W	D	L	F	A	PD	Pts
Long Buckby	12	12	0	0	299	77	222	24
Wellingborough	12	10	0	2	288	120	168	20
Kibworth	12	8	1	3	176	134	42	17
Worksop	12	7	1	4	126	98	28	15
South Leicester	12	7	0	5	184	110	74	14
Lutterworth	12	6	0	6	132	108	24	12
Lincoln	12	6	0	6	159	146	13	12
Grimsby	12	5	1	6	138	164	-26	11
West Bridgford	12	6	0	6	168	182	-14	10
Mellish	12	5	0	7	117	187	-70	10
Coalville	12	2	1	9	108	170	-62	5
Kesteven	12	2	0	10	84	192	-108	4
Dronfield	12	0	0	12	62	353	-291	0

Ashby Parva, Nr Lutterworth, Leics LE17 5HY. Tel: (H) 0455 209053 Tel: (W) 0788 577191
Fixtures Secretary: Chris Payne, Cawder Ghyll, Shawell, Nr Lutterworth, Leics LE17 6AG.
Club Colours: Red, green & white hoops.

MELLISH RFC
Ground Address: The Memorial Ground, Plains Road, Mapperley, Nottingham NG3 5RT. Tel: 0602 266653
Club Secretary: Mark JB Wrench, 1 Arndale Road, Sherwood, Nottingham NG5 3GT. Tel: (H) 0602 264991 Tel: (W) 0602 282000
Fixtures Secretary: Graham Preston, 29a Little Ealing Lane, Ealing, London W5 4EB. Tel: (H) 081 579 1049
Club Colours: Black, yellow & green.

MODERNS RFC
Ground Address: Ferryfield, Main Road, Wilford, Nottingham. Tel: 0602 811374
Club Secretary: Alex Shipley, 84 Dean Close, Wollaton, Nottingham NG8 2BX. Tel: (H) 0602 285666
Fixtures Secretary: Alistair Clarke, 17 Mountsorrel Drive, Abbey Park, West Bridgford, Nottingham NG2 6LJ. Tel: (H) 0602 819207 Tel (W) 0602 781203
Club Colours: Red & white.

SOUTH LEICESTER RFC
Ground Address: Welford road, Wigston, Leicester LE18 1TE. Tel: 0533 882066
Club Secretary: Richard Dowdall, 4 Bodmin Avenue, Wigston, Leicester. Tel: (H) 0533 885606
Fixtures Secretary: David Cottom, 11 Heather Way, Countesthorpe, Leicester. Tel: (H) 0533 773615
Club Colours: Green & white hoops.

WEST BRIDGFORD RFC
Ground Address: The Memorial Ground, Stamford Road, West Bridgford, Nottingham. Tel: 0602 232506
Club Secretary: K Howells, 117 Mount Pleasant, Keyworth, Nottingham NE12 5ES. Tel: (H) 0602 374468
Fixtures Secretary: B Najdan, 41 Blake Road, West Bridgford, Nottingham. Tel: (H) 0602 816853
Club Colours: Black with red & gold hoops, black shorts & stockings.

WORKSOP RUFC
Ground Address: Stubbing Meadows, Stubbing Lane, Worksop, Notts. Tel: 0909 484247
Club Secretary: John H Gibson, c/o Worksop Rugby Club, Stubbing Lane, Worksop, Notts. Tel: (H) 0909 482439 Tel: (W) 0909 482439
Fixtures Secretary: Nick Gibson, 12 Maple Drive, Worksop, Notts S81 0LR. Tel: (H) 0909 487506
Club Colours: Black & white hoops, black shorts.

MIDLAND DIVISION

September 17 (Week 3)
Ashbourne   v Bakewell Mannerians
East Leake   v Kesteven
Glossop   v Dronfield
Long Eaton   v Nottingham Casuals
Melbourne   v Leesbrook Asterdale
Southwell   v Sleaford

September 24 (Week 4)
Bakewell Mannerians v Southwell
Dronfield   v Stamford
Kesteven   v Glossop
Leesbrook Asterdale v East Leake
Nottingham Casuals   v Melbourne
Sleaford   v Long Eaton

October 1 (Week 5)
East Leake v Nottingham Casuals
Glossop   v Leesbrook Asterdale
Long Eaton v Bakewell Mannerians
Melbourne   v Sleaford
Southwell   v Ashbourne
Stamford   v Kesteven

October 15 (Week 7)
Ashbourne   v Long Eaton
Bakewell Mannerians v Melbourne
Kesteven   v Dronfield
Leesbrook Asterdale v Stamford
Nottingham Casuals   v Glossop
Sleaford   v East Leake

October 22 (Week 8)
Dronfield   v Leesbrook Asterdale
East Leake v Bakewell Mannerians
Glossop   v Sleaford
Long Eaton v Southwell
Melbourne   v Ashbourne
Stamford   v Nottingham Casuals

October 29 (Week X2)
Ashbourne   v East Leake
Bakewell Mannerians v Glossop
Leesbrook Asterdale v Kesteven
Nottingham Casuals   v Dronfield
Sleaford   v Stamford
Southwell   v Melbourne

January 7 (Week 17)
Dronfield   v Sleaford
East Leake v Southwell
Glossop   v Ashbourne
Kesteven   v Nottingham Casuals
Melbourne   v Long Eaton
Stamford   v Bakewell Mannerians

January 14 (Week 18)
Ashbourne   v Stamford
Bakewell Mannerians v Dronfield
Long Eaton   v East Leake
Nottingham Casuals   v Leesbrook Asterdale
Sleaford   v Kesteven
Southwell   v Glossop

February 11 (Week 22)
Dronfield   v Ashbourne
East Leake   v Melbourne
Glossop   v Long Eaton
Kesteven   v Bakewell Mannerians
Leesbrook Asterdale v Sleaford
Stamford   v Southwell

February 25 (Week 24)
Ashbourne   v Kesteven
Bakewell Mannerians v Leesbrook Asterdale
Long Eaton   v Stamford
Melbourne   v Glossop
Sleaford   v Nottingham Casuals
Southwell   v Dronfield

March 4 (Week 25)
Dronfield   v Long Eaton
Glossop   v East leake
Kesteven   v Southwell
Leesbrook Asterdale v Ashbourne
Nottingham Casuals   v Bakewell Mannerians
Stamford   v Melbourne

March 25 (Week 28)
Ashbourne   v Nottingham Casuals
Bakewell Mannerians v Sleaford
East Leake   v Stamford
Long Eaton   v Kesteven
Melbourne   v Dronfield
Southwell   v Leesbrook Asterdale

April 8 (Week 30)
Dronfield   v East Leake
Kesteven   v Melbourne
Leesbrook Asterdale v Long Eaton
Nottingham Casuals   v Southwell
Sleaford   v Ashbourne
Stamford   v Glossop

NOTTS, LINCS & DERBY ONE

ASHBOURNE RUFC
Ground Address:The Recreation Ground, Ashbourne, Derbyshire
Club Secretary: Steve Jones, 20 North Leys, Ashbourne,
Derbyshire DE6 1DQ. Tel: (H) 0335 344753 Tel: (W) 0335
343821
Fixtures Secretary: Ian Jones, 18 Oak Crescent, Ashbourne,
Derbyshire. Tel: (H) 0335 344894 Tel (W) 0335 343243
Club Colours: Navy & old gold hoops.

BAKEWELL MANNERIANS RUFC
Ground Address:The Showground, Coombs Road, Bakewell,
Derbyshire.
Club Secretary: Tom Furness, Fern Bank, Brookfield Lane,
Bakewell, Derbyshire DE45 1AN. Tel: (H) 0629 812863 Tel:
(W) 0629 580000 x7186
Fixtures Secretary: John Oldfield, Oldfield Design, Riverside
Works, Buxton Road, Bakewell, Derbyshire DE45 1GJ. Tel:
(H) 0629 813186 Tel (W) 0629 813301
Club Colours: Dark blue, light blue & white hooped shirts,
navy shorts.

DRONFIELD RUFC
Ground Address:Dronfield (Gosforth) School, Carr Lane,
Dronfield Woodhouse, Nr Sheffield. Tel: 0742 890913
Club Secretary: Richard Nixon, 129 Ridgeway Road, Sheffield
S12 2SQ. Tel: (H) 0742 398510 Tel: (W) 0709 828500
Fixtures Secretary: Andy Longden, 109 Tadcaster Road,
Sheffield S8 0RA. Tel: (H) 0742 589643
Club Colours: Red shirts, black shorts.

EAST LEAKE RFC
Ground Address:East Leake Leisrue Centre, Lantern Lane,
East Leake, Notts. New ground: Costock Road Ravilion,
Costock Road, East Leake. Tel: 0509 852956
Club Secretary: Paul R Cobbin, 15 Old Way, Hathern,
Loughborough, Leicestershire LE12 5NH. Tel: (H) 0509
646354 Tel: (W) 0374 773514
Fixtures Secretary: Michael Kirton, 1 Coe Avenue,
Loughborough, Leics LE11 0SE. Tel: (H) 0509 217636 Tel (W)
0850 101635
Club Colours: Maroon & white hooped shirts & socks, black
shorts.

GLOSSOP RUFC
Ground Address:Hargate Hill Lane, Charlesworth,
Broadbottom, Hyde, Cheshire, SK13 9JL. Tel: 0457 864553
Club Secretary: Alastair May, 6 Kinder Grove, Romilet,
Stockport, SK6 4EU. Tel: (H) 061 427 5774 Tel: (W) 0457
864553
Fixtures Secretary: Dave Gerrard, 11 Burnside, Hadfield,
Hyde, Cheshire, SK14 8DX. Tel: (H) 0457 865014 Tel (W)
0742 735030
Club Colours: Blue and white quartered shirts.

KESTEVEN
Ground Address:Woodnook, Nr Grantham, Lincolnshire. Tel:
0476 64887
Club Secretary: Mr NJ Pert, 8 High Street, Ropsley, Nr
Grantham. Tel: (H) 0476 585352 Tel: (W) 0476 616314
Fixtures Secretary: Mr D Gilbert, 3 Blue Town, Skillington,
Nr Grantham. Tel: (H) 0476 860676 Tel (W) 0476 860676
Club Colours: Black shirts, white shorts.

LEESBROOK ASTERDALE RUFC
Ground Address:Asterdale Centre, Borrowash Road, Spondon,
Derby. Tel: 0332 668656
Club Secretary: Leon Davies, c/o DRS Victoria Chambers, 60
London Road, Derby DE1 2PA. Tel: (W) 0332 290188
Fixtures Secretary: Leigh Woodside, 1 South Drive,
Chaddesden, Derby DE21 6RZ. Tel: (H) 0332 673872 Tel (W)
0332 247658
Club Colours: Black, white, green & blue quarters, black
shorts.

LONG EATON RUFC
Ground Address:West Park, Long Eaton, Notts.
Club Secretary: Tony Suiter, 102 Trowell Grove, Long Eaton,
Notts NG10 4BB. Tel: (H) 0602 721267 Tel: (W) 0602 344776
Fixtures Secretary: Martyn Smith, 4 Hawthorne Avenue, Long
Eaton NG10 3NF. Tel: (H) 0602 736135 Tel (W) 0533 487101
Club Colours: Blue & white quartersw, black shorts, blue &
white socks.

FINAL TABLE

	P	W	D	L	F	A	PD	Pts
Ilkeston	12	12	0	0	250	92	158	24
Glossop	12	9	0	3	243	99	144	18
Stamford	12	6	2	4	162	109	53	14
Southwell	12	6	2	4	196	197	-1	14
Nottingham Cas	12	7	1	4	228	172	56	13
Sleaford	12	6	1	5	115	134	-19	13
Ashbourne	12	5	4	3	198	112	86	12
Bakewell Manns	12	6	0	6	178	169	9	12
East Leake	12	5	2	5	146	127	19	4
Long Eaton	12	5	0	7	185	155	30	2
Market Rsn & Louth	12	3	0	9	138	262	-124	2
Keyworth	12	2	0	10	112	274	-162	2
Meden Vale	12	0	0	12	73	322	-249	0

MELBOURNE RFC
Ground Address:Recreation Ground, Cockshot Lane,
Melbourne, Derbyshire.
Club Secretary: Miss Victoria Coley, 43 Vicarage Road,
Mickleover, Derby. Tel: (H) 0332 511233 Tel: (W) 0332
242424
Fixtures Secretary: Mr D Carver, 21 Selina Street, Melbourne,
Derby. Tel: (H) Melbourne 864446 Tel (W) Melbourne 864446
Club Colours: Bottle green shirts, white shorts.

NOTTINGHAM CASUALS RFC
Ground Address:Canal Side, Meadow Road, Beeston Rylands,
Nottingham NG9 1JG. Tel: 0602 250135
Club Secretary: A Rothera, 36 Harcourt Street, Beeston,
Nottingham NG9 1EY. Tel: (H) 0602 257427 Tel: (W) 0602
514489
Fixtures Secretary: J Lillestone, 16 Chapel Fields, Swinford,
Leics LE17 6BS. Tel: (H) 0788 860530
Club Colours: White with maroon hoops.

SLEAFORD RFC
Ground Address:Sleaford RFC, East Road, Sleaford. Tel:
0529 303335
Club Secretary: Andrew Sharpe, 5 Pinewood Drive,
Grantham, Lincs NG31 8QQ. Tel: (H) 0476 70976 Tel: (W)
0476 66363
Fixtures Secretary: George Marsh, 37 Meadow Field,
Sleaford. Tel: (H) 0529 303859
Club Colours: Red & black hooped shirts, black shorts, red
socks.

SOUTHWELL RUFC
Ground Address:Pentelows, Park Lane, Southwell, Notts. Tel:
0636 812576
Club Secretary: Tim Brooks, 116 Westgate, Southwell, Notts
NG25 0LT. Tel: (H) 0636 816189 Tel: (W) 0602 812125
Fixtures Secretary: Alaster Anderson, 76 Bonner Lane,
Calverton, Notts. Tel: (H) 0602 652268 Tel (W) 0636 814667
Club Colours: Maroon shirts, navy blue shorts.

STAMFORD RUFC
Ground Address:Hambleton Road, Stamford, Lincs. Tel: 0780
52180
Club Secretary: NM Jolly, 21 Chatsworth Road, Stamford,
Lincs. Tel: (H) 0780 52134 Tel: (W) 0780 720501
Fixtures Secretary: A Baker, 27 Queens Walk, Stamford,
Lincs. Tel: (H) 0780 56367
Club Colours: Purple, black & white, black shorts.

MIDLAND DIVISION

NOTTS, LINCS & DERBY TWO 1994-95 FIXTURES

January 7 (Week 17)
Ashfield Swans v Buxton
Barton & District v Meden Vale
Bingham v Boston
East Retford v Market Rasen & Louth
North Kesteven v Keyworth
Rolls Royce v All Spartans

September 17 (Week 3)
All Spartans v Market Rasen & Louth
Ashfield Swans v Barton & District
Buxton v Boston
Keyworth v Meden Vale
North Kesteven v East Retford
Rolls Royce v Notts Constabulary

January 14 (Week 18)
All Spartans v North Kesteven
Boston v Barton & District
Buxton v Bingham
Keyworth v Ashfield Swans
Market Rasen & Louth v Notts Constabulary
Meden Vale v East Retford

September 24 (Week 4)
Barton & District v Bingham
Boston v Keyworth
East Retford v Ashfield Swans
Market Rasen & Louth v Rolls Royce
Meden Vale v All Spartans
Notts Constabulary v North Kesteven

February 11 (Week 22)
Ashfield Swans v All Spartans
Barton & District v Buxton
Bingham v Keyworth
East Retford v Boston
North Kesteven v Rolls Royce
Notts Constabulary v Meden Vale

October 1 (Week 5)
All Spartans v Boston
Ashfield Swans v Notts Constabulary
Bingham v East Retford
Keyworth v Buxton
North Kesteven v Market Rasen & Louth
Rolls Royce v Meden Vale

February 25 (Week 24)
All Spartans v Bingham
Boston v Notts Constabulary
Buxton v East Retford
Keyworth v Barton & District
Meden Vale v Market Rasen & Lough
Rolls Royce v Ashfield Swans

October 15 (Week 7)
Boston v Rolls Royce
Buxton v All Spartans
East Retford v Barton & District
Market Rasen & Louth v Ashfield Swans
Meden Vale v North Kesteven
Notts Constabulary v Bingham

March 4 (Week 25)
Ashfield Swans v North Kesteven
Barton & District v All Spartans
Bingham v Rolls Royce
East Retford v Keyworth
Market Rasen & Louth v Boston
Notts Constabulary v Buxton

October 22 (Week 8)
All Spartans v Keyworth
Ashfield Swans v Meden Vale
Barton & District v Notts Constabulary
Bingham v Market Rasen & Louth
North Kesteven v Boston
Rolls Royce v Buxton

April 8 (Week 30)
Barton & District v North Kesteven
Bingham v Ashfield Swans
East Retford v Rolls Royce
Market Rasen & Lough v Keyworth
Meden Vale v Buxton
Notts Constabulary v All Spartans

October 29 (Week X2)
Boston v Ashfield Swans
Buxton v North Kesteven
Keyworth v Rolls Royce
Market Rasen & Louth v Barton & District
Meden Vale v Bingham
Notts Constabulary v East Retford

NOTTS, LINCS & DERBY TWO

ALL SPARTANS RUFC
Ground Address: Sutton Lawn, Station Road, Sutton in Ashfield, Notts. Tel: 0623 554554
Club Secretary: Joe Higgins, 7 Blenheim Close, Forest Town, Mansfield, Notts NG19 0PN. Tel: (H) 0623 641985
Fixtures Secretary: John Chambers, 12 Berry Hill Lane, Mansfield, Notts NG18 4BQ. Tel: (H) 0623 641391
Club Colours: Blue shirts with broad amber hoop, black shorts, blue socks.
ASHFIELD SWANS RUFC
Ground Address: Ashfield School, Sutton Road, Kirkby in Ashfield, Notts. Tel: 0623 752403
Club Secretary: Stephen Trainer, 12 Belfry Close, Broadlands Park, Kirkby-in-Ashfield, Notts NG17 8NS. Tel: (H) 0623 443744 Tel: (W) 0602 657276
Fixtures Secretary: Peter Bonsor, 3 Lindley Street, Selston, Notts NG16 6DP. Tel: (H) 0773 860872
Club Colours: Red & black quarters, black shorts.
BARTON & DISTRICT RUFC
Ground Address: Mill Lane, Barrow-on-Humber, South Humberside.
Club Secretary: Tim Phipps, 4 West Acridge, Barton-on-Humber, South Humberside. Tel: (H) 0652 632373 Tel: (W) 0724 847888
Fixtures Secretary: Andy Snowden, Western Villa, High Burbage, Winteringham, South Humberside. Tel: (H) 0724 734629
Club Colours: Red & white hoops.
BINGHAM RUFC
Ground Address: Town Pavilion, Brendon Grove, Wynhill, Bingham, Notts. Tel: 0949 832874
Club Secretary: JW Mitton, 10 Dark Lane, Whatton, Notts NG13 9FE. Tel: (H) 0949 51238 Tel: (W) 0602 350928
Fixtures Secretary: RJ Williams, Crown House, High Street, Collingham, Notts. Tel: (H) 0636 823307
Club Colours: Green & red hoops.
BOSTON RFC
Ground Address: Great Fen Road, Wyberton, Boston, Lincs PE2 7PB. Tel: 0205 362683
Club Secretary: Mrs Lynn Creasey, 48 Glen Drive, Boston, Lincs PE21 7QB. Tel: (H) 0205 356753 Tel: (W) 0205 313000
Fixtures Secretary: Mr T Bembridge, 5 Blackthorne Lane, Boston, Lincs PE21 9BG. Tel: (H) 0205 351973
Club Colours: Blue & white hoops.
BUXTON RUFC
Ground Address: Fairfield Centre, Victoria Park Road, Fairfield, Buxton, Derbyshire. Tel: 0298 24081
Club Secretary: DR Allsop, Flat 1, 155 Park Road, Buxton. Tel: (H) 0298 22517 Tel: (W) 0298 22517
Fixtures Secretary: P Campbell, 7 Sylvan Cliff, Buxton. Tel: (H) 0298 73112
Club Colours: Navy, red & gold hoops.
EAST RETFORD RUFC
Ground Address: Club House, Ordsall Road, Retford, Nottinghamshire. Tel: 0777 703243
Club Secretary: EM Henderson, 51 Trent Street, Nottinghamshire DN22 6NG. Tel: (H) 0777 706987 Tel: (W) 0909 476724
Fixtures Secretary: BJ Dudley, 21 Southfall Close, Ranskill, Nottinghamshire. Tel: (H) 0777 818616 Tel (W) 0724 784433
Club Colours: Green & amber horizontal hoops.
KEYWORTH RFC
Ground Address: The Pavilion, Willoughby Lane, Widmerpool, Nottinghamshire NG2 6EZ. Tel: 0602 375579
Club Secretary: MP Tyrrell, 60 Peterborough Road, Farcet, Peterborough, Cambs PE7 3BN. Tel: (H) 0733 310468 Tel: (W) 0733 310468
Fixtures Secretary: D Hathaway, 5 Brockwood Crescent,

FINAL TABLE

	P	W	D	L	F	A	PD	Pts
Leesbrook	12	12	0	0	378	57	321	24
Melbourne	12	9	1	2	262	75	187	19
Notts Cons	12	9	1	2	212	137	75	19
East Retford	12	9	0	3	243	110	113	18
Ashfield Swans	12	7	2	3	135	126	9	16
Rolls Royce	12	5	1	6	196	154	42	11
Buxton	12	5	0	7	176	152	24	10
Boston	12	3	3	6	121	186	-65	9
All Spartans	12	4	1	7	103	174	-71	9
Bingham	12	3	1	8	60	212	-152	5
Boots Athletic	12	2	0	10	107	277	-170	4
Nottinghamians	12	2	2	8	77	240	-163	2
Stamford College	12	2	0	10	61	231	-170	2

Keyworth, Nottingham NG12 5HQ. Tel: (H) 0602 374380 Tel (W) 0602 760614
Club Colours: Black with gold stripes or gold with black stripes.
MARKET RASEN & LOUTH RUFC
Ground Address: Willingham Road, Market Rasen, Lincs. Tel: 0673 843162
Club Secretary: B Harper, Newgoby, Church Lane, Manby, Louth, Lincs, LN11 8HL. Tel: (H) 0507 327318
Fixtures Secretary: J Hole, Manesty, 1 Castle Walk, Caistor, Lincoln, LN7 6UG. Tel: (H) 0472 851653
Club Colours: Red & green.
MEDEN VALE RFC
Ground Address: Welbeck Colliery Miners Welfare Institute, Elkesley Road, Meden Vale, Notts. Tel: 0623 842267
Club Secretary: W Booth, 32 Morven Terrace, Warsop, Notts. Tel: (H) 0623 846530
Fixtures Secretary: E Davison, 25 Egmanton Road, Meden Vale, Notts. Tel: (H) 0623 842018
Club Colours: Red & black quarters, black shorts & socks.
NORTH KESTEVEN RUFC
Ground Address:PFA Sports & Social Club, rear of Memorial Hall, Newark road, North Hykeham, Lincoln. Tel: 0522 680193
Club Secretary: Kevin Flynn, 20 Stenigot Close, Doddiston Park, Lincoln LN6 3PB. Tel: (H) 0522 692409 Tel: (W) 0526 320472 x7247
Fixtures Secretary: Nigel Thomas, 192 Hykeham Road, Lincoln LN6 8AR. Tel: (H) 0522 696666
Club Colours: Black shirt with white, emerald & scarlet bands, black shorts.
NOTTINGHAMSHIRE CONSTABULARY RFC
Ground Address: Mellish RFC, Plains Road, Mapperley, Nottingham. Tel: 0602 266655
Club Secretary: Ian Winton, Olde Breck, 4 Hall Mews, Main Street, Papplewick, Nottingham. Tel: (H) 0602 640364 Tel: (W) 0602 482999
Fixtures Secretary: Martin Hewith, 10 The Mount, Redhill, Nottingham. Tel: (H) 204996 Tel (W) 0602 420999
Club Colours: Black/green quarters, black shorts.
ROLLS-ROYCE RFC
Ground Address: Merrill Way, Allenton, Derby. Tel: 0332 249167
Club Secretary: Neil Coleman, 64 Western Road, Mickleover, Derby, DE3 5GP. Tel: (H) 0332 518505 Tel: (W) 0332 249647
Fixtures Secretary: TBD.
Club Colours: Maroon/sky blue quarters.

MIDLAND DIVISION

NOTTS, LINCS & DERBY THREE 1994-95 FIXTURES

September 17 (Week 3)
Bolsover v Castle Donington
Boots Athletic v Stamford College
Gainsborough v Skegness
Belper v Ollerton
Nottinghamians v Tupton
Cotgrave v Horncastle

September 24 (Week 4)
Castle Donington v Boots Athletic
Stamford College v Gainsborough
Skegness v Belper
Ollerton v Nottinghamians
Tupton v Cotgrave
Horncastle v Derby University

October 1 (Week 5)
Boots Athletic v Bolsover
Gainsborough v Castle Donington
Belper v Stamford College
Nottinghamians v Skegness
Cotgrave v Ollerton
Derby v Tupton

October 15 (Week 7)
Bolsover v Gainsborough
Castle Donington v Belper
Stamford College v Nottinghamians
Skegness v Cotgrave
Ollerton v Derby University
Tupton v Horncastle

October 22 (Week 8)
Gainsborough v Boots Athletic
Belper v Bolsover
Nottinghamians v Castle Donington
Cotgrave v Stamford College
Derby University v Skegness
Horncastle v Ollerton

October 29 (Week X2)
Boots Athletic v Belper
Bolsover v Nottinghamians
Castle Donington v Cotgrave
Stamford College v Derby University
Skegness v Horncastle
Ollerton v Tupton

January 7 (Week 17)
Belper v Gainsborough
Nottinghamians v Boots Athletic
Cotgrave v Bolsover
Derby University v Castle Donington
Horncastle v Stamford College
Tupton v Skegness

January 14 (Week 18)
Gainsborough v Nottinghamians
Boots Athletic v Cotgrave
Bolsover v Derby University
Castle Donington v Horncastle
Stamford College v Tupton
Skegness v Ollerton

February 11 (Week 22)
Nottinghamians v Belper
Cotrave v Gainsborough
Derby University v Boots Athletic
Horncastle v Bolsover
Tupton v Castle Donington
Ollerton v Stamford College

February 25 (Week 24)
Belper v Cotgrave
Gainsborough v Derby University
Boots Athletic v Horncastle
Bolsover v Tupton
Castle Donington v Ollerton
Stamford College v Skegness

March 4 (Week 25)
Cotgrave v Nottinghamians
Derby University v Belper
Horncastle v Gainsborough
Tupton v Boots Athletic
Ollerton v Bolsover
Skegness v Castle Donington

March 25 (Week 28)
Nottinghamians v Derby University
Belper v Horncastle
Gainsborough v Tupton
Boots Athletic v Ollerton
Bolsover v Skegness
Castle Donington v Stamford College

April 8 (Week 30)
Derby University v Cotgrave
Horncastle v Nottinghamians
Tupton v Belper
Ollerton v Gainsborough
Skegness v Boots Athletic
Stamford College v Bolsover

NOTTS, LINCS & DERBY THREE

BELPER RUFC
Ground Address:Eyes Meadow, Duffield, Derbyshire.
Club Secretary: Chris Smith, Hillcrest, Hillcliffe Lane,
Turnditch, Derbyshire DE5 2EA. Tel: (H) 0773 550702
Tel: (W) 0332 332248
Fixtures Secretary: William Butler, 11 Pingle Crescent,
Belper, Derbyshire. Tel: (H) 0773 827116
Club Colours: Black & white hoops.

BOLSOVER RUFC
Ground Address:Oxcroft Rugby Ground, Stanfree,
Bolsover, Chesterfield, Derbyshire.
Club Secretary: Lynda Knight, 24 Shuttleworth Road,
Bolsover, Cheserfield, Derbyshire S44 6PA. Tel: (H) 0246
822418
Fixtures Secretary: Peter East, Coronation Cottage, Calow
Green, Chesterfield, Derbyshire S44 5XQ. Tel: (H) 0246
209686
Club Colours: Blue, gold & white hoops, blue shorts.

BOOTS ATHLETIC RUFC
Ground Address:1 Holme Road, Lady Bay, West
Bridgford, Nottingham. Tel: 0602 492388
Club Secretary: David Bright, c/o 218 Rutland Road,
West Bridgford, Nottingham. Tel: (W) 0602 592294
Fixtures Secretary: Mike Freemantle, 18 Kirkby Close,
Southwell, Notts NG25 0DG. Tel: (H) 0636 816433 Tel
(W) 0636 830302
Club Colours: Sky & navy blue quarters.

CASTLE DONINGTON RUFC
Ground Address:The Spittal Playing Fields, The Spittal,
Castle Donington, Derbyshire. Tel: (via Cross Keys pub)
0332 812214
Club Secretary: A Hackett, The Old Bakery, Thringstone,
Leicestershire LE67 5AP. Tel: (H) 0530 223599 Tel: (W)
0831 675987
Fixtures Secretary: Mr P Parry, 93 Park Lane, Castle
Donington, Derbyshire. Tel: (H) 0332 810351
Club Colours: Red & black quarters, black shorts, red &
black hoops on socks.

COTGRAVE COLLIERY RFC
Ground Address:Cotgrave Community Centre,
Woodview, Cotgrave, Nottinghamshire. Tel: 0602 892916
Club Secretary: Mr JP Robinson, 10 Fosse Walk,
Cotgrave, Nottingham NG12 3NZ. Tel: (H) 0602 892501
Fixtures Secretary: Mr I Jowett, 25 Rivermead, Cotgrave,
Nottingham. Tel: (H) 0602 899949
Club Colours: Claret & blue quarters.

GAINSBOROUGH RUFC
Ground Address:Rose Leisure, North Warren Road,
Gainsborough, Lincs. Tel: 0427 612915
Club Secretary: AC Lobley, Church View Cottage,
Gringley Road, Walkeringham, South Yorkshire
DN10 4HT. Tel: (H) 0427 890951 Tel: (W) 0427 612885
Fixtures Secretary: A Russell, Plot 29, The Meadows,
Holme Lane, Messingham. Tel: (H) 0427 616828
Club Colours: All black.

HORNCASTLE RFC
Ground Address:The Playing Fields, The Wong, Boston
Road, Horncastle. Tel: 0507 526 742
Club Secretary: Miss Teri Livingstone, 15a North Street,
Horncastle, Lincolnshire, LN9 5EB. Tel: (H) 0507 525568
Fixtures Secretary: Jeff Bentley, 1 Albert Cottages,
Chapel Lane, Legbourne, Gooth, Lincs, LN11 8LW. Tel:
(H) 0507 600318
Club Colours: Green & gold quarters, black shorts.

NOTTINGHAMIANS RFC
Ground Address:Adbolton Lane, West Bridgford,
Nottingham. Tel: 0602 811372
Club Secretary: Martin Wynne-Jones, 31 Ribblesdale
road, Sherwood, Nottingham NG5 3GY. Tel: (H) 0602
674901 Tel: (W) 0602 358565
Fixtures Secretary: Phil Quinn, 80 Dunster Road,

FINAL TABLE

	P	W	D	L	F	A	PD	Pts
North Kesteven	12	11	1	0	406	64	342	23
Barton & District	12	11	0	1	241	83	158	22
Derby College	12	7	0	5	178	142	36	14
Skegness	12	6	1	5	123	148	-25	13
Belper	12	6	0	6	147	128	19	12
Cotgrave	12	6	0	6	158	153	5	12
Tupton	12	5	1	6	121	152	-31	11
Gainsborough	12	4	2	6	127	123	4	10
Ollerton & Beverct	12	5	0	7	140	145	-5	10
Horncastle	12	5	0	7	164	280	-116	10
Bourne	12	4	0	8	189	220	-31	8
Cleethorpes	12	4	0	8	87	261	-174	8
Hope Valley	12	1	1	10	89	271	-182	3

Newthorpe, Notts NG16 2DW. Tel: (H) 0773 710668 Tel
(W) 0602 418418
Club Colours: Black, white & purple hoops.

OLLERTON RFC
Ground Address:Boughton Sports Field, Boughton
Village Hall, Church Road, Boughton, Newark, Notts.
Club Secretary: DG Price, Lathkill, Harrow Farm,
Tuxford Road, Boughton, Newark, Notts NG22 9JZ. Tel:
(H) 0623 860871
Fixtures Secretary: DG Price, Lathkill, Harrow Farm,
Tuxford Road, Boughton, Newark, Notts NG22 9JZ. Tel:
(H) 0623 860871
Club Colours: Yellow & blue hoops.

SKEGNESS RUFC
Ground Address:Wainfleet Road, Skegness. Tel: 0754
765699
Club Secretary: Alan Hawkes, Grunters Grange, East
Keal, Spilsby, Lincs. Tel: (H) 0790 752788
Fixtures Secretary: Jeremy Kendall, Flat 1, 12 Prince
Alfred Avenue, Skegness PE25 2UH. Tel: (H) 0754
761903 Tel (W) 0754 610101
Club Colours: Royal blue & white hoops, navy shorts.

STAMFORD COLLEGE RFC
Ground Address:Stamford College of Further Education,
Drift Road, Stamford, Lincs.
Club Secretary: Mr SD Harker, 31 Mountbatten Avenue,
Stamford, Lincs PE9 1HU. Tel: (H) 0780 53069
Fixtures Secretary: Brian Lonslow, 6 Park View, Barnack
Road, Stamford, Lincs PE9 2NG. Tel: (H) 0780 66195
Club Colours: Red & green hoops.

TUPTON RUFC
Ground Address:Recreation Ground, North Side, Tupton,
Chesterfield.
Club Secretary: Steve Robinson, 7 Gladstone Road,
Chesterfield, Derbyshire S40 4TE. Tel: (H) 0246 202857
Tel: (W) 0246 217522
Fixtures Secretary: Mr A Simpson, The End House,
Heath, Chesterfield S44 5RX. Tel: (H) 0246 850310
Club Colours: Navy blue with 3 yellow bands, black
shorts.

UNIVERSITY OF DERBY RUFC
Ground Address:University of Derby, Kedleston Road,
Derby, DE22 1GB. Tel: 0332 622222
Club Secretary: Dave French, 73 Cedar Street, Derby,
DE22 1GE. Tel: (H) 0332 371275 Tel: (W) 0332 622222
Ext 176
Fixtures Secretary: John Braybrooke, c/o Students'
Union, University of Derby, Kedleston Rd, Derby. Tel: (H)
0773 714856
Club Colours: Red & blue quarters.

MIDLAND DIVISION

NOTTS, LINCS & DERBY FOUR 1994-95 FIXTURES

September 17 (Week 3)
Cleethorpes v Bilsthorpe
Hope Valley v Yarborough Bees
Whitwell v Sutton Bonington

September 24 (Week 4)
Bilsthorpe v Bourne
Sutton Bonington v Hope Valley
Yarborough Bees v Cleethorpes

October 1 (Week 5)
Bourne v Yarborough Bees
Cleethorpes v Sutton Bonington
Hope Valley v Whitwell

October 15 (Week 7)
Sutton Bonington v Bourne
Whitwell v Cleethorpes
Yarborough Bees v Bilsthorpe

October 22 (Week 8)
Bilsthorpe v Sutton Bonington
Bourne v Whitwell
Cleethorpes v Hope Valley

October 29 (Week X2)
Hope Valley v Bourne
Sutton Bonington v Yarborough Bees
Whitwell v Bilsthorpe

November 12 (Week 10)
Bilsthorpe v Hope Valley
Bourne v Cleethorpes
Yarborough Bees v Whitwell

January 7 (Week 17)
Bilsthorpe v Cleethorpes
Sutton Bonington v Whitwell
Yarborough Bees v Hope Valley

January 14 (Week 18)
Bourne v Bilsthorpe
Cleethorpes v Yarborough Bees
Hope Valley v Sutton Bonington

February 11 (Week 22)
Sutton Bonington v Cleethorpes
Whitwell v Hope Valley
Yarborough Bees v Bourne

February 25 (Week 24)
Bilsthorpe v Yarborough Bees
Bourne v Sutton Bonington
Cleethorpes v Whitwell

March 4 (Week 25)
Hope Valley v Cleethorpes
Sutton Bonington v Bilsthorpe
Whitwell v Bourne

March 25 (Week 28)
Bilsthorpe v Whitwell
Bourne v Hope Valley
Yarborough Bees v Sutton Bonington

April 8 (Week 30)
Cleethorpes v Bourne
Hope Valley v Bilsthorpe
Whitwell v Yarborough Bees

NOTTS, LINCS & DERBY FOUR

BILSTHORPE RUFC
Ground Address:Bilsthorpe Sports Ground, Gakring
Road, Bilsthorpe, Newark, Notts. Tel: 0623 870049
Club Secretary: Terry Brown, 34 Church Street,
Bilsthorpe, Newark, Notts NG22 8PR. Tel: (H) 0623
411462
Fixtures Secretary: Andrew Marsden, 22 Greenwood
Avenue, Edwinstowe, Mansfield, Notts NG21 9QL. Tel:
(H) 0623 824767
Club Colours: Home: Black & yellow reversed quarters.
Away: Green, black & yellow hoops.
BOURNE RUFC
Ground Address:Milking Nook Drive, Spalding Road,
Bourne, Lincs. Tel: 0778 393346
Club Secretary: Andrew J Rowe, 54 North Road, Bourne,
Lincs PE10 9BT. Tel: (H) 0778 424353 Tel: (W) 0933
57511
Fixtures Secretary: Martyn Hunter, 16 Rochester Court,
Bourne, Lincs. Tel: (H) 0778 426536
Club Colours: Navy with amber hoop.
CLEETHORPES RUFC
Ground Address:Wilton Road, Cleethorpes. Tel: 0472
812936
Club Secretary: Alan Clark, 10 Cambridge Street,
Cleethorpes, South Humberside DN35 8HB. Tel: (H) 0472
692716 Tel: (W) 0469 572464
Fixtures Secretary: John Walsham, 38 Richmond Road,
Cleethorpes. Tel: (H) 0472 699322
Club Colours: Gold with blue hoops.
HOPE VALLEY RUFC
Ground Address:Castleton Playing Fields, Hollowford
Road, Castleton. Tel: c/o 0433 620247
Club Secretary: Ian Broad, 10 Farndale Road, Hillsboro',
Sheffield S6 1SH. Tel: (H) 0742 338264
Fixtures Secretary: Andy Woodall, 3 Brough Cottages,
Brough, Bradwell S30 2HG. Tel: (H) 0433 620698
Club Colours: Purple, green & white quarters, black shorts.
SUTTON BONNINGTON RFC
Ground Address:University of Nottingham, Faculty of
Agriculture, Sutton Bonnington, Loughborough, Leic.
LE12 5RD. Tel: 0602 515151 EXT 8648
Club Secretary: James Dunthorne. As above during term
time.
Club Colours: Black and green quarters, black shorts.
WHITWELL (1985) RUFC
Ground Address:Markland Campus, North Derbyshire
Tertiary College, Sheffield Road, Creswell, Notts. Tel:
0909 724908
Club Secretary: Mrs Jill Marshall, 3 Duke Street,
Whitwell, Worksop, Notts S80 4TH. Tel: (H) 0909 722060
Tel: (W) 0909 722060
Fixtures Secretary: Mr A Lamb, 5 Johns Street, Creswell,
Notts S80 4DF. Tel: (H) 0909 724753
Club Colours: Green shirts with black swirl.
YARBOROUGH BEES RFC
Ground Address:Yarborough Sports Centre, Riseholme
Road, Lincoln. Tel: 0522 524228
Club Secretary: H Sampson, 7 Shannon Avenue, Lincoln
LN6 7JG. Tel: (H) 0522 691631 Tel: (W) 0522 584510
Fixtures Secretary: D Small, 7 Wigsley Road, Doddington
Park, Lincoln. Tel: (H) 0522 690037
Club Colours: Maroon & amber.

FINAL TABLE

	P	W	D	L	F	A	PD	Pts
Bolsover	10	8	1	1	142	79	63	17
Yarborough Bees	10	5	2	3	121	75	46	12
Whitewell	10	6	0	4	154	110	44	12
Castle Donington	10	5	2	3	135	97	38	12
Sutton Bonnington	10	3	1	6	116	119	-3	7
Bilsthorpe	10	0	0	10	27	215	-188	0

Bolsover and Castle Donington promoted due to Rule 11(f)

MIDLAND DIVISION

EAST MIDLAND & LEICESTERSHIRE ONE 1994-95 FIXTURES

January 7 Week 17)
Market Bosworth v Melton Mowbray
Northampton Mens Own v Daventry
Northampton Old Scouts v Aylestone St James
Oadby Wyggestonians v St Neots
Old Bosworthians v Bedford Queens
Old Northamptonians v Dunstablians

September 17 (Week 3)
Bedford Queens v Dunstablians
Daventry v Melton Mowbray
Northampton Mens Own v Old Northamptonians
Oadby Wyggestonians v Market Bosworth
Old Bosworthians v Loughborough
St Neots v Aylestone St James

September 24 (Week 4)
Aylestone St James v Daventry
Dunstablians v Old Bosworthians
Loughborough v Northampton Mens Own
Market Bosworth v Northampton Old Scouts
Melton Mowbray v Bedrford Queens
Old Northamptonians v Oadby Wyggestonians

October 1 (Week 5)
Bedford Queens v Aylestone St James
Daventry v St Neots
Northampton Mens Own v Dunstablians
Northampton Old Scouts v Old Northamptonians
Oadby Wyggestonians v Loughborough
Old Bosworthians v Melton Mowbray

October 15 (Week 7)
Aylestone St James v Old Bosworthians
Dunstablians v Oadby Wuggestonians
Loughborough v Northampton Old Scouts
Melton Mowbray v Northampton Mens Own
Old Northamptonians v Market Bosworth
St Neots v Bedford Queens

October 22 (Week 8)
Bedford Queens v Daventry
Market Bosworth v Loughborough
Northampton Mens Own v Aylestone St James
Northampton Old Scouts v Dunstablians
Oadby Wyggestonians v Melton Mowbray
Old Bosworthians v St Neots

October 29 (Week X2)
Aylestone St James v Oadby Wyggestonians
Daventry v Old Bosworthians
Dunstablians v Market Bosworth
Loughborough v Old Northamptonians
Melton Mowbray v Northampton Old Scouts
St Neots v Northampton Mens Own

January 14 (Week 18)
Aylestone St James v Market Bosworth
Bedford Queens v Northampton Mens Own
Daventry v Oadby Wyggestonians
Dunstablians v Loughborough
Melton Mowbray v Old Northamptonians
St Neots v Northampton Old Scouts

February 11 (Week 22)
Loughborough v Melton Mowbray
Market Bosworth v St Neots
Northampton Mens Own v Old Bosworthians
Northampton Old Scouts v Daventry
Oadby Wyggestonians v Bedford Queens
Old Northamptonians v Aylestone St James

February 25 (Week 24)
Aylestone St James v Loughborough
Bedford Queens v Northampton Old Scouts
Daventry v Market Bosworth
Melton Mowbray v Dunstablians
Old Bosworthians v Oadby Wyggestonians
St Neots v Old Northamptonians

March 4 (Week 25)
Dunstablians v Aylestone St James
Loughborough v St Neots
Market Bosworth v Bedford Queens
Northampton Old Scouts v Old Bosworthians
Oadby Wyggestonians v Northampton Mens Own
Old Northamptonians v Daventry

March 25 (Week 28)
Aylestone St James v Melton Mowbray
Bedford Queens v Old Northamptonians
Daventry v Loughborough
Northampton Mens Own v Northampton Old Scouts
Old Bosworthians v Market Bosworth
St Neots v Dunstablians

April 8 (Week 30)
Dunstablians v Daventry
Loughborough v Bedford Queens
Market Bosworth v Northampton Mens Own
Melton Mowbray v St Neots
Northampton Old Scouts v Oadby Wyggestonians
Old Northamptonians v Old Bosworthians

EAST MIDLANDS & LEICS ONE

AYLESTONE ST JAMES RFC
Ground Address:Covert Lane, Scraptoft, Leicester. Tel: 0533 866481
Club Secretary: KWI Ridge. Tel: (W) 0533 608187
Fixtures Secretary: P Chapman, 8 Valentine Road, Leicester. Tel: (H) 0533 431826
Club Colours: Blue & white hoops.
BEDFORD QUEENS RUFC
Ground Address:Allen Park, Old Ford End Road, Bedford. Tel: 0234 211151
Club Secretary: JBG Cunningham, Flat 4, 16 Adelaide Square, Bedford, Beds MK40 2RN. Tel: (H) 0234 269085 Tel: (W) 0234 347111
Fixtures Secretary: Mr A Radnor, 133 Ireland, Shefford, Beds SG17 5GL. Tel: (H) 0462 816175
Club Colours: Maroon & white hoops, navy blue shorts, maroon & white socks.
DAVENTRY RFC
Ground Address:Stefen Hill, Western Avenue, Daventry, Northants NN11 4ST. Tel: 0327 703802
Club Secretary: Richard Roy, 5 Warwick Street, Daventry, Northants NN11 4AJ. Tel: (H) 0327 310477 Tel: (W) 0327 72921
Fixtures Secretary: Graham Woodliffe, Checkley Cottage, Chapel Street, Charwelton, Daventry, Northants NN11 3YU. Tel: (H) 0327 61461 Tel (W) 0327 709137
Club Colours: All black.
DUNSTABLIANS RUFC
Ground Address:Bidwell Park, Bedford Road, Houghton Regis, Dunstable, Beds. Tel: 0582 866555
Club Secretary: Paul Freeman, 19 Preston Road, Toddington, Nr Dunstable, Beds LU5 6EG. Tel: (H) 0525 874550 Tel: (W) 0234 328111
Fixtures Secretary: Mr Lynn Sanford, 62 Marlin Road, Luton LU4 0SJ. Tel: (H) 0582 602777
Club Colours: Black, red & silver.
LOUGHBOROUGH RFC
Ground Address:The Clubhouse, Derby Road Playing Fields, Derby Road, Loughborough. Tel: 0509 216093
Club Secretary: Anne Murphy, 51 Park Road, Loughborough, LE11 2ED. Tel: (H) 0509 231575
Club Colours: Navy blue & old gold.
MARKET BOSWORTH RFC
Ground Address:Cadeby Lane, Cadeby, Market Bosworth. Tel: 0455 291340
Club Secretary: G Donnelly, 23 NOrfolk Road, Desford, Leicester LE9 9HR. Tel: (H) 0455 823522 Tel: (W) 0455 232328
Fixtures Secretary: P Spencer, 10 Beaumont Avenue, Hinckley, Leics LE10 0JU. Tel: (H) 0455 633364 Tel (W) 0455 230804
Club Colours: Blue, gold & white hoops.
MELTON MOWBRAY RFC
Ground Address:Saxby Road, Melton Mowbray, Leicestershire LE13. Tel: 0664 43342
Club Secretary: Mr Colin Cross, 15 Fernie Avenue, Melton Mowbray, Leicestershire LE13. Tel: (H) 0664 61702
Fixtures Secretary: Mr Tony Middleton, 13 Birch Close, Melton Mowbray, Leicestershire LE13. Tel: (H) 0664 67042
Club Colours: Maroon. Away: Yellow.
NORTHAMPTON MEN'S OWN RFC
Ground Address:Stoke Road, Ashton, Northampton NN7 2JN. Tel: 0604 862463
Club Secretary: John Goold, 38 Millway, Duston, Northampton NN5 6ES. Tel: (H) 0604 756297
Fixtures Secretary: Ernie Dalby, 39 Forest Road, Piddington, Northampton NN7 2DA. Tel: (H) 0604 870609 Tel (W) 0302 556398
Club Colours: White with blue hoops, navy blue shorts.

FINAL TABLE

	P	W	D	L	F	A	PD	Pts
Huntingdon	12	9	1	2	261	110	151	19
Oadby Wygstonians	12	9	1	2	218	109	109	19
Market Bosworth	12	11	0	1	308	87	221	18
St Neots	12	6	2	4	144	91	53	14
Old Bosworthians	12	7	0	5	165	170	-5	14
Northampton M O	12	6	1	5	153	134	19	13
Dunstablians	12	5	1	6	163	180	-17	11
Northampton O S	12	6	0	6	194	168	26	10
Aylestone St James	12	4	1	7	121	158	-37	9
Loughborough	12	3	0	9	112	196	-84	6
Daventry	12	3	1	8	108	210	-102	5
Melton Mowbray	12	2	1	9	103	224	-121	5
Brackley	12	2	1	9	64	277	-213	3

NORTHAMPTON OLD SCOUTS RFC
Ground Address:Rushmere Road, Northampton. Tel: 0604 33639
Club Secretary: Bob Letty, 49 Barley Hill Road, Northampton NN3 5JA. Tel: (H) 0604 493727
Fixtures Secretary: Keith Shurville, 41 Churchill Avenue, Northampton. Tel: (H) 0604 494374
Club Colours: Navy, green, red & yellow hoops.
OADBY WYGGESTONIAN RFC
Ground Address:Oval Park, Wigston Road, Oadby, Leicester. Tel: 0533 714848
Club Secretary: Jim Kilgallen, 75 Leicester Road, Oadby, Leicester LE2 4DF. Tel: (H) 0533 713987 Tel: (W) 0533 858032
Fixtures Secretary: Ian Turvey, 15 Bakewell Road, Wigston, Leicester LE18 1FF. Tel: (H) 0533 571669
Club Colours: Black, white & gold hooped jerseys, black shorts.
OLD BOSWORTHIANS RFC
Ground Address:Hinckley Road, Leicester Forest East, Leicester. Tel: 0533 387136
Club Secretary: Grahame D Spendlove-Mason, Croft House Farm, Post Office Lane, Newton Harcourt, Leics LE8 0FN. Tel: (H) 0533 592965 Tel: (W) 0533 557803
Fixtures Secretary: Colin Hughes, 97 Rosslyn Road, Whitwick, Leics LE67 5PV. Tel: (H) 0530 834493 Tel (W) 0509 611011 x44102
Club Colours: Navy & sky blue.
OLD NORTHAMPTONIANS RFC
Ground Address:Sports Field, Billing Road, Northampton. Tel: 0604 34045
Club Secretary: K Napier, 627 Wellingborough Road, Northampton NN3 3AR. Tel: (H) 0604 415269 Tel: (W) 0604 33329
Fixtures Secretary: D Summers, 94 Upper Turiff Street, Northampton NN11 5HR. Tel: (H) 0604 28454
Club Colours: Cardinal, navy & gold hoops.
ST NEOTS RUFC
Ground Address:The Common, St Neots. Tel: 0480 474285
Club Secretary: Ray London, 14 St James Court, Eynesbury, St Neots PE19 2QQ. Tel: (H) 0480 390135 Tel: (W) 0480 812202
Fixtures Secretary: Keith Sandford, 36 Avenue Road, St Neots PE19 1LJ. Tel: (H) 0480 472812 Tel (W) 0234 274049
Club Colours: Light blue with broad navy hoop.

MIDLAND DIVISION

September 17 (Week 3)
Wigston v Bedford Swifts
Wellingborough OGs v Rushden/Higham
Brackley v Oakham
Bugbrooke v Colworth House
Aylestonians v Birstall
Northampton Casuals v St Ives

September 24 (Week 4)
Bedford Swifts v Northampton Casuals
Rushden/Higham v Old Ashbeians
Oakham v Wellingborough OGs
Colworth House v Brackley
Birstall v Bugbrooke
St Ives v Aylestonians

October 1 (Week 5)
Aylestonians v Bedford Swifts
Northampton Casuals v Wigston
Bugbrooke v St Ives
Brackley v Birstall
Wellingborough OGs v Colworth House
Old Ashbeians v Oakham

October 15 (Week 7)
Wigston v Aylestonians
Bedford Swifts v Bugbrooke
Oakham v Rushden/Higham
Colworth House v Old Ashbeians
Birstall v Wellingborough OGs
St Ives v Brackley

October 22 (Week 8)
Brackley v Bedford Swifts
Bugbrooke v Wigston
Aylestonians v Northampton Casuals
Wellingborough OGs v St Ives
Old Ashbeians v Birstall
Rushden/Higham v Colworth House

October 29 (Week X2)
Bedford Swifts v Wellingborough OGs
Wigston v Brackley
Northampton Casuals v Bugbrooke
Colworth House v Oakham
Birstall v Rushden/Higham
St Ives v Old Ashbeians

January 7 (Week 17)
Old Ashbeians v Bedford Swifts
Wellingborough OGs v Wigston
Brackley v Northampton Casuals
Bugbrooke v Aylestonians
Rushden/Higham v St Ives
Oakham v Birstall

January 14 (Week 18)
Aylestonians v Brackley
Northampton Casuals v Wellingborough OGs
Wigston v Old Ashbeians
Bedford Swifts v Rushden/Higham
Birstall v Colworth House
St Ives v Oakham

February 11 (Week 22)
Oakham v Bedford Swifts
Rushden/Higham v Wigston
Old Ashbeians v Northampton Casuals
Wellingborough OGs v Aylestonians
Brackley v Bugbrooke
Colworth House v St Ives

February 25 (Week 24)
Bugbrooke v Wellingborough OGs
Aylestonians v Old Ashbeians
Northampton Casuals v Rushden/Higham
Wigston v Oakham
Bedford Swifts v Colworth House
St Ives v Birstall

March 4 (Week 25)
Birstall v Bedford Swift
Colworth House v Wigston
Oakham v Northampton Casuals
Rushden/Higham v Aylestonians
Old Ashbeians v Bugbrooke
Wellingborough OGs v Brackley

March 25 (Week 28)
Brackley v Old Ashbeians
Bugbrooke v Rusden/Higham
Aylestonians v Oakham
Northampton Casuals v Colworth House
Wigston v Birstall
Bedford Swifts v St Ives

April 8 (Week 30)
St Ives v Wigston
Birstall v Northampton Casuals
Colworth House v Aylestonians
Oakham v Bugbrooke
Rushden/Higham v Brackley
Old Ashbeians v Wellingborough OGs

EAST MIDLANDS & LEICS TWO

AYLESTONIANS RFC
Ground Address:Knighton Lane East, Leicester. Tel: 0533 834899
Club Secretary: Mr C Cooper, 31 Rockingham Close, Leicester. Tel: (H) 0533 740922
Fixtures Secretary: Mr G Gaunt, 15 Brookes Avenue, Croft, Leicester. Tel: (H) 0455 282052
Club Colours: Red, white & blue hoops.

BEDFORD SWIFTS RUFC
Ground Address:Bedford Athletics Stadium, Barkers Lane, Bedford MK41 9SA. Tel: 0234 351115
Club Secretary: Trevor N Stewart, 64 Ravensden Road, Renhold, Bedford MK41 0JY. Tel: (H) 0234 771828 Tel: (W) 0767 681491
Fixtures Secretary: Mr Stan Davidson, 136 Chantry Avenue, Kempston, Beedford. Tel: (H) 0234 857529
Club Colours: Amber & royao blue hooped shirts, navy socks & shorts.

BIRSTALL RFC
Ground Address:Longslade Community College, Wanlip Lane, Birstall, Leicester. Tel: 0533 674211
Club Secretary: Mr C Blakesley, 39 Ashfield Drive, Anstey, Leicester. Tel: (H) 0533 351254
Fixtures Secretary: Mr J Cross, 10 Riverside Close, Birstall, Leicester LE4 4EH. Tel: (H) 0533 673307
Club Colours: Green, black & white hoops, black shorts.

BRACKLEY RUFC
Ground Address:Pavillons Way, Brackley, Northants. Tel: 0280 700685
Club Secretary: Mrs Sue Cooper, Octavian Way, Brackley, Northants. Tel: (H) 0280 704711
Fixtures Secretary: Mr Martin Budd, 6 Hollies Court, Brittania Road, Banbury, Oxon. Tel: (H) 0295 273957
Club Colours: Royal blue & white quarters, blue shorts.

BUGBROOKE RUFC
Ground Address:The Playing Fields, Pilgrims Lane, Bugbrooke, Northants. Tel: 0604 831137
Club Secretary: Mr John Gowen, 46 Granary Road, East Hunsbury, Northampton NN4 0XA. Tel: (H) 0604 705273 Tel: (W) 0604 671176
Fixtures Secretary: Mr Terry Newcombe, 31 Georges Ave, Bugbrooke, Northants NN7 3PP. Tel: (H) 0604 831806
Club Colours: Bottle green shirts, gold collar & cuffs, green shorts, green socks with gold hoops.

COLWORTH HOUSE RUFC
Ground Address:Unilever Researchy, Colworth House, Sharnbrook, Bedford MK44 1LQ. Tel: 0234 838671
Club Secretary: Dr Paul Dunnett, Barden Cottage, 37 Sandy Road, Willington, Bedford MK44 3QS. Tel: (H) 0234 838671 Tel: (W) 0234 222857
Fixtures Secretary: Paul Stuart, 62 Cornland, Bedford MK41 8HZ. Tel: (H) 0234 269262 Tel (W) 0234 222217
Club Colours: Emerald green with black shorts & socks.

NORTHAMPTON CASUALS RFC
Ground Address:Rushmills House, Bedford road, Rushmills, Northampton. Tel: 0604 36716
Club Secretary: Mr S M Tee, 32 Duston Wildes, Duston, Northampton NN5 6ND. Tel: (H) 0604 587982 Tel: (W) 0602 582938
Fixtures Secretary: Mr MD Askew, 60 Hinton Road, Kingsthorpe, Northampton. Tel: (H) 0604 821148
Club Colours: Black with amber band.

OAKHAM RFC
Ground Address:The Showground, Barleythorpe Road, Oakham, Rutland. Tel: 0572 724206
Club Secretary: Peter Bateman, 26 Well Street, Langham, Oakham, Rutland LE15 7JS. Tel: (H) 0572 756143 Tel: (W) 0533 550020
Fixtures Secretary: Peter Bateman, 26 Well Street, Langham, Oakham, Rutland LE15 7JS. Tel: (H) 0572 756143
Club Colours: Black with amber hooped shirts.

FINAL TABLE

	P	W	D	L	F	A	PD	Pts
O Northamptonians	12	11	0	1	338	64	274	22
Bedford Queens	12	10	1	1	244	66	178	21
Oakham	12	9	0	3	267	123	144	18
Wellingborough O G	12	8	2	2	189	119	70	18
Rushden & Higham	12	4	5	3	183	85	98	13
Bugbrooke	12	6	0	6	139	217	-78	12
Northampton Cas	12	4	3	5	133	131	2	11
Birstall	12	5	1	6	168	170	-2	11
Aylestonians	12	4	3	5	157	164	-7	11
Wigston	12	4	1	7	130	192	-62	9
St Ives	12	2	2	8	117	219	-102	6
Old Ashbeians	12	2	0	10	95	204	-109	4
New Parks O Boys	12	0	0	12	26	432	-406	0

OLD ASHBEIANS RFC
Ground Address:Nottingham Road, Ashby, Leics. Tel: 0530 413992
Club Secretary: J Mitchell, 50 Pennine Way, Ashby, Leics LE65 1EW. Tel: (H) 0530 415284 Tel: (W) 0623 22148
Fixtures Secretary: A Patrick, 20 Tithe Close, Thringstone, Mr Coalville, Leics LE67 8LZ. Tel: (H) 0530 222076
Club Colours: Maroon & sky blue hoops, navy shorts.

RUSHDEN AND HIGHAM RFC
Ground Address:Manor Park, Bedford Road, Rushden, Northants NN10 0SA. Tel: 0933 312071
Club Secretary: Steve Miles, 9 Grange Road, Little Cransley, Northants NN14 1PH. Tel: (H) 0536 790429 Tel: (W) 0604 235410
Fixtures Secretary: Terry Dancer, 4 Orwell Close, Raunds, Northants NN9 6SG. Tel: (H) 0933 624889 Tel (W) 0933 404205
Club Colours: Black & white hoops.

ST IVES RUFC
Ground Address:St Ivo Outdoor Centre, California Road, St Ives, Huntingdon, Cambs PE17 4SJ. Tel: 0480 465485
Club Secretary: M Prince, 59 Erica Road, St ives, Huntingdon, Cambs. Tel: (H) 0480 381091
Fixtures Secretary: R Kamper, Kayakampa, Parkhall Road, Somersham, Huntingdon, Cambs. Tel: (H) 0487 842261 Tel (W) 0487 880535
Club Colours: Royal blue shirts, black shorts.

WELLINGBOROUGH OLD GRAMMARIANS RFC
Ground Address:Memorial Sportsfield, Sanders Road, Finedown Road Industrial Estate, Wellingborough, Northants. Tel: 0933 279316
Club Secretary: Paul Bush, 33 Newtown Road, Little Irchester, Wellingborough, Northants NN8 2DX. Tel: (H) 0933 441663 Tel: (W) 0933 277432
Fixtures Secretary: Paul Bush, 33 Newtown Road, Little Irchester, Wellingborough, Northants NN8 2DX. Tel: (H) 0933 441663 Tel (W) 0933 277432
Club Colours: Claret & white hoops, black shorts.

WIGSTON RFC
Ground Address:Leicester Road, Countesthorpe, Leicester. Tel: 0533 771153
Club Secretary: Steve Benton, 5 Ramsdean Avenue, Wigston, Leicester LE18 1DX. Tel: (H) 0533 889381 Tel: (W) 0533 556776 Fax: 0533 556940
Fixtures Secretary: Steve Benton, 5 Ramsdean Avenue, Wigston, Leicester LE18 1DX. Tel: (H) 0533 889381 Tel (W) 0533 556776 Fax: 0533 556940
Club Colours: Purple, black, gold & silver chest & arm bands.

411

MIDLAND DIVISION

EAST MIDLAND & LEICESTERSHIRE THREE 1994-95 FIXTURES

September 17 (Week 3)
Old Newtonians v Corby
New Parks v Westwood
Anstey v Old Wellingburians
Kempston v Oundle
Deepings v Northampton Heathens

September 24 (Week 4)
Corby v New Parks
Northampton Heathens v West Leicester
Vauxhall v Deepings
Old Wellingburians v Kempston
Westwood v Anstey

October 1 (Week 5)
New Parks v Old Newtonians
Anstey v Corby
Kempston v Westwood
Deepings v Oundle
West Leicester v Vauxhall

October 15 (Week 7)
Old Newtonians v Anstey
Corby v Kempston
Vauxhall v Northampton Heathens
Oundle v West Leicester
Old Wellingburians v Deepings

October 22 (Week 8)
Anstey v New Parks
Kempston v Old Newtonians
Deepings v Westwood
West Leicester v Old Wellingburians
Northampton Heathens v Oundle

October 29 (Week X2)
Corby v Deepings
New Parks v Kempston
Oundle v Vauxhall
Old Wellingburians v Northampton Heathens
Westwood v West Leicester

January 7 (Week 17)
Kempston v Anstey
Deepings v Old Newtonians
West Leicester v Corby
Nothampton Heathens v Westwood
Vauxhall v Old Wellingburians

January 14 (Week 18)
Old Newtonians v West Leicester
Corby v Northampton Heathens
New Parks v Deepings
Old Wellingburians v Oundle
Westwood v Vauxhall

February 11 (Week 22)
Deepings v Anstey
West Leicester v New Parks
Northampton Heathens v Old Newtonians
Vauxhall v Corby
Oundle v Westwood

February 24 (Week 24)
Old Newtonians v Vauxhall
Corby v Oundle
New Parks v Northampton Heathens
Anstey v West Leicester
Kempston v Deepings
Westwood v Old Wellingburians

March 4 (Week 25)
West Leicester v Kempston
Northampton Heathens v Anstey
Vauxhall v New Parks
Oundle v Old Newtonians
Old Wellingburians v Corby

March 25 (Week 28)
Old Newtonians v Old Wellingburians
Corby v Westwood
New Parks v Oundle
Anstey v Vauxhall
Kempston v Northampton Heathens

April 8 (Week 30)
West Leicester v Deepings
Vauxhall v Kempston
Oundle v Anstey
Old Wellingburians v New Parks
Westwood v Old Newtonians

EAST MIDLANDS & LEICS THREE

ANSTEY RFC
Ground Address: Link Road Playing Fields, Link Road, Anstey, Leicester.
Club Secretary: AN Duffield, 10 Pinewood Close, Anstey Heights, Leicester LE4 1ER. Tel: (H) 0533 355986 Tel: (W) 0533 621221
Fixtures Secretary: M Strong, 18 Netherfield Road, Anstey. Tel: (H) 0533 350840
Club Colours: Black shirts & shorts.

CORBY RFC
Ground Address: Northen Park, Rockingham Triangle, Corby, Northants. Tel: 0536 204466
Club Secretary: George A Ewen, 24 Charnwood Road, Corby, Northants NN17 1XS. Tel: (H) 0536 201788 Tel: (W) 0536 265291
Fixtures Secretary: Steve McEachran, 4 Tavistock Square, Corby, Northants. Tel: (H) 0860 780606
Club Colours: Red & white quarters.

DEEPINGS RUFC
Ground Address: Linchfield Road, Deeping St James, Peterborough. Tel: 0778 345228
Club Secretary: Brian Kirby, 4 Woodcroft Close, Market Deeping, Peterborough PE5 8BT. Tel: (H) 0778 343048 Tel: (W) 0733 68989 x4173
Fixtures Secretary: Keith Smith, 17 Burchnall Close, Deeping St James, Peterborough PE6 8QJ. Tel: (H) 0778 346411 Tel (W) 0533 765755
Club Colours: Black, green & gold hoops, black shorts.

KEMPSTON RUFC
Ground Address:c/o Cutler Hammer Sports & Social Club, 134 High Street, Kempston, Beds. Tel: 0234 852499
Club Secretary: Mr SF Templeman, 56 Millwright Way, Flitwick, Beds MK45 1BQ. Tel: (H) 0525 718858 Tel: (W) 0525 718858
Fixtures Secretary: Mr D McConnell, 8 Addington Close, Bedford, Beds. Tel: (H) 0234 211849 Tel (W) 0234 341234
Club Colours: Red & black with red V sash.

NEW PARKS RFC
Ground Address: New Parks Community College, Greencoat Road, Leicester LE3 6RN. Tel: 0533 872115/6
Club Secretary: A Newcombe, 37 Copeland Avenue Forest Way, Leicester LE3 9BT. Tel: (H) 0533 871618 Tel: (W) 0533 759588
Fixtures Secretary: DP Bullock, 17 Digby Close, Leicester. Tel: (H) 0533 890649
Club Colours: Dark blue with light blue chevron to front.

NORTHAMPTON HEATHENS RFC
Ground Address: The Racecourse, Northampton. Tel: 0604 39250
Club Secretary: Martin Labrum, 101 Yeomans Meadow, Northampton NN4 9YX. Tel: (H) 0604 765287 Tel: (W) 0604 765287 Fax: 0604 702838 (H&W)
Fixtures Secretary: Derek Hodgkinson, 5 Pine Trees, Weston Favell, Northampton NN3 3ET. Tel: (H) 0604 416442 Tel (W) 0708 731100
Club Colours: 3' black with alternate 1' gold hoops.

OLD NEWTONIANS RFC
Ground Address: Hinckley Road (A47), Leicester Forest East, Leicester. Tel: 0533 392389
Club Secretary: GA Clark, 250 Wigston Lane, Aylestone, Leicester LE2 8DH. Tel: (H) 0533 832309
Fixtures Secretary: Peter Muggleton, 16 Bruxby Street, Syston, Leicester. Tel: (H) 0533 694704 Tel (W) (Message only) 0533 530066 x4223
Club Colours: Navy base with white, green, red, white central band.

OLD WELLINGBURIANS RFC
Ground Address: The Embankment Club, Wellingborough.
Club Secretary: Mark Thompson, 60 Glenfield Drive, South Doddington, Northants NN9 7TE. Tel: (W) 0324 343221
Club Colours: Green, Gold, Mauve.

FINAL TABLE

	P	W	D	L	F	A	PD	Pts
Bedford Swifts	11	11	0	0	311	60	251	22
Colworth House	11	10	0	1	313	85	228	20
Corby	11	7	1	3	261	129	132	15
Oundle	11	7	1	3	159	104	55	15
Kempston	11	6	0	5	209	109	100	12
Deepings	11	6	0	5	170	153	17	12
Westwood	11	4	1	6	89	120	-31	9
Anstey	11	4	1	6	136	178	-42	9
Old Newtonians	11	4	0	7	113	138	-25	8
Old Wellingburians	11	3	0	8	137	349	-212	6
West Leicester	11	2	0	9	103	234	-131	4
Burbage	11	0	0	11	36	378	-342	0

OUNDLE RFC
Ground Address: Occupation Road, Oundle, Peterborough. Tel: 0832 273101
Club Secretary: Roger Smith, 6 Pheasant Way, Yaxley, Peterborough PE7 3HN. Tel: (H) 0733 242344 Tel: (W) 0733 556610
Fixtures Secretary: Mr Fred King, 13 Chapel Street, Titchmarsh, Nr Kettering, Northants. Tel: (H) 0832 734659
Club Colours: Black with red & white hoop.

VAUXHALL MOTORS RUFC
Ground Address: Brache Estate, Osbourne Road, Luton, Bedfordshire. Tel: 0582 454785
Club Secretary: Mr P McIntyre (Paul), 5 Tracey Court, 76 Hibbert Street, Luton, Bedfordshire LU1 3XH. Tel: (H) 0582 23168
Fixtures Secretary: Mr Frank J Brown, 17 Byron Crescent, Flitwick, Bedfordshire. Tel: (H) 0525 712818 Tel (W) 0525 404242
Club Colours: Blue with 3' gold hoops, black shorts, blue & gold socks.

WEST LEICESTER RFC
Ground Address: St Mary's Fields, Narborough Road, Leicester. Tel: 0533 540634
Club Secretary: GE Topley, 8 Hillsborough Road, Glen Parva, Leicester LE2 9PL. Tel: (H) 0533 774119 Tel: (W) 0533 888951
Fixtures Secretary: A Lee, 15 Chestnut Close, Littlethorpe, Leicester LE9 5HN. Tel: (H) 0533 863557
Club Colours: Red jerseys, white shorts, black socks.

WESTWOOD RUFC
Ground Address: Phorpres Club, London Road, Peterborough. Tel: 0733 343501
Club Secretary: Kenneth Barnes, 17 St Peter's Walk, Yaxley, Peterborough PE7 3ET. Tel: (H) 0733 241382
Fixtures Secretary: Peter Tartelin, Flat 20, Fenland Court, West End, Whittleset, Peterborough PE7 1HR. Tel: (H) 0733 350632 Tel (W) 0234 225404
Club Colours: Red & white hoops.

MIDLAND DIVISION

EAST MIDLAND & LEICESTERSHIRE FOUR 1994-95 FIXTURES

September 17 (Week 3)
Biddenham v Cosby
Clapham v Braunstone
Shepshed v Burbage

September 24 (Week 4)
Burbage v Biddenham
Cosby v Clapham
Thorney v Shepshed

October 1 (Week 5)
Biddenham v Thorney
Clapham v Burbage
Shepshed v Braunstone

October 15 (Week 7)
Braunstone v Biddenham
Cosby v Shepshed
Thorney v Clapham

October 22 (Week 8)
Biddenham v Shepshed
Braunstone v Cosby
Burbage v Thorney

October 29 (Week X2)
Clapham v Biddenham
Cosby v Burbage
Thorney v Braunstone

November 26 (Week 12)
Burbage v Braunstone
Clapham v Shepshed
Cosby v Thorney

January 7 (Week 17)
Braunstone v Clapham
Burbage v Shepshed
Cosby v Biddenham

January 14 (Week 18)
Biddenham v Burbage
Clapham v Cosby
Shepshed v Thorney

February 11 (Week 22)
Braunstone v Shepshed
Burbage v Clapham
Thorney v Biddenham

February 25 (Week 24)
Biddenham v Braunstone
Clapham v Thorney
Shepshed v Cosby

March 4 ((Week 25)
Cosby v Braunstone
Shepshed v Biddenham
Thorney v Burbage

March 25 (Week 28)
Biddenham v Clapham
Braunstone v Thorney
Burbage v Cosby

April 8 (Week 30)
Braunstone v Burbage
Shepshed v Clapham
Thorney v Cosby

EAST MIDLANDS & LEICS FOUR

BIDDENHAM RFC
Ground Address: The Pavilion, Deep Spinney,
Biddenham, Beds.
Club Secretary: Mr Trevor Sparks, 19 Deep Spinney,
Biddenham MK40 4QJ. Tel: (H) 0234 327845 Tel: (W)
0234 750422
Fixtures Secretary: Mr Kevin Weedon, 11 Darlow Drive,
Biddenham, Beds MK40 4AX. Tel: (H) 0234 269194 Tel
(W) 0234 215300
Club Colours: Green & cream quarters.

BRAUNSTONE TOWN RFC
Ground Address: Mossdale Meadows, The Kingsway,
Braunstone, Leicester
Club Secretary: P S Clarke, 28 Park Road, Wisston,
Leicester LE18 4QD. Tel: (H) 0533 773507 (W) 0455
822441
Club Colours: Maroon & gold. Black shorts.

BURBAGE RFC
Ground Address: John Cleveland College, Butt Lane,
Hinckley, Leics.
Club Secretary: CM Startin, 102 Strathmore Road,
Hinckley, Leicsw LE10 0LR. Tel: (H) 0455 634073 Tel:
(W) 0455 637841
Fixtures Secretary: R Sansome, 98 Hinckley Road,
Burbage, Leics. Tel: (H) 0455 610266
Club Colours: Green & white hoops.

CLAPHAM RUFC
Ground Address: Twinwoods Road, Clapham, Beds.
Club Secretary: DR Tough, Millbrook House, 109 High
Street, Riseley, Beds MK44 1DF. Tel: (H) 0234 708453
Tel: (W) 0433 314281
Fixtures Secretary: R Baker, 82 High Street, Oakley, Beds
MK43 7RH. Tel: (H) 0234 824092
Club Colours: Blue & gold quarters.

COSBY RFC
Ground Address: Victory Park, Park Road, Cosby,
Leicester.
Club Secretary: CW Elliott, 9 Wavertree Close, Cosby,
Leicester LE9 5TN. Tel: (H) 0533 841746 Tel: (W) 0530
510051
Fixtures Secretary: CW Elliott, 9 Wavertree Close,
Cosby, Leicester LE9 5TN. Tel: (H) 0533 841746 Tel (W)
0530 510051
Club Colours: Black shirts, black shorts.

SHEPSHED RFC
Ground Address: Hind Leys College, Forest Street,
Shepshed, Leicestershire LE12 9DB. Tel: 0509 503592
Club Secretary: Mrs Sue Patterson, c/o Shepshed RFC,
Hind Leys College, Forest Street, Shepshed, Leicestershire
LE12 9DB. Tel: (H) 0509 265847
Fixtures Secretary: RWP Short, 40D Loughborough
Road, Shepshed, Leicestershire LE12 9DN. Tel: (H) 0509
503592 Tel (W) 0860 113479
Club Colours: Red & black quarters. Change: Red & black.

THORNEY RUFC
Ground Address: Thorney Park, Wisbech Road, Thorney,
Cambs.
Club Secretary: Mr Paul Smith, 154 Wisbech Road,
Thorney, Cambs PE6 0SE. Tel: (H) 0733 270552
Fixtures Secretary: Mr Dick Turner, 1415 Lincoln Road,
Peterborough. Tel: (H) 0733 571259 Tel (W) 0733 63232
Club Colours: Navy & gold quarters. Change: Navy.

FINAL TABLE

	P	W	D	L	F	A	PD	Pts
Vauxhall Motors	12	11	0	1	395	35	360	22
Northampton Hns	12	9	0	3	224	131	93	18
Thorney	12	8	0	4	127	139	-12	16
Braunstone Town	12	7	0	5	209	123	86	14
Cosby	12	4	0	8	80	181	-101	8
Clapham Twinwds	12	3	0	9	111	323	-212	6
Potton	12	0	0	12	64	278	-214	0

LONDON & SOUTH EAST DIVISION

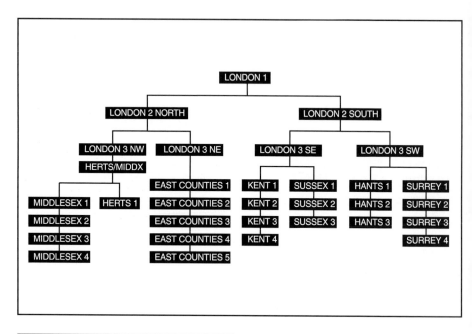

COMPETITION SUB-COMMITEE

CHAIRMAN
R. Tennant, 57 Boveney Road, Forest Hill, London SE23 3NL (H) 081 699 9025.

SECRETARY
M.A. Ward, 3 Rookery Close, Oulton Broad, Lowestoft, Suffolk NR33 9NZ (H) 0502 566169 (B) 0502 711343 (F) 0502 712660

EASTERN COUNTIES
F.A.G. Ford, "Fairhaven", 36 Haynes Road, Hornchurch, Essex RM11 2HT (H) 0708 45787

HAMPSHIRE
Lt. Cl. D. McF. Hathorn, 3 Broomacres, Fleet, Aldershot, Hampshire GU13 9UU (H) 0252 621565

HERTFORDSHIRE
D.J. Williams, 7 Sadlers Way, Hertford, Herts SG14 2DZ (H) 0992 586744

KENT
D. Attwood, 6 Somerset Gardens, Lewisham, London, SE13 7SY (H) 081 691 2820.

MIDDLESEX
D.C. Ransom, 2 Powis Court, The Rutts, Bushey Heath, Hertfordshire WD2 1LL (H) 081 950 5871 (B) 081 848 8744.

SURREY
H. Brady, 16 Selwood Terrace, London SW7 3QG (H) 071 370 1078.

SUSSEX
P Sealey, 15 Hart Close, Uckfield, Sussex TN22 2DA (H) 0825 763293 (B) 0732 863868.

CO-OPTED
F Pugh, 42 Duchess Drive, Newmarket, Suffolk CB8 8AG

LONDON & SOUTH EAST DIVISION

Officials contd.

L.E.A.F. FUND MANAGER
F Pugh, 42 Duchess Drive, Newmarket, Suffolk CB8 8AG (H) 0483 575742

RFU REPRESENTATIVES (COMPETITION SUB-COMMITTEE)
L.C.K. Angel, 1 Rochford Road, Basingstoke, Hampshire RG21 1TQ (H) 0256 27935 (B) 0256 844844 Ext 4584.
G.G. Smith, The Old Rectory, Provender Lane, Norton, Faversham, Kent ME13 0SU (H) 0795 521166

LEAGUE SECRETARIES
London One George Ford, "Fairhaven", 36 Haynes Road, Hornchurch, Essex RM11 2HT (H) 0402 457807
London Two North David Williams, 7 Sadlers Way, Hertford, Herts SG14 2DZ (H) 0992 586744
London Two South & London Three South-West Lt. Col. D. McF. Hathorn, 3 Broomacres, Fleet, Aldershot, Hampshire, GU13 9UU (H) 0252 621565
London Three North-West C. Pool, Esq., 24 Firs Walk, Tewin Wood, Welwyn, Hertfordshire, AL6 0NZ (H) 0438 798469
London Three North-East M. J. Stott, Brick Kiln Farm, North Walsham, Norfolk (H) 0692 403096.
London Three South-East Dennis Attwood, 6 Somerset Gardens, Lewisham, London SE13 7SY. (H) 081 691 2820.
Hertfordshire/Middlesex D. Gershlick, 20a The Avenue, Potters Bar, Hertfordshire EN6 1EB (H) 0707 644433
Herts All Leagues C. Pool, Esq., 24 Firs Walk, Tewin Wood, Welwyn, Herts AL6 0NZ. (H) 0438 798469
Middlesex One R Willingale, Fairmile Farm Cottage, Cobham, Surrey KT11 1JY (H) 0932 866927
Middlesex Two P. Astbury, 32 Kneller Gardens, Isleworth, Middlesex (H) 081 898 5372.
Middlesex Three A. Rabjohn, 62 Central Avenue, Hounslow, Middlesex (H) 081 894 1850.
Middlesex Four Brian East, 17 Waterloo Road, London, N19 5NJ (H) 071 272 5686 (W) 071 485 4100
Hampshire One and Two J Sneezum, Bursledon Lodge, Salterns Lane, Old Bursledon, Southampton, Hampshire SO3 8DH (H) 0703 402286
Surrey General A Manly, The Ramtop, 28 Harestone Lane, Caterham, Surrey CR3 6BD (H) 0883 340252 (W) 081 760 0200
Surrey One R. Greer Kirkwood, 63 Shaftesbury Way, Strawberry Hill, Twickenham TW2 5RW (H) 081 898 1767.

Surrey Two J.S. Laidman, 2 West Dene, Park Lane, Cheam, Surrey (H) 081 643 2919.
Surrey Three M P Tanner, 1 Woodland Way, Morden, Surrey SM4 4DS (H) 081 540 5784 (W) 0923 214123
Surrey Four R.V. Miller, Flat 3, 127 Barnet Wood Road, Ashtead, Surrey (H) 0372 278486.
Eastern Counties One, Two Mike Tuck, 51 Highfield Road, Billericay, Essex CM11 2PE (H) 0277 655483.
Eastern Counties Three and Four Ron Hatch, 99 Ernest Road, Wivenhoe, Essex CO7 9LJ (H) 0206 823548
Eastern Counties Five Roger Wyatt, Stone Cottage, The Green, Beyton, Suffolk IP30 9AF (H) 0359 270410
Sussex all Leagues J.M. Carrington, 1 Graftons, Christ's Hospital, Horsham, Sussex RH13 7LU (H) 0403 260556.
Kent One and Two J. Carley, Trinity Court, Easole Street, Nonnington, Kent CT15 4HE. (H) 0304 841066.
Kent Three and Four R. Fisher, 7 Manwood Close, Sittingbourne, Kent ME10 4QL (H) 0795 471433 (W) 0634 388765.

LONDON & SOUTH EASTCHAMPIONS ROLL OF HONOUR 1993/94

London 1
Barking RUFC

London 2 North
Ruislip RFC

London 2 South
Esher RFC

London 3 NE
Romford & Gidea Park RFC

London 3 NW
Staines RFC

London 3 SE
Gravesend RFC

London 3 SW
Portsmouth RFC

Herts/Middx
Barnet RFC

Middlesex 1
Mill Hill RFC

Middlesex 2
Old Pauline FC

Middlesex 3
Bank of England RFC

Middlesex 4
London French RFC

Herts 1
St Albans RFC

Eastern Counties 1
Maldon RUFC

Eastern Counties 2
Diss RFC

Eastern Counties 3
Old Cooperians' RFC

Eastern Counties 4
Hadleigh RUFC

Eastern Counties 5
Mersea Island RFC

Kent 1
Park House FC

Kent 2
Old Shootershillians RFC

Kent 3
Old Gravesendians RFC

Kent 4
Old Olavians RFC

Sussex 1
Heathfield & Waldron RFC

Sussex 2
Pulborough RFC

Hants 1
Gosport & Gareham RFC

Hants 2
Esso (Fawley) RFC

Surrey 1
Wimbledon RFC

Surrey 2
Old Cranleighans RFC

Surrey 3
Woking RFC

Surrey 4
Egham RFC

LONDON & SOUTH EAST DIVISION FEATURED CLUBS

GRAVESEND

Gravesend bounced back after relegation in 1992-93 to win London's League Three South East with a perfect record from 12 matches played and an overwhelming 315-57 points situation.

Led with inspiration by Rob Bardell they are now naturally looking for even further success and a club which managed wins over such higher rated teams as Thurrock, Sidcup, Dorking, Thanet Wanderers and Bishop's Stortford must be taken seriously.

Bob attributes much of their success to a strong first team squad with plenty of tries being scored, the front runners being Matt Merrison, Dave Vaughan and Kevin Taplin, who are part of a blend of experience and promising players, the former represented by Malcolm Willden, Stuart McBride, Jerry Shelton and Andy Love who are well supported by such newcomers as Mike Delay, Jason Smith and Gareth Williams.

Of the regular first team players 28 are former club colts and they have thriving youth, junior and mini sections, which is not only good for the future but also for team spirit in an area of England where a successful outfit such as Gravesend is essential for the prosperity of the game.

OLD HAMPTONIANS

Old Hamptonians may have missed out on a second successive promotion season — they managed only third place in Midlesex One with eight of their 12 matches won for an impressive 291-139 points situation — but they had a far from disappointing season, as any side that reaches a Twickenham final will rightly claim. And the final of the Pilkington Shield is the top honour that any so called 'minnows' club can seek. To achieve this superb performance they had to play through eight rounds of hard knock-out competition and in the last three of them the going was tough. Bishopston held them to 26-11 and then they had an old boys' 'Derby' with Old Caterhamians, which was won 15-3 thanks to an excellent performance by their pack.

That took them to Northampton's Franklin's Gardens ground and a semi-final against highly fancied Kidderminster Carolians, which produced a nail-biting 10-6 victory and a trip to Twickenham, where their luck finally ran out against another surprise finalist in Malvern. Two penalties by centre Prichard were not enough to bring victory against determined opponents and despite brave efforts from the whole team and notably skipper Zander, the back row of Clarke, Carmody and Cooke and the half backs Bugler and Turnill it was not to be their day, although it was a memorable occasion and a better game than the one which was to follow between Bath and Leicester.

Now they must — and will — pick themselves up and gain that elusive promotion to higher things.

Opposite: Old Hamptonians RFC. Above Gravesend RFC

LONDON & SOUTH EAST DIVISION

LONDON ONE
1994-95
FIXTURES

September 17 (Week 3)
Camberley v Old Mid-Whitgiftians
Eton Manor v Southend
Streatham-Croydon v Ruislip
Sutton & Epsom v Esher
Maidstone v Guildford & God'ming
Harlow v Old Colfeians

September 24 (Week 4)
Old Mid-Whitgiftians v Harlow
Old Colfeians v Maidstone
Guildford & God'ming v Sutton & Epsom
Esher v Streatham-Croydon
Ruislip v Eton Manor
Southend v Ealing

October 1 (Week 5)
Maidstone v Old Mid-Whitgiftians
Harlow v Camberley
Ealing v Ruislip
Eton Manor v Esher
Streatham-Croydon v Guildford & God'ming
Sutton & Epsom v Old Colfeians

October 15 (Week 7)
Camberley v Maidstone
Old Mid-Whitgiftians v Sutton & Epsom
Old Colfeians v Streatham-Croydon
Guildford & God'ming v Eton Manor
Esher v Ealing
Ruislip v Southend

October 22 (Week 8)
Streatham-Croydon v Old Mid-Whitgiftians
Sutton & Epsom v Camberley
Maidstone v Harlow
Southend v Esher
Ealing v Guildford & God'ming
Eton Manor v Old Colfeians

October 29 (Week X2)
Harlow v Sutton & Epsom
Camberley v Streatham-Croydon
Old Mid-Whitgiftians v Eton Manor
Old Colfeians v Ealing
Guildford & God'ming v Southend
Esher v Ruislip

January 7 (Week 17)
Ealing v Old Mid-Whitgiftians
Eton Manor v Camberley
Streatham-Croydon v Harlow
Sutton & Epsom v Maidstone
Ruislip v Guildford & God'ming
Southend v Old Colfeians

January 14 (Week 18)
Maidstone v Streatham-Croydon
Harlow v Eton Manor
Camberley v Ealing
Old Mid-Whitgiftians v Southend
Old Colfeians v Ruislip
Guildford & God'ming v Esher

February 11 (Week 22)
Ruislip v Old Mid-Whitgiftians
Southend v Camberley
Ealing v Harlow
Eton Manor v Maidstone
Streatham-Croydon v Sutton & Epsom
Esher v Old Colfeians

February 25 (Week 24)
Sutton & Epsom v Eton Manor
Maidstone v Ealing
Harlow v Southend
Camberley v Ruislip
Old Mid-Whitgiftians v Esher
Old Colfeians v Guildford & God'ming

March 4 (Week 25)
Guildford & God'ming v Old Mid-Whitgiftians
Esher v Camberley
Ruislip v Harlow
Southend v Maidstone
Ealing v Sutton & Epsom
Eton Manor v Streatham-Croydon

March 25 (Week 28)
Streatham-Croydon v Ealing
Sutton & Epsom v Southend
Maidstone v Ruislip
Harlow v Esher
Camberley v Guildford & God'ming
Old Mid-Whitgiftians v Old Colfeians

April 8 (Week 30)
Old Colfeians v Camberley
Guildford & God'ming v Harlow
Esher v Maidstone
Ruislip v Sutton & Epsom
Southend v Streatham-Croydon
Ealing v Eton Manor

LONDON ONE

CAMBERLEY RFC
Ground Address: Watchetts Recreation Ground, Park Road, Camberley, Surrey GU15 2SR. Tel: 0276 25395
Club Secretary: P Bland, 20 Moulsham Lane, Yateley, Camberley, Surrey GU17 7QY. Tel: (H) 0252 878934
Fixtures Secretary: Bill Fletcher, 63 Rookwood Avenue, Owlsmoor, Camberley, Surrey GU15 4TY. Tel: (H) 0344 777701 Tel (W) 0344 51555
Club Colours: Black & amber hoops.

EALING FC
Ground Address: Berkeley Avenue, Greenford, Middlesex UB6 0NZ. Tel: 081 422 0868
Club Secretary: Mr D Bugeja, 7 Bradley Gardens, Ealing, London W13 8HE. Tel: (H) 081 997 9982 Tel: (W) 0344 872677
Fixtures Secretary: Mr P Monteith, 3 The Ruddings, Wheldrake, York. Tel: (H) 0904 448809 Tel (W) 071 204 2932
Club Colours: Green with white hoops.

ESHER RFC
Ground Address:369 Molesley Road, Hersham, Surrey KT12 3PF. Tel: 0932 224834
Club Secretary: AR Till, 25 Motspur Park, New Malden, Surrey KT3 6PS. Tel: 081 942 1380
Fixtures Secretary: S Gardner, 72 Chesil Street, Winchester, Hants SO32 8HK. Tel: (H) 0962 869846 Tel (W) 0245 705075
Club Colours: Black & amber.

ETON MANOR RFC
Ground Address: The Eastway Sports Centre, Quartermile Lane, London E10. Tel: 081 555 2670
Club Secretary: John Ayling, 44 Lytton Road, Leytonstone, London E11 1JH. Tel: (H) 081 558 1800
Fixtures Secretary: Mr Martin Scott, 24 Preston Drive, Wanstead, London E11 2JB. Tel: (H) 081 530 4451
Club Colours: Dark blue shirts with light blue hoop, dark blue shorts.

GUILDFORD & GODALMING RFC
Ground Address: Broadwater, Guildford Road, Godalming, Surrey GU7 3BU. Tel: 0483 416199
Club Secretary: Alan Bird, The Old Barn, Fernhurst Green, Haslemere, Surrey GU27 3HY. Tel: (H) 0428 653359
Fixtures Secretary: Len Bodill, 4 Orchard Road, Burpham, Guildford, Surrey GU4 7JH. Tel: (H) 0483 570580
Club Colours: Green & white hoops.

HARLOW RUFC
Ground Address: Ram Gorse, Elizabeth Way, Harlow, Essex CM20 2JQ. Tel: 0279 429750
Club Secretary: Jo Riddell, 30 Portland Road, Bishops Stortford, Herts CM23 3SJ. Tel: (H) 0279 657596 Tel: (W) 0279 657596
Fixtures Secretary: John Pendleton, 59 Priory Court, Harlow, Essex CM18 7AZ. Tel: (H) 0729 439265
Club Colours: Red shirts with green collars & cuffs, white shorts.

MAIDSTONE FC
Ground Address: The William Day Memorial Ground, The Mote, Willow Way, Maidstone, Kent ME15 7RN. Tel: 0622 754159
Club Secretary: Mr David Pares, Minster Lodge, Otham Lane, Bearsted, Maidstone, Kent ME15 8SL. Tel: (H) 0622 861246 Tel: (W) 0622 691567
Fixtures Secretary: AF Kelleher, 5 Conway Road, Maidstone, Kent ME16 0HD. Tel: (H) 0622 754872 Tel (W) 0622 754872
Club Colours: Red, white & black hoops.

OLD COLFEIANS RFC
Ground Address: Horn Park, Eltham Road, Lee, London SE12. Tel: 081 852 1181
Club Secretary: Dai Andrew, 80 Dallinger Road, Lee, London SE12 0TH. Tel: (H) 081 857 4036 Tel: (W) 081 680 2255/9011
Fixtures Secretary: John Nunn, The Mount, 27 Westmount Road, Eltham, London SE9 1JB. Tel: (H) 081 850 1853
Club Colours: Blue, black, maroon & old gold bands, navy shorts & socks.

FINAL TABLE

	P	W	D	L	F	A	PD	Pts
Barking	12	10	1	1	290	149	141	21
Ealing	12	9	0	3	271	141	130	18
Camberley	12	9	0	3	242	137	105	18
Sutton & Epsom	12	7	1	4	271	207	64	15
Harlow	12	6	0	6	223	217	6	12
Guildfrd & Godming	12	6	0	6	162	162	0	12
Old Mid Whitgiftian	12	6	0	6	143	163	-20	12
Eton Manor	12	5	1	6	178	176	2	11
Streatham-Croydon	12	5	1	6	166	183	-17	11
Old Colfeians	12	5	0	7	166	221	-55	10
Thurrock	12	3	1	8	138	204	-66	7
Dorking	12	3	0	9	171	220	-49	6
Old Alleynian	12	1	1	10	135	376	-241	3

OLD MID-WHITGIFTIAN RFC
Ground Address: Lime Meadow Avenue, Sanderstead, Surrey CR2 9AS. Tel: 081 657 2014
Club Secretary: Mike Ricca, Keepers Cottage, 14 Worcester Road, Sutton, Surrey SM2 6PE. Tel: (H) 081 643 4185
Fixtures Secretary: League contact: Andy Hillburn, 47A Foxearth Road, Selsdon, South Croydon, Surrey CR2 8EL. Tel: (H) 0651 1825 Tel (W) 071 917 8888 x4435
Club Colours: Dark blue jerseys, shorts & socks.

RUISLIP RFC
Ground Address: West End Road, Ruislip, Middlesex HA4 6DR. Tel: 0895 633102
Club Secretary: Michael A Searls, 16 Park Way, Rickmansworth, Herts WD3 2AT. Tel: (H) 0923 773903 Tel: (W) 071 357 1000
Fixtures Secretary: Steve Hazell, Milestones, 23 Hopfield Avenue, Byfleet, Surrey. Tel: (H) 0932 354060 Tel (W) 081 641 7070
Club Colours: Maroon & white hooped shirts, white shorts, maroon socks.

SOUTHEND RFC
Ground Address: Warners Bridge Park, Sumpters Way, Southend on Sea, Essex, S52 5RR. Tel: 0702 546682
Club Secretary: D J Dilley, The Pimple, 106 Woodside, Leigh on Sea, Essex, S59 4RB. Tel: (H) 0702 523553 Tel: (W) 0702 546682
Fixtures Secretary: T H Webb, 28 St James Gardens, Westcliffe on Sea, Essex. Tel: (H) 0702 342888
Club Colours: Chocolate and white.

STREATHAM & CROYDON RFC
Ground Address: Rosevale, 159 Brigstock Road, Thornton Heath, Surrey CR7 7JP. Tel: 081 684 1502
Club Secretary: I Fenn, Flat 1, 24 Kestrel Avenue, London SE24 0ED. Tel: (H) 071 733 3775
Fixtures Secretary: RV Towers, 24 Ernest Grove, Beckenham, Kent BR3 3JF. Tel: (H) 081 658 2333 Tel (W) 081 698 8911
Club Colours: Maroon shirts, white shorts.

SUTTON & EPSOM RFC
Ground Address: Cuddington Court, Rugby Lane, West Drive, Cheam, Surrey SM2 7NF. Tel: 081 642 0280
Club Secretary: DR Poole, Maple Drive, Heath Drive, Warton on the Hill, Surrey KT20 7QJ. Tel: (H) 0737 814130
Fixtures Secretary: I Frazer, 111 Benhill Road, Sutton, Surrey SM1 3RR. Tel: (H) 081 643 4835 Tel (W) 071 510 8549
Club Colours: Black & white hoops.

LONDON & SOUTH EAST DIVISION

LONDON TWO NORTH
1994-95
FIXTURES

September 17 (Week 3)
Norwich v Brentwood
Romford & Gidea Park v Cheshunt
Finchley v Staines
Old Gaytonians v Bishop's Stortford
Woodford v Thurrock
Chingford v Old Verulamians

September 24 (Week 4)
Brentwood v Chingford
Old Verulamians v Woodford
Thurrock v Old Gaytonians
Bishop's Stortford v Finchley
Staines v Romford & Gidea Park
Cheshunt v Cambridge

October 1 (Week 5)
Woodford v Brentwood
Chingford v Norwich
Cambridge v Staines
Romford & Gidea Park v Bishop's Stortford
Finchley v Thurrock
Old Gaytonians v Old Verulamians

October 15 (Week 7)
Norwich v Woodford
Brentwood v Old Gaytonians
Old Verulamians v Finchley
Thurrock v Romford & Gidea Park
Bishop's Stortford v Cambridge
Staines v Cheshunt

October 22 (Week 8)
Finchley v Brentwood
Old Gaytonians v Norwich
Woodford v Chingford
Cheshunt v Bishop's Stortford
Cambridge v Thurrock
Romford & Gidea Park v Old Verulamians

October 29 (Week X2)
Chingford v Old Gaytonians
Norwich v Finchley
Brentwood v Romford & Gidea Park
Old Verulamians v Cambridge
Thurrock v Cheshunt
Bishop's Stortford v Staines

January 7 (Week 17)
Cambridge v Brentwood
Romford & Gidea Park v Norwich
Finchley v Cingford
Old Gaytonians v Woodford
Staines v Thurrock
Cheshunt v Old Verulamians

January 14 (Week 18)
Woodford v Finchley
Chingford v Romford & Gidea Park
Norwich v Cambridge
Brentwood v Cheshunt
Old Verulamians v Staines
Thurrock v Bishop's Stortford

February 11 (Week 22)
Staines v Brentwood
Cheshunt v Norwich
Cambridge v Chingford
Romford & Gidea Park v Woodford
Finchley v Old Gaytonians
Bishop's Stortford v Old Verulamians

February 25 (Week 24)
Old Gaytonians v Romford & Gidea Park
Woodford v Cambridge
Chingford v Cheshunt
Norwich v Staines
Brentwood v Bishop's Stortford
Old Verulamians v Thurrock

March 4 (Week 25)
Thurrock v Brentwood
Bishop's Stortford v Norwich
Staines v Chingford
Cheshunt v Woodford
Cambridge v Old Gaytonians
Romford & Gidea Park v Finchley

March 25 (Week 28)
Finchley v Cambridge
Old Gaytonians v Cheshunt
Woodford v Staines
Chingford v Bishop's Stortford
Norwich v Thurrock
Brentwood v Old Verulamians

April 8 (Week 30)
Old Verulamians v Norwich
Thurrock v Chingford
Bishop's Stortford v Woodford
Staines v Old Gaytonians
Cheshunt v Finchley
Cambridge v Romford & Gidea Park

LONDON TWO NORTH

BISHOP'S STORTFORD RFC
Ground Address:Silver Leys, Hadham Road, Bishop's
Stortford, Hertfordshire CM23 2QE. Tel: 0279 652092
Club Secretary: John Robinson, 193 Heath Row, Bishop's
Stortford, Herts CM23 5BX. Tel: (H) 0279 657104 Tel: (W)
0582 24182
Fixtures Secretary: Mrs Jenny Lancey, 41 Appleton Fields,
Bishop's Stortford, Herts CM23 4DR. Tel: (H) 0279 651061
Club Colours: Royal blue & white.

BRENTWOOD RFC
Ground Address:King George V Playing Fields, Ingrave
Road, Brentwood, Essex. Tel: 0277 210267
Club Secretary: Mr RW Glasby, 29 Painswick Avenue,
Stanford-le-Hope, Essex SS17 8HR. Tel: (H) 0375 671755 Tel:
(W) 0702 74496
Fixtures Secretary: Mr A Joselyn, 15 Chandlers Walk,
Kelvedon Common, Brentwood CM15 0XL. Tel: (H) 0277
373690 Tel (W) 071 357 2770
Club Colours: Claret, grey & white hoops.

CAMBRIDGE RUFC
Ground Address:Grantchester Road, Cambridge CB3 9ED.
Tel: 0223 312437
Club Secretary: Mr DJ Martin, 45 York Street, Cambridge
CB1 2PZ. Tel: (H) 0223 314705 Tel: (W) 0223 845985
Fixtures Secretary: Mr A Curtis, Kendal Lodge, Church End,
Coton, Cambridge CB3 7PN. Tel: (H) 0954 211724
Club Colours: Blood & sand hoops, white shorts.

CHESHUNT RFC
Ground Address:Rosedale Sports Club, Andrews Lane,
Cheshunt, Herts EN7 6TB. Tel: 0992 623983
Club Secretary: RP Jackson, 18 Churchbury Road, Enfield,
Middlesex EN1 3HR. Tel: (H) 081 342 0329 Tel: (W) 071 283
6293
Fixtures Secretary: Peter Thompson, 7 Harrison's Walk,
Cheshunt, Herts EN8 8PT. Tel: (H) 0992 633027
Club Colours: Green & white.

CHINGFORD RFC
Ground Address:Lea Valley Playing Fields, Waltham Way,
Chingford, London E4 7SR. Tel: 081 529 4879
Club Secretary: Howard K Hartley, 85 Whitehall Gardens,
Chingford, London E4 6EJ. Tel: (H) 081 559 4821
Fixtures Secretary: Peter Wilton, 39 College Gardens,
Chingford, London E4. Tel: (H) 081 529 2052 Tel (W) 081 529
4879
Club Colours: Black jerseys with royal blue & white hoops,
white shorts, blue socks.

FINCHLEY RFC
Ground Address:Summers Lane, Finchley, London N12 0PD.
Tel: 081 445 3746
Club Secretary: Mr C Elliott, 3 Mount Pleasant Road, Ealing,
London W5. Tel: (H) 081 998 9669 Tel: (W) 0252 346305
Fixtures Secretary: Mr L Gibbons, 14 Church Hill Road, East
Barnet, EN4 8XD. Tel: (H) 081 368 7253
Club Colours: Red & white hoops.

NORWICH RFC
Ground Address:Beeston Hyrne, North Walsham Road,
Norwich NR12 7BW. Tel: 0603 426259 or 0603 484861
(answerphone)
Club Secretary: Chris Gillham, Eversheds, Paston House,
Princes Street, Norwich NR3 1BD. Tel: (H) 0603 58439 Tel:
(W) 0603 272727
Fixtures Secretary: Steve Henson.
Club Colours: Maroon, green & gold jerseys, blue shorts, navy
blue socks with maroon, green & gold hooped tops.

OLD GAYTONIANS RFC
Ground Address:South Vale, Harrow, Middlesex HA1 3PN.
Tel: 081 423 4133
Club Secretary: Tony Usher, 9 Paynesfield Road, Bushey
Heath, Herts WD2 1PQ. Tel: (H) 081 950 2956 Tel: (W) 0784
241731
Fixtures Secretary: Brian Kennett, 102 Cleveland Road,
London W13 0EL. Tel: (H) 081 998 2879 Tel (W) 081 231 2128
Club Colours: White with broad band of chocolate, green &
blue.

FINAL TABLE

	P	W	D	L	F	A	PD	Pts
Ruislip	12	9	2	1	196	95	101	20
Old Verulamians	12	9	1	2	203	102	101	19
Bishops' Stortford	12	9	1	2	175	131	44	17
Cambridge	12	7	2	3	214	130	84	16
Cheshunt	12	8	1	3	190	96	94	15
Norwich	12	6	1	5	143	122	21	13
Old Gaytonians	12	5	1	6	178	142	36	11
Chingford	12	4	2	6	178	120	58	10
Woodford	12	5	0	7	152	198	-46	10
Finchley	12	4	1	7	107	146	-39	9
Brentwood	12	3	1	8	103	223	-120	7
Upper Clapton	12	1	1	10	51	226	-175	3
Old Edwardians	12	1	0	11	69	228	-159	0

OLD VERULAMIAN RFC
Ground Address:Cotlandswick, London Colney, Nr St Albans,
Hertfordshire AL2 1DW. Tel: 0727 822929
Club Secretary: AB Charlwood, 12 Waverley Road, St
Albans, Hertfordshire AL3 5PA. Tel: (H) 0727 846923 Tel: (W)
071 638 5858
Fixtures Secretary: Mrs R Halford, 21 Marshalswick Lane, St
Albans, Hertfordshire AL1 4UR. Tel: (H) 0727 830732 Tel (W)
0920 830230
Club Colours: Royal blue with gold V, white shorts.

ROMFORD & GIDEA PARK RFC
Ground Address:Crowlands, Crow Lane, Romford, Essex
RM7 0EP. Tel: 0708 760068
Club Secretary: DGE Davies, 25 Stanley Avenue, Gidea Park,
Romford, Essex RM2 5DL. Tel: (H) 0708 724870 Tel: (W) 081
592 4193
Fixtures Secretary: K Parry, 112 London Road, Brentwood,
Essex CM14 4NS. Tel: (H) 0277 224881 Tel (W) 081 592 5623
Club Colours: Black with white, purple & white bands across
chest and arms.

STAINES RFC
Ground Address:The Reeves, Feltham Hill Road, Hanworth,
Feltham, Middlesex TW13 7NB. Tel: 081 890 3051
Club Secretary: WR Johnston, 4 April Close, Feltham,
Middlsex TW13 7JQ. Tel: (H) 081 384 6330 Tel: (W) 081 759
2141 x233
Fixtures Secretary: EJ de Voil, 94 Groveley Road,
Sunbury-on-thames, Middlesex TW16 7TB. Tel: (H) 081 890
6643 Tel (W) 071 248 1117 Fax: 071 248 1118
Club Colours: Blue & red jerseys, white shorts, blue & red
stockings.

THURROCK RFC
Ground Address:Oakfield, Long Lane, Grays, Essex. Tel:
0375 374877
Club Secretary: J Keefe, 20 Archates Avenue, Grays, Essex
RM16 6QS. Tel: (H) 0375 381763
Fixtures Secretary: A McGready, 97 High Road, Orsett, Essex
RM16 3LB. Tel: (H) 0375 891954
Club Colours: Black & white hooped shirts, black shorts &
stockings.

WOODFORD RFC
Ground Address:Highams, High Road, Woodford Green,
Essex IG9 9LB. Tel: 081 504 6769
Club Secretary: Mr RF Perryman, 7 Brancepeth Gardens,
Buckhurst Hill, Essex IG9 5JL. Tel: (H) 081 505 5973 Tel: (W)
081 556 9721
Fixtures Secretary: Mr M Whiteley, 62 Beresford Road,
London E4. Tel: (H) 081 524 2737 Tel (W) 071 865 5870
Club Colours: Lavender, black & white.

LONDON & SOUTH EAST DIVISION

LONDON THREE NORTH WEST 1994-95 FIXTURES

September 17 (Week 3)
Barnet v Letchworth
Old Albanians v Welwyn
Old Merchant Taylors v Upper Clapton
Old Millhillians v Hertford
Grasshoppers v Old Elizabethans
London New Zealand v Lensbury

September 24 (Week 4)
Letchworth v London New Zealand
Lensbury v Grasshoppers
Old Elizabethans v Old Millhillians
Hertford v Old Merchant Taylors
Upper Clapton v Old Albanians
Welwyn v Kingsburians

October 1 (Week 5)
Grasshoppers v Letchworth
London New Zealand v Barnet
Kingsburians v Upper Clapton
Old Albanians v Hertford
Old Merchant Taylors v Old Elizabethans
Old Millhillians v Lensbury

October 15 (Week 7)
Barnet v Grasshoppers
Letchworth v Old Millhillians
Lensbury v Old Merchant Taylors
Old Elizabethans v Old Albanians
Hertford v Kingsburians
Upper Clapton v Welwyn

October 22 (Week 8)
Old Merchant Taylors v Letchworth
Old Millhillians v Barnet
Grasshoppers v London New Zealand
Welwyn v Hertford
Kingsburians v Old Elizabethans
Old Albanians v Lensbury

October 29 (Week X2)
London New Zealand v Old Millhillians
Barnet v Old Merchant Taylors
Letchworth v Old Albanians
Lensbury v Kingsburians
Old Elizabethans v Welwyn
Hertford v Upper Clapton

January 7 (Week 17)
Kingsburians v Letchworth
Old Albanians v Barnet
Old Merchant Taylors v London New Zealand
Old Millhillians v Grasshoppers
Upper Clapton v Old Elizabethans
Welwyn v Lensbury

January 14 (Week 18)
Grasshoppers v Old Merchant Taylors
London New Zealand v Old Albanians
Barnet v Kingsburians
Letchworth v Welwyn
Lensbury v Upper Clapton
Old Elizabethans v Hertford

February 11 (Week 22)
Upper Clapton v Letchworth
Welwyn v Barnet
Kingsburians v London New Zealand
Old Albanians v Grasshoppers
Old Merchant Tayors v Old Millhillians
Hertford v Lensbury

February 25 (Week 24)
Old Millhillians v Old Albanians
Grasshoppers v Kingsburians
London New Zealand v Welwyn
Barnet v Upper Clapton
Letchworth v Hertford
Lensbury v Old Elizabethans

March 4 (Week 25)
Old Elizabethans v Letchworth
Hertford v Barnet
Upper Clapton v London New Zealand
Welwyn v Grasshoppers
Kingsburians v Old Millhillians
Old Albanians v Old Merchant Taylors

March 25 (Week 28)
Old Merchant Taylors v Kingsburians
Old Millhillians v Welwyn
Grasshoppers v Upper Clapton
London New Zealand v Hertford
Barnet v Old Elizabethans
Letchworth v Lensbury

April 8 (Week 30)
Lensbury v Barnet
Old Elizabethans v London New Zealand
Hertford v Grasshoppers
Upper Clapton v Old Millhillians
Welwyn v Old Merchant Taylors
Kingsburians v Old Albanians

LONDON THREE NORTH WEST

BARNET RFC
Ground Address:Byng Road, Barnet, herts. Tel: 081 449 0040
Club Secretary: Nigel Oram, Salisbury Cottage, Essendon,
Hertsw AL9 6AU. Tel: (H) 0707 268481 Tel: (W) 071 621 1224
Fixtures Secretary: Peter Glenister, 47 Bury Lane, Codicote,
Hitchin, Herts SG4 8XX. Tel: (H) 0438 820692
Club Colours: Dark blue & claret.

GRASSHOPPERS RFC
Ground Address:Macfarlane Sports Field, Macfarlane Lane,
off Syon Lane, Osterley, Middlesex. Tel: 081 568 0010
Club Secretary: Mr AJ Huckle, 142 West Drayton Road,
Hillingdon, Middlesex UB8 3LF. Tel: (H) 081 561 6164
Fixtures Secretary: Mr Andy Brown, 44 Thornbury Road,
Isleworth, Middlesex. Tel: (H) 081 560 4844 Tel (W) 081 560
2583
Club Colours: Green, black & gold.

HERTFORD RFC
Ground Address:Highfields, Hoe Lane, Ware, Herts SG12
9NZ. Tel: 0920 462975
Club Secretary: Mr AK Sparks, 29 Wilton Crescent, Hertford,
Herts SG13 8JS. Tel: (H) 0992 589364 Tel: (W) 0279 439161
Fixtures Secretary: Mr DJ Williams, 7 Sadlers Way, Hertford,
Herts SG14 2DZ. Tel: (H) 0992 586744
Club Colours: Black, royal blue & gold jerseys, black shorts.

KINGSBURIANS RFC
Ground Address:Northwick Park Pavilion, Northwick Park,
The Fairway, North Wembley, Middlesex. Tel: 081 904 4414
Club Secretary: Neil Keeler, 25 Lansdown Road, Stanmore,
Middlesex HA7 2RX. Tel: (H) 081 954 7211
Fixtures Secretary: Bruce Bland, 10 Clitheroe Avenue,
Rayners Lane, Harrow, Middlesex HA2 9UX. Tel: (H) 081 868
5244 Tel (W) 081 204 4442
Club Colours: Black & amber hoops, black shorts. Change:
Black shirts.

LENSBURY
Ground Address:Lensbury Club, Broom Road, Teddington,
Middx TW11 9NU. Tel: 081 977 8821
Club Secretary: M O'Gara, 13 Bryanston Avenue,
Twickenham, Middx TW2 6HP. Tel: (H) 081 898 7359 Tel:
(W) 0252 625 121
Fixtures Secretary: Mr S Riach, Deva, 12 Blackwood Close,
West Byfleet, Surrey KT14 6PW. Tel: (H) 0932 340601 Tel
(W) 0784 245058
Club Colours: Purple, orange & black hoops.

LETCHWORTH GARDEN CITY RUFC
Ground Address:Baldock road, Letchworth. Tel: 0462 682554
Club Secretary: JP Donegan, 9 Byrd Walk, Baldock Herts
SG7 6LN. Tel: (H) 0462 491360 Tel: (W) 0462 442800
Fixtures Secretary: Chris Priestley, 88 Cowslip Hill,
Letchworth, Herts. Tel: (H) 0462 686768 Tel (W) 071 3236990
Club Colours: Black & amber hooped jerseys, black shorts &
stockings.

LONDON NEW ZEALAND RFC
Ground Address:c/o Osterley Sports & Social Club, Tentelow
Lane, Osterley, Middx. Tel: 081 574 3774
Club Secretary: Team Manager: Tudor Davies, 46 Lamorna
Grove, Stanmore, Middx HA7 1PQ. Tel: (H) 081 952 6822 Tel:
(W) 081 208 0022
Fixtures Secretary: Richard Peacock, Oakfell, Downley
Common, High Wycombe, Bucks. Tel: (H) 0494 448157 Tel
(W) 081 907 7799
Club Colours: All black.

OLD ALBANIAN RFC
Ground Address:Beech Bottom, Old Harpenden Road, St
Albans, Herts. Tel: 0727 864476
Club Secretary: Peter Lipscomb, 35 Gurney Court Road, St
Albans, Herts AL1 4QU. Tel: (H) 0727 863621 Tel: (W) 081
784 5924
Fixtures Secretary: David Verdon, Pine Lodge, Hook Heath
Road, Woking, Surrey. Tel: (H) 0483 764937 Tel (W) 071 538
8860
Club Colours: Red, blue & gold hooped shirts.

FINAL TABLE

	P	W	D	L	F	A	PD	Pts
Staines	12	11	0	1	291	195	22	
Letchworth	12	10	0	2	267	102	165	18
Grasshoppers	12	9	0	3	211	133	78	18
O. Merchnt Taylors	12	8	0	4	192	172	20	16
Hertford	12	7	0	5	154	171	-17	14
Lensbury	12	10	0	2	223	117	106	10
London N. Zealand	12	5	0	7	158	180	-22	10
Welwyn	12	5	0	7	162	236	-74	10
Old Elizabethans	12	4	0	8	172	193	-21	8
Old Albanians	12	4	0	8	155	230	-75	8
Kingsburians	12	3	0	9	113	178	-65	6
Fullerians	12	2	0	10	83	200	-117	4
Old Meadonians	12	0	0	12	64	237	-173	0

OLD ELIZABETHANS (BARNET) RFC
Ground Address:Gipsy Corner, Mays Lane (Barnet Gate Lane
End), Barnet, Hertfordshire EN5 2AG. Tel: 081 449 9481
Club Secretary: Michael Parker, 4 Cedar Avenue, East Barnet,
Hertfordshire EN4 8DY. Tel: (H) 081 368 4767 Tel: (W) 071
290 4042
Fixtures Secretary: John Fuller, 109 Margaret Road, New
Barnet, Herts EN4 9RA. Tel: (H) 081 449 0590
Club Colours: Light blue & dark blue hoops.

OLD MERCHANT TAYLORS' FC
Ground Address:Durrants, Lincoln Way, Croxley Green, Nr
Rickmansworth, Hertfordshire WD3 3ND. Tel: 0923 773014
Club Secretary: MG Foster, The White House, 16 New Road,
Croxley Green, Hertfordshire WD3 3ND. Tel: (H) 0923 775793
Fixtures Secretary: GW Shilling, The Lodge, Wellingrove,
Woodcock Hill, Rickmansworth, Herts WD3 1PT. Tel: (H)
0923 774506 Tel (W) 0923 774506
Club Colours: White jerseys, black shorts.

OLD MILLHILLIANS RFC
Ground Address:Pinner Park, Headstone Lane, North Harrow,
Middlesex HA2 6BR. Tel: 081 428 2281
Club Secretary: M Leon, Wildacre, Bushfield Road,
Bovingdon, Herts HP3 0QR. Tel: (H) 0442 833665
Fixtures Secretary: P Foottit, 38 Birkbeck Road, London NW7
4AA. Tel: (H) 081 906 3060 Tel (W) 081 367 7711
Club Colours: Chocolate & white hoops.

UPPER CLAPTON FC
Ground Address:The Clubhouse, Upland Road, Thornwood
Common, Epping, Essex CM16 6NL. Tel: 0992 572588
Club Secretary: David Miller, 13 Rushfield, Sawbridgeworth,
Herts CM21 9NF. Tel: (H) 0279 724849 Tel: (W) 081 309 6398
Fixtures Secretary: Nick Slate, The Cock Public House,
Church Road, Henham, Nr Bishop's Stortford, Herts. Tel: (H)
0279 850347
Club Colours: 7' red & white hoops.

WELWYN RFC
Ground Address:Hobbs Way, Colgrove, Welwyn Garden City,
Herts. Tel: 0707 329116
Club Secretary: JM Sargeant, 67 Woodhall Lane, Welwyn
Garden City, Herts AL7 3TG. Tel: (H) 0707 331186 Tel: (W)
0707 326318
Fixtures Secretary: N Aldridge, 9 Marsden Close, Welwyn
Garden City, Herts AL7 6JF. Tel: (H) 0707 321012 Tel (W) 081
758 6000
Club Colours: Maroon & white hoops, blue shorts, maroon
stockings.

LONDON & SOUTH EAST DIVISION

HERTFORDSHIRE/ MIDDLESEX ONE 1994-95 FIXTURES

September 17 (Week 3)
Hemel Hempstead v Fullerians
Centaurs v Hitchin
St. Mary's Hospital v Mill Hill
Hendon v Hampstead
Harpenden v St. Albans
Haringey v Old Meadonians

September 24 (Week 4)
Fullerians v Haringey
Old Meadonians v Harpenden
St. Albans v Hendon
Hampstead v St. Mary's Hospital
Mill Hill v Centaurs
Hitchin v Uxbridge

October 1 (Week 5)
Harpenden v Fullerians
Haringey v Hemel Hempstead
Uxbridge v Mill Hill
Centaurs v Hamsptead
St. Mary's Hospital v St. Albans
Hendon v Old Meadonians

October 15 (Week 7)
Hemel Hempstead v Harpenden
Fullerians v Hendon
Old Meadonians v St. Mary's Hospital
St. Albans v Centaurs
Hampstead v Uxbridge
Mill Hill v Hitchin

October 22 (Week 8)
St. Mary's Hospital v Fullerians
Hendon v Hemel Hempstead
Harpenden v Haringey
Hitchin v Hampstead
Uxbridge v St. Albans
Centaurs v Old Meadonians

October 29 (Week X2)
Haringey v Hendon
Hemel Hempstead v St. Mary's Hospital
Fullerians v Centaurs
Old Meadonians v Uxbridge
St. Albans v Hitchin
Hampstead v Mill Hill

January 7 (Week 17)
Uxbridge v Fullerians
Centaurs v Hemel Hempstead
St. Mary's Hospital v Haringey
Hendon v Harpenden
Mill Hill v St. Albans
Hitchin v Old Meadonians

January 14 (Week 18)
Harpenden v St. Mary's Hospital
Haringey v Centaurs
Hemel Hempstead v Uxbridge
Fullerians v Hitchin
Old Meadonians v Mill Hill
St. Albans v Hampstead

February 11 (Week 22)
Mill Hill v Fullerians
Hitchin v Hemel Hempstead
Uxbridge v Haringey
Centaurs v Harpenden
St. Mary's Hospital v Hendon
Hampstead v Old Meadonians

February 25 (Week 24)
Hendon v Centaurs
Harpenden v Uxbridge
Haringey v Hitchin
Hemel Hempstead v Mill Hill
Fullerians v Hampstead
Old Meadonians v St. Albans

March 4 (Week 25)
St. Albans v Fullerians
Hampstead v Hemel Hempstead
Mill Hill v Haringey
Hitchin v Harpenden
Uxbridge v Hendon
Centaurs v St. Mary's Hospital

March 25 (Week 28)
St. Mary's Hospital v Uxbridge
Hendon v Hitchin
Harpenden v Mill Hill
Haringey v Hampstead
Hemel Hempstead v St. Albans
Fullerians v Old Meadonians

April 8 (Week 30)
Old Meadonians v Hemel Hempstead
St. Albans v Haringey
Hampstead v Harpenden
Mill Hill v Hendon
Hitchin v St. Mary's Hospital
Uxbridge v Centaurs

HERTS & MIDDLESEX

CENTAURS RFC
Ground Address:Gower Road, Syon Lane, Osterley, Middlesex. Tel: 081 560 4500
Club Secretary: Mr M Ryole, 218 Meadvale Road, Ealing, London, W5 1LT. Tel: (H) 081 991 1439 Tel: (W) 0784 461 666
Fixtures Secretary: Jerry Goldie, 23 Northumberland Avenue, Isleworth, Midd. TW7 5HZ. Tel: (H) 081 568 7240 Tel (W) 071 837 3627
Club Colours: Light blue & dark blue hoops.
FULLERIANS RUFC
Ground Address:Watford Grammer School, New Field, Coninges Drive, Watford, Herts. Tel: 0923 224483
Club Secretary: Nick Thomas, 12 Hempstead Road, Kings Langley, Herts WD4 7AD.
Fixtures Secretary: John Ayres, 9 Church Grove, Little Chalfont, Buckinghamshire, HP6 6SH. Tel: (H) 0494 763 266 Tel (W) 081 469 2244
Club Colours: Black, red & green hoops, white shorts.
HAMPSTEAD RFC
Ground Address:The Heath Extension, Hampstead Way, London NW11. Tel: 071 794 4805
Club Secretary: Stephen John Loffler, 14 Grey Close, London NW11 6QG. Tel: (H) 081 458 6512 Tel: (W) 081 759 4822
Fixtures Secretary: Charles Scully, 4 Monmouth Close, Beaumont Park, Chiswick, London W4 5DQ. Tel: (H) 081 742 2550 Tel (W) (Mobile) 0836 666381
Club Colours: Claret, white & yellow.
HARINGEY RFC
Ground Address:New River Sports Centre, White Hart Lane, Wood Green, London N22 5QW. Tel: Clubhouse: 081 888 9299. Reception: 081 881 1926
Club Secretary: Glynne Jones, 44 Park Hall Road, East Finchley, London N2 9PX. Tel: (H) 081 883 8091
Fixtures Secretary: Colin Field, 2 Highview Close, Potters Bar, Herts. Tel: (H) 0707 645557 Tel (W) 081 340 1771
Club Colours: Green, scarlet & white.
HARPENDEN RFC
Ground Address:Redbourn Lane, Harpenden, Herts AL5 2BA. Tel: 0585 460711
Club Secretary: M Aldous-Ball, 4 Wells Close, Harpenden, Herts AL5 3LQ. Tel: (H) 0582 461527 Tel: (W) 081 979 9951
Fixtures Secretary: Andy Finch, 3 Doon Court, 46 Luton Road, Harpenden, Herts. Tel: (H) 0582 713797 Tel (W) 0438 7555376
Club Colours: Brown & white quartered shirts.
HEMEL HEMPSTEAD (CAMELOT) RUFC
Ground Address:The Club House, Chauldon Lane, Hemel Hempstead, Herts, HP1 2BS. Tel: 0442 230 353 (Admin) 0442 213 408 (Public)
Club Secretary: John Clapham, 49 Brook Court, Watling Street, Radlett, Herts, WD7 7JA. Tel: (H) 0923 852 104
Fixtures Secretary: Adrian Wakefield, 23 Riverside Court, River Beach, Broom Water, Teddington, Midd. Tel: (H) 081 977 0746 Tel (W) 071 930 2399
Club Colours: Royal blue with white hoop.
HENDON RFC
Ground Address:Copthall Playing Fields, Great North Way, Hendon, London NW4. Tel: 081 203 1737
Club Secretary: T Brownsell, 9 Winscombe Way, Stanmore, Middlesex HA7 3AX. Tel: (H) 081 954 7060
Fixtures Secretary: C Silver, 7 Castellane Close, Stanmore, Middlesex HA7 3TN. Tel: (H) 081 954 9641
Club Colours: Bottle green, black & white.
HITCHIN RFC
Ground Address:King George V Playing Field, Old Hale Way, Hitchin, Herts. Tel: 0462 432679
Club Secretary: Stephen Ward, 73 Millstream Close, Hitchin, Herts SG4 0DB. Tel: (H) 0462 455358 Tel: (W) 071 860 2147

FINAL TABLE

	P	W	D	L	F	A	PD	Pts
Barnet	12	10	0	2	210	119	91	20
Old Millhillians	12	11	0	1	360	90	270	18
Hampstead	12	9	0	3	257	114	143	16
Uxbridge	12	8	0	4	204	106	98	16
Haringey	12	8	0	4	214	179	35	16
St. Mary's Hospital	12	7	0	5	137	233	4	14
Hendon	12	5	0	7	131	206	-75	10
Harpenden	12	5	0	7	144	220	-76	10
Hemel Hempstead	12	4	0	8	147	180	-33	8
Centaurs	12	4	0	8	128	162	-34	8
Hitchin	12	3	0	9	118	235	-117	6
Harrow	12	3	0	9	131	274	-143	6
Antlers	12	1	0	11	98	261	-163	2

Fixtures Secretary: Malcolm Ward, 10 Roman Road, Baldock, Herts SG7 6PN. Tel: (H) 0462 893071
Club Colours: Maroon shirts, white shorts.
MILL HILL RFC
Ground Address:Page Street, Mill Hill, London NW7 2ER. Tel: 081 203 0685
Club Secretary: Bruce A Williams, 56 Kingshill Avenue, Kenton, Harrow, Middlesex HA3 8LB. Tel: (H) 081 907 6765 Tel: (W) 081 424 1367
Fixtures Secretary: Peter J Braddock, 43 Winstre Road, Boreham Wood, Hertfordshire WD6 5DR. Tel: (H) 081 953 6500 Tel (W) 081 953 6500
Club Colours: Chocolate & gold hoops.
OLD MEADONIANS RFC
Ground Address:Riverside Lands, Chiswick, London W4. Tel: 081 994 6956
Club Secretary: RF Udwin, 62 Somerset Road, Chiswick, London W4 5DN. Tel: (H) 081 994 6623 Tel: (W) 081 994 6623
Fixtures Secretary: R Willingale, Fairmile Farm Cottage, Denby Road, Cobham, Surrey KT11 1JY. Tel: (H) 0932 866927 Tel (W) 0932 866927
Club Colours: Maroon & pale blue hoops.
ST ALBANS RFC
Ground Address:Bogeymead Spring, Oaklands Lane, Smallford, St. Albans, Herts AL4. Tel: 081 205 1213 x285
Club Secretary: John Gregory, 58 Luton Lane, Redbourn, Herts AL3 7PY. Tel: (H) 0582 792798 Tel: (W) 081 205 1213 x285
Fixtures Secretary: Gregory Thomas, 176 Park Street Lane, Park Street, St Albans AL2 2AT. Tel: (H) 0727 873004
Club Colours: Royal blue & gold hoops.
ST MARY'S HOSPITAL RFC
Ground Address:Udney Park Road, Teddington, Middlesex. Tel: 081 977 3100
Club Secretary: RAL Young, FRCS, West Middlesex University Hospital, Twickenham Road, Isleworth, Middx TW7 6AF. Tel: (H) 081 891 0638 Tel: (W) 081 565 5768
Fixtures Secretary: Professor P Sever FRCP, St Mary's Hospital Medical School, Norfolk Place, London W2. Tel (W) 071 725 1117
Club Colours: Navy blue & white.
UXBRIDGE RFC
Ground Address:Uxbridge Cricket Club, Park Road, Uxbridge, UB8 1NR. Tel: 0895 237
Club Secretary: Richard Jones, 103 Swakeleys Road, Ickenham, Middlesex, UB10 8DH. Tel: (H) 0895 675387 Tel: (W) 071 356 8806
Fixtures Secretary: P John, 4 The Avenue, Old Windsor, Berks, SL4 2RS. Tel: (H) 0753 867 678 Tel (W) 0895 832 323 Ext 6226
Club Colours: Red, black & white hooped shirts, black shorts.

LONDON & SOUTH EAST DIVISION

MIDDLESEX ONE
1994-95
FIXTURES

January 7 (Week 17)
Belsize Park v Roxeth Manor O B
Wembley v Twickenham
Harrow v Sudbury Court
Old Haberdashers v Civil Service
Old Hamptonians v Old Pauline
Old Actonians v Hackney

September 17 (Week 3)
Twickenham v Roxeth Manor O B
Wembley v Old Actonians
Harrow v Old Hamptonians
Old Haberdashers v Antlers
Civil Service v Old Pauline
Sudbury Court v Hackney

January 14 (Week 18)
Civil Service v Harrow
Sudbury Court v Wembley
Twickenham v Belsize Park
Roxeth Manor O B v Old Actonians
Hackney v Old Hamptonians
Old Pauline v Antlers

September 24 (Week 4)
Roxeth Manor O B v Sudbury Court
Hackney v Civil Service
Old Pauline v Old Haberdashers
Antlers v Harrow
Old Hamptonians v Wembley
Old Actonians v Belsize Park

February 11 (Week 22)
Old Hamptonians v Roxeth Manor O B
Old Actonians v Twickenham
Belsize Park v Sudbury Court
Wembley v Civil Service
Harrow v Old Haberdashers
Antlers v Hackney

October 1 (Week 5)
Civil Service v Roxeth Manor O B
Sudbury Court v Twickenham
Belsize Park v Old Hamptonians
Wembley v Antlers
Harrow v Old Pauline
Old Haberdashers v Hackney

February 25 (Week 24)
Old Haberdashers v Wenbley
Civil Service v Belsize Park
Sudbury Court v Old Actonians
Twickenham v Old Hamptonians
Roxeth Manor O B v Antlers
Hackney v Old Pauline

October 15 (Week 7)
Twickenham v Civil Service
Roxeth Manor O B v Old Haberdashers
Hackney v Harrow
Old Pauline v Wembley
Antlers v Belsize Park
Old Hamptonians v Old Actonians

March 4 (Week 25)
Old Pauline v Roxeth Manor O B
Antlers v Twickenham
Old Hamptonians v Sudbury Court
Old Actonians v Civil Service
Belsize Park v Old Haberdashers
Wembley v Harrow

October 22 (Week 8)
Harrow v Roxeth Manor O B
Old Haberdashers v Twickenham
Civil Service v Sudbury Court
Old Actonians v Antlers
Belsize Park v Old Pauline
Wembley v Hackney

March 25 (Week 28)
Harrow v Belsize Park
Old Haberdashers v Old Actonians
Civil Service v Old Hamptonians
Sudbury Court v Antlers
Twickenham v Old Pauline
Roxeth Manor O B v Hackney

October 29 (Week X2)
Sudbury Court v Old Haberdashers
Twickenham v Harrow
Roxeth Manor O B v Wembley
Hackney v Belsize Park
Old Pauline v Old Actonians
Antlers v Old Hamptonians

April 8 (Week 30)
Hackney v Twickenham
Old Pauline v Sudbury Court
Antlers v Civil Service
Old Hamptonians v Old Haberdashers
Old Actonians v Harrow
Belsize Park v Wembley

MIDDLESEX ONE

ANTLERS RFC
Ground Address: Bushy Park, Teddington, Middlesex.
Tel: 081 977 4989
Club Secretary: PJ Woolgar, 114 Elgin Avenue, Ashford,
Middx TW15 1QG. Tel: (H) 0784 259734 Tel: (W) 0268
544001
Fixtures Secretary: R Bromfield, 104 Station Road,
Hampton, Middx. Tel: (H) 081 979 5635
Club Colours: Dark blue.

BELSIZE PARK RFC
Ground Address:c/o Hendon RFC, Copthall Sports
Centre, Hendon Way, Hendon, NW London. Tel: 071 794
4910
Club Secretary: Sebastian Colquhoun, 9 Regency Lawn,
Croftdown Road, London NW5 1HF. Tel: (H) 071 485
5767 Tel: (W) 071 477 5537
Fixtures Secretary: Hugh Reeve-Tucker, 5 Algarve Road,
London SW18 3EQ. Tel: (H) 081 874 5907 Tel (W) 071
234 4822
Club Colours: Lavender & black.

CIVIL SERVICE FC (RU)
Ground Address: Dukes Meadows, Riverside Drive,
Chiswick, London W4. Tel: 081 994 1202
Club Secretary: N G Alway, 20 Herndon Road, London,
SW18 2DG. Tel: (H) 081 870 6818 Tel: (W) 071 583 5333
Fixtures Secretary: R Hulme, 64 Walmington Fold,
London N12. Tel: (H) 081 346 1557
Club Colours: White shirts, blue shorts.

HACKNEY RFC
Ground Address: Spring Hill Ground, Spring Hill,
Hackney, London E5. Tel: 081 806 5289
Club Secretary: Howard Gross, 50 Cassland Road,
Hackney, London E9 7AW. Tel: (H) 081 986 3783 Tel:
(W) 081 923 9005
Fixtures Secretary: Bob Brown, 73 Purdy Street, Bow,
London E3. Tel: (H) 071 537 7306 Tel: (W) 071 729 5477
Club Colours: Gold, blue & green quarters.

HARROW RFC
Ground Address: Grovefield, Wood Lane, Stanmore,
Middx. Tel: 081 954 2615
Club Secretary: Mr Steven Riley, 16 Grange Avenue,
Stanmore, Middx HA7 2HZ. Tel: (H) 081 907 6748 Tel:
(W) 0941 105118
Fixtures Secretary: Mr Peter Pope, 16 Kenilworth Drive,
Croxley Green, Hertfordshire. Tel: (H) 0923 241504 Tel
(W) 0923 778111
Club Colours: Navy blue jerseys with 1@ white hoops.

OLD ACTONIANS RFC
Ground Address: Gunnersby Drive, off Popes Lane,
Ealing, London W5. Tel: 081 567 4556
Club Secretary: Mr Peter Mullen, 67 Barton Court, Barons
Court Road, London W14 9EH. Tel: (W) 071 962 3426
Fixtures Secretary: Mr D Sommerville, 4 The Common,
Ealing, London W5 3TR. Tel: (H) 081 567 3002 Tel (W)
071 831 6351
Club Colours: Blue & white hoops, red collars.

OLD HABERDASHERS RFC
Ground Address: Croxdale Road, Theobald Street,
Borehamwood, Hertfordshire WD6 4PY. Tel: 081 953 1987
Club Secretary: A J S Alexander, 26 Little Bushey Lane,
Bushey Heath, Hertfordshire. Tel: (H) 081 950 1495
Club Colours: Blue, white & magenta.

OLD HAMPTONIANS RFC
Ground Address: The Pavilion, Dean Road, Hampton,
Middlesex. Tel: 091 979 2784
Club Secretary: Ian Strutt, 132 Peregrine Road,
Sunbury-on-Thames, Middlesex TW16 6JL. Tel: (H) 0932
782019 Tel: (W) 0941 106939
Fixtures Secretary: Nick Bugler, 14 Sidney Road,
Teddington TW11 8PQ. Tel: (H) 081 977 1654
Club Colours: Black, gold & silver hoops.

FINAL TABLE

	P	W	D	L	F	A	PD	Pts
Mill Hill	12	12	0	0	311	91	220	24
Roxeth Manor O.B.	12	9	0	3	143	93	50	18
Old Hamptonians	12	8	0	4	291	139	152	16
Civil Service	12	8	0	4	217	102	115	16
Wembley	11	7	0	4	220	120	100	14
Old Actonians	12	6	1	5	203	180	23	13
Old Haberdashers	12	5	1	6	136	198	-62	11
Twickenham	12	5	0	7	165	139	26	10
Sudbury Court	11	4	0	7	112	200	-88	8
Old Abbotstonians	12	3	2	7	133	243	-110	8
Hackney	12	3	1	8	126	219	-93	7
Old Isleworthians	12	3	1	8	93	211	-118	7
Hamrsmith & Fulhm	12	1	0	11	75	290	-215	2

Old Abbotstonians also relegated

OLD PAULINE FC
Ground Address: Speer Road, Thames Ditton, Surrey KT7
0PW. Tel: 081 398 1858
Club Secretary: Tim JD Cunis, 62 Derby Road, East
Sheen, London SW14 7DP. Tel: (H) 081 878 3099
Fixtures Secretary: John A Howard, 93A Richmond Park
Road, Kingston, Surrey KT2 6AF. Tel: (H) 081 541 3817
Tel (W) 081 941 4431
Club Colours: Red, white & black hoops.

ROXETH MANOR OLD BOYS RFC
Ground Address: City of Westminster, Harrow College of
Further Education, Watford Road, Harrow, Middlesex.
Club Secretary: D R Pearham, 26 Yeading Avenue,
Harrow, Middlesex, HA2 9RN. Tel: (H) 081 868 1799
Club Colours: All black.

SUDBURY COURT RFC
Ground Address: Vale Farm, East Lane, North Wembley,
Middx. Tel: 081 904 8485
Club Secretary: Derek Gray, 33 Northwick Park Road,
Harrow, Middx. Tel: (H) 081 427 4155 Tel: (W) 021 456
4411
Fixtures Secretary: D Roxborough, 72A Locket Road,
Harrow, Middx. Tel: (H) 081 861 4362
Club Colours: Dark blue, red & white.

TWICKENHAM RFC
Ground Address: Park Fields, South Road, Hunton,
Middlesex. Tel: 081 979 2427
Club Secretary: Tony Kay, 29 Grange Avenue,
Twickenham, Middlesex TW2 5TW. Tel: (H) 081 898
7210 Tel: (W) 081 898 7210
Fixtures Secretary: Martin Mitchell, 41 Northolme Road,
Highbury, London N5 2UX. Tel: (H) 071 359 1224
Club Colours: Red & black irregular hoops.

WEMBLEY RFC
Ground Address: Cedars Hall, Chicheley Road, Harrow
Weald HA3 6QL. Tel: 081 420 1789
Club Secretary: Noreen Conlon, 62 Canterbury Way,
Croxley Green, Rickmansworth, Herts WD3 3SS. Tel: (H)
0923 230640 Tel: (W) 081 420 1789
Fixtures Secretary: Chris Green, 26 Anmersh Grove,
Stanmore, Middx.
Club Colours: Maroon & amber quarters.

LONDON & SOUTH EAST DIVISION

MIDDLESEX TWO
1994-95
FIXTURES

September 17 (Week 3)
Old Abbotstonians v London Nigerian
Old Isleworthians v Old Grammarians
Barclays Bank v Thamesians
Enfield Ignatians v Pinner & Grammarians
Feltham v Bank Of England
Hammersmith & F'm v Hayes

September 24 (Week 4)
London Nigerian v Hammersmith & F'm
Hayes v Feltham
Bank of England v Enfield Ignatians
Pinner & Grammarians v Barclays Bank
Thamesians v Old Isleworthians
Old Grammarians v H.A.C.

October 1 (Week 5)
Feltham v London Nigerian
Hammersmith & F'm v Old Abbotstonians
H.A.C. v Thamesians
Old Isleworthians v Pinner & Grammarians
Barclays Bank v Bank of England
Enfield Ignatians v Hayes

October 15 (Week 7)
Old Abbotstonians v Feltham
London Nigerian v Enfield Ignatians
Hayes v Barclays Bank
Bank of England v Old Iseworthians
Pinner & Grammarians v H.A.C.
Thamesians v Old Grammarians

October 22 (Week 8)
Barclays Bank v London Nigerian
Enfield Ignatians v Old Abbotstonians
Feltham v Hammersmith & F'm
Old Gramarrians v Pinner & Grammarians
H.A.C. v Bank of England
Old Isleworthians v Hayes

October 29 (Week X2)
Hammersmith & F'm v Enfield Ignatians
Old Abbotstonians v Barclays Bank
London Nigerian v Old Isleworthians
Hayes v H.A.C.
Bank of England v Old Grammarians
Pinner & Grammarians v Thamesians

January 7 (Week 17)
H.A.C. v London Nigerian
Old Isleworthians v Old Abbotstonians
Barclays Bank v Hammersmith & F'm
Enfield Ignatians v Feltham
Thamesians v Bank of England
Old Grammarians v Hayes

January 14 (Week 18)
Feltham v Barclays Bank
Hammersmith & F'm v Old Isleworthians
Old Abbotstonians v H.A.C.
London Nigerian v Old Grammarians
Hayes v Thamesians
Bank of England v Pinner & Grammarians

February 11 (Week 22)
Thamesians v London Nigerian
Old Grammarians v Old Abbotstonians
H.A.C. v Hammersmith & F'm
Old Isleworthians v Feltham
Barclays Bank v Enfield Ignatians
Pinner & Grammarians v Hayes

February 25 (Week 24)
Enfield Ignatians v Old Isleworthians
Feltham v H.A.C.
Hammersmith & F'm v Old Grammarians
Old Abbotstonians v Thamesians
London Nigerian v Pinner & Grammarians
Hayes v Bank of England

March 4 (Week 25)
Bank of England v London Nigerian
Pinner & Grammarians v Old Abbotstonians
Thamesians v Hammersmith & F'm
Old Grammarians v Feltham
H.A.C. v Enfield Ignatians
Old Isleworthians v Barclays Bank

March 25 (Week 28)
Barclays Bank v H.A.C.
Enfield Ignatians v Old Grammarians
Feltham v Thamesians
Hammersmith & F'am v Pinner & Grammarians
Old Abbotstonians v Bank of England
London Nigerian v Hayes

April 8 (Week 30)
Hayes v Old Abbotstonians
Bank of England v Hammersmith & F'm
Pinner & Grammarians v Feltham
Thamesians v Enfield Ignatians
Old Grammarians v Barclays Bank
H.A.C. v Old Isleworthians

MIDDLESEX TWO

BANK OF ENGLAND RFC
Ground Address:Priory Lane, Roehampton, London
SW15 5JQ. Tel: 081 876 8417
Club Secretary: BS Brown, 62 Gilpin Avenue, East
Sheen, London SW14 8QY. Tel: (H) 081 878 3396 Tel:
(W) 071 601 4949
Fixtures Secretary: BS Brown, 62 Gilpin Avenue, East
Sheen, London SW14 8QY. Tel: (H) 081 878 3396 Tel (W)
071 601 4949
Club Colours: Blue, gold & white hoops.
BARCLAYS BANK RFC
Ground Address:Park View Road, Ealing, London W5
2JF. Tel: 081 998 4904
Club Secretary: Mike J Allen, 12 Laburnum Way,
Bromley, Kent. Tel: (H) 081 457 2097 Tel: (W) 071 491
8687
Fixtures Secretary: D Martin Bevan-Jones, 23 Cypress
Avenue, Whitton, Middlesex. Tel: (H) 081 898 4107 Tel
(W) 071 696 2865
Club Colours: Maroon jerseys with gold band edged in
silver, black shorts.
ENFIELD IGNATIANS RFC
Ground Address:Enfield Playing Fields, Donkey Lane,
Carterhatch Lane, Enfield, Middx. Tel: 081 363 2877
Club Secretary: Glyn Jones, 45 Halifax Road, Enfield,
Middx. Tel: (H) 091 366 3207 Tel: (W) 081 967 9474
Fixtures Secretary: Peter Tiervan, 19 Hawkwood
Crescent, London E4. Tel: (H) 081 529 8130
Club Colours: Blue & gold.
FELTHAM RFC
Ground Address:Park Road, Hanworth, Middlesex, TW13
7EY. Tel: 081 894 3609
Club Secretary: B J Wilkins, 29 Gibbon Road, Kingston
Upon Thames, Surrey, KT2 6AD.
Club Colours: Light blue, dark blue, gold hoop.
HAMMERSMITH & FULHAM RFC
Ground Address:Hurlingham Stadium, Hurlingham Park,
Hurlingham Road, London SW6. Tel: 071 736 5186
Club Secretary: Chris Cuthbertson, 17 Wheatsheaf Wharf,
Wheatsheaf Lane, London SW6 6LS. Tel: (H) 071 381
5064 Tel: (W) 071 233 5611
Fixtures Secretary: Lyndon Walters, 32 Chapel Road,
Hounslow TW3 1JL. Tel: (H) 081 572 3853 Tel (W) 071
962 8047
Club Colours: Red with white & navy bands.
HAYES RFC
Ground Address:Grosvenor Playing Fields, Kingshill
Avenue, Hayes, Middx. Tel: 081 845 4963
Club Secretary: Mr R Hall, 2 Fulwood Close, Church
Road, Hayes, Middx UB3 2NF. Tel: (H) 081 573 7133
Fixtures Secretary: N Fretwell, 5 Sandgate House,
Queens Walk, Ealing, London W5 1TN. Tel: (H) 081 991
1652 Tel (W) 0459 114864 (pager)
Club Colours: Navy blue.
HONOURABLE ARTILLERY COMPANY RFC
Ground Address:Honourable Artillery Company, Artillery
Ground, Armoury House, City Road, London EC1Y 2BQ.
Club Secretary: Colin Pritchard, 31 Bedford Avenue,
Little Chalfont, Bucks HP6 6PS. Tel: (H) 0494 762982
Fixtures Secretary: Colin Pritchard, 31 Bedford Avenue,
Little Chalfont, Bucks HP6 6PS. Tel: (H) 0494 762982
Club Colours: Maroon & dark blue hoops.
LONDON NIGERIAN RFC
Ground Address:Barnes Copthall Playing Fields, Great
North Way, Hendon, London NW4. Tel: 081 203 1237
Club Secretary: Babs Akin-Olugbemi, 3 Glebe Road,
Hornsey, London N8 7DA. Tel: (H) 081 341 2371 Tel: (W)
081 341 2371
Fixtures Secretary: Fola Odetoyinbo, 130 Fleet Road,
Hampstead, London NW3. Tel: (H) 071 267 8788 Tel (W)
071 490 1638

FINAL TABLE

	P	W	D	L	F	A	PD	Pts
Old Paulines	12	10	0	2	220	98	122	20
Belsize Park	12	9	0	3	244	129	115	18
Pinner & Gramrians	12	9	0	3	209	113	96	18
Thamesians	12	9	1	2	290	150	140	15
Enfield Ignatians	12	7	1	4	212	142	70	15
Barclays Bank	12	7	0	5	200	187	13	12
H.A.C.	12	6	1	5	216	211	5	11
Feltham	12	4	2	6	126	161	-35	10
Old Grammarians	12	3	2	7	149	145	4	8
Hayes	12	4	0	8	145	199	-54	8
London Cornish	12	3	1	8	118	184	-66	7
Orleans F.P.	12	1	0	11	66	350	-284	-2
Osterley	12	1	0	11	66	350	-284	-2

Club Colours: Black. Change: Green & white.
OLD ABBOTSTONIANS RFC
Ground Address:Pole Hill Open Spaces, Raeburn Road,
Hayes, Middlesex. Tel: 081 845 1452
Club Secretary: Mr Geln Baptista, 2 Denecroft Crescent,
Hillingdon, Middlesex UB10 9HU. Tel: (H) 0895 231748
Tel: (W) 071 798 7699
Fixtures Secretary: Mr Denis Halloran, 8 Swallow Drive,
Northolt, Middlesex UB5 6UJ. Tel: (H) 081 842 2154 Tel
(W) 0895 272090
Club Colours: Blue & red quarters.
OLD GRAMMARIANS RFC
Ground Address:Worlds End Lane, Green Dragon Lane,
Grange Park, Enfield, Middlesex.
Club Secretary: Brian Calderwood, 17 Birch Crescent,
Aylesford, Kent ME20 7QE. Tel: (H) 0622 718350 Tel:
(W) 0622 710811
Fixtures Secretary: Mike Holt, 64 Chandos Road, London
N2 9AP. Tel: (H) 081 883 4016
Club Colours: Navy, light blue & red.
OLD ISLEWORTHIANS RFC
Ground Address:Memorial Ground, Wood Lane,
Isleworth, Middlesex. Tel: 081 560 7949
Club Secretary: Huw Davies, 230 Whitton Dene,
Isleworth, Middlesex TW7 7LU. Tel: (H) 081 898 5924
Tel: (W) 071 315 6023
Fixtures Secretary: Richard Crow, 14 Heathfield South,
Twickenham TW2 7SS. Tel: (H) 081 892 8901 Tel (W)
071 702 5134
Club Colours: Blue jerseys with horizontal red band &
grey stripe, white & red socks.
PINNER & GRAMMARIANS RFC
Ground Address:Shaftesbury Playing Fields, Grimsdyke
Road, Hatch End, Pinner, Middx. Tel: 081 428 3136
Club Secretary: David Hiles, 31 Lulworth Close, South
Harrow, Middx HA2 9NR. Tel: (H) 081 864 0787
Fixtures Secretary: Phil Skelton, 38 Chamberlaine Way,
Pinner, Middx HA5 2AX. Tel: (H) 081 429 4095
Club Colours: Navy with 1' scarlet hoops.
THAMESIANS RFC
Ground Address:Richmond-upon-Thames College,
Egerton Road, Twickenham, Middlesex TW2 7SJ. Tel: 081
894 3110
Club Secretary: EJ Burrows, 133 Cranleigh Road, Lower
Feltham, Middlesex TW13 4QA. Tel: (H) 081 890 7162
Tel: (W) 081 977 0637
Fixtures Secretary: J Taylor, 14 Strathern Avenue,
Whitton, Middlesex TW2 6JU. Tel: (H) 081 894 6174 Tel
(W) 081 974 5565
Club Colours: Maroon & green.

LONDON & SOUTH EAST DIVISION

MIDDLESEX THREE
1994-95
FIXTURES

September 24 (Week 4)
Northolt v London French
Old Tottonians v London Cornish
St. Nicholas Old Boys v London Exiles
U.C.S. Old Boys v Orleans F.P.

October 1 (Week 5)
London French v U.C.S. Old Boys
Orleans F.P. v Southgate
London Exiles v Old Tottonians
London Cornish v Osterley

October 15 (Week 7)
Southgate v London French
U.C.S. Old Boys v Northolt
Osterley v London Exiles
St. Nicholas Old Boys v Orleans F.P.

October 22 (Week 8)
Northolt v Southgate
London French v St. Nicholas Old Boys
Orleans F.P. v Old Tottonians
London Exiles v London Cornish

October 29 (Week X2)
Old Tottonians v London French
St. Nicholas Old Boys v Northolt
Southgate v U.C.S. Old Boys
Osterley v Orleans F.P

January 7 (Week 17)
U.C.S. Old Boys v St. Nicholas Old Boys
Northolt v Old Tottonians
London French v Osterley
Orleans F.P. v London Cornish

January 14 (Week 18)
London Cornish v London French
Osterley v Northolt
Old Tottonians v U.C.S. Old Boys
St. Nicholas Old Boys v Southgate
London Exiles v Orleans F.P.

February 11 (Week 22)
Southgate v Old Tottonians
U.C.S. Old Boys v Osterley
Northolt v London Cornish
London French v London Exiles

February 25 (Week 24)
London Exiles v Northolt
London Cornish v U.C.S. Old Boys
Osterley v Southgate
Old Tottonians v St. Nicholas Old Boys

March 4 (Week 25)
St. Nicholas Old Boys v Osterley
Southgate v London Cornish
U.C.S. Old Boys v London Exiles
London French v Orleans F.P.

March 25 (Week 28)
Orleans F.P. v Northolt
London Exiles v Southgate
London Cornish v St. Nicholas Old Boys
Osterley v Old Tottonians

MIDDLESEX THREE

LONDON CORNISH RFC
Ground Address:Richardson-Evans Memorial Ground, Roehampton Vale, London. Tel: 081 788 3638 (Groundsman)
Club Secretary: S Lang, 31 Coleshill Road, Teddington, Middlesex TW11 0LL. Tel: (H) 081 943 0931 Tel: (W) 071 633 0344
Fixtures Secretary: G Reed, 35 Cathcart Road, London SW10 7JG. Tel (W) 071 837 2507
Club Colours: Black with narrow gold hoops.
LONDON EXILES RUFC
Ground Address:Barn Elms Sports Centre, Queen Elizabeth Walk, Barnes, Lodon SW15 0DG. Tel: 081 876 7685
Club Secretary: President: Tim Edghill, 114 Rannock Road, London W6 9SW. Tel: (H) 081 748 3167 Tel: (W) 071 413 1313
Fixtures Secretary: Tim Edghill, 114 Rannock Road, London W6 9SW. Tel: (H) 081 748 3167 Tel (W) 071 413 1313
LONDON FRENCH RFC
Ground Address:Barn Elms East Playing Fields, Rocks Lane, Barnes, London SW13.
Club Secretary: A James, 2 Oak End Cottages, Lower Road, Gerrards Cross, Buckinghamshire SL9 0PY. Tel: (H) 0753 892108 Tel: (W) 071 629 8191
Fixtures Secretary: H Smith, 28 Hazelbank Court, Hazelbank, Chertsey TK16 8PE. Tel: (H) 0932 560680 Tel (W) 071 250 8913
Club Colours: French blue shirts, white shorts, red socks.
NORTHOLT RFC
Ground Address:Cayton Park, Cayton Road, Greenford, Middlesex UB6 8BJ. Tel: 081 813 1701
Club Secretary: Colin Nicholl, 43 Columbia Avenue, Ruislip, Middlesex HA4 9SU. Tel: (H) 081 866 8201 Tel: (W) 081 975 2209
Fixtures Secretary: /League contact: Geoff Payne, 16 Brackenbridge Drive, South Ruislip, Middlesex HA4 0NG. Tel: (H) 081 845 0874 Tel (W) 071 361 2642
Club Colours: Sky & navy blue hoops, navy shorts, sky & navy socks. Change: White shirts.
OLD TOTTONIANS RFC
Ground Address:Churchfields, Harrow Drive, Great Cambridge Road, Edmonton, London N9. Tel: 081 364 3099
Club Secretary: Trevor de la Salle, 55 Welsummer Way, Le Motte Chase, Cheshunt, Herts EN8 0UG. Tel: (H) 0992 638492 Tel: (W) 0494 444811
Fixtures Secretary: John Cockrill, 7 Sutherland Way, Cuffley, Herts EN6 4EG. Tel: (H) 0707 872507 Tel (W) 071 278 7373
Club Colours: Blue & amber hoops.
ORLEANS FP
Ground Address:off Richard Road (by the Crown Public House). Twickenham. Tel: 081 892 5743
Club Secretary: Steve Frost, 13 Langham Place, Chiswick W4 2QL. Tel: (H) 081 747 5026 Tel: (W) 081 943 5331
Fixtures Secretary: Kevin Mullen, 7 Sussex Avenue, Isleworth. Tel: (H) 081 560 0564
Club Colours: Maroon, gold & white hoops.
OSTERLEY RFC
Ground Address:Tentelow Lane, Norwood Green, Southall, Middlesex. Tel: 081 574 3774
Club Secretary: A Matthews, 22 Elthorne Park Road, Hanwell, London W7 1JB. Tel: (H) 081 579 2046 Tel: (W) 081 754 1010
Fixtures Secretary: J Green, 92 Roxburghe Avenue, Isleworth, Middlesex. Tel: (H) 081 568 5557
Club Colours: Black & white hoops.

FINAL TABLE

	P	W	D	L	F	A	PD	Pts
Bank of England	9	8	1	0	279	109	170	17
London Nigerians	9	8	0	1	282	80	202	16
London Exiles	8	6	0	2	227	94	133	12
St. Nicholas O B	9	5	1	3	97	108	-11	11
U.C.S. Old Boys	9	4	2	3	272	106	166	10
Northolt	9	3	1	5	144	138	6	7
Old Tottonians	9	2	1	6	57	146	-89	5
St. Barts. Hospital	8	2	1	5	79	229	-150	5
Royal Free Hosp	9	2	0	7	103	268	-165	4
Quintin	9	0	1	8	53	315	-262	1

SOUTHGATE RFC
Ground Address:Northern Telecom, Oakleigh Road South, New Southgate, London N11 1HB. Tel: 081 945 2655/2181
Club Secretary: David Hockey, 5 The Vineries, Enfield, Middlesex EN1 3DQ. Tel: (H) 081 342 0202 Tel: (W) 071 270 3874
Fixtures Secretary: Simon Stormer, 21 Woodhall House, Woodhall Parade, Cole Green Lane, Welwyn Garden City AL7 3PU. Tel: (H) 0707 324731 Tel (W) 081 945 3219
Club Colours: Dark blue, light blue & gold hoops.
ST NICHOLAS OLD BOYS RFC
Ground Address:Ickenham Cricket Club, Oak Avenue, Ickenham, Middlesex. Tel: 0895 639366
Club Secretary: Mr DW Price, 143 Myrtleside Close, Northwood, Middlesex HA6 2GB. Tel: (H) 0923 827317 Tel: (W) 071 403 9984
Fixtures Secretary: Mr Ross Telfer. Tel: (H) 081 248 4844 Tel (W) 0753 507937
Club Colours: Red shirts, white shorts, black socks.
UCS OLD BOYS RFC
Ground Address:Farm Avenue, London NW2. Tel: 081 452 4337
Club Secretary: Paul Gyf, 63 Blackhorse Lane, South Mimms EN6 3PS. Tel: (H) 0707 643156 Tel: (W) 081 345 4643
Fixtures Secretary: Andrew Wiseman, 37 Connaught Avenue, London E4 7AE.

LONDON & SOUTH EAST DIVISION

MIDDLESEX FOUR
1994-95
FIXTURES

September 24 (Week 4)
Middlesex Hospital v G.W.R.
British Airways v St. Bart's Hospital
Kodak v Quintin
St. George's Hospital v University College
Meadhurst v Stanmore

October 1 (Week 5)
G.W.R. v St. George's Hospital
St. Bart's Hospital v Meadhurst
Quintin v Brtish Airways
University College v Kodak
Middlesex Hospital v Stanmore

October 15 (Week 7)
Kodak v G.W.R.
St. George's Hospital v Middlesex Hospital
Stanmore v St. Bart's Hospital
British Airways v University College
Meadhurst v Quintin

October 22 (Week 8)
Middlesex Hospital v Kodak
G.W.R. v British Airways
University College v Meadhurst
Stanmore v St. George's Hospital
Quintin v St. Bart's Hospital

October 29 (Week X2)
Meadhurst v G.W.R.
British Airways v Middlesex Hospital
Kodak v St. George's Hospital
Quintin v Stanmore
St. Bart's Hospital v University College

January 14 (Week 18)
St. George's Hospital v British Airways
Middlesex Hospital v Meadhurst
G.W.R. v St. Bart's Hospital
University College v Quintin
Kodak v Stanmore

February 11 (Week 22)
Quintin v G.W.R.
St. Bart's Hospital v Middlesex Hospital
Meadhurst v St. George's Hospital
British Airways v Kodak
Stanmore v University College

February 25 (Week 24)
Kodak v Meadhurst
St. George's Hospital v St. Bart's Hospital
Middlesex Hospital v Quintin
G.W.R. v University College
Stanmore v British Airways

March 4 (Week 25)
Stanmore v G.W.R.
University College v Middlesex Hospital
Quintin v St. George's Hospital
St. Bart's Hospital v Kodak
Meadurst v British Airways

MIDDLESEX FOUR

BRITISH AIRWAYS RFC
Ground Address:British Airways Clubs, The Concorde
Centre, Crane Lodge Road, High Street, Cranford, Middx.
Tel: 081 562 0291
Club Secretary: Kieran Donaghy, 36 Welland Close,
Langley, Berkshire SL3 8UP. Tel: (H) 0753 545916 Tel:
(W) 081 562 2130
Fixtures Secretary: Peter Attard, 38 Hounslow Road,
Feltham, Middlesex TW13 9DG. Tel: (H) 081 751 1605
Tel (W) 0956 511460
Club Colours: Red, white & blue quarters.
THE GREAT WESTERN RAILWAY RFC
Ground Address: Castlebar Park, Vallis Way, Argyle
Road, West Ealing , London, W13 0DD. Tel: 081 998 7928.
Club Secreatry: R J W Sullivan, 100 Westcott Crescent,
Hanwell, London, W7 1PB. Tel: (H) 081 575 6074.
Club Colours: Cardinal red & black.
KODAK RFC
Ground Address:Kodak Sports Ground, Harrow View,
Harrow, Middlesex, HA1 4TY. Tel: 081 427 2642
Club Secretary: Paul Childs, 44 Roe Green, Kingsbury,
London, NW9 0PE. Tel: (H) 061 206 0199 Tel: (W) 081
982 4502
Club Colours: Green & gold.
MEADHURST RFC
Ground Address:Meadhurst Sports & Social Club,
Chertsey Road, Sunbury-on-Thames, Middlesex TW16
7LN. Tel: 0932 763500
Club Secretary: Brian Messenger, BP Chemicals, Poplar
House, Chertsey Road, Sunbury-on-Thames, Middlesex
TW16 7LL. Tel: (H) 081 332 7635 Tel: (W) 0932 774054
Fixtures Secretary: Maggie Farmer, 30 Waldemar
Avenue, Ealing, London W13 9PY. Tel: (H) 081 840 0297
Tel (W) 071 829 3941
Club Colours: Green & yellow.
MIDDLESEX HOSPITAL RUFC
Ground Address:Athletic Ground, Perry Street,
Chislehurst, Kent. Tel: 081 467 3859
Club Secretary: c/o Students Union. Tel: (H) 071 580
7310
ST BARTHOLOMEWS HOSPTIAL RUFC
Ground Address:Perry Street, Foxbury, Chislehurst, Kent.
Tel: 081 467 9452
Club Secretary: Alastair Watt, 79 Kenilworth Road,
London E(5RB. Tel: (H) 081 895 7305 Tel: (W) 071 253
1161/1100 (leave message)
Fixtures Secretary: Alastair Watt, 79 Kenilworth Road,
London E9 5RB. Tel: (H) 081 985 7305 Tel (W) 071 253
1161/1100 (leave message)
Club Colours: White & thin black hoops.
ST GEORGES HOSPITAL RFC
Ground Address: Royal Dental Hospital Ground, Stoke
Road, Cobham, Surrey. Tel: 0932 864341.
Club Secretary: Dr W Landells, Histopathology Dept, St
Helier, Wrythe Lane, Carsholton, Surrey. Tel: (H) 081 946
9408 (W) 081 644 4343.
Club Colours: Green & gold hoops.
THE QUINTIN RFC
Ground Address:Quintin Hogg Memorial Ground,
Cavendish Road, Grove Park, Chiswick, London W4. Tel:
081 994 1554
Club Secretary: Nigel Smith, 4 Australia Avenue,
Maidenhead, Berks SL6 7DJ. Tel: (H) 0628 75899 Tel: (W)
0628 595971
Fixtures Secretary: Colin Smith, 34 Oakdean Drive,
Surbiton, Surrey KT5 9NH. Tel: (H) 081 337 9631
Club Colours: Red & green hoops, blue shorts.

FINAL TABLE

	P	W	D	L	F	A	PD	Pts
London French	8	8	0	0	265	67	198	16
Southgate	8	7	0	1	201	66	135	14
Meadhurst	7	4	0	3	154	73	81	8
Kodak	7	4	0	3	92	85	7	8
British Airways	6	3	0	3	106	113	-7	6
St. Georges Hosp	6	2	0	4	75	115	-40	4
Middlesex Hospital	6	1	0	5	27	189	-162	2
University College	4	0	0	4	0	67	-67	0
G.W.R.	6	0	0	6	42	187	-145	0

UNIVERSITY COLLEGE LONDON RFC
Ground Address: Shenley Sports Grounds, Bell Lane,
London Colney, Shenley, Hertfordshire. Tel: 0727 22215.
Club Secretary: Richard A M Newberry, UCLRFC,
Student's Union, 25 Gordon Street, London, WC1H 0AH.
Tel: (H) 071 387 3611.
Club Colours: Purple, black, blue quarters, black shorts.

LONDON & SOUTH EAST DIVISION

HERTFORDSHIRE ONE
1994-95
FIXTURES

September 24 (Week 4)
Q.E.II v Royston
Tring v Watford
Stevenage v Old Ashmoleans
Hatfield v Datchworth

October 1 (Week 5)
Bacavians v Hatfield
Datchworth v Stevenage
Old Ashmoleans v Tring
Watford v Q.E.II
Royston v Old Stanfordians

October 15 (Week 7)
Stevenage v Bacavians
Old Stanfordians v Watford
Q.E.II v Old Ashmoleans
Tring v Datchworth

October 22 (Week 8)
Bacavians v Tring
Datchworth v Q.E.II
Old Ashmoleans v Old Standfordians
Watford v Royston

October 29 (Week 9)
Q.E.II v Bacavians
Stevenage v Hatfield
Royston v Old Ashmoleans
Old Stanfordians v Datchworth

January 7 (Week 17)
Hatfield v Tring
Bacavians v Old Stanfordians
Datchworth v Royston
Old Ashmoleans v Watford

Janaury 14 (Week 18)
Royston v Bacavians
Q.E.II v Hatfield
Tring v Stevenage
Watford v Datchworth

February 11 (Week 22)
Stevenage v Q.E.II
Hatfield v Old Standfordians
Bacavians v Watford
Datchworth v Old Ashmoleans

February 25 (Week 24)
Old Ashmoleans v Bacavians
Royston v Hatfield
Old Stanfordians v Stevenage
Q.E.II v Tring

March 4 (Week 25)
Tring v Old Stanfordians
Stevenage v Royston
Hatfield v Watford
Bacavians v Datchworth

March 25 (Week 30)
Old Ashmoleans v Hatfield
Watford v Stevenage
Royston v Tring
Old Stanfordians v Q.E.II

HERTFORDSHIRE ONE

BACAVIANS RFC
Ground Address:British Aerospace Sports & Social Club, Brafbury House, Brafbury End, Stevenage, Herts. Tel: 0438 312985
Club Secretary: Richard Stephens, 18 Russell Close, Stevenage, Herts SG2 8PB. Tel: (H) 0438 351971 (answerphone)
Fixtures Secretary: Fred McCarthy, 106 Raleigh Crescent, Stevenage. Tel: (H) 0438 364641 (answerphone)
Club Colours: Green shirts with amber hoop, white shorts, green socks.
DATCHWORTH RFC
Ground Address:Datchworth Green, Datchworth, Herts. Tel: 0438 812490
Club Secretary: Mrs LD Wyatt, 7 Hazeldell, Watton-at-Stone, Hertford SG14 3SL. Tel: (H) 0920 830407 Tel: (W) 0920 830407
Fixtures Secretary: Mr D Muncaster, 16 The Paddocks, Codicote, Herts SG4 8YX. Tel: (H) 0438 821262 Tel (W) 071 368 4515
Club Colours: Green shirts & socks, black shorts.
HATFIELD RFC
Ground Address:Roe Hill Sports Ground, Briars Lane, Roe Hill, Hatfield, Herts. Tel: 0707 269814
Club Secretary: Mark Gates, 21 Gresford Close, St Albans, Herts, AL4 0UB. Tel: (H) 0727 861721 Tel: (W) 071 327 4585
Fixtures Secretary: Amy Nicholson, 43 Handside Lane, Welwyn Gardens City, Herts. Tel: (H) 0707 326660
Club Colours: Green, gold, brown and white quarters.
OLD ASHMOLEAN RFC
Ground Address:Ashmole School, Burleigh Gardens, Southgate, N14. Tel: 081 368 4984
Club Secretary: Mr D Hickey, Flat 9, Apex Lodge, 35 Lyonsdown Road, New Barnet, Hertfordshire, EN5 1JG. Tel: (H) 081 441 3545 Tel: (W) 081 886 3344 Clubhouse
Fixtures Secretary: Mr S Stamp, 9 Kenwood House, 74 Wellington Road, Enfield, EN1 2NZ. Tel: (H) 081 364 3213
Club Colours: Scarlet & emerald hoops.
OLD STANFORDIANS RFC
Ground Address:Buntingford Community Centre, Buntingford, Herts. Tel: 0763 273230
Club Secretary: Ted Moody, Croft House Cottage, High Lane, Stanstead, Essex CM24 8LQ.
Fixtures Secretary: Ted Moody, Croft House Cottage, High Lane, Stanstead, Essex CM24 8LQ.
Club Colours: Black with a purple hoop.
QUEEN ELIZABETH II RFC
Ground Address:Hatfield Hyde Sports Club, King George V Playing Fields, Beehive Lane, Welwyn Garden City, Hertfordshire, AL7 4BP. Tel: 0707 326700
Club Secretary: Steve Murray, 227 Colebrook Lane, Loughton, Essex IG10 2HG. Tel: 081 508 5532 Tel: (W) 071 918 3712
Club Colours: Myrtle green & amber.
ROYSTON RFC
Ground Address:The Heath Sporting Club, Baldock Road, Royston, Herts SG8 5PG. Tel: 0763 243613
Club Secretary: Mrs Peggy Compton, 12 Abbots Close, Lithington, Royston, Herts SG8 0QQ. Tel: (H) 0763 852788
Fixtures Secretary: Godfrey Everett, 24 Clarence Way, Bassingbourn, Royston SG8 5LT. Tel: (H) 0763 243846
Club Colours: Black & white hoops, black shorts, black socks.

FINAL TABLE

	P	W	D	L	F	A	PD	Pts
St Albans	9	9	0	0	321	47	274	16
Datchworth	9	7	0	2	237	45	192	14
Old Ashmoleans	9	7	0	2	166	73	93	14
Watford	9	6	0	3	112	89	23	12
Tring	9	6	0	3	271	89	182	10
Old Stanfordians	9	4	0	5	85	154	-69	8
Bacavians	9	3	0	6	74	158	-84	6
Hatfield	9	2	0	7	24	274	-250	4
Royston	9	1	0	8	59	179	-120	0
Q.E. II Hospital	9	0	0	9	19	260	-241	-2
Stevenage							0	-3

STEVENAGE RUFC
Ground Address:North Road, Old Town, Stevenage, Herts. Tel: 0438 359788
Club Secretary: Chris Welch, Holmwood, Todds Green, Stevenage, Herts. Tel: (H) 0438 728505 Tel: (W) 0438 744543
Fixtures Secretary: Chris Hill, 21 Jessop Road, Stevenage, Herts. Tel: (H) 0438 313996
Club Colours: Green Y gold hoops with dark green shorts.
TRING RFC
Ground Address:Pendley Sports Centre, Cow Lane, Tring, Herts. Tel: 0442 825710
Club Secretary: Malcolm rose, 25 Grenadine Way, Tring, Herts HP23 5EA. Tel: (H) 0442 827165 Tel: (W) 0628 486969 x211
Fixtures Secretary: Peter Wilson, 10A Woodley Grove, Enfield, Middx EN2 0EA. Tel: (H) 081 482 4187
Club Colours: Black & gold.
WATFORD RFC
Ground Address:Radlett Road, Watford, Herts. Tel: 0923 243292
Club Secretary: Keven Tagg, 13 Cannon Road, Watford, Herts WD1 8BB. Tel: (H) 0923 441006 Tel: (W) 071 945 4903
Fixtures Secretary: Bob Wynne, 125 North Approach, Garston, Herts. Tel: (H) 0923 678928 Tel (W) 0923 242261
Club Colours: Red, white & blue hoops, black shorts, red socks.

LONDON & SOUTH EAST DIVISION

LONDON THREE NORTH EAST
1994-95 FIXTURES

September 17 (Week 3)
West Norfolk v Rochford
Colchester v Basildon
Ipswich v Braintree
Old Edwardians v Chelmsford
Shelford v Woodbridge
Maldon v Campion

September 24 (Week 4)
Rochford v Maldon
Campion v Shelford
Woodbridge v Old Edwardians
Chelmsford v Ipswich
Braintree v Colchester
Basildon v Bury St. Edmunds

October 1 (Week 5)
Shelford v Rochford
Maldon v West Norfolk
Bury St. Edmunds v Braintree
Colchester v Chelmsford
Ipswich v Woodbridge
Old Edwardians v Campion

October 15 (Week 7)
West Norfolk v Shelford
Rochford v Old Edwardians
Campion v Ipswich
Woodbridge v Colchester
Chelmsford v Bury St. Edmunds
Braintree v Basildon

October 22 (Week 8)
Ipswich v Rochford
Old Edwardians v West Norfolk
Shelford v Maldon
Basildon v Chelmsford
Bury St. Edmunds v Woodridge
Colchester v Campion

October 29 (Week X2)
Maldon v Old Edwardians
West Norfolk v Ipswich
Rochford v Colchester
Campion v Bury St. Edmunds
Woodbridge v Basildon
Chelmsford v Braintree

January 7 (Week 17)
Bury St. Edmunds v Rochford
Colchester v West Norfolk
Ipswich v Maldon
Old Edwardians v Shelford
Braintree v Woodbridge
Basildon v Campion

January 14 (Week 18)
Sheldon v Ipswich
Maldon v Colchester
West Norfolk v Bury St. Edmunds
Rochford v Basildon
Campion v Braintree
Woodbridge v Chelmsford

February 11 (Week 22)
Braintree v Rochford
Basildon v West Norfolk
Bury St. Edmunds v Maldon
Colchester v Shelford
Ipswich v Old Edwardians
Chelmsford v Campion

February 25 (Week 24)
Old Edwardians v Colchester
Shelford v Bury St. Edmunds
Maldon v Basildon
West Norfolk v Braintree
Rochford v Chelmsford
Campion v Woodbridge

March 4 (Week 25)
Woodbridge v Rochford
Chelmsford v West Norfolk
Braintree v Maldon
Basildon v Shelford
Bury St. Edmunds v Old Edwardians
Colchester v Ipswich

March 25 (Week 28)
Ipswich v Bury St. Edmunds
Old Edwardians v Basildon
Shelford v Braintree
Maldon v Chelmsford
West Norfolk v Woodbridge
Rochford v Campion

April 8 (Week 30)
Campion v West Norfolk
Woodbridge v Maldon
Chelmsford v Sheldon
Braintree v Old Edwardians
Basildon v Ipswich
Bury St. Edmunds v Colchester

LONDON THREE NORTH EAST

BASILDON RFC
Ground Address: Gardiners Close, Basildon, Essex. Tel: 0268 533136
Club Secretary: RJ Phillips, 118 Great Spenders, Basildon, Essex SS14 2NT. Tel: (H) 0268 284942
Fixtures Secretary: LA Hymans, 32 Devon Way, Canvey Island, Essex SS8 9YD. Tel: (H) 0268 693899 Tel (W) 0850 500159
Club Colours: Green & white shirts, white shorts.
BRAINTREE RUFC
Ground Address: The Clubhouse, Beckers Green Road, Braintree, Essex CM7 6PR. Tel: 0376 322282
Club Secretary: Mrs C Wadforth, 8 Chelmer Road, Braintree, Essex CM7 6PY. Tel: (H) 0376 341642
Fixtures Secretary: Mr S Ross, 12 Kelso Close, Great Horksley, Colchester, Essex. Tel: (H) 0206 271007
Club Colours: Black & amber.
BURY ST EDMUNDS RUFC
Ground Address: The Haberden, Southgate Green, Bury St Edmunds, Suffolk. Tel: 0284 753920
Club Secretary: Mr Martin Peacock, 31 Plovers Way, Bury St Edmunds, Suffolk. Tel: (H) 0284 761536 Tel: (W) 0284 754450
Fixtures Secretary: Mrs Carol Palombo, 41 Oakes Road, Bury St Edmunds. Tel: (H) 0284 761871
Club Colours: Green & amber quarters, black shorts, amber socks.
CAMPION RFC
Ground Address: Cottons Park, Cottons Approach, Romford, Essex RM7 7AA. Tel: 0708 753209
Club Secretary: P O'Brien, 68 Lancaster Drive, Elm Park, Hornchurch, Essex RM12 5ST. Tel: (H) 0708 446980 Tel: (W) 0708 342827
Fixtures Secretary: Kevin O'Neill, 26 Priests Field, Ingrave, Brentwood CM13 3QJ. Tel: (H) 0277 811742
CHELMSFORD RFC
Ground Address: Coronation Park, Timsons Lane, Springfield, Chelmsford, Essex CM2 6AG. Tel: 0245 261159
Club Secretary: D Triggs, Fir Trees, Riffhams Lane, Danbury, Essex CM3 4DS. Tel: (H) 0245 226001
Fixtures Secretary: Ian Stuart, 49 Hillside Grove, Chelmsford, Essex CM2 9DA. Tel: (H) 0245 352790 Tel (W) 0279 647366
Club Colours: Navy blue shirts & shorts.
COLCHESTER RFC
Ground Address: Mill Road, Mile End, Colchester, C04 5JF. Tel: 0206 851610
Club Secretary: Ron Hatch, 99 Ernest Road, Wivenhow, C07 9LJ. Tel: (H) 0206 823548
Fixtures Secretary: Jon Roberts, 5 Spencer Close, Maldon, CM9 6BX. Tel: (H) 0621 854043
Club Colours: Black.
IPSWICH RUFC
Ground Address: Humber Doucy Lane, Ipswich, Suffolk. Tel: 0473 724072
Club Secretary: Mr SE Gaskin, 6 Parkside Avenue, Westerfield Road, Ipswich, suffolk. Tel: (H) 0473 258803 Tel: (W) 0473 217920
Fixtures Secretary: Mrs Lisa Greetham, 159 Woodbridge Road, Ispwich, Suffolk. Tel: (H) 0473 233731 Tel (W) 0473 724072 (club)
Club Colours: Black & amber hoops.
MALDON RUFC
Ground Address: Drapers Farm Sports Club, Drapers Chase, Goldhanger Road, Maldon, Essex. Tel: 0621 852152
Club Secretary: Mike Beckwith, Oakwood, The Mallows, Fambridge Road, Maldon, Essex CM9 6BJ. Tel: (H) 0621 857106 Tel: (W) 0702 218104
Fixtures Secretary: N Manning, 57 Larch Walk, Maldon, Essex CM9 7TS (Also all League correspondence). Tel:

FINAL TABLE

	P	W	D	L	F	A	PD	Pts
Romfrd & Gidea Pk	12	12	0	0	310	63	247	24
Ipswich	12	9	1	2	212	81	131	19
Woodbridge	12	8	0	4	131	148	-17	16
Braintree	12	7	0	5	140	112	28	14
Rochford	12	6	1	5	150	127	23	13
Colchester	12	6	0	6	131	101	30	12
Bury St. Edmunds	12	6	0	6	165	146	19	12
Campton	12	5	1	6	161	236	-75	11
Chelmsford	12	4	2	6	100	153	-53	10
Basildon	12	4	1	7	170	206	-36	9
Shelford	12	4	0	8	141	158	-17	8
Westcliff	12	3	0	9	112	174	-62	4
Saffron Walden	12	1	0	11	97	315	-218	2

(H) 0621 856073
Club Colours: Royal blue & white.
OLD EDWARDIAN RFC
Ground Address: Westlands Playing Fields, London Road, Romford, Essex.
Club Secretary: P J Hensher, 108 Stanley Avenue, Gidea Park, Romford, Essex. Tel: (H) 0708 764429 Tel: (W) 081 597 1126
Club Colours: Navy shirts, white shorts, red socks.
ROCHFORD HUNDRED RFC
Ground Address: The Clubhouse, Magnolia Road, Hawkwell, Rochford, Essex SS4 3AD. Tel: 0702 544021
Club Secretary: R Simon Wakefield, 54 Parklands Drive, Springfield, Chelmsford, Essex CM1 5SP. Tel: (H) 0245 266158 Tel: (W) 0702 541581
Fixtures Secretary: Mr Michael Tuck, 51 Highfield Road, Billericay, Essex. Tel: (H) 0277 655483
Club Colours: Black shirts & shorts, black & white socks.
SHELFORD RUFC
Ground Address: Davey Field, Cambridge Road, Great Shelford, Cambridge. Tel: 0223 843357
Club Secretary: Christine Jeffery, 58 Macaulay Avenue, Great Shelford, Cambridge CB2 5AE. Tel: (H) 0223 844605 Tel: (W) 0223 415814
Fixtures Secretary: Mike Whibley, Driftway House, 111a Glebe Road, Cambridge CB1 4TE. Tel: (H) 0223 214070
Club Colours: Maroon & white hoops.
WEST NORFOLK RUFC
Ground Address: Gatehouse Lane, North Wootton, King's Lynn, Norfolk. Tel: 0553 631307
Club Secretary: JA Williams, 1 Courtnell Place, Springwood, King's Lynn, Norfolk PE30 4TW. Tel: (H) 0553 760986 Tel: (W) 0603 627107
Fixtures Secretary: K Foreman, 1 Caretakers House, NORCAT, Tennyson Avenue, King's Lynn, Norfolk. Tel: (H) 0553 764391
Club Colours: Frecnh grey with cerise band, navy blue shorts.
WOODBRIDGE RUFC
Ground Address: Hatchley Barn, Bromeswell, Woodridge, Suffolk IP12 2PP. Tel: 0394 460630
Club Secretary: John Blake, Brackendale, Bromeswell, Woodbridge IP12 2PP. Tel: (H) 0394 460447 Tel: (W) 0394 460447
Fixtures Secretary: Bruce Harrington, 24 Bury Hill Close, Melton, Woodbridge IP12 1LE. Tel: (H) 0394 386208 Tel (W) 0502 562262
Club Colours: Tide blue.

LONDON & SOUTH EAST DIVISION

EASTERN COUNTIES ONE
1994-95
FIXTURES

January 7 (Week 17)
Diss v Holt
Westcliff v Harwich & Dovercourt
Newmarket v Bancroft
Wymondham v Canvey Island
Ravens v Upminster
Ely v Lowestoft & Yarmouth

September 17 (Week 3)
Harwich & Dovercourt v Holt
Westcliff v Ely
Newmarket v Ravens
Wymondham v Saffron Walden
Canvey Island v Upminster
Bancroft v Lowestoft & Yarmouth

January 14 (Week 18)
Canvey Island v Newmarket
Bancroft v Westcliff
Harwich & Dovercourt v Diss
Holt v Ely
Lowestoft & Yarmouth v Ravens
Upminster v Saffron Walden

September 24 (Week 4)
Holt v Bancroft
Lowestoft & Yarmouth v Canvey Island
Upminster v Wymondham
Saffron Walden v Newmarket
Ravens v Westcliff
Ely v Diss

February 11 (Week 22)
Ravens v Holt
Ely v Harwich & Dovercourt
Diss v Bancroft
Westcliff v Canvey Island
Newmarket v Wymondham
Saffron Walden v Lowestoft & Yarmouth

October 1 (Week 5)
Canvey Island v Holt
Bancroft v Harwich & Dovercourt
Diss v Ravens
Westcliff v Saffron Walden
Newmarket v Upminster
Wymondham v Lowestoft & Yarmouth

February 25 (Week 24)
Wymondham v Westcliff
Canvey Island v Diss
Bancroft v Ely
Harwich & Dovercourt v Ravens
Holt v Saffron Walden
Lowestoft & Yarmouth v Upminster

October 15 (Week 7)
Harwich & Dovercourt v Canvey Island
Holt v Wymondham
Lowestoft & Yarmouth v Newmarket
Upminster v Westcliff
Saffron Walden v Diss
Ravens v Ely

March 4 (Week 25)
Upminster v Holt
Saffron Walden v Harwich & Dovercourt
Ravens v Bancroft
Ely v Canvey Island
Diss v Wymondham
Westcliff v Newmarket

October 22 (Week 8)
Newmarket v Holt
Wymondham v Harwich & Dovercourt
Canvey Island v Bancroft
Ely v Saffron Walden
Diss v Upminster
Westcliff v Lowestoft & Yarmouth

March 25 (Week 28)
Newmarket v Diss
Wymondham v Ely
Canvey Island v Ravens
Bancroft v Saffron Walden
Harwich & Dovercourt v Upminster
Holt v Lowestoft & Yarmouth

October 29 (Week X2)
Bancroft v Wymondham
Harwich & Dovercourt v Newmarket
Holt v Westcliff
Lowestoft & Yarmouth v Diss
Upminster v Ely
Saffron Walden v Ravens

April 8 (Week 30)
Lowestoft & Yarmouth v Harwich & Dovercourt
Upminster v Bancroft
Saffron Walden v Canvey Island
Ravens v Wymondham
Ely v Newmarket
Diss v Westcliff

EASTERN COUNTIES ONE

BANCROFT RFC
Ground Address: Buckhurst Way, Buckhurst Hill, Essex IG9 6JD. Tel: 081 504 0429
Club Secretary: SB Thirsk, 4 Bentley Way, Woodford Green, Woodford Green IG8 0SE. Tel: (H) 081 504 1468 Tel: (W) 0279 441111
Fixtures Secretary: G Wiseman, 13 Dene Road, Buckhurst Hill, Essex. Tel: (H) 081 504 7647 Tel (W) 071 930 9711
Club Colours: Blue, black, claret & light blue hoops.

CANVEY ISLAND RUFC
Ground Address: Tewkes Creek, Dovervelt Road, Canvey Island, Essex. Tel: 0268 681881
Club Secretary: Martin Powell, 7 Chichester Close, Canvey Island, Essex SS8 0DZ. Tel: (H) 0268 695130 Tel: (W) 071 418 3270
Fixtures Secretary: Don Maclean, 9 St Luke's Close, Canvey Island, Essex SS8 9NF. Tel: (H) 0268 694771
Club Colours: Red & blue.

DISS RFC
Ground Address: Mackenders, Bellrope Lane, Roydon, Diss, Norfolk IP21 3RG. Tel: 0379 642891
Club Secretary: NP Kingsley, Spralle & Kingsley, 16 Broad Street, Bungay, Suffolk. Tel: (W) 0986 892721
Fixtures Secretary: J Green, Greenacres, Langmere Road, Dickleborough, Diss. Tel (W) 0379 741705
Club Colours: Royal blue & white.

ELY RFC
Ground Address: The Club House, Little Downham road, Ely, Cambs. Tel: 0353 662363
Club Secretary: Richard Wilding, 12 West End, Ely, Cambs CB6 3BY. Tel: (H) 0353 665963
Fixtures Secretary: Martin Hammond, 5 Common Lane, Southery, Norfold PE38 0PB. Tel: (H) 0366 6400
Club Colours: Black & gold hoops.

HARWICH & DOVERCOURT RUFC
Ground Address: Swimming Pool road, Wick Lane, Dovercourt, Harwich. Tel: 0255 240225
Club Secretary: Steve Race, 11 The Ridgeway, Dovercourt, Harwich, Essex CO12 4AT. Tel: (H) 0255 507992 Tel: (W) 0255 241124
Fixtures Secretary: Barry Male, 28 Mayes Lane, Ramsey, Harwich, Essex CO12 5EJ. Tel: (H) 0255 886165 Tel (W) 0255 502246
Club Colours: Black & white hoops or plain red.

HOLT RFC
Ground Address: Bridge Road, High Kelling, Holt, Norfolk NR25 6QT. Tel: 0263 712191
Club Secretary: MD Bush, The Warren, Sir Williams Lane, Aylsham, Norwich NR11 6AW. Tel: (H) 0263 732051 Tel: (W) 0603 867355
Fixtures Secretary: J Lockhart, April Cottage, The Rosary, Mulbarton, Norwich NR14 8AL. Tel: (H) 0508 570835 Tel (W) 0603 628251
Club Colours: Black shirts, shorts & socks.

LOWESTOFT & YARMOUTH RUFC
Ground Address: Gunton Park, off Corton Long Lane, Old Lane, Corton, Nr Lowestoft. Tel: Lowestoft 730350
Club Secretary: June Nelson, 70 Upper Cliff Road, Gorleston, Great Yarmouth NR31 6AJ. Tel: (H) Great Yarmouth 653095 Tel: (W) Great Yarmouth 656071
Fixtures Secretary: Andrew Warnes, 7 St Margaret's Road, Lowestoft. Tel: (H) Loestoft 519192 Tel (W) Great Yarmouth 844911
Club Colours: Blue & white hoops.

NEWMARKET RUFC
Ground Address: Scaltback Middle School, Exning Road, Newmarket, Suffolk CB8 0DJ. Tel: 0638 663082
Club Secretary: JW Paxton, 7 Beechwood Close, Exning, Newmarket, Suffolk CB8 7EL. Tel: (H) 0638 577251 Tel: (W) 0638 577251

FINAL TABLE

	P	W	D	L	F	A	PD	Pts
Maldon	12	11	0	1	274	86	188	22
West Norfolk	12	10	0	2	240	99	141	20
Lowestoft & Yarmth	12	9	0	3	288	107	181	18
Wymondham	12	8	0	4	294	120	174	16
Canvey Island	12	9	0	3	191	150	41	16
Bancroft	12	6	1	5	157	148	9	13
Ely	12	5	1	6	141	231	-90	11
Ravens	12	5	0	7	105	210	-105	10
Upminster	12	4	1	7	98	159	-61	9
Harwich & Doverct	12	3	2	7	105	138	-33	6
Newmarket	12	3	0	9	118	179	-61	6
Cantabrigian	12	1	1	10	77	286	-209	3
Wanstead	12	1	0	11	89	264	-175	2

Fixtures Secretary: John Taylor, 32 High Street, Stetchworth, Newmarket CB8 9TJ. Tel: (H) 0638 507483 Tel (W) 0638 507483
Club Colours: Emerald green & black hoops.

RAVENS RFC
Ground Address: British Gas Sports Ground, Southend Road, London E6. Tel: 081 472 8000
Club Secretary: AC Guest, 57 Shaftesbury Road, Forest Gate, London E7 8PD. Tel: (H) 081 471 7571
Fixtures Secretary: AC Guest, 57 Shaftesbury Road, Forest Gate, London E7 8PD. Tel: (H) 081 471 7571
Club Colours: Navy blue & old gold hoops. Change: All black.

SAFFRON WALDEN RFC
Ground Address: Springate, Henham, Nr Bishop's Stortford, Herts. Tel: 0279 850791
Club Secretary: Nick Webber, Aldridges Farm, Maple Lane, Wimbush, Saffron Walden. Tel: (H) 0799 599440
Fixtures Secretary: John Hamilton, Smiths Cottage, Smiths Green, Takeley, Herts CN22 6NR. Tel: (H) 0279 870828
Club Colours: Myrtle green & gold jerseys, white shorts.

UPMINSTER RFC
Ground Address: Hall Lane Playing Fields, Hall Lane, Upminster, Essex. Tel: 0708 220320
Club Secretary: M Eve, 142 Cranston Park Avenue, Upminster, Essex RM14 3XJ. Tel: (H) 0708 225383 Tel: (W) 0708 858935
Fixtures Secretary: Ken Ewen, 8 Ravens Dale, Basildon, Essex. Tel: (H) 0268 285102
Club Colours: Yellow & blue hoops.

WESTCLIFF RFC
Ground Address: The Gables, Aviation Way, Southend-on-Sea, Essex SS2 6UN. Tel: 0702 541499
Club Secretary: Richard J Davies, 88 Flemming Avenue, Leigh-on-Sea, Essex SS9 3AX. Tel: (H) 0702 72140 Tel: (W) 0375 652025
Fixtures Secretary: Greg Horan, 30 Beresford Gardens, Benfleet, Essex SS7 2SA. Tel: (H) 0702 555389
Club Colours: Maroon & old gold.

WYMONDHAM RUFC
Ground Address: Foster Harrison Memorial Ground, Tutles Lane East, Wymondham, Norfold. Tel: 0953 607332
Club Secretary: M Warren, 67 Hawkes Lane, Bracon Ash, Norfolk NR14 8EW. Tel: (H) 0508 570669 Tel: (W) 0603 616112
Fixtures Secretary: J Titlow Shingles, Marlingford Road, Barford, Norfolk. Tel: (H) 0603 881151 Tel (W) 0603 760511
Club Colours: Red & black.

LONDON & SOUTH EAST DIVISION

EASTERN COUNTIES TWO
1994-95
FIXTURES

September 17 (Week 3)

Clacton	v	Ilford Wanderers
Thetford	v	Loughton
Wanstead	v	Old Cooperians
Lakenham-Hewett	v	Cantabrigian
Thames	v	Met. Police
Old Bealonians	v	East London

September 24 (Week 4)

Ilford Wanderers	v	Old Bealonians
East London	v	Thames
Met. Police	v	Lakenham-Hewett
Cantabrigian	v	Wanstead
Old Cooperians	v	Thetford
Loughton	v	Old Palmerians

October 1 (Week 5)

Thames	v	Ilford Wanderers
Old Bealonians	v	Clacton
Old Palmerians	v	Old Cooperians
Thetford	v	Cantabrigian
Wanstead	v	Met. Police
Lakenham-Hewett	v	East London

October 15 (Week 7)

Clacton	v	Thames
Ilford Wanderers	v	Lakenham-Hewett
East London	v	Wanstead
Met. Police	v	Thetford
Cantabrigian	v	Old Palmerians
Old Cooperians	v	Loughton

October 22 (Week 8)

Wanstead	v	Ilford Wanderers
Lakenham-Hewett	v	Clacton
Thames	v	Old Bealonians
Loughton	v	Cantabrigian
Old Palmerians	v	Met. Police
Thetford	v	East London

October 29 (Week X2)

Old Bealonians	v	Lakenham-Hewett
Clacton	v	Wanstead
Ilford Wanderers	v	Thetford
East London	v	Old Palmerians
Met. Police	v	Loughton
Cantabrigian	v	Old Cooperians

January 7 (Week 17)

Old Palmerians	v	Ilford Wanderers
Thetford	v	Clacton
Wanstead	v	Old Bealonians
Lakenham-Hewett	v	Thames
Old Cooperians	v	Met. Police
Loughton	v	East London

January 14 (Week 18)

Thames	v	Wanstead
Old Bealonians	v	Thetford
Clacton	v	Old Palmerians
Ilford Wanderers	v	Loughton
East London	v	Old Cooperians
Met. Police	v	Cantabrigian

February 11 (Week 22)

Old Cooperians	v	Ilford Wanderers
Loughton	v	Clacton
Old Palmerians	v	Old Bealonians
Thetford	v	Thames
Wanstead	v	Lakenham-Hewett
Cantabrigian	v	East London

February 25 (Week 24)

Lakenham-Hewett	v	Thetford
Thames	v	Old Palmerians
Old Bealonians	v	Loughton
Clacton	v	Old Cooperians
Ilford Wanderers	v	Cantabrigian
East London	v	Met. Police

March 4 (Week 25)

Met. Police	v	Ilford Wanderers
Cantabrigian	v	Clacton
Old Cooperians	v	Old Bealonians
Loughton	v	Thames
Old Palmerians	v	Lakenham-Hewett
Thetford	v	Wanstead

March 25 (Week 28)

Wanstead	v	Old Palmerians
Lakenham-Hewett	v	Loughton
Thames	v	Old Cooperians
Old Bealonians	v	Cantabrigian
Clacton	v	Met. Police
Ilford Wanderers	v	East London

April 8 (Week 30)

East London	v	Clacton
Met. Police	v	Old Bealonians
Cantabrigian	v	Thames
Old Cooperians	v	Lakenham-Hewett
Loughton	v	Wanstead
Old Palmerians	v	Thetford

EASTERN COUNTIES TWO

BEALONIANS RUFC
Ground Address:Beal High School, Woodford Bridge Road, Woodford Avenue, Ilford, Essex. Tel: Clubhouse: 081 554 5333
Club Secretary: MP March, 22 Landview Gardens, Marden Ash, Ongar, Essex CM5 9EQ. Tel: (H) 0277 363403 Tel: (W) 02068 526856
Fixtures Secretary: Steve Morris, 436 Ilford Lane, Ilford, Essex IG1. Tel: (H) 081 553 9679 Tel (W) 071 234 3021
Club Colours: Red & black quarters.

CANTABRIGIAN RUFC
Ground Address:Sedley Taylor Road, Cambridge CB2 2PW. Tel: 0223 213061
Club Secretary: RL Ladds, 4 Flamsteed Road, Cambridge CB1 3QU. Tel: (H) 0223 249008 Tel: (W) 0223 61111
Fixtures Secretary: ST Barrett, 42 Melvin Way, Histon, Cambridge CB4 4HZ. Tel: (H) 0223 237040 Tel (W) 0223 315315 x2206
Club Colours: Navy blue & white hoops.

CLACTON RUFC
Ground Address:Clubhouse, Valley Road, Clacton, Essex. Tel: 0255 421002
Club Secretary: Brian White, 80 Vista Road, Clacton, Essex CO15 5JD. Tel: (H) 0255 432270 Tel: (W) 0255 222606
Fixtures Secretary: Alan Lee, 82 High Street, Walten-on-Naze. Tel: (H) 0255 678793 Tel (W) 0255 678795
Club Colours: Maroon chirts, blue shorts.

EAST LONDON RFC
Ground Address:Holland Road, West Ham, London, E15 3BP. Tel: 071 474 6761
Club Secretary: Ray James, 43 Bounds Oak Way, Southborough, Tonbridge Wells, Kent, TN4 0TW. Tel: (H) 0892 512798 Tel: (W) 0342 410166
Fixtures Secretary: Ian Bessant, 111 Croydon Road, Plaiston, London E13. Tel: (H) 071 474 3770 Tel (W) 071 474 3770
Club Colours: Maroon & navy hoops (or quarters), black shorts, maroon & navy socks.

ILFORD WANDERERS RFC
Ground Address:Forest Road, Barkingside, Ilford, Essex. Tel: 081 500 4622
Club Secretary: Alan Lewis, 161A Albborough Road south, Seven Kings, Ilford, Essex IG3 8HU. Tel: (H) 081 597 1158 Tel: (W) 081 594 4894
Fixtures Secretary: Beiron Rees, 161A Aldborough Road South, Seven Kings, Ilford, Essex IG3 8HU. Tel: (H) 081 597 1158 Tel (W) 081 592 7861
Club Colours: Red, green & white hoops.

LAKENHAM-HEWETT RFC
Ground Address:Hilltop Sports Centre, Norwich Road, Swardeston, Norwich, Norfolk. Tel: 05087 78826
Club Secretary: Phil Boyce, 2 Branksome Road, Norwich. Tel: (H) 0603 54208
Fixtures Secretary: (League contact) Bruce Ridgeway, Rye House, Newton Street, Newton St Faith, Norwich. Tel: (H) 0603 897771 Tel (W) 0603 628333 x271
Club Colours: Red shirts & socks, white shorts.

LOUGHTON RFC
Ground Address:Squirrels Lane, Hornbeam Road, Buckhurst Hill, Essex. Tel: 081 504 0065
Club Secretary: Stephen King, 290 Blackhorse Lane, Walthamstow, London, E17 5QH. Tel: (H) 081 531 4466 Tel: (W) 071 792 1200
Fixtures Secretary: Brian Westley, 30 The Avenue, St Pauls Cray, Orpington, Kent, BR5 3DJ. Tel: (H) 081 302 0755 Tel (W) 071 256 4483
Club Colours: White with black hoop botwoon green hoops.

FINAL TABLE

	P	W	D	L	F	A	PD	Pts
Diss	12	11	0	1	292	56	236	22
Holt	12	10	0	2	253	92	161	20
East London	12	11	0	1	237	79	158	20
Thames Sports	12	6	2	4	172	117	55	14
Loughton	12	7	1	4	212	115	97	13
Clacton	12	6	1	5	140	160	-20	13
Thetford	12	6	1	5	138	176	-38	13
Lakenham Hewett	12	3	2	7	107	286	-179	8
Old Bealonians	12	3	0	9	139	194	-55	6
Old Palmerians	12	2	2	8	73	161	-88	6
Met.Pol. Chigwell	12	2	2	8	109	236	-127	6
Crusaders	12	4	0	8	130	206	-76	4
Ipswich YMCA	12	1	1	10	113	237	-124	3

METROPOLITAN POLICE CHIGWELL RFC
Ground Address: Metropolitan Police Sports Club, Chigwell Hall, High Road, Chigwell, Essex Tel 081 500 2735
Club Secretary: Malcolm Bartlett, 11 Fairfield Road, Ongar, Essex. Tel (h) 0277 363206
Club Colours: Royal Blue Shirts, black shorts, red socks.

OLD COOPERIANS RUFC
Ground Address:Eastbrook School, Dagenham Road, Dagenham, Essex.
Club Secretary: John C Green, Greenlow House, Melbourn, Herts SG8 6DG. Tel: (H) 0763 260624 Tel: (W) 0279 652214
Fixtures Secretary: Dave Russell, 51 Perth Road,Letton, London E10. Tel: (H) 081 539 0794
Club Colours: Dark blue shirts with light blue & gold hoops.

OLD PALMERIANS RUFC
Ground Address:Palmers College, Chadwell Road, Grays, Essex. Tel: 0375 370121
Club Secretary: Carwyn Owen, 1B Rose Cottage, South Stifford, Grays, Essex RM16 1YD. Tel: (H) 0375 378668
Fixtures Secretary: John McClean, 97c Oakley Drive, Leigh-on-Sea, Essex. Tel: (H) 0702 711288
Club Colours: Light & dark blue hoops.

THAMES RFC
Ground Address:St Cedd's Playing Fields, Garrow Lane, Aveley, Essex.
Club Secretary: David Northfield, 179 Blackshots Lane, Grays, Essex RM16 2LL. Tel: (H) 0375 371125 Tel: (W) 0268 402239 Mobile: 0956 518257
Fixtures Secretary: Tony Smith, 33 Chester Place, Chelmsford, Essex. Tel: (H) 0245 281951 Tel (W) 071 325 1432
Club Colours: Emerald green & black hoops.

THETFORD RFC
Ground Address:Mundford Road, Thetford, Norfolk. Tel: 0842 755176
Club Secretary: Peter Gandlin, 67 Nunnery Drive, Thetford, Norfolk. Tel: (H) 0842 750416 Tel: (W) 0842 750415
Fixtures Secretary: Paul Lumley, 2 Dial House, Old Market Street, Thetford, Norfolk IP24 2EQ. Tel: (H) 0842 752620 Tel (W) 0440 820994
Club Colours: Red & white hoops.

WANSTEAD RFC
Club Secretary: MJ Curry, 48 Wellesley Road, Wanstead, London E11 2MF. Tel: (H) 081 989 0507 Tel: (W) 0850 801877
Fixtures Secretary: T Elliot, 18 Highbury Gardens, Seven Kings IG3 8AA. Tel: (H) 081 599 2743
Club Colours: Royal blue & white hoops.

443

LONDON & SOUTH EAST DIVISION

EASTERN COUNTIES THREE 1994-95 FIXTURES

January 7 (Week 17)
Sth. Woodham Ferrers v Felixstowe
Haverhill & Dist v Fakenham
Southwold v Thurston
Crusaders v Stowmarket
Redbridge v Broadland
Beccles v Ipswich Y.M.C.A.

September 17 (Week 3)
Fakenham v Felixstowe
Haverhill & Dist v Beccles
Southwold v Redbridge
Crusaders v Hadleigh
Stowmarket v Broadland
Thurston v Ipswich Y.M.C.A.

January 14 (Week 18)
Stowmarket v Southwold
Thurston v Haverhill & Dist
Fakenham v Sth. Woodham Ferrers
Felixstowe v Beccles
Ipswich Y.M.C.A. v Redbridge
Broadland v Hadleigh

September 24 (Week 4)
Felixstowe v Thurston
Ipswich Y.M.C.A. v Stowmarket
Broadland v Crusaders
Hadleigh v Southwold
Redbridge v Haverhill & Dist
Beccles v Sth. Woodham Ferrers

Fabruary 11 (Week 22)
Redbridge v Felixstowe
Beccles v Fakenham
Sth. Woodham Ferrers v Thurston
Haverhill & Dist v Stowmarket
Southwold v Crusaders
Hadleigh v Ipswich Y.M.C.A.

October 1 (Week 5)
Stowmarket v Felixstowe
Thurston v Fakenham
Sth. Woodham Ferrers v Redbridge
Haverhill & Dist v Hadleigh
Southwold v Broadland
Crusaders v Ipswich Y.M.C.A.

February 25 (Week 24)
Crusaders v Haverhill
Stowmarket v Sth. Woodham Ferrers
Thurston v Beccles
Fakenham v Redbridge
Felixstowe v Hadleigh
Ipswich Y.M.C.A. v Broadland

October 15 (Week 7)
Fakenham v Stowmarket
Felixstowe v Crusaders
Ipswich Y.M.C.A. v Southwold
Broadland v Haverhill & Dist
Hadleigh v Sth. Woodham Ferrers
Redbridge v Beccles

March 4 (Week 25)
Broadland v Felixstowe
Hadleigh v Fakenham
Redbridge v Thurston
Beccles v Stowmarket
Sth. Woodham Ferrers v Crusaders
Haverhill & Dist v Southwold

October 22 (Week 8)
Southwold v Felixstowe
Crusaders v Fakenham
Stowmarket v Thurston
Beccles v Hadleigh
Sth. Woodham Ferrers v Broadland
Haverhill & Dist v Ipswich Y.M.C.A.

March 25 (Week 28)
Southwold v Sth. Woodham Ferrers
Crusaders v Beccles
Stowmarket v Redbridge
Thurston v Hadleigh
Fakenham v Broadland
Felixstowe v Ipswich Y.M.C.A.

October 29 (Week X2)
Thurston v Crusaders
Fakenham v Southwold
Felixstowe v Haverhill & Dist
Ipswich Y.M.C.A. v Sth. Woodham Ferrers
Broadland v Beccles
Hadleigh v Redbridge

April 8 (Week 30)
Ipswich Y.M.C.A. v Fakenham
Broadland v Thurston
Hadleigh v Stowmarket
Redbridge v Crusaders
Beccles v Southwold
Sth. Woodham Ferrers v Haverhill & Dist

444

EASTERN COUNTIES THREE

BECCLES RUFC
Ground Address: Beef Meadow, Common Lane, Beccles. Tel: 0502 712016
Club Secretary: David Smith, 4 The View, Shipmeadow, Beccles, Suffolk NR34 8EX. Tel: (H) 0502 711947 Tel: (W) 0502 715518
Fixtures Secretary: Ben Goode, 28 Ringsfield Road, Beccles NR34 9PF. Tel: (H) 0502 714514
Club Colours: Green & black quarters.

BROADLAND RFC
Ground Address: Cobholm Playing Fields, Cobholm, Great Yarmouth, Norfolk.
Club Secretary: Miss Annie Blizzard, 30 Wolseley Road, Southtown, Great Yarmouth, Norfolk NR30 0EJ. Tel: (H) 0493 440143
Fixtures Secretary: Mr David Inverarity, 16 Beeleigh Way, Beeleigh Green, Caister, Great Yarmouth, Norfolk NR30 5UP. Tel: (H) 0493 377576 Tel (W) 0493 661407
Club Colours: Red, white & blue hoops.

CRUSADERS RFC
Ground Address: Little Melton, Norwich, Norfolk. Tel: 0603 811157
Club Secretary: Mr Tim Holliday, 19 Hobart Close, Wymondham, Norfolk NR18 0EQ. Tel: (H) 0953 601101 Tel: (W) 0603 662496
Fixtures Secretary: Mr Mike Bridgeman, 4 Bensley Road, Norwich NR2 3JS. Tel: (H) 0603 250926 Tel (W) 0603 417500
Club Colours: Gold & green hoops.

FAKENHAM RUFC
Ground Address: Old Wells Road, Fakenham, Norfolk. Tel: 0328 851007
Club Secretary: Miss Alie Vogel, 2 Constitution Hill, Fakenham, Norfolk NR21 9EF. Tel: (H) 0328 851218
Fixtures Secretary: Chris Evans, 64 Boyd Avenue, Toftwood, East Dereham, Norfolk NR1G 1ND. Tel: (H) 0362 694537
Club Colours: Light blue & black.

FELIXSTOWE RUFC
Ground Address: The Clubhouse, Coronation Sports Field, Mill Lane, Felixstowe, Suffolk IP11 8LN. Tel: 0394 270150
Club Secretary: David Richardson, 5 Estuary Drive, Felixstowe, Suffolk IP11 9TL. Tel: (H) 0394 285047 Tel: (W) 0394 670845
Fixtures Secretary: Derek O'Gallighan, 77 Phillip Avenue, Felixstowe, Suffolk IP11 8PJ. Tel: (H) 0394 277114 Tel (W) 0473 654289
Club Colours: Black & white hooped shirts, black shorts, black socks.

HADLEIGH RUFC
Ground Address: Layham Road Sports Ground, Hadleigh, Ipswich, Suffolk IP7 5NE. Tel: 0473 824217
Club Secretary: Andrew Hunkin, 7 Yeoman Way, Hadleigh, Ipswich, Suffolk. Tel: (H) 0473 824448 Tel: (W) 0473 825745
Fixtures Secretary: Alan Murray, Clematis Cottage, Hintlesham, Ipswich, Suffolk. Tel: (H) 0473 652448
Club Colours: Maroon & white hoops or maroon, white & amber hoops.

HAVERHILL & DISTRICT RUFC
Ground Address: Castle Playing Fields, Burton End, School Lane, Haverhill, Suffolk. Tel: 0440 702871
Club Secretary: Clive D Farrow, 27 Broad Street, Haverhill, Suffolk CB9 9HD. Tel: (H) 0440 63766 Tel: (W) 0440 703551
Fixtures Secretary: A Hope, 2 Clare Road, Arrendene Park, Haverhill, Suffolk CB9 9JP. Tel: (H) 0440 63555 Tel (W) 0440 704444
Club Colours: Maroon & blue quartered shirts, black shorts & socks.

IPSWICH YM RUFC
Ground Address: Ipswich YM Sports Ground, The Street, Rushmore, Ipswich, Suffolk. Tel: 0473 713807
Club Secretary: RM Daniels, 85 Western Avenue, Felizstowe, Suffolk IP11 9NT. Tel: (H) 0394 283907 Tel: (W) 0473 543850
Fixtures Secretary: Rob Hullis, 2 Godbold Close, Kesgrave, Ipswich IP5 7SE. Tel: (H) 0473 625027 Tel (W) 0473 622701
Club Colours: Maroon & amber hoops.

FINAL TABLE

	P	W	D	L	F	A	PD	Pts
Old Cooperians	11	11	0	0	237	69	168	22
Ilford Wanderers	11	9	0	2	219	87	132	18
Fakeham	11	7	0	4	148	101	47	14
Sth Wdhm Ferrers	11	6	1	4	148	82	66	13
Haverhill	11	6	0	5	198	84	114	12
Thurston	11	5	1	5	185	126	59	11
Stowmarket	11	5	1	5	125	89	36	11
Felixtowe	11	5	0	6	148	139	9	10
Beccles	11	4	1	6	192	161	31	9
Southwold	11	3	0	8	131	128	3	6
Redbridge	11	3	0	8	117	234	-117	6
Old Brentwoods	11	0	0	11	17	565	-548	0
London Hospital							0	-1
(Expelled from League for 1994-95 Season)								

METROPOLITAN POLCE CHIGWELL RFC
Ground Address: Chigwell Hall, High Road, Chigwell, Essex. Tel: 081 500 2755
Club Secretary: Malcolm Barrett, 11 Fairfield Road, Ongar, Essex CM5 9HJ. Tel: (H) 0277 364205 Tel: (W) 071 275 5221
Fixtures Secretary: Jim Harding, 37 Abbey Road, Hulbridge, Mr Hockley, Essex. Tel: (H) 0702 230713
Club Colours: Royal blue shirts, black shorts, red socks.

REDBRIDGE RFC
Ground Address: Blake Hall Road Sports Centre, Blake Hall Road, Wanstead, London E11. Tel: 081 989 1673
Club Secretary: John Beth, 25 Ackroyd Drive, Bow, London E3 4JY. Tel: (H) 071 987 4203 Tel: (W) 081 981 3206
Fixtures Secretary: Lloyd Evans, 46 Westbury Road, Barking, Essex IG1 7PQ. Tel: (H) 081 594 8408 Tel (W) 081 471 8229
Club Colours: Navy blue.

SOUTH WOODHAM FERRERS RFC
Ground Address: Saltcoats Pavilion, Saltcoats, South Woodham Ferrers, Essex. Tel: 0245 320041
Club Secretary: Mrs Susan Williams, 2 Took Drive, South Woodham Ferrers, Essex CM3 5RL. Tel: (H) 0245 325987
Fixtures Secretary: Mr B Gittos, 12 Hillcrest, South Woodham Ferrers, Essex. Tel: (H) 0245 324603
Club Colours: Black shirts, shorts & socks.

SOUTHWOLD RFC
Ground Address: The Pavilion, The Common, Southwold, Suffolk.
Club Secretary: Andy Toone, 17 Portsch Close, Carlton Colville, Lowestoft, Suffolk NR33 8TY. Tel: (H) 0502 515649 Tel: (W) 0502 566321
Fixtures Secretary: Benny Churchyard, Osborne House, Ilketshall St Lawrence, Beccles, Suffolk. Tel: (H) 0986 781356
Club Colours: Black & amber hoops.

STOWMARKET RUFC
Ground Address: Chilton Fields Sports Club, Chilton Fields, Chilton Way, Stowmarket, Suffolk. Tel: 0449 613181
Club Secretary: N Pearman, 5 Milden Close, Stowmarket, Suffolk IP14 2RF. Tel: (H) 0449 774250 Tel: (W) 0449 612401
Fixtures Secretary: Jim Lawson, 2 Childer Road, Stowmarket, Suffolk IP14 1PP. Tel: (H) 0449 613833
Club Colours: Navy blue with white, red & white central band.

THURSTON RUFC
Ground Address: Robinson Field, Ixworth Road, Thurston, Suffolk. Tel: 0359 232450
Club Secretary: Mark G Abbas, The Fieldings, New Green, Thurston, Suffolk IP31 3SD. Tel: (H) 0359 232546 Tel: (W) 0245 358522
Fixtures Secretary: Bruce Workmaster, 30 Trinity Mews, Bury St Edmunds, Suffolk. Tel: (H) 0284 756565 Tel (W) 0284 756565
Club Colours: Blue with red collar.

LONDON & SOUTH EAST DIVISION

EASTERN COUNTIES FOUR
1994-95 FIXTURES

September 17 (Week 3)
Wisbech v Dereham
Mayfield v Ongar
Essex Police v Billericay
May & Baker v Mersea Island
March v Burnham-on-Crouch

September 24 (Week 4)
Witham v March
Burnham-on-Crouch v May & Baker
Mersea Island v Essex Police
Billericay v Mayfield
Ongar v Brightlingsea

October 1 (Week 5)
March v Dereham
Brightlingsea v Billericay
Mayfield v Mersea Island
Essex Police v Burnham-on-Crouch
May & Baker v Witham

October 15 (Week 7)
Wisbech v March
Dereham v May & Baker
Witham v Essex Police
Burnham-on-Crouch v Mayfield
Mersea Island v Brightlingsea
Billericay v Ongar

October 22 (Week 8)
Essex Police v Dereham
May & Baker v Wisbech
Ongar v Mersea Island
Brightlingsea v Burnham-on-Crouch
Mayfield v Witham

October 29 (Week X2)
Wisbech v Essex Police
Dereham v Mayfield Old Boys
Witham v Brightlingsea
Burnham-on-Crouch v Ongar
Mersea Island v Billericay

January 7 (Week 17)
Brightlingsea v Dereham
Mayfield v Wisbech
May & Baker v March
Billericay v Burnham-on-Crouch
Ongar v Witham

January 14 (Week 18)
March v Essex Police
Wisbech v Brightlingsea
Dereham v Ongar
Witham v Billericay
Burnham-on-Crouch v Mersea Island

February 11 (Week 22)
Billericay v Dereham
Ongar v Wisbech
Mayfield v March
Essex Police v May & Baker
Mersea Island v Witham

February 25 (Week 24)
May & Baker v Mayfield
March v Brightlingsea
Wisbech v Billericay
Dereham v Mersea Island
Witham v Burnham-on_Crouch

March 4 (Week 25)
Burnham-on-Crouch v Dereham
Mersea Island v Wisbech
Ongar v March
Brightlingsea v May & Baker
Mayfield v Essex Police

March 25 (Week 28)
Essex Police v Brightlingsea
May & Baker v Ongar
March v Billericay
Wisbech v Burnham-on-Crouch
Dereham v Witham

April 8 (Week 30)
Witham v Wisbech
Mersea Island v March
Billericay v May & Baker
Ongar v Essex Police
Brightlingsea v Mayfield

EASTERN COUNTIES FOUR

BILLERICAY RFC
Ground Address: Willowbrook, Stock Road, Stock, Billericay, Essex. Tel: 0277 841442
Club Secretary: GJ Buggle, 96 Norsey View Drive, Billericay, Essex CM12 0QU. Tel: (W) 0375 677777
Fixtures Secretary: M Scoggins, 38 St Mary's Drive, South Benfleet, Essex SS7 1LB. Tel: (H) 0268 751007 Tel (W) 0268 756276
Club Colours: Black with single gold hoop.

BRIGHTLINGSEA RFC
Ground Address: Strangers Corner, Brightlingsea, Essex. Tel: 0206 304946
Club Secretary: James McClure, 10 Pertwee Close, Brightlingsea, Essex CO7 0RT. Tel: (H) 0206 304761 Tel: (W) 0268 525631
Fixtures Secretary: Trevor Andrews, 1 Tabor Close, Brightlingsea, Essex CO7 0QS. Tel: (H) 0206 302235
Club Colours: Scarlet shirts, black shorts & socks.

BURNHAM-ON-CROUCH RUFC
Ground Address: Dengie Hundred Sports Centre, Millfields, Station Road, Burnham-on-Crouch, Essex CM0 8HS. Tel: Office: 0621 784633 Bar: 0621 784656
Club Secretary: Mr Warwick Bridge, 12 Glendale Road, Burnham-on-Crouch, Essex CM0 8LY. Tel: (H) 0621 783807
Fixtures Secretary: Mr Warwick Bridge, 12 Glendale Road, Burnham-on-Crouch, Essex CM0 8LY. Tel: (H) 0621 783807
Club Colours: Navy blue & amber hoops.

DEREHAM RUFC
Ground Address: Moorgate, Dereham, Norfolk.
Club Secretary: Barbara Endresen, 1 Bayfield Avenue, Dereham, Norfolk NR19 1PH. Tel: (H) 0362 691487
Fixtures Secretary: Mark Brown, 47 Hillcrest Avenue, Toftwood, Dereham, Norfolk. Tel: (H) 0362 698588
Club Colours: Maroon.

ESSEX POLICE RFC
Ground Address: Police Headquarters, Sandford Road, Chelmsford, Essex. Tel: 0245 452221
Club Secretary: Jenny Halford, 54 Peel Road, Chelmsford CM2 6AL. Tel: (H) 0245 262017
Fixtures Secretary: Mike Hall, Weapons Training Department, Police Headquarters, PO Box 2, Springfield, Chelmsford, Essex CM2 6DA. Tel: (H) 0245 265794 Tel (W) 0245 452441 Fax: 0245 452831
Club Colours: Royal blue & white.

MARCH BRAZA RUFC
Ground Address: Braza Sports Pavilion, Sports Field, Elm Road, March, Cambridgeshire.
Club Secretary: Mr C Amps, 10 Swallow Way, March, Cambridgeshire. Tel: (H) 0354 57040
Fixtures Secretary: Mr I Woodward, 34b Westfield Road, Manea, March, Cambridgeshire. Tel: (H) 0354 680445
Club Colours: 1st XV: Maroon & white hoops. 2nd XV: Maroon tops.

MAY AND BAKER RUFC
Ground Address: Rhone Poulenc Rorer, Painham Road South, Dagenham RM10 7XS (Entrance to sports ground in Dagenham Road). Tel: 081 919 3156
Club Secretary: Terry Simmons, 105 Alibon Road, Dagenham, Essex RM10 8DE. Tel: (H) 081 593 2630 Tel: (W) 081 919 2579
Fixtures Secretary: Mike Parnell, The Old Post Office, High Easter, Chelmsford, Essex. Tel: (H) 0245 231302
Club Colours: Black with single red hoop, black shorts, red stockings.

FINAL TABLE

	P	W	D	L	F	A	PD	Pts
Hadleigh	12	12	0	0	264	111	153	24
Broadland	12	58	1	3	144	133	11	17
Billericay	12	7	2	3	207	98	109	16
March	12	7	1	4	195	155	40	15
May & Baker	11	6	1	4	160	132	28	13
Witham	12	6	0	6	134	141	-7	12
Brightlingsea	12	5	1	6	190	139	51	11
Ongar	11	5	0	6	106	147	-41	10
Burnham-on-Crouch	12	3	2	7	115	120	-5	8
Wisbech	12	4	0	8	107	145	-38	8
Dereham	12	4	0	8	141	187	-46	8
Essex Police	12	4	0	8	132	215	-83	8
Swaffam	12	2	0	10	105	277	-172	4

MAYFIELD RUFC
Ground Address: Whitbread Playing Fields, Durham Avenue, off Prospect Avenue, Woodford Green, Essex.
Club Secretary: Alan Gold, 6 Boxted Close, Buckhurst Hill, Essex IG9 6BX. Tel: (H) 081 505 7084 Tel: (W) 0708 764086
Fixtures Secretary: John Allum, Flat 8, 29 Eastcourt House, Eastwood Road, Goodmayes, Essex. Tel: (H) 081 599 6730
Club Colours: Green & white quarters.

MERSEA ISLAND RFC
Ground Address: Youth Camp, East Road, East Mersea, Essex.
Club Secretary: Tony Eves, Dormy House, Lower Road, Peldon, Essex CO5 7QR. Tel: (H) 0206 735537 Tel: (W) 0206 735537
Fixtures Secretary: Graham Woods, 24 Church Field, West Mersea, Essex. Tel: (H) 0206 383525
Club Colours: Blue & white quarters.

ONGAR RFC
Ground Address: Lone Lane, Ongar, Essex. Tel: 0277 363838
Club Secretary: N Doubleday, 105 Roundhills, Waltham Abbey, Essex EN9 1TF. Tel: (H) 0992 768950 Tel: (W) 0992 788557
Fixtures Secretary: Peter Hodgson, 16 Northcourt, Summerfields, Ingatestone, Essex CM4 0BD. Tel: (H) 0277 354404 Tel (W) 0836 615535
Club Colours: Blue with amber band.

WISBECH RUFC
Ground Address: Chapel Road, Wisbech, Cambridgeshire. Tel: 0945 63666
Club Secretary: JRC Pallant, 139 Lynn Road, Wisbech, Cambridgeshire PE13 3DH. Tel: (H) 0945 588147 Tel: (W) 0354 54321
Fixtures Secretary: DH Dobson, 5 Buckingham Walk, Wisbech, Cambridgeshire. Tel: (H) 0945 61223
Club Colours: Red shirts, blue shorts.

WITHAM RUFC
Ground Address: Spa Road, Witham, Essex, CM8 1UN. Tel: 0376 511066
Club Secretary: T M Whelan, Shortland, Highfields Road, Witham, Essex, CM8 2HJ. Tel: (H) 0376 515871
Fixtures Secretary: A Downes, The Old Manse, Manse Chase, Maldon, Essex. Tel: (H) 0621 857 593
Club Colours: Brown & white hoops, navy shorts.

LONDON & SOUTH EAST DIVISION

EASTERN COUNTIES FIVE
1994-95
FIXTURES

March 25 (Week 28)
Rayleigh v Dagenham
Swaffham v Sizewell
Essex County Council v Burwell
Norwich Union v Sawston

October 1 (Week 5)
Dagenham v Stanford le Hope
Sawston v Essex County Council
Burwell v Swaffham
Sizewell v Rayleigh

October 15 (Week 7)
Stanford le Hope v Sizewell
Essex County Council v Norwich Union
Swaffham v Sawston
Rayleigh v Burwell

October 22 (Week 8)
Burwell v Stanford le Hope
Sizewell v Dagenham
Sawston v Rayleigh
Norwich Union v Swaffham

October 29 (Week X2)
Dagenham v Burwell
Stanford le Hope v Sawston
Rayleigh v Norwich Union
Swaffham v Essex County Council

January 14 (Week 18)
Norwich Union v Stanford le Hope
Sawston v Dagenham
Burwell v Sizewell
Essex County Council v Rayleigh

February 11 (Week 22)
Sizewell v Sawston
Dagenham v Norwich Union
Stanford le Hope v Essex County Council
Rayleigh v Swaffham

February 25 (Week 24)
Swaffham v Stanford le Hope
Essex County Council v Dagenham
Norwich Union v Sizewell
Sawston v Burwell

March 4 (Week 25)
Burwell v Norwich Union
Sizewell v Essex County Council
Dagenham v Swaffham
Stanford le Hope v Rayleigh

EASTERN COUNTIES FIVE

BURWELL RFC
Ground Address: Fen Edge, The Recreation Ground,
Hythe Lane, Burwell, Cambridge.
Club Secretary: Chris Stearne, 16 Priory Close, Burwell,
CB5 0HW. Tel: (H) 0638 743676 Tel: (W) 0638 743 097
Fixtures Secretary: B Mitchell, 24 Ness Road, Burwell,
Cambs. Tel: (H) 0638 743 950
Club Colours: Scarlet.
DAGENHAM RFC
Ground Address: Central Park Pavilion, Rainham Road,
North Dagenham, Essex.
Club Secretary: Mr RJ Moreton, 21 Central Park Avenue,
Dagenham, Essex RM10 7DA. Tel: (H) 081 984 8444 Tel:
(W) 0860 821799
Fixtures Secretary: Mr RL Yates, 76 Hardie Road,
Dagenham, Essex. Tel: (H) 081 252 1405
Club Colours: Red & white quarters.
ESSEX COUNTY COUNCIL RFC
Ground Address: Lordship Lane, Writtle, Chelmsford,
Essex.
Club Secretary: David Sharp, 67 Clements Green Lane,
South Woodham Ferrers, Chelmsford, Essex CM3 5JS. Tel:
(H) 0245 323490 Tel: (W) 0268 702336
Fixtures Secretary: David Sharp, 67 Clements Green
Lane, South Woodham Ferrers, Chelmsford, Essex CM3
5JS. Tel: (H) 0245 323490 Tel (W) 0268 702336
Club Colours: Red & white quarters, blue shorts, red socks.
NORWICH UNION RFCE
Ground Address: Pinebanks, White Farm Lane, Harvey
Lane, Norwich, Norfolk. Tel: 0603 33752
Club Secretary: Paul D Osborne, 22 Impala Close,
Sprowston, Norwich, Norfolk NR6 7PN. Tel: (H) 0603
483142 Tel: (W) 0603 683723
Fixtures Secretary: Mark L Howell, 165 Christchurch
Road, Norwich, Norfolk NR2 3PJ. Tel (H) 0603 501503
Tel (W) 0603 622200
Club Colours: Green & white quarters, white shorts, green
socks.
RAYLEIGH WYVERNS RFC
Ground Address: John Fisher Playing Fields, Little
Wheatleys Chase, Rayleigh, Essex.
Club Secretary: SJ Earl, 22 The Fairway, Leigh-on-Sea,
Essex SS9 4QL. Tel: (H) 0702 524111 Tel: (W) 081 502
1423
Fixtures Secretary: M Sheppard, 19 Mortimer Road,
Rayleigh, Essex. Tel: (H) 0268 781152
Club Colours: Scarlet & emerald quarters.
SAWSTON RUFC
Ground Address: Sawston College, New Road, Sawston
CB2 4BP.
Club Secretary: Paul Clerke, 1 Crossways, Linton,
Cambridge. Tel: (H) 0223 891365 Tel: (W) 081 965 0313
Fixtures Secretary: Phil Mason, 6 Stanstead Road,
Elsenham, Bishop's Stortford, Herts. Tel: (H) 0279 812545
Tel (W) 071 374 4055
Club Colours: Navy, black & white.
SIZEWELL RUFC
Ground Address: Sizewell Sports & Social Club, King
George's Avenue, Leiston, Suffolk. Tel: 0728 830115
Club Secretary: Alan Biddle, 71 Carr Avenue, Leiston
IP16 4JA. Tel: (H) 0728 830930 Tel: (W) 0394 444325
Fixtures Secretary: Tony Gibson, 5 Ashwood Cottages,
The Old Abbey Estate, Eastbridge, Suffolk IP16 4SR. Tel:
(H) 0728 833251 Tel (W) 0728 833251
Club Colours: Royal blue. Change: Dark blue & light blue
hoops.
STANFORD LE HOPE RFC
Ground Address: Stanford Recreation Ground, Billet Lane,
Stanford le Hope, Essex. Tel: 0375 640957
Club Secretary: Arlan Roach, 159 Lodge Lane, Grays,
Essex RM17 5PS. Tel: (H) 0375 377798 Tel: (W) 0860

FINAL TABLE

	P	W	D	L	F	A	PD	Pts
Mersea Island	11	9	2	0	248	43	205	20
Mayfield Old Boys	10	9	1	0	205	47	158	17
Swaston	11	6	2	3	192	85	107	14
Stanford	10	6	1	3	281	118	163	13
Burwell	11	6	0	5	212	120	92	12
Essex University	10	5	1	4	308	179	129	11
Essex C Council	10	5	1	4	232	166	66	11
Norwich Union	11	4	2	5	190	114	76	10
Dagenham	11	5	0	6	201	155	46	10
Leiston	11	2	0	9	120	290	-170	4
Mistley	10	1	0	9	64	668	-604	2
Watton	10	0	0	10	57	325	-268	0

790093 Fax: 0375 378077
Fixtures Secretary: Albert Higgs, 18 Gooderham House,
Godman Road, Chadwell St Mary, Essex RM16 4TW. Tel:
(H) 0375 841803
Club Colours: Red & white hoops.
SWAFFHAM RUFC
Ground Address: North Pickenham Road, Swaffham,
Norfolk. Tel: 0760 724829
Club Secretary: Hugh Green, Gemini Cottage,
Weasenham St Peter, King's Lynn, Norfolk PE32 2TD.
Tel: (H) 0328 74269 Tel: (W) 0760 721281 Fax: 725084
Fixtures Secretary: Graham Robinson, 9 Beaumont Place,
Norwich, Norfolk NR2 2HH. Tel: (H) 0603 622696
Club Colours: Amber shirts, black shorts. Change: Black
shirts with amber hoops.

LONDON & SOUTH EAST DIVISION

LONDON TWO SOUTH
1994-95
FIXTURES

September 17 (Week 3)
Thanet Wanderers v Old Wimbledonians
Portsmouth v Sidcup
Westcombe Park v Horsham
Charlton Park v Dorking
Old Blues v Old Alleynian
Old Juddian v Old Reigatian

September 24 (Week 4)
Old Wimbledonians v Old Juddian
Old Reigatian v Old Blues
Old Alleynian v Charlton Park
Dorking v Westcombe Park
Horsham v Portsmouth
Sidcup v Gravesend

October 1 (Week 5)
Old Blues v Old Wimbledonians
Old Juddian v Thanet Wanderers
Gravesend v Horsham
Portsmouth v Dorking
Westcombe Park v Old Alleynian
Charlton Park v Old Reigatian

October 15 (Week 7)
Thanet Wanderers v Old Blues
Old Wimbledonians v Charlton Park
Old Reigatian v Westcombe Park
Old Alleynian v Portsmouth
Dorking v Gravesend
Horsham v Sidcup

October 22 (Week 8)
Westcombe Park v Old Wimbledonians
Charlton Park v Thanet Wanderers
Old Blues v Old Juddian
Sidcup v Dorking
Gravesend v Old Alleynian
Portsmouth v Old Reigatian

October 29 (Week X2)
Old Juddian v Charlton Park
Thanet Wanderers v Westcombe Park
Old Wimbledonians v Portsmouth
Old Reigation v Gravesend
Old Alleynian v Sidcup
Dorking v Horsham

January 7 (Week 17)
Gravesend v Old Wimbledonians
Portsmouth v Thanet Wanderers
Westcombe Park v Old Juddian
Charlton Park v Old Blues
Horsham v Old Alleynian
Sidcup v Old Reigatian

January 14 (Week 18)
Old Blues v Westcombe Park
Old Juddian v Portsmouth
Thanet Wanderers v Gravesend
Old Wimbledonians v Sidcup
Old Reigatian v Horsham
Old Alleynian v Dorking

February 11 (Week 22)
Horsham v Old Wimbledonians
Sidcup v Thanet Wanderers
Gravesend v Old Juddian
Portsmouth v Old Blues
Westcombe Park v Charlton Park
Dorking v Old Reigatian

February 25 (Week 24)
Charlton Park v Portsmouth
Old Blues v Gravesend
Old Juddian v Sidcup
Thanet Wanderers v Horsham
Old Wimbledonians v Dorking
Old Reigatian v Old Alleynian

March 4 (Week 25)
Old Alleynian v Old Wimbledonians
Dorking v Thanet Wanderers
Horsham v Old Juddian
Sidcup v Old Blues
Gravesend v Charlton Park
Portsmouth v Westcombe Park

March 25 (Week 28)
Westcombe Park v Gravesend
Charlton Park v Sidcup
Old Blues v Horsham
Old Juddian v Dorking
Thanet Wanderers v Old Alleynian
Old Wimbledonians v Old Reigatian

April 8 (Week 30)
Old Reigatian v Thanet Wanderers
Old Alleynian v Old Juddian
Dorking v Old Blues
Horsham v Charlton Park
Sidcup v Westcombe Park
Gravesend v Portsmouth

LONDON TWO SOUTH

CHARLTON PARK RFC
Ground Address: Pippenhall Sports Ground, Avery Hill Park, Footscray Road, Eltham, London SE9. Tel: 081 850 0408
Club Secretary: Nick Hollier, 5 Brunswick Road, Bexleyheath, Kent DA6 8EL. Tel: (H) 081 301 1210 Tel: (W) 081 303 7777 x2419
Fixtures Secretary: Roger Foxon, 245 McLeod Road, Abbey Wood, London SE2 0YJ. Tel: (H) 081 473 0004 Tel (W) 071 250 3055 x2120 (nights)
Club Colours: Red & white shirts, blue shorts, red socks.
DORKING RFC
Ground Address: Big Field, Kiln Lane, Brockham, Dorking, Surrey. Tel: 0737 844282
Club Secretary: PJ Curran, Silveracre, Camilla Drive, Westhumble, Dorking, Surrey RH5 6BU. Tel: (H) 0306 884649 Tel: (W) 081 643 7221
Fixtures Secretary: Mark Kenway, 11 Ansell Road, Dorking, Surrey. Tel: (H) 0306 880291 Tel (W) 071 327 5212
Club Colours: Red & white hoops.
GRAVESEND RFC
Ground Address: The Rectory Field & Club House, Milton Road, Gravesend, Kent DA12 2PP. Tel: 0474 534840
Club Secretary: John Moore Esq, 375A Singledell Road, Gravesend, Kent DA11 7RL. Tel: (H) 0474 362998
Fixtures Secretary: RA Wright, 43 Alanbrooke, Gravesend, Kent DA12 1NA. Tel: (H) 0474 327303
Club Colours: 4' black & white hoops.
HORSHAM RUFC
Ground Address: Hammer Pond Road, Coolhurst, Horsham, West Sussex. Tel: 0403 265027
Club Secretary: BR Lewis Esq, 2 Wain End, Horsham, West Sussex RH12 5TQ. Tel: (H) 0403 266267
Fixtures Secretary: G Curtis Esq, The Bunglaow, Church Road, Mannings Heath, Horsham, West Sussex RH13 6JE. Tel: (H) 0403 268262 Tel (W) 0444 458166
Club Colours: Green & white.
OLD ALLEYNIAN FC
Ground Address: Dulwich Common, Dulwich, London SE21 7HA. Tel: 081 693 2402
Club Secretary: RA (Joe) Crow, 13 Gable Court, Lawrie Park Avenue, London SE26 6HR. Tel: (H) 081 778 2868
Fixtures Secretary: Alastair N Capon, 2 Cranmore Road, Chislehurst, Kent BR7 6EP. Tel: (H) 081 851 7510
Club Colours: Dark blue, light blue & black hoops.
OLD BLUES RFC
Ground Address: Arthur Road, Motspur Park, New Malden, Surrey KT3 6PT. Tel: 081 336 2566
Club Secretary: Ian Hoskins, 1 Oak Tree Drive, Englefield Green, Surrey TW20 0NR. Tel: (H) 0784 436707 Tel: (W) 0784 436707
Fixtures Secretary: Gile Simons, 66B Gowrie Road, London SW11 5NR. Tel: (H) 071 207 0010 Tel (W) 071 628 2411
Club Colours: French navy, cardinal & old gold.
OLD JUDDIAN RFC
Ground Address: Tonbridge Sports Ground, The Slade, Tonbridge, Kent. Tel: 0732 358548
Club Secretary: Steve Davey, 35 Dowgate Close, Tonbridge, Kent. Tel: (H) 0732 357429 Tel: (W) 0732 866066
Fixtures Secretary: Tony Russell, 28 Whistler Road, Tonbridge, Kent TN10 4RD. Tel: (H) 0732 355582
Club Colours: Claret & light blue hooped jerseys, navy blue shorts.
OLD REIGATIAN
Ground Address: Ors Field, Park Lane, Reigate, Surrey RH2 8JX. Tel: 0737 245634
Club Secretary: Todd Budgen, Flat 1, 20 Alders Road, Reigate, Surrey RH2 8ED. Tel: (H) 0737 223806 Tel: (W) 0708 730333

FINAL TABLE

	P	W	D	L	F	A	PD	Pts
Esher	12	10	2	0	387	95	292	22
Westcombe Park	12	10	1	1	259	130	129	21
Thanet Wanderers	12	6	2	4	243	171	72	14
O. Wimbledonians	12	6	1	5	208	176	32	13
Horsham	12	6	1	5	205	196	9	13
Charlton Park	12	6	1	5	172	208	-36	13
Sidcup	12	6	0	6	208	174	34	12
Old Blues	12	5	2	5	157	139	18	12
Old Reigatian	12	4	2	6	124	162	-38	10
Old Juddian	12	5	0	7	230	292	-62	10
Lewes	12	3	2	7	135	187	-52	8
Worthing	12	4	0	8	107	163	-56	6
K.C.S. Old Boys	12	0	0	12	94	436	-342	0

Fixtures Secretary: Keith Ireland, 36 Barrow Green Road, Oxted, Surrey RH8 0NM. Tel: (H) 0883 712713 Tel (W) 081 651 6321
Club Colours: Blue, green & white.
OLD WIMBLEDONIANS RFC
Ground Address:104 Cottenham Park Road, Raynes Park, London SW20 0DS. Tel: 081 879 0700
Club Secretary: C O'Rourke, 103 Cannon Hill Lane, Merton Park, London SW20 9LE. Tel: (H) 081 540 6615 Tel: (W) 081 424 0382
Fixtures Secretary: R Nolan, 156 Horton Hill, Epsom, Surrey KT19 8ST. Tel: (H) 0372 727063
Club Colours: Green, maroon & gold hoops.
PORTSMOUTH RFC
Ground Address: Rugby Camp, Norway Road, Portsmouth PO3 5HR. Tel: 0705 876185
Club Secretary: Ian Henderson, Flat 1, 22 High Street, Old Portsmouth, PO1 2CR. Tel: (H) 0705 876185 Tel: (W) 0329 876185
Fixtures Secretary: Maurice Twells, Yore Cottage, 1 Chackridge Road, Cosham, Portsmouth PO6 2BE. Tel: (H) 0705 389350 Tel (W) 0705 370660
Club Colours: Black with single white & gold hoop.
SIDCUP FC
Ground Address: Crescent Farm, Sydney Road, Sidcup, Kent DA14 6RA. Tel: 081 300 2336
Club Secretary: Allan Jones, 53 Goodwin Drive, Sidcup, Kent DA14 4NX. Tel: (H) 081 302 2382
Fixtures Secretary: Malcolm J Leamon, 4 Glenhouse Road, Eltham, London SE9 1JH. Tel: (H) 081 859 5598
Club Colours: White. Change: Maroon.
THANET WANDERERS RUFC
Ground Address: St Peters Recreation Ground, Callis Court Road, Broadstairs, Kent.
Club Secretary: Peter Hawkins, 51 Park Road, Ramsgate, Kent CT11 9TL. Tel: (H) 0843 593142 Tel: (W) 0843 593142
Fixtures Secretary: Peter Hawkins, 51 Park Road, Ramsgate, Kent CT11 9TL. Tel: (H) 0843 295159
Club Colours: Blue, black & yellow hoops.
WESTCOMBE PARK RFC
Ground Address: Goddington Dene, Goddington Lane, Orpington, Kent BR6 9SH. Tel: 0689 834902
Club Secretary: Robin Taylor, 24 Pinchbeck Road, Green Street Green, Orpington, Kent BR6 6DR. Tel: (H) 0689 855052 Tel: (W) 081 310 9868 Car: 0374 212029
Fixtures Secretary: John Bellinger, The Butry, 32A Courtyard, Eltham, London SE9 5QE. Tel: (H) 081 850 7280
Club Colours: Navy & white hoops, navy shorts, navy & white hooped hose.

LONDON & SOUTH EAST DIVISION

LONDON THREE SOUTH EAST 1994-95 FIXTURES

January 7 (Week 17)
Canterbury v Lewes
Old Beccehamians v Park House
Heathfield & Waldron v Brockleians
Erith v Beckenham
Haywards Heath v Brighton
Chichester v East Grinstead

September 17 (Week 3)
Park House v Lewes
Old Beccehamians v Chichester
Heathfield & Waldron v Haywards Heath
Erith v Worthing
Beckenham v Brighton
Brockleians v East Grinstead

January 14 (Week 18)
Beckenham v Heathfield & Waldron
Brockleians v Old Beccehamians
Park House v Canterbury
Lewes v Chichester
East Grinstead v Haywards Heath
Brighton v Worthing

September 24 (Week 4)
Lewes v Brockleians
East Grinstead v Beckenham
Brighton v Erith
Worthing v Heathfield & Waldron
Haywards Heath v Old Beccehamians
Chichester v Canterbury

February 11 (Week 22)
Haywards Heath v Lewes
Chichester v Park House
Canterbury v Brockleians
Old Beccehamians v Beckenham
Heathfield & Waldron v Erith
Worthing v East Grinstead

October 1 (Week 5)
Beckenham v Lewes
Brockleians v Park House
Canterbury v Haywards Heath
Old Beccehamians v Worthing
Heathfield & Waldron v Brighton
Erith v East Grinstead

February 25 (Week 24)
Erith v Old Beccehamians
Beckenham v Canterbury
Brockleians v Chichester
Park House v Haywards Heath
Lewes v Worthing
East Grinstead v Brighton

October 15 (Week 7)
Park House v Beckenham
Lewes v Erith
East Grinstead v Heathfield & Waldron
Brighton v Old Beccehamians
Worthing v Canterbury
Haywards Heath v Chichester

March 4 (Week 25)
Brighton v Lewes
Worthing v Park House
Haywards Heath v Brockleians
Chichester v Beckenham
Canterbury v Erith
Old Beccehamians v Heathfield & Waldron

October 22 (Week 8)
Heathfield & Waldron v Lewes
Erith v Park House
Beckenham v Brockleians
Chichester v Worthing
Canterbury v Brighton
Old Beccehamians v East Grinstead

March 25 (Week 28)
Heathfield & Waldron v Canterbury
Erith v Chichester
Beckenham v Haywards Heath
Brockleians v Worthing
Park House v Brighton
Lewes v East Grinstead

October 29 (Week X2)
Brockleians v Erith
Park Houee v Heathfield & Waldron
Lewes v Old Beccehamians
East Grinstead v Canterbury
Brighton v Chichester
Worthing v Haywards Heath

April 8 (Week 30)
East Grinstead v Park House
Brighton v Brockleians
Worthing v Beckenham
Haywards Heath v Erith
Chichester v Heathfield & Waldron
Canterbury v Old Beccehamians

LONDON THREE SOUTH EAST

BECKENHAM RFC
Ground Address: Balmoral Avenue, Elmers End, Beckenham, Kent BR3 3RD. Tel: 081 650 7176
Club Secretary: League contact: Paul Bailey, 128 Lennard Road, Beckenham, Kent BR3 1QP. Tel: (H) 081 778 3053
Fixtures Secretary: John Arger, 15 Thatcher Road, Staplehurst, Kent TN12 0ND. Tel: (H) 0580 891550
Club Colours: Royal blue & old gold hoops.

BRIGHTON FC
Ground Address: Waterhall Playing Fields, Waterhall Road, Patcham, Brighton, Sussex, BN1 8YR. Tel: 0273 562729
Club Secretary: Edward D'arcy, Bailey House, Barttelot Road, Horsham, W Sussex, RH12 1XG. Tel: (H) 0273 885407 Tel: (W) 0403 250277
Fixtures Secretary: Ray Greenwood, 11 Lyminster Ave, Brighton, BN1 8JL. Tel: (H) 0273 502898
Club Colours: Blue shirts/socks, red socks.

BROCKLEIANS RFC
Ground Address: Eltham Palace Road, Eltham, London SE9. Tel: 081 850 8650
Club Secretary: RJC Ellery, 13 Peacock Gardens, Selsdon CR2 8TE. Tel: (H) 081 657 7973
Fixtures Secretary: G Wright, 3 Birling Avenue, Bearsted, Maidstone ME14 4DG. Tel: (H) 0622 38396
Club Colours: Chocolate, emerald & old gold.

CANTERBURY RFC
Ground Address: The Pavilion, Merton Lane, Canterbury, Kent. Tel: 0227 768958
Club Secretary: TDO Hall, Whiteacre Farmhouse, Whiteacre Lane, Waltham, Canterbury, Kent CT4 5SR. Tel: (H) 0227 700344 Tel: (W) 0227 763939
Fixtures Secretary: Graham Brookes, 4 Forestry Cottages, Sole Street, Crundale, Canterbury, Kent CT4 7ES. Tel: (H) 0227 700535 Tel (W) 0233 812181
Club Colours: Black & amber hoops, black shorts.

CHICHESTER RFC
Ground Address: Oaklands Park, (entrance via Wellington Road), Chichester, W Sussex. Tel: 0243 779820
Club Secretary: Simon Hill, St Ronans, 8 Clayton Road, Selsey, West Sussex.
Fixtures Secretary: Mike French. Tel: (H) 0705 482382
Club Colours: Light & dark blue hoops.

EAST GRINSTEAD RFC
Ground Address: Saint Hill Ground, Saint Hill Road, Saint Hill, East Grinstead, West Sussex. Tel: 0342 322338
Club Secretary: Philip Davis Evans, 21 Hackenden Close, East Grinstead, West Sussex RH19 3DR. Tel: (H) 0342 314413
Fixtures Secretary: RP Russell, 1 Rose Cottages, Plaistow Street, Lingfield, Surrey RH7 6AU. Tel: (H) 0342 834648 Tel (W) 081 668 8859
Club Colours: Blue shirts with a broad white hoop.

ERITH RFC
Ground Address: Northumberland Heath Playing Fields, Sussex Road, Erith, Kent. Tel: 0322 432295
Club Secretary: JN McConville, 18 Buxton Road, Erith, Kent DA8 3BJ. Tel: (H) 0322 337064 Tel: (W) 081 303 5696
Fixtures Secretary: Mr S Button, 26 Pilgrims View, Greenhithe, Kent DA9 9BQ. Tel: (H) 0322 387689
Club Colours: Light blue & dark blue hoops.

HAYWARDS HEATH RFC
Ground Address: The Clubhouse, Whitemans Green, Cuckfield, Haywards Heath, West Sussex. Tel: 0444 413950
Club Secretary: Mel Cook, Tinkers, Summerhill Lane, Haywards Heath, West Sussex. Tel: (H) 0444 452327 Tel: (W) 071 753 1972
Fixtures Secretary: Ian Beckett, 94 Sunnywood Drive, Haywards Heath, West Sussex. Tel: (H) 0444 412576

FINAL TABLE

	P	W	D	L	F	A	PD	Pts
Gravesend	12	12	0	0	315	57	258	24
Beckenham	12	9	0	3	165	73	92	18
Brockleians	12	8	0	4	213	94	119	16
Canterbury	12	8	0	4	206	103	103	16
Haywards Heath	12	7	0	5	145	139	6	14
Old Beccehamian	12	6	0	6	151	116	35	12
Brighton	12	6	0	6	150	181	-31	12
Chichester	12	5	1	6	120	161	-41	11
East Grinstead	12	4	1	7	163	247	-84	9
Erith	12	4	0	8	142	139	3	8
Gillingham Anchrian	12	4	0	8	105	231	-126	8
Tunbridge Wells	12	3	0	9	111	264	-153	6
Hove	12	1	0	11	91	272	-181	2

Club Colours: Red & black quartered jerseys, black shorts.

HEATHFIELD & WALDRON RFC
Ground Address: Hardy Roberts Playing Fields, Cross in Hand, Heathfield, East Sussex. Tel: 0435 863396
Club Secretary: Peter R Mercer, Mapsedge, Cross in Hand, Heathfield, East Sussex TN21 0TA. Tel: (H) 0435 863396 Tel: (W) 0424 775999
Fixtures Secretary: Kelvin Bromley, Sandy Cross Cottage, Sandy Cross, Heathfield, East Sussex. Tel: (H) 0435 864928
Club Colours: Green & white hooped shirts, white shorts.

LEWES RFC
Ground Address: Stanley Turner Sports Ground, Kingston Road, Lewes, East sussex BN7 3NB. Tel: 0273 473732
Club Secretary: AH Powell, 29 Cradle Hill Road, Seaford, East Sussex BN25 3JA. Tel: (H) 0323 893094
Fixtures Secretary: K Gordon, Lynstead, Coopers Green, Uckfield, East Sussex TN22 4AT. Tel: (H) 0825 732440
Club Colours: Blue & white hoops.

OLD BECCEHAMIAN RFC
Ground Address: Sparrows Den, Corkscrew Hill, West Wickham, Kent BR4 9BB. Tel: 081 777 8105
Club Secretary: Bill Gault, 45 Bushey Way, Beckenham, Kent BR3 2TA. Tel: (H) 081 650 6854 Tel: (W) 081 658 7211
Fixtures Secretary: /President: Clive Putner, 12 Manor Road, West Wickham, Kent. Tel: (H) 081 777 6307 Tel (W) 081 650 9253
Club Colours: Black, white & maroon hoops.

PARK HOUSE FC
Ground Address: Barnet Wood Road (south side), Hayes, Kent. Tel: 081 462 7318
Club Secretary: Robert D Elves, 380 Blackfen Road, Sidcup, Kent DA15 9NZ. Tel: (H) 081 304 9170 Tel: (W) 0474 853731
Fixtures Secretary: James McGarey, Greenways, 5 Pondfield Road, Hayes, Kent BR2 7HS. Tel: (H) 081 462 1130 Tel: (W) 071 357 5512
Club Colours: Black & red shirts, black shorts, red socks.

WORTHING RFC
Ground Address: The Rugby Park, Roundstone Lane, Angmering, West Sussex. Tel: Tel & Fax: 0903 784706
Club Secretary: Chris Packwood, 15 Anscombe Close, Worthing, West Sussex. Tel: (H) 0903 505250 Tel: (W) 0903 238273
Fixtures Secretary: Paul Hughes, 74 Lanfranc Road, Worthing, West Sussex. Tel: (H) 0903 209053 Tel (W) 0732 361500
Club Colours: Royal blue with gold & chocolate hoops. Change: Gold.

LONDON & SOUTH EAST DIVISION

KENT ONE
1994-95
FIXTURES

September 17 (Week 3)
Betteshanger	v	Dartfordians
Met. Police	v	Old Dunstonians
Gillingham Anchorians	v	Medway
Old Elthamians	v	Old Shootershillians
Bromley	v	Tunbridge Wells
Sheppey	v	Greenwich Academicals

September 24 (Week 4)
Dartfordians	v	Sheppey
Greenwich Academicals	v	Bromley
Tunbridge Wells	v	Old Elthamians
Old Shootershillians	v	Gillingham Anchorians
Medway	v	Met. Police
Old Dunstonians	v	Sevenoaks

October 1 (Week 5)
Bromley	v	Dartfordians
Sheppey	v	Betteshanger
Sevenoaks	v	Medway
Met. Police	v	Old Shootershillians
Gillingham Anchorians	v	Tunbridge Wells
Old Elthamians	v	Greenwich Academicals

October 15 (Week 7)
Betteshanger	v	Bromley
Dartfordians	v	Old Elthamians
Greenwich Academicals	v	Gillingham Anchorians
Tunbridge Wells	v	Met. Police
Old Shootershillians	v	Sevenoaks
Medway	v	Old Dunstonians

October 22 (Week 8)
Gillingham Anchorians	v	Dartfordians
Old Elthamians	v	Betteshanger
Bromley	v	Sheppey
Old Dunstonians	v	Old Shootershillians
Sevenoaks	v	Tunbridge Wells
Met. Police	v	Greenwich Academicals

October 29 (Week X2)
Sheppey	v	Old Elthamians
Betteshanger	v	Gillingham Anchorians
Dartfordians	v	Met. Police
Greenwich Academicals	v	Sevenoaks
Tunbridge Wells	v	Old Dunstonians
Old Shootershillians	v	Medway

January 7 (Week 17)
Sevenoaks	v	Dartfordians
Met. Police	v	Betteshanger
Gillingham Anchorians	v	Sheppey
Old Elthamians	v	Bromley
Medway	v	Tunbridge Wells
Old Dunstonians	v	Greenwich Academicals

January 14 (Week 18)
Bromley	v	Gillingham Anchorians
Sheppey	v	Met. Police
Betteshanger	v	Sevenoaks
Dartfordians	v	Old Dunstonians
Greenwich Academicals	v	Medway
Tunbridge Wells	v	Old Shootershillians

February 11 (Week 22)
Medway	v	Dartfordians
Old Dunstonians	v	Betteshanger
Sevenoaks	v	Sheppey
Met. Police	v	Bromley
Gillingham Anchorians	v	Old Elthamians
Old Shootershillians	v	Greenwich Academicals

February 25 (Week 24)
Old Elthamians	v	Met. Police
Bromley	v	Sevenoaks
Sheppey	v	Old Dunstonians
Betteshanger	v	Medway
Dartfordians	v	Old Shootershillians
Greenwich Academicals	v	Tunbridge Wells

March 4 (Week 25)
Tunbridge Wells	v	Dartfordians
Old Shootershillians	v	Betteshanger
Medway	v	Sheppey
Old Dunstonians	v	Bromley
Sevenoaks	v	Old Elthamians
Met. Police	v	Gillingham Anchorians

March 25 (Week 28)
Gillingham Anchorians	v	Sevenoaks
Old Elthamians	v	Old Dunstonians
Bromley	v	Medway
Sheppey	v	Old Shootershillians
Betteshanger	v	Tunbrisge Wells
Dartfordians	v	Greenwich Academicals

April 8 (Week 30)
Greenwich Academicals	v	Betteshanger
Tunbridge Wells	v	Sheppey
Old Shootershillians	v	Bromley
Medway	v	Old Elthamians
Old Dunstonians	v	Gillingham Anchorians
Sevenoaks	v	Met. Police

KENT ONE

BETTESHANGER CW RFC
Ground Address: Welfare Ground, Cavell Square, Deal, Kent. Clubhouse: Welfare Club (First floor), Cowdray Square, Deal, Kent. Tel: 0304 365090
Club Secretary: MS Rickatson, 40 Mongeham Road, Great Mongeham, Deal, Kent CT14 9PQ. Tel: (H) 0304 361178
Fixtures Secretary: RJ Pinnick, 65 Courtenay Road, Dunkirk, Faversham, Kent ME13 9LH. Tel: (H) 0227 750530 Tel (W) 0227 750530
Club Colours: Red & white hoops.

BROMLEY RFC
Ground Address: Barnet Wood Road, Hayes Common, Bromley, Kent. Tel: 081 462 3430
Club Secretary: Mr A Lauder, 32 Turnpike Drive, Pratts Bottom, Orpington, Kent BR6 7SJ. Tel: (H) 0689 855004 Tel: (W) 0322 343239
Fixtures Secretary: Mr A McIntosh, 1 Gundulph Road, Bromley, Kent. Tel: (H) 081 460 8049
Club Colours: Black & amber hooped jerseys, black shorts & stockings.

DARTFORDIANS RFC
Ground Address: Bourne Road, Bexley, Kent. Tel: 0322 524176
Club Secretary: Jack Morris, 7 Irving Way, Swanley, Kent BR8 7EP. Tel: (H) 0322 669817
Fixtures Secretary: D Rapley, 11 Felhampton Road, New Eltham, London SE9. Tel: (H) 081 857 6198
Club Colours: Maroon & old gold shirts, navy shorts.

GILLINGHAM ANCHORIANS RUFC
Ground Address: Watling Street Playing Fields, off Darland Avenue, Gillingham, Kent. Tel: 0634 851495
Club Secretary: John Jennings, 49 Marshall Road, Gillingham, Kent ME8 0AW. Tel: (H) 0634 233431
Fixtures Secretary: Neil Cripps, 2 Derwent Way, Rainham, Gillingham, Kent ME8 0BX. Tel: (H) 0634 373156 Tel (W) 0322 276831
Club Colours: Purple, black & white hoops, black shorts.

GREENWICH ACADEMICALS RFC
Ground Address: Sparrows Farm Centre, University of Greenwich, Sparrows Lane, New Eltham, London SE9 2BU. Tel: 081 859 2921
Club Secretary: John Baker, 31 Willow Avenue, Swanley, Kent BR8 8AT. Tel: (H) 0322 614513
Fixtures Secretary: GD (Dusty) Miller, 85 Earlshall Road, London SE9 1PP. Tel: (H) 081 850 2794 Tel (W) 081 850 2794
Club Colours: Green with red, gold & red bands.

MEDWAY RFC
Ground Address: Priestfields Recreation Ground, Rochester, Kent ME1 3AD. Tel: 0634 847737
Club Secretary: Andy Green, 18a City Way, Rochester, Kent ME1 2AB. Tel: (H) 0634 818428
Fixtures Secretary: Jim Hillier, 9 Oxford Road, Gillingham, Kent ME7 4BP. Tel: (H) 0634 572440 Tel (W) 0322 391747
Club Colours: Scarlet & gold hoops, navy blue shorts.

MET POLICE HAYES RFC
Ground Address: Metropolitan Police, The Warren Sports Club, Croydon Road, Hayes, Kent BR2 0BN. Tel: 081 462 1266
Club Secretary: Mr Chris McHale, 18 Elm Road, Warlingham, Surrey.
Fixtures Secretary: Mr George Strachan, 244 Pickhurst Lane, West Wickham, Kent BR4 0HN. Tel: (H) 081 462 7996
Club Colours: Blue & maroon quarters, black shorts, blue & maroon hooped socks.

OLD DUNSTONIAN RFC
Ground Address: St Dunstan's Lane, Langley Park, Beckenham, Kent BR3 3SS. Tel: 081 650 1779
Club Secretary: MA Rogers, Aboyne, Pickhurst Lane, West Wickham, Kent BR4 0HN. Tel: (H) 081 462 3064

FINAL TABLE

	P	W	D	L	F	A	PD	Pts
Park House	12	10	1	1	306	77	229	21
Sevenoaks	11	9	0	2	299	103	196	18
Darfordians	12	8	1	3	286	182	104	17
Sheppey	12	7	1	4	215	150	65	15
Medway	11	7	0	4	199	144	55	14
Bromley	12	7	0	5	178	162	16	14
Old Dunstonians	12	6	0	6	283	174	109	12
Met. Police Hayes	11	5	1	5	129	147	-18	11
Betteshanger	12	5	0	7	144	259	-115	10
Thames Polytechnic	12	4	1	7	128	249	-121	9
Snowden C.W.	12	4	0	8	116	278	-162	8
New Ash Green	12	1	1	10	82	212	-130	3
Nat. West. Bank	11	0	0	11	91	319	-228	0

Tel: (W) 071 379 7383
Fixtures Secretary: PW France, 5 The Mead, West Wickham, Kent BR4 0BA. Tel: (H) 081 776 0872 Tel (W) 071 261 3368
Club Colours: Navy blue & white circlet.

OLD ELTHAMIANS RFC
Ground Address: Foxbury Avenue, Chislehurst, Kent, BR7 6HA. Tel: 081 467 14296
Club Secretary: Gareth Evinson, 23 Woodmere, Court Road, Eltham, SE9 5NT. Tel: (H) 081 850 7400 Tel: (W) 071 895 2643
Club Colours: Amber & royal blue hoops.

OLD SHOOTERSHILLIANS RFC
Ground Address: Entrance between 123 & 125 Mayday Gardens, Kidbrooke, London SE3 8NP. Tel: 081 856 1511
Club Secretary: K Bailey, 13 Linden Avenue, Dartford, Kent DA1 2RA. Tel: (H) 0322 276129 Tel: (W) 0206 43331 Fax: 0206 563788
Fixtures Secretary: I Trevett Esq, 28 Reventlow Road, New Eltham, London SE9 2DJ. Tel: (H) 081 859 0746 Tel (W) 071 514 4389
Club Colours: Red, blue, green, yellow.

SEVENOAKS RFC
Ground Address: Knole Paddock, Plymouth Drive, Sevenoaks, Kent TN13 3RP. Tel: 0732 452027
Club Secretary: John Maslin, 198 Chesterfield Drive, Sevenoaks, Kent TN13 2EH. Tel: (H) 0732 460910 Tel: (W) 071 528 1888
Fixtures Secretary: Howard Pearl, Nearly Corner, Neaversham, Nr Sevenoaks, Kent TN15 6NQ. Tel: (H) 0732 763431 Tel (W) 071 432 3292
Club Colours: Blue & gold hoops.

SHEPPEY FC
Ground Address: The Ditch, Lower Road, Minster, Sheerness, Kent. Tel: 0795 872082
Club Secretary: Mrs Linda Neal, 16 New Road, Minster, Sheerness, Kent ME12 3PX. Tel: (H) 0795 873983 Tel: (W) 0634 832160
Fixtures Secretary: Mr Gerry Lawson, 435 Minster Road, Minster, Sheerness, Kent ME12 3NS. Tel: (H) 0795 875120
Club Colours: White shirts with single red hoop, black shorts.

TUNBRIDGE WELLS RFC
Ground Address: St Marks, Frant Road, Tunbridge Wells, Kent. Tel: 0892 522748
Club Secretary: Andy Hill, 18 Lime Hill Road, Tunbridge Wells, Kent. Tel: (H) 0892 548114
Fixtures Secretary: Sue Kench, 63 Frant Road, Tunbridge Wells, Kent. Tel: (H) 0892 533397
Club Colours: Royal blue & white hoops, white shorts, royal blue socks.

LONDON & SOUTH EAST DIVISION

KENT TWO
1994-95
FIXTURES

September 17 (Week 3)
Midland Bank v Deal Wanderers
Ashford v Old Gravesendians
New Ash Green v Vigo
Sittingbourne v Folkestone
Dover v Nat. West. Bank
Snowdown C.W. v Cranbrook

September 24 (Week 4)
Deal Wanderers v Snowdon C.W.
Cranbrook v Dover
Nat. West. Bank v Sittingbourne
Folkestone v New Ash Green
Vigo v Ashford
Old Gravesendians v Whitstable

October 1 (Week 5)
Dover v Deal Wanderers
Snowdon C.W. v Midland Bank
Whitstable v Vigo
Ashford v Folkestone
New Ash Green v Nat. West. Bank
Sittingbourne v Cranbrook

October 15 (Week 7)
Midland Bank v Dover
Deal Wanderers v Sittingbourne
Cranbrook v New Ash Green
Nat. West. Bank v Ashford
Folkestone v Whitstable
Vigo v Old Gravesendians

October 22 (Week 8)
New Ash Green v Deal Wanderers
Sittingbourne v Midland Bank
Dover v Snowdown C.W.
Old Gravesendians v Folkestone
Whitstable v Nat. West. Bank
Ashford v Cranbrook

October 29 (Week X2)
Snowdown C.W. v Sittingbourne
Midland Bank v New Ash Green
Deal Wanderers v Ashford
Cranbrook v Whitstable
Nat. West. Bank v Old Gravesendians
Folkestone v Vigo

January 7 (Week 17)
Whitstable v Deal Wanderers
Ashford v Midland Bank
New Ash Green v Snowdown C.W.
Sittingbourne v Dover
Vigo v Nat. West. Bank
Old Gravesendians v Cranbrook

January 14 (Week 18)
Dover v New Ash Green
Snowdown C.W. v Ashford
Midland Bank v Whitstable
Deal Wanderers v Old Gravesendians
Cranbrook v Vigo
Nat. West. Bank v Folkestone

February 11 (Week 22)
Vigo v Deal Wanderers
Old Gravesendians v Midland Bank
Whitstable v Snowdown C.W.
Ashford v Dover
New Ash Green v Sittingbourne
Folkestone v Cranbrook

February 25 (Week 24)
Sittingbourne v Ashford
Dover v Whitstable
Snowdon C.W. v Old Gravesendians
Midland Bank v Vigo
Deal Wanderers v Folkestone
Cranbrook v Nat. West. Bank

March 4 (Week 25)
Nat. West. Bank v Deal Wanderers
Folkestone v Midland Bank
Vigo v Snowdown C.W.
Old Gravesendians v Dover
Whitstable v Sittingbourne
Ashford v New Ash Green

March 25 (Week 28)
New Ash Green v Whitstable
Sittingbourne v Old Gravesendians
Dover v Vigo
Snowdown C.W. v Folkestone
Midland Bank v Nat. West. Bank
Deal Wanderers v Cranbrook

April 8 (Week 30)
Cranbrook v Midland Bank
Nat. West. Bank v Snowdown C.W.
Folkestone v Dover
Vigo v Sittingbourne
Old Gravesendians v New Ash Green
Whitstable v Ashford

KENT TWO

ASHFORD (KENT) RFC
Ground Address:Kinneys Field, Bybrook Ground, Canterbury Road, Bybrook, Ashford, Kent. Tel: 0233 640905
Club Secretary: Sue Lat, Field Cottage, Faversham Road, Kennington, Ashford, Kent TN25 4PQ. Tel: (H) 0233 623921
Fixtures Secretary: Colin Yalden, 23 Weavers Way, Ashford, Kent TN23 2DY. Tel: (H) 0233 640905
Club Colours: Red, gold & black hoops.

CRANBROOK RFC
Ground Address:Tomlin Ground, Angley Road, Staplehurst, Kent TN17 3LB. Tel: 0580 712777
Club Secretary: David Davies, Beeches, Station Road, Staplehurst, Kent TN12 0QG. Tel: (H) 0580 891448 Tel: (W) 071 287 2777
Fixtures Secretary: R Turner, 52 Franklin Drive, Grove Green, Maidstone ME14 5SY. Tel: (H) 0622 735763 Tel (W) 071 826 0426
Club Colours: Magenta & white.

DEAL WANDERERS SPORTS CLUB RUFC
Ground Address:Western Road, Deal, Kent. Tel: 0304 365892
Club Secretary: R Dorling, 13 Halsatt Road, Deal, Kent. Tel: (H) 0304 363629
Club Colours: Blue & yellow hoops.

DOVER RFC
Ground Address:The Pavilion, Crabble Athletic Ground, Crabble Road, River, Dover, Kent. Tel: 0304 210296
Club Secretary: JD Thomas, Karma, Minnis Lane, River, Dover CT17 0PT. Tel: (H) 0304 822169
Fixtures Secretary: R Dixon, 2 Roman Way, St Margaret's a/c, Nr Dover, Kent. Tel: (H) 0304 852776
Club Colours: Dark blue & light blue hoops.

FOLKESTONE RFC
Ground Address:New Burlington Field, Bargrave, Nr Folkestone.
Club Secretary: BG Keating, Carbery, Church Hill, Hythe CT21 5DW. Tel: (H) 0303 264604 Tel: (W) 0303 850206
Fixtures Secretary: J Richards, 19 Oast Meadow, Willesborough, Ashford, Kent TN24 0AS. Tel: (H) 0233 660162 Tel (W) 0233 644095
Club Colours: Emerald green & white hoops.

MIDLAND BANK RFC
Ground Address:Lennard Road, Beckenham, Kent. Tel: 081 778 7784
Club Secretary: C Rouse, 59 Crantock Road, London SE6. Tel: (H) 081 698 4327
Fixtures Secretary: JRD Hayhow, Five Trees, 36 Holbrook Lane, Chislehurst, Kent BR7 6PF. Tel: (H) 081 467 3314 Tel (W) 071 623 9333
Club Colours: Green shirts, blue shorts. Change: Red shirts.

NAT WEST BANK RFC
Ground Address:Copers Cope Road, Lower Sydenham BR3 1NZ. Tel: 081 650 9217/4559
Club Secretary: J Longhurst, 8 Lydia Cottages, Wrotham Road, Gravesend, Kent DA11 0QE. Tel: (H) 0474 333955 Tel: (W) 071 491 4500
Fixtures Secretary: GWC Teale, 17 Queensway, Coney Hall, West Wickham, Kent BR4 9EP. Tel: (H) 081 462 9288 Tel (W) 071 726 1702
Club Colours: Light blue & dark blue hoops.

NEW ASH GREEN RFC
Ground Address:The Pavilion, New Ash Green, Kent. Tel: 0474 874660
Club Secretary: K Milner, Ash House, Ash Road, New Ash Green, Kent, DA3 9JD. Tel: (W) 0474 872746
Club Colours: Green & black quarters.

OLD GRAVESENDIANS RFC
Ground Address:Fleetway Sports Ground, Bronte View, Parrock Road, Gravesend, Kent. Tel: 0474 365503
Club Secretary: Tim Mulholland, 9 Milton Court, Gravesend, Kent, DA12 1ND. Tel: (H) 0474 325895 Tel: (W) 071 601 5222
Club Colours: Light & dark blue hoops.

SITTINGBOURNE RUFC
Ground Address:UK Paper Leisure Club, Gore Court Road, Sittingbourne, Kent. Tel: 0795 477047
Club Secretary: J Chapman, 4 Morris Court Close, Bapchild, Sittingbourne, Kent, ME9 9PL. Tel: (H) 0795 475668 Tel: (W) 0634 271681
Club Colours: Amber with single blue hoop.

SNOWDOWN COLLIERY WELFARE RFC
Ground Address:Welfare Ground, Aylesham, Canterbury, Kent. Tel: 0304 840278
Club Secretary: EJ Sullivan, 4 Burgess Road, Aylesham, Canterbury, Kent CT3 3AU. Tel: (H) 0304 840052
Fixtures Secretary: Alan Booth, 91 Milner Crescent, Aylesham, Canterbury, Kent. Tel: (H) 0304 840619
Club Colours: Red & blue hoops.

VIGO RFC
Ground Address:Swanswood Field, Harvel Road, Harvel. Tel: 0732 823830
Club Secretary: Mr N Simpson, Pitfield House, Meopham Green, Meopham, Kent DA13 0PZ. Tel: (H) 0474 812707 Tel: (W) 081 854 1331
Fixtures Secretary: John Taylor, Sandon, Burnt House Lane, Hawley, Dartford. Tel: (H) 0322 227363 Tel (W) 071 488 0733 x318
Club Colours: Red jerseys, black shorts, black stockings.

WHITSTABLE RFC
Ground Address:Church Street Playing Fields, Thanet Way, Whitstable, Kent. Tel: c/o 0227 265500
Club Secretary: Colin James, 71 Swalecliffe Court Drive, Whitstable, Kent CT5 2NF. Tel: (H) 0227 793031
Fixtures Secretary: Roger Dengate, 70 Regent Street, Whitstable, Kent CT5 1JQ. Tel: (H) 0227 264604 Tel (W) 0304 812501 x205
Club Colours: Royal blue & white hooped shirts.

FINAL TABLE

	P	W	D	L	F	A	PD	Pts
O. Shootershillians	12	10	0	2	234	63	171	20
Old Elthamians	12	10	0	2	170	65	105	16
Dover	12	7	1	4	142	108	34	15
Folkestone	11	7	0	4	136	139	-3	14
Deal	11	7	0	4	122	147	-25	14
Vigo	12	6	1	5	113	109	4	13
Cranbrook	12	5	1	6	201	146	55	11
Midland Bank	12	5	0	7	187	165	22	10
Ashford	12	4	2	6	144	129	15	10
Sittingbourne	12	3	2	7	116	141	-25	8
Bexley	12	4	0	8	110	211	-101	8
Tonbridge	11	3	1	7	120	160	-40	7
Lloyds Bank	11	1	0	10	54	266	-212	2

LONDON & SOUTH EAST DIVISION

KENT THREE
1994-95
FIXTURES

September 24 (Week 4)
Bexley   v   Aylesford
Lordswood   v   Darenth Valley
Tonbridge   v   Greenwich
Old Olavians   v   Citizens
Lloyds Bank   v   Old Williamsonians

October 1 (Week 5)
Aylesford   v   Old Olavians
Darenth Valley   v   Lloyds Bank
Greenwich   v   Lordswood
Citizens   v   Tonbridge
Bexley   v   Old Williamsonians

October 15 (Week 7)
Tonbridge   v   Aylesford
Old Olavians   v   Bexley
Old Williamsonians   v   Darenth Valley
Lordswood   v   Citizens
Lloyds Bank   v   Greenwich

October 22 (Week 8)
Bexley   v   Tonbridge
Aylesford   v   Lordswood
Citizens   v   Lloyds Bank
Old Williamsonians   v   Old Olavians
Greenwich   v   Darenth Valley

October 29 (Week X2)
Lloyds Bank   v   Aylesford
Lordswood   v   Bexley
Tonbridge   v   Old Olavians
Greenwich   v   Old Williamsonians
Darenth Valley   v   Citizens

January 14 (Week 18)
Old Olavians   v   Lordswood
Bexley   v   Lloyds Bank
Aylesford   v   Darenth Valley
Citizens   v   Greenwich
Tonbridge   v   Old Williamsonians

February 11 (Week 22)
Greenwich   v   Aylesford
Darenth Valley   v   Bexley
Lloyds Bank   v   Old Olavians
Lordswood   v   Tonbridge
Old Williamsonians   v   Citizens

February 25 (Week 24)
Tonbridge   v   Lloyds Bank
Old Olavians   v   Darenth Valley
Bexley   v   Greenwich
Aylesford   v   Citizens
Old Williamsonians   v   Lordswood

March 4 (Week 25)
Old Williamsonians   v   Aylesford
Citizens   v   Bexley
Greenwich   v   Old Olavians
Darenth Valley   v   Tonbridge
Lloyds Bank   v   Lordswood

KENT THREE

AYLESFORD RFC
Ground Address:Adj. Ferry Fields, Hall Road, Aylesford.
Club Secretary: Kevin D Burbidge, 77 Holsborough Road,
Snodland, Kent ME6 5PA. Tel: (H) 0634 Tel: (W) 0474
337571
Fixtures Secretary: David Enston, 47 Hornbeam Close,
Larkfield, Aylesford, Kent ME20 6LZ. Tel: (H) 0732
842666
Club Colours: Red shirts, black shorts, red socks.
BEXLEY RFC
Ground Address:Hall Place Park, Bourne Road, Bexley,
Kent.
Club Secretary: Peter Butler, 194 Claremont Road,
Hextable, Kent BR8 7QU. Tel: (H) 0322 664389
Fixtures Secretary: James Butler, 39 Baldwyns Road,
Bexley, Kent. Tel: (H) 0322 522693
Club Colours: Royal blue & white hooped shirts, blue
shorts, blue socks with white tops.
CITIZENS RFC
Ground Address:ULC Athletic Ground, Perry Street,
Chislehurst, Kent. Tel: 081 467 3859
Club Secretary: CR Southgate, Suny Bank, Kingsland,
Leominster, Herefordshire HR6 9SE. Tel: (H) 0568 708010
Tel: (W) 0568 708050
Fixtures Secretary: RJ Mannell, 281 Green Lane, London
SE9 3TB. Tel: (H) 081 857 3057
Club Colours: Black with maroon & white hoops.
DARENTH VALLEY RFC
Ground Address:Leigh City Technology College, Green
Street, Green Road, Dartford, Kent DA1 1QE. Tel: 0322
290801
Club Secretary: Ashley Rivett, 9 St Martins Drive,
Eynsford, Kent DA4 0EY. Tel: (H) 0322 862387
Fixtures Secretary: Stuart Sullivan, 18 Egerton Avenue,
Hextable, Kent BR8 7LQ. Tel: (H) 0322 667218 Tel (W)
071 600 0505
Club Colours: Black shirts with white V, black shorts.
GREENWICH RFC
Ground Address:The Pavilion, Old Mill Road, Plumstead,
London, SE18. Tel: 081 854 8637
Club Secretary: A J Smith, 41 Ashden Drive, Dartford,
Kent, DA1 3L2. Tel: (H) 0322 222832
Club Colours: Red & black quarters, black shorts.
LLOYDS BANK RFC
Ground Address:Lloyds Bank Sports Club, Copers Cope
Road, New Beckenham, Kent. Tel: 081 658 3818
Club Secretary: Bob Brazier, 2 Crushes Close, Hutton,
Brentwood, Essex CM13 1PB. Tel: (H) 0277 213626 Tel:
(W) 0277 227272
Fixtures Secretary: Alan Stow, 4 Silkham Road, Oxted,
Surrey RH8 0NP. Tel: (H) 0883 717565
Club Colours: White with magenta & black horizontal
hoops.
LORDSWOOD RFC
Ground Address:Martin Grove, North Dare Way,
Lordswood, Chatham, Kent. Tel: 0634 669138
Club Secretary: Huw thomas, 97 Ballens Road,
Lordswood. Tel: (H) 0634 867045
Fixtures Secretary: Andy Foley, 10 Bankside, Chatham,
Kent ME5 0BY. Tel: (H) 0634 404664
Club Colours: Amber & black. Change: Red.
OLD OLAVIANS RFC
Ground Address:St Olave's School, Gollington Lane,
Orpington, Kent. Tel: 0689 830744
Club Secretary: S R Gill, 19 Forrwich Close, Orpington,
Kent, BR6 OTT. Tel: (H) 0689 836858 Tel: (W)
Club Colours: Purple, black & white

FINAL TABLE

	P	W	D	L	F	A	PD	Pts
O. Gravesendians	9	7	0	2	165	86	79	14
Whitstable	9	7	0	2	115	83	32	14
Darenth Valley	9	6	0	3	135	95	40	12
Old Williamsonians	9	5	0	4	158	85	73	10
Linton	9	5	0	4	127	102	25	10
Lordswood	9	4	0	5	85	119	-34	8
Citizens	9	4	0	5	67	102	-35	8
Kent Police	9	3	0	6	119	96	23	6
S.T.C. Footscray	9	3	0	6	47	147	-100	6
Orpington	9	1	0	8	72	175	-103	2

OLD WILLIAMSONIAN RFC
Ground Address:Sir Joseph Williamson's Mathematical
School, Maidstone Road, Rochester. Tel: 0634 842883
Club Secretary: Simon Riddiford, 72 Castle Avenue,
Rochester, Kent ME1 2DY. Tel: (H) 0634 408511
Fixtures Secretary: Graham Richards, 76 Valley View
Road, Rochester. Tel: (H) 0634 848700
Club Colours: Navy blue with single gold hoop.
TONBRIDGE RFC
Ground Address:The Clubhouse, Avebury Avenue,
Tonbridge, Kent. Tel: 0732 350067
Club Secretary: James Lark, 7 Newton Avenue,
Tonbridge, Kent, TN10 4RP. Tel: (H) 0732 354581 Tel:
(W) 0732 368326
Club Colours: Chocolate & old gold hoops.

LONDON & SOUTH EAST DIVISION

KENT FOUR
1994-95
FIXTURES

March 25 (Week 28)
Kent Police v Faversham
Westerham v Edenbridge
Footscray v Orpington

September 24 (Week 4)
Westerham v Kent Police
Footscray v Edenbridge
Faversham v Orpington

October 1 (Week 5)
Kent Police v Footscray
Westerham v Faversham
Edenbridge v Orpington

October 15 (Week 7)
Footscray v Westerham
Orpington v Kent Police
Faversham v Edenbridge

October 22 (Week 8)
Kent Police v Edenbridge
Westerham v Orpington
Footscray v Faversham

October 29 (Week X2)
Orpington v Footscray
Edenbridge v Westerham
Faversham v Kent Police

January 14 (Week 18)
Kent Police v Westerham
Edenbridge v Footscray
Orpington v Faversham

February 11 (Week 22)
Orpington v Edenbridge
Footscray v Kent Police
Faversham v Westerham

February 25 (Week 24)
Edenbridge v Faversham
Westerham v Footscray
Kent Police v Orpington

March 4 (Week 25)
Orpington v Westerham
Faversham v Footscray
Edenbridge v Kent Police

KENT FOUR

EDENBRIDGE
Ground Address: The Recreation Ground, Lingfield Road, Edenbridge, Kent. Tel: 0732 862435
Club Secretary: Ron Mitchell, Amberly, Crouch House Road, Edenbridge, Kent TN8 5EE. Tel: (H) 0732 863385 Tel: (W) 0732 863385
Fixtures Secretary: Ron Mitchell, Amberly, Crouch House Road, Edenbridge, Kent TN8 5EE. Tel: (H) 0732 863385 Tel (W) 0732 863385
Club Colours: Black & amber hoops.

FAVERSHAM RUFC
Ground Address: The Lodge, Faversham Recreation Ground, Faversham, Kent ME13 8HA. Tel: Pat Rowan, 14 Abbey Street, Faversham, Kent ME13 7BE
Club Secretary: 0795 590252. Tel: (H) 0634 577555 Tel: (W) 0634 577555
Fixtures Secretary: Neil Vining, 120 Whitstable Road, Faversham, Kent ME13 8BT. Tel: (H) 0795 535956
Club Colours: Sky blue & white.

FOOTSCRAY RUFC (FORMERLY STC FOOTSCRAY)
Club Secretary: Stephen Roberts, 279 Burnt Oak Lane, Sidcup, Kent DA15 8LR. Tel: (H) 091 302 7141 Tel: (W) 0753 679253
Fixtures Secretary: Tony Codd, 74 Felthampton Road, New Eltham, London SE9 3NX. Tel: (H) 081 857 6040 Tel (W) 071 832 5484
Club Colours: Blue & gold hoops.

KENT POLICE RUFC
Ground Address: Police Headquarters, Sutton Road, Maidstone (A299 out of Maidstone twon centre, fork left along A274, police HQ 1.5 miles on right). Tel: 0622 690690
Club Secretary: PC Dave Greenwood, Traffic Central, London Road, Aylesford, Kent. Tel: (H) 0634 714029 Tel: (W) 0622 608166
Fixtures Secretary: PC Dave Greenwood, Traffic Central, London Road, Aylesford, Kent. Tel: (H) 0634 714029 Tel (W) 0622 608166
Club Colours: Red, blue & white hoops.

ORPINGTON RFC
Ground Address: Hoblingwell Wood, Leesons Way, St Pauls Cray, Orpington, Kent BR5 2QB. Tel: 0689 823913
Club Secretary: Ken Hall, The Lodge, ORFC, Leesons Way, St Pauls Cray, Orpington, Kent BR5 2QB. Tel: (H) 0689 896262 Tel: (W) 0689 823913
Fixtures Secretary: Les Whittingham, 246 Bexley Road, Eltham, London SE9 2PJ. Tel: (H) 081 850 8004 (after 2pm)
Club Colours: Black & amber hoops.

WESTERHAM RFC
Ground Address: King George Playing Fields, Westerham, Kent.
Club Secretary: S Richardson, 44 Pennycroft, Off Pixton Way, Forestdale, CR0 9LL. Tel: (H) 081 651 4302 Tel: (W) 081 654 3181
Club Colours: Black & white quarters.

FINAL TABLE

	P	W	D	L	F	A	PD	Pts
Old Olvanians	10	9	0	1	362	44	318	18
Greenwich	10	8	0	2	239	56	183	16
Edenbridge	10	6	0	4	148	77	71	12
Faversham	10	4	0	6	61	131	-70	8
Westerham	10	2	0	8	23	291	-268	4
Centurians	10	1	0	9	54	288	-234	2

LONDON & SOUTH EAST DIVISION

SUSSEX ONE
1994-95
FIXTURES

January 7 (Week 17)
Ditchling v Uckfield
Crawley v Hastings & Bexhill
Eastbourne v Burgess Hill
Old Brightonians v Bognor
Hove v Seaford
Crowborough v Pulborough

September 17 (Week 3)
Hastings & Bexhill v Uckfield
Crawley v Crowborough
Eastbourne v Hove
Old Brightonians v Sun Alliance, Horsham
Bognor v Seaford
Burgess Hill v Pulborough

January 14 (Week 18)
Bognor v Eastbourne
Burgess Hill v Crawley
Hastings & Bexhill v Ditchling
Uckfield v Crowborough
Pulborough v Hove
Seaford v Sun Alliance, Horsham

September 24 (Week 4)
Uckfield v Burgess Hill
Pulborough v Bognor
Seaford v Old Brightonians
Sun Alliance, Horsham v Eastbourne
Hove v Crawley
Crowborough v Ditchling

February 11 (Week 22)
Hove v Uckfield
Crowborough v Hastings & Bexhill
Ditchling v Burgess Hill
Crawley v Bognor
Eastbourne v Old Brightonians
Sun Alliance, Horsham v Pulborough

October 1 (Week 5)
Bognor v Uckfield
Burgess Hill v Hastings & Bexhill
Ditchling v Hove
Crawley v Sun Alliance, Horsham
Eastbourne v Seaford
Old Brightonians v Pulborough

February 25 (Week 24)
Old Brightonians v Crawley
Bognor v Ditchling
Burgess Hill v Crowborough
Hastings & Bexhill v Hove
Uckfield v Sun Alliance, Horsham
Pulborough v Seaford

October 15 (Week 7)
Hastings & Bexhill v Bognor
Uckfield v Old Brightonians
Pulborough v Eastbourne
Seaford v Crawley
Sun Alliance, Horsham v Ditchling
Hove v Crowborough

March 4 (Week 25)
Seaford v Uckfield
Sun Alliance, Horsham v Hastings & Bexhill
Hove v Burgess Hill
Crowborough v Bognor
Ditchling v Old Brightonians
Crawley v Eastbourne

October 22 (Week 8)
Eastbourne v Uckfield
Old Brightonians v Hastings & Bexhill
Bognor v Burgess Hill
Crowborough v Sun Alliance, Horsham
Ditchling v Seaford
Crawley v Pulborough

March 25 (Week 28)
Eastbourne v Ditchling
Old Brightonians v Crowborough
Bognor v Hove
Burgess Hill v Sun Alliance, Horsham
Hastings & Bexhill v Seaford
Uckfield v Pulborough

October 29 (Week X2)
Burgess Hill v Old Brightonians
Hastings & Bexhill v Eastbourne
Uckfield v Crawley
Pulborough v Ditchling
Seaford v Crowborough
Sun Alliance, Horsham v Hove

April 8 (Week 30)
Pulborough v Hastings & Bexhill
Seaford v Burgess Hill
Sun Alliance, Horsham v Bognor
Hove v Old Brightonians
Crowborough v Eastbourne
Ditchling v Crawley

SUSSEX ONE

BOGNOR RFC
Ground Address:Hawthorn Recreation Ground, Hampshire Avenue, Bognor Regis, West Sussex PO21 5JY.
Club Secretary: Guy Tompkins, 11 Gilwynes, Aldwick Fields, Bognor Regis, West sussex. Tel: (H) 0243 868643 Tel: (W) 0903 239084
Fixtures Secretary: Dean Dewey, 39 Carlton Avenue, Rose Green, Bognor Regis. Tel: (H) 0243 266185
Club Colours: Purple, green & white hoops, black shorts, green socks.

BURGESS HILL RFC
Ground Address:Poveys Close, Burgess Hill, West Sussex RH15 9TA. Tel: 0444 232221
Club Secretary: M J Bushell Esq, 4 Kirdford Close, Burgess Hill, West Sussex RH15 0BW. Tel: (H) 0444 246750 Tel: (W) 0273 440420
Fixtures Secretary: R Packham Esq, 5 Condor Way, Burgess Hill, West Sussex RH15 9QB. Tel: (H) 0444 235162 Tel (W) 081 668 1500
Club Colours: All black. Change: Black & yellow.

CRAWLEY RFC
Ground Address:Willoughby Field, 1 Field Avenue, Crawley, Sussex. Tel: 0293 533995
Club Secretary: Ray Lloyd, 105 Gales Drive, Three Bridges, Crawley, Sussex, RH10 1QD. Tel: (H) 0243 536664 Tel: (W) 071 865 5723
Club Colours: Maroon & blue.

CROWBOROUGH RFC
Ground Address:Steel Cross, Crowborough, East Sussex. Tel: 0892 654832
Club Secretary: Gavin Tyler, 109 Fermor Way, Crowborough, East Sussex TN6 3BH. Tel: (H) 0892 665153 Tel: (W) 0892 515121
Fixtures Secretary: John Gibb, 42 Belvedere Gardens, Crowborough, East Sussex TN6 2LS. Tel: (H) 0892 667984
Club Colours: Cherry with white hoops.

DITCHLING
Ground Address:The Playing Fields, Lewes Road, Ditchling, Sussex. Tel: 0273 843423
Club Secretary: Justin Wallden, 10 Station Road, Burgess Hill, West Sussex RH15 9DQ. Tel: (H) 0444 239347 Tel: (W) 0444235664
Fixtures Secretary: Vernon Atkinson, 19 Wolstonbury Court, Burgess Hill, West Sussex RH15 9DP. Tel: (H) 0444 233249 Tel (W) 081 681 5500
Club Colours: Bottle green shirts, white shorts, green socks.

EASTBOURNE RFC
Ground Address:Park Avenue, Mapden Park, Eastbourne, East Sussex BN22 7QN. Tel: 0323 503076
Club Secretary: David Johnson, 11 The Hoo, Church Street, Willingdon, Eastbourne. Tel: (H) 0323 506489
Fixtures Secretary: Mark Westlake, 3 The Game Lodge, Letheren Place, Eastbourne BN21 1HL. Tel: (H) 0323 410786 Tel (W) 0273 606766 x33852
Club Colours: Blue & yellow hoops.

HASTINGS & BEXHILL RFC
Ground Address:The Polegrove, Brockley Road, Bexhill-on-Sea. Tel: 0424 210224
Club Secretary: R W Ellis, 24 Cranston Avenue, Bexhill-on-Sea, East Sussex, TN39 3QD. Tel: (H) 0424 731486 Tel: (W) 0424 439888
Club Colours: Blue & white hoops.

HOVE FC
Ground Address:The New Pavilion, Hove Park, Hove, East Sussex. Tel: 0273 505103
Club Secretary: R Griffin Esq, 117 Valley Drive, Withdean, Brighton, East Sussex. Tel: (H) 0273 504190
Fixtures Secretary: Mike Richardson, 6 Wayside, Westdene, Brighton, East Sussex BN1 5HL. Tel: (H) 0273

FINAL TABLE

	P	W	D	L	F	A	PD	Pts
Heathfld & Waldren	11	10	1	0	373	41	332	21
Uckfield	11	10	0	1	216	74	142	20
Crawley	11	8	1	2	225	71	154	17
Bognor	11	8	0	3	204	142	62	16
Hastings & Bexhill	11	7	0	4	244	143	101	14
Seaford	11	5	0	6	122	174	-52	10
Burgess Hill	11	4	0	7	143	236	-93	8
Eastbourne	11	3	0	8	141	173	-32	6
Crowborough	11	3	0	8	112	195	-83	6
Ditchling	11	3	0	8	92	288	-196	6
Old Brightonians	11	2	0	9	87	199	-112	4
B.A. Wingspan	11	2	0	9	71	294	-223	4

500512 Tel (W) 081 644 4388
Club Colours: Maroon & sky blue hoops.

OLD BRIGHTONIAN RFC
Ground Address:c/o Brighton Rugby Football Club, The Club House, Water Hall, Mill Road, Patcham, Brighton, Sussex BN1 8ZD. Tel: 0273 562729
Club Secretary: CD Loadsman, 20 Meadow Close, Hove, Sussex. Tel: (H) 0273 552988 Tel: (W) 0273 736000
Fixtures Secretary: P Rumney, 17 Benett Drive, Hove, Sussex3 BN3 6PL. Tel: (H) 0273 504981
Club Colours: Light blue, magenta & navy hoops.

PULBOROUGH RFC
Ground Address:Sports & Social Club, Rectory Lane, Pulborough, West Sussex. Tel: 0798 873020
Club Secretary: Chaz Trenam, 126 Flansham Lane, Felpham, Bognor Regis, West Sussex PO22 6BB. Tel: (H) 0243 584924 Tel: (W) 071 377 7000 x2950
Fixtures Secretary: Michael Ford, 11 Arun Prospect, Station Road, Pulborough RH29 1AW. Tel: (H) 0798 875452
Club Colours: Black & white hoops.

SEAFORD RFC
Ground Address:Salts Recreation Ground, The Esplanade, Seaford, Sussex. Tel: 0323 892355
Club Secretary: EA Pugh, Shottery, 19 Chyngton Road, Seaford, Sussex BN25 4HL. Tel: (H) 0323 892020
Fixtures Secretary: R Ungoed, 5 The Ridgeway, Seaford, Sussex. Tel: (H) 0323 893688
Club Colours: Scarlet shirts, navy shorts.

SUN ALLIANCE HORSHAM RFC
Ground Address:Meadowlands, North Heath Lane, Horsham, West Sussex. Tel: 0403 253814
Club Secretary: BR Lewis Esq, 2 Wain End, Horsham, West Sussex RH12 5TQ. Tel: (H) 0403 266267
Fixtures Secretary: S West Esq, 31 Redford Avenue, Horsham, West Sussex RH12 2HW. Tel: (H) 0403 269836 Tel (W) 0403 232323 x4285
Club Colours: Yellow & blue.

UCKFIELD RFC
Ground Address:Hempstead Fields, Manor Park, Uckfield, Sussex. Tel: 0825 768956
Club Secretary: Jerry Miller, 8 Streele View, Uckfield, Sussex TN22 1UG. Tel: (H) 0825 767861 Tel: (W) 0892 503143
Fixtures Secretary: Mrs Maureen Poole, Pentlands, 9 Keld Avenue, Uckfield, Sussex. Tel: (H) 0825 761151
Club Colours: Amber & purple.

LONDON & SOUTH EAST DIVISION

SUSSEX TWO
1994-95
FIXTURES

March 25 (Week 28)
Plumpton   v   Sussex Police
Newick   v   B.A. Wingspan
St. Francis   v   Hellingly

September 24 (Week 4)
Newick   v   Plumpton
St. Francis   v   B.A. Wingspan
Sussex Police   v   Hellingly

October 1 (Week 5)
Plumpton   v   St. Francis
Newick   v   Sussex Police
B.A. Wingspan   v   Hellingly

October 15 (Week 7)
St. Francis   v   Newick
Hellingly   v   Plumpton
Sussex Police   v   B.A. Wingspan

October 22 (Week 8)
Plumpton   v   B.A. Wingspan
Newick   v   Hellingly
St. Francis   v   Sussex Police

October 29 (Week X2)
Hellingly   v   St. Francis
B.A. Wingspan   v   Newick
Sussex Police   v   Plumpton

January 14 (Week 18)
Plumpton   v   Newick
B.A. Wingspan   v   St. Francis
Hellingly   v   Sussex Police

February 11 (Week 22)
Hellingly   v   B.A. Wingspan
St. Francis   v   Plumpton
Sussex Police   v   Newick

February 25 (Week 24)
B.A. Wingspan   v   Sussex Police
Newick   v   St. Francis
Plumpton   v   Hellingly

March 4 (Week 25)
Hellingly   v   Newick
Sussex Police   v   St. Francis
B.A. Wingspan   v   Plumpton

SUSSEX TWO

BRITISH AIRWAYS (WINGSPAN) RUFC
Ground Address: Bewbush Leisure Centre, Breezehurst Drive, Bewbush, Crawley. Tel: 0293 546477
Club Secretary: Keri Matthews, 3 Comptons Court, Comptons Lane, Horsham RH13 6TA. Tel: (H) 0403 272865
Fixtures Secretary: Harry Townsend, 6 Manor Road, East Grinstead, Sussex RH19 1LR. Tel: (H) 0342 322508 Tel (W) 0342 322508
Club Colours: Red, white & blue.

HELLINGLY RFC
Ground Address: Hellingly Sports Club, Horsebridge, Nr Hailsham, East Sussex.
Club Secretary: Ross Hollister, 17 Sycamore Drive, Hailsham, East Sussex BN27 3TT. Tel: (H) 0323 840756
Fixtures Secretary: Tim Bowler, Brook House, Lower Horsebridge, Hailsham, East Sussex. Tel: (H) 0323 845838
Club Colours: Amber & black.

NEWICK RFC
Ground Address: Newick Recreational Ground, George V Recreation Ground, Allington Road, Newick, East Sussex. Tel: 0825 773293
Club Secretary: Judy Whiteman, 29 Hatmers Hill, Newick, East Sussex, BN8 4QU. Tel: (H) 0825 723615 Tel: (W) 0825 764829
Club Colours: Maroon & white hoops.

PLUMPTON RFC
Ground Address: Plumpton Racecourse, Plumpton, West Sussex.
Club Secretary: Mr C Woodward, 2 Monks Way, Lewes, West Sussex BN7 2EX. Tel: (H) 0273 890202
Fixtures Secretary: Mr Graham Glindinning, 57 Carlyle Avenue, Brighton BN2 4DR. Tel: (H) 0273 620585
Club Colours: Maroon & gold.

ST FRANCIS RFC
Ground Address: Broadfield Playing Fields, Broadfield, Crawley, Sussex.
Club Secretary: League contact: JW Wright, 220 Weald Drive, Furnach Green, Crawley, West Sussex RH10 6NJ. Tel: (H) 0293 529065
Fixtures Secretary: Vince McGahan, 24 Cobbles Crescent, Northgate, Crawley, West Sussex. Tel: (H) 0293 547194 Tel (W) 0293 503278
Club Colours: Black with a blue & white hoop.

SUSSEX POLICE RFC
Ground Address: Waterhall Playing Fields, Waterhall Road, Patcham, Brighton, Sussex BN1 8YR. Tel: 0273 562729
Club Secretary: Dc P Johnson, Police Station, Kingsham Road, Chichester, Sussex PO19 2AD. Tel: (H) 0243 267819 Tel: (W) 0243 536733 x20252
Fixtures Secretary: Ps C Gale, PSU Department, Police Headquarters, Malling House, Lewes, Sussex. Tel (W) 0273 475432 x52305
Club Colours: Dark blue shirts & shorts. Change: Blue & gold quartered shirts.

FINAL TABLE

	P	W	D	L	F	A	PD	Pts
Pulborough	7	7	0	0	166	42	124	14
Sunallon	7	6	0	1	173	51	122	12
St Francis	7	5	0	2	95	62	33	10
Hellingly	7	4	0	3	134	84	50	8
Sussex Police	7	2	0	5	75	125	-50	4
Newick	7	2	0	5	82	144	-62	4
lumpton	7	2	0	5	53	129	-76	4
Midhurst	7	0	0	7	44	185	-141	0

LONDON & SOUTH EAST DIVISION

SUSSEX THREE
1994-95
FIXTURES

March 25 (Week 28)
Arun v Shoreham
Gatwick Handling v Rye
Midhurst v Robertsbridge

September 24 (Week 4)
Gatwick Handling v Arun
Midhurst v Rye
Shoreham v Robertsbridge

October 1 (Week 5)
Arun v Midhurst
Gatwick Handling v Shoreham
Rye v Robertsbridge

October 15 (Week 7)
Midhurst v Gatwick Handling
Robertsbridge v Arun
Shoreham v Rye

October 22 (Week 8)
Arun v Rye
Gatwick Handling v Robertsbridge
Midhurst v Shoreham

October 29 (Week X2)
Robertsbridge v Midhurst
Rye v Gatwick Handling
Shoreham v Arun

January 14 (Week 18)
Arun v Gatwick Handling
Rye v Midhurst
Robertsbridge v Shoreham

February 11 (Week 22)
Robertsbridge v Rye
Midhurst v Arun
Shoreham v Gatwick Handling

February 25 (Week 24)
Rye v Shoreham
Gatwick Handling v Midhurst
Arun v Robertsbridge

March 4 (Week 25)
Robertsbridge v Gatwick Handling
Shoreham v Midhurst
Rye v Arun

SUSSEX THREE

ARUN RUFC
Ground Address: Littlehampton School, Hill Road,
Littlehampton, Sussex. Tel: 0903 713944
Club Secretary: Paul Best, 9 St Mary's Close,
Littlehampton, Sussex BA17 5PZ. Tel: (H) 0903 723969
Fixtures Secretary: Neil Cousine, 16 Trinity Way,
Littlehampton. Tel: (H) 0903 713756
Club Colours: Red, navy blue & white quarters
GATWICK HANDLING RUFC
Ground Address: Willoughby Fields, Ifield Avenue,
Crawley.
Club Secretary: Jill Coomber, 2 Warnham Road,
Broadbridge Heath, Horsham, West Sussex, RH12 3JZ.
Tel: (H) 0403 257527 Tel: (W) 0293 502855
Fixtures Secretary: Ruth Barnes, 25 Victoria Close,
Burgesshill, West Sussex, RH15 9QS. Tel: (H) 0444
233421 Tel (W) 0293 502548
Club Colours: Black and red trim.
MIDHURST RFC
Ground Address: The Sports Pavilion, Cowdray Ruins,
Midhurst, West Sussex. Tel: 0730 816658
Club Secretary: Simon Flint, Broadoak, Chichester Road,
Midhurst, West Sussex GU29 9PF. Tel: (H) 0730 816465
Tel: (W) 081 390 1144
Fixtures Secretary: Simon Fay, Bradshaws Barn, Bepton
Road, Bepton, Midhurst, West Sussex.
Club Colours: Yellow with a blue hoop.
ROBERTSBRIDGE RUFC
Ground Address: Robertsbridge Community College,
Knelle Rd, Robertsbridge, East Sussex. Tel: 0580 880360
Club Secretary: M Eldridge, 36 Old Harrow Rd, St
Leonards o/s, East Sussex. Tel: (H) 0424 427933 Tel: (W)
0424 853481
Fixtures Secretary: G Vincent, Upper Maisonette, 120
Braybrook Rd, St Leonards o/s, East Sussex. Tel: (H) 0424
438984 Tel (W) 0424 853481
Club Colours: Blue/black quarters.
RYE RFC
Ground Address: New Road, Rye, East Sussex.
Club Secretary: J Bowen, 15 Southundercliff, Rye, East
Sussex TN31 7HN. Tel: (H) 0797 226597 Tel: (W) 0850
598358
Fixtures Secretary: W Sherwood, 5 Pottingfield Road,
Rye, East Sussex. Tel: (H) 0797 226714
Club Colours: Red & white quarters.
SHOREHAM RFC
Ground Address: Kings Manor School, Kingston Lane,
Shoreham.
Club Secretary: Ron Beal, 20 St Giles Close, Shoreham
BN43 6GR. Tel: (H) 0273 884827 Tel: (W) 0273 624242
Fixtures Secretary: Peter Spruce, Flat 13, Seabrook Court,
Cecil Road, Lancing BN15 8HS. Tel: (H) 0903 756306 Tel
(W) 0903 509669
Club Colours: Amber & bottle green quarters.

LONDON & SOUTH EAST DIVISION

LONDON THREE
SOUTH WEST
1994-95 FIXTURES

September 17 (Week 3)
Old Emanuel v Guy's Hospital
Eastleigh v Wimbledon
Alton v Purley
Old Walcountians v Old Guildfordians
K.C.S. Old Boys v Gosport
Cranleigh v Warlington

September 24 (Week 4)
Guy's Hospital v Cranleigh
Warlingham v K.C.S. Old Boys
Gosport v Old Walcountians
Old Guildfordians v Alton
Purley v Eastleigh
Wimbledon v Southampton

October 1 (Week 5)
K.C.S. Old Boys v Guy's Hospital
Cranleigh v Old Emanuel
Southampton v Purley
Eastleigh v Old Guildfordians
Alton v Gosport
Old Walcountians v Warlingham

October 15 (Week 7)
Old Emanuel v K.C.S. Old Boys
Guy's Hospital v Old Walcountians
Warlingham v Alton
Gosport v Eastleigh
Old Guildfordians v Southampton
Purley v Wimbledon

October 22 (Week 8)
Alton v Guy's Hospital
Old Walcountians v Old Emanuel
K.C.S. Old Boys v Cranleigh
Wimbledon v Old Guildfordians
Southampton v Gosport
Eastleigh v Warlington

October 29 (Week X2)
Cranleigh v Old Walcountians
Old Emanuel v Alton
Guy's Hospital v Eastleigh
Warlingham v Southampton
Gosport v Wimbledon
Old Guildfordians v Purley

January 7 (Week 17)
Southampton v Guy's Hospital
Eastleigh v Old Emanuel
Alton v Cranleigh
Old Walcountians v K.C.S. Old Boys
Purley v Gosport
Wimbledon v Warlington

January 14 (Week 18)
K.C.S. Old Boys v Alton
Cranleigh v Eastleigh
Old Emanuel v Southampton
Guy's Hospital v Wimbledon
Warlingham v Purley
Gosport v Old Guildfordians

February 11 (Week 22)
Purley v Guy's Hospital
Wimbledon v Old Emanuel
Southampton v Cranleigh
Eastleigh v K.C.S. Old Boys
Alton v Old Walcountians
Old Guildfordians v Warlingham

February 25 (Week 24)
Old Walcountians v Eastleigh
K.C.S. Old Boys v Southampton
Cranleigh v Wimbledon
Old Emanuel v Purley
Guy's Hospital v Old Guildfordians
Warlingham v Gosport

March 4 (Week 25)
Gosport v Guy's Hospital
Old Guildfordians v Old Emanuel
Purley v Cranleigh
Wimbledon v K.C.S. Old Boys
Southampton v Old Walcountians
Eastleigh v Alton

March 25 (Week 28)
Alton v Southampton
Old Walcountians v Wimbledon
K.C.S. Old Boys v Purley
Cranleigh v Old Guildfordians
Old Emanuel v Gosport
Guy's Hospital v Warlingham

April 8 (Week 30)
Warlingham v Old Emanuel
Gosport v Cranleigh
Old Guildfordians v K.C.S. Old Boys
Purley v Old Walcountians
Wimbledon v Alton
Southampton v Eastleigh

LONDON THREE SOUTH WEST

ALTON RFC
Ground Address:Anstey Park, Anstey Lane, Alton, Hants.
Tel: 0420 82076
Club Secretary: Jerry Pugh, 8 Silver Birch Close, Liss,
Hants, GU33 7HP. Tel: (H) 0730 895248 Tel: (W) 0730
894638
Fixtures Secretary: Martin Simpson, 10 Gauvain Close,
Alton, Hants, GU34 2SB. Tel: (H) 0420 86880
Club Colours: Red shirts, black shorts.

CRANLEIGH RFC
Ground Address:Wildwood Lane, Cranleigh, Surrey. Tel:
0483 275843
Club Secretary: Mrs I Spong, Millook, New Park Road,
Cranleigh, Surrey GU6 7HJ. Tel: (H) 0483 272700
Fixtures Secretary: Mr D Coward, 2 Dover Court,
Cranleigh, Surrey GU6 7EZ. Tel: (H) 0483 271247
Club Colours: Navy & red quarters.

EASTLEIGH RFC
Ground Address:Bishopstoke Road, Eastleigh, Hants. Tel:
0703 641312
Club Secretary: Brian Booth, 72 Station Road, Netley
Abbey, Southampton SO3 5AF. Tel: (H) 0703 452718 Tel:
(W) 0256 51658
Fixtures Secretary: John Sneezum, Bursledon Lodge,
Salterns Lane, Old Bursledon, Southampton SO3 8DH. Tel:
(H) 0703 402286 Tel (W) 0703 616941
Club Colours: Black, amber & red.

GOSPORT & FAREHAM RFC
Ground Address:Gosport Park, Dolphin Crescent,
Gosport, Hampshire PO12 2HQ. Tel: 0705 589852
Club Secretary: Mrs Susan Pazdzierski, 18 Palmerston
Avenue, Fareham, Hants PO16 7DP. Tel: (H) 0329 232173
Fixtures Secretary: Mr Peter Tomlinson, 18 Freemantle
Road, Gosport PO12 4RD. Tel: (H) 0705 589661
Club Colours: Royal blue & old gold.

GUY'S HOSPITAL RFC
Ground Address:Honor Oak Park, London SE23 1NW.
Tel: 081 690 1612
Club Secretary: League contact: Graham Bevan, 49
Lockyer Estate, Kipling Street, London SE1 3RX. Tel: (H)
071 403 6906
Fixtures Secretary: Graham Bevan, 49 Lockyer Estate,
Kipling Street, London SE1 3RX. Tel: (H) 071 403 6906

KCS OLD BOYS RFC
Ground Address:Arthur Road, Motspur Park, Surrey KT3
6LX. Tel: 081 336 2512
Club Secretary: Noel M Crockford, 78 Claygate Lane,
Hinchley Wood, Surrey KT10 0BJ. Tel: (H) 081 398 7474
Tel: (W) 081 390 0483
Fixtures Secretary: Andy Todd, 5 Wendover Drive, New
Malden, Surrey KT3 5RN. Tel: (H) 081 942 0048 Tel (W)
081 395 3808
Club Colours: Red, blue & old gold hoops.

OLD EMANUEL RFC
Ground Address:Blagdon House, Blagdon Lane, New
Malden, Surrey KT3 4PU. Tel: 081 942 3857
Club Secretary: Ian Blair, 28 Hunters Road, Chessington,
Surrey KT9 1RU. Tel: (H) 081 397 1272 Tel: (W) 071 872
3349
Fixtures Secretary: John Monkhouse, 26 Oriental Road,
Woking, Surrey GU22 7AH. Tel: (H) 04837 64114 Tel (W)
09323 55144
Club Colours: White.

OLD GUILDFORDIANS RFC
Ground Address:The Pavilion, Stoke Park, London Road,
Guildford, Surrey. Tel: 0483 300752
Club Secretary: DJ Pym, Flat 3, 4 Guildown Road,
Guildford, Surrey GU2 5EN. Tel: (H) 0483 69953 Tel: (W)
0483 403534
Fixtures Secretary: G Hills, 28 Bannister Close, Wheeler
Lane, Witley, Surrey GU8 5RR. Tel: (H) 0428 684337 Tel

FINAL TABLE

	P	W	D	L	F	A	PD	Pts
Portsmouth	12	9	2	1	224	104	120	20
Old Guildfordians	12	8	1	3	223	117	106	17
Alton	12	8	1	3	230	139	91	17
Guy's Hospital	12	8	0	4	166	124	42	16
Purley	12	8	0	4	146	144	2	16
Warlingham	12	6	2	4	176	136	40	14
Old Walcountians	12	5	4	3	180	148	32	14
Old Emanuel	12	5	1	6	241	207	34	11
Eastleigh	12	4	0	8	99	210	-111	8
Southampton	12	3	0	9	103	210	-107	6
Cranleigh	12	2	0	10	110	244	-134	4
Winchester	12	2	1	9	170	243	-73	3
United Serv Por	12	4	0	8	132	174	-42	2

(W) 071 234 9000
Club Colours: Green with narrow red & white hoops,
green shorts, red socks.

OLD WALCOUNTIANS RFC
Ground Address:Clockhouse, Carshalton Road,
Woodmansterne, Banstead, Surrey SM7 3HU. Tel: 0737
354348
Club Secretary: RA Tait, Flat 3, 58 Mulgrave Road,
Sutton, Surrey SM2 6LX. Tel: (H) 081 661 6391 Tel: (W)
081 688 9243
Fixtures Secretary: S Barry, 23 Parklands, Lynwood
Road, Redhill, Surrey RH1 2JF. Tel: (H) 0737 762892
Club Colours: Black, blue & gold.

PURLEY RFC
Ground Address:Parson's Pightle, Old Coulsdon, Surrey
CR3 1EE. Tel: 0737 553042
Club Secretary: Mr IA Martin, 41 Court Road, Caterham,
Surrey CR3 5RJ. Tel: (H) 0883 348509
Fixtures Secretary: M tidy, 29 Pleasant View Road,
Crowborough, East Sussex TN6 2UU. Tel: (H) 0892
652378 Tel (W) 0860 399601 (Mobile)
Club Colours: Black & white hoops, white shorts.

SOUTHAMPTON RFC
Ground Address:Test Playing Fields, Lower Brownhill
Road, Millbrook, Southampton. Tel: 0703 737777
Club Secretary: Tony Sharpe, 6 Berkeley Road,
Southampton SO15 2JB. Tel: (H) 0703 492429 Tel: (W)
0850 884753 (Mobile)
Fixtures Secretary: George Materna, 29 Netley Firs Road,
Hedge End, Southampton SO30 4AY. Tel: (H) 0489
786704 Tel (W) 0489 886611
Club Colours: Red & white hoops, navy shorts, red socks.

WARLINGHAM RFC
Ground Address:Limpsfield Road, Hamsey Green,
Warlingham, Surrey CR6 9RB. Tel: 0883 622825
Club Secretary: Chris Cave, 57 Ridge Langley,
Sanderstead, South Croydon, Surrey CR2 0AP. Tel: (H)
081 651 0742 Tel: (W) 071 826 8789
Fixtures Secretary: Paul Fettes, 63 Mitchley Hill,
Sanderstead, South Croydon, Surrey. Tel: (H) 081 657
7629
Club Colours: Royal blue & white hoops, navy shorts.

WIMBLEDON RFC
Ground Address:Beverley Meads, Barham Road, Copse
Hill, Wimbledon, London SW20 0ET. Tel: 081 946 3156
Club Secretary: David Dixon-Smith, 42 Princes Road,
Wimbledon, London SW19 8RB. Tel: (W) 081 543 6244
Fixtures Secretary: Mr M Keene, 17 Auriol Park Road,
Worcester Park, Surrey KT4 7DP. Tel: (H) 081 337 6036
Tel (W) 071 261 3255
Club Colours: Maroon & Cambridge blue.

LONDON & SOUTH EAST DIVISION

HAMPSHIRE ONE
1994-95
FIXTURES

September 17 (Week 3)
Esso v Millbrook
Trojans v Tottonians
Winchester v Isle of Wight
Farnborough v U.S. Portsmouth
Sandown & Shanklin v New Milton
Jersey v Guernsey

September 24 (Week 4)
Millbrook v Jersey
Guernsey v Sandown & Shanklin
New Milton v Farnborough
U.S. Portsmouth v Winchester
Isle of Wight v Trojans
Tottonians v Petersfield

October 1 (Week 5)
Sandown & Shanklin v Millbrook
Jersey v Esso
Petersfield v Isle of Wight
Trojans v U.S. Portsmouth
Winchester v New Milton
Farnborough v Guernsey

October 15 (Week 7)
Esso v Sandown & Shanklin
Millbrook v Farnborough
Guernsey v Winchester
New Milton v Trojans
U.S. Portsmouth v Petersfield
Isle of Wight v Tottonians

October 22 (Week 8)
Winchester v Millbrook
Farnborough v Esso
Sandown & Shanklin v Jersey
Tottonians v U.S. Portsmouth
Petersfirld v New Milton
Trojans v Guernsey

October 29 (Week X2)
Jersey v Farnborough
Esso v Winchester
Millbrook v Trojans
Guernsey v Petersfield
New Milton v Tottonians
U.S. Portsmouth v Isle of Wight

January 7 (Week 17)
Petersfield v Millbrook
Trojans v Esso
Winchester v Jersey
Farnborough v Sandown & Shanklin
Isle of Wight v New Milton
Tottonians v Guernsey

January 14 (Week 18)
Sandown & Shanklin v Winchester
Jersey v Trojans
Esso v Petersfield
Millbrook v Tottonians
Guernsey v Isle of Wight
New Milton v U.S. Portsmouth

February 11 (Week 22)
Isle of Wight v Millbrook
Tottonians v Esso
Petersfield v Jersey
Trojans v Sandown & Shanklin
Winchester v Farnborough
U.S. Portsmouth v Guernsey

February 25 (Week 24)
Farnborough v Trojans
Sandown & Shanklin v Petersfield
Jersey v Tottonians
Esso v Isle of Wight
Millbrook v U.S. Portsmouth
Guernsey v New Milton

March 4 (Week 25)
New Milton v Millbrook
U.S. Portsmouth v Esso
Isle of Wight v Jersey
Tottonians v Sandown & Shanklin
Petersfield v Farnborough
Trojans v Winchester

March 25 (Week 28)
Winchester v Petersfield
Farnborough v Tottonians
Sandown & Shanklin v Isle of Wight
Jersey v U.S. Portsmouth
Esso v New Milton
Millbrook v Guernsey

April 8 (Week 30)
Guernsey v Esso
New Milton v Jersey
U.S. Portsmouth v Sandown & Shanklin
Isle of Wight v Farnborough
Tottonians v Winchester
Petersfield v Trojans

HAMPSHIRE ONE

ESSO (FAWLEY) RFC
Ground Address:Esso Recreation Club, Long Lane,
Holbury Hants. Tel: 0703 893750
Club Secretary: Alan McElevey, 32 Butts Ash Avenue,
Hythe, Southampton SO4 6RE. Tel: (H) 0703 840201 Tel:
(W) 0703 895400
Fixtures Secretary: J Plumley, 4 Roseberry Avenue,
Hythe, Southampton. Tel: (H) 0703 845472
Club Colours: Red shirts, blue shorts, red socks.
FARNBOROUGH RFC
Ground Address:Tilebarn Close, Cove, Farnborough,
Hampshire GU14 8LS. Tel: 0252 542750
Club Secretary: Adrian Hathaway, 2 Tees Close, Cove,
Farnborough, Hampshire. Tel: 0252 626242
Fixtures Secretary: Barry Mackay, 43 The Grove,
Farnborough, Hampshire GU14 6QS. Tel: (H) 0252
512363
Club Colours: Light & dark blue hoops.
GUERNSEY RUFC
Ground Address:Footes Lane, St Peter Port, Guernsey.
Tel: 0481 54590
Club Secretary: BJ Mildon, PO Box 181, St Peter Port,
Guernsey. Tel: (H) 0481 65493 Tel: (W) 0481 715055
Fixtures Secretary: A Towers, PO Box 181, St Peter Port,
Guernsey. Tel: (H) 0481 48921 Tel (W) 0481 726521
Club Colours: Green & white.
ISLE OF WIGHT RFC
Ground Address:Wootton Recreation Ground, Wootton
Bridge, Nr Ryde, Isle of Wight. Tel: 0983 883240
Club Secretary: T Allen, 19 Victoria Grove, East Cowes,
Isle of Wight PO32 6DJ. Tel: (H) 0983 280549 Tel: (W)
0983 283659
Fixtures Secretary: S Lucy, The Paddocks, Morton Road,
Brading, Isle of Wight PO36 0BJ. Tel: (H) 0983 406801
Club Colours: Dark blue & gold hoops.
JERSEY RFC
Ground Address:Rue des Landes, St Peter, Jersey,
Channel Islands. Tel: 42255
Club Secretary: Michael T Vibert, PO Box 141, St Peter,
Jersey JE4 33365. Tel: (H) 0534 33483 Tel: (W) 0534
33365
Fixtures Secretary: T Lapidus Esq, Greenview Farm, St
Martin, Jersey, Channel Islands. Tel: (H) 0534 85\64100
Tel (W) 0534 864455
Club Colours: Red & white.
MILLBROOK RFC
Ground Address:Lordshill Recreation Centre, Redbridge
Lane, Southampton. Tel: 0703 739759
Club Secretary: Miss J Neagle, 27 Gemini Close,
Lordshill, Southampton SO16 8BG. Tel: (H) 0703 736474
Tel: (W) 0703 636362
Fixtures Secretary: Mr W Renwick, 2 Centaury Gardens,
Morton Heath SO5 7NY. Tel: (H) 0703 601680 Tel (W)
0705 494847
Club Colours: Scarlet & emerald hoops.
NEW MILTON RFC
Ground Address:Ashley Sports Ground, Ashley, New
Milton, Hants. Tel: 0425 610401
Club Secretary: NE Hanmer, Walsingham, Andrew Lane,
Ashley, New Milton, Hants BH25 5QD. Tel: (H) 0425
612613 Tel: (W) 0590 682495
Fixtures Secretary: J Jupe, 9 Molyneaux Road, Ashley,
New Milton, Hants. Tel: 0425 612184
Club Colours: Green & white quarters.
PETERSFIELD RFC
Ground Address:Penns Place, Petersfield, Hants GU31
4EX. Tel: 0730 264588
Club Secretary: Peter J Williamson, 20 Bridge Meadows,
Liss, Hants GU33 7JY. Tel: (H) 0730 894542 Tel: (W)
0256 841919
Fixtures Secretary: David Church, Downwands,

FINAL TABLE

	P	W	D	L	F	A	PD	Pts
Gosport	12	11	0	1	323	70	253	22
Jersey	12	11	0	1	348	101	247	20
Millbrook	12	10	0	2	343	96	247	20
Tottonians	12	8	0	4	166	106	60	14
Petersfield	12	7	0	5	222	173	49	14
Isle of Wight	12	7	0	5	173	149	24	14
Farnborough	12	5	0	7	159	178	-19	10
Trojans	12	5	0	7	134	279	-145	10
New Milton	12	4	0	8	126	274	-148	8
Sandwn & Shanklin	12	4	0	8	105	262	-157	8
Fareham Heathens	12	4	0	8	122	302	-180	6
Andover	12	2	0	10	156	173	-17	4
Romsey	12	0	0	12	84	298	-214	0

Foxcombe, South Harting, Petersfield GU31 5PJ. Tel: (H)
0730 825288
Club Colours: Red with a single white hoop.
SANDOWN & SHANKLIN RUFC
Ground Address:The Clubhouse, The Fairway, Sandown,
IOW PO36 9ES. Tel: 0983 404707
Club Secretary: Brian Smith, 3 Carter Street, Sandown,
IOW PO36 8BL. Tel: (H) 0983 403298
Fixtures Secretary: Colin Bond, c/o The Warden's Chalet,
Sandown Bay Holiday Centre, Yaverland, Sandown IOW.
Tel: (H) 0983 406129
Club Colours: Navy blue & white close hooped shirts,
navy blue shorts & socks.
TOTTONIANS RFC
Ground Address:Totton College, Water Lane, Totton,
Hants.
Club Secretary: AD Hamilton, Wedgewood, Winsor
Road, Winsor, Southampton, Hants SO40 2HN. Tel: (H)
0703 813217 Tel: (W) Fax: 0703 814092
Fixtures Secretary: S Anderson, 14 Lovage Gardens,
Totton, Southampton SO40 5NP. Tel: (H) 0703 870985
Club Colours: White, green & black hoops.
TROJANS FC
Ground Address:Stoneham Park, Stoneham Lane,
Eastleigh, Hants SO50 9HT. Tel: 0703 612400/613068
Club Secretary: JWJ Mist, Westbury House, 14 Bellevue
Road, Southampton SO15 2AY. Tel: (H) 0703 583450 Tel:
(W) 0703 332844
Fixtures Secretary: CG Holt, The Chase, 338 Hill Lane,
Southampton SO15 2PH. Tel (W) 0703 330993
Club Colours: Blue with red hoops.
UNITED SERVICES PORTSMOUTH RFC
Ground Address:Burnaby Road, Portsmouth, Hants. Tel:
0705 825394
Club Secretary: John Collins, 4 Neelands Grove,
Paulsgrove, Portsmouth, Hants PO6 4QL. Tel: (H) 0705
380859 Tel: (W) 0705 333579
Fixtures Secretary: Brian Hookway, 5 Hamilton Road,
Southsea, Portsmouth, Hants PO5 2LX. Tel: (H) 0705
817271 Tel (W) 0705 822351 x25805
Club Colours: Blue & red hoops, blue shorts.
WINCHESTER RFC
Ground Address:Nuns Road, Winchester, Hants. Tel:
0962 863405
Club Secretary: D Allum, 20 Chawton Close, Harestock,
Winchester, Hants. Tel: (H) 0962 882658
Fixtures Secretary: D Watters, Conkers, The Pastures,
Kingsworthy, Winchester, Hants. Tel: (H) 0962 880659 Tel
(W) 0703 266355
Club Colours: Black & amber. Change: Green.

LONDON & SOUTH EAST DIVISION

September 17 (Week 3)
A.C. Delco v Ventnor
Fareham Heathens v Andover
Overton v Fordingbridge

September 24 (Week 4)
Andover v A.C. Delco
Romsey v Overton
Fordingbridge v Fareham Heathens

October 1 (Week 5)
A.C. Delco v Fordingbridge
Ventnor v Andover
Fareham Heathens v Romsey

October 15 (Week 7)
Fordingbridge v Ventnor
Romsey v A.C. Delco
Overton v Fareham Heathens

October 22 (Week 8)
A.C. Delco v Overton
Ventnor v Romsey
Andover v Fordingbridge

October 29 (Week X2)
Romsey v Andover
Overton v Ventor
Fareham Heathens v A.C. Delco

November 19 (Week 11)
Ventnor v Fareham Heathens
Andover v Overton
Fordingbridge v Romsey

January 7 (Week 17)
Ventnor v A.C. Delco
Andover v Fareham Heathens
Fordingbridge v Overton

January 14 (Week 18)
A.C. Delco v Andover
Overton v Romsey
Fareham Heathens v Fordingbridge

February 11 (Week 22)
Fordingbridge v A.C. Delco
Andover v Ventnor
Romsey v Fareham Heathens

February 25 (Week 24)
Ventnor v Fordingbridge
A.C. Delco v Romsey
Fareham Heathens v Overton

March 4 (Week 25)
Overton v A.C. Delco
Romsey v Ventnor
Fordingbridge v Andover

March 25 (Week 28)
Andover v Romsey
Ventnor v Overton
A.C. Delco v Fareham Heathens

April 8 (Week 30)
Fareham Heathens v Ventnor
Overton v Andover
Romsey v Fordingbridge

HAMPSHIRE TWO

AC DELCO RFC
Ground Address:AC Delco Sports & Social Club,
Stoneham Lane, Eastleigh, Southampton. Tel: 0703 613334
Club Secretary: Peter Watson, 37 Wallisdean Avenue,
Fareham, Hants PO14 1HR. Tel: (H) 0329 23260
Fixtures Secretary: Simon Fitzjohn, 104 Alma Road,
Portswood, Southampton SO14 6UW. Tel: (H) 0703
324061 Tel (W) 0703 511811
Club Colours: Red & blue quarters.

ANDOVER RFC
Ground Address: The Goodship Ground, Foxcotte Park,
Hatherden Road, Charlton, Andover, Hants SP11 0HN. Tel:
0264 339518
Club Secretary: WAJ Kent, Croye Lodge, 3 The Avenue,
Andover, Hants SP10 3EL. Tel: (H) 0264 324963 Tel: (W)
0926 844755
Fixtures Secretary: RJ Smith, 17 Longstock Close,
Andover, Hants SP10 3UN. Tel: (H) 0264 359491 Tel (W)
0264 332299
Club Colours: Black.

FAREHAM HEATHENS RFC
Ground Address: Cams Alders Sports Centre, Highfield
Avenue, Fareham, Hampshire. Tel: 0329 221793
Club Secretary: CR Townsend, 9 Daisy Lane, Locksheath,
Southampton SO3 6RA. Tel: (H) 0489 574945 Tel: (W)
0329 220844 (P/T only)
Fixtures Secretary: Mr CEM Turner, 4 Walberton
Avenue, Cosham, Portsmouth, Hampshire PO6 2JH. Tel:
(H) 0705 370139
Club Colours: Red & black quarters.

FORDINGBRIDGE RFC
Ground Address: Recreation Ground, Fordingbridge,
Hants. Tel: 0425 652047
Club Secretary: SCJ Godden, 157 Station Road,
Fordingbridge, Hants SP6 1DF. Tel: (H) 0425 654069
Fixtures Secretary: J Trim, Trees, Fryern Court Road,
Fordingbridge, Hants SP6 1NG. Tel: (H) 0425 655156 Tel
(W) 0425 652254
Club Colours: Sky blue. Change: Black & white quarters.

OVERTON RUFC
Ground Address: Town Meadow, High Street, Overton,
Basingstoke, Hants (on B3400). Tel: 0256 462827 (Alec
Coles, Fixture Secretary)
Club Secretary: Colin Gordon, 5 Millstream Close,
Andover, Hants SP10 2NB. Tel: (H) 0264 333140 Tel: (W)
0264 224477
Fixtures Secretary: Alec Coles, 15 Rochford Road,
Basingstoke, Hants RG21 1TQ. Tel: (H) 0256 462827
Club Colours: Royal blue. Change: Red, white & blue
hoops.

ROMSEY RUFC
Ground Address: The Sports Centre, Southampton Road,
Romsey, Hants. Tel: 0794 515103
Club Secretary: Andrew R Mott, 8 Harefield Court,
Romsey, Hampshire SO51 7NN. Tel: (H) 0794 512989 Tel:
(W) 0725 512777
Fixtures Secretary: Andrew R Mott, 8 Harefield Court,
Romsey, Hampshire SO51 7NN. Tel: (H) 0794 512989 Tel
(W) 0725 512777
Club Colours: Blue & gold hoops, blue shorts.

VENTNOR RFC
Ground Address: Watcombe Bottom, Whitwell Road,
Ventnor, IOW. Tel: 0983 854155
Club Secretary: John Adams, B1-1K, Avenue Road,
Wroxall, IOW PO38 3EG. Tel: (H) 0983 854201
Fixtures Secretary: Marvin Champion, The HOmestead,
Monkton Street, Ryde, Isle of Wight. Tel: (H) 0983 566896
Tel (W) 0705 876001
Club Colours: Blue with white band.

FINAL TABLE

	P	W	D	L	F	A	PD	Pts
Esso	11	11	0	0	451	37	414	22
Guernsey	11	9	0	2	432	85	347	18
A.C. Delco	11	9	0	2	245	83	162	18
Fordingbridge	11	8	0	3	266	91	175	16
Ventnor	11	7	0	4	297	101	196	14
Overton	11	7	0	4	218	117	101	14
Waterlooville	11	5	0	6	83	291	-208	10
Alresford	11	4	0	7	116	293	-177	8
Fleet	11	3	0	8	108	290	-182	6
Nomads	11	2	0	9	99	374	-275	4
Ellingham	11	1	0	10	50	356	-306	2
Basingstke Wombts	11	0	0	11	61	308	-247	0

LONDON & SOUTH EAST DIVISION

HAMPSHIRE THREE
1994-95
FIXTURES

March 25 (Week 28)
Waterlooville   v   Basingstoke Wombats
Alresford   v   Ellingham
Fleet   v   Nomads

September 24 (Week 4)
Alresford   v   Waterlooville
Fleet   v   Ellingham
Basingstoke Wombats   v   Nomads

October 1 (Week 5)
Waterlooville   v   Fleet
Alresford   v   Basingstoke Wombats
Ellingham   v   Nomads

October 15 (Week 7)
Fleet   v   Alresford
Nomads   v   Waterlooville
Basingstoke Wombats   v   Ellingham

October 22 (Week 8)
Waterlooville   v   Ellingham
Alresford   v   Nomads
Fleet   v   Basingstoke Wombats

October 29 (Week X2)
Nomads   v   Fleet
Ellingham   v   Alresford
Basingstoke Wombats   v   Waterlooville

January 14 (Week 18)
Waterlooville   v   Alresford
Ellingham   v   Fleet
Nomads   v   Basingstoke Wombats

February 11 (Week 22)
Nomads   v   Ellingham
Fleet   v   Waterlooville
Basingstoke Wombats   v   Alresford

February 25 (Week 24)
Ellingham   v   Basingstoke Wombats
Alresford   v   Fleet
Waterlooville   v   Nomads

March 4 (Week 25)
Nomads   v   Alresford
Basingstoke Wombats   v   Fleet
Ellingham   v   Waterlooville

HAMPSHIRE THREE

ALRESFORD RFC
Ground Address: Bighton CC.
Club Secretary: Andrew Martin, 19 Bell House,
Tichborne Down, Alresford, Hants SO24 9PA. Tel: (H)
0962 735124 Tel: (W) 0705 487431
Fixtures Secretary: R Howard, The Horse & Groom,
Broad Street, Alresford, Hants. Tel: (H) 0962 734809 Tel
(W) 0962 734809
Club Colours: Black, green & gold hoops.
BASINGSTOKE WOMBATS RFC
Ground Address: Hockey Club, Down Grange, Pack Lane,
Basingstoke.
Club Secretary: David Thurston, 3 Musket Copse,
Chineham, Basingstoke, Hampshire. Tel: (H) 0256 462672
Tel: (W) 0256 817640
Club Colours: Red, green, yellow & blue quarters.
ELLINGHAM & RINGWOOD RFC
Ground Address: Picket Post, Ringwood, Hants. Tel: 0425
476668
Club Secretary: Douglas Middleton, 56 Eastfield Lane,
Ringwood, Hants, BH24 1QP. Tel: (H) 0425 475521 Tel:
(W) 0202 893000
Fixtures Secretary: Philip Lambert, 44 Waterloo Way,
Ringwood, Hants. Tel: (H) 0425 476643
Club Colours: Blue with amber hoop.
FLEET RUFC
Ground Address: Wavel Cody School, Lynchford Road,
Farnborough, Hants.
Club Secretary: Merrik Knight, 31 Osborne Road,
Farnborough, Hants GU14 6AE. Tel: (H) 0252 518798 Tel:
(W) 081 563 4945
Fixtures Secretary: Richard Bawden, 63 Queens Road,
Farnborough, Hants GU14 6JP. Tel: (H) 0252 513304 Tel
(W) 0483 575211
Club Colours: Royal blue & red shirts, royal blue shorts.
NOMADS RUFC
Ground Address: Farlington Recreation Ground, Eastern
Road, Portsmouth, Hants. Tel: 0705 643991
Club Secretary: Ken Walker, 130 Portchester Road,
Fareham, Hants PO16 8QP. Tel: (H) 0329 237584 Tel: (W)
0705 297273
Fixtures Secretary: Mr Barry Bridgman, 216
Southampton Road, Paulsgrove, Hants PO6 4RZ. Tel: (H)
0705 326046 Tel (W) 0705 624212
Club Colours: Red & black irregular hoops.
WATERLOOVILLE RFC
Ground Address: Rowlands Avenue Sports Club,
Rowlands Avenue, Waterlooville, Hants.
Club Secretary: John Kingdon, 40 Jubilee Road,
Waterlooville, Hants. Tel: (H) 0705 612739
Club Colours: Sky blue, white & green.

Hampshire Three is a New League for the
1994-95 Season formed from last year's
Hampshire Three

LONDON & SOUTH EAST DIVISION

SURREY ONE
1994-95
FIXTURES

September 17 (Week 3)
Shirley Wanderers v Raynes Park
Chobam v John Fisher Old Boys
Old Cranleighans v Old Reedonians
Effingham v Farnham
Old Rutlishians v Kingston
Old Whitgiftians v Barnes

September 24 (Week 4)
Raynes Park v Old Whitgiftians
Barnes v Old Rutlishians
Kingston v Effingham
Farnham v Old Cranleighans
Old Reedonians v Chobham
John Fisher Old Boys v University Vandals

October 1 (Week 5)
Old Rutlishians v Raynes Park
Old Whitgiftians v Shirley Wanderers
University Vandals v Old Reedonians
Chobham v Farnham
Old Cranleighans v Kingston
Effingham v Barnes

October 15 (Week 7)
Shirley Wanderers v Old Rutlishians
Raynes Park v Effingham
Barnes v Old Cranleighans
Kingston v Chobham
Farnham v University Vandals
Old Reedonians v John Fisher Old Boys

October 22 (Week 8)
Old Cranleighans v Raynes Park
Effingham v Shirley Wanderers
Old Rutlishians v Old Whitgiftians
John Fisher Old Boys v Farnham
University Vandals v Kingston
Chobham v Barnes

October 29 (Week X2)
Old Whitgiftians v Effingham
Shirley Wanderers v Old Cranleighans
Raynes Park v Chobham
Barnes v University Vandals
Kingston v John Fisher Old Boys
Farnham v Old Reedonians

January 7 (Week 17)
University Vandals v Raynes Park
Chobham v Shirley Wanderers
Old Cranleighans v Old Whitgiftians
Effingham v Old Rutlishians
Old Reedonians v Kingston
John Fisher Old Boys v Barnes

January 14 (Week 18)
Old Rutlishians v Old Cranleighans
Old Whitgiftians v Chobham
Shirley Wanderers v University Vandals
Raynes Park v John Fisher Old Boys
Barnes v Old Reedonians
Kingston v Farnham

February 11 (Week 22)
Old Reedonians v Raynes Park
John Fisher Old Boys v Shirley Wanderers
University Vandals v Old Whitgiftians
Chobham v Old Rutlishians
Old Cranleighans v Effingham
Farnham v Barnes

February 25 (Week 24)
Effingham v Chobham
Old Rutlishians v University Vandals
Old Whitgiftians v John Fisher Old Boys
Shirley Wanderers v Old Reedonians
Raynes Park v Farnham
Barnes v Kingston

March 4 (Week 25)
Kingston v Raynes Park
Farnham v Shirley Wanderers
Old Reedonians v Old Whitgiftians
John Fisher Old Boys v Old Rutlishians
University Vandals v Effingham
Chobham v Old Cranleighans

March 25 (Week 28)
Old Cranleighans v University Vandals
Effingham v John Fisher Old Boys
Old Rutlishians v Old Reedonians
Old Whitgiftians v Farnham
Shirley Wanderers v Kingston
Raynes Park v Barnes

April 8 (Week 30)
Barnes v Shirley Wanderers
Kingston v Old Whitgiftians
Farnham v Old Rutlishians
Old Reedonians v Effingham
John Fisher Old Boys v Old Cranleighans
University Vandals v Chobham

SURREY ONE

BARNES RFC
Ground Address:Barn Elms, Queen Elizabeth Walk, Barnes,
London SW15 0DG. Tel: 081 876 7685
Club Secretary: Mr Paul Kirby, 53 Stanhope Gardens, London
SW7 5RF. Tel: (H) 071 373 0120 Tel: (W) 071 602 5678
Fixtures Secretary: Mr Sean Briggs, 48 Bolingbroke Road,
London W14. Tel: (H) 071 603 5766 Tel (W) 071 629 9292
Club Colours: Green & gold hoops, green shorts.

CHOBHAM RFC
Ground Address:Fowlers Wells, Windsor Road, Chobham,
Surrey GU24 8NA. Tel: 0276 858616
Club Secretary: A Thomas, Hazel Cottage, Viggory Lane,
Horsell, Woking, Surrey GU21 4XH. Tel: (H) 0483 720810
Tel: (W) 0483 761036
Fixtures Secretary: Wallace Hooper, 8 Fowlers Mead,
Chobham, Woking GU24 8LF. Tel: (H) 0276 858661
Club Colours: Scarlet & gold hoops on dark blue jersey.

EFFINGHAM RFC
Ground Address:King George V Playing Fields, Browns Lane,
Effingham, Surrey. Tel: 0372 458845
Club Secretary: MC Wheeler, 34 Oakfields, Broadacres,
Guildford, Surrey GU3 3AU. Tel: (H) 0483 36022
Fixtures Secretary: E Newton, 42 Milney Road, Kingston,
Surrey KT1 2AU. Tel: (H) 081 549 8213 Tel (W) 071 738 1122
Club Colours: Emerald green & amber hoops, black shorts.

FARNHAM RUFC
Ground Address:Westfield Lane, Wrecclesham, Farnham,
Surrey GU10 4QP. Tel: 0252 721138
Club Secretary: Derek R Wall, 22 Hope Lane, Farnham,
Surrey GU9 0HZ. Tel: (H) 0252 710476
Fixtures Secretary: JF Robertson, Akora, 98 Shoreham Road,
Farnham, Surrey GU9 8SE. Tel: (H) 0252 712387
Club Colours: Black & white hoops, black shorts.

JOHN FISHER OLD BOYS RFC
Ground Address:192 Limpsfield Road, Hamsey Green,
Warlingham, Surrey. Tel: 0883 625149
Club Secretary: Tony Spong, 26 Glanfield Road, Beckenham,
Kent BR3 3JU. Tel: (H) 081 658 5189 Tel: (W) 071 437 4831
Fixtures Secretary: Simon Sterling, 3 Archers Court, 13a
Nottingham Road, Croydon, Surrey. Tel: (H) 081 649 8910 Tel
(W) 081 681 2222
Club Colours: Old, blue & white hoops, blue shorts, hooped
socks.

KINGSTON RFC
Ground Address:King Edward Sports Ground, Hook Road,
Chessington, Surrey KT9 1PL. Tel: 081 397 8385
Club Secretary: IM Barnes, 4 Kenley Road,
Kingston-on-Thames, Surrey KT1 3RW. Tel: (H) 081 336 1481
Tel: (W) 071 406 7361
Fixtures Secretary: K Walker, 3 Woodcote Side, Epsom,
Surrey KT18 7HB. Tel: (H) 0372 741791
Club Colours: Maroon & white hoops, blue shorts.

OLD CRANLEIGHAN RFC
Ground Address:Old Portsmouth Road, Thames Ditton,
Surrey KT7 0HB. Tel: 081 398 3092
Club Secretary: Mark Lubbock, 52 Sarsfeld Road, London
SW12 8HN. Tel: (H) 081 672 1310 Tel: (W) 071 638 1111
Fixtures Secretary: Tony Price, 32 Beverley Road, New
Malden, Surrey KT3 4AW. Tel: (H) 081 949 1194 Tel (W) 081
533 7588
Club Colours: Blue, white & gold hoops.

OLD REEDONIANS RFC
Ground Address:North Avenue, Whiteley Village, off
Burwood Road, Walton-on-Thames, surrey. Tel: 09328 49616
Club Secretary: John Rogers, 8 Model Cottages, East Sheen,
London SW14 7PH. Tel: (H) 081 876 1512
Fixtures Secretary: Adrian Procter, 4 Friston Street, Fulham,
London SW6 3AT. Tel: (H) 071 731 3791 Tel (W) 081 974
6150
Club Colours: Red, white, light blue, dark blue hoops.

FINAL TABLE

	P	W	D	L	F	A	PD	Pts
Wimbledon	12	10	0	2	258	60	198	20
University Vandals	12	10	0	2	218	66	152	20
Old Whitgiftians	12	10	0	2	199	97	102	20
John Fisher O B	12	9	0	3	173	165	8	18
Shirley Wanderers	12	5	1	6	116	117	-1	11
Kingston	12	5	0	7	143	149	-6	10
Raynes Park	12	4	2	6	85	114	-29	10
Barnes	12	5	0	7	153	191	-38	10
Old Reedonians	12	5	0	7	122	222	-100	10
Effingham	12	4	0	8	156	164	-8	8
Chobam	12	4	0	8	130	160	-30	8
Old Rutlishians	12	4	0	8	146	189	-43	8
Mitcham	12	1	1	10	67	272	-205	3

OLD RUTLISHIANS RFC
Ground Address:The Clubhouse, Poplar Road, Merton Park,
London SW19 3JS. Tel: 081 540 3678
Club Secretary: WH Griffin, 68 Love Lane, Morden, Surrey
SM4 6LP. Tel: (H) 081 395 1875
Fixtures Secretary: S Thompson, 100 Aylward Road, Merton
Park, London SW20 9AQ. Tel: (H) 081 540 5676
Club Colours: Gold, azure, silver & black.

OLD WHITGIFTIAN RFC
Ground Address:Croham Manor Road, South Croydon,
Surrey, CR2 7BG. Tel: 081 688 3248
Club Secretary: Geoff Austin, 97 Clifton Road,
Kingston-Upon-Thames, Surrey, KT2 6PL. Tel: (H) 081 549
3757 Tel: (W) 071 926 6100
Fixtures Secretary: Andrew Stone, 10 Frenches Court,
Frenches Road, Redhill, Surrey, RH1 2HD. Tel: (H) 0737
773648 Tel (W) 0932 336000
Club Colours: Red, black & blue hooped shirts, white shorts.

RAYNES PARK RFC
Ground Address:Taunton Avenue, Raynes Park, London
SW20.
Club Secretary: Russell Price, 101 Belmont Avenue, New
Malden, Surrey KT3 6QE. Tel: (H) 081 949 2448 Tel: (W) 071
976 7199
Fixtures Secretary: Peter Tuesley, 7 South View, Bromley,
Kent BR1 3DR. Tel: (H) 081 464 3781 Tel (W) 071 638 0297
Club Colours: Blue jerseys with gold band, blue shorts &
socks.

SHIRLEY WANDERERS RUFC
Ground Address:Kent Gate, Addington Road, West Wickham,
Kent. Tel: 081 777 5298
Club Secretary: Martin Stone, 251 Quentin Court, Regency
Walk, Shirley, Croydon, Surrey. Tel: (H) 081 777 6712
Fixtures Secretary: Geoff Jeffcoat, 96 Woodland Way, West
Wickham, Kent BR4 9LT. Tel: (H) 081 777 5174 Tel (W) 081
761 3000
Club Colours: All white.

UNIVERSITY VANDALS RFC
Ground Address:Brownacres, The Towing Path,
Walton-on-Thames, Surrey. Tel: 0932 227659
Club Secretary: AMG Williams, 7 Clarence Close,
Walton-on-Thames, Surrey KT12 5JX. Tel: (H) 0932 229727
Tel: (W) 071 259 6633
Fixtures Secretary: CJ Cockrean Esq, 94 Albany Road,
Hersham, Walton-on-Thames, Surrey. Tel: (H) 0932 226837
Club Colours: Black, purple & emerald green.

LONDON & SOUTH EAST DIVISION

SURREY TWO
1994-95
FIXTURES

September 17 (Week 3)
Cobham v Old Haileyburians
Mitcham v London Fire Brigade
Old Tiffinians v BEC Old Boys
Old Caterhamians v Woking
Law Society v Wandsworthians
Merton v Reigate & Redhill

September 24 (Week 4)
Old Haileyburians v Merton
Reigate & Redhill v Law Society
Wandworthians v Old Caterhamians
Woking v Old Tiffinians
BEC Old Boys v Mitcham
London Fire Brigade v Chipstead

October 1 (Week 5)
Law Society v Old Haileyburians
Merton v Cobham
Chipstead v BEC Old Boys
Mitcham v Woking
Old Tiffinians v Wandsworthians
Old Caterhamians v Reigate & Redhill

October 15 (Week 7)
Cobham v Law Society
Old Haileyburians v Old Caterhamians
Reigate & Redhill v Old Tiffinians
Wandsworthians v Mitcham
Woking v Chipstead
BEC Old Boys v London Fire Brigade

October 22 (Week 8)
Old Tiffinians v Old Haileyburians
Old Caterhamians v Cobham
Law Society v Merton
London Fire Brigade v Woking
Chipstead v Wandsworthians
Mitcham v Reigate & Redhill

October 29 (Week X2)
Merton v Old Caterhamians
Cobham v Old Tiffinians
Old Haileyburians v Mitcham
Reigate & Redhill v Chipstead
Wandsworthians v London Fire Brigade
Woking v BEC Old Boys

January 7 (Week 17)
Chipstead v Old Haileyburians
Mitcham v Cobham
Od Tiffinians v Merton
Old Caterhamians v Law Scoiety
BEC Old Boys v Wandsworthians
London Fire Brigade v Reigate & Redhill

January 14 (Week 18)
Law Society v Old Tiffinians
Merton v Mitcham
Cobham v Chipstead
Old Haileyburians v London Fire Brigade
Reigate & Redhill v BEC Old Boys
Wandsworthians v Woking

February 11 (Week 22)
BEC Old Boys v Old Haileyburians
London Fire Brigade v Cobham
Chipstead v Merton
Mitcham v Law Scoiety
Old Tiffinians v Old Caterhamians
Woking v Reigate & Redhill

February 25 (Week 24)
Old Caterhamians v Mitcham
Law Society v Chipstead
Merton v London Fire Brigade
Cobham v BEC Old Boys
Old Haileyburians v Woking
Reigate & Redhill v Wandsworthians

March 4 (Week 25)
Wandsworthians v Old Haileyburians
Woking v Cobham
BEC Old Boys v Merton
London Fire Brigade v Law Society
Chipstead v Old Caterhamians
Mitcham v Old Tiffinians

March 25 (Week 28)
Old Tiffinians v Chipstead
Old Caterhamians v London Fire Brigade
Law Society v BEC Old Boys
Merton v Woking
Cobham v Wandsworthians
Old Haileyburians v Reigate & Redhill

April 8 (Week 30)
Reigate & Redhill v Cobham
Wandsworthians v Merton
Woking v Law Scoiety
BEC Old Boys v Old Caterhamians
London Fire Brigade v Old Tiffinians
Chipstead v Mitcham

SURREY TWO

BEC OLD BOYS RFC
Ground Address:Northey Avenue, Cheam, Surrey. Tel:
081 642 3423
Club Secretary: Carol Sanders, 58 Pollards Hill North,
Norbury, London, SW16 4NL. Tel: (H) 081 764 0912
Club Colours: Blue, old gold & white hoops.
CHIPSTEAD RFC
Ground Address:Chipstead Meads, High Road, Chipstead,
Surrey. Tel: 0737 553055
Club Secretary: AD Malyon, 4 Hillside Road, East Ewell,
Epsom, Surrey KT17 3EH. Tel: (H) 081 393 3578 Tel: (W)
081 680 1017
Fixtures Secretary: A Carr, 53 Woodplace Lane,
Coulsdon, Surrey CR5 1NE. Tel: (H) 0737 551919 Tel (W)
071 792 4666
Club Colours: Blue 7 gold hoops.
COBHAM RFC
Ground Address:Old Surbitonians Memorial Ground,
Fairmile Lane, Cobham, Surrey. Tel: 0932 863245
Club Secretary: IJ Johnson, 209 Portsmouth Road,
Cobham, Surrey KT11 1JR. Tel: (H) 0932 862694 Tel: (W)
081 942 1033
Fixtures Secretary: G Finch, 23 Arlington Road, Surbiton,
Surrey. Tel: (H) 081 399 3049 Tel (W) 081 680 1700
Club Colours: Blue, maroon & gold quarters.
LAW SOCIETY RFC
Ground Address:c/o Old Wimbledonians Cricket Club,
Clayton Road, Hook, Surrey. Tel: 081 397 1962
Club Secretary: A Signy, 61 Ferntower Road, London, N5
2JE.
Club Colours: Maroon & black hoops.
LONDON FIRE BRIGADE RFC
Ground Address:LFCDA Welfare Fund Sports Ground,
Banstead Road, Ewell, Surrey. Tel: 081 394 1946/393 0446
Club Secretary: Stephen Foy, 24 Kent House, Hogarth
Estate, Chiswick, London, W4 2JS. Tel: (H) 081 994 3819
Tel: (W) 071 587 4736
Club Colours: Red, old gold, black.
MERTON RFC
Ground Address:Morden Recreation Ground, Faversham
Road, Morden, Surrey SM4. Tel: 081 646 5192
Club Secretary: Robert Smith, 16 Leppoc Road, Clapham,
London SW4 9LT. Tel: (H) 071 622 3729
Fixtures Secretary: Tom Wild, 78 Arundel Avenue,
Sanderstead, South Croydon, Surrey. Tel: (H) 081 651
6454 Tel (W) 081 302 8500
Club Colours: Black, gold & white quartered shirts, black
shorts, black socks.
MITCHAM RUFC
Ground Address:Rosehill Recreation Ground, Rosehill,
Sutton, Surrey.
Club Secretary: S Payne, 70 Morton Gardens, Wallington,
Surrey. Tel: (H) 081 715 4087 Tel: (W) 081 658 7626
Fixtures Secretary: G Ashburn, 90 Gravel Hill, Selsdon,
Surrey. Tel: (H) 081 654 4771 Tel (W) 081 686 2599
Club Colours: Lavender & green.
OLD CATERHAMIAN
Ground Address:Park Avenue, Caterham, Surrey. Tel:
0883 343488
Club Secretary: Peter Smith, Three Chimneys, Gravelly
Hill, Caterham, Surrey CR3 6ES. Tel: (H) 0883 347919
Tel: (W) 0883 347919
Fixtures Secretary: Mark Rowland, 1 Southcote Road,
Merstham, Surrey RH1 3LJ. Tel: (H) 0734 644135 Tel (W)
0737 775160
Club Colours: Black, amber, silver & mauve, black shorts.

FINAL TABLE

	P	W	D	L	F	A	PD	Pts
Old Cranleighans	12	12	0	0	247	95	152	22
Farnham	12	11	0	1	209	81	128	22
Old Haileyburians	12	8	0	4	237	192	45	16
Merton	12	7	1	4	165	99	66	15
Law Society	12	7	0	5	166	114	52	14
Old Caterhamians	12	6	0	6	233	115	118	12
Bec Old Boys	12	5	1	6	192	127	65	9
Cobham	12	4	1	7	129	135	-6	9
Chipstead	12	5	2	5	218	107	111	8
Old Tiffinians	12	4	0	8	163	131	32	8
Wansworthians	12	4	0	8	115	274	-159	8
Reigate & Redhill	12	0	0	12	55	401	-346	-2
Charing X/W Hosp							0	-10

(Withdrawn from League for '93-94 Season)

OLD HAILEYBURIANS RFC
Ground Address:27 Ruxley Lane, Kingston Road, Ewell.
Tel: 081 393 3901
Club Secretary: R Sheen, 29 Kenilworth Ave, Wimbledon
Sw19 7LN. Tel: (H) 081 879 7581 Tel: (W) 071 782 0990
Club Colours: Magenta and white.
OLD TIFFINIAN RFC
Ground Address:Grist Memorial Ground, Summer Road,
off Hampton Court Way, East Molesey, Surrey. Tel: 081
398 1391
Club Secretary: B A Bench, 12 Angas Court, Pine Grove,
Weybridge, Surrey. Tel: (H) 0932 842533 Tel: (W) 081
549 9222
Fixtures Secretary: R G Kirkwood, 63 Shaftesbury Way,
Strawberry Hill, Twickenham, Middlesex. Tel: (H) 081 898
1767
Club Colours: Violet, white & navy blue.
REIGATE & REDHILL RFC
Ground Address:Eric Hodgkins Memorial Ground, Colley
Lane, Reigate, Surrey RH2 9JL. Tel: 0737 221110
Club Secretary: Norman Phillips, 19 Linnell Road,
Redhill, Surrey RH1 4DH. Tel: (H) 0737 769258 Tel: (W)
081 577 4526
Fixtures Secretary: Clive Harrington, 66 Somerset Road,
Meadvale, Redhill, Surrey RH1 6LT. Tel: (H) 0737 247067
Tel (W) 081 666 0201
Club Colours: Dark blue with light blue hooped jerseys,
blue shorts.
WANDSWORTHIANS RFC
Ground Address:Kings College Playing Fields, Windsor
Avenue, New Malden, Surrey KT3 5HA. Tel: 081 942 0495
Club Secretary: Ian Maclean, Lancaster House, More
Lane, Esher, Surrey. Tel: (H) 0372 463121
Fixtures Secretary: Gary Kirkwood, 53 Leominster Road,
Morden, Surrey SM4 6HT. Tel: (H) 081 640 0263 Tel (W)
081 665 3756
Club Colours: Maroon, white & gold hoops.
WOKING RFC
Ground Address:Byfleet Recreation Ground, Rectory
Road, Byfleet, Surrey.
Club Secretary: Mr S Elder, Corner House, 64 Chertsey
Road, Byfleet, Surrey. Tel: (H) 0932 343003
Fixtures Secretary: Mr Ian Vousden, 142 Blackmore
Crescent, Sheerwater, Woking, Surrey. Tel: (H) 0483
715715 Tel (W) 0374 624753
Club Colours: Blue & gold hoops.

LONDON & SOUTH EAST DIVISION

SURREY THREE
1994-95
FIXTURES

September 24 (Week 4)
Lightwater v Haslemere
Old Pelhamians v Battersea Ironsides
Croydon v Egham
Old Bevonians v Old Freemans
Old Suttonians v Old Johnians

October 1 (Week 5)
Haslemere v Old Suttonians
Old Johnians v Old Bevonians
Old Freemans v Croydon
Egham v Old Pelhamians
Battersea Ironsides v London Media

October 15 (Week 7)
Old Bevonians v Haslemere
Old Suttonians v Lightwater
London Media v Egham
Old Pelhamians v Old Freemans
Croydon v Old Johnians

October 22 (Week 8)
Lightwater v Old Bevonians
Haslemere v Croydon
Old Johnians v Old Pelhamians
Old Freemans v London Media
Egham v Battersea Ironsides

October 29 (Week X2)
Old Pelhamians v Haslemere
Croydon v Lightwater
Old Bevonians v Old Suttonians
Battersea Ironsides v Old Freemans
London Media v Old Johnians

January 7 (Week 17)
Old Suttonians v Croydon
Lightwater v Old Pelhamians
Haslemere v London Media
Old Johnians v Battersea Ironsides
Old Freemans v Egham

January 14 (Week 18)
Battersea Ironsides v Haslemere
London Media v Lightwater
Old Pelhamians v Old Suttonians
Croydon v Old Bevonians
Egham v Old Johnians

February 11 (Week 22)
Old Bevonians v Old Pelhamians
Old Suttonians v London Media
Lightwater v Battersea Ironsides
Haslemere v Egham
Old Johnians v Old Freemans

February 25 (Week 24)
Old Freemans v Haslemere
Egham v Lightwater
Battersea Ironsides v Old Suttonians
London Media v Old Bevonians
Old Pelhamians v Croydon

March 4 (Week 25)
Croydon v London Media
Old Bevonians v Battersea Ironsides
Old Suttonians v Egham
Lightwater v Old Freemans
Haslemere v Old Johnians

March 25 (Week 28)
Old Johnians v Lightwater
Old Freemans v Old Suttonians
Egham v Old Bevonians
Battersea Ironsides v Croydon
London Media v Old Pelhamians

SURREY THREE

BATTERSEA IRONSIDES RFC
Ground Address: Battersea Ironsides Sports & Social Club, Openview, Earlsfield, London SW17. Tel: 081 879 9913
Club Secretary: Martin Paul Tanner, 1 Woodland Way, Morden, Surrey SM4 4DS. Tel: (H) 081 540 5784
Fixtures Secretary: Tony S'zulc, 63 Chelsham Road, London SW4 6NN. Tel: (H) 071 622 7694 Tel (W) 0956 501794
Club Colours: Green & white.

CROYDON RFC
Ground Address: Lydhams Road (junction with King Henry's Drive), Keston, Bromley, Kent. Tel: 0959 573409
Club Secretary: Trevor Davies, 62 Coulsdon Road, Coulsdon, Surrey CR5 2LB. Tel: (H) 081 668 4864 Tel: (W) 071 233 0288
Fixtures Secretary: Bob Goodwin, 298 Grange Road, London SE19. Tel: (H) 653 8919
Club Colours: Black, magenta & white.

EGHAM RFC
Ground Address: Strodes College, High Street, Egham, Surrey TW20.
Club Secretary: Tony Codling, Brookside, 18 Vicarage Avenue, Egham, Surrey TW20 8NW. Tel: (H) 0784 434139 Tel: (W) 0784 432366
Fixtures Secretary: Gerard O'Grady, 79 Quincy Road, Egham, Surrey TW20 9JJ. Tel: (H) 0784 472585
Club Colours: Medium blue with gold hoop.

HASLEMERE RFC
Ground Address: The Pavilion, Woolmer Hill Sports Ground, Haslemere, Surrey GU27 1QA. Tel: 0428 643072
Club Secretary: Colin Andrews, Combodene, Portsmouth Road, Hindhead, Surrey GU26 6TQ. Tel: (H) 0428 604511 Tel: (W) 071 828 7998
Fixtures Secretary: Joe Riley, 4 New Mill Cottages, Critchmere Lane, Haslemere, Surrey GU27 3RA. Tel: (H) 0428 652869 Tel (W) 0483 68889
Club Colours: Mid blue & white hoops.

LIGHTWATER RUFC
Ground Address: The Sports Centre, The Avenue, Lightwater, Surrey, GU18 5RG. Tel: 0276 472664
Club Secretary: A Sharpe, 66 Cedar Close, Bagshot, Surrey, GU19 5AB. Tel: (H) 0276 472994
Club Colours: Green & white quarters, black shorts.

LONDON MEDIA RUFC
Ground Address: Battersea Park, Albert Bridge Road Entrance, Battersea, London.
Club Secretary: Nick Field, 18 Walton Way, West Acton. Tel: (H) 081 993 5909 Tel: (W) 071 278 2656
Fixtures Secretary: Mike Jefferies, 64A Rosendale Road, West Dulwich, London SE21 8DP. Tel: (H) 081 761 2346 Tel (W) 071 831 2981
Club Colours: Black & white quarters.

OLD BEVONIANS RFC
Ground Address: Ballard Coombe, Robin Hood's Way, Kingston Vale, London SW15 3QX. Tel: 081 942 2907
Club Secretary: Mr Ian James Cecil, 53 Orme Road, Kingston upon Thames KT1 3SD. Tel: (H) 081 942 0152 Tel: (W) 071 329 3910
Fixtures Secretary: Mr Alex Kerr, 427 West Barnes Lane, New Malden, Surrey KT3 6PA. Tel: (H) 081 949 2009
Club Colours: Black, amber & green hoops.

OLD FREEMEN'S RFC
Ground Address: Old Fremen's Memorial Clubhouse, City of London Freemen's School, Ashtead Park, Ashtead, Surrey KT21 1ET. Tel: 0372 274158
Club Secretary: JG Wild, Beeches, Ermyn Way, Leatherhead, Surrey KT22 8TW. Tel: (H) 0372 276085 Tel: (W) 0483 729661
Fixtures Secretary: MJ Bailey, 123 Overdale, Ashtead, Surrey KT21 1PZ. Tel: (H) 0372 278505 Tel (W) 081 642

FINAL TABLE

	P	W	D	L	F	A	PD	Pts
Woking	12	11	1	0	291	79	212	23
London Fire Brig.	11	10	1	0	202	93	109	21
Battersea Ironsides	12	10	0	2	299	76	223	20
London Media	12	7	1	4	267	146	121	15
Old Pelhamians	12	7	0	5	230	150	80	14
Old Suttonians	11	5	0	6	143	137	6	10
Lightwater	12	4	2	6	169	168	1	10
Old Bevonians	12	5	0	7	138	191	-53	10
Haslemere	12	5	0	7	136	215	-79	10
Royal Holloway Coll	11	3	0	8	154	206	-52	6
Croydon	12	3	0	9	57	314	-257	6
Kings Coll Hosp	11	2	0	9	93	246	-153	4
Old Freemans	12	1	1	10	72	230	-158	3

Only Kings College Hospital relegated

3419/081 642 5685
Club Colours: Blue, maroon & gold hoops, dark blue shorts.

OLD JOHNIANS RFC
Ground Address:OJ RFC, Oaken Lane, Hinchley Wood, Surrey.
Club Secretary: Tim Gunther, 44 Temperley Road, Clapham, WS12 8QF. Tel: (W) 071 929 4037
Fixtures Secretary: Patrick Rogers, 115a Allfarthing Lane, Wandsworth, London, SW18 2AU. Tel: (H) 081 871 9857 Tel (W) 071 580 4441
Club Colours: Green & white hoops.

OLD PELHAMIANS RFC
Ground Address: Poulter Park, Bishopsford Road (A217), Mitcham, Surrey. Tel: 081 648 3755
Club Secretary: John Winter, 20 Blake's Terrace, New Malden, Surrey KT3 6ET. Tel: (H) 081 395 9549 Tel: (W) 071 815 7128
Fixtures Secretary: Dave Turner, 49 Chelsham Road, Clapham, London SW4 6NN. Tel: (H) 071 627 4778 Tel (W) 071 926 9449
Club Colours: All black.

OLD SUTTONIANS RFC
Ground Address: Walch Pavilion, Priest Hill, Banstead Road, Ewell, Surrey. Tel: 081 393 7427
Club Secretary: Mr SJ Udall, 16 Kingsdown Road, Cheam, Sutton, Surrey SM3 8NY. Tel: (H) 081 644 7259 Tel: (W) 0992 560330
Fixtures Secretary: Mr I Connell, 43 Grove Avenue, Sutton, Surrey SM1 2DF. Tel: (H) 081 642 8915
Club Colours: Red, white & black hoops.

481

LONDON & SOUTH EAST DIVISION

SURREY FOUR
1994-95
FIXTURES

September 24 (Week 4)
Economicals v Racal Decca
Surrey Police v Kings College Hospital
Old Epsomians v Sun Alliance
Oxted v Old Wellingtonian
Surrey University v Kew Occasionals

October 1 (Week 5)
Racal Decca v Surrey University
Kew Occasionals v Oxted
Old Wellingtonian v Old Epsomians
Sun Alliance v Surrey Police
Kings College Hospital v Royal Holloway Coll

October 15 (Week 7)
Oxted v Racal Decca
Surrey University v Economicals
Royal Holloway Coll v Sun Alliance
Surrey Police v Old Wellingtonian
Old Epsomians v Kew Occasionals

October 22 (Week 8)
Ecomonicals v Oxted
Racal Decca v Old Epsomians
Kew Occasionals v Surrey Police
Old Wellingtonian v Royal Holloway Coll
Sun Alliance v Kings College Hospital

October 29 (Week X2)
Surrey Police v Racal Decca
Old Epsomians v Economicals
Oxted v Surrey University
Kings College Hospital v Old Wellingtonian
Royal Holloway Coll v Kew Occasionals

January 7 (Week 17)
Surrey University v Old Epsomians
Economicals v Surrey Police
Racal Decca v Royal Holloway Coll
Kew Occasionals v Kings College Hospital
Old Wellington v Sun Alliance

January 14 (Week 18)
Kings College Hospital v Racal Decca
Royal Holloway Coll v Economicals
Surrey Police v Surrey University
Old Epsomians v Oxted
Sun Alliance v Kew Occasionals

February 11 (Week 22)
Oxted v Surrey Police
Surrey University v Royal Holloway Coll
Economicals v Kings College Hospital
Racal Decca v Sun Alliance
Kew Occasionals v Old Wellingtonian

February 25 (Week 24)
Old Wellingtonian v Racal Decca
Sun Alliance v Economicals
Kings College Hospital v Surrey University
Royal Holloway Coll v Oxted
Surrey Police v Old Epsomians

March 4 (Week 25)
Old Epsomians v Royal Holloway Coll
Oxted v Kings College Hospital
Surrey University v Sun Alliance
Economicals v Old Wellingtonian
Racal Decca v Kew Occasionals

March 25 (Week 28)
Kew Occasionals v Economicals
Old Wellingtonian v Surrey University
Sun Alliance v Oxted
Kings College Hospital v Old Epsomians
Royal Holloway Coll v Surrey Police

SURREY FOUR

ECONOMICALS RUFC
Ground Address:LSE Sports Ground, Windsor Avenue, New Malden, Surrey. Tel: 081 942 1229
Club Secretary: Steve Bowen, 97 Salehurst Road, Crofton Park, London SE4 1AR. Tel: (H) 081 690 5393 Tel: (W) 071 486 1234
Fixtures Secretary: Steve Bowen, 97 Salehurst Road, Crofton Park, London SE4 1AR. Tel: (H) 081 690 5393 Tel (W) 071 486 1234
Club Colours: Green & white hoops.
KEW OCCASIONALS
Ground Address: Westminster University Sports Ground, Cavendish Road (off Hartington Road) Chiswick W4 3UH. Tel 081 994 1554.
Club Secretary: Mrs L S Role, 68 Rosebury Rd, London SW6 2NG. Tel (H) 071 736 8469. (W) 071 836 1225
Club Colours: Pink shirts, blue shorts.
KINGS COLLEGE HOSPITAL RFC
Ground Address: The Griffin, 12 Dulwich Village, Dulwich, London SE24. Tel: 081 693 6900
Club Secretary: James O'Beirne, KCHRFC, Kings College Hospital Medical School, Rugby Pigeon Hole, Bessemer Road, London SE5 9PJ. Tel: (H) 071 737 5841 Tel: (W) 071 737 4000 x4050/1 Fax: 737 0210
Fixtures Secretary: James Piers, KCHRFC, Rugby Pigeon Hole, Kings College Hospital Medical School, Bessemer Road, London SE5 9PJ.
Club Colours: 1st XV: Navy, sky, maroon hoops or quarters.
OLD EPSOMIAN RFC
Club Secretary: TJ Goodger, 53 Braithwaite Gardens, Stanmore, Middlesex HA7 2QG. Tel: (H) 081 907 3886
Fixtures Secretary: S Schlaefli, 40 Broadhurst Gardens, Reigate, Surrey RG2 8AW. Tel: (H) 0737 244983
Club Colours: Blue tops, white shorts.
OLD WELLINGTONIAN RFC
Ground Address:27 Ruxley Lane, Kingston Road, Ewell. Tel: 081 393 3901
Club Secretary: Hugh Salmon, 30 Bennerley Road, London, SW11 6DS. Tel: (H) 071 223 9297
Fixtures Secretary: Robert Collins, Top Flat, 10 Hildyard Road, Fulham, London, SW6 1SQ. Tel: (H) 071 386 0331
Club Colours: Orange, yellow and blue stripe on black.
OXTED RFC
Ground Address: Holland Field, Holland Road, Hurst Green, Oxted, Surrey. Tel: 0883 717468
Club Secretary: BN Knight, 3 Geary Close, Smallfield, Horley, Surrey RH6 9QA. Tel: (H) 0342 844227
Fixtures Secretary: M Branson, 41 Grantwood Close, Redhill, Surrey RH1 5SN. Tel: (H) 0883 717488
Club Colours: Blue & red hoops.
RACAL-DECCA RFC
Ground Address: Racal-Decca Sports & Social Club, Kingston Road, Tolworth KT5 9NU. Tel: 081 337 0519
Club Secretary: William Tracy, 102 Clapham Common, Northside, London SW4 9SQ. Tel: (H) 071 228 2787 Tel: (W) 081 754 6456
Fixtures Secretary: William Tracy, 102 Clapham Common, Northside, London SW4 9SQ. Tel: (H) 071 228 2787 Tel (W) 081 754 6456
Club Colours: Blue & white hoops.
ROYAL HOLLOWAY COLLEGE RFC
Ground Address:'Nobles', RHUL, Englefield Green, Egham, Surrey, TW20 0EX.
Club Secretary: K J Wheaton, Students Union, RHUL, Egham Hill, Egham, Surrey. Tel: (H) 0784 471178 Tel: (W) 0784 435035
Club Colours: Purple & green.

FINAL TABLE

	P	W	D	L	F	A	PD	Pts
Egham	8	8	0	0	247	40	207	16
Old Johnians	8	7	0	1	204	57	147	14
Surrey Police	8	5	0	3	157	76	81	10
Surrey University	8	5	0	3	132	98	34	10
Old Epsomians	8	5	0	3	156	124	32	10
Oxted	8	2	0	6	91	130	-39	4
Racal Decca	8	1	0	7	73	137	-64	2
Sun Alliance	8	1	0	7	28	370	-342	2

SUN ALLIANCE, RAYNES PARK RFC
Ground Address: Sun Aliance London Club, Fairways, Off Church Walk, Raynes Park, London, SW20 9DN. Tel: 081 542 2824
Club Secretary: B Williams, 121 Midfield Way, St Paul's Cray, Orpington, Kent, BR5 2QW. Tel: (H) 081 302 4630 Tel: (W) 071 734 7211 Ext 4353
Fixtures Secretary: As club secretary.
Club Colours: Red & blue hoops.
SURREY POLICE RFC
Ground Address: Police HQ, Mount Browne, Sandy Lane, Guildford GU1 3HG. Tel: 0483 571212 x2760
Club Secretary: Shane Burrows, 4 Junewood Close, Woodham, New Haw, Addlestone, Surrey KT15 3PX. Tel: (H) 0932 344607 Tel: (W) 0483 571212
Fixtures Secretary: Phil Brown, Kingston Rise, New Haw, Addlestone, Surrey. Tel: (H) 0932 349874 Tel (W) 0483 571212 x5360
Club Colours: All black, red socks.
UNIVERSITY OF SURREY RFC
Ground Address: Varsity Centre Sports Pavilion, Egerton, Guildford, Surrey. Tel: 0483 259393 x9242
Club Secretary: Paul Gamble, SURFC, c/o Students Union, University of Surrey, Guildford, Surrey GU2 5XH.
Fixtures Secretary: Robert Haggart, 38 Recreation Road, Guildford, Surrey GU2. Tel: (H) 0483 69905
Club Colours: Black with blue, red & gold hoops.

SOUTH WEST DIVISION

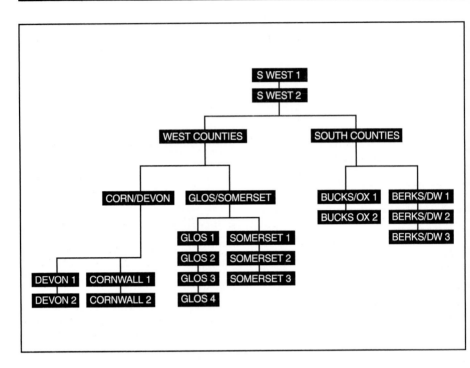

OFFICIALS 1994-95

CHAIRMAN, League Sub-Committee
Dr. C.V. Phillips, "Barlowena", Alexandra Road, Illogan, Cornwall, TR16 4EN (H) 0209 842660
LEAGUES CO-ORDINATING SECRETARY
Jack D. Wooldridge, 16 Grange Drive, Durleigh, Bridgwater, Somerset, TA6 7LL (H) 0278 422009
LEAGUE SECRETARIES
South West One & South West Two Jack D. Wooldridge, 16 Grange Drive, Durleigh, Bridgwater, Somerset, TA6 7LL (H) 0278 422009.
Western Counties Mike Gee, Suhaila, 7 Hellesvane Close, St Ives, Cornwall, TR6 7HQ (H) 0736 797168.
Southern Counties Trevor Palm, 13 Dolesford Road, Aylesbury, Bucks (H) 0296 81847 (B) 0753 533223.
Cornwall/Devon Geoff Simpson, 108 Pattison Drive, Mainstone, Plymouth, Devon, PL6 8RU (H) 0752 707432.
Devon One & Devon Two Geoff Simpson, 108 Pattison Drive, Mainstone, Plymouth, Devon. (H) 0752 707432.

Cornwall One & Cornwall Two Beverley Davis, 8 Penrose Road, Helston, Cornwall, TR13 8TP (H) 0326 563744.
Glos/Somerset & Somerset One Bill Bishop, "Hellvellyn", 1 Wiltshire Place, Kingswood, Bristol, Avon BS15 4XA.(H) 0272 575729 (B) 0272 352017.
Somerset Two & Somerset Three Clive MacDonald, 8 Sycamore Drive, Crewkerne, Somerset, TA18 7BT (H) 0460 76136.
Glos One, Glos Two, Glos Three & Glos Four Allan Townsend, St Kelelm, 2 Kencourt Close, Kenilworth Avenue, Gloucester, GL2 0QL (H) 0452 522721.
Berk/Dorset & Wilts One, Berk/Dorset & Wilts Two & Berk/Dorset & Wilts Three Tony Bott, Kew House, Anchor Road, Calne, Wilts SN11 8DI (H) 0860 448328 (B)0249 821448.
Bucks/Oxon One & Bucks/Oxon Two Brian Flanders, Old Cross House, Coscote, Didcot, Oxon, OX11 0NP (H) 0235 816523.
COMMITTEE MEMBERS
Stanley Oswin, Manor Farmhouse, Appleton, Abingdon, Oxon OX13 5JR (H) 0865 862954
Tony Boyer, 11 Christopher Court, Boundary Road, Newbury, Berks RG14 7PQ (H) 0635 40574

SOUTH WEST DIVISION

ADMINISTRATIVE RULES

1. MATCH RESULTS REPORTING INSTRUCTIONS

ALL LEAGUES

(i) Home Clubs will telephone the First Eleven Sports Agency on (0734) 311244 as soon as possible after the end of the game and certainly before 6.00pm, with the Match Result.

(ii) Both Clubs in each game will complete a Match Result Card, listing the team and replacements in block letters, with initials and the Match Result. The card must be signed by the Match Referee and posted, first class, to the First Eleven Sports Agency, by first post Monday latest.

2. NOTIFICATION OF RESULTS

Club Secretaries are responsible for their Club's compliance with the rules for notification of results. Failure to telephone and card-in the match result and team and replacements list, within the time limits laid down, will incur a fine for each offence of £10.00. Offending Clubs will be notified of fines imposed, failure to pay within 28 days will result in the offending Club being deducted two Competition points. Any outstanding fines at the end of the Season can result in points deduction in the following Season.

3. POSTPONED MATCHES

Club Secretaries of Clubs with Home matches must, in the event of a postponement of any League match, immediately inform the First Eleven Sports Agency on (0734) 861593 and their appropriate League Secretary. In addition, they must also notify the Agency and the League Secretary within SEVEN days, of the date of the re-arranged fixture.

In the absence of a notification of a mutually acceptable re-arranged date within the time specified, the League Secretary will direct the Clubs to play on a specified date. Postponed matches must be arranged to take place on the next available Saturday.

4. PLAYER REGISTRATION FORMS

All Player Registration Forms must, on completion, be forwarded to: The Registrar, PO Box 11, Reading RG6 3DT. Faxed registration forms will not be accepted.

5. CLUBS JOINING COURAGE LEAGUES

All Clubs wishing to join the Courage Leagues should ensure that their membership of the Rugby Football Union has been accepted by 1st May to qualify for entry in the following Season.

6. CHANGE OF CLUB'S NAME

(i) Any proposals to change the name of a Club must be notified to the Co-ordinating Secretary before 1st May for inclusion in the Season commencing the September following.

(ii) Any Clubs proposing a merger should note the regulation in respect of Club mergers contained in the Rugby Football Union's Handbook.

SOUTH WEST CHAMPIONS ROLL OF HONOUR 1993/94

South West 1
Henley RFC

South West 2
Gloucester Old Boys RFC

Western Counties
Old Patesians RFC

Southern Counties
Bournemouth RFC

Cornwall/Devon
Devon & Cornwall Constabulary RFC

Devon 1
Honiton RFC

Devon 2
Salcombe RFC

Cornwall 1
Saltash RFC

Cornwall 2
St Agnes RFC

Glos & Somerset
Dings Crusaders RFC

Gloucestershire 1
Stow-on-the-Wold & District RFC

Gloucestershire 2
Hucclecote Old Boys RFC

Gloucestershire 3
Bishopston RFC

Gloucestershire 4
Tewkesbury RFC

Somerset 1
Midsomer Norton RFC

Somerset 2
The Tor RFC

Somerset 3
St Brendans Old Boys RFC

Bucks & Oxon 1
Amersham & Chiltern RFC

Bucks & Oxon 2
Phoenix RFC

Berks, Dorset & Wilts 1
Devizes RFC

Berks, Dorset & Wilts 2
Blandford RFC

Berks, Dorset & Wilts 3
Berkshire Shire Hall RUFC

Launceston RFC

SOUTH WEST DIVISION
FEATURED TEAMS

GLOUCESTER OLD BOYS

Gloucester Old Boys have been just about the most consistent junior club in the whole of the short history of the Courage Leagues. Starting in 1987-88 in Gloucester Three they have never finished below second place in any division and only failed to gain promotion in 1989-90 from Gloucester One when their runners-up spot was not duly rewarded, although as champions the following season they did go up.

Founded in 1904 they have always been hard nuts to crack, but their latest run of success has been phenominal and last season another perfect record in South West Two left them only one rung on the ladder away from senior status. Their 12 victories were achieved with a 343-83 points situation and they also reached the final of the Gloucestershire County Cup. In all games they won 29, drew one and lost one for an overall 899-236 points position with 124 tries having been scored and only 16 conceded.

This side originally formed from three local grammar schools had six players in the most recent Gloucestershire county side - Paul Mansell, brothers Simon and Steve Baldwin (the former skippering the team), Jeff Cole, Nigel Smart and Andy Vicary. A further player — No 8 Kevin Hemming — was selected but missed out as the game was cancelled. He managed 135 points during the season including 25 tries, while wing Gareth Gwillin managed 15 from 19 games and Andy Broady landed 250 points.

Simon Baldwin is a fine example of the club's spirit. He joined at the age of 12 (as did eight others from the superb side) and has already been the field boss for four seasons — with another to follow. As back-up the club has a fine chairman in Roy Hill, an excellent first team manager (Ray Ellis), dedicated coaches in Viv Wooley, Les James and Gerry Artus and a fine trainer in Kenny Clapton.

The way for 'GOB' is still up. Watch them again this season!

LAUNCESTON

Launceston again narrowly missed promotion from the Western Counties league — this time through inconsistency which left them in third place — but they struck a blow for East Cornwall by landing the county cup with a succession of victories over higher placed clubs starting with South West Two Penryn in the last eight (25-13 away), followed by a tight semi-final at home to St Ives (14-10) and then a marvellous final success against National League Redruth (24-14).

They were also the only side to beat league champions Old Patesians (a 36-16 drubbing) and had notable away 'friendly' wins over Weston-super-Mare (25-18) and the high flying Taunton side (15-7). All this means a Pilkington Cup place in the new season, when they also intend to take that Western League title at last.

Led on the field by Roddy Statton for three seasons with great zest they also have a superb coaching staff led by Mick Stephens, ably assisted by Steve Brown and completed by none other than former England hooker Graham Dawe.

To back up their drive for the top Launceston have greatly improved their facilities, which now include floodlights, six changing rooms, a new kitchen and enlarged bar. To add to all this they have taken the initiative locally by running a Floodlit Cup for local junior clubs and their own second team.

The ground is beautifully situated along the River Tamar close to the county border with Devon. It is meant to be — and is — a joy for visitors except, they hope, in the playing sense!

Gloucester Old Boys RFC

SOUTH WEST DIVISION

SOUTH WEST ONE
1994-95
FIXTURES

September 17 (Week 3)
Barnstaple v Newbury
Brixham v Gloucester OB
Cheltenham v Stroud
Cinderford v Sherborne
Salisbury v Maidenhead
Taunton v Torquay

September 24 (Week 4)
Gloucester OB v Cinderford
Maidenhead v Barnstaple
Newbury v St Ives
Sherborne v Cheltenham
Stroud v Taunton
Torquay v Salisbury

October 1 (Week 5)
Barnstaple v Torquay
Cheltenham v Gloucester OB
Cinderford v Brixham
Salisbury v Stroud
St Ives v Maidenhead
Taunton v Sherborne

October 15 (Week 7)
Brixham v Cheltenham
Gloucester OB v Taunton
Maidenhead v Newbury
Sherborne v Salisbury
Stroud v Barnstaple
Torquay v St Ives

October 22 (Week 8)
Branstaple v Sherborne
Cheltenham v Cinderford
Newbury v Torquay
Salisbury v Gloucester OB
St Ives v Stroud
Taunton v Brixham

October 29 (Week X2)
Brixham v Salisbury
Cinderford v Taunton
Gloucester OB v Barnstaple
Sherborne v St Ives
Stroud v Newbury
Torquay v Maidenhead

January 7 (Week 17)
Barnstaple v Brixham
Maidenhead v Stroud
Newbury v Sherborne
Salisbury v Cinderford
St Ives v Gloucester OB
Taunton v Cheltenham

January 14 (Week 18)
Brixham v St Ives
Cheltenham v Salisbury
Cinderford v Barnstaple
Gloucester OB v Newbury
Sherborne v Maidenhead
Stroud v Torquay

February 11 (Week 22)
Barnstaple v Cheltenham
Maidenhead v Gloucester OB
Newbury v Brixham
Salisbury v Taunton
St Ives v Cinderford
Torquay v Sherborne

February 25 (Week 24)
Brixham v Maidenhead
Cheltenham v St Ives
Cinderford v Newbury
Gloucester OB v Torquay
Sherborne v Stroud
Taunton v Barnstaple

March 4 (Week 25)
Barnstaple v Salisbury
Maidenhead v Cinderford
Newbury v Cheltenham
St Ives v Taunton
Stroud v Gloucester OB
Torquay v Brixham

March 25 (Week 28)
Brixham v Stroud
Cheltenham v Maidenhead
Cinderford v Torquay
Gloucester OB v Sherborne
Salisbury v St Ives
Taunton v Newbury

April 8 (Week 30)
Maidenhead v Taunton
Newbury v Salisbury
Sherborne v Brixham
St Ives v Barnstaple
Stroud v Cinderford
Torquay v Cheltenham

SOUTH WEST ONE

BARNSTAPLE RFC
Ground Address: Pottington Road, Barnstaple EX31 1DZ.
Tel: 0271 45627
Club Secretary: RM Pettifer, Baileys Cottage, Lake,
Barnstaple EX31 3HU. Tel: (H) 0271 73475 Tel: (W) 0271
46710
Fixtures Secretary: D Stubbs, Marigold Cottage, Two
Pots, Ilfracombe. Tel: (H) 0271 866315 Tel (W) 0271
45296
Club Colours: Red shirts, white shorts.

BRIXHAM RFC
Ground Address: Ashley Park, Higher Ranscombe Road,
Brixham. Tel: 0803 882162/0803 855511 (O)
Club Secretary: JD Irvine Esq BEM, 1 Great Rea Road,
Brixham, South Devon TQ5 9SW. Tel: (H) 0803
8822190803 855511
Fixtures Secretary: Danny Irvine, 1 Great Rea Road,
Brixham TQ5 9SW.
Club Colours: Black with 6' white band. Change: Red.

CHELTENHAM RFC
Ground Address: Prince of Wales Stadium, Tommy
Taylor's Lane, Cheltenham, Glos GL50 4NJ. Tel: 0242
525393
Club Secretary: Tom Parker, 39 Long Mynd Avenue,
Cheltenham, Glos GL51 5QT. Tel: (H) 0242 521076
Fixtures Secretary: Mike Edwards, 2 Greenbank Cottage,
Piccadilly, Guiting Power, Glos GL54 5UT. Tel: (H) 0451
850232 Tel (W) 0452 419666
Club Colours: Black & red hoops.

CINDERFORD RFC
Ground Address: Recreation Ground, Dockham Road,
Cinderford, Glos. Tel: 0594 822673
Club Secretary: Mrs M Beavis, 5 Abbots Road,
Cinderford, Glos GL14 3BN. Tel: (H) 0594 823779
Fixtures Secretary: Mr J Gazzard, 1 Wedgewood
Crescent, Cinderford, Glos. Tel: (H) 0594 822333 Tel (W)
0452 371221
Club Colours: Red, black & amber.

GLOUCESTER OLD BOYS' RFC
Ground Address: Horton Road, Gloucester GL1 3PX. Tel:
0452 302390
Club Secretary: Norman P Partridge, 17 Armscroft Place,
Barnwood, Gloucester GL2 0SW. Tel: (H) 0452 527658
Tel: (W) 0452 302088
Fixtures Secretary: Chris J Read, 21 Meadowleaze,
Longlevens, Gloucester GL2 0PW. Tel: (H) 0452 306491
Tel (W) 0452 424418
Club Colours: Claret, gold & navy.

MAIDENHEAD RUFC
Ground Address: Braywick Park, Maidenhead SL6 1BN.
Tel: 0628 29663
Club Secretary: Mr DA Bartley SAMS, Tars Platt,
Cookham Dean Common, Maidenhead SL6 1BN. Tel: (H)
0628 482749 Tel: (W) 0628 532010
Fixtures Secretary: Mr AG Cowen, 31 Furze Platt Road,
Maidenhead SL6 7NE. Tel: (H) 0628 29237
Club Colours: Magenta, violet & black.

NEWBURY RFC
Ground Address: Pinchington Lane, Newbury, Berkshire
RG14 7HB. Tel: & Fax: 0635 40103
Club Secretary: Vernon Lewis, 76 Monks Lane, Newbury,
Berkshire. Tel: (H) 0635 44308
Fixtures Secretary: Richard Little, 27 Lipscomb Close,
Hermitage, Newbury. Tel: (H) 0635 200904
Club Colours: Navy & sky irregular hoops.

SALISBURY RFC
Ground Address: Castle Road, Salisbury SP1 3SA. Tel:
0722 325317
Club Secretary: LE Macey, 33 Montague Road, West
Harnham, Salisbury SP2 8NL. Tel: (H) 0722 322056 Tel:
(W) 0722 327801

FINAL TABLE

	P	W	D	L	F	A	PD	Pts
Henley	12	12	0	0	328	125	203	24
Cheltenham	12	11	0	1	312	119	193	22
Newbury	12	8	1	3	173	165	8	17
St Ives	12	7	1	4	181	138	43	15
Barnstaple	12	7	0	5	161	142	19	14
Torquay	12	5	2	5	125	160	-35	12
Salisbury	12	5	0	7	105	118	-13	10
Stroud	12	4	2	6	165	237	-72	10
Cinderford	12	4	1	7	140	167	-27	9
Brixham	12	3	1	8	112	209	-97	7
Maidenhead	12	3	0	9	139	177	-38	6
Sherborne	12	3	0	9	153	220	-67	6
Gordon League	12	1	2	9	102	219	-117	4

Fixtures Secretary: RH Rowland, 1 Lode Hill, Downton,
Wilts SP5 3PW. Tel: (H) 0725 512064
Club Colours: Green & white.

SHERBORNE RFC
Ground Address: The Terrace Club, Terrace Playing
Fields, Sherborne, Dorset. Tel: 0935 812478
Club Secretary: Mrs Sarah Hill, Wescot, Westbury,
Sherborne, Dorset DT9 3RA. Tel: (H) 0935 813663
Fixtures Secretary: Mrs Val Rushton, 2 Sackmore Green,
Marnhull, Sturminster Newton, Dorset DT10 1PW. Tel:
(H) 0258 820195
Club Colours: Black.

ST IVES RFC
Ground Address: Alexandra Road, St ives, Cornwall. Tel:
0736 795346
Club Secretary: JC Guppy, Cedar Court Bungalow,
Lelant, St ives, Cornwall TR26 3JP. Tel: (H) 0736 755127
Fixtures Secretary: NA Simpson, Gillan Cottage, The
Belyars, St Ives, Cornwall. Tel: (H) 0736 798169 Tel (W)
0736 794424
Club Colours: Navy blue & white.

STROUD RFC
Ground Address: Fromehall Park, Stroud, Glos GL5 3HS.
Tel: 0453 763019
Club Secretary: NF Hall, 1 Elm Terrace, Foxmoor Lane,
Ebley, Stroud, Glos GL5 4QH. Tel: (H) 0453 824321 Tel:
(W) 0453 763462
Fixtures Secretary: Russell Hillier, Marijon, Pagan Hill
Lane, Stroud, Glos GL5 4AW. Tel: (H) 0453 764381 Tel
(W) 0275 464441
Club Colours: Blue & white hoops.

TAUNTON RFC
Ground Address: Priory Park, Priory Bridge Road,
Taunton, Somerset TA1 1XQ. Tel: 0823 275670
Club Secretary: Peter Hancock, 21 Kirke Grove, Taunton,
Somerset TA2 8SB. Tel: (H) 0823 277982
Fixtures Secretary: Rodney Reed, 22 Burrow Drive,
Taunton. Tel: (H) 0823 276354 Tel (W) 0823 337900
x3375
Club Colours: Crimson, black & white hoops.

TORQUAY ATHLETIC RFC
Ground Address: Recreation Ground, Sea Front, Torquay.
Tel: 0803 293842
Club Secretary: Robin Foster, 110 Duchy Drive, Preston
Down, Paignton, Torquay, TQ3 1EX. Tel: (H) 0803
529508 Tel: (W) 0803 655002
Fixtures Secretary: Dave Thompson, 44 Bidwell Brook
Drive, Churston, Paignton. Tel: (H) 0803 845115
Club Colours: Black and white.

SOUTH WEST DIVISION

SOUTH WEST TWO
1994-95
FIXTURES

September 17 (Week 3)
Banbury v Gordon League
Bournemouth v Aylesbury
Bridgwater v Oxford
Combe Down v Swanage & Wareham
Marlow v Penryn
Matson v Old Patesians

September 24 (Week 4)
Aylesbury v Matson
Gordon League v Marlow
Old Patesians v Combe Down
Oxford v Clevedon
Penryn v Bridgwater
Swanage & Wareham v Banbury

October 1 (Week 5)
Banbury v Old Patesians
Bridgwater v Gordon League
Clevedon v Penryn
Combe Down v Aylesbury
Marlow v Swanage & Wareham
Matson v Bournemouth

October 15 (Week 7)
Aylesbury v Banbury
Bournemouth v Combe Down
Gordon League v Clevedon
Old Patesians v Marlow
Penryn v Oxford
Swanage & Wareham v Bridgwater

October 22 (Week 8)
Banbury v Bournemouth
Bridgwater v Old Patesians
Clevedon v Swanage & Wareham
Combe Down v Matson
Marlow v Aylesbury
Oxford v Gordon League

October 29 (Week X2)
Aylesbury v Bridgwater
Bournemouth v Marlow
Gordon League v Penryn
Matson v Banbury
Old Patesians v Clevedon
Swanage & Wareham v Oxford

January 7 (Week 17)
Banbury v Combe Down
Bridgwater v Bournemouth
Clevedon v Aylesbury
Marlow v Matson
Oxford v Old Patesians
Penryn v Swanage & Wareham

January 14 (Week 18)
Aylesbury v Oxford
Bournemouth v Clevedon
Combe Down v Marlow
Matson v Bridgwater
Old Patesians v Penryn
Swanage & Wareham v Gordon League

February 11 (Week 22)
Bridgwater v Combe Down
Clevedon v Matson
Gordeon League v Old Patesians
Marlow v Banbury
Oxford v Bournemouth
Penryn v Aylesbury

February 25 (Week 24)
Aylesbury v Gordon League
Banbury v Bridgwater
Bournemouth v Penryn
Combe Down v Clevedon
Matson v Oxford
Old Patesians v Swanage & Wareham

March 4 (Week 25)
Bridgwater v Marlow
Clevedon v Banbury
Gordon League v Bournemouth
Oxford v Combe Down
Penryn v Matson
Swanage & Wareham v Aylesbury

March 25 (Week 28)
Aylesbury v Old Patesians
Banbury v Oxford
Bournemouth v Swanage & Wareham
Combe Down v Penryn
Marlow v Clevedon
Matson v Gordon League

April 8 (Week 30)
Clevedon v Bridgwater
Gordon League v Combe Down
Old Patesians v Bournemouth
Oxford v Marlow
Penryn v Banbury
Swanage & Wareham v Matson

SOUTH WEST TWO

AYLESBURY RUFC
Ground Address: Ostlers Field, Brook End, Weston Turville, Aylesbury, Buckinghamshire. Tel: 0296 612556
Club Secretary: Andrew McKechnie, 20 Whieelwrights, Weston Turville, Aylesbury, Bucks. Tel: (H) 0296 613001
Fixtures Secretary: James Williams, 11 Little Mollards, Wingrave, Aylesbury, Bucks. Tel: (H) 0296 688249
Club Colours: Magenta & black.

BANBURY RUFC
Ground Address: Banbury School, Ruskin Road, Banbury, Oxon.
Club Secretary: M Thomas, 24 Poplars Road, Chacombe, Banbury, Oxon OX17 2JY. Tel: (H) 0295 711582 Tel: (W) 0295 267511
Club Colours: Dark blue & white hoops.

BOURNEMOUTH RFC
Ground Address: Chapel Gate, Parley Lane, Christchurch, Dorset BH23 6BD. Tel: 0202 581933
Club Secretary: Mike Wilkes, 581 Christchurch Road, Bournemouth, Dorset BH1 4BU. Tel: (H) 0202 395168 Tel: (W) 0202 302345
Fixtures Secretary: Ian Mure, 17 Barn Road, Broadstone, Dorset BH18 8NH. Tel: (H) 0202 696331 Tel (W) 0202 684684
Club Colours: Sable & or (black with gold hoops).

BRIDGWATER & ALBION RFC
Ground Address: Bath Road, Bridgwater, Somerset. Tel: 0278 423900
Club Secretary: Anthony Pomeroy, Hafod-y-gân, Newton Road, North Petherton, Somerset TA6 6SN. Tel: (H) 0278 662181 Tel: (W) 0278 455631 Fax: 0278 444361
Fixtures Secretary: Ralph Sealey, 1 Capes Close, Bridgwater, Somerset. Tel: (H) 0278 444757
Club Colours: Scarlet, amber & black.

CLEVEDON RFC
Ground Address: Coleridge Vale Playing Fields, Clevedon, Avon. Tel: 0275 877772
Club Secretary: RG Legge, 2 Kingston Avenue, Clevedon, Avon BS21 6DS. Tel: (H) 0275 874624 Tel: (W) 0272 291031 x2995
Fixtures Secretary: J Evans, 79 Kenn Road, Clevedon, Avon. Tel: (H) 0275 871443
Club Colours: Gold & royal blue.

COMBE DOWN RFC
Ground Address: Holly's Corner, North Road, Combe Down, Bath. Tel: 0225 832075
Club Secretary: N Williams, 2 Abbey View Gardens, Widcombe, Bath BA2 6DQ. Tel: (H) 0225 312405 Tel: (W) 0225 444222 x3347
Fixtures Secretary: Wyn Bailey, 2 Warbler Close, Trowbridge, Wilts. Tel: (H) 0225 760217 Tel (W) 0225 466122
Club Colours: Black & amber.

GORDON LEAGUE RFC
Ground Address: Hempsted Lane, Hempsted, Gloucester GL2 6JN. Tel: 0452 303434Mr WR King
Club Secretary: 361 Innsworth Lane, Churchdown, Gloucester GL3 1EY. Tel: (H) 0452 856787 Tel: (W) 0452 371371 x2656
Fixtures Secretary: Mr A Jenkins, 14 Galspick Way, Longlevens, Gloucester. Tel: (H) 0452 305239
Club Colours: White with red sash.

MARLOW RUFC
Ground Address: Riverwoods Drive, Marlow, Bucks SL7 1QU. Tel: Office: 0628 483911 Clubhouse: 0628 477054
Club Secretary: Graham Cutts, 6 Eastern Dene, Hazlemere, Bucks HP15 7BT. Tel: (H) 0494 711391 Tel: (W) 0494 431717
Fixtures Secretary: Graham Cutts, 6 Eastern Dene, Hazlemere, Bucks HP15 7BT. Tel: (H) 0494 711391 Tel (W) 0494 431717

FINAL TABLE

	P	W	D	L	F	A	PD	Pts
Gloucester O B	12	12	0	0	343	83	260	24
Taunton	12	11	0	1	296	130	166	22
Matson	12	9	0	3	222	99	123	18
Bridgwater & Albion	12	9	0	3	251	135	116	18
Oxford	12	7	0	5	200	218	-18	14
Clevedon	12	6	0	6	220	214	6	12
Aylesbury	12	6	0	6	194	210	-16	12
Swanage & Wrhm	12	5	0	7	162	268	-106	10
Combe Down	12	4	1	7	208	167	41	9
Banbury	12	2	2	8	129	223	-94	6
Marlow	12	2	2	8	126	228	-102	6
Penryn	12	2	1	9	131	254	-123	5
Windsor	12	0	0	12	126	379	-253	0

Club Colours: Black & white hoops, black shorts.

MATSON RFC
Ground Address: Redwell Road, Matson, Gloucester GL4 9JG. Tel: 0452 528963
Club Secretary: Gilbert Locke, 39 Oxmoor, Abbeydale, Gloucester GL4 9XW. Tel: (H) 0452 419587 Tel: (W) 0452 712802
Fixtures Secretary: Colin Thornton, 43 Brimsome Meadow, Highnam, Gloucester. Tel: (H) 0452 383138 Tel (W) 0594 844877
Club Colours: Black shirts, white shorts.

OLD PATESIANS RFC
Ground Address: Everest Road, Leckhampton, Cheltenham, Gloucestershire. Tel: 0242 524633
Club Secretary: Peter McMurray, Avon, Victoria Terrace, Cheltenham, Gloucestershire GL52 6BN. Tel: (H) 0242 570947 Tel: (W) 0242 515881
Fixtures Secretary: Steven Cohen, Rosslyn, Moorend Grove, Leckhampton, Cheltenham, Gloucestershire. Tel: (H) 0242 520873 Tel (W) 0242 221221 x281
Club Colours: Magenta, blue & white hoops.

OXFORD RFC
Ground Address: North Hinksey Village, Oxford. Tel: 0865 243984
Club Secretary: R Martin, Pantiles, 22 Didcot Road, Long Wittenham, Oxon OX14 4PZ. Tel: (H) 0865 407528
Fixtures Secretary: V Baskerville, 19 Holliers Crescent, Middle Barton, Chipping Norton OX7 7HE. Tel: (H) 0869 47495
Club Colours: Green, black & silver.

PENRYN RFC
Ground Address: The Memorial Ground, Kernick Road, Penryn, Cornwall TR10 8QP. Tel: 0326 372239
Club Secretary: Mrs MSD O'Neill, 80 Bohelland Road, Penryn, Cornwall TR10 8DY. Tel: (H) 0326 373283
Fixtures Secretary: Mr K Loft, 6 Bellevue, Penryn, Cornwall. Tel: (H) 0326 372862
Club Colours: Black & red hoops.

SWANAGE & WAREHAM RFC
Ground Address: Bestwall, Wareham, Dorset BH20 4AY. Tel: 0929 552224
Club Secretary: Kevin Large, 84 Victoria Avenue, Swanage, Dorset. Tel: (H) 0929 426823 Tel: (W) 0929 425818
Fixtures Secretary: John M Hopkins, Sospan, Greenclose Lane, Wimborne, Dorset BH21 9AL. Tel: (H) 0202 886804
Club Colours: Maroon shirts, white shorts.

SOUTH WEST DIVISION

WESTERN COUNTIES 1994-95 FIXTURES

September 17 (Week 3)
Bideford v Avonmouth OB
Crediton v Dings Crusaders
Devonport Services v Spartans
Drybrook v D & C Police
Okehampton v Launceston
Old Culverhaysians v Tiverton

September 24 (Week 4)
Avonmouth OB v Crediton
D & C Police v Devonport Services
Dings Crusdaers v Drybrook
Launceston v Penzance-Newlyn
Spartans v Old Culverhaysians
Tiverton v Okehampton

October 1 (Week 5)
Crediton v Bideford
Devonport Services v Dings Crusaders
Drybrook v Avonmouth OB
Okehampton v Spartans
Old Curverhaysians v D & C Police
Penzance-Newlyn v Tiverton

October 15 (Week 7)
Avonmouth OB v Devonport Services
Bideford v Drybrook
D & C Police v Okehampton
Dings Crusaders v Old Culverhaysians
Spartans v Penzance-Newlyn
Tiverton v Launceston

October 22 (Week 8)
Devonport Services v Bideford
Drybrook v Crediton
Launceston v Spartans
Okehampton v Dings Crusaders
Old Culverhaysians v Avonmouth OB
Penzance-Newlyn v D & C Police

October 29 (Week X2)
Avonmouth OB v Okehampton
Bideford v Old Culverhaysians
Crediton v Devonport Services
D & C Police v Launceston
Dings Crusaders v Penzance-Newlyn
Spartans v Tiverton

January 7 (Week 17)
Devonport Services v Drybrook
Launceston v Dings Crusaders
Okehampton v Bideford
Old Culverhaysians v Crediton
Penzance-Newlyn v Avonmouth OB
Tiverton v D & C Police

January 14 (Week 18)
Avonmouth OB v Launceston
Bideford v Penzance-Newlyn
Crediton v Okehampton
D & C Police v Spartans
Dings Crusaders v Tiverton
Drybrook v Old Culverhaysians

February 11 (Week 22)
Launceston v Bideford
Okehampton v Drybrook
Old Culverhaysians v Devonport Services
Penzance-Newlyn v Crediton
Spartans v Dings Crusaders
Tiverton v Avonmouth OB

February 25 (Week 24)
Avonmouth v Spartans
Bideford v Tiverton
Crediton v Launceston
Devonport Services v Okehampton
Dings Crusaders v D & C Police
Drybrook v Penzance-Newlyn

March 4 (Week 25)
D & C Police v Avonmouth OB
Launceston v Drybrook
Okehampton v Old Culverhaysians
Penzance-Newlyn v Devonport Services
Spartans v Bideford
Tiverton v Crediton

March 25 (Week 28)
Avonmouth OB v Dings Crusaders
Bideford v D & C Police
Crediton v Spartans
Devonport Services v Launceston
Drybrook v Tiverton
Old Culverhaysians v Penzance-Newlyn

April 8 (Week 30)
D & C Police v Crediton
Dings Crusaders v Bideford
Launceston v Old Culverhaysians
Penzance-Newlyn v Okehampton
Spartans v Drybrook
Tiverton v Devonport Services

WESTERN COUNTIES

AVONMOUTH OLD BOYS RFC
Ground Address: Barracks Lane, Avonmouth, Bristol. Tel:
0272 829093
Club Secretary: IK McNab, 48 Nibley Road,
Shirehampton, Bristol, Avon BS11 9XR. Tel: (H) 0272
823870 Tel: (W) 0222 666659
Fixtures Secretary: A Woodruff, 69 Prior Road,
Shirehampton, Bristol. Tel: (H) 0272 826160 Tel (W) 0272
364903
Club Colours: Black with single 4' red band.
BIDEFORD RFC
Ground Address: King George's Field, Bank End,
Bideford, Devon. Tel: 0237 474049
Club Secretary: Bernard A Ridd, Higher Benton, Bratton
Fleming, Devon EX32 7LF. Tel: (H) 0598 710298 Fax:
0598 710894
Fixtures Secretary: B Cork, 4 Park Lane, Bideford,
Devon. Tel: (H) 0237 479841 Tel (W) 0237 479841
Club Colours: Red & white hoops.
CREDITON RFC
Ground Address: Exhibition Road, Crediton EX17 1BY.
Tel: 0363 772784
Club Secretary: Mr P Gibbings, 80 Greenway, Crediton
EX17 3LP. Tel: (H) 0363 774820
Fixtures Secretary: Mr KS Pitt, Tannery Farm, Bow,
Devon EX17 6JP. Tel: (H) 0363 82230
Club Colours: Black & amber.
DEVON & CORNWALL CONSTABULARY RFC
Ground Address: Middlemoor Police HQ, Exeter, Devon.
Tel: 0392 52101
Club Secretary: Mr S Bassett, c/o Tavistock Police
Station, Bedford Square, Tavistock, Devon. Tel: (H) 0822
854510 Tel: (W) 0822 612217
Fixtures Secretary: Mr N Jones, c/o Paignton Police
Station. Tel (W) 0803 865126
Club Colours: White with black hoops.
DEVONPORT SERVICES RFC
Ground Address: The Rectory, Second Avenue,
Devonport, Plymouth PL1 5QE. Tel: 0752 501559
Club Secretary: Lt Cdr M Waythe, Field Gun Office,
HMS Drake, HM Naval Base, Plymouth. Tel: (H) 0752
848802 Tel: (W) 0752 555483
Fixtures Secretary: Lr Cdr R Wiltcher, Staff of Flag
Officer Plymouth, Mount Wise, Devonport, Plymouth. Tel:
(H) 0752 481589 Tel (W) 0752 501425
Club Colours: Navy blue shirts & shorts, red socks.
DINGS CRUSADERS RFC
Ground Address: Shaftesbury Crusade, Landseer Avenue,
Lockleaze, Bristol BS7. Tel: 0272 691367
Club Secretary: Gerry Williams, 22 Crowther Road,
Horfield, Bristol BS7 9NS. Tel: (H) 0272 516059 Tel: (W)
0272 436205
Fixtures Secretary: Terry Webb, 50 Monks Park Avenue,
Horfield, Bristol BS7 0UH. Tel: (H) 0272 692749
Club Colours: Royal blue & black.
DRYBROOK RFC
Ground Address: Mannings Ground, High Street,
Drybrook, Glos. Tel: 0594 542595
Club Secretary: Glyn Tingle, Southview, Hazel Hill,
Drybrook, Glos GL17 9HH. Tel: (H) 0594 543294 Tel:
(W) 0594 542769
Fixtures Secretary: Paul Gaylard, 10 Holywell Road,
Mitcheldean, Glos. Tel: (H) 0594 542104 Tel (W) 0594
542461 x1264
Club Colours: Green with black on white band.
LAUNCESTON RFC
Ground Address: The New Club House, Polson,
Launceston, Cornwall. Tel: 0566 773406
Club Secretary: Mr R Wilkinson, St Dominick House,
The Walk, Launceston, Cornwall PL15 8BP. Tel: (H) 0566
772433

FINAL TABLE

	P	W	D	L	F	A	PD	Pts
Old Patesians	12	10	1	1	215	99	116	21
Tiverton	12	10	0	2	197	130	67	20
Launceston	12	8	0	4	204	110	94	16
Penzance-Newlyn	12	8	0	4	185	124	61	16
Devonport Serv	12	6	1	5	183	128	55	13
O Culverhaysians	12	6	0	6	178	207	-29	12
Drybrook	12	5	0	7	140	181	-41	10
Crediton	12	5	0	7	121	192	-71	10
Spartans	12	4	1	7	132	160	-28	9
Avonmouth O B	12	4	1	7	146	193	-47	9
Bideford	12	3	1	8	128	163	-35	7
Okehampton	12	3	1	8	80	132	-52	7
Wiveliscombe	12	3	0	9	103	193	-90	6

Fixtures Secretary: Mr S Gill, Lower West Curry, Boyton,
Launceston, Cornwall. Tel: (H) 0566 85310
Club Colours: Black.
OKEHAMPTON RFC
Ground Address: Oaklands Park Showfield, Okehampton,
Devon. Tel: 0837 52508
Club Secretary: Ted Cann, 11 Exeter Road, Okehampton,
Devon EX20 1NN. Tel: (H) 0837 52759
Fixtures Secretary: David Dixon, Mistlebank, Ramsley
Road, South Zeal, Nr Okehampton, Devon. Tel: (H) 0837
840818
Club Colours: Maroon & amber hoops.
OLD CULVERHAYSIANS RFC
Ground Address: Glasshouse Ground, Bradford Road,
Combe Down, Bath, Avon. Tel: 0225 832081
Club Secretary: Mike Harding, 6 Gages Close,
Kingswood, Bristol BS15 2UH. Tel: (H) 0272 475862 Tel:
(W) 0272 517272
Fixtures Secretary: Bob Toghill, The Parsonage, The
Street, Rush Hill, Farrington Gurney, Bristol BS18 5UB.
Tel: (H) 0761 453553
Club Colours: Black.
PENZANCE & NEWLYN RFC
Ground Address: Westholme, Alexandra Road, Penzance,
Cornwall. Tel: 0736 64227
Club Secretary: AR Blewett, 17 Church Street, Newlyn,
Penzance, Cornwall TR18 5JY. Tel: (H) 0736 62562
Fixtures Secretary: A Edwards, Chy Kembro, Boslandew
Hill, Paul, Penzance, Cornwall TR19 6UD. Tel: (H) 0736
731042 Tel (W) 0736 331166
Club Colours: Black, white & red.
SPARTANS RFC
Ground Address: Archdeacon Meadow (at rear of cattle
market), Gloucester. Tel: 0452 410552
Club Secretary: Phil Minns, 8 Sebert Street, Kingsholm,
Gloucester GL1 3BP. Tel: (H) 0452 500122
Club Colours: Red.
TIVERTON RFC
Ground Address: Coronation Field, Bolham Road,
Tiverton, Devon EX16 6SG. Tel: 0884 252271
Club Secretary: Michael Alan Heard, 6 Norwood Road,
Tiverton, Devon EX16 6BD. Tel: (H) 0884 258600 Tel:
(W) 0392 384773
Fixtures Secretary: Raymond Takel, 90 Westexe South,
Tiverton, Devon. Tel: (H) 0884 257526 Tel (W) 0884
257777 x282(B)
Club Colours: Light & dark blue.

SOUTH WEST DIVISION

CORNWALL/DEVON 1994-95 FIXTURES

September 17 (Week 3)
Ivybridge   v   Exmouth
Paignton   v   Honiton
Plymouth CS   v   Newquay Hornets
South Molton   v   Teignmouth
Truro   v   Sidmouth
Veor   v   Saltash

September 24 (Week 4)
Exmouth   v   Hayle
Honiton   v   Plymouth CS
Newquay Hornets   v   Veor
Saltash   v   South Molton
Sidmouth   v   Ivybridge
Teignmouth   v   Truro

October 1 (Week 5)
Hayle   v   Sidmouth
Ivybridge   v   Teignmouth
Plymouth CS   v   Paignton
South Molton   v   Newquay Hornets
Truro   v   Saltash
Veor   v   Honiton

October 15 (Week 7)
Honiton   v   South Molton
Newquay Hornets   v   Truro
Paignton   v   Veor
Saltash   v   Ivybridge
Sidmouth   v   Exmouth
Teignmouth   v   Hayle

October 22 (Week 8)
Exmouth   v   Teignmouth
Hayle   v   Saltash
Ivybridge   v   Newquay Hornets
South Molton   v   Paignton
Truro   v   Honiton
Veor   v   Plymouth CS

October 29 (Week X2)
Honiton   v   Ivybridge
Newquay Hornets   v   Hayle
Paignton   v   Truro
Plymouth CS   v   South Molton
Saltash   v   Exmouth
Teignmouth   v   Sidmouth

January 7 (Week 17)
Exmouth   v   Newquay Hornets
Hayle   v   Honiton
Ivybridge   v   Paignton
Sidmouth   v   Saltash
South Molton   v   Veor
Truro   v   Plymouth CS

January 14 (Week 18)
Honiton   v   Exmouth
Newquay Hornets   v   Sidmouth
Paignton   v   Hayle
Plymouth CS   v   Ivybridge
Saltash   v   Teignmouth
Veor   v   Truro

February 11 (Week 22)
Exmouth   v   Paignton
Hayle   v   Plymouth CS
Ivybridge   v   Veor
Sidmouth   v   Honiton
Teignmouth   v   Newquay Hornets
Truro   v   South Molton

February 25 (Week 24)
Honiton   v   Teignmouth
Newquay Hornets   v   Saltash
Paignton   v   Sidmouth
Plymouth CS   v   Exmouth
South Molton   v   Ivybridge
Veor   v   Hayle

March 4 (Week 25)
Exmouth   v   Veor
Hayle   v   South Molton
Ivybridge   v   Truro
Saltash   v   Honiton
Sidmouth   v   Plymouth CS
Teignmouth   v   Paignton

March 25 (Week 28)
Honiton   v   Newquay Hornets
Paignton   v   Saltash
Plymouth CS   v   Teignmouth
South Molton   v   Exmouth
Truro   v   Hayle
Veor   v   Sidmouth

April 8 (Week 30)
Exmouth   v   Truro
Hayle   v   Ivybridge
Newquay Hornets   v   Paignton
Saltash   v   Plymouth CS
Sidmouth   v   South Molton
Teignmouth   v   Veor

CORNWALL & DEVON

EXMOUTH RFC
Ground Address:Imperial Recreation Ground, Royal Avenue, Exmouth, Devon. Tel: 0395 263665
Club Secretary: Stuart (Kes) Kesteven, 56 Marpool Hill, Exmouth, Devon EX8 2LH. Tel: (H) 0395 263351 Tel: (W) 0392 73614
Fixtures Secretary: Phil Gillgan, 9 Westminster Close, Exmouth, Devon EX8 5QS. Tel: (H) 0395 270936 Tel (W) 0392 77888
Club Colours: Heliotrope & white.

HAYLE RFC
Ground Address:Memorial Park, Marsh Lane, Hayle, Cornwall. Tel: 0736 753320
Club Secretary: Clive Rowe, Lanskyber, 3 Churchtown, Gwinear, Hayle, Cornwall TR27 5JZ. Tel: (H) 0736 850389
Fixtures Secretary: Mike Gee, Suhaili, 7 Hellesvean Close, St Ives, Cornwall TR26 2HQ. Tel: (H) 0736 797168
Club Colours: Green, black & white.

HONITON RFC
Ground Address:Allhallows Playing Fields, Northcote Lane, Honiton, Devon. Tel: 0404 41239
Club Secretary: Mr DB Todd, Omega, Sidmouth Road, Honiton, Devon EX14 8BE. Tel: (H) 0404 41608
Fixtures Secretary: Mr K Clark, Millhouse, Millhayes, Stockland, Nr Honiton, Devon. Tel: (H) 0404 881249 Tel (W) 0404 41866
Club Colours: Red, amber & black hoops.

IVYBRIDGE RFC
Ground Address:Cross-in-Hand, Exeter Road, Ivybridge. Tel: 0752 894392
Club Secretary: John Naylor, Trem-y-wawr, Crescent Road, Ivybridge, Devon PL21 0BP. Tel: (H) 0752 892412 Tel: (W) 0752 892516
Fixtures Secretary: Brian Bullock, 39 Savery Close, Ivybridge PL21 0NA. Tel: (H) 0752 894109
Club Colours: Green, white & black.

NEWQUAY HORNETS RFC
Ground Address:Newquay Sports Centre, Tretherras, Newquay, Cornwall. Tel: 0637 875533
Club Secretary: Russell Edwards, 17 St Thomas Road, Newquay, Cornwall TR7 1RS. Tel: (H) 0637 871479 Tel: (W) 0637 871479
Fixtures Secretary: Reg Roberts, 18 St Anne's Road, Newquay, Cornwall. Tel: (H) 0637 874568
Club Colours: Green & white.

PAIGNTON RFC
Ground Address:Queens Park, Queens Road, Paignton. Tel: 0803 557715
Club Secretary: Ray Squires, 67 Brantwood Drive, Paignton TQ4 5HY. Tel: (H) 0803 554360
Fixtures Secretary: Mrs Andrea Platt, 72 Osney Crescent, Paignton TQ4 5EZ. Tel: (H) 0803 521646
Club Colours: Red & white hoops.

PLYMOUTH CIVIL SERVICE RFC
Ground Address:Civil Season Sports Club, Beacon Down, Recreation Road, Plymouth PL2 3WA. Tel: 0752 702303
Club Secretary: Danny R Avery, 25 Weston Mill Hill, Weston Mill, Plymouth PL5 2AR. Tel: (H) 0752 365830 Tel: (W) 0752 552182
Fixtures Secretary: Stewart Brown, 35 Knapps Close, Elburton, Plymouth PL9 8UX. Tel: (H) 0752 492216 Tel (W) 0752 557258
Club Colours: Red & white shirts, black shorts, red socks.

SALTASH RFC
Ground Address:Moorlands Lane, Burraton, Saltash, Cornwall. Tel: 0752 847227
Club Secretary: Mr DR Jenkins, Windward, St Anns Chapel, Gunnislake, Cornwall PL18 9HQ. Tel: (H) 0822 832785

FINAL TABLE

	P	W	D	L	F	A	PD	Pts
Devon & Cnwll Pol	12	9	0	3	223	105	118	18
Exmouth	12	8	0	4	233	169	64	16
Hayle	12	7	0	5	132	132	0	14
Paignton	12	6	1	5	177	134	43	13
Teignmouth	12	6	1	5	192	195	-3	13
Truro	12	6	1	5	113	118	-5	13
Sidmouth	12	6	1	5	167	178	-11	13
Newquay Hornets	12	6	0	6	180	161	19	12
Plymouth C S	12	5	2	5	109	153	-44	12
South Molton	12	5	0	7	212	220	-8	10
Veor	12	4	1	7	150	166	-16	9
Ivybridge	12	4	1	7	131	176	-45	9
Liskeard-Looe	12	2	0	10	85	197	-112	4

Fixtures Secretary: L Maher, 17 Liskeard Road, Saltash, Cornwall. Tel (W) 0752 845559
Club Colours: Black, gold & red hoops.

SIDMOUTH RFC
Ground Address:Blackmore Ground, Heydon's Lane, Sidmouth, Devon. Tel: 0395 516816
Club Secretary: Brian Showell, 3 Connaught Close, Sidmouth, Devon EX10 8TU. Tel: (H) 0395 512055
Fixtures Secretary: T O'Brien, 2 Rivulet Cottages, Sidford, Sidmouth, Devon. Tel: (H) 0395 577403
Club Colours: Green jerseys, white shorts.

SOUTH MOLTON RFC
Ground Address:Pathfields, Station Road, South Molton, Devon EX36 3LH. Tel: 0769 572024
Club Secretary: Mrs Anne White, 8 Duke Street, South Molton, Devon EX36 3AL. Tel: (H) 0769 573741 Tel: (W) 0769 573204 Fax: 573200
Fixtures Secretary: Mr D Cronk, Old Rectory, Rose Ash, South Molton, Devon. Tel: (H) 0769 550402
Club Colours: Black.

TEIGNMOUTH RFC
Ground Address:Bitton Park Sports Ground, Bitton Park Road, Teignmouth, Devon TQ14 9DR. Tel: 0626 774714
Club Secretary: Mr Robert Loveridge, 59 Second Avenue, Teignmouth, Devon TQ14 9DN. Tel: (H) 0626 775891 Tel: (W) 0626 774556
Fixtures Secretary: Mr Brian Abraham, 16 Gloucester Road, Teignmouth. Tel: (H) 0626 776346
Club Colours: Red, white & black hoops.

TRURO RFC
Ground Address:St Clements Hill, Truro, Cornwall TR1 1NY. Tel: 0872 74750
Club Secretary: Philip A Rowe, 36 Chirgwin Road, Truro, Cornwall TR1 1TT. Tel: (H) 0872 71915 Tel: (W) 0872 224202
Fixtures Secretary: Philip Lear, 5 Carclew Street, Truro, Cornwall TR1 2DY. Tel: (H) 0872 260741 Tel (W) 0872 73479
Club Colours: Blue & amber quarters.

VEOR RFC
Ground Address:Wheal Gerry, Cliff View Road, Camborne, Cornwall.
Club Secretary: Bert Barber JP, 86 Dolcoath Road, Camborne, Cornwall TR14 8RP. Tel: (H) 0209 710593 Tel: (W) 0752 665951
Fixtures Secretary: Paul Pascoe, 18 Condurrow Road, Beacon, Camborne, Cornwall. Tel: (H) 0209 716535
Club Colours: Amber shirts, black shorts.

SOUTH WEST DIVISION

DEVON ONE
1994-95
FIXTURES

September 17 (Week 3)
Exeter Saracens v Dartmouth
Ilfracombe v Tavistock
Kingsbridge v Withycombe
Old Plymothian v Newton Abbot
Old Technicians v Salcombe
Prince Rock v Old Public Oaks

September 24 (Week 4)
Dartmouth v Ilfracombe
Newton Abbot v Topsham
Old Public Oaks v Old Technicians
Salcombe v Old Plymothian
Tavistock v Kingsbridge
Withycombe v Prince Rock

October 1 (Week 5)
Ilfracombe v Exeter Saracens
Kingsbridge v Dartmouth
Old Plymothian v Old Public Oaks
Old Technicians v Withycombe
Prince Rock v Tavistock
Topsham v Salcombe

October 15 (Week 7)
Dartmouth v Prince Rock
Exeter Saracens v Kingsbridge
Old Public Oaks v Topsham
Salcombe v Newton Abbot
Tavistock v Old Technicians
Withycombe v Old Plymothian

October 22 (Week 8)
Kingsbridge v Ilfracombe
Newton Abbot v Old Public Oaks
Old Plymothian v Tavistock
Old Technicians v Dartmouth
Prince Rock v Exeter Saracens
Topsham v Withycombe

October 29 (Week X2)
Dartmouth v Old Plymothian
Exeter Saracens v Old Technicians
Ilfracombe v Prince Rock
Old Public Oaks v Salcombe
Tavistock v Topsham
Withycombe v Newton Abbot

January 7 (Week 17)
Newton Abbot v Tavistock
Old Plymothian v Exeter Saracens
Old Technicians v Ilfracombe
Prince Rock v Kingsbridge
Salcombe v Withycombe
Topsham v Dartmouth

January 14 (Week 18)
Dartmouth v Newton Abbot
Exeter Saracens v Topsham
Ilfracombe v Old Plymothian
Kingsbridge v Old Technicians
Tavistock v Salcombe
Withycombe v Old Public Oaks

February 11 (Week 22)
Newton Abbot v Exeter Saracens
Old Plymothian v Kingsbridge
Old Public Oaks v Tavistock
Old Technicians v Prince Rock
Salcombe v Dartmouth
Topsham v Ilfracombe

February 25 (Week 24)
Dartmouth v Old Public Oaks
Exeter Saracens v Salcombe
Ilfracombe v Newton Abbot
Kingsbridge v Topsham
Prince Rock v Old Plymothian
Tavistock v Withycombe

March 4 (Week 25)
Newton Abbot v Kingbridge
Old Plymothian v Old Technicians
Old Public Oaks v Exeter Saracens
Salcombe v Ilfracombe
Topsham v Prince Rock
Withycombe v Dartmouth

March 25 (Week 28)
Dartmouth v Tavistock
Exeter Saracens v Withycombe
Ilfracombe v Old Public Oaks
Kingsbridge v Salcombe
Old Technicians v Topsham
Prince Rock v Newton Abbot

April 8 (Week 30)
Newton Abbot v Old Technicians
Old Public Oaks v Kingsbridge
Salcombe v Prince Rock
Tavistock v Exeter Saracens
Topsham v Old Plymothian
Withycombe v Ilfracombe

DEVON ONE

DARTMOUTH RFC
Ground Address:The Clubhouse, Roseville Street,
Dartmouth, South Devon. Tel: 0803 833994
Club Secretary: Ms A Reaburn, 7 Crowthers Hill,
Dartmouth, Devon TQ6 9QX. Tel: (H) 0803 832957
Club Colours: Emerald & scarlet.
EXETER SARACENS RFC
Ground Address:Exhibition Field, Summer Lane,
Whipton, Exeter. Tel: 0392 462651
Club Secretary: Peter Blackmore, 1 Vieux Close,
Behindhayes, Otterton, Budleigh Salterton, Devon EX9
7JT. Tel: (H) 0395 67777 Tel: (W) 0395 264373
Fixtures Secretary: Dave McIlroy, Downderry, 7 West
Clyst, Pinhoe, Exeter EX1 3TP. Tel: (H) 0392 469146 Tel
(W) 0392 55554
Club Colours: Red shirts, black shorts.
ILFRACOMBE RFC
Ground Address:Brimlands, Hillsborough Road,
Ilfracombe, Devon. Tel: 0271 864249
Club Secretary: Andrew Burke, 14 South Burrow Road,
Ilfracombe, Devon EX34 8JE. Tel: (H) 0271 882819 Tel:
(W) 0271 72128
Fixtures Secretary: John Williams, 5 Castle Hill Villas,
Ilfracombe, Devon. Tel: (H) 0271 865677
Club Colours: Blue & white hoops.
KINGSBRIDGE RFC
Ground Address:High House, Kingsbridge, Devon TQ7
1JL. Tel: 0548 852051
Club Secretary: Martn Newman, Fourwinds, 46 Saffron
Park, Kingsbridge, Devon TQ7 1RL. Tel: (H) 0548 853976
Tel: (W) 0548 853101
Fixtures Secretary: Arthur Ball, 7 Riverview Place,
Kingsbridge, Devon. Tel: (H) 0548 852182
Club Colours: Blue & white.
NEWTON ABBOT RFC
Ground Address:Rackenhayes, Kingsteignton Road,
Newton Abbot, Devon. Tel: 0626 54150
Club Secretary: Mrs Sherril Lock, 38 Mile End Road,
Newton Abbot, Devon TQ12 1RW. Tel: (H) 0626 54835
Tel: (W) 0803 312861
Fixtures Secretary: Allan Baker, 5 Westward View,
Newton Abbot, Devon. Tel: (H) 0626 61494
Club Colours: All white.
OLD PLYMOTHIANS & MANHAMEADIAN RFC
Ground Address:South West, Bickleigh Down Lane,
Roborough, Plymouth.
Club Secretary: E J Bolster, 22 Castle Close, Lower
Compton, Plymouth, PL3 6JS. Tel: (H) 0752 223908 Tel:
(W) 0752 673626
Fixtures Secretary: Simon Matthews, 14 Trevians Road,
Eggluckland, Plymouth. Tel: (H) 0752 780114 Tel (W)
0392 382457
Club Colours: Claret/blue quarters.
OLD PUBLIC OAKS RFC
Ground Address:King George V Playing Fields, Elburton,
Plymouth. Tel: Clubhouse: 0752 252039
Club Secretary: GH Mathews, 25 Colwill Road,
Mainstone Estate, PLymouth PL6 8RP. Tel: (H) 0752
707363 Tel: (W) 0752 663231
Fixtures Secretary: N Jordan, 112A Underwood Road,
Plympton, Plymouth PL7 3TA. Tel: (H) 0752 330455 Tel
(W) 0752 663231
Club Colours: Green & gold hoops.
OLD TECHNICIANS RFC
Ground Address:Weston Mill Oak Villa, Ferndale Road,
Plymouth, Devon. Tel: 0752 363352
Club Secretary: Steve Reeves, 3A Clowance Street,
Devonport, Plymouth PL1 4LJ. Tel: (H) 0752 605318

FINAL TABLE

	P	W	D	L	F	A	PD	Pts
Honiton	12	10	1	1	236	79	157	21
Newton Abbot	12	9	0	3	283	119	164	18
Tavistock	12	8	1	3	230	114	116	17
Old Public Oaks	12	8	0	4	291	150	141	16
Topsham	12	8	0	4	222	89	133	16
Old Plymothian	12	7	1	4	166	130	36	15
Kingsbridge	12	6	0	6	143	156	-13	12
Exeter Saracens	12	5	0	7	111	186	-75	10
Ilfracombe	12	5	0	7	96	192	-96	10
Withycombe	12	4	1	7	109	158	-49	9
Old Technicians	12	4	0	8	99	151	-52	8
Dartmouth	12	1	0	11	92	251	-159	2
Jesters	12	1	0	11	45	348	-303	2

PRINCE ROCK RFC
Ground Address:Seaton Barracks, Crownhill, Plymouth.
Club Secretary: DW Bishop, 19 Grafton Road, Mutley,
Plymouth PL4 6QR. Tel: (H) 0752 220031
Fixtures Secretary: L Fowdon, 1 Hayes Road, Oreston,
Plymouth. Tel: (H) 0752 405018
Club Colours: Amber shirts, white shorts.
SALCOMBE RFC
Ground Address:Twomgades, Camperdown Road,
Salcombe TQ8 8AX. Tel: 0548 842639
Club Secretary: GS Jacobs, Cornerways, Bonaventure
Road, Salcombe, Devon TQ8 8BG. Tel: (H) 0548 844123
Fixtures Secretary: I Vaissiere, The Wood, D'Courcy
Road, Salcombe, Devon TQ8 8LQ. Tel: (H) 0548 842778
Club Colours: Red & white or black & white.
TAVISTOCK RFC
Ground Address:Sandy Park, Trelawney Road, Tavistock,
Devon. Tel: 0822 618275
Club Secretary: Mr T Masters, St Peters, 10 Uplands,
Tavistock, Devon PL19 8ET. Tel: (H) 0822 614323 Tel:
(W) 0566 774211
Fixtures Secretary: Cedric Sutton, 121 Plymouth Road,
Tavistock, Devon PL19 9DT. Tel: (H) 0822 615829
Club Colours: Black with red hoops.
TOPSHAM RFC
Ground Address:Bonfire Field, Topsham, Devon. Tel:
0392 873651
Club Secretary: David Burdick, 21 Victoria Road,
Topsham, Devon EX3 0EU. Tel: (H) 0392 873065 Tel:
(W) 0626 863140 Fax: 0626 866551
Fixtures Secretary: Paul Pirongs, The Dutch House, The
Strand, Topsham, Devon. Tel: (H) 0392 877347 Tel (W)
0626 52655
Club Colours: Light & dark blue hoops.
WITHYCOMBE RFC
Ground Address:Raleigh Park, Hulham Road,
Withycombe, Exmouth, Devon. Tel: 0395 266762
Club Secretary: Mr M Norman, 2 Claremont Lane,
Exmouth EX8 2LE. Tel: (H) 0395 270644
Fixtures Secretary: Peter Cozens, 2 Meadow Street,
Exmouth, Devon EX8 1LH. Tel: (H) 0395 269970
Club Colours: Emerald green & black hoops. Change:
Yellow with narrow green & black hoops.

SOUTH WEST DIVISION

<table>
<tr><td>

**DEVON TWO
1994-95
FIXTURES**

</td></tr>
</table>

September 17 (Week 3)
Axminster v Jesters
Devonport HSOB v Cullompton
North Tawton v Plymouth Argaum
Plymouth YMCA v Totnes
Plympton Victoria v Torrington
Plymstock v Tamar Saracens

September 24 (Week 4)
Cullompton v North Tawton
Jesters v St Columba
Plymouth Argaum v Plymouth YMCA
Tamar Saracens v Axminster
Torrington v Plymstock
Totnes v Plympton Victoria

October 1 (Week 5)
Axminster v Torrington
North Tawton v Devonport HSOB
Plymouth YMCA v Cullompton
Plympton Victoria v Plymouth Argaum
Plymstock v Totnes
St Columba v Tamar Saracens

October 15 (Week 7)
Cullompton v Plympton Victoria
Devonport HSOB v Plymouth YMCA
Plymouth Argaum v Plymstock
Tamar Saracens v Jesters
Torrington v St Columba
Totnes v Axminster

October 22 (Week 8)
Axminster v Plymouth Argaum
Jesters v Torrington
Plymouth YMCA v North Tawton
Plympton Victoria v Devonport HSOB
Plymstock v Cullompton
St Columba v Totnes

October 29 (Week X2)
Cullompton v Axminster
Devonport HSOB v Plymstock
North Tawton v Plympton Victoria
Plymouth Argaum v St Columba
Torrington v Tamar Saracens
Totnes v Jesters

January 7 (Week 17)
Axminster v Devonport HSOB
Jesters v Plymouth Argaum
Plympton Victoria v Plymouth YMCA
Plymstock v North Tawton
St Columba v Cullompton
Tamar Saracens v Totnes

January 14 (Week 18)
Cullompton v Jesters
Devonport HSOB v St Columba
North Tawton v Axminster
Plymouth Argaum v Tamar Saracens
Plymouth YMCA v Plymstock
Totnes v Torrington

February 11 (Week 22)
Axminster v Plymouth YMCA
Jesters v Devonport HSOB
Plymstock v Plympton Victoria
St Columba v North Tawton
Tamar Saracens v Cullompton
Torrington v Plymouth Argaum

February 25 (Week 24)
Cullompton v Torrington
Devonport HSOB v Tamar Saracens
North Tawton v Jesters
Plymouth Argaum v Totnes
Plymouth YMCA v St Columba
Plumpton Victoria v Axminster

March 4 (Week 25)
Axminster v Plymstock
Jesters v Plymouth YMCA
St Columba v Plympton Victoria
Tamar Saracens v North Tawton
Torrington v Devonport HSOB
Totnes v Cullompton

March 25 (Week 28)
Cullompton v Plymouth Argaum
Devonport HSOB v Totnes
North Tawton v Torrington
Plymouth YMCA v Tamar Saracens
Plympton Victoria v Jesters
Plymstock v St Columba

April 8 (Week 30)
Jesters v Plymstock
Plymouth Argaum v Devonport HSOB
St Columba v Axminster
Tamar Saracens v Plympton Victoria
Torrington v Plymouth YMCA
Totnes v North Tawton

DEVON TWO

AXMINSTER RUFC
Ground Address: Gammons Hill, Kilmington, Axminster, Devon. Tel: 0297 32016
Club Secretary: Nikki Parker, 74 The Cricketers, Axminster, Devon EX13 5RH. Tel: (H) 0297 35893 Tel: (W) 0297 22932
Fixtures Secretary: Nigel Powell, 6 Fairfield Close, Axminster, Devon EX13 5LP. Tel: (H) 0297 34938
Club Colours: Red & royal blue.
CULLOMPTON RFC
Ground Address: Stafford Park, Knowle Lane, Cullompton, Devon EX15 1PZ. Tel: 0884 32480
Club Secretary: Nigel Nichols, 91 Bilbie Close, Cullompton, Devon EX15 1LG. Tel: (H) 0884 38365
Fixtures Secretary: Matthew Weetman, 64 Langlands Road, Cullompton, Devon EX15 1JD. Tel: (H) 0884 32736
Club Colours: Scarlet & black hoops.
DEVONPORT HIGH SCHOOL OLD BOYS' RFC
Ground Address: Devonport High School for Boys, Paradise Road, Millbridge, Devonport, Plymouth PL1 5DP. Tel: 0752 564682
Club Secretary: Mr GK Simpson, 108 Pattinson Drive, Mainstone, Plymouth, Devon PL6 8RU. Tel: (H) 0752 707432 Tel: (W) 0752 563001
Fixtures Secretary: Mr DA Morgan, Sheba, Downderry, Cornwall PL11 3JA. Tel: (H) 05035 594
Club Colours: Green, black & white irregular hoops.
JESTERS RFC
Ground Address: Marsh Meadows, Lower Leigham, Plym Valley, Devon.
Club Secretary: Debbie Hancock, 61 Powisland Drive, Derriford, Plymouth PL6 6AD. Tel: (H) 0752 773469
Fixtures Secretary: John Gillen, Bassett House, Hatches Green, Gunnislake, Cornwall. Tel: (H) 0822 832919 Tel (W) 0752 701521
Club Colours: Red, white, gold & black quarters.
NORTH TAWTON RFC
Ground Address: The Butts, Bartn Street, NOrth Tawton, Devon.
Club Secretary: Mrs Gillian Mary Hoggins, The Old Forge, 33 North Street, North Tawton, Devon EX20 2DE. Tel: (H) 0837 82516
Fixtures Secretary: Mr Colin Sharp, 74 Fore Street, North Tawton, Devon EX20 2ED. Tel: (H) 0837 82869 Tel (W) 0837 82224
Club Colours: Black & amber or plain amber.
PLYMOUTH ARGAUM RFC
Ground Address: The Clubhouse, Blackeven Hill, Bickleigh Down Road, Roborough, Plymouth, Devon. Tel: 0752 772156
Club Secretary: PA Evans, 34A Park View, Knighton Road, St Judes, Plymouth PL4 9BY. Tel: (H) 0752 672030 Tel: (W) 0752 385402
Fixtures Secretary: I Roberts, 31 Grasmere Close, Derriford, Plymouth PL6 5HE. Tel: (H) 0752 779163
Club Colours: Green, black & white.
PLYMOUTH YM RFC
Ground Address: Suttons Field, John Kitto Community College, Burrington Way, Honicknowle, Plymouth. Tel: 0752 702492
Club Secretary: Mr Jim Mather, 126 Pike Road, Efford, Plymouth. Tel: (H) 0752 268169
Fixtures Secretary: Mr Bob Pearce, 24 East Park Avenue, Mutley, Plymouth. Tel: (H) 0752 663442
Club Colours: Red with black & white hoops.
PLYMPTON VICTORIA RFC
Ground Address: King George V Playing Fields, Elburton, Plymstock, Plymouth, Devon.
Club Secretary: GB Knight, 62 The Mead, Plympton, Plymouth, Devon PL7 4HT. Tel: (H) 0752 342888

FINAL TABLE

	P	W	D	L	F	A	PD	Pts
Salcombe	11	10	0	1	327	79	248	20
Prince Rock	11	10	0	1	232	87	145	20
Torrington	11	9	0	2	246	111	135	18
Totnes	11	7	0	4	151	117	34	14
Cullompton	11	6	1	4	218	109	109	13
North Tawton	11	6	0	5	86	169	-83	12
Plymouth Argaum	11	4	0	7	135	173	-38	8
Plymstock	11	4	0	7	114	185	-71	8
St Columba	11	2	2	7	122	121	1	6
Tamar Saracens	11	2	1	8	76	206	-130	5
Devonport HSOB	11	2	0	9	72	212	-140	4
Plymouth YMCA	11	2	0	9	96	306	-210	4

Fixtures Secretary: P Evans, 9 Brookingfield Close, Plympton, Plymouth. Tel: (H) 0752 347311
Club Colours: Red & white quarters.
PLYMSTOCK RFC
Ground Address: King George V Playing Fields, Elburton, Plymouth, Devon.
Club Secretary: Mrs Rosemary Holloway, 45 Southern Way, Plymstock, Plymouth, Devon PL9 8TB. Tel: (H) 0752 404578
Fixtures Secretary: Mr Nigel Higginson, 6 Brockley Road, Laira, Plymouth, Devon PL3 6BT. Tel: (H) 0752 260008 Tel (W) 0752 491410
Club Colours: Blue shirts, black shorts.
ST COLUMBA TORPOINT RFC
Ground Address: Defiance Field, Torpoint, Cornwall.
Club Secretary: Peter Charles Summers, 112 Rochford Crescent, Ernesettle, Plymouth, Devon PL5 2QD. Tel: (H) 0752 362785 Tel: (W) 0752 552115
Fixtures Secretary: Peter Charles Summers, 112 Rochford Crescent, Ernesettle, Plymouth, Devon PL5 2QD. Tel: (H) 0752 362785 Tel (W) 0752 552115
TAMAR SARACENS RFC
Ground Address: Parkway Sports Club, Ernesettle Lane, Ernesettle, Plymouth, Devon. Tel: 0752 363080
Club Secretary: K McDermottroe, 8 Pinewood Close, Plympton, Plymouth, Devon PL7 3DW. Tel: (H) 0752 344639 Tel: (W) 0752 364341
Fixtures Secretary: J Bentley, 29 Dunster Close, Plympton, Plymouth PL7 3FN. Tel: (H) 0752 345020 Tel (W) 0752 364341
Club Colours: Black with red, green & white hoops.
TORRINGTON RUFC
Ground Address: Donnacroft Fields, Hatchmoor Road, Torrington, North Devon.
Club Secretary: Mr NS Parker, 8 Hodges Walk, Torrington, North Devon EX38 7NP. Tel: (H) 0805 624216
Fixtures Secretary: Mr D Glover, Hayedown, Little Torrington, Torrington, North Devon. Tel: (H) 0805 624566
Club Colours: Green, black & white hoops.
TOTNES
Ground Address: The Borough Park, Totnes, Devon TQ9 5XX. Tel: 0803 867796
Club Secretary: Miss J Pantry, 50 Punchards Down, Follaton, Totnes, Devon TQ9 5FC. Tel: (H) 0803 864581 Tel: (W) 0803 866560
Fixtures Secretary: Roger Lang, 42 The Carrions, Totnes, Devon TQ9 5SX. Tel: (H) 0803 864516
Club Colours: Royal blue & white.

SOUTH WEST DIVISION

CORNWALL ONE
1994-95
FIXTURES

September 17 (Week 3)
Bude v Bodmin
Falmouth v St Agnes
Illogan Park v Stithians
Liskeard-Looe v Wadebridge
St Austell v Helston

October 1 (Week 5)
Bodmin v Liskeard-Looe
Helston v Perranporth
St Agnes v Illogan Park
Stithians v St Austell
Wadebridge v Falmouth

October 15 (Week 7)
Falmouth v Bodmin
Illogan Park v Wadebridge
Liskeard-Looe v Bude
Perranporth v Stithians
St Austell v St Agnes

October 29 (Week X2)
Bodmin v Illogan Park
Bude v Falmouth
St Agnes v Perranporth
Stithians v Helston
Wadebridge v St Austell

January 7 (Week 17)
Falmouth v Liskeard-Looe
Helston v St Agnes
Illogan Park v Bude
Perranporth v Wadebridge
St Austell v Bodmin

January 14 (Week 18)
Bodmin v Perranporth
Bude v St Austell
Liskeard-Looe v Illogan Park
St Agnes v Stithians
Wadebridge v Helston

February 11 (Week 22)
Helston v Bodmin
Illogan Park v Falmouth
Perranporth v Bude
St Austell v Liskeard-Looe
Stithians v Wadebridge

February 25 (Week 24)
Bodmin v Stithians
Bude v Helston
Falmouth v St Austell
Liskeard-Looe v Perranporth
Wadebridge v St Agnes

March 4 (Week 25)
Helston v Liskeard-Looe
Perranporth v Falmouth
St Agnes v Bodmin
St Austell v Illogan Park
Stithians v Bude

March 25 (Week 28)
Bodmin v Wadebridge
Bude v St Agnes
Falmouth v Helston
Illogan Park v Perranporth
Liskeard-Looe v Stithians

April 8 (Week 30)
Helston v Illogan Park
Perranporth v St Austell
St Agnes v Liskeard-Looe
Stithians v Falmouth
Wadebridge v Bude

CORNWALL ONE

BODMIN RFC
Ground Address: Cliffden Park, Bodmin, Cornwall. Tel: 0208 74629
Club Secretary: A Cornish, 11 Springwell View, Love Lane, Bodmin, Cornwall PL31 2QP. Tel (H) 0208 75519 (W) 0208 79128 x 218
Fixtures Secretary: A Rowe, 6 Treburdon Drive, Roche, St Austell, Cornwall PL26 8QB. Tel (H) 0726 890670
Club Colours: Light blue with navy band.
BUDE RFC
Ground Address: Bencoolen Meadow (off Kings Hill), Bude, Cornwall. Tel: 0288 354795
Club Secretary: Miss Marilyn Cockbill, 2 Lee Cottages, Morwenstow, Bude EX23 9HT. Tel: (H) 0288 331690 Tel: (W) 0409 254101
Fixtures Secretary: Mr John Boundy, Linhays, Buttsbeare Cross, Bridgerule, Holsworthy, Devon. Tel: (H) 0288 81296 Tel (W) 0288 353766
Club Colours: Maroon & sky blue.
FALMOUTH RFC
Ground Address: Dracaena Avenue, Falmouth, Cornwall. Tel: 0326 311304
Club Secretary: JK Dryden, 15 Pengarth Road, Falmouth, Cornwall TR11 2TY. Tel: (H) 0326 316644 Tel: (W) 0326 311644
Fixtures Secretary: GV Wilkes, 17 Rose Valley, Three Milestones, Truro, Cornwall. Tel: (H) 0872 77249 Tel (W) 0872 74451
Club Colours: Black & white.
HELSTON RFC
Ground Address: King George V Playing Fields, Clodgey Lane, Helston. Tel: 0326 573423
Club Secretary: Mrs BA Davis, 8 Penrose Road, Helston, Cornwall TR13 8TP. Tel: (H) 0326 563744 Tel: (W) 0209 215620
Fixtures Secretary: Mrs BA Davis, 8 Penrose Road, Helston, Cornwall TR13 8TP. Tel: (H) 0326 563744 Tel (W) 0209 215620
Club Colours: Navy & white hoops.
ILLOGAN PARK RFC
Ground Address: Paynters Lane End, Illogan, Redruth, Cornwall.
Club Secretary: A Baldwin, 1 Killigrew Place, Falmouth. Tel: (H) 0326 311 442
Fixtures Secretary: G Roberts, 28 Treberran Gardens, Toivaddon, Camborne. Tel: (H) 0209 717559
Club Colours: old & black.
LISKEARD-LOOE RFC
Ground Address: Lux Park, Liskeard. Tel: 0579 342665
Club Secretary: Geoff Collings, Little Polscoe, Lostwithiel, Cornwall PL22 0HS. Tel: (H) 0208 873201 Tel: (W) 0208 873201
Fixtures Secretary: Geoff Collings, Little Polscoe, Lostwithiel, Cornwall PL22 0HS. Tel: (H) 0208 873201 Tel (W) 0208 873201
Club Colours: Red & black 4' hoops.
PERRANPORTH RFC
Ground Address: Ponsmere Valley, Perranporth, Cornwall. Tel: 0872 57
Club Secretary: Mr Nik Lewis, Cornerways, Perranwell Road, Goonhaven, Nr Truro, Cornwall TR4 9JL. Tel: (H) 0872 571217
Fixtures Secretary: Mr John Smeadon, Nanparra Cottage, Granny's Lane, Perranporth, Cornwall. Tel: (H) 0872 573015
Club Colours: Green & gold.

FINAL TABLE

	P	W	D	L	F	A	PD	Pts
Saltash	10	9	1	0	319	48	271	19
Falmouth	10	6	1	3	247	104	143	13
Helston	10	6	1	3	207	72	135	13
St Ausell	10	6	1	3	211	114	97	13
Bude	10	6	1	3	131	112	19	13
Wadebridge Cams	10	6	1	3	109	103	6	13
Bodmin	10	4	2	4	163	141	22	10
Illogan Park	10	4	0	6	91	156	-65	8
Stithians	10	3	0	7	150	190	-40	6
Redruth Albany	10	1	0	9	61	232	-171	2
St Just	10	0	0	10	41	458	-417	-2

ST AGNES RFC
Ground Address: Enys Parc, Polberro, St Agnes, Cornwall. Tel: 0872 552363
Club Secretary: Mr T Barnes, T & JB Produce Ltd, Stanley Way, Cardrew Industrial Estate, Redruth, Cornwall TR15 1SP. Tel: (H) 0209 890218 Tel: (W) 0209 314477
Fixtures Secretary: Mr Bob Howard, Wheal Friendly Chalets, Roughwood, Rocky Lane, St Agnes. Tel: (H) 0872 553160 Tel (W) 0872 553160
Club Colours: Black & red hoops.
ST AUSTELL RFC
Ground Address: Tregorrick Lane, St Austell, Cornwall PL26 7AG. Tel: 0726 76300
Club Secretary: Jerry Yeoman, c/o St Austell RFC, Tregorrick Lane, St Austell, Cornwall PL26 7AG. Tel: (W) 0726 76300
Fixtures Secretary: Howard Roberts, Trethevy Farm, Par, Cornwall. Tel: (H) 0726 812065
Club Colours: Red & white hoops.
STITHIANS RFC
Ground Address: Playing Field, Stithians.
Club Secretary: T J Knight, 6 Chainwalk Drive, Kenwyn, Truro, Cornwall. Tel: (H) 0872 70849 Tel: (W) 0872 76116
Fixtures Secretary: C Burley, 54 Collins Parc, Stithians, Truro, Cornwall. Tel: (H) 0209 860148
Club Colours: Maroon.
WADEBRIDGE CAMELS RFC
Ground Address: Molesworth Field, Egloshaule, Wadebridge, Cornwall.
Club Secretary: Mark Richards, Perlees Farm, St Breock, Wadebridge, Cornwall PL27 7HU. Tel: (H) 020881 2848 Tel: (W) 0726 860308
Fixtures Secretary: Chris Taylor, Penhale, Whitecross, Wadebridge, Cornwall. Tel: (H) 020881 3919
Club Colours: Chocolate & gold.

SOUTH WEST DIVISION

CORNWALL TWO
1994-95
FIXTURES

April 8 (Week 30)
Redruth Albany v Lankelly
Roseland v St Day
St Just v Camborne SoM

September 17 (Week 3)
Lankelly v Camborne SoM
Redruth Albany v Roseland
St Just v St Day

October 1 (Week 5)
Camborne SoM v Roseland
St Day v Redruth Albany
St Just v Lankelly

October 15 (Week 7)
Lankelly v St Day
Redruth Albany v Camborne SoM
Roseland v St Just

October 29 (Week X2)
Camborne SoM v St Day
Roseland v Lankelly
St Just v Redruth Albany

January 7 (Week 17)
Camborne SoM v St Just
Lankelly v Redruth Albany
St Day v Roseland

February 11 (Week 22)
Camborne SoM v Lankelly
Roseland v Redruth Albany
St Day v St Just

February 25 (Week 24)
Lankelly v St Just
Redruth Albany v St Day
Roseland v Camborne SoM

March 4 (Week 25)
Camborne SoM v Redruth Albany
St Day v Lankelly
St Just v Roseland

March 25 (Week 28)
Lankelly v Roseland
Redruth Albany v St Just
St Day v Camborne SoM

CORNWALL TWO

CAMBORNE SCHOOL OF MINES RFC
Ground Address:The Memorial Ground, Boundervean Lane, Penponds, Camborne. Tel: 0209 612959 Clubhouse: 0209 711935
Club Secretary: Dr CV Phillips, Barlowena, Alexandra Road, Illogen, Redruth, Cornwall TR16 4EN. Tel: (H) 0209 842660 Tel: (W) 0209 714866
Fixtures Secretary: DR CV Phillips, Barlowena, Alexandra Road, Illogen, Redruth, Cornwall TR16 4EN. Tel: (H) 0209 842660 Tel (W) 0209 714866
Club Colours: Navy, gold & silver hoops or quarters.
LANKELLY-FOWEY RFC
Ground Address:Lankelly Farm, Lankelly Lane, Fowey.
Club Secretary: DL Sainsbury, 2 Saffron Close, Fowey, Cornwall PL23 1EU. Tel: (H) 0726 832342 Tel: (W) 0726 832342
Fixtures Secretary: R Sainsbury, 21 Wood Lane, Tywardreath. Tel: (H) 814035 Tel (W) 861140
Club Colours: Navy blue & white hoops, black shorts.
REDRUTH ALBANY RFC
Ground Address:Trewirgie Mill, Redruth. Tel: 0209 216945
Club Secretary: Simon Johns, 41 Rose Road, Redruth. Tel: (W) 0326 211945
Fixtures Secretary: Jan Wills, 1 Church Street, St Day. Tel: (H) 0209 820872 Tel (W) 0209 820171
Club Colours: Blue and white.
ROSELAND RFC
Ground Address:Philleigh, Truro, Cornwall. Tel: 0872 580254
Club Secretary: CR Thomas, Parton Vrane, Gerrans, Portscatho, Truro, Cornwall TR2 5ET. Tel: (H) 0872 580495 Tel: (W) 0872 580495
Fixtures Secretary: CJ Trerise, Omega, West End, Blackwater, Truro, Cornwall. Tel: (H) 0972 560248 Tel (W) 0872 320000
Club Colours: Navy & scarlet.
ST DAY RFC
Ground Address:The Playing Field, St Day, Redruth, Cornwall.
Club Secretary: PC Newcombe, 21 Martinvale Parc, Mount Ambrose, Redruth, Cornwall TR15 1SD. Tel: (H) 0209 212834 Tel: (W) 0872 76477
Fixtures Secretary: KP Bawden, 34 Veor House, South Terrace, Camborne TR14 8SS. Tel: (H) 0209 716023 Tel (W) 0736 793808
Club Colours: White with red band.
ST JUST RFC
Ground Address:Tregeseal, St Just, Penwith, Cornwall TR19 7PF. Tel: 0736 788593
Club Secretary: Hon Secretary, St Just RFC, Tregeseal, St Just, Penwith, Cornwall TR19 7PF.
Fixtures Secretary: P Whiteman, Ashmore Cottage, Kellynack, St Just, Penwith, Cornwall. Tel: (H) 0736 788150 Tel (W) 0736 788150
Club Colours: Black.

FINAL TABLE

	P	W	D	L	F	A	PD	Pts
St Agnes	10	10	0	0	217	73	144	20
Perranporth	10	8	0	2	110	62	48	16
St Day	10	5	0	5	132	112	20	10
Roseland	10	4	0	6	127	152	-25	8
Camborne S o M	10	3	0	7	102	137	35	6
Lankelly Fowey	10	0	0	10	73	225	-152	0

SOUTH WEST DIVISION

GLOUCESTER/SOMERSET 1994-95 FIXTURES

September 17 (Week 3)
Bristol Harlequins v Cirencester
Hornets v O. Redcliffians
Keynsham v Oldfield OB
Midsomer Ntn v Thornbury
North Bristol v Whitehall
Stow-on-the-Wold v St Mary's OB

September 24 (Week 4)
Cirencester v Midsomer Ntn
O. Redcliffians v Wiveliscombe
Oldfield OB v Hornets
St Mary's OB v North Bristol
Thornbury v Stow-on-the-Wold
Whitehall v Keynsham

October 1 (Week 5)
Hornets v Whitehall
Keynsham v St Mary's OB
Midsomer Ntn v Bristol Harl
North Bristol v Thornbury
Stow-on-the-Wold v Cirencester
Wiveliscombe v Oldfield OB

October 15 (Week 7)
Bristol Harlequins v Stow-on-the-Wold
Cirencester v North Bristol
Oldfield OB v O. Redcliffians
St Mary's OB v Hornets
Thornbury v Keynsham
Whitehall v Wiveliscombe

October 22 (Week 8)
Hornets v Thornbury
Keynsham v Cirencester
North Bristol v Bristol Harlequins
O. Redcliffians v Whitehall
Stow-on-the-Wold v Midsomer Ntn
Wiveliscombe v St Mary's OB

October 29 (Week X2)
Bristol Harlequins v Keynsham
Cirencester v Hornets
Midsomer Ntn v North Bristol
St Mary's OB v O. Redcliffians
Thornbury v Wiveliscombe
Whitehall v Oldfield OB

January 7 (Week 17)
Hornets v Bristol Harlequins
Keynsham v Midsomer Ntn
North Bristol v Stow-on-the-Wold
O. Redcliffians v Thornbury
Oldfield OB v St Mary's OB
Wiveliscombe v Cirencester

January 14 (Week 18)
Bristol Harlequins v Wiveliscombe
Cirencester v O. Redcliffians
Midsomer Ntn v Hornets
St Mary's OB v Whitehall
Stow-on-the-Wold v Keynsham
Thornbury v Oldfield OB

February 11 (Week 22)
Hornets v Stow-on-the-Wold
Keynsham v North Bristol
O. Redcliffians v Bristol Harlequins
Oldfield OB v Cirencester
Whitehall v Thornbury
Wiveliscombe v Midsomer Ntn

February 25 (Week 24)
Bristol Harlequins v Oldfield OB
Cirencester v Whitehall
Midsomer Ntn v O. Redcliffians
North Bristol v Hornets
Stow-on-the-Wold v Wiveliscombe
Thornbury v St Mary's OB

March 4 (Week 25)
Hornets v Keynsham
O. Redcliffians v Stow-on-the-Wold
Oldfield OB v Midsomer Ntn
St Mary's OB v Cirencester
Whitehall v Bristol Harlequins
Wiveliscombe v North Bristol

March 25 (Week 28)
Bristol Harlequins v St Mary's OB
Cirencester v Thornbury
Keynsham v Wiveliscombe
Midsomer Ntn v Whitehall
North Bristol v O. Redcliffians
Stow-on-the-Wold v Oldfield OB

April 8 (Week 30)
O. Redcliffians v Keynsham
Oldfield OB v North Bristol
St Mary's OB v Midsomer Ntn
Thornbury v Bristol Harlequins
Whitehall v Stow-on-the-Wold
Wiveliscombe v Hornets

GLOUCESTERSHIRE & SOMERSET

BRISTOL HARLEQUINS RUFC
Ground Address: Valhalla, Broomhill Road, Brislington,
Bristol BS4. Tel: 0272 721650
Club Secretary: Mr P Broome, 1 Ketch Road, Knowle,
Bristol (League Sec: Mr C Croot, 29 Calcott Road, Knowle,
Bristol. Tel: 0272 777445). Tel: (H) 0272 713815 Tel: (W)
0272 721261
Fixtures Secretary: Mr E Morrison, 4 Lowbourne,
Whitchurch, Bristol. Tel: (H) 0275 83 Tel (W) 0272 362016
Club Colours: Blue, black & white.
CIRENCESTER RFC
Ground Address: The White Way, Cirencester, Glos. Tel:
0285 654434
Club Secretary: Richard H Evans, 66 Rose Way,
Cirencester, Glos GL7 1PS. Tel: (H) 0285 640954 Tel: (W)
0285 720593
Fixtures Secretary: John Lawrence, Timberley, Winstone,
Cirencester, Glos GL7 7JU. Tel: (H) 0285 821435
Club Colours: Red & black hoops, black shorts.
HORNETS RFC
Ground Address: Hutton Moor Road, Weston-super-Mare,
Avon BS22 8LY. Tel: 0934 621433
Club Secretary: Tony Wilson, 29 Grove Road,
Weston-super-Mare, Avon BS22 8EY. Tel: (H) 0934
415240
Fixtures Secretary: Dave Pollard, 216 Locking Road,
Weston-super-Mare, Avon BS23 3LU. Tel: (H) 0934
624912
Club Colours: Black & amber.
KEYNSHAM RFC
Ground Address: The Crown Fields, Bristol Road,
Keynsham, Bristol BS18 2BE. Tel: 0272 867879
Club Secretary: Dermot G Courtier, 15 Montague Road,
Saltford, Bristol BS18 3LA. Tel: (H) 0225 873522 Tel: (W)
0793 541010 x208
Fixtures Secretary: John Holliday, 38 Forty Avenue,
Filton, Bristol BS7 0RW. Tel: (H) 0272 691821
Club Colours: Amber, black shorts, black socks with 3
amber bands.
MIDSOMER NORTON RFC
Ground Address: Norton Down Playing Fields, Norton
Down, Stratton in the Fosse, Somerset BA3 4RW. Tel:
0761 412827
Club Secretary: JV Presley, 73 Welton Grove, Midsomer
Norton, Bath, Avon BA3 2TT. Tel: (H) 0761 416089 Tel:
(W) 0749 682267
Fixtures Secretary: Brian Willcox, Fossil Place, Chicks
Lane, Ston Easton, Somerset BA3 4BY. Tel: (H) 0761
241477
Club Colours: Scarlet.
NORTH BRISTOL RFC
Ground Address: Oaklands, Gloucester Road,
Almondsbury, Bristol BS12 (M5 junction 16). Tel: 0454
612740
Club Secretary: GH Hill, 7 Keinton Walk, Henbury,
Bristol BS10 7EE. Tel: (H) 0272 508123
Fixtures Secretary: D Kettlewell, 227 Gloucester Road,
Patchway, Bristol BS12 5AD. Tel: (H) 0454 613418
Club Colours: Royal blue & scarlet hoops.
OLD REDCLIFFIANS RFC
Ground Address: Stockwood Lane, Brislington, Bristol.
Tel: 0272 778501
Club Secretary: Richard Yandell, 11 Imperial Walk,
Knowle, Bristol BS14 9AD. Tel: (H) 0272 777657 Tel:
(W) 0272 823382
Club Colours: Red & black hoops.
OLDFIELD OLD BOYS RFC
Ground Address: Shaft Road, Combe Down, Bath. Tel:
0225 834135
Club Secretary: Steve Godwin, 12 Lime Grove Gardens,
Bath, Avon BA2 4HE. Tel: (H) 0225 318612 Tel: (W)

FINAL TABLE

	P	W	D	L	F	A	PD	Pts
Dings Crusaders	12	12	0	0	262	100	162	24
St Mary's Old Boys	12	11	0	1	296	117	179	22
Keynsham	12	8	1	3	346	188	158	17
Hornets	12	7	0	5	258	120	138	14
Bristol Harlequins	12	6	1	5	148	108	40	13
Whitehall	12	6	0	6	152	121	31	12
Thornbury	12	6	0	6	181	183	-2	12
Oldfield Boys	12	6	0	6	143	214	-71	12
Old Redcliffians	12	4	1	7	189	178	11	9
North Bristol	12	4	1	7	132	136	-4	9
Cirencester	12	3	0	9	152	319	-167	6
Frome	12	2	0	10	117	311	-194	4
Coney Hill	12	1	0	11	67	348	-281	2

0258 451441
Fixtures Secretary: Gary Lynch, 6 Ivy Grove, Southdown,
Bath. Tel: (H) 0225 333823
Club Colours: Maroon & gold.
ST MARY'S OLD BOYS RFC
Ground Address: Northwood Park, Trench Lane,
Winterbourne, Bristol. Tel: 0454 250489
Club Secretary: Mrs L Collins, 18 Belmont Road, St
Andrews, Bristol BS6 5AS. Tel: (H) 0272 249879
Fixtures Secretary: Mr S Radford, 19 Stanshawe Close.
Tel: (H) 0454 618753 Tel (W) 0272 362507
Club Colours: Emerald green & black.
STOW-ON-THE-WOLD & DISTRICT RFC
Ground Address: Oddington Road, Stow-on-the-Wold,
Glos. Tel: 0451 830887
Club Secretary: Mr NP Drury, Aston House, Broadwell,
Moreton-in-Marsh, Glos GL56 0TJ. Tel: (H) 0451 830961
Tel: (W) 0608 650428
Fixtures Secretary: Mr B Proctor, 33 Cleevemont,
Evesham Road, Cheltenham, Glos. Tel: (H) 0242 234199
Club Colours: Black & white hoops.
THORNBURY RFC
Ground Address: Cooper's Farm, Lower Morton,
Thornbury. Tel: 0454 412096
Club Secretary: HR Bowker, 2 Bruncksea Road, Filton
Park, Bristol BS7 0SE. Tel: (H) 0272 698744 Tel: (W)
0272 299511
Fixtures Secretary: MR Carling, 57 Ashgrove, Thornbury,
Bristol BS12 1BH. Tel: (H) 0454 415083
Club Colours: Black & amber hoops.
WHITEHALL RFC
Ground Address: Speedwell Recreation Ground, Foundry
Lane, Speedwell, Bristol (No correspondencev to ground
address). Tel: 0272 659636
Club Secretary: JW Lewis, 113 Dundridge Lane, St
George, Bristol.
Fixtures Secretary: A Ferguson, 8 Stoneleigh Road,
Knowle,Bristol BS4 2RJ. Tel: (H) 0272 772898
Club Colours: Myrtle & gold.
WIVELISCOMBE RFC
Ground Address: Recreation Ground, West Road,
Wiveliscombe, Somerset TA4. Tel: 0984 623897
Club Secretary: Mr A Weaver, 21 Mount Street, Bishop's
Lydeard, Taunton, Somerset TA4 3AN. Tel: (H) 0823
433632
Fixtures Secretary: Mr C Mann, Lockyers, Fore Street,
Milverton, Somerset TA4 1JU. Tel: (H) 0823 400673
Club Colours: Blue with red sash.

SOUTH WEST DIVISION

GLOUCESTERSHIRE ONE 1994-95 FIXTURES

September 17 (Week 3)
Barton Hill OB v Bream
Cheltenham North v Widden OB
Coney Hill v Old Richians
Frampton Cotterell v Old Cryptians
Longlevens v Brockworth
Painswick v Hucclecote OB

September 24 (Week 4)
Bream v Coney Hill
Brockworth v Painswick
Hucclecote OB v Cleve
Old Cryptians v Cheltenham North
Old Richians v Frampton Cotterell
Widden OB v Longlevens

October 1 (Week 5)
Cheltenham North v Old Richians
Cleve v Brockworth
Coney Hill v Barton Hill OB
Frampton Cotterell v Bream
Longlevens v Old Cryptians
Painswick v Widden OB

October 15 (Week 7)
Barton Hill OB v Frampton Cotterell
Bream v Cheltenham North
Brockworth v Hucclecote OB
Old Cryptians v Painswick
Old Richians v Longlevens
Widden OB v Cleve

October 22 (Week 8)
Cheltenham North v Barton Hill OB
Cleve v Old Cryptians
Frampton Cotterell v Coney Hill
Hucclecote OB v Widden OB
Longlevens v Bream
Painswick v Old Richians

October 29 (Week X2)
Barton Hill OB v Longlevens
Bream v Painswick
Coney Hill v Cheltenham North
Old Cryptians v Hucclecote OB
Old Richians v Cleve
Widden OB v Brockworth

January 7 (Week 17)
Brockworth v Old Cryptians
Cheltenham North v Frampton Cotterell
Cleve v Bream
Hucclecote OB v Old Richians
Longlevens v Coney Hill
Painswick v Barton Hill OB

January 14 (Week 18)
Barton Hill OB v Cleve
Bream v Hucclecote OB
Coney Hill v Painswick
Frampton Cotterell v Longlevens
Old Cryptians v Widden OB
Old Richians v Brockworth

February 11 (Week 22)
Brockworth v Bream
Cleve v Coney Hill
Hucclecote OB v Barton Hill OB
Longlevens v Cheltenham North
Painswick v Frampton Cotterell
Widden OB v Old Richians

February 25 (Week 24)
Barton Hill OB v Brockworth
Bream v Widden OB
Cheltenham North v Painswick
Coney Hill v Hucclecote OB
Frampton Cotterell v Cleve
Old Richians v Old Cryptians

March 4 (Week 25)
Brockworth v Coney Hill
Cleve v Cheltenham North
Hucclecote OB v Frampton Cotterell
Old Cryptians v Bream
Painswick v Longlevens
Widden OB v Barton Hill OB

March 25 (Week 28)
Barton Hill OB v Old Cryptians
Bream v Old Richians
Cheltenham North v Hucclecote OB
Coney Hill v Widden OB
Frampton Cotterell v Brockworth
Longlevens v Cleve

April 8 (Week 30)
Brockworth v Cheltenham North
Cleve v Painswick
Hucclecote OB v Longlevens
Old Cryptians v Coney Hill
Old Richians v Barton Hill OB
Widden OB v Frampton Cotterell

GLOUCESTERSHIRE ONE

BARTON HILL OLD BOYS RUFC
Ground Address: Duncombe Lane, Speedwell, Bristol.
Tel: 0272 583541
Club Secretary: Keith Strickland, 18 The Close,
Soundwell, Bristol BS16 4PH. Tel: (H) 657614 Tel: (W)
0272 825145
Fixtures Secretary: Paul Uppington, 18 Eaton Close,
Fishponds, Bristol. Tel: (H) 650340
Club Colours: White shirts with cherry red band, black
shorts, red & white hooped socks.
BREAM RFC
Ground Address: High Street, Bream, Nr Lydney, Glos,
GL15 6JG. Tel: 0594 562320
Club Secretary: John Grail, 31 Highbury Road, Bream, Nr
Lydney, Glos, GL15 6EF. Tel: (H) 0594 562737 Tel: (W)
0594 562320
Fixtures Secretary: Trevor Evans, High Bank, Whitecroft
Road, Bream, Nr Lydney, Glos, Gl15. Tel: (H) 0594 562
Club Colours: Red & black.
BROCKWORTH RFC
Ground Address: Mill Lane, Brockworth, Glos. Tel: 0452
862556
Club Secretary: RJ Cassidy, 90 Boverton Drive,
Brockworth, Glos GL3 4BS. Tel: (H) 0452 862621 Tel:
(W) 0452 413531
Fixtures Secretary: S Bace, 19 Castle Hill Drive,
Brockworth, Glos GL3 4PQ. Tel: (H) 0452 863385 Tel (W)
0452 528686 x2285
Club Colours: Black & white.
CHELTENHAM NORTH RFC
Ground Address: Stone Orchard Road, Bishop's Cleeve,
Cheltenham. Tel: 0242 675968
Club Secretary: Andrew Page, Baytrees, 3 Chargrove
Lane, Upatherley, Cheltenham GL51 5LP. Tel: (H) 0242
510932
Fixtures Secretary: P Shand, 96 Netherwood Gardens,
Cheltenham GL51 8LG. Tel: (H) 0242 574962
Club Colours: Black with one red band.
CLEVE RFC
Ground Address: Bromley Heath Road, Downend, Bristol
BS16 6HY. Tel: 0272 560323
Club Secretary: R Pocock, 44 Spring Hill, Kingswood,
Bristol BS15 1XT. Tel: (H) 0272 611079
Fixtures Secretary: Mr LA Millard, 177 Lodgecauseway,
Fishponds, Bristol BS16 3QE. Tel: (H) 0272 656673
Club Colours: Maroon & black shorts.
CONEY HILL RUFC
Ground Address:1 Metz Way, Coney Hill, Gloucester
GL4 7RQ. Tel: 0452 306239
Club Secretary: DC Veale, 13 Stanway Road, Coney Hill,
Gloucester GL4 7RE. Tel: (H) 0452 306510 Tel: (W) 0452
863906
Fixtures Secretary: DA Carter, 55 Paygrove Lane,
Longlevens, Gloucester GL2 0BA. Tel: (H) 0452 500424
Club Colours: Amber, black & white hoops.
FRAMPTON COTTERELL RFC
Ground Address: School Road, Frampton Cotterell,
Bristol. Tel: 0454 772947
Club Secretary: Mrs Sue Soper, 58 Lower Chapel Lane,
Frampton Cotterell, Bristol BS17 2RH. Tel: (H) 0454
772095 Tel: (W) 0272 297867
Fixtures Secretary: Mr Chris Belsten, 31 Cornwall
Crescent, North Yate, Bristol. Tel: (H) 0454 324759
Club Colours: Green, black & gold shirts, black shorts &
socks.
HUCCLECOTE OLD BOYS RFC
Club Secretary: John E Ring, 9 Conway Road,
Hucclecote, Gloucester GL3 3PD. Tel: (H) 0452 618920
Fixtures Secretary: Colin Bevan, 2 Watermead Cottages,
Green Street, Brockworth, Glos GL3 4RB. Tel: (H) 0452
863689

FINAL TABLE

	P	W	D	L	F	A	PD	Pts
Stow-on-the-Wold	12	11	0	1	268	109	159	22
Cheltenham North	12	9	2	1	306	121	185	20
Bream	12	10	0	2	221	117	104	20
Longlevens	12	9	1	2	238	109	129	19
Cleve	12	7	1	4	322	114	208	15
Brockworth	12	7	0	5	200	194	6	14
Frampton Cotterell	12	5	1	6	163	263	-100	11
Old Richians	12	4	1	7	137	229	-92	9
Old Cryptians	12	2	2	8	119	243	-124	6
Painswick	12	3	0	9	95	221	-126	6
Widden Old Boys	12	3	0	9	104	240	-136	6
Saintbridge	12	3	0	9	115	266	-151	6
Ashley Down O B	12	1	0	11	139	201	-62	2

Club Colours: Amber & black.
LONGLEVENS RFC
Ground Address: Longford Lane, Longlevens, Gloucester.
Tel: 0452 306880
Club Secretary: Colin Dunford, 66 Estcourt Road,
Gloucester GL1 3LG. Tel: (H) 0452 522795 Tel: (W) 0452
411666
Fixtures Secretary: Mark Dunford, 22 Hayes Court,
Longford, Gloucester. Tel: (H) 0452 311750 Tel (W) 0242
221221
Club Colours: Red.
OLD CRYPTIANS RFC
Ground Address: Memorial Ground, Tuffley Avenue,
Gloucester GL1 5NS. Tel: 0452 520052
Club Secretary: GS Hill, 244 Stroud Road, Gloucester
GL4 0AU. Tel: (H) 0452 521651 Tel: (W) 0454 260681
Fixtures Secretary: DL Howell, 255c Stroud Road,
Gloucester. Tel: (H) 0452 414010 Tel (W) 0452 425611
Club Colours: Maroon & yellow shirts, black shorts,
maroon socks.
OLD RICHIANS RFC
Ground Address: Sandyleaze, Longlevens, Gloucester.
Tel: 0452 524649
Club Secretary: Paul Toleman, 4 Upper Rea, Hempsted,
Gloucester GL2 6LR. Tel: (H) 0452 422274 Tel: (W) 0452
422274 Fax: 0452 416138
Fixtures Secretary: Pete Samuel, 72 Tewkesbury Road,
Longford, Gloucester. Tel: (H) 0452 308086 Tel (W) 0452
331511
Club Colours: Royal blue & gold hoops.
PAINSWICK RFC
Ground Address: Broadham Sports Field, Stroud Road,
Painswick. Tel: 0452 813861
Club Secretary: Mr D Patrick, Rose Cottage, Tibbiwell
Lane, Painswick, Stroud, Glos. Tel: (H) 0452 814104
Club Colours: Cherry & white.
WIDDEN OLD BOYS RFC
Ground Address: Memorial Ground, Tuffley Avenue,
Gloucester. Tel: 0452 304080
Club Secretary: Mr Chris Hinde, 32 Millfields,
Hucclecote, Gloucester. Tel: (H) 0452 617010
Fixtures Secretary: Mr Mike Taylor, 285 Tuffley Lane,
Tuffley, Gloucester. Tel: (H) 0452 413480 Tel (W) 0452
413480
Club Colours: Nyrtle green.

SOUTH WEST DIVISION

GLOUCESTERSHIRE TWO
1994-95
FIXTURES

September 17 (Week 3)
Bishopston	v	Ashley Down OB
Bristol Saracens	v	Saintbridge FP
Cheltenham CS	v	Tredworth
Cheltenham Saracens	v	O Bristolians
Cotham Park	v	Chosen Hill FP
Kingswood	v	Tetbury

September 24 (Week 4)
Ashley Down OB	v	Kingswood
Chosen Hill FP	v	Bristol Tel Area
O Bristolians	v	Cotham Park
Saintbridge FP	v	Cheltenham CS
Tetbury	v	Bristol Saracens
Tredworth	v	Cheltenham Saracens

October 1 (Week 5)
Bristol Saracens	v	Ashley Down OB
Bristol Tel Area	v	O Bristolians
Cheltenham CS	v	Tetbury
Cheltenham Saracens	v	Saintbridge FP
Cotham Park	v	Tredworth
Kingswood	v	Bishopston

October 15 (Week 7)
Ashley Down OB	v	Cheltenham CS
Bishopston	v	Bristol Saracens
O Bristolians	v	Chosen Hill FP
Saintbridge FP	v	Cotham Park
Tetbury	v	Cheltenham Saracens
Tredworth	v	Bristol Tel Area

October 22 (Week 8)
Bristol Saracens	v	Kingswood
Bristol Tel Area	v	Saintbridge
Cheltenham CS	v	Bishopston
Cheltenham Saracens	v	Ashley Down OB
Chosen Hill FP	v	Tredworth
Cotham Park	v	Tetbury

October 29 (Week X2)
Ashley Down OB	v	Cotham Park
Bishopston	v	Cheltenham Saracens
Kingswood	v	Cheltenham CS
Saintbridge FP	v	Chosen Hill FP
Tetbury	v	Bristol Tel Area
Tredworth	v	O Bristolians

January 7 (Week 17)
Bristol Tel Area	v	Ashley Down OB
Cheltenham CS	v	Bristol Saracens
Cheltenham Saracens	v	Kingswood
Chosen Hill FP	v	Tetbury
Cotham Park	v	Bishopston
O Bristolians	v	Saintbridge FP

January 14 (Week 18)
Ashley Down OB	v	Chosen Hill FP
Bishopston	v	Bristol Tel Area
Bristol Saracens	v	Cheltenham Saracens
Kingswood	v	Cotham Park
Saintbridge FP	v	Tredworth
Tetbury	v	O Bristolians

February 11 (Week 22)
Bristol Tel Area	v	Kingswood
Cheltenham Saracens	v	Cheltenham CS
Chosen Hill FP	v	Bishopston
Cotham Park	v	Bristol Saracens
O Bristolians	v	Ashley Down OB
Tredworth	v	Tetbury

February 25 (Week 24)
Ashley Down OB	v	Tredworth
Bishopston	v	O Bristolians
Bristol Saracens	v	Bristol Tel Area
Cheltenham CS	v	Cotham Park
Kingswood	v	Chosen Hill FP
Tetbury	v	Saintbridge FP

March 4 (Week 25)
Bristol Tel Area	v	Cheltenham CS
Chosen Hill FP	v	Bristol Saracens
Cotham Park	v	Cheltenham Saracens
O Bristolians	v	Kingswood
Saintbridge FP	v	Ashley Down OB
Tredworth	v	Bishopston

March 25 (Week 28)
Ashley Down OB	v	Tetbury
Bishopston	v	Saintbridge FP
Bristol Saracens	v	O Bristolians
Cheltenham CS	v	Chosen Hill FP
Cheltenham Saracens	v	Bristol Tel Area
Kingswood	v	Tredworth

April 8 (Week 30)
Bristol Tel Area	v	Cotham Park
Chosen Hill FP	v	Cheltenham Saracens
O Bristolians	v	Cheltenham CS
Saintbridge FP	v	Kingswood
Tetbury	v	Bishopston
Tredworth	v	Bristol Saracens

GLOUCESTERSHIRE TWO

ASHLEY DOWN OLD BOYS RFC
Ground Address: Bonnington Walk, Lockleaze, Bristol.
Tel: 0272 312642
Club Secretary: MJ Delderfield, 1 Charlton Gardens,
Brentry, Bristol BS10 6LU. Tel: (H) 0272 504360 Tel: (W)
0452 653826
Fixtures Secretary: R Johnson, 46 Kendal Road, Horfield,
Bristol BS7 0DU. Tel: (H) 0272 691581 Tel (W) 0272 796408
Club Colours: Purple & white.
BISHOPSTON RFC
Ground Address: Bonnington Walk, Lockleaze, Bristol.
Tel: 0272 691916
Club Secretary: Jim Hockley, 21 Pinewood Close,
Westbury-on-Trym, Bristol BS9 4AJ. Tel: (H) 0272
623509 Tel: (W) 0272 291031 x2390
Fixtures Secretary: Stuart Brain, 9 Chewton Close,
Fishponds, Bristol BS16 3SR. Tel: (H) 0272 585560
Club Colours: Red with black hoop.
BRISTOL SARACENS RFC
Ground Address: Station Road, Cribbs Causeway,
Henbury, Bristol. Tel: 0272 500037
Club Secretary: AE Swash, 6 Downs Road,
Westbury-on-Trym, Bristol BS9 3TX. Tel: (H) 0272
629047 Tel: (W) 0626 832283
Fixtures Secretary: Chris Matthews, 6 Wellington Drive,
Henleaze, Bristol BS9 4SR. Tel: (H) 0272 243696 Tel (W)
0454 419008
Club Colours: Myrtle green & white hoops, black shorts.
BRISTOL TELEPHONE AREA RFC
Ground Address:BTRA Sports Ground, Stockwood Lane,
Stockwood, Bristol BS14. Tel: 0275 891776
Club Secretary: Mike Cross, 21 Grangeville Close,
Longwell Green, Bristol BS15 6YA. Tel: (H) 0272 325146
Tel: (W) 0272 519912
Fixtures Secretary: Chris Watts, 22 Ladman Road,
Stockwood, Bristol. Tel: (H) 0275 837472 Tel (W) 0272
650011
Club Colours: Blue with red & white V neck.
CHELTENHAM CIVIL SERVICE RFC
Ground Address: Civil Service Sports Ground, Tewkesbury
Road, Uckington, Cheltenham, Glos. Tel: 0242 608424
Club Secretary: Brian Didlick, 15 Stoneville Street,
Cheltenham, Glos GL51 8PH. Tel: (H) 0242 519285
Fixtures Secretary: Nigel Holdsworth, 9 The Tullworths,
Longford, Glos GL2 9RF. Tel: (H) 0452 504671 Tel (W)
0452 306522 x275
Club Colours: Navy blue. Change: Light blue & red.
CHELTENHAM SARACENS RFC
Ground Address: King George V Playing Fields, Brooklyn
Road, Cheltenham, Glos.
Club Secretary: Colin Wheeler, Bredon School, Pull
Court, Bushley, Nr Tewkesbury, Glos GL20 6AH. Tel: (H)
0684 294119 Tel: (W) 0684 293156
Fixtures Secretary: Dave Garside, 1 Solway Road,
Springbank, Cheltenham, Glos GL51 0LY. Tel: (H) 0242
515177
Club Colours: Blue with gold circlet.
CHOSEN HILL FORMER PUPILS RFC
Ground Address: Brookfield Road, Churchdown,
Gloucester GL3 2PL. Tel: 0452 712384
Club Secretary: Colin Yeates, 14 Drews Court,
Churchdown, Gloucester GL3 2LD. Tel: (H) 0452 712827
Tel: (W) 0242 230881
Fixtures Secretary: Ian Yeates, 20 Westover Court,
Churchdown, Gloucester GL3 1AL. Tel: (H) 0452 713502
Tel (W) 0242 527511
Club Colours: Myrtle green & white.
COTHAM PARK RFC
Ground Address: Beggar Bush Lane, Failand, Bristol. Tel:
0275 392501
Club Secretary: Frank Nesbitt, 9 Wood End Walk, Bristol

FINAL TABLE

	P	W	D	L	F	A	PD	Pts
Hucclecote O B	12	11	0	1	211	118	93	22
Barton Hill	12	10	1	1	279	69	210	21
Old Bristolians	12	9	1	2	227	133	94	19
Cheltenham Sara	12	9	1	2	195	120	75	19
Chosen Hill FP	12	8	0	4	181	127	54	16
Cheltenham C S	12	5	1	6	146	118	28	11
Tetbury	12	4	3	5	195	193	2	11
Bristol Telephones	12	5	0	7	137	190	-53	10
Bristol Saracens	12	4	1	7	122	142	-20	9
Tredworth	12	3	1	8	178	197	-19	7
Cotham Park	12	3	1	8	109	213	-104	7
Chipping Sodbury	12	1	0	11	105	221	-116	2
Dursley	12	1	0	11	97	341	-244	2

BS9 2JB. Tel: (H) 0272 687746
Fixtures Secretary: Mike Gill, 8 Holmwood, Bristol BS9
3EB. Tel: (H) 0272 500361 Tel (W) 0272 306200
Club Colours: Black & white.
KINGSWOOD RFC
Ground Address: Church Avenue Playing Field, London
Road, Warmley, Nr Bristol. Tel: 0272 675001
Club Secretary: Roger Clease, 166 Mounthill Road,
Kingswood, Avon BS15 2SX. Tel: (H) 0272 750890 Tel:
(W) 0272 701549
Fixtures Secretary: Nick Long, 119 Woodland Way,
Kingswood, Avon BS15 1PY. Tel: (H) 0272 608804
Club Colours: Sky blue & brown.
OLD BRISTOLIANS RFC
Ground Address: Memorial Playing Field, Failand, Bristol.
Tel: 0275 392137
Club Secretary: Mr S (St John) Williams, 7 Old Sweed
Avenue, Stoke Bishop, Bristol BS9 1SD. Tel: (H) 0272
685136 Tel: (W) 0272 295077
Fixtures Secretary: Mr D (Don) Furze, 103 Manor Road,
Keynsham, Bristol BS18 1SF. Tel: (H) 0272 865222 Tel
(W) 0272 797687
Club Colours: Maroon, amber & green.
SAINTBRIDGE FP RFC
Ground Address: Saintbridge Sports Centre, Painswick
Road, Gloucester. Tel: 0452 303768
Club Secretary: PK Fritchley, 195 Seymour Road,
Gloucester GL1 5HR (Courage Rep: Kevin Hopson, 23
Silver Close, Tuffley, Gloucester GL4 0RJ). Tel: (H) 0452
418427 Tel: (W) 0374 121389
Fixtures Secretary: Mr A Stephenson, 10 Brookside Villas,
Coronation Grove, Gloucester GL2 0SS. Tel: (H) 0452 306158
Club Colours: Navy blue, royal blue & gold rings, black shorts.
TETBURY RFC
Ground Address: Recreation Ground, New Church Street,
Tetbury, Glos.
Club Secretary: Mrs SP Dyer, Prince of Wales Inn, West
Street, Tetbury, Glos GL8 8DR. Tel: (H) 0666 502318 Tel:
(W) 0666 502318
Fixtures Secretary: Mr C Robins, 18 Clarrie Road,
Tetbury, Glos. Tel: (H) 0666 504362
Club Colours: Black with amber hoops.
TREDWORTH RUFC
Ground Address: The Linnet, King Edwards Avenue,
Gloucester. Tel: 0452 308939
Club Secretary: Howard Kenneth Spock, Salem, 1
Ashcroft Close, Gloucester. Tel: (H) 0452 302699 Tel: (W)
0635 840391
Fixtures Secretary: R Williams, 16 Highworth Road,
Gloucester. Tel: (H) 0452 411338
Club Colours: Green & black.

SOUTH WEST DIVISION

GLOUCESTERSHIRE THREE 1994-95 FIXTURES

September 17 (Week 3)
Aretians v Southmead
Broad Plain v Westbury-on-Severn
Dursley v Smiths Ind
Minchinhampton v Cainscross
O Colstonians v Chipping Sodbury
Tewkesbury v O Elizabethans

September 24 (Week 4)
Cainscross v Aretians
Chipping Sodbury v Dursley
O Elizabethans v Glos Civil Ser
Smiths Ind v Broad Plain
Southmead v Tewkesbury
Westbury-on-Severn v Minchinhampton

October 1 (Week 5)
Aretians v Westbury-on-Severn
Broad Plain v Chipping Sodbury
Dursley v O Colstonians
Glos Civil Ser v Southmead
Minchinhampton v Smiths Ind
Tewkesbury v Cainscross

October 15 (Week 7)
Cainscross v Glos Civil Ser
Chipping Sodbury v Minchinhampton
O Colstonians v Broad Plain
Smiths Ind v Aretians
Southmead v O Elizabethans
Westbury-on-Severn v Tewkesbury

October 22 (Week 8)
Aretians v Chipping Sodbury
Broad Plains v Dursley
Glos Civil Ser v Westbury-on-Severn
Minchinhampton v O Colstonians
O Elizabethans v Cainscross
Tewkesbury v Smiths Ind

October 29 (Week X2)
Cainscross v Southmead
Chipping Sodbury v Tewkesbury
Dursley v Minchinhampton
O Colstonians v Aretians
Smiths Ind v Glos Civil Ser
Westbury-on-Severn v O Elizabethans

January 7 (Week 17)
Aretians v Dursley
Glos Civil Ser v Chipping Sodbury
Minchinhampton v Broad Plain
O Elizabethans v Smiths Ind
Southmead v Westbury-on-Severn
Tewkesbury v O Colstonians

January 14 (Week 18)
Broad Plain v Aretians
Chipping Sodbury v O Elizabethans
Dursley v Tewkesbury
O Colstonians v Glos Civil Ser
Smiths Ind v Southmead
Westbury-on-Severn v Cainscross

February 11 (Week 22)
Aretians v Minchinhampton
Cainscross v Smiths Ind
Glos Civil Ser v Dursley
O Elizabethans v O Colstonians
Southmead v Chipping Sodbury
Tewkesbury v Broad Plain

February 25 (Week 24)
Broad Plain v Glos Civil Ser
Chipping Sodbury v Cainscross
Dursley v O Elizabethans
Minchinhampton v Tewkesbury
O Colstonians v Southmead
Smiths Ind v Westbury-on-Severn

March 4 (Week 25)
Cainscross v O Colstonians
Glos Civil Ser v Minchinhampton
O Elizabethans v Broad Plain
Southmead v Dursley
Tewkesbury v Aretians
Westbury-on-Severn v Chipping Sodbury

March 25 (Week 28)
Aretians v Glos Civil Ser
Broad Plain v Southmead
Chipping Sodbury v Smiths Ind
Dursley v Cainscross
Minchinhampton v O Elizabethans
O Colstonians v Westbury-on-Severn

April 8 (Week 30)
Cainscross v Broad Plain
Glos Civil Ser v Tewkesbury
O Elizabethans v Aretians
Smiths Ind v O Colstonians
Southmead v Minchinhampton
Westbury-on-Severn v Dursley

GLOUCESTERSHIRE THREE

ARETIANS RFC
Ground Address: The Clubhouse, Station Road, Little Stoke, Bristol. Tel: 0454 612004
Club Secretary: Andy Vaughan, 42 Elm Close, Little Stoke, Bristol BS12 6RQ. Tel: (H) 0272 756513 Tel: (W) 0272 557767
Fixtures Secretary: Andy Williams, 145 Finch Road, Chipping Sudbury, Bristol BS17 6JB. Tel: (H) 0454 310849
Club Colours: Black.

BROAD PLAIN RFC
Ground Address: Hartcliffe School, Bishport Avenue, Hartcliffe, Bristol. Tel: 0272 649757
Club Secretary: Don Collins, 77 Lake Road, Henleaze, Bristol BS10 5JE. Tel: (H) 0272 622094 Tel: (W) 0272 248051
Fixtures Secretary: John Daveridge, 115 Ravenshill Road, Knowle, Bristol. Tel: (H) 0272 771823
Club Colours: Blue, maroon & gold hoops. Change: Maroon & gold quarters.

CAINSCROSS RFC
Ground Address: Victory Park, Ebley, Stroud, Glos. Tel: 0453 766707
Club Secretary: WR Tocknell, Pendaleon House, Selsley Road, North Woodchester, Stroud, Glos GL5 5PH. Tel: (H) 0453 872333 Tel: (W) 0453 762773
Fixtures Secretary: D Roberts, The Mallards, Bristol Road, Stonehouse, Glos. Tel: (H) 0453 824694
Club Colours: Amber & blue.

CHIPPING SODBURY RFC
Ground Address: The Ridings, Wickwar Road, Chipping Sodbury, Bristol. Tel: 0554 312852
Club Secretary: M J Kirkham, 27 Sutherland Ave, Yate, Bristol, BS17 5UE. Tel: (H) 0454 324496
Fixtures Secretary: Tony Windsor, The Bungalow, King Edmunds School, Sunbridge Park Road, Yate, Bristol. Tel: (H) 0454 315959
Club Colours: Black. Change various.

DURSLEY RFC
Ground Address: Hounds Green, Stinchcombe, Dursley, Glos. Tel: 0453 543693
Club Secretary: Simon Bilous, 32 Second Avenue, Highfields, Dursley, Glos GL11 4PE. Tel: (H) 0453 547443
Fixtures Secretary: Steve Tocknell, 57 Shutehay Drive, Cam, Dursley, Glos GL11 5UU. Tel: (H) 0453 544236
Club Colours: Maroon with amber band.

GLOUCESTER CIVIL SERVICE RFC
Ground Address:CSSA Eastcourd Road, Gloucester. Tel: 0452 28317
Club Secretary: David M Oliver, 60 Larkhay Road, Hucclecote, Gloucester GL3 3NB. Tel: (H) 0452 613418
Fixtures Secretary: Dave Wilks, 19 Hillcot Close, Quedgeley, Gloucester. Tel: (H) 0452 724536 Tel (W) 0684 297393
Club Colours: Red & blue hoops.

MINCHINHAMPTON RFC
Ground Address: Minchinhampton Sports & Social Club, Tobacconist Road, Minchinhampton, Glos. Tel: 0453 882636
Club Secretary: Robert Edmonds, Woodlands Cottage, 205 Slad Road, Stroud, Glos. Tel: (H) 0453 766662 Tel: (W) 0452 308989
Fixtures Secretary: Pete Weaving, 14 Langtoft Road, Stroud, Glos. Tel: (H) 0453 755561
Club Colours: 1st VX: Black shorts, shirts green/black/white hoops. 2nd XV: Black shorts, shirts green/white hoops.

OLD COLSTONIANS RFC
Ground Address: New Road, Stoke Gifford, Bristol. Tel: 0272 690009
Club Secretary: David C Parker, 37 Ratcliffe Drive, Stoke Gifford, Bristol BS12 6TX. Tel: (H) 0272 697438 Tel: (W)

FINAL TABLE

	P	W	D	L	F	A	PD	Pts
Bishopston	12	10	1	1	259	53	206	21
Kingswood	12	10	1	1	231	111	120	21
Cainscross	12	10	0	2	279	125	154	20
Smiths (Industries)	12	9	0	3	212	125	87	18
Southmead	12	8	0	4	243	109	134	16
Westbury on Sevrn	12	7	0	5	182	109	73	14
Aretians	12	6	0	6	169	169	0	12
Old Elizabethans	12	4	0	8	163	218	-55	8
Gloucester C S	12	3	2	7	122	210	-88	8
Old Colstonians	12	3	1	8	127	157	-30	7
Broad Plain	12	2	1	9	181	281	-100	5
Bristol Aero Co	12	1	2	9	72	247	-175	4
Gloucester All Blues	12	1	0	11	65	391	-326	2

0275 555431
Fixtures Secretary: Dr Bill Burrows, The Firs, Westend, Wickwar, Wotton-under-Edge, Glos. Tel: (H) 0454 294312 Tel (W) 0454 842214
Club Colours: Black, blue & gold hoops.

OLD ELIZABETHANS RFC
Ground Address: Severn Road, Hallen, Bristol. Tel: 0272 591072
Club Secretary: David Langdon, 13 Gloucester Street, Wotton-under-Edge, Glos GL12 7DN. Tel: (H) 0453 845349 Tel: (W) 0272 668431
Fixtures Secretary: Philip Cheek, 25 Broadway Road, Bishopston, Bristol. Tel: (H) 0272 249202 Tel (W) 0272 821000
Club Colours: White blue & old gold quarters or hoops.

SMITHS INDUSTRIES RFC
Ground Address: The Newlands, Evesham Road, Bishops Cleeve, Cheltenham, Glos. Tel: 0242 672752
Club Secretary: Gerald Owen, 79 Station Road, Bishops Cleeve, Cheltenham, Glos. Tel: (H) 0242 676345 Tel: (W) 0242 673333 x2966
Fixtures Secretary: Robert Etchells, 179 Broadoak Way, Hatherley, Cheltenham, Glos. Tel: (H) 0242 528921 Tel (W) 0684 290243
Club Colours: White with three royal blue hoops.

SOUTHMEAD RFC
Ground Address: Greenway Centre, Doncaster Road, Southmead, Bristol. Tel: 593060
Club Secretary: John Cockwell, 7 Reon Lane, Bedminster, Bristol. Tel: (H) 632979
Fixtures Secretary: Mike Haddow, 20 Braydon Avenue, Little Stoke, Bristol. Tel: (H) 0454 614019
Club Colours: Blue shirts with emerald green hoops.

TEWKESBURY RFC
Ground Address: The Vineyards, Tewkesbury. Mail to: 64a High Street, Tewkesbury, Glos. Tel: 0684 294364
Club Secretary: Derek Bailey, 14 King John's Court, King John's Island, Tewkesbury, Glos GL20 6EG. Tel: (H) 0684 293197 Tel: (W) 0684 274945
Fixtures Secretary: Paul Cole, 7 East Street, Tewkesbury, Glos. Tel: (W) 295932
Club Colours: Black & amber.

WESTBURY-ON-SEVERN RFC
Ground Address: Parish Grounds, Westbury-on-Severn, Glos. Tel: 0452 760751
Club Secretary: Phil Bleathman, The Hollies, Elton, Westbury-on-Severn, Glos GL14 1JJ. Tel: (H) 0452 760751 Tel: (W) 0452 760751
Fixtures Secretary: Tony Osborne, 42 Baynham Road, Mickledean, Glos GL17 0JR. Tel: (H) 0594 542613 Tel (W) 0452 760209/760747
Club Colours: Royal blue & white hoops.

SOUTH WEST DIVISION

GLOUCESTERSHIRE FOUR 1994-95 FIXTURES

September 17 (Week 3)
Dowty v Glos Police
Newent v Wotton-under-Edge
Pilning v Bristol Aero Co

September 24 (Week 4)
Glos All Blues v Dowty
Glos Police v Bristol Aero Co
Newent v Pilning

October 1 (Week 5)
Bristol Aero Co v Glos All Blues
Newent v Glos Police
Wooton-under-Edge v Pilning

October 15 (Week 7)
Dowty v Newent
Glos All Blues v Wotton-under-Edge
Glos Police v Pilning

October 22 (Week 7)
Glos All Blues v Glos Police
Newent v Bristol Aero Co
Pilning v Dowty

October 29 (Week X2)
Bristol Aero Co v Pilning
Dowty v Glos All Blues
Glos Police v Wotton-under-Edge

January 7 (Week 17)
Glos All Blues v Bristol Aero Co
Pilning v Newent
Wotton-under-Edge v Dowty

January 14 (Week 18)
Bristol Aero Co v Newent
Dowty v Wotton-under-Edge
Pilning v Glos Police

February 11 (Week 22)
Bristol Aero Co v Wotton-under-Edge
Glos Police v Dowty
Newent v Glos All Blues

February 25 (Week 24)
Bristol Aero v Glos Police
Glos All Blues v Pilning
Wotton-under-Edge v Newent

March 4 (Week 25)
Dowty v Bristol Aero Co
Glos Police v Glos All Blues
Pilning v Wotton-under-Edge

March 25 (Week 28)
Dowty v Pilning
Glos Police v Newent
Wotton-under-Edge v Glos All Blues

April 1 (Week 29)
Bristol Aero Co v Dowty
Glos All Blues v Newent
Wotton-under-Edge v Glos Police

April 8 (Week 30)
Newent v Dowty
Pilning v Glos All Blues
Wotton-under-Edge v Bristol Aero Co

GLOUCESTERSHIRE FOUR

BRISTOL AEROPLANE CO RFC
Ground Address: Bristol Aerospace Welfare Association Sports Ground, 589 Southmead Road, Filton, Bristol BS12 7DG. Tel: 0272 768066
Club Secretary: Neil Elliott, 20 Franklin Court, Caxton Gate, Redcliffe BS1 6FJ. Tel: (H) 0272 254997 Tel: (W) 0272 795399
Fixtures Secretary: Roy Williams, 90 Cock Road, Kingswood, Bristol BS15 2SL. Tel: (H) 0272 678600 Tel (W) 0272 568775
Club Colours: Red, white & blue hoops.

DOWTY RFC
Ground Address: Dowty Sports and Social Scoiety, Staverton Division, Down Hatherly Lane, Glos. GL2 9QD. Tel: 0452 714567
Club Secretary: A D Green, Willows, Reddings Road, Cheltenham, Glos. Tel: (H) 0425 856937 Tel: (W) 0242 533068
Club Colours: Blue & white hoops.

GLOUCESTER ALL BLUES RFC
Ground Address: The Oxleaze, Westgate Street, Gloucester. Tel: 0452 306984
Club Secretary: Mr GR Selwyn, Millbank, Chessgrove Lane, Longhope, Gloucester GL17 0LE. Tel: (H) 0452 831215 Tel: (W) 0452 529553
Fixtures Secretary: Mr M Heath, 35 Dimore Close, Hardwicke, Gloucester. Tel: (H) 0452 728159
Club Colours: Dark blue shirts, shorts & socks with white top.

GLOUCESTERSHIRE CONSTABULARY RFC
Ground Address:c/o Dowty Sports & Social Club, Down Hatherly Lane, Staverton, Glos. Tel: 0452 712223
Club Secretary: Alex Drummond, The Orchard, Green Lane, Churchdown, Glos. Tel: (H) 0452 712709 Tel: (W) 0242 276453
Fixtures Secretary: Peter Haines, Savanah, Caincross Road, Stroud, Glos. Tel: (H) 0453 765003 Tel (W) 0242 276427
Club Colours: All black.

NEWENT RFC
Ground Address: The Recreation Ground, Watery Lane, Newent, Glos. Tel: 0531 821517
Club Secretary: Keri Evans, 303 Foley Road, Newent, Glos GL18 1ST. Tel: (H) 0531 822328
Fixtures Secretary: James Coull, Mayfield, Tibberton, Glos GL2 8EB. Tel: (H) 0452 790621
Club Colours: Green & gold with V.

PILNING RFC
Ground Address: The Pitch, Beach Road, Severn Beach, Bristol. Tel: 0454 633549
Club Secretary: Mrs A Long, 38 Wainbridge Crescent, Pilning, Bristol BS12 3LJ. Tel: (H) 0454 633204
Fixtures Secretary: Mr M O'Brien, 19 Prospect Road, Severn Beach, Bristol BS12. Tel: (H) 0454 633768
Club Colours: Blue & white hoops. Change: All black.

WOTTON RFC
Ground Address: New Road, Wotton-Under-Edge, Changing Rooms, KLB School. Tel: 0453 842626
Club Secretary: C R Baker, 13 Bradley Street, Wotton-Under-Edge, Glos, GL12 7AP. Tel: (H) 0453 842455
Fixtures Secretary: R Flippence, 22 Bearlands, Wotton-Under-Edge, Glos. GL12 7SF. Tel: (H) 0453 844958
Club Colours: Black & amber hoops & black shorts.

FINAL TABLE

	P	W	D	L	F	A	PD	Pts
Tewkesbury	12	12	0	0	272	62	210	24
Minchinhampton	12	9	1	2	259	105	154	19
Pilning	12	6	1	5	130	106	24	13
Gloucs Police	12	6	0	6	126	137	-11	12
Dowty	12	5	0	7	131	112	19	10
Newent	12	3	0	9	140	203	-63	6
Wotton-under-Edge	12	0	1	11	29	362	-333	1

SOUTH WEST DIVISION

SOMERSET ONE
1994-95
FIXTURES

September 17 (Week 3)
Chard v Frome
Gordano v Yeovil
Minehead v Yatton
N Petherton v Old Sulians
St Bernadette v Walcot OB
Tor v Wellington

September 24 (Week 4)
Frome v Gordano
Old Sulians v Minehead
Walcot OB v Wells
Wellington v St Bernadette
Yatton v Tor
Yeovil v N Petherton

October 1 (Week 5)
Gordano v Chard
Minehead v Yeovil
N Petherton v Frome
St Bernadette v Yatton
Tor v Old Sulians
Wells v Wellington

October 15 (Week 7)
Chard v N Petherton
Frome v Minehead
Old Sulians v St Bernadette
Wellington v Walcot OB
Yatton v Wells
Yeovil v Tor

October 22 (Week 8)
Minehead v Chard
N Petherton v Gordano
St Bernadette v Yeovil
Tor v Frome
Walcot OB v Yatton
Wells v Old Sulians

October 29 (Week X2)
Chard v Tor
Frome v St Bernadette
Gordano v Minehead
Old Sulians v Walcot OB
Yatton v Wellington
Yeovil v Wells

January 7 (Week 17)
Minehead v N Petherton
St Bernadette v Chard
Tor v Gordano
Walcot OB v Yeovil
Wellington v Old Sulians
Wells v Frome

January 14 (Week 18)
Chard v Wells
Frome v Walcot OB
Gordano v St Bernadette
N Petherton v Tor
Old Sulians v Yatton
Yeovil v Wellington

February 11 (Week 22)
St Bernadette v N Petherton
Tor v Minehead
Walcot OB v Chard
Wellington v Frome
Wells v Gordano
Yatton v Yeovil

February 25 (Week 24)
Chard v Wellington
Frome v Yatton
Gordano v Walcot OB
Minehead v St Bernadette
N Petherton v Wells
Yeovil v Old Sulians

March 4 (Week 25)
Old Sullivans v Frome
St Bernadette v Tor
Walcot OB v N Petherton
Wellington v Gordano
Wells v Minehead
Yatton v Chard

March 25 (Week 28)
Chard v Old Sulians
Frome v Yeovil
Gordano v Yatton
Minehead v Walcot OB
N Petherton v Wellington
Tor v Wells

April 8 (Week 30)
Old Sulians v Gordano
Walcot OB v Tor
Wellington v Minehead
Wells v St Bernadette
Yatton v N Petherton
Yeovil v Chard

SOMERSET ONE

CHARD RFC
Ground Address: The Park, Essex Close, Chard, Somerset.
Tel: 0460 62495
Club Secretary: Mr NJ Urch, 2 South View, Listers Hill,
Ilminster, somerset TA19 0EJ. Tel: (H) 0460 57864 Tel:
(W) 0935 702913 Fax: 0935 4168
Fixtures Secretary: Mr M Berry, 27 Halcombe, Chard,
Somerset. Tel: (H) 0460 67549 Tel (W) 0460 53221 Fax:
0460 57832
Club Colours: Black, red & gold.
FROME RFC
Ground Address: Gypsy Lane, Frome, Somerset BA11
2NA. Tel: 0373 462506
Club Secretary: PF Holdaway, 4 Market Place, Nunney,
Frome, Somerset. Tel: (H) 0373 836821
Fixtures Secretary: John RJ Griffiths, 33 Innox Hill,
Frome, Somerset BA11 2LN. Tel: (H) 0373 462537 Tel
(W) 0985 213595
Club Colours: Red, white & black hoops.
GORDANO RFC
Ground Address: The National Stadium, Caswell Lane,
Portbury, Nr Bristol, Avon BS20 9UF. Tel: 0275 373486
Club Secretary: SE Costley, 17 Gordano Gardens,
Easton-in-Gordano, Nr Bristol, Avon BS20 0PD. Tel: (H)
0275 373948 Tel: (W) 0860 210822
Fixtures Secretary: A Stanton, 7 Halswell Drive,
Clevedon, Avon. Tel: (H) 0275 877103
Club Colours: Red & black hoops.
MINEHEAD BARBARIANS RFC
Ground Address: Tom Stewart Field, Ellicombe,
Minehead TA24 6TR. Tel: 0643 707155/705662
Club Secretary: Malcolm Parslow, Ladbrook, The
Holloway, Minehead TA24 5PB. Tel: (H) 0643 702101
Fixtures Secretary: Michael Turner, 4 Wristland Road,
Watchet TA23. Tel: (H) 0984 631170
Club Colours: Black & white hoops.
NORTH PETHERTON RUFC
Ground Address: Beggars Brook, North Petherton,
Somerset. Tel: 0278 663028
Club Secretary: Mr P Lees, Warden's Bungalow,
Baymead Meadow, North Petherton, Somerset TA6 6QW.
Tel: (H) 0278 662734 Tel: (W) 0278 783371
Fixtures Secretary: Mr J Upfield, 12 Pilots Helm, North
Petherton. Tel: (H) 0278 663892 Tel (W) (Mobile) 0836
757839
Club Colours: Black & white hoops.
OLD SULIANS RFC
Ground Address: Lansdown Road, Bath, Avon BA1 9BH.
Tel: 0225 310201
Club Secretary: Terry Haines, 24 Rockliffe Avenue, Bath,
Avon BA2 6QP. Tel: (H) 0225 465107 Tel: (W) 0272
797540
Fixtures Secretary: Tony Slee, 8 Heathfield Close,
Weston, Bath, Avon BA1 4NW. Tel: (H) 0225 317256
Club Colours: Blue with red band.
ST BERNADETTE RFC
Ground Address: Bamfield, Hengrove Park, Whitchurch,
Bristol. Tel: 0275 891500
Club Secretary: Barry Taylor, 39 Woodleigh Gardens,
Whitchurch, Bristol BS14 9JA. Tel: (H) 0275 831880
Fixtures Secretary: Brian Murphy, 4 Rookery Way,
Whitchurch, Bristol BS14. Tel: (H) 0275 837702
Club Colours: Green & blue hoops.
THE TOR RFC
Ground Address: Lowerside Park, Lowerside Lane,
Glastonbury, Somerset BA9 9AE. Tel: 0458 832236
Club Secretary: Malcolm Dykes, 1 Lovells,
Baltonsborough, Glastonbury, Somerset BA6 8QP. Tel: (H)
0458 50498 Tel: (W) 0935 402215
Fixtures Secretary: Keith Elver, 170 Strode Road, Street,
Somerset. Tel: (H) 0458 47284 Tel (W) 0749 673199

FINAL TABLE

	P	W	D	L	F	A	PD	Pts
Midsomer Norton	12	11	1	0	309	107	202	23
Yatton	12	9	1	2	192	111	81	19
Walcot Old Boys	12	9	0	3	325	141	184	18
St Bernadettes OB	12	9	0	3	219	129	90	18
Wellington	12	9	0	3	231	159	72	18
North Petherton	12	8	0	4	206	151	55	16
Minehead Barbs	12	5	0	7	125	199	-74	10
Wells	12	4	0	8	134	153	-19	8
Chard	12	4	0	8	107	213	-106	8
Old Sulians	12	4	0	8	131	253	-122	8
Yeovil	12	2	0	10	143	209	-66	4
Imperial	12	2	0	10	80	241	-161	4
Stothert & Pitt	12	1	0	11	91	227	-136	2

Club Colours: Maroon.
WALCOT OLD BOYS RFC
Ground Address: Albort Field, Lansdown, Bath. Tel: 0225
330199
Club Secretary: K Jones, 14 Canterbury Road, Oldfield
Park, Bath BA2 3LG. Tel: (H) 0225 427045 Tel: (W) 0245
712051
Fixtures Secretary: B Richman, 14 Primrose Hill, Weston,
Bath BA1 3UT. Tel: (H) 0225 422989
Club Colours: Blue & white hoops.
WELLINGTON RFC
Ground Address: The Athletic Ground, Corams Lane,
Wellington, Somerset. Tel: 0823 663758
Club Secretary: BK Colman, Meadowside, Mantle Street,
Wellington, Somerset TA21 8BG. Tel: (H) 0823 663307
Tel: (W) 0823 333451 x5121
Fixtures Secretary: GR Vickery, 7 Seymour Street,
Wellington, Somerset. Tel: (H) 0823 664695 Tel (W) 0823
335166
Club Colours: Red & black.
WELLS RFC
Ground Address: Charter Way, The Portway (off A371),
Wells, Somerset BA5 2FB. Tel: 0749 672823
Club Secretary: Mr AC Cox, 10 Mount Pleasant Avenue,
Well,s somerset BA5 2JQ. Tel: (H) 0749 673407
Fixtures Secretary: Mrs C Sullivan, 3 Bignall Road Close,
Wells, Somerset BA5 2EE. Tel: (H) 0749 679248
Club Colours: Black & white hoops. Change: Red.
YATTON RFC
Ground Address: North End, Yatton, Avon BS19. Tel:
0934 832085
Club Secretary: John Crabtree, 11 Old Park Road,
Clevedon, Avon BS21 7JH. Tel: (H) 0275 876954 Tel: (W)
0272 432399
Fixtures Secretary: Chris Bates, 17 Yewtree Park,
Congresbury, Avon. Tel: (H) 0934 838642
Club Colours: Amber & black.
YEOVIL RFC
Ground Address: Johnson Park, Ilchester Road, Yeovil,
Somerset BA21 3NY. Tel: 0935 74433
Club Secretary: Mr William Harding, 43 Ivel Court,
Yeovil, Somerset BA21 4HX. Tel: (H) 0935 78084 Tel:
(W) 0935 703794
Fixtures Secretary: Martin Western, 158 Roseberry
Avenue, Yeovil, Somerset. Tel: (H) 0935 73386 Tel (W)
0935 31313
Club Colours: Yellow & blue hoops.

SOUTH WEST DIVISION

SOMERSET TWO
1994-95
FIXTURES

September 17 (Week 3)
Avon	v	Westlands
Nailsea & Backwell	v	Cheddar Valley
Chew Valley	v	Blagdon
Crewkerne	v	Old Ashtonians
Imperial	v	Winscombe
St Brendans OB	v	Bath Old Eds

September 24 (Week 4)
Bath Old Eds	v	Stot & Pitt
Blagdon	v	Imperial
Cheddar Valley	v	Avon
Old Ashtonians	v	St Brendans OB
Westlands	v	Chew Valley
Winscombe	v	Crewkerne

October 1 (Week 5)
Avon	v	Nailsea & Backwell
Chew Valley	v	Cheddar Valley
Crewkerne	v	Blagdon
Imperial	v	Westlands
St Brendans OB	v	Winscombe
Stot & Pitt	v	Old Ashtonians

October 15 (Week 7)
Nailsea & Backwell	v	Chew Valley
Blagdon	v	St Brendans OB
Cheddar Valley	v	Imperial
Old Ashtonians	v	Bath Old Eds
Westlands	v	Crewkerne
Winscombe	v	Stot & Pitt

October 22 (Week 8)
Bath Old Eds	v	Winscombe
Chew Valley	v	Avon
Crewkerne	v	Cheddar Valley
Imperial	v	Nailsea & Backwell
St Brendans OB	v	Westlands
Stot & Pitt	v	Blagdon

October 29 (Week X2)
Avon	v	Imperial
Nailsea & Backwell	v	Crewkerne
Blagdon	v	Bath Old Eds
Cheddar Valley	v	St Brendans OB
Westlands	v	Stot & Pitt
Winscombe	v	Old Ashtonians

January 7 (Week 17)
Bath Old Eds	v	Westlands
Crewkerne	v	Avon
Imperial	v	Chew Valley
Old Ashtonians	v	Blagdon
St Brendans OB	v	Nailsea & Backwell
Stot & Pitt	v	Cheddar Valley

January 14 (Week 18)
Avon	v	St Brendans OB
Nailsea & Backwell	v	Stot & Pitt
Blagdon	v	Winscombe
Cheddar Valley	v	Bath Old Eds
Chew Valley	v	Crewkerne
Westlands	v	Old Ashtonians

February 11 (Week 22)
Bath Old Eds	v	Nailsea & Backwell
Crewkerne	v	Imperial
Old Ashtonians	v	Cheddar Valley
St Brendans OB	v	Chew Valley
Stot & Pitt	v	Avon
Winscombe	v	Westlands

February 25 (Week 24)
Avon	v	Bath Old Eds
Nailsea & Backwell	v	Old Ashtonians
Cheddar Valley	v	Winscombe
Chew Valley	v	Stot & Pitt
Imperial	v	St Brendans OB
Westlands	v	Blagdon

March 4 (Week 25)
Bath Old Eds	v	Chew Valley
Blagdon	v	Cheddar valley
Old Ashtonians	v	Avon
St Brendans OB	v	Crewkerne
Stot & Pitt	v	Imperial
Winscombe	v	Nailsea & Backwell

March 25 (Week 28)
Avon	v	Winscombe
Nailsea & Backwell	v	Blagdon
Cheddar Valley	v	Westlands
Chew Valley	v	Old Ashtonians
Crewkerne	v	Stot & Pitt
Imperial	v	Bath Old Eds

April 8 (Week 30)
Bath Old Eds	v	Crewkerne
Blagdon	v	Avon
Old Ashtonians	v	Imperial
Stot & Pitt	v	St Brendans OB
Westlands	v	Nailsea & Backwell
Winscombe	v	Chew Valley

SOMERSET TWO

AVON RFC
Ground Address: Hicksfield, London Rd, Batheaston, Bath. Tel: 0225 852 446
Club Secretary: Kevin Newton, 2 Dene Villas, Tunley, Bath, Avon, BA3 1EB. Tel: (H) 0761 471 149
Fixtures Secretary: D Waters, 10 Stepney Walk, Whitehall, Bristol. Tel: (H) 0272 350 847 Tel (W) 0272 350 847
Club Colours: Graduating black to amber through hoops.

BATH OLD EDWARDIANS RFC
Ground Address: School Playing Field, Bathampton, Vath. Tel: 0225 462354
Club Secretary: Philip C Stuart-Harris, 8 Beaufort East, London Road, Bath BA1 6QD. Tel: (H) 0225 338215 Tel: (W) 0225 448944
Fixtures Secretary: Rory O'Connell, Riverside Cottage, Swineford, Bristol BS15 6LW. Tel: (H) 0272 325932 Tel (W) 0275 340343
Club Colours: Maroon, gold & blue.

BLAGDON RFC
Ground Address: The Mead, Blagdon, Nr Bristol. Tel: 0761 463196
Club Secretary: Andy McKeown, 4 Prospect Cottages, High Street, Winford, Nr Bristol BS18 8EQ. Tel: (H) 0275 472439 Tel: (W) 0272 644809
Fixtures Secretary: Mark Ryan, Flat 9, Old Rectory, Pilgrims Way, Chew Stoke, Bristol BS18 8TX. Tel: (H) 0275 333778 Tel (W) 0272 264662
Club Colours: Green.

CHEDDAR VALLEY RFC
Ground Address: Sharpham Road, Cheddar, Somerset. Tel: 0934 743623
Club Secretary: Ceri Davies, 16 Round Oak Grove, Cheddar, Somerset, BS27 3BW. Tel: (H) 0934 744167
Fixtures Secretary: Derek Buxton, Hillingdon, Cliff Street, Cheddar. Tel: (H) 0934 742 050
Club Colours: Scarlet & sky blue hoops.

CHEW VALLEY OLD BOYS RFC
Ground Address: Lobingtons, Chew Lane, Chew Stoke, Bristol BS18.
Club Secretary: T Weatherley, 10 Malago Walk, The Ridings, Bishopsworth, Bristol BS13 8NZ. Tel: (H) 0272 783216
Fixtures Secretary: R Martin, 66 Meadowside Drive, Whitchurch, Bristol. Tel: (H) 0275 832547
Club Colours: White with large green hoops.

CREWKERNE RFC
Ground Address: Henhayes Lane, Crewkerne, Somerset. Tel: 0460 76422
Club Secretary: RG Physick, 4 Henley View, Crewkerne, Somerset TA18 8JD. Tel: (H) 0460 75482
Fixtures Secretary: D Holley, Shortlands, Back Lane, North Perrott. Tel: (H) 0460 76449
Club Colours: Red & black hoops.

IMPERIAL RFC
Ground Address: West Town Lane, Knowle, Bristol BS14 9EA. Tel: 0275 546000
Club Secretary: Stuart A Eld, 43 Avonleigh Road, Bedminster, Bristol BS3 3HS. Tel: (H) 0272 631688
Fixtures Secretary: John Hamblin, 65 Stoneyfields, Easton-in-Gordano, Bristol. Tel: (H) 0275 372854
Club Colours: Myrtle & amber.

NAILSEA & BACKWELL RFC
Ground Address: North Street, Nailsea.
Club Secretary: AP Nelson, 51 Westway, Nailsea, Bristol BS19 1EF. Tel: (H) 0275 851340
Fixtures Secretary: N Williams, 11 Cerney Gardens, Nailsea, Bristol BS19 2TT. Tel: (H) 0275 856990 Tel (W) 0272 205210
Club Colours: Black with yellow, white & blue bands.

FINAL TABLE

	P	W	D	L	F	A	PD	Pts
Tor	12	11	0	1	314	61	253	22
Gordano	12	11	0	1	244	88	156	22
Crewkerne	12	8	1	3	227	147	80	17
Blagdon	12	7	0	5	191	161	30	14
Westland	12	7	0	5	147	158	-11	14
Winscombe	12	6	1	5	185	149	36	13
Chew Valley	12	6	0	6	167	148	19	12
Avon	12	5	0	7	105	186	-81	10
Backwell	12	4	1	7	122	205	-83	9
Bath Old Eds	12	4	0	8	154	154	0	8
Old Ashtonians	12	3	0	9	96	208	-112	6
Avondale	12	2	1	9	115	214	-99	5
Bath Saracens	12	2	0	10	107	295	-188	4

OLD ASHTONIANS RFC
Ground Address: Ashton Park School, Blackmoors Lane, Bower Ashton, Bristol.
Club Secretary: Ian Reed, The Bear Hotel, 261/3 Hotwells Road, Hotwells, Bristol BS8 4SF. Tel: (H) 0272 268385 Tel: (W) 0272 268385
Fixtures Secretary: Mr T Excell, 18 Perrycroft Road, Birshopsworth, Bristol. Tel: (H) 0272 642352
Club Colours: Blue shirts with white, green & yellow band, black shorts, yellow socks.

ST BRENDAN'S OLD BOYS RFC
Ground Address: Combination Ground, Northway, Filton, Bristol BS12 7QG. Tel: 0272 692793
Club Secretary: RA Kolanko, 91 Church Road, Horfield, Bristol BS7 8SD. Tel: (H) 0272 241390 Tel: (W) 0272 666861
Fixtures Secretary: S McAlinden, 50 Grangeville Close, Longwell Green, Bristol BS15 6YJ. Tel: (H) 0272 326203 Tel (W) 0454 312001
Club Colours: Old gold & maroon hoops.

STOTHERT & PITT RFC
Ground Address:(a) Adamsfield, Corston, Bath (b) Newtonfield, Lower Bristol Road, Bath. Tel: (a) None (b) 0225 425569
Club Secretary: RV Garraway, 2 Westfield Park South, Lower Weston, Bath BA1 3HT. Tel: (H) 0225 316863 Tel: (W) 0225 428321
Fixtures Secretary: JP Burcombe, 199 Whiteway Road, Southdown, Bath BA2 2RG. Tel: (H) 0225 425909 Tel (W) 0225 448266
Club Colours: Blue, black & amber.

WESTLAND RFC
Ground Address: Bunford Lane, Yeovil, Somerset. Tel: 0935 74297
Club Secretary: Ian Prestwood, 11 Hillingdon Court, Abbey Manor Park, Yeovil, Somerset BA21 3TA. Tel: (H) 0935 72878 Tel: (W) 0935 22298
Fixtures Secretary: Mark Davidge, 30 Trellech Court, Abbey Manor Park, Yeovil, Somerset BA21 3TE. Tel: (H) 0935 73390 Tel (W) 0935 703231
Club Colours: Maroon & sky blue quarters.

WINSCOMBE RFC
Ground Address: Lonefield Recreation Ground, Winscombe, Avon. Tel: 0934 842720
Club Secretary: Alun George, 9 Goosey Lane, St Georges, Weston-super-Mare, Avon BS22 0XA. Tel: (H) 0934 515397
Fixtures Secretary: Adie Ellis, 20 Wimblestone Road, Winscombe, Avon. Tel: (H) 0934 843087 Tel (W) 0272 823564
Club Colours: Black with white band.

SOUTH WEST DIVISION

SOMERSET THREE
1994-95 FIXTURES

September 17 (Week 3)
Aller v Avonvale
British Gas v Martock
Burnham-on-Sea v Morganians
Castle Cary v Bath Harlequins
Wincanton v Bath Saracens

September 24 (Week 4)
Avonvale v Castle Cary
Bath Harlequins v Wincanton
Bath Saracens v British Gas
Martock v Burnham-on-Sea
Morganians v Aller

October 1 (Week 5)
Aller v Castle Cary
British Gas v Bath Harlequins
Burnham-on-Sea v Bath Saracens
Morganians v Martock
Wincanton v Avonvale

October 15 (Week 7)
Avonvale v British Gas
Bath Harlequins v Burnham-on-Sea
Bath Saracens v Morganians
Castle Cary v Wincanton
Martock v Aller

October 22 (Week 8)
Aller v Wincanton
British Gas v Castle Cary
Burnham-on-Sea v Avonvale
Martock v Bath Saracens
Morganians v Bath Harlequins

October 29 (Week X2)
Avonvale v Morganians
Bath Harlequins v Martock
Bath Saracens v Aller
Castle Cary v Burnham-on-Sea
Wincanton v British Gas

November 12 (Week 10)
Bath Saracens v Bath Harlequins
British Gas v Aller
Burnham-on-Sea v Wincanton
Martock v Avonvale
Morganians v Castle Cary

November 19 (Week 11)
Aller v Bath Harlequins
Avonvale v Bath Saracens
British Gas v Burnham-on-Sea
Castle Cary v Martock
Wincanton v Morganians

January 7 (Week 17)
Bath Harlequins v Avonvale
Bath Saracens v Castle Cary

Burnham-on-Sea v Aller
Martock v Wincanton
Morganians v British Gas

January 14 (Week 18)
Avonvale v Aller
Bath Harlequins v Castle Cary
Bath Saracens v Wincanton
Martock v British Gas
Morganians v Burnham-on-Sea

February 11 (Weeek 22)
Aller v Morganians
British Gas v Bath Saracens
Burnham-on-Sea v Martock
Castle Cary v Avonvale
Wincanton v Bath Harlequins

February 25 (Week 24)
Avonvale v Wincanton
Bath Harlequins v British Gas
Bath Saracens v Burnham-on-Sea
Castle Cary v Aller
Martock v Morganians

March 4 (Week 25)
Aller v Martock
British Gas v Avonvale
Burnham-on-Sea v Bath Harlequins
Morganians v Bath Saracens
Wincanton v Castle Cary

March 11 (Week 26)
Avonvale v Burnham-on-Sea
Bath Harlequins v Morganians
Bath Saracens v Martock
Castle Cary v British Gas
Wincanton v Aller

March 25 (Week 28)
Aller v Bath Saracens
British Gas v Wincanton
Burnham-on-Sea v Castle Cary
Martock v Bath Harlequins
Morganians v Avonvale

April 8 (Week 30)
Aller v British Gas
Avonvale v Martock
Bath Harlequins v Bath Saracens
Castle Cary v Morganians
Wincanton v Burnham-on-Sea

April 15 (Week 31)
Bath Harlequins v Aller
Bath Saracens v Avonvale
Burnham-on-Sea v British Gas
Martock v Castle Cary
Morganians v Wincanton

April 22 (Week 32)
Aller v Burnham-on-Sea
Avonvale v Bath Harlequins
British Gas v Morganians
Castle Cary v Bath Saracens
Wincanton v Martock

SOMERSET THREE

ALLER RFC
Ground Address: Westfield, Curry Rivel, Somerset. Tel:
0458 252687
Club Secretary: Mark Roddie, The Annexe, Heron House,
North Street, Langport, Somerset TA10 9RQ. Tel: (H) 0458
253599 Tel: (W) 0458 273740
Fixtures Secretary: Mark Roddie, The Annexe, Heron
House, North Street, Langport, Somerset TA10 9RQ. Tel:
(H) 0458 253599 Tel (W) 0458 273740
Club Colours: Red & green hoops.

AVONVALE RFC
Ground Address: Bathford Playing Fields, Bathford, Bath,
Avon. Tel: 0225 858295
Club Secretary: Martin Bath, 30 Forrester Green, Colerne,
Nr Chippenham, Wiltshire SN14 8EB. Tel: (H) 0225
742396 Tel: (W) 0831 600314
Fixtures Secretary: Steve Vowles, 72 Locksbrook Road,
Lower Weston, Bath BA1 3ES. Tel: (H) 0225 333852 Tel
(W) 0225 766451
Club Colours: Navy blue & white.

BATH HARLEQUINS RFC
Ground Address: Lansdown North, Lansdown Road,
Lansdown, Bath. Tel: 0225 427969
Club Secretary: Christopher Jordan, 3 St James Street,
Bath BA1 2TW. Tel: (H) 0225 338254
Fixtures Secretary: Tony Doel, 1 Kingsmead Court, Bath
BA1 1XB. Tel: (H) 0225 482712 Tel (W) 0225 708842
Club Colours: Red, white & black quarters.

BATH SARACENS RFC
Ground Address: Civil Service Ground, Claverton Down,
Bath, Avon. Tel: 0225 832403
Club Secretary: Neil D Pirie, Poolemead Road, Twerton,
Bath, Avon BA2 1QP. Tel: (H) 0225 314521 Tel: (W) 0225
384577
Fixtures Secretary: Mr R Lawrence, 91 Englishcombe
Lane, Bath, Avon. Tel: (H) 0225 427356
Club Colours: Blue with red & gold bands.

BRITISH GAS (BRISTOL) RFC
Ground Address: The Beeches, Broomhill Road,
Brislington, Bristol 4. Tel: 0272 719701
Club Secretary: Richard Alan Griffin, 28 Whitchurch
Road, Bishopsworth, Bristol 3 BS13 7RT. Tel: (H) 0272
645373
Fixtures Secretary: David Hackling, 95 Bailbrook Lane,
Lower Stainswick, Bath BA1 7AL. Tel: (H) 0225 336121
Club Colours: Blue & white hoops.

BURNHAM ON SEA RFC
Ground Address: Base Clubhouse, Stoppens Road,
Burnham on Sea, Somerset, TA8 2DE. Tel: 0278 788355
Club Secretary: David Baxter, Flat 4, Ashcombe House,
188 Berrow Road, Burnham on Sea, Somerset, TA8 2JE.
Tel: (H) 0278 781323 Tel: (W) 0278 435284
Fixtures Secretary: Gareth Berry, 86 Burnham Road,
Highbridge, Burnham on Sea, Somerset. Tel: (H) 0278
786456
Club Colours: Broad blue and white hoops.

CASTLE CARY RFC
Ground Address: Brookhouse Field, Alhampton, Castle
Cary, Somerset.
Club Secretary: A J Bailey, 2 Enfield Terrace, Weymouth
Road, Evercreech, Somerset, BA4 6JE. Tel: (H) 0749
830268 Tel: (W) 0860 544558
Fixtures Secretary: C Watts, 15 Woodford Green,
Ansford, Castle Cary.
Club Colours: Red & black hoops.

FINAL TABLE

	P	W	D	L	F	A	PD	Pts
St Brendans O B	16	15	0	1	511	101	410	30
Cheddar Valley	16	14	0	2	493	110	383	28
Burnham on Sea	16	10	0	6	211	175	36	20
South West Gas	16	7	1	8	200	253	-53	15
Morganians	16	7	1	8	121	224	-103	15
Castle Cary	16	7	0	9	172	297	-125	14
Wincanton	16	5	0	11	261	347	-86	10
Aller	16	3	0	13	149	385	-236	6
Martock	16	3	0	13	136	362	-226	2

MARTOCK RFC
Ground Address: The Nags Head, East Street, Martock,
Somerset TA12 6JQ.
Club Secretary: D F Pates, The South Grange, Water
Street, Martock, Somerset, TA12 6JN. Tel: (H) 0935
825268 Tel: (W) 0935 825268
Club Colours: Green & black quarters.

MORGANIANS RFC
Ground Address: Chedzoy Lane, Bridgwater, Somerset.
Tel: 0278 423434
Club Secretary: PA Culverwell, 30 Edinburgh Road,
Bridgwater, Somerset TA6 6EJ. Tel: (H) 0278 459922
Fixtures Secretary: D Bryant, 140 Stoddons Road,
Burnham-on-Sea, Somerset. Tel: (H) 0278 788058
Club Colours: Navy blue with red & gold hoops.

WINCANTON RUFC
Ground Address: Lattiford, Wincanton (Farmer's field).
Club Secretary: Mr Terry Kitts, 1 Quarry Cottage, North
Cheriton, Templecombe, Somerset BA8 0AP. Tel: (H)
0963 33020 Tel: (W) 0963 33234
Fixtures Secretary: Mr Ray Holder, 21 Whieathill Way,
Milborne Port, Somerset. Tel: (H) 0963 251227
Club Colours: Black & amber.

SOUTH WEST DIVISION

September 17 (Week 3)
Amersham & Chilt v Wimborne
Bicester v Abbey
Bletchley v Slough
Dorchester v Windsor
Olney v Chippenham
Oxford Marathon v Bracknell

September 24 (Week 4)
Abbey v Bletchley
Bracknell v Amersham & Chilt
Chippenham v Oxford Marathon
Slough v Olney
Wimborne v Dorchester
Windsor v Devizes

October 1 (Week 5)
Amersham & Chilt v Chippenham
Bletchley v Bicester
Devizes v Wimborne
Dorchester v Bracknell
Olney v Abbey
Oxford Marathon v Slough

October 15 (Week 7)
Abbey v Oxford Marathon
Bicester v Olney
Bracknell v Divizes
Chippenham v Dorchester
Slough v Amersham & Chilt
Wimborne v Windsor

October 22 (Week 8)
Amersham & Chilt v Abbey
Devizes v Chippenham
Dorchester v Slough
Olney v Bletchley
Oxford Marathon v Bicester
Windsor v Bracknell

October 29 (Week X2)
Abbey v Dorchester
Bicester v Amersham & Chilt
Bletchley v Oxford Marathon
Bracknell v Wimborne
Chippenham v Windsor
Slough v Devizes

January 7 (Week 17)
Amersham & Chilt v Bletchley
Devizes v Abbey
Dorchester v Bicester
Oxford Marathon v Olney
Wimborne v Chippenham
Windsor v Slough

January 14 (Week 18)
Abbey v Windsor
Bicester v Devizes
Bletchley v Dorchester
Chippenham v Bracknell
Olney v Amersham & Chilt
Slough v Wimborne

February 11 (Week 22)
Amersham & Chilt v Oxford Mara
Bracknell v Slough
Devizes v Bletchley
Dorchester v Olney
Wimborne v Abbey
Windsor v Bicester

February 25 (Week 24)
Abbey v Bracknell
Bicester v Wimborne
Bletchley v Windsor
Olney v Devizes
Oxford Marathon v Dorchester
Slough v Chippenham

March 4 (Week 25)
Bracknell v Bicester
Chippenham v Abbey
Devizes v Oxford Marathon
Dorchester v Amersham & Chilt
Wimborne v Bletchley
Windsor v Olney

March 25 (Week 28)
Abbey v Slough
Amersham & Chilt v Devizes
Bicester v Chippenham
Bletchley v Bracknell
Olney v Wimborne
Oxford Marathon v Windsor

April 8 (Week 30)
Bracknell v Olney
Chippenham v Bletchley
Devizes v Dorchester
Slough v Bicester
Wimborne v Oxford Marathon
Windsor v Amers & Chilt

SOUTHERN COUNTIES

ABBEY RFC
Ground Address: Rosehill, Peppard Road, Emmer Green, Reading, Berks. Tel: 0734 722881
Club Secretary: Adrian Curd, 18 Pell Street, Reading, Berks. Tel: (H) 0734 391865 Tel: (W) 071 588 2345
Fixtures Secretary: Lynne Lef, Cotswold, Behoes Lane, Woodcote, Oxon. Tel: (H) 0491 680102
Club Colours: Navy blue with green & white hoops.

AMERSHAM & CHILTERN RFC
Ground Address: Ash Grove, Weedon Lane, Amersham, Bucks HP6 5QU. Tel: 0494 725161
Club Secretary: Ian McKenzie, 17 Highover Park, Amersham, Bucks HP7 0BN. Tel: (H) 0494 431966
Fixtures Secretary: Roger Cook, 120 Chestnut Lane, Amersham, Bucks HP6 6DZ. Tel: (H) 0494 433144
Club Colours: Claret & white.

BICESTER RUFC
Ground Address: Oxford Road, Bicester, Oxon OX6 8AB. Tel: 0869 241000
Club Secretary: Bernard Evans, 3 Hethe Road, Cottisford, Nr Brackley, Northants NN13 5SR. Tel: (H) 0280 847250 Tel: (W) 0296 432091
Fixtures Secretary: George Davis, 166 Barry Avenue, Bicester OX6 8WP. Tel: (H) 0869 241993 Tel (W) 0869 241993
Club Colours: Red, brown & yellow hoops.

BLETCHLEY RUFC
Ground Address: Manor Fields, Bletchley, Milton Keynes. Tel: 0908 372298
Club Secretary: Robin Bowen-Williams, 130 Water Eaton Road, Bletchley, Milton Keynes MK2 3AJ. Tel: (H) 0908 378120 Tel: (W) 0908 376614
Fixtures Secretary: Jon Austin, 17 Statham Place, Oldbrook, Milton Keynes. Tel: (H) 0908 608326 Tel (W) 071 918 5242
Club Colours: Burgundy & white.

BRACKNELL RFC
Ground Address: Lily Hill Park, Lily Hill Road, Bracknell, Berks RG12 2UG. Tel: 0344 424013
Club Secretary: JC Hood, 39 East Stratton Close, Forest Park, Bracknell, Berks RG12 3XY. Tel: (H) 0344 488024 Tel: (W) 081 750 5005
Fixtures Secretary: Mr E Brown, 57 Chesterblade Lane, Bracknell, Berks. Tel: (H) 0344 412041
Club Colours: Green gold & black, black shorts & socks.

CHIPPENHAM FC
Ground Address: Allington Field, Frogwell, Chippenham, Wiltshire SN14 2XZ. Tel: 0249 446997
Club Secretary: J Wilding, 8 Foscote Cottages, Grittleton, Chippenham, Wiltshire SN14 6AD. Tel: (H) 0249 782611 Tel: (W) 0793 522688
Fixtures Secretary: A Lloyd, 27 Lords Mede, Chippenham, Wiltshire. Tel: (H) 0249 656793
Club Colours: Black & white hoops.

DEVIZES RFC
Ground Address: Chivers Ground Sports Club, London Road, Devizes, Wilts. Tel: 0380 723763
Club Secretary: MJ Maudrell, Manor Farmhouse, Calstone, Calne, Wilts SN11 8PY. Tel: (H) 0249 812373 Tel: (W) 0249 812373
Fixtures Secretary: Dan Gaiger, 67 Queens Road, Devizes SN10 5HR. Tel: (H) 0380 722480 Tel (W) 0380 722412
Club Colours: Black & white.

DORCHESTER RFCW
Ground Address: Coburg Road, Dorchester, Dorset. Tel: 0305 265692
Club Secretary: Mr Graham Aspley, 5 Nappers Court, Charles Street, Dorchester, Dorset DT1 1EE. Tel: (H) 0305 814802 Tel: (W) 0305 269944
Fixtures Secretary: Tony Foot, 25 Cromwell Road, Dorchester, Dorset DT1 2DN. Tel: (H) 0305 250137 Tel

FINAL TABLE

	P	W	D	L	F	A	PD	Pts
Bournemouth	12	12	0	0	293	64	229	24
Bracknell	12	10	0	2	294	90	204	20
Dorchester	12	9	0	3	267	111	156	18
Chippenham	12	7	1	4	182	149	33	15
Olney	12	7	0	5	230	169	61	14
Abbey	12	6	1	5	150	143	7	13
Wimborne	12	6	0	6	163	156	7	12
Bletchley	12	5	1	6	120	177	-57	11
Bicester	12	3	2	7	185	199	-14	8
Oxford Marathon	12	3	2	7	164	195	-31	8
Slough	12	3	1	8	75	228	-153	7
Redingensians	12	2	0	10	68	276	-208	4
Wootton Bassett	12	1	0	11	125	359	-234	2

(W) 0305 264426
Club Colours: Green & white hoops.

OLNEY RFC
Ground Address: Recreation Ground, East Street, Olney, Bucks. Tel: 0234 712880
Club Secretary: Stuart Parkin, West View Farm, Olney, Bucks MK46 5EX. Tel: (H) 0234 713165 Tel: (W) 0234 711792
Fixtures Secretary: Bob Taylor, 24 Elmlea Drive, Olney, Bucks. Tel: (H) 0234 712111 Tel (W) 0831 462021
Club Colours: Cerise & French grey.

OXFORD MARATHON RFC
Ground Address: Horspath Road Recreation Ground, Horspath, Cowley, Oxford. Tel: 0865 775765
Club Secretary: AWG Barson, 97 Oxford Road, Garsington, Oxford. Tel: (H) 0865 361540
Fixtures Secretary: Graham Heal, 28 Evenlode Drive, Berinsfield, Oxford. Tel: (H) 0865 340652
Club Colours: Dark blue & amber hoops.

SLOUGH RFC
Ground Address: Tamblyn Fields, Upton Court Park, Slough, Berkshire SL3 7LT. Tel: 0753 522107/692115
Club Secretary: Malcolm Carter, 65 Wavell Road, Maidenhead, Berkshire SL6 5AB. Tel: (H) 0628 25640 Tel: (W) 0628 25640
Fixtures Secretary: Clive Blackman, 11 Coleridge Crescent, Colnbrook, Slough, Berkshire SL3 0PY. Tel: (H) 0753 684403
Club Colours: Green jerseys with a 6' white hoop, navy blue shorts, bottle green stockings.

WIMBORNE RFC
Ground Address: Leigh Park, Wimborne, Dorset. Tel: 0202 882602
Club Secretary: Graham Reeves, 37 Leigh Gardens, Wimborne, Dorset BH21 2ES. Tel: (H) 0202 889526
Fixtures Secretary: Michael Moysey, 42 Lacey Drive, Wimborne, Dorset. Tel: (H) 0202 841478
Club Colours: Black shirts, black shorts, black socks with white tops.

WINDSOR RFC
Ground Address: Home Park, Datchet Road, Windsor, Berks. Tel: 0753 868391
Club Secretary: NC Tysoe, Rosewood Cottage, Burledon Road, Ascot, Berks. Tel: (H) 0344 22900 Tel: (W) 0753 861381
Fixtures Secretary: A Davies, 46 Buckland Avenue, Slough SL3 7PH. Tel: (H) 0753 536642 Tel (W) 0831 297141
Club Colours: Black, green, gold & maroon quarters.

SOUTH WEST DIVISION

BUCKS/OXON ONE
1994-95
FIXTURES

September 17 (Week 3)
Abingdon v Beaconsfield
Buckingham v Pennanians
Chinnor v Drifters
Grove v Witney
Oxford Old Boys v Chesham
Phoenix v Littlemore

September 24 (Week 4)
Beaconsfield v Chinnor
Chesham v Buckingham
Drifters v Oxford Old Boys
Littlemore v Grove
Pennanians v Phoenix
Witney v Milton Keynes

October 1 (Week 5)
Buckingham v Drifters
Chinnor v Abingdon
Grove v Pennanians
Milton Keynes v Littlemore
Oxford Old Boys v Beaconsfield
Phoenix v Chesham

October 15 (Week 7)
Abingdon v Oxford Old Boys
Beaconsfield v Buckingham
Chesham v Grove
Drifters v Phoenix
Littlemore v Witney
Pennanians v Milton Keynes

October 22 (Week 8)
Buckingham v Abingdon
Grove v Drifters
Milton Keynes v Chesham
Oxford Old Boys v Chinnor
Phoenix v Beaconsfield
Witney v Pennanians

October/29 (Week X2)
Abingdon v Phoenix
Beaconsfield v Grove
Chesham v Witney
Chinnor v Buckingham
Drifters v Milton Keynes
Pennanians v Littlemore

January 7 (Week 17)
Buckingham v Oxford Old Boys
Grove v Abingdon
Littlemore v Chesham
Milton Keynes v Beaconsfield
Phoenix v Chinnor
Witney v Drifters

January 14 (Week 18)
Abingdon v Milton Keynes
Beaconsfield v Witney
Chesham v Pennanians
Chinnor v Grove
Drifters v Littlemore
Oxford Old Boys v Phoenix

February 11 (Week 22)
Grove v Oxford Old Boys
Littlemore v Beaconsfield
Milton Keynes v Chinnor
Pennanians v Drifters
Phoenix v Buckingham
Witney v Abingdon

February 25 (Week 24)
Abingdon v Littlemore
Beaconsfield v Pennanians
Buckingham v Grove
Chinnor v Witney
Drifters v Chesham
Oxford Old Boys v Milton Keynes

March 4 (Week 25)
Chesham v Beaconsfield
Grove v Phoenix
Littlemore v Chinnor
Milton Keynes v Buckingham
Pennanians v Abingdon
Witney v Oxford Old Boys

March 25 (Week 28)
Abingdon v Chesham
Beaconsfield v Drifters
Buckingham v Witney
Chinnor v Pennanians
Oxford Old Boys v Littlemore
Phoenix v Milton Keynes

April 8 (Week 30)
Chesham v Chinnor
Drifters v Abingdon
Littlemore v Buckingham
Milton Keynes v Grove
Pennanians v Oxford Old Boys
Witney v Phoenix

BUCKS & OXON ONE

ABINGDON RFC
Ground Address: Abingdon RFC, Southern Sports Park, Lambrock Way, Abingdon, Oxon, OX14 5TJ. Tel: 0235 553810
Club Secretary: Dr Anthony P Lavers, 8 Champs Close, Abingdon, Oxon, OX14 2NQ. Tel: (H) 0235 526448 Tel: (W) 0865 483489
Fixtures Secretary: Chris Thomas, 15 Withington Court, Abingdon, OX14 3QA. Tel: (H) 0235 528730 Tel (W) 0235 533482
Club Colours: Emerald and amber hoops, black shorts, emerald socks.

BEACONSFIELD RFC
Ground Address: Oak Lodge Meadow, Windsor End, Beaconsfield, Buckinghamshire. Tel: 0494 673783
Club Secretary: Chairman: George Parker, 1 Thames Close, Bourne End, Bucks SL8 5QJ. Tel: (H) 0628 522297 Tel: (W) 0494 472626
Fixtures Secretary: David White, 9 The Closes, Haddenham, Aylesbury, Bucks HP17 8JN. Tel: (H) 0844 291716 Tel (W) 0494 675432
Club Colours: Green & gold hoops.

BUCKINGHAM RUFC
Ground Address: Floyd Field, Moreton Road, Maids Moreton, Buckingham MK18 1RF. Tel: 0280 815474
Club Secretary: FM Gemmell, 22 Elmfields Gate, Winslow, Bucks MK18 3JG. Tel: (H) 0296 714640 Tel: (W) 0628 893772
Fixtures Secretary: FAW Smith, 10 Mare Leys, Linden Village, Buckingham. Tel: (H) 0280 815634
Club Colours: Green & white hoops, black shorts.

CHESHAM RUFC
Ground Address: Ground: Chesham Moor. Club House: Amy Lane. Tel: Ground: 0494 783068. Club House: 0494 783635
Club Secretary: MM Hogg, 37 Lye Green Road, Chesham, Bucks HP5 3LS. Tel: (H) 0494 791656 Tel: (W) 0494 771576
Fixtures Secretary: Dick King, 75 Darvell Drive, Chesham HP5 2QN. Tel: (H) 0494 786056 Tel (W) 081 868 2674
Club Colours: Claret & blue bands.

CHINNOR RFC
Ground Address: Kingsey Road, Thame, Oxon. Tel: 0844 213735
Club Secretary: Jon Durrant, 17a Worminghamm Road, Oakley, Aylesbury, Bucks HP18 9QU. Tel: (H) 0844 238030
Fixtures Secretary: Kevin Robinson, The Limes, 31 Oxford Road, Thame, Oxon OX9 2AJ. Tel: (H) 0844 213822
Club Colours: Black & white hooped shirts, white shorts.

DRIFTERS RFC
Ground Address: Farnham Common Sports Club, One Pin Lane, Farnham Common, Bucks.. Tel: 0753 644190
Club Secretary: Patrick Spellman, 44 Iverdale Close, Iver, Bucks, SL0 9RL. Tel: (H) 0753 654153
Fixtures Secretary: Dave Hancock, 19 Thurston Road, Slough, Berks.. Tel: (H) 0753 576512
Club Colours: Black with magenta hoops.

GROVE RFC
Ground Address: Grove Recreation Ground, Cane Lane, Grove. Tel: 0235 762750
Club Secretary: Mr R Teasdale, Manor Bungalow, Denchworth, Watage, Oxfordshire OX12 0DX. Tel: (W) 0235 772900 x325
Fixtures Secretary: Mr A DAvies, 6 Culham Close, Abingdon, Oxfordshire OX14 2AS. Tel: (H) 0235 533568
Club Colours: Red, white & blue hooped jerseys, white shorts, red socks.

LITTLEMORE RFC
Ground Address: Peers School, Sandy Lane West, Littlemore, Oxon. Tel: 0865 715776
Club Secretary: C D Bowler, 40 South Avenue, Kidlington, Oxon, OX5 1DQ. Tel: (H) 0865 375279 Tel (W) 0865 376427
Fixtures Secretary: F Hardie, 40 Cardinal Close, Littlemore, Oxford.
Club Colours: White shirt & shorts, royal blue socks.

FINAL TABLE

	P	W	D	L	F	A	PD	Pts
Amersham & Chilt	12	12	0	0	493	63	430	24
Chinnor	12	10	0	2	293	122	171	20
Witney	12	8	0	4	193	110	83	16
Oxford Old Boys	12	7	1	4	206	134	72	15
Milton Keynes	12	6	1	5	215	189	26	13
Grove	12	6	0	6	133	105	28	12
Drifters	12	5	2	5	132	141	-9	12
Beaconsfield	12	6	0	6	180	193	-13	12
Chesham	12	5	0	7	139	219	-80	10
Pennanians	12	4	1	7	132	254	-122	9
Abingdon	12	2	0	10	117	304	-187	4
Littlemore	12	3	1	8	128	282	-154	3
Chipping Norton	12	1	0	11	56	301	-245	2

MILTON KEYNES RUFC
Ground Address: Field Lane, Greenleys, Wolverton, Milton Keynes. Tel: 0908 313858
Club Secretary: Mr Peter Hemingway, 6 Malvern Drive, Hilltop, Stony Stratford, Milton Keynes. Tel: (H) 0908 564931 Tel: (W) 081 863 5611 x2474
Fixtures Secretary: Mr V Wilcox, 8 Caxton Road, Wolverton, Milton Keynes. Tel: (H) 0908 313083
Club Colours: Black shirt with single white chest band, black shorts & socks.

OXFORD OLD BOYS RFC
Ground Address: Marston Ferry Road, Oxford, Oxon. Tel: 0865 52813
Club Secretary: Mr Richard Wardle, 4 St Leonards Road, Headington, Oxford OX3 8AA. Tel: (H) 0865 69442
Fixtures Secretary: Mr Terry Whitelow, 41 Church Hill Road, Cowley, Oxford. Tel: (H) 0865 716351
Club Colours: Maroon & white hoops, blue shirts, red socks.

PENNANIANS RUFC
Ground Address: Farnham Park, Beaconsfield Road, Farnham Common, Bucks. Tel: 0753 646252
Club Secretary: Eleanor James, 47 Pearl Gardens, Cippenham, Slough, Berkshire SL1 2YX. Tel: (H) 0753 516856 Tel: (W) 0628 70021
Fixtures Secretary: Richard Kearney, 14 Churchfields Mews, Wexham Road, Slough, Berks. Tel: (H) 0753 824155
Club Colours: Black shirts & shorts, red socks.

PHOENIX RC
Ground Address: The Sports Ground, Institute Road, Taplow, Berks. Tel: 0628 664319
Club Secretary: Mr Steve Lucas, Mole End, 4 Chiltern Road, Burnham, Bucks SL1 7NQ. Tel: (H) 0628 605557 Tel: (W) 0628 70969
Fixtures Secretary: Mr Russell Dixon, 3 Merlin Close, Winkfield, Berks. Tel: (H) 0344 886633 Tel (W) 0753 554500
Club Colours: Red shirts with black hoops or red & black quarteras, black shorts.

WITNEY RFC
Ground Address: The Clubhouse, Hailey Road, Witney, Oxon. Tel: 0993 771043
Club Secretary: Chris Birks, 112 Colwell Drive, Witney, Oxon OX8 7NH. Tel: (H) 0993 778341
Fixtures Secretary: Pete Holiday, 179 Corn Street, Witney. Tel: (H) 0993 705327
Club Colours: Black hoops on sky blue.

SOUTH WEST DIVISION

BUCKS/OXON TWO
1994-95
FIXTURES

September 17 (Week 3)
Chipping Norton v Wheatley
Didcot v Gosford
Harwell v Winslow
T. Valley Police v Cholsey

September 24 (Week 4)
Chipping Norton v Gosford
Harwell v Didcot
Wheatley v Cholsey
Winslow v T. Valley Police

October 1 (Week 5)
Didcot v Chipping Norton
Gosford v Wheatley
T. Valley Police v Harwell
Winslow v Cholsey

October 15 (Week 7)
Cholsey v Chipping Norton
Harwell v Gosford
Wheatley v T. Valley Police
Winslow v Didcot

October 22 (Week 8)
Chipping Norton v T. Valley Police
Cholsey v Harwell
Didcot v Wheatley
Gosford v Winslow

October 29 (Week X2)
Chipping Norton v Harwell
Gosford v Cholsey
T. Valley Police v Didcot
Wheatley v Winslow

January 7 (Week 17)
Cholsey v Didcot
Harwell v Wheatley
T. Valley Police v Gosford
Winslow v Chipping Norton

January 14 (Week 18)
Cholsey v T. Valley Police
Gosford v Didcot
Wheatley v Chipping Norton
Winslow v Harwell

February 11 (Week 22)
Cholsey v Wheatley
Didcot v Harwell
Gosford v Chipping Norton
T. Valley Police v Winslow

February 25 (Week 24)
Chipping Norton v Didcot
Cholsey v Winslow
Harwell v T. Valley Police
Wheatley v Gosford

March 4 (Week 25)
Chipping Norton v Cholsey
Didcot v Winslow
Gosford v Harwell
T. Valley Police v Wheatley

March 25 (Week 28)
Harwell v Cholsey
T. Valley Police v Chipping Norton
Wheatley v Didcot
Winslow v Gosford

April 1 (Week 29)
Cholsey v Gosford
Didcot v T. Valley Police
Harwell v Chipping Norton
Winslow v Wheatley

April 8 (Week 30)
Chipping Norton v Winslow
Didcot v Cholsey
Gosford v T. Valley Police
Wheatley v Harwell

BUCKS & OXON TWO

CHIPPING NORTON RUFC
Ground Address: Greystones, Burford Road, Chipping Norton, Oxon. Tel: 0608 643968
Club Secretary: A Cripps, 4 Portland Place, Chipping Norton, Oxon OX7 5AG. Tel: (H) 0608 641182 Tel: (W) 0608 643911
Fixtures Secretary: A Cripps, 4 Portland Place, Chipping Norton, Oxon OX7 5AG. Tel: (H) 0608 641182 Tel (W) 0608 643911
Club Colours: Red & black hoops.

CHOLSEY RFC
Ground Address: Hithercroft Road, Wallingford, Oxon. Tel: 0491 835044
Club Secretary: GA Thompson, 13 The Murren, Wallingford OX10 9DZ. Tel: (H) 0491 836910 Tel: (W) 071 245 6262
Fixtures Secretary: M Porter, 3 Starlings Drive, Tilehurst, Reading, Berks RG3 5ST. Tel: (H) 0734 410946 Tel (W) 0734 393939
Club Colours: Black & amber.

DIDCOT RUFC
Ground Address: Edmonds Park, Paris Road, Didcot (No correspondence to this address).
Club Secretary: Mrs Jane Llewellyn, 54 Loyd Road, Didcot, Oxon OX11 8JJ. Tel: (H) 0235 813634
Fixtures Secretary: Stewart Watson, 16 Eden Court, Didcot, Oxon OX11 7RH. Tel: (H) 0235 811625 Tel (W) 0235 432567
Club Colours: Red & white hoops, white shorts.

GOSFORD ALL BLACKS RFC
Ground Address: Langford Lane, Kidlington, Oxon. Tel: 0865 373994
Club Secretary: Dr Steve Butcher, 16 The Paddocks, Yarnton, Kidlington, Oxon. Tel: (H) 0865 373106 Tel: (W) 0865 844019
Fixtures Secretary: Dave Duthie, 10 Lovell Close, Ducklington, Witney, Oxon. Tel: (H) 0993 702261
Club Colours: All black.

HARWELL RUFC
Ground Address: Central Sports Field, Aere Harwell, Didcot, Oxon.
Club Secretary: C F Bartlett, 66 Upthorps Drive, Wantage, Oxon, OX12 7DG. Tel: (H) 0235 767596
Fixtures Secretary: Jenny Bosley, 55 West Lockinge, Wantage, Oxon. Tel: (H) 0235 833688
Club Colours: Navy blue, light blue & white hoops.

THAMES VALLEY POLICE RFC
Ground Address:c/o Oxford RFC, Southern Bypass, North Hinksey, Oxford. Tel: 0865 243984
Club Secretary: David McWhirter, c/o Control Rooms Department, Police HQ, Kidlington, Oxford OX5 2NX. Tel: (H) 0865 820508 Tel: (W) 0865 846607
Fixtures Secretary: David McWhirter, c/o Control Rooms Department, Police HQ, Oxford OX5 2NX. Tel: (H) 0865 820508 Tel (W) 0865 846607
Club Colours: Old gold jerseys, dark blue shorts. Change: Bottle green jerseys, dark blue shorts.

WHEATLEY
Ground Address: The Playing Fields, Holton, Wheatley, Oxon. Tel: 0865 873476
Club Secretary: Mrs Elaine Murray, The Mead, 56 Clifden Road, Worminghall, Bucks HP18 9JP. Tel: (H) 0844 338940 Tel: (W) 0844 261966
Fixtures Secretary: Mr Bryn Davies, 13 Pelham Road, Thame, Oxon. Tel: (H) 0844 261615
Club Colours: Purple & white, black shorts.

FINAL TABLE

	P	W	D	L	F	A	PD	Pts
Phoenix	16	15	0	1	504	55	449	30
Buckingham	16	14	0	2	385	109	276	28
Gosford All Blacks	16	8	1	7	202	149	53	17
Wheatley	16	8	0	8	174	162	12	16
Harwell	16	8	0	8	169	267	-98	16
Didcot	16	6	1	9	156	251	-95	13
Cholsey	16	5	1	10	184	295	-111	11
Thames Val Police	16	4	1	1	112	204	-92	9
Winslow	16	2	0	14	59	453	-394	4

WINSLOW RUFC
Ground Address: The Winslow Centre, Park Road, Winslow, Buckingham, MK18.
Club Secretary: Duncan C.A. Wigley, 18 Offas Lane, Winslow, Buckingham, MK18 3JS. Tel: (H) 0296 713136 Tel: (W) 0296 851616
Fixtures Secretary: Mr S Spoors, 99 High Street, Winslow, Buckingham, MK18. Tel: (H) 0296 714694 Tel (W) 0296 391749
Club Colours: Blue & gold — hoops.

SOUTH WEST DIVISION

BERKS, DORSET & WILTS ONE 1994-95 FIXTURES

September 17 (Week 3)
Aldermaston v Wootton Bassett
Blandford v Marlborough
Redingensians v Lytchett Minster
Swindon College v Supermarine
Swindon v Corsham
Thatcham v Weymouth

September 24 (Week 4)
Corsham v Melksham
Lytchett Minster v Swindon College
Marlborough v Aldermaston
Supermarine v Thatcham
Weymouth v Swindon
Wootton Bassett v Redingensians

October 1 (Week 5)
Aldermaston v Blandford
Melksham v Weymouth
Redingensians v Marlborough
Swindon College v Wootton Bassett
Swindon v Supermarine
Thatcham v Lytchett Minster

October 15 (Week 7)
Blandford v Redingensians
Lytchett Minster v Swindon
Marlborough v Swindon College
Supermarine v Melksham
Weymouth v Corsham
Wootton Bassett v Thatcham

October 22 (Week 8)
Corsham v Supermarine
Melksham v Lytchett Minster
Redingensians v Aldermaston
Swindon College v Blandford
Swindon v Wootoon Bassett
Thatcham v Marlborough

October 29 (Week X2)
Aldermaston v Swindon College
Blandford v Thatcham
Lytchett Minster v Corsham
Marlborough v Swindon
Supermarine v Weymouth
Wootton Bassett v Melksham

January 7 (Week 17)
Corsham v Wootton Bassett
Melksham v Marlborough
Swindon College v Redingensians
Swindon v Blandford
Thatcham v Aldermaston
Weymouth v Lytchett Minster

January 14 (Week 18)
Aldermaston v Swindon
Blandford v Melksham
Lytchett Minster v Supermarine
Marlborough v Corsham
Redingensians v Thatcham
Wootton Bassett v Weymouth

February 11 (Week 22)
Corsham v Blandford
Melksham v Aldermaston
Supermarine v Wootton Bassett
Swindon v Redingensians
Thatcham v Swindon College
Weymouth v Marlborough

February 25 (Week 24)
Aldermaston v Corsham
Blandford v Weymouth
Marlborough v Supermarine
Redingensians v Melksham
Swindon College v Swindon
Wootton Bassett v Lytchett Minster

March 4 (Week 25)
Corsham v Redingensians
Lytchett Minster v Marlborough
Melksham v Swindon College
Supermarine v Blandford
Swindon v Thatcham
Weymouth v Aldermaston

March 25 (Week 28)
Aldermaston v Supermarine
Blandford v Lytchett Minster
Marlborough v Wootton Bassett
Redingensians v Weymouth
Swindon College v Corsham
Thatcham v Melksham

April 8 (Week 30)
Corsham v Thatcham
Lytchett Minster v Aldermaston
Melksham v Swindon
Supermarine v Redingensians
Weymouth v Swindon College
Wootton Bassett v Blandford

BERKS, DORSET & WILTS ONE

ALDERMASTON RUFC
Ground Address: Aldermaston Recreation Ground, AWE, Aldermaston, Reading, Berks RG7 4PR. Tel: 0734 817603
Club Secretary: K Jones, 13 Stratfield Road, Basingstoke, Hants RG21 2RS. Tel: (H) 0256 811175 Tel: (W) 0734 814111 x6750
Fixtures Secretary: A Cuss, 39 Beaconsfield Road, Basingstoke, Hants RG21 3DQ. Tel: (H) 0256 24129 Tel (W) 0252 525425
Club Colours: Scarlet. Change: White.

BLANDFORD RFC
Ground Address: Larksmead, Blandford. Clubhouse: 53A East Street, Blandford, Dorset. Tel: 0258 450665
Club Secretary: Mr RJ Hewlett
Fixtures Secretary: Dave Stringer, 21 Damory Street, Blandford, Dorset DT11 7EU. Tel: (H) 0258 456954 Tel (W) 0258 453698
Club Colours: Gold & brown with red & white hoop.

CORSHAM RFC
Ground Address: Lacock Road, Corsham, Wilts SN13 9QG. Tel: 0249 701064
Club Secretary: JG Wiltshire, 84 Springfield Close, Rudloe, Copsham, Wilts SN13 0JR. Tel: (H) 0225 810800
Fixtures Secretary: R Slade, 46 Paul Street, Copsham, Wilts. Tel: (H) 0249 712683
Club Colours: Red & white hoops.

LYTCHETT MINSTER RUFC
Ground Address: South Manor Drive, Lytchett Minster, Poole, Dorset.
Club Secretary: DH Smurthwaite, Staddlestones, Chesel Bourne, Dorchester, Dorset DT2 7NJ. Tel: (H) 0258 837796 Tel: (W) 0202 622413
Fixtures Secretary: M Hobson, Broomheyes, Beacon Hill, Poole, Dorset. Tel: (H) 0202 623287
Club Colours: Red & blue hoops, white shorts.

MARLBOROUGH RFC
Ground Address: The Common, Marlborough. Tel: 0672 514717
Club Secretary: RM Nocton, 2 West End, West Overton, Marlborough. Tel: (W) 0672 513471
Fixtures Secretary: Alec Thomas, 2 Dando Drive, Marlborough. Tel: (H) 0672 512296 Tel (W) 0249 813051
Club Colours: Black & amber hoops, black shorts.

MELKSHAM RFC
Ground Address: Avon Sports & Social Club, Melksham House, Melksham, Wilts. Tel: 0225 703265
Club Secretary: Mr AC Butcher, 37 Locking Close, Bowerhill, Melksham, Wilts SN12 6XZ. Tel: (H) 0225 707426
Fixtures Secretary: Mrs Ruth Simmons, 4 Foresters Park Road, Melksham, Wilts SN12. Tel: (H) 0225 708154
Club Colours: Blue & sky blue hoops.

REDINGENSIANS RUFC
Ground Address: Old Bath Road, Sonning, Berks. Tel: 0734 695259
Club Secretary: JH Cook, 95 Century Court, Grove End Road, London NW8 9LD. Tel: (H) 071 289 1887 Tel: (W) 071 814 8700
Fixtures Secretary: JM Taylor, 3 The Cedars, Tilehurst, Reading RG3 6JW. Tel: (H) 0734 411444 Tel (W) 0734 393093
Club Colours: Dark blue, light blue & white hoops.

SUPERMARINE RFC
Ground Address: Supermarine Sports & Social Club, Highworth Road, South Marston, Swindon, Wilts. Tel: 0793 824828
Club Secretary: Ian Wood, 3 Vicarage Lane, Highworth, Swindon. Tel: (H) 0793 861542
Fixtures Secretary: Ian Frizzle, 277 Windrush, Highworth, Swindon. Tel: (H) 0793 763135
Club Colours: 1st XV: Light & dark blue quarters. Others: Light & dark blue hoops.

FINAL TABLE

	P	W	D	L	F	A	PD	Pts
Devizes	12	12	0	0	327	46	281	24
Swindon	12	11	0	1	435	58	377	22
Swindon College	12	9	0	3	248	124	124	18
Melksham	12	7	0	5	274	151	123	14
Corsham	12	7	0	5	144	119	25	14
Supermarine	12	6	0	6	178	177	1	12
Weymouth	12	5	0	7	241	196	45	10
Marlborough	12	5	0	7	210	185	25	10
Lytchett Minster	12	5	0	7	201	219	-18	10
Aldermaston	12	5	0	7	115	180	-65	10
North Dorset	12	4	1	7	142	261	-119	9
Bradford on Avon	12	1	1	10	98	208	-110	3
Puddletown	12	0	0	12	34	723	-689	0

SWINDON COLLEGE OLD BOYS RFC
Ground Address: New College, Helston Road, Swindon. Tel: 0793 611470
Club Secretary: Kevin Church, 34 Burnet Close, Haydon Wick, Swindon, Wilts SN2 2RT. Tel: (H) 0793 726541 Tel: (W) 0793 537831
Fixtures Secretary: Philip Tyler, 12 Tower View, Faringdon, Oxfordshire SN7 7UN. Tel: (H) 0367 242386 Tel (W) 0367 241698
Club Colours: Red & black quarters.

SWINDON RFC
Ground Address: Greenbridge Road, Swindon. Tel: 0793 521148
Club Secretary: Mark Bates, 10 Eagle Close, Covingham, Swindon, Wilts SN3 5DN. Tel: (H) 0793 497134
Fixtures Secretary: Nick Jenkins, 20 Smitanbrook, Covingham, Swindon, Wilts. Tel: (H) 0793 693329
Club Colours: Navy blue & amber, white shorts.

THATCHAM RFC
Ground Address: Kennet School, Stoney Lane, Thatcham.
Club Secretary: Mark Ellis, 5 Sargood Close, Thatcham, Berkshire RG13 4FA. Tel: (H) 0635 869179 Tel: (W) 0252 801928
Fixtures Secretary: Bob Moore, 26 New Wokingham Road, Crowthorne, Berks RG11 6JJ. Tel: (H) 0344 776857
Club Colours: Red & navy quarters, navy shorts.

WEYMOUTH RFC
Ground Address: Monmouth Avenue, Weymouth, Dorset DT3 5HZ. Tel: 0305 778889
Club Secretary: Mrs G Llewellyn, 2 Goulds Hill Close, Upwey, Weymouth DT3 4LG. Tel: (H) 0305 812415
Fixtures Secretary: Mr RE Foyle, 12 Powys Close, Dorchester DT1 2RG. Tel: (H) 0305 266144
Club Colours: Light blue jerseys with dark blue circlet, black shorts, light & dark blue stockings.

WOOTTON BASSETT RFC
Ground Address: Rylands Field, Stoneover Lane, Wootton Bassett, Swindon, Wilts SN4 8QX. Tel: 0793 851425
Club Secretary: Colin Applegate, 26 Briars Close, Wootton Bassett, Wiltshire SN4 7HX. Tel: (H) 0793 850436 Tel: (W) 0793 496464 x151
Fixtures Secretary: Jim Brierley, 25 Broadtown Road, Broad Town, Wootton Bassett, Swindon, Wiltshire SN4 7RB. Tel: (H) 0793 731780
Club Colours: Black.

SOUTH WEST DIVISION

BERKS, DORSET & WILTS TWO 1994-95 FIXTURES

September 17 (Week 3)
Berks Shire Hall v Bournemouth Uni
Bradford-on-Avon v Trowbridge
Bridport v Westbury
North Dorset v Pewsey Vale
Oakmedians v Calne
Poole v Puddletown

September 24 (Week 4)
Bournemouth Uni v Bradford-on-Avon
Calne v Bridport
Pewsey Vale v Oakmedians
Puddletown v North Dorset
Trowbridge v Poole
Westbury v Warminster

October 1 (Week 5)
Bradford-on-Avon v Berks Shire Hall
Bridport v Pewsey Vale
North Dorset v Trowbridge
Oakmedians v Puddletown
Poole v Bournemouth Uni
Warminster v Calne

October 15 (Week 7)
Berks Shire Hall v Poole
Bournemouth Uni v North Dorset
Calne v Westbury
Pewsey Vale v Warminster
Puddletown v Bridport
Trowbridge v Oakmedians

October 22 (Week 8)
Bridport v Trowbridge
North Dorset v Berks Shire Hall
Oakmedians v Bournemouth Uni
Poole v Bradford-on-Avon
Warminster v Puddletown
Westbury v Pewsey Vale

October 29 (Week X2)
Berks Shire Hall v Oakmedians
Bournemouth Uni v Bridport
Bradford-on-Avon v North Dorset
Pewsey Vale v Calne
Puddletown v Westbury
Trowbridge v Warminster

January 7 (Week 17)
Bridport v Berks Shire Hall
Calne v Puddletown
North Dorset v Poole
Oakmedians v Bradford-on-Avon
Warminster v Bournemouth Uni
Westbury v Trowbridge

January 14 (Week 18)
Berks Shire Hall v Warminster
Bournemouth Uni v Westbury
Bradford-on-Avon v Bridport
Poole v Oakmedians
Puddletown v Pewsey Vale
Trowbridge v Calne

February 11 (Week 22)
Bridport v Poole
Calne v Bournemouth Uni
Oakmedians v North Dorset
Pewsey Vale v Trowbridge
Warminster v Bradford-on-Avon
Westbury v Berkshire Hall

February 25 (Week 24)
Berks Shire Hall v Calne
Bournemouth Uni v Pewsey Vale
Bradford-on-Avon v Westbury
North Dorset v Bridport
Poole v Warminster
Trowbridge v Puddletown

March 4 (Week 25)
Bridport v Oakmedians
Calne v Bradford-on-Avon
Pewsey Vale v Berks Shire Hall
Puddletown v Bournemouth Uni
Warminster v North Dorset
Westbury v Poole

March 25 (Week 28)
Berks Shire Hall v Puddletown
Bournemouth Uni v Trowbridge
Bradford-on-Avon v Pewsey Vale
North Dorset v Westbury
Oakmedians v Warminster
Poole v Calne

April 8 (Week 30)
Calne v North Dorset
Pewsey Vale v Poole
Puddletown v Bradford-on-Avon
Trowbridge v Berks Shire Hall
Warminster v Bridport
Westbury v Oakmedians

BERKS, DORSET & WILTS TWO

BERKSHIRE SHIRE HALL RUFC
Ground Address: Berkshire Sports & Social Club, Sonning Lane, Sonning, Reading, Berks. Tel: 0734 691340
Club Secretary: Dave Norris, 74 Caldbeck Drive, Woodley, Reading, Berks. Tel: (H) 0734 696439 Tel: (W) 0344 713851
Fixtures Secretary: Steve Bentley, John Barleycorn Inn, Menorrd, Goring-on-Thames RG8 9DP. Tel: (H) 0491 872509
Club Colours: Yellow & blue hoops.

BOURNEMOUTH UNIVERSITY RFC
Ground Address: White Farm, Slades Farm, Ensbury Park, Bournemouth. Tel: 0202 595012
Club Secretary: Miss A Eaton, B'mth University, Poole House, Talbot Campus, Fern Barrow, Poole, Dorset, BH12 5BB. Tel: (H) 0202 595012 Tel: (W) 0202 595012
Fixtures Secretary: Dai Dower, Sports Dept, B'mth University, Poole House, Talbot Campus, Fern Barrow, Poole, Dorset, BH12 5BB. Tel: (H) 0202 595012 Tel (W) 0202 595012
Club Colours: Royal blue/navy & two white hoops.

BRADFORD ON AVON RFC
Ground Address: St Laurence School, Bradford on Avon.
Club Secretary: Nicholas Cordel, Summerleaze, Northend, Batheaston, Bath, Avon BA1 8ES. Tel: (H) 0390 860230 Tel: (W) 0225 858551
Fixtures Secretary: Andy Gerrish, 14 Huntington Street, Bradford on Avon, Wilts. Tel: (H) 0225 864165
Club Colours: Red & black.

BRIDPORT RFC
Ground Address: Bridport Leisure Centre, Skilling Hill Road, Bridport, Dorset DT6 5LN. Tel: 0308 427464
Club Secretary: RT Salt, 21 South Street, Bridport, Dorset DT6 3NR. Tel: (H) 0297 89237 Tel: (W) 0308 422236
Fixtures Secretary: J Greig, 94 West Bay Road, Bridport, Dorset DT6 4AX. Tel: (H) 0308 456692 Tel (W) 0308 424600
Club Colours: Dark blue.

CALNE RFC
Ground Address: The Recreation Ground, Anchor Rd, Calne, Wilts, SN11 8JX. Tel: 0249 812206/814555
Club Secretary: Mr S A Gill, 1 Heddington Wick, Heddington, Calne, Wilts, SN11 0PB. Tel: (H) 0380 850909 Tel: (W) 0793 485337
Fixtures Secretary: Mr M Otridge, 29 Westerham Walk, Sands farm, Calne, Wilts, SN11 8LP. Tel: (H) 0249 821593
Club Colours: Royal blue & white hoop.

NORTH DORSET RFC
Ground Address: Slaughtergate, Longbury Hill Lane, Gillingham, Dorset SP8 5SY. Tel: 0747 822748
Club Secretary: Paul Phillips, 10 Black Lawn, Gillingham, Dorset SP8 4SD. Tel: (H) 0747 825271 Tel: (W) 0373 831800
Fixtures Secretary: Jez Spicer, 6 Hawthorn Avenue, Wyke, Gillingham, Dorset SP8 4ST. Tel: (H) 0747 824871
Club Colours: Green & navy.

OAKMEADIANS RFC
Ground Address: Meyrick Park Pavilion, Meyrick Park, Bournemouth BH2 6LJ. Tel: 0202 789497
Club Secretary: Mrs A Cope, 3 Comber Road, Moordown, Bournemouth BH9 2XG. Tel: (H) 0202 520170
Fixtures Secretary: Mr & Mrs J Phillips, 47 Headswell Avenue, Bournemouth BH10 6JX. Tel: (H) 0202 525311
Club Colours: Royal blue & white hoops.

FINAL TABLE

	P	W	D	L	F	A	PD	Pts
Blandford	12	12	0	0	342	91	251	24
Thatcham	12	10	1	1	219	83	136	21
Bournemouth Univ	12	9	0	3	253	156	97	18
Trowbridge	12	8	0	4	313	137	176	16
Calne	12	7	0	5	303	167	136	14
Oakmedians	12	6	1	5	172	191	-19	13
Bridport	12	5	1	6	178	179	-1	11
Poole	12	5	1	6	119	224	-105	11
Westbury	12	4	0	8	152	180	-28	8
Warminster	12	3	2	7	155	217	-62	8
Tadley	12	3	1	8	173	146	27	7
Hungerford	12	2	1	9	122	222	-100	5
Minety	12	0	0	12	32	540	-508	0

PEWSEY VALE RFC
Ground Address: Pewsey Vale School Playing Fields, Wilcot Road, Pewsey, Wiltshire. Tel: 0672 62218
Club Secretary: David Aroskin, 20A Rawlins Road, Pewsey, Wiltshire SN9 5EB. Tel: (H) 0672 62218 Tel: (W) 0672 62218
Fixtures Secretary: Vivian Philips, 8 Miller Close, Chirton, Devizes, Wiltshire SN10. Tel: (H) 0380 840516 Tel (W) 0980 665371
Club Colours: Red, royal blue, white & black quarters.

POOLE RFC
Ground Address: Turlin Moor, Blandford Road, Hamworthy, Poole, Dorset. Tel: 0202 687170
Club Secretary: Roderick JP Knight, 58 Wareham Road, Lytchett Matravers, Dorset BH16 6DS. Tel: (H) 0202 622288 Tel: (W) 0305 251414
Fixtures Secretary: G Allsopp, 15 Guest Avenue, Poole, Dorset BH23 2JA. Tel: (H) 0202 733908
Club Colours: Blue & amber.

PUDDLETOWN RFC
Ground Address: Green Fields, Piddlehinton, Dorchester, Dorset DT2 7VA. Tel: 0305 848808
Club Secretary: Philip Barnard, 21 Harveys Terrace, Dorchester, Dorset DT1 1LE. Tel: (H) 0305 251087 Tel: (W) 0305 267411
Fixtures Secretary: Philip Smeeth, 21 London Close, Piddlehinton, Dorchester, Dorset DT2 7TQ. Tel: (H) 0300 348310
Club Colours: Red jerseys, black shorts, red socks.

TROWBRIDGE RFC
Ground Address: Green Lane, Ashton Park, Trowbridge, Wilts. BA14 7DH. Tel: 0225 761389
Club Secretary: B Parfitt, 60 Paxcroft, Trowbridge, Wilts. BA14 7DJ. Tel: (H) 0225 761760
Club Colours: Light blue, dark blue & gold.

WARMINSTER RFC
Ground Address: The Pavilion, Warminster Cricket Club, Sambourne Road, Warminster, Wiltshire. Tel: 0985 219039
Club Secretary: Simon Pick, 95 Portway, Warminster, Wiltshire BA12 0AA. Tel: (H) 0985 847756
Fixtures Secretary: Phil Doyle, 12 Stuarts Green, Warminster, Wilts. Tel: (H) 0985 215927
Club Colours: Royal blue with gold hoop.

WESTBURY RFC
Ground Address: Leighton Sports Ground, Wellhead Lane, Westbury, Wiltshire. Tel: 0373 826438
Club Secretary: Philip Osborne, 1 Nightingale Drive, Westbury, Wiltshire BA13 3XY. Tel: (H) 0373 827951
Fixtures Secretary: Mark Knott, Slate Cottage, 30 Fore Street, Warminster, Wilts. Tel: (H) 0985 215054
Club Colours: Green & black hoops.

SOUTH WEST DIVISION

BERKS, DORSET & WILTS THREE 1994-95 FIXTURES

September 17 (Week 3)
Cricklade   v Tadley
Dorset Police v Minety
Pioneers   v Christchurch
Portcastrians v Hungerford

September 24 (Week 4)
Christchurch v Cricklade
Colerne   v Portcastrians
Hungerford v Pioneers
Tadley   v Dorset Police

October 1 (Week 5)
Cricklade   v Hungerford
Dorset Police v Christchurch
Minety   v Tadley
Pioneers   v Colerne

October 15 (Week 7)
Christchurch v Minety
Colerne   v Cricklade
Hungerford v Dorset Police
Portcastrians v Pioneers

October 22 (Week 8)
Cricklade   v Portcastrians
Dorset Police v Colerne
Minety   v Hungerford
Tadley   v Christchurch

October 29 (Week X2)
Colerne   v Minety
Hungerford v Tadley
Pioneers   v Cricklade
Portcastrians v Dorset Police

November 19 (Week 11)
Christchurch v Hungerford
Dorset Police v Pioneers
Minety   v Portcastrians
Tadley   v Colerne

December 3 (Week 13)
Colerne   v Christchurch
Cricklade   v Dorset Police
Pioneers   v Minety
Portcastrians v Tadley

January 7 (Week 17)
Christchurch v Portcastrians
Hungerford v Colerne
Minety   v Cricklade
Tadley   v Pioneers

January 14 (Week 18)
Christchurch v Pioneers
Hungerford v Portcastrians
Minety   v Dorset Police
Tadley   v Cricklade

January 21 (Week 19)
Cricklade   v Christchurch
Dorset Police v Tadley
Pioneers   v Hungerford
Portcastrians v Colerne

February 4 (Week 21)
Christchurch v Dorset Police
Colerne   v Pioneers
Hungerford v Cricklade
Tadley   v Minety

February 11 (Week 22)
Cricklade   v Colerne
Dorset Police v Hungerford
Minety   v Christchurch
Pioneers   v Portcastrians

February 25 (Week 24)
Christchurch v Tadley
Colerne   v Dorset Police
Hungerford v Minety
Portcastrians v Cricklade

March 4 (Week 25)
Cricklade   v Pioneers
Dorset Police v Portcastrians
Minety   v Colerne
Tadley   v Hungerford

March 25 (Week 28)
Colerne   v Tadley
Hungerford v Christchurch
Pioneers   v Dorset Police
Portcastrians v Minety

April 1 (Week 29)
Christchurch v Colerne
Dorset Police v Cricklade
Minety   v Pioneers
Tadley   v Portcastrians

April 8 (Week 30)
Colerne   v Hungerford
Cricklade   v Minety
Pioneers   v Tadley
Portcastrians v Christchurch

BERKS, DORSET & WILTS THREE

CHRISTCHURCH
Ground Address: Grange Road, Somerford, Christchurch, Dorset BH23 4JE. Tel: 0202 404279
Club Secretary: Nigel Kennett, c/o Siemens Plessey Systems, Grange Road, Somerford, Christchurch, Dorset BH23 4JE. Tel: (W) 0202 404175
Fixtures Secretary: Andy Jolley, 35 Russell Drive, Mudeford, Christchurch, Dorset. Tel: (H) 0202 481482 Tel (W) 0202 407800
Club Colours: Royal blue & white hoops.

COLERNE RFC
Ground Address: Higgins Field, Bath Road, Colerne, Wilts.. Tel: 0225 742835
Club Secretary: Karen Sayers, Daubeneys Stable Cottage, High St, Colerne, Wilts, SN14 8DB. Tel: (H) 0225 744355 Tel: (W) 0272 861717
Fixtures Secretary: Richard Grieshaber, 35 Martins Croft, Colerne, Chippenham, Wiltshire.
Club Colours: Black.

CRICKLADE RFC
Ground Address: Hatchets, Cricklade, Wilts.
Fixtures Secretary: Vaughan Jelley, 43 North Meadow Road, Cricklade SN6 6LT. Tel: (H) 0793 752296
Club Colours: Red & green quarters.

DORSET POLICE RFC
Ground Address: Dorset Police HQ, Winfrith, Nr Dorchester, Dorset. Tel: 0929 462727 x3797
Club Secretary: Phil Morgan Haye, 17 Halstock Crescent, Canford Heath, Poole, Dorset BH17 9BD. Tel: (H) 0202 697987 Tel: (W) 0929 462727 x3797
Fixtures Secretary: Chris Jenkins, CID Office, Bournemouth Police Station, Madeira Road, Bournemouth, Dorset. Tel (W) 0202 222115
Club Colours: Black & green hoops.

HUNGERFORD RFC
Ground Address: The Cricket Pavilion, Hungerford Common, Hungerford, Berks. Tel: 0488 682663
Club Secretary: Jeremy Smeddle, 5 Hawthorne Way, Great Shefford, Nr Newbury, Berks RG16 7BT. Tel: (H) 0488 648231 Tel: (W) 0895 862432
Fixtures Secretary: Peter Goodwin, 42 Grange Court, Boundary Road, Newbury, Berks. Tel: (H) 0635 45887 Tel (W) 0635 48222
Club Colours: Claret & porter.

MINETY RFC
Ground Address: The Playing Fields, Silver Street, Minety, Wiltshire. Tel: 0666 860802
Club Secretary: Mr Kevin Vancil, 12 Essex Walk, Walcot, Swindon, Wiltshire SN3 3EY. Tel: (H) 0793 525898 Tel: (W) 0793 574514 x4945
Fixtures Secretary: Mr David Miller, 98 Sandringham Drive, Swindon SN3 1JF. Tel: (H) 0793 481028 Tel (W) 1793 644542
Club Colours: Green & purple.

PIONEERS (BOVINGTON) RFC
Ground Address: Bovington Middle School, Bovington, Dorset BH20 6NU. Tel: 0929 405229
Club Secretary: Mr Gary Somerset, 39 Victoria Close, Bovington, Dorset BH20 6HY. Tel: (H) 0929 463176
Fixtures Secretary: Gareth Angel, 1 Cologne Road, Bovington, Dorset BH20 6NU. Tel: (H) 0929 405229 Tel (W) 0929 462495
Club Colours: Amber & royal blue.

FINAL TABLE

	P	W	D	L	F	A	PD	Pts
Berkshire Shire H	10	8	1	1	250	72	178	17
Portcastrians	10	6	1	3	173	97	76	13
Pewsey Vale	10	6	1	3	137	104	33	13
Colerne	10	5	0	5	129	103	26	10
Pioneers	10	3	1	6	116	115	1	7
Christchurch	10	0	0	10	50	364	-314	0

Pewsey Vale promoted ahead of Portcastrians under Rule 11(f)

PORTCASTRIAN RFC
Ground Address: Iford Playing Fields, Iford Lane, Bournemouth.
Club Secretary: Martin Leadbitter, 127 Stourvale Road, Bournemouth BH6 5HE. Tel: (H) 0202 421463 Tel: (W) 0703 644599
Fixtures Secretary: Gary Fretton, 59 The Grove, Moordown, Bournemouth. Tel: (H) 0202 526215 Tel (W) 0860 665295
Club Colours: Red, yellow & blue hoops.

TADLEY RFC
Ground Address: Red Lane, Aldermaston, Reading, Berks. Tel: 0734 700072
Club Secretary: Roy Mears, 18 Tewkesbury Close, Basingstoke, Hants RG24 9DU. Tel: (H) 0256 461612
Fixtures Secretary: Roy Mears, 18 Tewkesbury Close, Basingstoke, Hants RG24 9DU. Tel: (H) 0256 461612
Club Colours: Black with amber hoop. Change: Amber with black hoop.

RUGBY SPECIALISTS Bourne Sports

COURAGE

CRT7.

CRT2.

CRT8.

CRT1.

CRT5.

CRT6.

CRT3.

COURAGE
RUGBY TACKLE   RANGE

CRT1 Rugby Jersey - 100% cotton, long sleeves rugby jersey, embroidered badge, unisex, generous sizes, all our usual quality features, taped inside collar, reinforced seams and snug stretch cuffs, sizes S, M, L, XL.
CRT1. Usual £29.95 **League price £25.00**

CRT2 Rugby Jersey - 100% cotton, long sleeves with all features of CRT1 in alternative design, sizes S, M, L, XL.
CRT2. Usual £29.95 **League price £25.00**

CRT3 Polo Shirt - Fashionable Polo Shirt, comfortable 50/50 poly-cotton fabric with embroidered badge, sizes S, M, L, XL.
CRT3. Usual £13.99 **League price £12.50**

CRT4 Training Jacket - Two Colour Jacket in hard wearing 100% cotton drill with embroidered badge, sizes S, M, L, XL, XXL, not illustrated
CRT4. Usual £24.95 **League price £21.00**

CRT5 Sweatshirt - Heavy fleece sweatshirt, 50/50 poly-cotton in navy with embroidered logo, sizes S, M, L, XL. Usual £17.99 **League price £15.**

CRT6 Hooded Top - Fashionable garment, 50/50 poly-cotton with embroidered badge, sizes S, M, L, XL. **CRT6.** Usual £26.95 **League price £24.**

CRT7 Cap - Pro style cap adjustable to any size, embroidered logo, **£9.95**
CRT7. Usual £9.95 **League price £8.95**

CRT8 T-Shirt - Printed T-Shirt, 50/50 poly-cotton, sizes available S, M, L, XL, XXL, **£10.95**
CRT8. Usual £10.95 **League price £8.00**

BOURNE SPORTS

**Bourne Sports, Church Street
Stoke-on-Trent, ST4 1DJ**

**Tel: 0782 410411.
Fax: 0782 411072**

All orders value £40 and over post free. Other orders plus £3 postage and packing. Send cheque/postal order or telephone your order quoting Access, Visa, American Express, Diners Card, or Switchcard.

Special Prices for Courage League Players

OTHER MAJOR STATISTICS 1993-94

NEW ZEALAND TOUR TO ENGLAND, SCOTLAND & WALES

OCTOBER, NOVEMBER & DECEMBER 1993

23rd October 1993	v London Division	Twickenham	W39-12
26th October 1993	v Midland Division	Leicester	W12-6
30th October 1993	v South West Division	Redruth	W19-15
2nd November 1993	v North Division	Anfield, Liverpool	W27-21
7th November 1993	v England A	Gateshead	W26-12
10 November 1993	v South of Scotland	Gala	W84-5
13th November 1993	v Scotland A	Old Anniesland, Glasgow	W20-9
16th November 1993	v Scotland Development XV	Myreside, Edinburgh	W31-12
20th November 1993	v SCOTLAND	Murrayfield	W51-15
23rd November 1993	v England Emerging Players	Gloucester	W30-19
27th November 1993	v ENGLAND	Twickenham	L9-15
30th November 1993	v Combined Services	Devonport	W13-3
4th December 1993	v Barbarians	Cardiff	W25-10

Summary: Played 13, won 12, lost 1, points for 386, against 154
Tries scored 42, conceded 5

9th Match, Saturday 20th November 1993 at Murrayfield
SCOTLAND 15   NEW ZEALAND 51

G Hastings 4 PG, Chalmers 1 PG

Wilson 3 Tries, Ellis 2 Tries, Brooke 1 Try, Bunce 1 Try, Cooper 2 PG, 4 Cons, Wilson 1 Con

Half Time: 9-22

SCOTLAND: G Hastings (Watsonians) (captain); A Stanger (Hawick), I Jardine (Stirling County), G Shiel (Melrose), S Hastings (Watsonians); C Chalmers (Melrose), A Nicol (Dundee High School FP); A Watt (Glasgow High/Kelvinside), K Milne (Heriot's FP), P Burnell (London Scottish), D McIvor (Edinburgh Academicals), D Cronin (London Scottish), A Macdonald (Heriot's FP), R Wainwright (Edinburgh Academicals), G Weir (Melrose). Replacements: D Wyllie (Stewart's-Melville FP) for Chalmers 57 mins, C Hogg (Melrose) for Cronin 61 mins. Temporary Replacements: B Redpath (Melrose) for Nicol 8-10 mins, K Logan (Stirling County) for G Hastings 37-40 mins.

NEW ZEALAND: J Timu (Otago); J Wilson (Otago), F Bunce (North Harbour), M Cooper (Waikato), V Tuigamala (Auckland); M Ellis (Otago), S Forster (Otago); C Dowd (Auckland), S Fitzpatrick (Auckland) (captain), O Brown (Auckland), J Joseph (Otago), I Jones (North Auckland), S Gordon (Waikato), Z Brooke (Auckland), A Pene (Otago).

Referee: F Burger, South Africa

11th Match, Saturday 27th November 1993 at Twickenham
ENGLAND 15   NEW ZEALAND 9

Andrew 1 DG, Callard 4 PG

Wilson 3 PG

Half Time: 6-0

ENGLAND: J Callard (Bath); T Underwood (Leicester), W Carling (Harlequins (captain), P de Glanville (Bath), R Underwood (Leicester/RAF); R Andrew (Wasps), K Bracken (Bristol); J Leonard (Harlequins), B Moore (Harlequins), V Ubogu (Bath), T Rodber (Northampton), M Johnson (Leicester), N Redman (Bath), B Clarke (Bath), D Richards (Leicester)

NEW ZEALAND: J Timu (Otago); J Wilson (Otago), F Bunce (North Harbour), E Clarke (Auckland), V Tuigamala (Auckland); M Ellis (Otago), S Forster (Otago); C Dowd (Auckland), S Fitzpatrick (Auckland) (captain), O Brown (Auckland), J Joseph (Otago), I Jones (North Auckland), S Gordon (Waikato), Z Brooke (Auckland), A Pene (Otago)

Referee: F Burger, South Africa

INTERNATIONAL TOURS

JAPAN TOUR OF WALES
September & October 1993

v Wales A	Llanell	L5-61
v Dunvant	Dunvant	W24-23
v East Wales	Abertillery	L12-38
v West Wales	Narberth	W26-10
v Heineken Select XV	Pontypridd	W39-10
v **WALES**	Cardiff Arms Park	L5-55

Summary of Results

P	W	D	L	F	A
6	3	0	3	111	197

AUCKLAND IN ENGLAND & SCOTLAND — November 1993

v Scottish Exiles	Richmond	W33-12
v Edinburgh	Meggetland	W27-21
v Scottish Districts	Hawick	L19-24
v Bedford	Bedford	W51-3
v Bristol	Bristol	W44-7
v West Hartlepool	West Hartlepool	W34-8
v Wasps	Sudbury	W28-25

Summary of Results

P	W	D	L	F	A
7	6	0	1	236	100

Saturday 16th October 1993   **At Cardiff Arms Park**

WALES 55   JAPAN 5

I Evans(2T), Gibbs(2T), Jenkins(T)(5C), Moon(T),   Williams(T)
Lewis(T), Rayer(T), Clement(T)

Wales: A Clement (Swansea), I Evans (Llanelli) (caotain), S Gibbs (Swansea), N Jenkins (Pontypridd), N Walker (Cardiff), A Davies (Cardiff), R Moon (Llanelli), M Griffiths (Cardiff), A Lamerton (Llanelli), J Davies (Neath), S Davies (Swansea), A Copsey (Llanelli), Gareth Llewellyn (Neath), L Jones (Llanelli), E Lewis (Llanelli). Replacements: M Rayer (Cardiff) for Walker 27 mins, R Bidgood (Newport) for Evans 72 mins.

Japan: T Matsuda (Toshiba), I Williams (Kobe Steel), M Fujikake (World), E Kutsuki (Toyota Motor), Y Yoshida (Isetan), S Aoki (Ricoh), Y Nagatomo (Suntory), O Ota (NEC), M Kunda (Toshiba Fuchu) (captain), R Takahashi (Toyota Motor), S Kaleta (Ricoh), Y Sakuraba (Nippon Steel), B Ferguson (Hino Motor), H Ouchi (Ryukoku University), S Latu (Sanyo).

AUSTRALIA IN NORTH AMERICA AND FRANCE — Oct & Nov 1993

In North America

v United States	Riverside, California	W26-22
v Canada 'A'	Calgary	W40-3
v **CANADA**	Calgary	W43-16

In France

v Aquitaine XV	Dax	W30-15
v S W Selection	Agen	W20-19
v Languedoc-Roussillon	Narbonne	W35-18
v S E France	Grenoble	W24-23
v **FRANCE**	Bordeaux	L13-16
v Cote d'Azur	Toulon	L15-21
v **FRANCE**	Paris	W24-3
v French Barbarians	Clermont Ferrand	W43-26

Summary of Results

P	W	D	L	F	A
11	9	0	2	313	182

CANADA 'A' TOUR TO ENGLAND & WALES — March 1994

v North Division	Fylde	L8-18
v Newbridge	Newbridge	W9-8
v Wales A	Cardiff Arms Park	L11-42
v London Division	Twickenham	L9-25
v England Emerging	Richmond Athletic Ground	L9- 23

Summary of Results

P	W	D	L	F	A
5	1	—	4	46	116

SOUTH AFRICA TOUR TO ARGENTINA — Oct & Nov 1993

v Cordoba		W55-37
v Buenos Aires XV		L27-28
v Tucuman		W40-12
v **ARGENTINA**	Buenos Aires	W29-26
v Rosario		W40-26
v **ARGENTINA**	Buenos Aires	W52-23

Summary of Results

P	W	D	L	F	A
6	5	0	1	243	152

INTERNATIONAL TOURS

ENGLAND TOUR TO SOUTH AFRICA MAY & JUNE 1994
Results (after seven matches)

Wed, May 18	Orange Free State	Bloemfontein	L11-22
Sat, May 21	Natal	Durban	L6-21
Wed, May 25	Western Transvaal	Potchefstroom	W26-24
Sat, May 28	Transvaal	Johannesburg	L21-24
Tue, May 31	South Africa 'B'	Kimberley	L6-19
Sat, June 4	SOUTH AFRICA	Pretoria	W32-15
Tue, June 7	Eastern Province	Port Elizabeth	W31-13
Sat, June 11	SOUTH AFRICA	Cape Town	L9-27

Summary: Played 8, won 3, lost 5, points for 152, against 165.

6th Match. v SOUTH AFRICA (1st Test)

Saturday, 4th June 1994. At Loftus Versfeld, Pretoria.

SOUTH AFRICA 15   ENGLAND 32
H.T. 6-23

Penalty-Goals: Joubert (5)

Tries: Clarke (1), Andrew (1). Dropped-Goal: Andrew
Penalty-Goals: Andrew (5). Conversions: Andrew (2)

SOUTH AFRICA: A Joubert (Natal); J Small (Natal), B Venter (Orange Free State), P Muller (Natal), C Williams (Western Province); H le Roux (Transvaal), J van der Westhuizen (Northern Transvaal); A H le Roux (Orange Free State), J Allan (Natal), B Swart (Transvaal), F Pienaar (Transvaal)(captain), H Strydom (Transvaal), S Atherton (Natal), F van Heerden (Western Province), C Strauss (Western Province). New caps: Venter, A H le Roux, van Heerden.

ENGLAND: P Hull (Bristol); T Underwood (Leicester), W Carling (Harlequins)(captain), P de Glanville (Bath), R Underwood (Leicester/Raf); R Andrew (Wasps), D Morris (Orrell); J Leonard (Harlequins), B Moore (Harlequins), V Ubogu (Bath), T Rodber (Northampton/Army), M Bayfield (Northampton), N Redman (Bath), B Clarke (Bath), D Richards (Leicester). Replacement: S Ojomoh (Bath) for Richards 58 minutes. New cap: Hull.

Referee: C Hawke, New Zealand.

8th Match. v SOUTH AFRICA (2nd Test)

Saturday, 11th June 1994. At Newlands, Cape Town.

SOUTH AFRICA 27   ENGLAND 9
H.T. 3-3

Tries: H P le Roux (1), Joubert (1)
Penalty-Goals: H P Le Roux (3), Joubert (2)
Conversion: Joubert

Penalty-Goals: Andrew (3)

SOUTH AFRICA: A Joubert (Natal); J Small (Natal), B Venter (Orange Free State), P Muller (Natal), C Williams (Western Province); H P le Roux (Transvaal), J Roux (Transvaal); B Swart (Transvaal), J Allan (Natal), J H S le Roux (Transvaal), F Pienaar (Transvaal)(captain), M Andrews (Natal), S Atherton (Natal), I Macdonald (Transvaal), A Richter (Northern Transvaal). Replacements: J van der Westhuizen (Northern Transvaal) for Williams 30 minutes, F van Heerden (Western Province) foer Macdonald 67 minutes. New caps: Roux, J H S le Roux.

ENGLAND: P Hull (Bristol); T Underwood (Leicester), W Carling (Harlequins)(captain), P de Glanville (Bath), R Underwood (Leicester/RAF); R Andrew (Wasps), D Morris (Orrell); J Leonard (Harlequins), B Moore (Harlequins), V Ubogu (Bath), T Rodber (Northampton/Army), M Bayfield (Northampton), N Redman (Bath), B Clarke (Bath), S Ojomoh (Bath). No new caps.

Referee: C Hawke, New Zealand.

INTERNATIONAL TOURS

FRANCE TOUR TO CANADA & NEW ZEALAND
JUNE & JULY 1994

Wed, June 1st	Canada 'A'	Toronto	W 34-31
Sat, June 4th	CANADA	Ottawa	L 16-18
Thu, June 9th	North Auckland	Whangarei	W28-23
Sun, June 12th	North Harbour'	Auckland	L 23-27
Wed, June 15th	Wairarapa-Bush	Masterton	W 53- 9
Sat, June 18th	New Zealand 'A'	Wanganui	W 33-25
Wed, June 22nd	Nelson-Bays	Nelson	W 46-18
Sun, June 26th	NEW ZEALAND	Christchurch	W 20- 8
Wed, June 29th	Hawke's Bay	Napier	L 25-30
Sun, July 3rd	NEW ZEALAND	Auckland	W 23-20

Summary: Played 10, won 7, lost 3, points for 301, against 209.

ITALY TOUR TO AUSTRALIA
JUNE 1994

Sun, June 5th	South Australia	Adelaide	W 60-12
Wed, June 8th	Sydney XV	Sydney	W 36-26
Sun, June 12th	Queensland XV	Brisbane	W 21-19
Wed, June 15th	Queensland Country	Toowoomba	W 57-13
Sat, June 18th	AUSTRALIA	Brisbane	L 20-23
Tue, June 22nd	New South Wales	Sydney	W 30-20
Sat, June 25th	AUSTRALIA	Melbourne	L 7-20

Summary: Played 7, won 5, lost 2, points for 231, against 133.

WALES TOUR & WORLD CUP MATCHES
MAY & JUNE 1994

Wed, May 18	PORTUGAL (RWC)	Lisbon	W 102-12
Sat, May 21	SPAIN (RWC)	Madrid	W 54- 0
Wed, June 8	Canadian Select XV	Hamilton	W 28-19
Sat, June 11	CANADA	Toronto	W 33-15
Sat, June 18	FIJI	Suva	W 23- 8
Wed, June 22	TONGA	Nuku'alofa	W 18- 9
Sun, June 26	WESTERN SAMOA	Apia	L 9-34

Summary: Played 7, won 6, lost 1, points for 267, against 97.

SCOTLAND TOUR TO ARGENTINA
MAY 7 JUNE 1994

We, May 25	v Buenos Aires Seleccion	Buenos Aires	D 24-24
Sa, May 28	v Cuyo	Mendoza	L 11-25
Tu, May 31	v Cordoba	Cordoba	W 40-14
Sa, June 4	v ARGENTINA	Buenos Aires	L 15-16
Tu, June 7	v Rosario	Rosario	L 16-27
Sa, June 11	v ARGENTINA	Buenos Aires	L 17-19

SUMMARY: Played 6, won 1, drawn 1, lost 4, points for 123, against 125.

FIVE NATIONS CHAMPIONSHIP 1994

Saturday, 15th January 1994 **At Parc des Princes, Paris**

FRANCE 35   IRELAND 15

Benetton(T), Lacroix(T)(3P)(3C), Saint-Andre(T),   Elwood(5P)
Merle(T)

Half Time: 16-12

France: J-L Sadourny (Colomiers), P Bernat-Salles (Pau), P Sella (Agen), T Lacroix (Dax), P Saint-Andre (Montferrand), A Penaud (Brive), F Galthie (Colomiers), L Armary (Lourdes), J-M Gonzales (Bayonne), P Gallart (Beziers), P Benetton (Agen), O Merle (Grenoble), O Roumat (Dax) (captain), A Benazzi (Agen), M Cecillon (Bourgoin). No new caps.

Ireland: C O'Shea (Lansdowne), R Wallace (Garryowen), V Cunningham (St. Mary's College), P Danaher (Garryowen), S Geoghegan (London Irish), E Elwood (Lansdowne), M Bradley (Cork Constitution) (captain), N Popplewell (Greystones), T Kingston (Dolphin), P Clohessy (Young Munster), M Galwey (Shannon), P Johns (Dungannon), N Francis (Old Belvedere), K O'Connell (Sunday's Well), B Robinson (Ballymena). Replacement: G Halpin (London Irish) for Clohessy 56 mins. New cap: O'Connell.

Referee: J Fleming, Scotland

Saturday 15th January 1994 **At Cardiff Arms Park**

WALES 29   SCOTLAND 6

Rayer(2T), Evans(T), N Jenkins(4P)(C)   Hastings(2P)

Half Time: 12-3

Wales: (Llanelli unless stated), A Clement (Swansea), I Evans (cpatain), M Hall (Cardiff), N Davies, N Walker (Cardiff), N Jenkins (Pontypridd), R Moon, R Evans, G Jenkins (Swansea), J Davies (Neath), P Davies, Gareth Llewellyn (Neath), E Lewis, M Perego, S Quinnell. Replacement: M Rayer (Cardiff) for Walker 11 mins. No new caps.

Scotland: G Hastings (Watsonians) (captain), A Stanger (Hawick), G Townsend (Gald), I Jardine (Stirling County), K Logan (Stirling County), C Chalmers (Melrose), A Nicol (Dundee High School FP), P Wright (Boroughmuir), K Milne (Heriot's FP), P Burnell (London Scottish), D Turnbull (Hawick), N Edwards (Northampton), S Munro (Glasgow High/Kelvinside), I Morrison (London Scottish), R Wainwright (Edinburgh Academicals). Replacements: G Weir (Melrose) for Morrison 18 mins. New cap: Munro.

Referee: P Robin, France

Saturday 5th February 1994 **At Murrayfield**

SCOTLAND 14   ENGLAND 15

Wainwright(T), Townsend(DG), G Hastings(2P)   Callard (5P)

Half Time: 5-3

Scotland: G Hastings (Watsonians) (captain), A Stanger (Hawick), S Hastings (Watsonians), D Wyllie (Stewart's-Melville FP), K Logan (Stirling County), G Townsend (Gala), G Armstrong (Jed-Forest), A Sharp (Bristol), K Milne (Heriot's FP), P Burnell (London Scottish), P Walton (Northampton), A Reed (Bath), S Munro (Glasgow High/Kelvinside), R Wainwright (Edinburgh Academicals), G Weir (Melrose). Replacements: I Smith (Gloucester) 67 for Wainwright, I Jardine (Stirling County) 70 for Wyllie. Temporary Replacement: B Redpath (Melrose) 50-51 for Armstrong. New caps: Sharp, Walton.

England: J Callard (Bath), R Underwood (Leicester), W Carling (Harlequins) (captain), P de Glanville (Bath), T Underwood (Leicester), R Andrew (Wasps), K Bracken (Bristol), J Leonard (Harlequins), B Moore (Harlequins), V Ubogu (Bath), J Hall (Bath), M Johnson (Leicester), M Bayfield (Northampton), N Back (Leicester), B Clarke (Bath). New cap: Back.

Referee: L McLachlan, New Zealand

IRELAND 15   WALES 17

Elwood(5P)   N Jenkins(T)(4P)

Ireland: C O'Shea (Lansdowne), R Wallace (Garryowen), M McCall (Bangor), P Danaher (Garryowen), S Geoghegan (London Irish), E Elwood (Lansdowne), M Bradley (Cork Constitution) (captain), N Popplewell (Greystones), T Kingston (Dolphin), P Clohessy (Young Munster), B Robinson (Ballymena), M Galwey (Shannon), N Francis (Old Belvedere), D McBride (Malone), P Johns (Dungannon). No new caps.

Wales: (Llanelli unless stated), A Clement (Swansea), I Evans (captain), M Hall (Cardiff), N Davies, W Proctor, N Jenkins (Pontypridd), R Moon, R Evans, G Jenkins (Swansea), J Davies (Neath), E Lewis, P Davies, Gareth Llewellyn (Neath), M Perego, S Quinnell. Replacement: S Hill (Cardiff) 43 for Proctor, M Rayer (Cardiff) 50 for Clement, R Jones (Swansea) for N Davies 74 mins. No new caps.

Referee: A Spreadbury, England

ENGLAND 12   IRELAND 13

Callard(4P)   Geoghegan(T), Elwood(2P)(C)

Half Time: 6-10

England: J Callard (Bath), T Underwood (Leicester), W Carling (Harlequins) (captain), P de Glanville (Bath), R Underwood (Leicester), R Andrew (Wasps), K Bracken (Bristol), J Leonard (Harlequins), B Moore (Leicester), V Ubogu (Bath), T Rodber (Northampton), M Johnson (Leicester), M Bayfield (Northampton), N Back (Leicester), S Ojomoh (Bath). New cap: Ojomoh.

Ireland: C O'Shea (Lansdowne), R Wallace (Garryowen), M Field (Malone), P Danaher (Garryowen), S Geoghegan (London Irish), E Elwood (Lansdowne), M Bradley (Cork Constitution) (captain), N Popplewell (Greystones), T Kingston (Dolphin), P Clohessy (Young Munster), B Robinson (Ballymena), M Galwey (Shannon), N Francis (Old Belvedere), D McBride (Malone), P Johns (Dungannon). Temporary replacement: K O'Connell (Sunday's Well) for Robinson 56-57 mins. New cap: Fiueld.

Referee: P Thomas, France

WALES 24   FRANCE 15

Quinnell(T), Walker(T), N Jenkins(4P)(C)   Roumat(T), Sella(T), Lacroix(P)(C)

Half Time: 11-3

Wales: (Llanelli unless stated), M Rayer (Cardiff), S Hill (Cardiff), M Hall (Cardiff), A Clement (Swansea), N Walker (Cardiff), N Jenkins (Pontypridd), R Moon, R Evans, G Jenkins (Swansea), J Davies (Neath), E Lewis, P Davies, Gareth Llewellyn (Neath) (captain), M Perego, S Quinnell. No new caps.

France: J-L Sadourny (Colomiers), E N'Tamack (Toulouse), P Sella (Agen), T Lacroix (Dax), P Saint-Andre (Montferrand), A Penaud (Brive), F Galthie (Colomiers), P Gallart (Beziers), J-M Gonzales (Bayonne), L Armary (Lourdes), P Benetton (Agen), O Roumat (Dax) (captain), O Merle (Grenoble), A Benazzi (Agen), M Cecillon (Bourgoin). New cap: N'Tamack

Referee: L McLachlan, New Zealand

IRELAND 6   SCOTLAND 6

Elwood(2P)   G Hastings(2P)

Ireland: C O'Shea (Lansdowne), R Wallace (Garryowen), M Field (Malone), P Danaher (Garryowen), S Geoghegan (London Irish), E Elwood (Lansdowne), M Bradley (Cork Constitution) (captain), N Popplewell (Greystones), T Kingston (Dolphin), P Clohessy (Young Munster), B Robinson (Ballymena), M Galwey (Shannon), N Francis (Old Belvedere), D McBride (Malone), P Johns (Dungannon). No new caps.

Scotland: G Hastings (Watsonians) (captain), A Stanger (Hawick), S Hastings (Watsonians), D Wyllie (Stewart's-Melville FP), K Logan (Stirling County), G Townsend (Gala), G Armstrong (Jed-Forest), A Sharp (Bristol), K Milne (Heriot's FP), P Burnell (London Scottish), P Walton (Northampton), A Reed (Bath), S Munro (Glasgow High/Kelvinside), I Smith (Gloucester), G Weir (Melrose). Temporary replacement: M Dods (Gala) for G Hastings 40 mins. New cap: Dods.

Referee: E Morrison, England

Saturday 19th March 1994   **At Twickenham**
ENGLAND 15   WALES 8
R Underwood(T), Rodber(T), Andrew(P)(C)   Walker(T), N Jenkins(P)

Half Time: 7-3

England: I Hunter (Northampton), T Underwood (Leicester), W Carling (Harlequins) (captain), P de Glanville (Bath), R Underwood (Leicester/RAF), R Andrew (Wasps), D Morris (Orrell), J Leonard (Harlequins), B Moore (Harlequins), V Ubogu (Bath), T Rodber (Northampton), M Johnson (Leicester), N Redman (Bath), B Clarke (Bath), D Richards (Leicester). Replacement: M Catt (Bath) for Andrew 76 mins. New cap: Catt.

Wales: (Llanelli unless stated), M Rayer (Cardiff), I Evans (captain), M Hall (Cardiff), N Davies, N Walker (Cardiff), N Jenkins (Pontypridd), R Moon, R Evans, G Jenkins (Swansea), J Davies (Neath), E Lewis, P Davies, Gareth Llewellyn (Neath), M Perego, S Quinnell. Replacement: A Copsey for Lewis 49 mins. No new caps.

Referee: J Fleming, Scotland

Saturday 19th March 1994   **At Murrayfield**
SCOTLAND 12   FRANCE 20
G Hastings(4P)   Sadourny(T), Saint-Andre(T), Lacroix(2P)(C),
                                       Montlaur(C)

Scotland: G Hastings (Watsonians) (captain), A Stanger (Hawick), S Hastings (Watsonians), D Wyllie (Stewart's-Melville FP), K Logan (Stirling County), G Townsend (Gala), S Redpath (Melrose), A Sharp (Bristol), K Milne (Heriot's FP), P Burnell (London Scottish), P Walton (Northampton), S Munro (Glasgow High/Kelvinside), A Reed (Bath), G Weir (Melrose), I Smith (Gloucester). No new caps.

France: J-L Sadourny (Colomiers), P Saint-Andre (Montferrand) (captain), P Sella (Agen), Y Delaigue (Toulon), W Techoueyres (SBUC), T Lacroix (Dax), A Macabiau (Perpignan), L Benezech (Racing Club), J-M Gonzales (Bayonne), L Seigne (Merignae), A Benazzi (Agen), O Merle (Grenoble), O Brouzet (Grenoble), L Cabannes (Racing Club), P Benetton (Agen). Replacement: P Moutlaur (Agen) for Lacroix 52 mins. New caps: Delaigue, Macabiau, Brouzet.

Referee: D Bevan, Wales

FINAL CHAMPIONSHIP TABLE							
	P	W	D	L	F	A	Pts
Wales	4	3	0	1	78	51	6
England	4	3	0	1	60	49	6
France	4	2	0	2	84	69	4
Ireland	4	1	1	2	49	70	3
Scotland	4	0	1	3	38	70	1

FIRA CHAMPIONSHIP

Sunday 17th October 1993   **At Brive**
FRANCE 51   ROMANIA 0
Bernat-Salles(3T), Sella(T), Merle(T), Loppy(T),
Lacroix(3P)(6C)

Half Time: 20-0

INTERNATIONAL FIXTURE AMENDMENT
On Page 10
Saturday March 4th
IRELAND will play FRANCE in Dublin, NOT Paris

UNDER 21 INTERNATIONALS

Sunday 7th November 1993   At Gateshead

ENGLAND UNDER-21 22   IRELAND UNDER-21 15
Ryan(2T), O'Leary(T), Handley(T), Stimpson(C)   Burke(DG)(4P)

Friday 14th January 1994   At Glamorgan Wanderers, Ely, Cardiff

WALES 36   SCOTLAND 0
S John(T), Davies(T), Reynolds(T), Thomas(T),
Appleyard(T), C John(3C)

Half Time: 10-0

INTERNATIONAL MATCHES

Wednesday 10th November 1993   At Cardiff Arms Park

WALES 24   CANADA 26
N Jenkins(8P)   Stuart(T), Charron(T), Rees(4P)(2C)

Half Time: 9-6

Saturday 13th November 1993   At Dublin

IRELAND 25   ROMANIA 3
Geoghegan(T), Elwood(6P)(C)   Rosu(P)

Half Time: 19-0

Saturday 18 December 1993   At Rovigo

ITALY 18   SCOTLAND A 15
Dominguez(6P)   Dods(5P)

Half Time: 9-9

'A' INTERNATIONALS 1993-94

Italy 18   Scotland 15
Scotland 24   Ireland 9
Ireland 10   Wales 20
Italy 9   England 15
England 29   Ireland 14
France 9   Scotland 12
France 20   England 8
Wales 21   France 8
Holland 14   England 56

UNDER 21 INTERNATIONALS 1993-94

England 22   Ireland 15   France 13   England 9
Wales 36   Scotland 0   Romania 8   Wales 12
Italy 6   England 43

CIS DIVISIONAL CHAMPIONSHIP

Saturday 16th October 1993   At Bath

SOUTH WEST 31   MIDLANDS 3

Lumsden(2T), Beal(T), Adebayo(T), Callard(3P)(C)   Hodgkinson(P)

Half Time: 17-3

South West: (Bath unless stated), J Callard, A Adebayo, P de Glanville, N Beal (Northampton), A Lumsden, M Catt, K Bracken (Bristol), C Clark, G Dawe, V Ubogu, J Hall (captain), N Redman, A Blackmore (Bristol), A Robinson, S Ojomoh.

Midlands: (Leicester unless stated), S Hodgkinson (Moseley), S Hackney, S Potter, I Bates, H Thorneycroft (Northampton), P Challinor (Harlequins), M Dawson (Northampton), G Rowntree, J Oliver (Northampton), D Garforth, C Barrow (Bristol), J Phillips (Northampton), S Lloyd (Moseley), C Millhouse (Northampton), D Richards (captain). Replacements: A Kardooni for Dawson 33 minutes, J Harris for Hodgkinson 58 minutes.

Referee: D Matthews, Liverpool

Saturday 16th October 1993   At Newcastle Gosforth

NORTH 21   LONDON 22

Mallinder(T), Fielden(T), Grayson(2DG)(P)(C)   Underwood(T), Carling(T), Hopley(T),
                                       Andrew(P)(2C)

Half Time: 9-14

North: I Hunter (Northampton), J Mallinder (Sale), M Fielden (Northampton), K Simms (Liverpool St. Helens) (captain), J Sleightholme (Wakefield), P Grayson (Northampton), D Scully (Wakefield), M Hynes (Orrell), G French (Orrell), S McMain (Sheffield), T Rodber (Northampton), D Baldwin (Sale), J Dixon (West Hartlepool), A Macfarlane (Sale), N Ashurst (Orrell).

London: (Wasps unless stated), H Davies, T Underwood (Leicester), W Carling (Harlequins), D Hopley, D O'Leary (Harlequins), R Andrew (captain), S Bates, J Leonard (Harlequins), B Moore (Harlequins), J Probyn, M Greenwood, A Snow (Harlequins), R Langhorn (Harlequins), D Ryan, L Dallaglio.

Referee: E Murray, Scotland

Saturday 23rd October 1993   At Gloucester

SOUTH WEST 29   NORTH 16

Hull(T), Adebayo(T), Ojomoh(T), Callard(4P)(C)   Mallinder(T), Grayson(DG)(2P)(C)

South West: (Bath unless stated), J Callard, P Holford (Gloucester), P de Glanville, N Beal (Northampton), A Adebayo, P Hull (Bristol), K Bracken (Bristol), C Clark (Oxford University & Bath), K Dunn (Wasps), D Hinkins (Bristol), J Hall (captain), D Sims (Gloucester), A Blackmore (Bristol), D Eves (Bristol), S Ojomoh.

North: I Hunter (Northampton), J Mallinder (Sale), M Fielden (Northampton), K Simms (Liverpool St. Helens) (captain), J Sleightholme (Wakefield), P Grayson (Northampton), D Scully (Wakefield), M Hynes (Orrell), G French (Orrell), S McMain (Sheffield), C Vyvyan (Wharfedale), D Baldwin (Sale), J Dixon (West Hartlepool), N Ashurst (Orrell), A MacFarlane (Sale). Replacement: G Ainscough (Orrell) for Mallinder 63 mins.

Referee: D McHugh, Cork

Saturday 30th October 1993   At Leicester

MIDLANDS 14   LONDON 23

Saunders(T), Packman(DG), Steel (2P)   Sheasby(T), Ryan(T), Andrew(DG)(2P)(C)

Half Time: 9-3

Midlands: (Leicester unless stated), J Steele (Northampton), E Saunders (Rugby), F Packman (Northampton), I Bates, H Thorneycroft (Northampton), J Harris, M Dawson (Northampton), G Rowntree, J Oliver (Northampton) (captain), D Garforth, J Wells, M Johnson, S Lloyd (Moseley), N Back, C Barrow (Bristol). Replacement: S Purdy (Moseley) for Bates 39 mins.

London: (Wasps unless stated), H Davies, D O'Leary (Harlequins), G Childs, D Hopley, C Oti, R Andrew (captain), S Bates, J Leonard (Harlequins), B Moore (Harlequins), A Mullins (Harlequins), M Greenwood, A Snow (Harlequins), D Ryan, R Jenkins (London Irish), C Sheasby (Harlequins).

Referee: A Spreadbury, Somerset

CIS DIVISIONAL CHAMPIONSHIP

MIDLANDS 9   NORTH 28

Stelle(3P)   Ashurst(T), Sleightholme(T), Simms(T),
Grayson(DG)(2P)(2C)

Half Time: 9-19

Midlands: (Leicester unless stated), J Steele (Northampton), S Hackney, S Purdy (Moseley), F Packman (Northampton), H Thorneycroft (Northampton), J Harris, A Kardooni, G Baldwin (Northampton), R Cockerill, D Garforth, J Wells, M Johnson, S Lloyd (Moseley), C Millhouse (Northampton), D Richards (captain). Replacement: I Skingsley (Bedford) for Lloyd 71 mins.

North: M Jackson (Wakefield), J Sleightholme (Wakefield), J Fletcher (Northampton), K Simms (Liverpool St. Helens) (captain), R Underwood (Leicester), P Grayson (Northampton), D Scully (Wakefield), P Lancaster (West Hartlepool), S Mitchell (West Hartlepool), S McMain (Sheffield), C Vyvyan (Wharfedale), J Dixon (West Hartlepool), C Cusani (Orrell), N Ashurst (Orrell), A MacFarlane (Sale).

Referee: E Morrison, Bristol

LONDON 17   SOUTH WEST 25

Alexander(T), Holford(4P)   Holford(T), Beal(DG), Hull(DG), Callard(4P)(C)

Half Time: 11-12

London: (Wasps unless stated), A Buzza, D O'Leary (Harlequins), H Davies, F Clough, J Alexander (Harlequins), G Gregory (Nottingham), S Bates (captain), G Holmes, G Botterman (Saracens), J Probyn, M Greenwood, A Snow (Harlequins), A Diprose (Saracens), M White, C Sheasby (Harlequins).

South West: (Bath unless stated), J Callard, M Lloyd, M Catt, N Beal (Northampton), P Holford (Gloucester), P Hull (Bristol), R Hill, C Clark (Oxford University & Bath), G Dawe (captain), D Hinkins (Bristol), S Ojomoh, A Blackmore (Bristol), R West (Gloucester), D Eves (Bristol), D Sims (Gloucester). Temporary replacement: K Dunn (Wasps) for Dawe 44-49 mins.

Referee: G Simmonds, Wales

FINAL TABLE						
	P	W	L	F	A	Pts
South West	3	3	0	85	36	6
London	3	2	1	62	60	4
North	3	1	2	68	60	2
Midlands	3	0	3	26	85	0

CIS COUNTY CHAMPIONSHIP

FINAL

Saturday, 16th April 1994   At Twickenham.

DURHAM 3   YORKSHIRE 26

DURHAM G Spearman (Blaydon); O Evans (West Hartlepool), I Bell (Hartlepool Rovers), P Nickalls (Rosslyn Park), C Mattison (Durham City); A Parker (West Hartlepool), S Kirkup (Durham City); R Naisbitt (Stockton) (captain), I Parnaby (Westoe), M Douthwaite (Stockton), S Musgrove (Westoe), G Wanless (Durham City), C Aldus (Stockton), D McKinnon (West Hartlepool), B Dixon (Stockton). Replacements: K McCallum (Durham City) for Evans 35 minutes, J Brown (Novocastrians) for Spearman 75 minutes.

YORKSHIRE D Breakwell (Leeds); M Harrison (Wakefield), B Barley (Sandal) (captain), S Burnhill (Cleckheaton), C Thornton (Leeds); K Plant (Rotherham), G Easterby (Harrogate); R Szabo (Wakefield), R Whyley (Harrogate), S McMain (Sheffield), C West (Rotherham), I Carroll (Otley), C Raducanu (Bradford & Bingley), N Hargreaves (Leeds), C Vyvyan (Wharfedale).

Referee A Spreadbury, Somerset.

UNDER 21's

FINAL

Saturday, 16th April 1994   At Twickenham.

EAST MIDLANDS 34   SURREY 22
Half-time 15-10.

EAST MIDLANDS (all Northampton S Montgomery; S Gross, M Foster (captain), S Pestell, C Moir; K Heitman, A Gallagher; M Valland, C Wilson, D Masters, J Wright, G Webster, C Knowles, A Pountney, G Seely. SCORERS: Tries: Gallagher (2), Moir (1), Masters (1). Dropped-Goal: Heitman. Pens: Heitman (3). Con: Heitman.

SURREY A Maddock (Wasps) (captain); J Blake (Rosslyn Park), D Fitzgerald (Rosslyn Park), J Keyter (Harlequins), S Roiser (Rosslyn Park); I Stent (Camberley), N Walshe (Rosslyn Park); A Poole (Sutton & Epsom), M Hynard (Bath), J Klass (Bristol), M Butterworth (Old Midwhitgifdtians), J Canham (Rosslyn Park), N Yeo (Harlequins), J Cowie (Rosslyn Park), T Thirwell (Wasps). Replacement: A Hutchinson (Harlequins) for Stent 60 minutes. SCORERS: Tries Roiser (1), Maddock (1), Blake (1). Pen: Maddock. Cons: Maddock (2).

CIS COUNTY CHAMPIONSHIP

FINAL TABLES

DIVISION 1 SOUTH	P	W	L	F	A	Pts
Cornwall	3	3	0	48	37	6
Gloucestershire	3	2	1	78	39	4
Hampshire	3	1	2	30	56	2
Middlesex	3	0	3	38	62	0

Cornwall and Gloucestershire qualify for semi-finals
Middlesex relegated to Division 2 South

DIVISION 1 NORTH	P	W	L	F	A	Pts
Yorkshire,3	3	0	78	14	6	
Durham	3	1	2	62	63	2
Lancashire	3	1	2	40	72	2
Northumberland	3	1	2	44	80	2

Yorkshire and Durham qualify for the semi-finals
Northumberland are relegated to Division 2 North

DIVISION 2 SOUTH	P	W	L	F	A	Pts
Surrey	3	2	1	0	48	28
Devon	3	1	1	1	31	40
Kent	3	1	0	2	52	41
Dorset & Wiltshire	3	1	0	2	49	71

Surrey are promoted to Division 1 South
Dorset & Wiltshire are relegated to Division 3 South

DIVISION 2 NORTH	P	W	L	F	A	Pts
Cheshire	3	3	0	65	47	6
Cumbria	3	2	1	57	46	4
Leicestershire	3	1	2	51	53	2
Warwickshire	3	0	3	51	78	0

Cheshire are promoted to Division 1 North
Warwickshire are relegated to Division 3 North

DIVISION 3 SOUTH	P	W	L	F	A	Pts
sussex	3	2	1	45	37	4
Buckinghamshire	3	2	1	36	40	4
Hertfordshire	3	1	2	48	44	2
Somerset	3	1	2	37	45	2

Sussex are promoted to Division 2 South
Somerset are relegated to Division 4 South

DIVISION 3 NORTH	P	W	L	F	A	Pts
Staffordshire	3	3	0	84	59	6
North Midlands	3	2	1	73	41	4
Notts Lincs & Derby	3	1	2	59	63	2
East Midlands	3	0	3	48	101	0

Staffordshire are promoted to Division 2 North

DIVISION 4 SOUTH	P	W	L	F	A	Pts
Oxfordshire	2	2	0	47	21	4
Berkshire	2	1	1	54	47	2
Eastern Counties	2	0	2	30	63	0

Oxfordshire are promoted to Division 3 South

Saturday 15th January 1994

YORKSHIRE 13   GLOUCESTERSHIRE 12

West(T), Plant(2P(C))   Hamlin(DG)(3P)

Half Time: 0-6

Yorkshire: T Stimpson (Durham University), J Eagle (Leeds), B Barley (Sandal) (captain), S Burnhill (Cleckheaton), C THornton (Leeds), K Plant (Rotherham), A Crawley (Bradford & BIngley), P Wright (Middlesborough), R Whyley (Harrogate), R Szabo (Wakefield), C West (Rotherham), P Taylor (Harrogate), C Raducanu (Bradford & Bingley), H Verity (Wharfedale), C Vyvyan (Wharfedale).

Gloucestershire: N Marment (Cheltenham), J Davies (Cheltenham), B Maslen (Gloucestershire), L Osborne (Berry Hill), D Cotterill (Bristol), M Hamlin (Moseley) (captain), G Shipton (Stroud), A Powles (Berry Hill), N Nelmes (Lydney), S Baldwin (Gloucester Old Boys), I Patten (Bristol), N Scrivens (Cirencester), J Brain (Cheltenham), R Lewis (Lydney), D Mann (Matson).

Referee: N Cousins, RFU

Saturday 5th February 1994   **At Redruth**

CORNWALL 9   DURHAM 14

Chapman(DG)(2P)   McKinnon(T), Bland(2DG)(P)

Half Time: 9-8

Cornwall: D Chapman (Camborne), D Weeks (Camborne), F Gadsdon (Camborne), A Mead (Redruth), I Pollard (Camborne), J Tucker (Launceston), R Nancekivell (Launceston), A Ellery (Redruth), B Andrew (Redruth), J Pearce (St Ives), S Berryman (Penzance & Newlyn, T Adams (Camborne), A Cook (Redruth) (captain), M Addinall (Penryn), J Atkinson (Penryn).

Durham: K McCallum (Durham City), C Evans (West Hartlepool), I Bell (Hartlepool Rovers), P Nickalls (Rosslyn Park), C Mattison (Durham City), J Bland (Durham City), S Kirkup (Durham City), G Naisbitt (Stockton) (captain), I Parnaby (Westoe), M Douthwaite (Stockton), S Musgrove (Westoe), G Wanless (Durham City), C Aldus (Stockton), D McKinnon (West Hartlepool), S Dixon (Stockton). Replacements: D Tweddle (Gateshead Fell) for Mattison 62 mins.

Referee: S Lander, Liverpool Society

INTERNATIONAL FIXTURE AMENDMENT
On Page 10
Saturday March 4th
IRELAND will play FRANCE in Dublin, NOT Paris

INTER-SERVICES TOURNAMENT

Saturday 26th March 1994

ROYAL NAVY 6   THE ARMY 18

Price(2P)   Powley(6P)

Half Time: 6-6

Royal Navy: J Coulton, C White, M Jarrett, D Oakley, S Brown, G Price, P Livingstone, D Honey, M Clay, S Gay, C Palmer, G Harrison, D Cross, S Jones (captain), R Armstrong. Replacement: K Eyre for Coulton 80 mins.

The Army: K Bowling, S Bartliff, S Powley, A Glasgow, J Fenn, S Commander, J Denwood, D Coghlan, J Brammer (captain), J Fowers, G James, D Dahinten, A Newsham, T Rodber, M Watson. Replacemenst: D Hall for Flowers 5 mins, D Orr Ewing for Dahintan 70 mins.

Referee: G Davies, Liverpool

Windsor Life Challenge Trophy

Wednesday 13th April 1994   **At Twickenham**

ROYAL NAVY 12   ROYAL AIR FORCE 22

Price (DG)(3P)   Raynor(2T), Roke(T), Underwood(T), Worrall (C)

Royal Navy: K Eyre, C White, M Jarrett, D Oakley, S Brown, G Price, P Livingstone, D Honey, M Clay, W Lee, I Dixon, G Harrison, D Cross, S Jones (captain), R Armstrong. Replacement: C Palmer for Jones 40 mins.

Royal Air Force: R Underwood, G Sharp, E Raynor, S Roke, S Crossland, P Hull, S Worrall (captain), A Billett, R Miller, B Williams, D Williams, B Richardson, R Burn, L Hibbert, D Parsonage.

Referee: A Rowden, Berkshire

S Worrall was making his 23rd Inter Srevices appearance — a record for the tournament.

Windsor Life Challenge Cup

Wednesday 20th April 19994

ROYAL AIR FORCE 28   THE ARMY 22

Sharp(2T), Raynor(T), Hull(DG), Worrall(P)(2C),   Rodber(2T), Watson(T), Jinks(T), Powley(C)
Hull(P)

Half Time: 20-10

Royal Air Force: R Underwood, G Sharp, E Raynor, S Roke, S Crossland, P Hull, S Worrall (captain), A Billett, S Miller, B Williams, D Williams, R Burn, B Richardson, L Hibbert, D Parsonage. Replacement: P Taylor for Richardson 34 mins.

The Army: K Bowling, S Bartliff, A Glasgow, S Powley, J Fenn, S Commander, J Merritt, D Hall, J Brammer (captain), J Fowers, T Rodber, A Newsham, D Dahinton, G James, M Watson. Replacemenst: D Coghlan for Flowers 41 mins, P Curtiss for James 56 mins, P Jinks for Brammer 78 mins.

Referee: G Hughes, Manchester

FINAL TABLE						
	P	W	L	F	A	Pts
Royal Air Force	2	2	0	50	34	4
The Army	2	1	1	40	34	2
Royal Navy	2	0	2	18	40	0

THE PILKINGTON CUP

FINAL

Saturday 7th May 1994   **At Twickenham**

BATH 21   LEICESTER 9

Swift(T), Catt(T), Callard(3P)(C)   Harris(3P)

Half Time 9-9

BATH: J Callard, A Swift, P de Glanville, M Catt, A Adebayo, S Barnes, R Hill, D Hilton, G Dawe, V Ubogu, J Hall(cpatain), N Redman, A Reed, A Robinson, B Clarke. Replacement: S Ojomoh for Robinson 49 mins.
LEICESTER: W Kilford, T Underwood, S Potter, L Boyle, R Underwood, J Harris, A Kardooni, G Rowntree, R Cockerill, D Garforth, J Wells, M Johnson, M Poole, N Back, D Richards(captain).
Referee: E Morrison, Bath

SEMI FINALS

Saturday 2nd April 1994   **At Stoop Memorial Ground, Twickenham**

HARLEQUINS 25   BATH 26

Pepper(T), Cassell(T), Challinor(DG)(P)(C)   Swift(2T), Barnes(T), Callard(T)(3C)

Half Time: 0-19

HARLEQUINS: K Bray, J Keyter, W Carling, G Thompson, D O'Leary, P Challinor, C Luxton, J Leonard, B Moore, A Mullins(captain), M Pepper, A Snow, P Thresher, M Russell, C Sheasby. Replacements: J Alexander for Thompson 40 mins, J Cassell for Sheasby 40 mins.
BATH: J Callard, A Swift, P de Glanville, M Catt, A Lumsden, S Barnes, R Hill, D Hilton, G Dawe, V Ubogu, J Hall(cpatain), M Haag, N Redman, A Robinson, B Clarke.
Referee: B Campsall, Yorkshire

At Orrell

ORRELL 18   LEICESTER 31

Wynn(T), Ainscough(T)(P)(C), Langford (P)   Potter(2T), Underwood(T), Harris(4P)(2C)

Half Time: 15-6

ORRELL: S Taberner(captain), J Naylor, I Wynn, S Langford, P Johnson, G Ainscough, D Morris, M Hynes, D French, D Southern, P Manley, C Cusani, C Cooper, D Cleary, S Bibby. Replacement: P Hamer for Taberner 62 mins. Sent-off: Cusani 71 mins.
LEICESTER: W Kilford, S Hackney, S Potter, L Boyle, R Underwood, J Harris, A Kardooni, G Rowntree, R Cockerill, D Garforth, J Wells, M Johnson, M Poole, W Drake-Lee, D Richards(captain).
Referee: A Spreadbury, Somerset

SIXTH ROUND

Gloucester 3	v	Orrell 10
Harlequins 26	v	Sale 13
Leicester 12	v	Moseley 6
Saracens 6	v	Bath 23

Played on Saturday 26th February 1994

FIFTH ROUND

Bath 14	v	Bristol 9
Gloucester 11	v	Northampton 6
Harlequins 23	v	West Hartlepool 15
Leicester 43	v	London Irish 10
Moseley 15	v	Fylde 6
Newcastle Gosforth 7	v	Orrell 12
Otley 7	v	Sale 58
Rosslyn Park 12	v	Saracens 29

Result of the Round:
Otley 7   v   Sale 58

FOURTH ROUND

Bath 24	v	Wasps 11
Blackheath 10	v	Leicester 16
Bristol 46	v	Henley 6
Harlequins 52	v	Basingstoke 3
Havant 13	v	London Irish 18
London Scottish 6	v	Fylde 8
Moseley 32	v	Winnington Park 6
Newcastle Gosforth 53	v	Bridgwater & Albion 10
Northampton 22	v	Waterloo 3
Nottingham 9	v	Gloucester 29
Orrell 55	v	Stourbridge 3
Otley 20	v	Wharfedale 3
Rosslyn Park 22	v	Coventry 15
Rugby 13	v	Sale 17
Saracens 26	v	B'ham & Solihull 3
Wakefield 17	v	West Hartlepool 18

Result of the Round:
Rugby 13   v   Sale 17
Played on Saturday 18th December 1993

THE PILKINGTON CUP

THIRD ROUND

Bi'ham & Solihull 13   v   Broughton Park 3
Bradford & Bingley 6   v   Fylde 13
Clifton 12   v   Bridgwater & Albion 24
Coventry 10   v   Preston Grasshoppers 5
Havant 24   v   Cambridge 13
Henley 17   v   North Walsham 3
Kettering 6   v   Stourbridge 13
New Brighton 3   v   Winnington Park 16
Rosslyn Park 38   v   Plymouth Albion 7
Sheffield 0   v   Wharfedale 20
Sudbury 6   v   Basingstoke 25
Played on Saturday 27th November 1993
Blackheath 21   v   London Welsh 9
Played on Sunday 28th November 1993
Sheffield 0   v   Wharfedale 20

SECOND ROUND

Amersham-Chiltern 5   v   London Welsh 23
Askeans 0   v   Basingstoke 6
Aspatria 17   v   Storubridge 22
B'ham & Solihull 7   v   Harrogate 3
Bradford & Bingley 23   v   Bedford 15
Brixham 3   v   North Walsham 3
(North Walsham qualify as away team)
Broughton Park 6   v   Morley 5
Camborne 20   v   Bridgwater & Albion 21
Coventry 33   v   York 19
Exeter 6   v   Clifton 9
Henley 65   v   St. Ives 0
High Wycombe 9   v   Preston Grasshoppers 20
Leeds 6   v   Kettering 13
Lydney 11   v   Havant 16
New Brighton 17   v   Liverpool St. Helens 12
Plymouth 22   v   Barking 11
Redruth 6   v   Rosslyn Park 30
Richmond 21   v   Blackheath 23
Sheffield 9   v   Hereford 8
Syston 9   v   Fylde 15
Tabard 9   v   Sudbury 33
Walsall 17   v   Wharfedale 22
Westcombe Park 6   v   Cambridge 21
Winnington Park 37   v   Durham City 3
Result of the Round:
Leeds 6   v   Kettering 13

FIRST ROUND

Alton 8   v   St. Ives 23
Berry Hill 15   v   Henley 20
Bradford & Bingley 12   v   Tynedale 6
Brixham 17   v   Reading 14
Broadstreet 6   v   B'ham & Solihull 17
Camborne 22   v   Wimborne 14
Cheshunt 8   v   High Wycombe 14
Chiltern 8   v   Worthing 0
Durham City 14   v   Wolverhampton 8
Kettering 8   v   Widnes 3
Lichfield 9   v   Walsall 14
London Welsh 44   v   Windsor 0
Lydney 64   v   Maidstone 0
New Brighton 14   v   Wigton 8
North Walsham 22   v   Metropolitan Police 3
Nuneaton 9   v   Hereford 11
Old Midwhitgiftians 8   v   Bridgwater & Albion 12
Preston Grasshoppers 38   v   Stoke-on-Trent 0
Ruislip 5   v   Tabard 30
Scunthorpe 6   v   Wharfedale 59
Southend 11   v   Cambridge 20
Stockton 8   v   Syston 11
Stourbridge 15   v   Camp Hill 10
Stroud 12   v   Basingstoke 16
Westcombe Park 20   v   Ealing 16
Weston-Super-Mare 10   v   Barking 39
Winnington Park 15   v   Rotherham 3
York 16   v   Kendal 15
Results of the Round:
Weston-Super-Mare 10   v   Barking 39
Southend 11   v   Cambridge 20

PILKINGTON SHIELD

Saturday 7th May 1994   At Twickenham

MALVERN 8   OLD HAMPTONIANS 6

Grundy(T)(P)   Prichard(2P)
                                          Half Time 0-3

MALVERN: S Fahey, D Grundy, G Richards, R James, A Johnson, D Green, G Henderson, S Cooper, P Morewood, C Campion, S Dixon, A McKelvie, A McBurney, M Wolfe, A Ridley(captain). Replacement: D Blinstone for Wolfe 75 mins.

OLD HAMPTONIANS: S Eggleton, A Mclenon, G Prichard, S Fox, A Mills-Leggett, N Bugler, E Turnill, A Glyn-Jones, S Zander(captain), J Clarke, L Gallant, J Lumley-Kelly, R Bowden, M Carmody, N Cooke.
Referee: A Spreadbury, Somerset

SEMI FINAL

Hucclecote Old Boys 6   v   Malvern 8
(at Coventry)
Kidderminster Carolians 6   v   Old Hamptonians 10
(at Northampton)
Played on Saturday 2nd April 1994

QUARTER FINAL

North
Edwardian 9   v   Malvern 9
(Malvern qualify as the away team)
Keswick 17   v   Kidderminster Carolians 27

South
Hucclecote Old Boys 11   v   Old Public Oaks 6
Old Caterhamians 3   v   Old Hamptonians 15
Played on Saturday 26th February 1994

ROUND SIX

North & Midlands

Atherstone 3	v	Keswick 10
Edwardian 22	v	St Albans 0
Kidderminster Carolians 14	v	Colne & Nelson 0
Malvern 20	v	Wibsey 13

London & South West

Barton Hill Old Boys 6	v	Hucclecote Old Boys 8
Bishopton 11	v	Old Hamptonians 26
Loughton 0	v	Old Caterhamians 14
Old Public Oaks 10	v	Woking 3

Played on Saturday 22nd January 1994

SCOTLAND

McEWAN'S SCOTTISH INTER-DISTRICT CHAMPIONSHIP 1993-94

Final Saturday 30th October 1993   at Melrose

SOUTH 28   GLASGOW 14

Nichol(T), Chalmers(T)(DG), Turnbull(T),   Brough(T), Barrett(3P)
Parker(2P), (2C)

Half Time: 25-8

South: (Melrose unless stated), M Dods (Gala), A Stanger (Hawick), S Nichol (Selkirk), A Shiel, G Parker, C Chalmers, R Redpath, G Isaac (Gala), J Hay (Hawick), H Hunter (Gala), D Turnbull (Hawick), R Brown (captain), G Weir, J Amos (Gala), C Hogg. Replacement: D Hunter (Selkirk) for Dods 56 mins.

Glasgow: (Stirling County inless stated), K Logan, A Turner, S McIntosh (West of Scotland), I Jardine, R Porter (Edinburgh Academicals), D Barrett (West of Scotland), F Scott (West of Scotland), A Watt (Glasgow High-Kelvinside), K McKenzie, G Robertson, F Wallace (Glasgow High-Kelvinside) (captain), S Hamilton, S Munro (Glasgow High-Kelvinside), J Busby (Glasgow High-Kelvinside), J Brough.
Referee: E Morrison, England

Other results:
Semi-finals (23rd October 1993)
Glasgow 21, v, Edinburgh 6 (at Hughenden)
South 27, v, North & Midlands 13 (at Jedburgh)

Third Place (30th October 1993)
Edinburgh 28, v, North & Midlands 25
(at Melrose)

McEWAN'S NATIONAL LEAGUE

FINAL TABLES 1993-94

DIVISION 1

	P	W	D	L	F	A	Pts
Melrose	13	12	0	1	410	192	24
Gala	12	9	0	3	274	214	18
Edinburgh Acads	13	8	1	4	265	183	17
Heriot's FP	12	7	0	5	230	224	14
Watsonians	13	7	0	6	276	337	14
Stirling County	12	6	1	5	227	163	13
Hawick	12	6	1	5	218	178	13
Jed-Forest	13	6	0	7	231	199	12
Currie	12	6	0	6	230	285	12
Stewart's/Melville	13	5	1	7	157	190	11
Boroughmuir	12	5	0	7	214	228	10
West of Scotland	13	4	1	8	235	279	9
Kelso	13	4	0	9	175	296	8
Selkirk	13	0	1	12	138	312	1

Champions: Melrose. Relegated: Kelso, Selkirk.

DIVISION 2

	P	W	D	L	F	A	Pts
Glasgow High/ Kelvinside	13	13	0	0	440	115	26
Dundee HS FP	12	11	0	1	395	80	22
Kirkcaldy	13	10	0	3	277	150	20
Edinburgh Wands	13	8	0	5	214	251	16
Musselburgh	13	7	0	6	204	185	14
Peebles	13	6	0	7	206	219	12
Glasgow Acads	13	5	1	7	237	276	11
Wigtownshire	13	5	0	8	172	241	10
Haddington	12	5	0	7	146	220	10
Grangemouth	13	4	1	8	201	293	9
Biggar	13	3	2	8	203	240	8
Preston Lodge FP	13	4	0	9	158	291	8
Clarkston	13	4	0	9	158	357	8
Ayr	13	3	0	10	168	261	6

Promoted: Glasgow High/Kelvinside (champions), Dundee High School FP. Relegated: Clarkston, Ayr

ALLOA BREWERY CUP

QUARTER FINALS

Glasgow High/Kelvinside 9   Stirling County 22
Heriot's FP 0   Boroughmuir 16
Kirkcaldy 9   Dundee HS FP 30
Watsonians 13   Stewart's-Melville FP 25

SEMI FINALS

Dundee HS FP 29   Stewart's-Melville FP 28
Stirling County 13   Boroughmuir 19

FINAL

Saturday, 7th May 1994   **At Meggetland**

BOROUGHMUIR 42   DUNDEE HIGH SCHOOL FP 18
H.T. 3-8.

Tries: Smith (1), Wright (1), Lineen (1), Burns (1), Stark (1). Penalty-goals: Easson (3). Conversions: Easson (4)

Tries: Waite (1), C Newton (1). Penalty-goals: J Newton (2). Conversion: J Newton

BOROUGHMUIR: N Marden; D Stark, S Lineen, D Laird, R Smith; B Easson, M Hall; G Wilson, N Dickson, P Wright, D Burns, G Hepburn, P Jennings, G Drummond, S Reid (captain).

DUNDEE HIGH SCHOOL FP: M Lamont; M Cousin, P Rouse, N Douglas, C Newton; J Newton, A Nicol; A Van der Esch, R Cairney, D Herrington, W Keys, S Campbell, A Baxter, M Waite, G Batchelor. Replacement: A Featherstone for Nicol 34 minutes. Temporary replacement: R MacFarlane.

Referee: J Bacigalupo, Edinburgh Wanderers.

CASTLEMAINE XXXX TROPHY

FINAL

Saturday, 7th May 1994

GARNOCK 6   FORRESTER22
H.T. 3-8

Penalty-goals: Jeans (2)

Tries: Whitelaw (1), Jeans (1) Penalty-goals: Dalgleish (4)

GARNOCK: K Jacobson; E Jeans, P McCarrol, J Nisbet, A Anderson; G Nisbet, D Musselbrook; I Hoynes, G Ward, J Goldie, A King, S Anderson, W Miller, A Brocket, S Livingstone. Replacement: W Walker for J Nisbet 43 minutes. Temporary replacement: A McLeary.
FORESTER FP: G McLoughlin; W Whitelaw, C Lewis, R Baldie, A Hamilton; P Dalgleish, M Proudfoot; J Bertram, B Duffie, A Sutton, S Hunter, P Reid, I Sutherland, A Clelland, G Hume. Temporary replacement: S Warner. Sent off: Proudfoot 36 minutes.

WALES

SWALEC CUP

FINAL

Saturday 7th May 1994   At Cardiff Arms Park

CARDIFF 15   LLANELLI 8

Hall(T), Rayer (T), A Davies (P)(C)   I Evans(T), Stephens(P)

Half Time: 15-8

CARDIFF: M Rayer, S Ford, M Hall (captain), M Laity, N Walker, A Davies, A Moore, M Griffiths, J Humphreys, L Mustoe, M Bennett, A Rees, D Jones, M Budd, O Williams. Temporary replacement: V Davies for Budd 22-28 mins.

LLANELLI: N Boobyer, I Evans, S Davies, N Davies, W Proctor, C Stephens, Rupert Moon(captain), R Evans, A Lamerton, H Williams- Jones, E Lewis, P Davies, A Copsey, M Perego, S Quinnell. Replacements: I Jones for S Davies 53 mins, P Jones for P Davies 54 Mins.

Referee: R Yeman, Port Talbot

SEMI FINALS

Saturday 16th April 1994   At The Gnoll, Neath

LLANELLI 23   MAESTEG 7

I Evans(T), Quinnell(T), R Evans(T), Strange(DG),   Watts(T)(C)
Stephens(P)(C)

Half Time: 5-7

LLANELLI: J Strange, I Evans, N Davies, N Boobyer, W Proctor, C Stephens, R Moon(captain), R Evans, A Lamerton, H Williams-Jones, M Perego, P Davies, A Copsey, L Jones, S Quinnell. Replacement: P JOnes for Copsey 79 mins.

MAESTEG: B Davey, D Williams, R Boobyer, G Wilcox, J Hopkins, M Watts, H Lewis, P Riley, L Gilby, P Pincher, P Buckle, L Harvey(captain), S Thomas, P Thomas, A Williams.

Referee: C Thomas, Swansea

At Rodney Parade, Newport

CARDIFF 8   PONTYPRIDD 6

Laity(T), Davies (P)   Cormack(2P)

Half Time: 0-6

CARDIFF: M Rayer, S Ford, M Hall (captain), C Laity, N Walker, A Davies, A Moore, M Griffiths, J Humphreys, L Mustoe, M Bennett, A Rees, D Jones, M Budd, O Williams. Replacement: P Sedgemore for Mustoe 70 mins. Temporary replacements: Sedgemore for Mustoe 11-13 mins, for Griffiths 13-22 mins.

PONTYPRIDD: M Black, D Manley, J Lewis, S Lewis, O Robins, C Cormack, Paul John, N Bezani(captain), Phil John, A Metcalfe, M Lloyd, G Prosser, M Rowley, R Collins, D McIntosh.

Referee: D Davies, WRU

QUARTER FINALS

Maesteg 35	v	Tenby United 7
Neath 3	v	Llanelli 7
Pontypridd 32	v	Newbridge 10
Played on Saturday 2nd April 1994		
Cardiff 20	v	South Wales Police 13

WALES

SWALEC CUP continued

ROUND SIX

Cardiff 15   v   Bridgend 6

Dunvant 8   v   Newbridge 16

Llanelli 57   v   Llandovery 5

Maesteg 11   v   Bonymaen 10

Maesteg Celtic 14   v   South Wales Police 37

Pontypridd 13   v   Swansea 3

Tenby United 23   v   Narberth 14

Ystradgynlais 3   v   Neath 26

Played on Saturday 26th February 1994

ROUND FIVE

Abercynon 12   v   Neath 19

Bonymaen 6   v   Tondu 0

Bridgend 29   v   Felinfoel 6

Cardiff 27   v   Oakdale 3

Dunvant 39   v   Pyle 10

Kidwelly 6   v   Llanelli 49

Llandovery 18   v   Mold 3

Maesteg 9   v   Glamorgan Wanderers 5

Maesteg Cletic 8   v   Talywain 3

Narberth 16   v   Nantymoel 6

Newbridge 32   v   Llanharan 3

Pontypridd 29   v   Aberavon 0

South Wales Police 10   v   Caerphilly 3

Swansea 70   v   Seven Sisters 6

Tenby United 18   v   Abercrave 13

Ystradgynlais 10   v   Newport 9

Result of the Round:

Ystradgynlais 10   v   Newport 9

HEINEKEN LEAGUE

FINAL TABLES 1993-94

DIVISION 1

	P	W	D	L	F	A	Pts
SWANSEA	22	20	0	2	459	264	40
Neath	22	17	2	3	581	286	36
Pontypridd	22	17	1	4	571	299	35
Cardiff	22	15	2	5	668	240	32
Llanelli	22	13	1	8	461	366	27
Bridgend	22	10	1	11	466	434	21
Newport	22	8	2	12	362	472	18
Newbridge	22	7	1	14	367	440	15
Pontypool	22	7	0	15	312	626	14
Dunvant	22	6	1	15	288	464	13
Aberavon	22	6	1	15	242	464	13
Cross Keys	22	0	0	22	239	751	0

DIVISION 2

	P	W	D	L	F	A	Pts
TREORCHY	22	20	1	1	425	200	41
Abertillery	22	15	1	6	473	242	31
Maesteg	22	13	1	8	376	259	27
S W Police	22	12	0	10	367	333	24
Tenby United	22	10	0	12	308	366	20
Llanharan	22	9	2	11	259	349	20
Narberth	22	10	0	12	273	294	20
Penarth	22	9	0	13	291	372	18
Ebbw Vale	22	8	2	12	279	321	18
Llandovery	22	8	1	13	269	370	17
Mountain Ash	22	8	0	14	275	333	16
Glamorgan Wan	22	6	0	16	262	418	12

IRELAND

INSURANCE CORPORATION LEAGUES

FIRST DIVISION

	P	W	D	L	F	A	Pts
Garryowen	10	8	0	2	172	108	16
Cork Con	10	7	0	3	201	123	14
Blackrock	10	7	0	3	137	99	14
Dungannon	10	5	0	5	181	130	10
Lansdowne	10	5	0	5	162	167	10
St Mary's	10	5	0	5	157	163	10
Y Munster	10	5	0	5	102	149	10
Shannon	10	4	0	6	107	104	8
Old Wesley	10	4	0	6	114	138	8
Greystones	10	4	0	6	97	156	8
Wanderers	10	1	0	9	141	243	2

Champions: Garryowen
Relegated: Wanderers and Greystones

SECOND DIVISION

	P	W	D	L	F	A	Pts
Instonians	10	8	0	2	205	100	16
Sunday's Well	10	8	0	2	184	118	16
Ballymena	10	7	0	3	214	125	14
Old Belvedere	10	7	0	3	141	125	14
Bangor	10	5	0	5	122	189	10
Terenure	10	4	1	5	149	112	9
Malone	10	4	1	5	125	141	9
Old Crescent	10	4	0	6	173	150	8
Dolphin	10	4	0	6	139	144	8
Galwegians	10	3	0	7	113	124	6
Ballina	10	0	0	10	72	309	0

Promoted: Instonians and Sunday's Well
Relegated: Ballina and Galwegians

IRISH PROVINCIAL CUP FINALS 1993-94

CONNACHT
Corinthians 14   Connemara 10

MUNSTER
Sunday's Wells 20   Young Munster 9

LEINSTER
Terenure College 12   Greystones 8

ULSTER
Dungannon 14   Instonians 10

IRISH INTERPROVINCIAL CHAMPIONSHIP 1993-94

Connacht 9 Munster 15
Ulster 21 Irish Exiles 3
Connacht 10 Ulster 39
Irish Exiles 8 Leinster 13
Irish Exiles 42 Connacht 12
Munster 21 Leinster 19
Leinster 25 Ulster 0
Munster 34 Irish Exiles 19
Ulster 24 Munster 21
Leinster 15 Connacht 11

FINAL TABLE

	P	W	L	F	A	Pts
Leinster	4	3	1	72	40	6
Ulster	4	3	1	84	59	6
Munster	4	3	1	91	71	6
Irish Exiles	4	1	3	72	80	2
Connacht	4	0	4	42	111	0

BARBARIANS 1993-94

In Britain

Exeter (Exeter)	W 59-14
Newport (Newport)	L 19-35
New Zealand (Cardiff)	L 12-25
Leicester (Leicester)	L 14-51
East Midlands (Northampton)	W 55-25
Cardiff (Cardiff)	W 53-27
Swansea (Swansea)	L 31-51

In Zimbabwe

Goshawks (Mutare)	W 53- 9
Matabeleland (Bulawayo)	W 35-23
Zimbabwe (Harare)	L 21-23

Summary
Played 10, won 5, lost 5 points for 352, against 283

UNIVERSITY MATCH

Tuesday 7th December 1993   **At Twickenham**

OXFORD 20   CAMBRIDGE 8

Du Toit(T), Boyle(DG), Rees(DG)(3P)   Boyd(T), Kennedy(DG)

Half Time: 9-3

Oxford University: *M Joy, R Wintle, L Boyle, E Raynor, T Watson, G Rees, *F du Toit, B Fennell, D Henderson, C Clark, *C Lion- Cachet (captain), *J Daniel, *D Evans, N Martin, A Aitken

Cambridge University: A Dalwood, A Arentsen, *P Flood, A Palfrey, A Boyd, A Kennedy, C Tynan, T Hughes, *A Read, *P Callow (captain), P Irons, R Bramley, S Roy, N Richardson, A Meadows. Replacement: W Thompson for Flood 68 mins. Temporary replacement: J Duckworth for Callow 32-34 mins.
* Denotes Old Blue

Referee: D Bevan, Wales

INTERNATIONAL FIXTURE AMENDMENT
On Page 10
Saturday March 4th
IRELAND will play FRANCE in Dublin, NOT Paris

UNIVERSITIES ATHLETIC UNION FINAL

NORTHUMBRIA UNI 13   WEST LONDON INSTITUTE 9

Miller(T), Eley(2P)(C)   Lee(3P)

Half Time: 10-3

Northumbria University: J Miller, D Bennett, A Redpath, M Tetlow, T Penn, A Scott, J Eley, R Fuller, D Hayes, S Bowden, M Corry (captain), J Fowler, S Owen, J Nicholson, J Ayton. Replacement: E Craig for Penn 79 mins.

West London Institute: D O'Leary, M Kemp, S Burns, G Harrison, R Francis, A Lee (captain), C Mahon, J Cooke, S Rodgers, O Pipe, C Clements, A Dougan, J Beddoe, J Potts, R Hill.
Referee: E Sklar, Argentina

HOSPITALS CUP — 1993-94

ST MARY'S 19   CHARING CROSS-WESTMINSTER 18

Boos(2T)(PT), Morgan(2C)   Sinclair(T), Rowe(T), Clift(P)(C)

Half Tine: 12-7

St Mary's Hospital: T Poole; C Boos, D Abrams, A Morgan, T Shephard; S Hakey, W Jackson (captain); A Evans, S White, N Hunt, J Torkington, M Crowther, M Tremelling, C Langrish, P Mitchell. Replacement: N Wood for Langrish 67 minutes.

Charing Cross-Westminster: A Redman; C Swart, G O'Driscoll, M Hutton, A Sinclair; D Clift, E Rowe; F Banks, A Dalrymple, A Norrish, M Jeffery, H Lewis, J Waite, J Hickey (captain), R Walker. Replacement: A Poulis for Lewis 46 minutes.
Referee: A Evans, RFU

UNIVERSITIES ATHLETIC UNION KNOCKOUT ROUNDS

Quarter Finals
Manchester 5   Northumbria 40
Durham 17   Sheffield Hallam 9
Swansea 17   Roehampton 18
Bath 16   West London Institute 28

Semi Finals
Durham 9   Northumbria 34
(at Gateshead)
Roehampton 19   West London Institute 24
(at Stoop Memorial Ground)

HOSPITALS CUP PRELIMINARY ROUNDS

1st Round
Guy's 27   Toyal Free 6
(Honor Oak)

2nd Round
St Bartholomew's 7   The London 10
(Cheshuht)
Guy's 12   Charing Cross-Westminster 18
(Honour Oak)
University College-Middlesex 0   St Mary's 20
(Cobham)
St Thomas's 6   King's College 7
(Stoke d'Abernon)

Semi-Finals
Charing Cross-Westminster 11   The London 0
(Old Deer Park)
St Mary's 48   King's College 8
(Old Deer Park)

COUNTY CUP FINALS 1993-94

All winners qualify for the Pilkington Cup except where stated.

NORTH DIVISION

Cheshire:	Winnington Park 30	New Brighton 12
Cumbria:	Wigton 19	Kendal 16
Durham:	Stockton 16	Hartlepool Rovers 14
Lancashire:	Waterloo 19	Orrell 6
Northumberland:	Gosforth 14	Tynedale 8
Yorkshire:	Wakefield 35	Sandal 8

MIDLAND DIVISION

East Midlands:	Stockwood Park 14	Long Buckby 8
Leicestershire:	Loughborough Students 35	Belgrave 0
Notts.,Lincs, & Derbys:	Scunthorpe 14	Mansfield 13
North Midlands:	Camp Hill 17	Worcester 11
Staffordshire:	Walsall 24	Stoke-on-Trent 6
Warwickshire:	Barkers' Butts 41	Old Coventrians 12
Shropshire*:	Newport 13	Whitchurch 3

* Do not qualify for Pilkington Cup.

SOUTH WEST DIVISION

Berkshire:	Reading 25	Maidenhead 13
Buckinghamshire:-	High Wycombe 16	Aylesbury 11
Devon:	Exeter 22	Plymouth Albion 6
Dorset & Wiltshire:	Sherborne 11	Salisbury 8
Cornwall:	Launceston 24	Redruth 14
Gloucestershire:	Matson 6	Gloucester Old Boys 5
Oxfordshire:	Henley 13	Banbury 12
Somerset:	Bridgwater 15	Clevedon 10
West Somerset*:	Wellington 8	Minehead 7

* Do not qualify for Pilkington Cup.

LONDON & SOUTH EAST DIVISION

Eastern Counties:	Southend 17	Sudbury 8
Hampshire:	Basingstoke 25	Alton 11
Hertfordshire:	Tabard 34	Old Albanians 13
Kent:	Old Colfeians 10	Charlton Park 10
	(Old Colfeians win 2-1 on penalties)	
Middlesex:	Ealing 15	Staines 10
Surrey:	Esher 9	Sutton & Epsom 3
Sussex:	Horsham 17	Lewes 0

HONG KONG SEVENS

FINAL

NEW ZEALAND 32   AUSTRALIA 20

Rush (2T), Lomu (T), Erenavula (T),
Osborne (T)(2C)

Williams (2T), Wilson (T), Gregan (T)

NEW ZEALAND: L Erenavula, G Osborne, J Tauiwi, P Woods, D Seymour, E Rush (captain), J Lomu.
AUSTRALIA: J Little, T Horan, D Campese (captain), G Gregan, I Tabua, D Wilson, J Williams. Replacement:
J Fenwicke for Tabua.

Group Matches

Group 'A'
Western Samoa 61   Sri Lanka 0
US Eagles 24   Sri Lanka 14
Western Samoa 33   US Eagles 10
Group 'B'
Ireland 40   Singapore 0
President's Seven 45   Singapore 0
President's Seven 22   Ireland 7
Group 'C'
Hong Kong 15   Scotland 5
Argentina 26   Hong Hong Kong 5
Scotland 24 Argentina 14

Group 'D'
Australia 29   Taiwan 0
Japan 17   Taiwan 12
Australia 54   Japan 0
Group 'E'
New Zealand 64   Malaysia 0
Tonga 45   Malaysia 7
New Zealand 38   Tonga 5
Group 'F'
France 26   Papua New Guinea 5
Papua New Guinea 26   Romania 5
France 40   Romania 5

Group 'G'
South Africa 63   Thailand 0
Canada 35   Thailand 0
South Africa 20   Canada 7
Group 'H'
Fiji 56   Portugal 7
South Korea 26   Portugal 10
Fiji 33   South Korea 0

Cup quarter-finals
Western Samoa 21   President's Seven 12
Argentina 0   Australia 43
New Zealand 21   France 12
South Africa 12   Fiji 14

Semi-finals
Western Samoa 17   Australia 20 (aet)
New Zealand 28   Fiji 14

SAVE & PROSPER MIDDLESEX SEVENS

Saturday, 14th May 1994   **At Twickenham.**

ORRELL 12   BATH 19

Naylor (T), Johnson (T)(C)

Rayner (T), Lumsden (T), Callard(T) (2C)

Half Time: 7-5

ORRELL: J Naylor, I Wynn, P Johnson (captain), A Healey; M Farr, J Clayton, H Parr.
BATH: A Lumsden, E Rayner, J Callard (captain), I Sanders; E Peters, G Adams, M Haag.

6th Round

Northampton 12 Rosslyn Park 26; Harlequins 19 Richmond 12; Orrell 17 Bristol 12 (after extra time);
Blackheath 7 Fiji Spartans 21; Zimbabwe 12 Loughborough University 21; Bath 28 London Scottish 26;
Gloucester 12 London Irish 17; Saracens 7 Wasps (holders) 5.

Quarter-finals
Rosslyn Park 21   Harlequins 10
Orrell 10   Fiji Spartans 7
Loughborough University 0   Bath 24
London Irish 5   Saracens 26

Semi-finals
Rosslyn Park 7   Orrell 10
Bath 19   Saracens 0.

Plate final
Wasps 22   Northampton 12.

WORTHINGTON BEST BITTER NATIONAL TENS

Monday, 2nd May 1994   at Kingsholm, Gloucester

Bristol 26   Gloucester 5

1st Round
Moseley 19   Harlequins 12
Bristol 47   London Irish 7
Orrell 17   Moseley 12
Wakefield 17   Bath 7
Wasps 33   Sale 7
Cardiff 40   West Hartlepool 7
Northampton 35   Saracens 10
Gloucester 12   Newcastle Gosforth 10

Quarter-finals
Bristol 19   Moseley 14
Wakefield 19   Orrell 5
Wasps 38   Cardiff 7
Gloucester 19   Northampton 0.

Semi-finals
Bristol 19   Wakefield 14
Gloucester 6   Wasps 0.

SUPER TEN TOURNAMENT

Pool 'A'
Queensland 44 Transvaal 19
Transvaal 35 Eastern Province 15
Eastern Province 10 Queensland 41
Transvaal 44 Otago 19
Otago 24 Queensland 18
Eastern Province 21 North Harbour 31
North Harbour 23 Otago 19
Otago 57 Eastern Province 24
North Harbour 19 Transvaal 6
Queensland 13 North Harbour 10

Pool 'B'
Waikato 16 New South Wales 43
New South Wales 25 Western Samoa 23
Auckland 27 Waikato 10
Waikato 18 Western Samoa 32
Natal walked over New South Wales
Western Samoa 15 Auckland 13 (in Auckland)
Natal 30 Waikato 24
Natal 48 Western Samoa 26
New South Wales 22 Auckland 19
Natal 14 Auckland 12

Final Tables

	P	W	L	F	A	Pts		P	W	L	F	A	Pts
QUEENSLAND	4	3	1	116	63	6	NATAL*	4	4	0	92	62	8
North Harbour	4	3	1	83	59	6	New South Wales*	4	3	1	90	58	6
Otago	4	2	2	119	109	4	Western Samoa	4	2	2	96	104	4
Transvaal	4	2	2	104	97	4	Auckland	4	1	3	71	61	2
Eastern Province	4	0	4	70	164	0	Waikato	4	0	4	68	132	0

* The Natal v New South Wales match was not played with the result and points being awarded to Natal.

FINAL

Natal 10   Queensland 21
Saturday, 14th May 1994. In Durban

WOMENS WORLD CUP

POOL 'A' (Melrose)
United States 111 Sweden 0
Japan 10 Sweden 5
United States 121 Japan 0
United States and Sweden qualify for quarter-finals.
POOL 'B' (Megetland):
England 66 Russia 0
Scotland 51 Russia 0
England 26 Scotland 0
England and Scotland qualify for quarter-finals.
POOL 'C' (Burnbrae)
France 70 Scottish Students 0
Ireland 18 Scottish Students 5

France 31 Ireland 0
France and Ireland qualify for quarter-finals.
POOL 'D' (Raeburn Place)
Wales 11 Canada 5
Wales 29 Kazakhstan 8
Canada 28 Kazakhstan 0
Wales and Canada qualify for quarter finals.
QUARTER-FINALS
England 26 Canada 10 (Gala)
Scotland 0 Wales 8 (Melrose)
United States 76 Ireland 0
France 99 Japan 0.

SEMI FINALS

UNITED STATES 56   WALES 15

United States: J Crawford; K McFarren, C Orsini, E Huffer, P Jervey; K Bergmann, P Connell; A Flavin, J Gray, M Sorrensen, S Hunt, A Williams, T Flanagan, L Spicer-Bourdon, B Bond (captain). Replacement: L Weix for Sorrensen 58 minutes. **Scorers:** Crawford (5), Jervey (1), Bergmann (1), Orsini (1). Pens: Bergmann (2). Cons: Bergmann (5)
Wales: K Richards; K Yau, E Davies, J Thomas, L Rickard; A Bennett, B Evans, T Wear, B Trotter, E Skiffington, J Morgan, K Eaves, H Cahalane, S Butler, L Burgess (captain). **Scorers:** Tries: Burgess (2), Evans (1). Referee: C Muir, Langholm.

ENGLAND 18   FRANCE 6

England: J Mitchell; P Blackett, P George, G Prangnell, A Cole; K Almond (captain), E Mitchell, J Mangham, N Ponsford, S Ewing, J Ross, S Wenn, H Stirrup, G Shore, G Burns. Replacement: J Vyvyan for J Mitchell 24 minutes. **Scorers:** Tries: Almond, 1 penalty try. Pens: Almond (2). Con: Almond.
France: C Lacommere; F Saudin, E Lafitte, A Hayraud, B de Barros; S Lamarque, M Sulpice; D Roussel, M Guichardon, S Girard, N Amiel captain, L St-Macary, V Lenoir, H Lacommere, N Bertranck. Replacement: I Rouet for Girard 48 minutes. **Scorer:** Pens: Hayraud (2).
Referee: K McCartney, Hawick.

FINAL

ENGLAND 38   UNITED STATES 23

England: J Mitchell; V Blackett, J Edwards, G Prangnell, A Cole; K Almond (captain), E Mitchell; J Mangham, N Ponsford, S Ewing, J Ross, S Wenn, H Stirrup, G Shore, G Burns. Replacements: J Chambers for Wenn 26 minutes, P George for Edwards 80 minutes. **Scorers:** Tries: J Mitchell (1), Burns (1), Edwards (1), 2 penalty tries. Pen: Almond. Cons: Almond (5).
United States: J Crawford; K McFarren, C Orsini, E Huffer, P Jerviy; J Bergmann, P Connell; A Flavin, J Gray, M Sorrensen, S Hunt, J Rutkowski, T Flanagan, L Spicer-Bourdon, B Bond (captain). **Scorers:** Tries: Crawford (2), Jervey (1), Huffer (1). Pen: Bergmann. Half-time: 26-10.
Referee: J Fleming, Boroughmuir.

3rd/4th place play-off
FRANCE 27   WALES 0

SHIELD
Semi-Finals (both at Melrose)
Scotland 10 Ireland 3
Canada 56 Japan 0
FINAL
CANADA 5   SCOTLAND 11
Third Place
Japan 3 Ireland 11

PLATE
Semi-Finals
Sweden 12 Kazakhstan 31
Scottish Students 12 Russia 24
FINAL
KAZAKHSTAN 29   SWEDEN 12
(all finals in Edinburgh)

1995 RUGBY WORLD CUP FIXTURES

Date	Pool	Match
MAY 1995		
Th 25th	A	Australia v South Africa (Cape Town)
Fr 26th	D	Scotland v Ivory Coast (Rustenburg)
	D	France v Tonga (Pretoria)
	A	Canada v Europe 3 (Port Elizabeth)
Sa 27th	B	Western Samoa v Europe 2 (East London)
	B	England v Argentina (Durban)
	C	Europe 1 v Asia (Bloemfontein)
	C	New Zealand v Ireland (Johannesburg)
Tu 30th	A	South Africa v Europe 3 (Cape Town)
	B	Western Samoa v Argentina (East London)
	D	France v Ivory Coast (Rustenburg)
	D	Scotland v Tonga (Pretoria)
We 31st	A	Australia v Canada (Port Elizabeth)
	B	England v Europe 2 (Durban)
	C	Ireland v Asia (Bloemfontein)
	C	New Zealand v Europe 1 (Johannesburg)
JUNE 1995		
Sa 3rd	A	Australia v Europe 3 (Stellenbosch)
	A	Canada v South Africa (Port Elizabeth)
	D	Tonga v Ivory Coast (Rustenburg)
	D	Scotland v France (Pretoria)
Su 4th	B	Argentina v Europe 2 (East London)
	B	England v Western Samoa (Durban)
	C	New Zealand v Asia (Bloemfontein)
	C	Ireland v Europe (Johannesburg)
Sa 10th	E	Winners D v Runners-up C (Durban)
	F	Winners A v Runners-up B (Johannesburg)
Su 11th	H	Winners B v Runners-up A (Cape Town)
	G	Winners C v Runners-up D
Sa 17th		Semi-final Winners E v Winners F (Durban)
Su 18th		Semi-final Winners G v Winners H (Cape Town)
Th 22nd		Third place play-off (Pretoria)
Sa 24th		**FINAL** (Johannesburg)

INTERNATIONAL FIXTURE AMENDMENT
On Page 10
Saturday March 4th
IRELAND will play FRANCE in Dublin, NOT Paris

CLUB INDEX

CLUB INDEX

CLUB INDEX

CLUB INDEX

CLUB INDEX

CLUB INDEX

CLUB INDEX

CLUB INDEX

CLUB INDEX

Vulcan RUFC	N-CLS	345	Whitley Bay Rockcliff RFC	N-NE2	353
Wadebridge Camels RFC	SW-CW1	501	Whitstable RFC	L-K2	457
Wakefield RFC	Nat-2	159	Whitwell (1985) RUFC	M-NLD4	407
Walcot Old Boys RFC	SW-S1	515	Wibsey RUFC	N-Y2	363
Wallasey RUFC	N-CE	347	Widden Old Boys RFC	SW-G1	507
Wallsend RFC	N-DN1	355	Widnes RUFC	N-N1	329
Walsall RFC	Nat-5N	286	Wigan RUFC	N-NW1	333
Wandsworthians RFC	L-SR2	479	Wigston RFC	M-EML2	411
Wanstead RFC	L-EC2	443	Wigton RUFC	N-N1	329
Warley RFC	M-NM1	391	Willenhall RFC	M-M2	377
Warlingham RFC	L-L3SW	469	Wilmslow RUFC	N-NW1	333
Warminster RFC	SW-BDW2	529	Wimbledon RFC	L-L3SW	469
Warrington RUFC	N-CLS	345	Wimborne RFC	SW-SC	521
Warwick RFC	M-SW3	387	Winaton Vulcans RUFC	N-DN2	357
Warwickshire Constabulary RFC	M-SW2	385	Wincanton RUFC	SW-S3	519
Washington RUFC	N-DN3	359	Winchester RFC	L-HA1	471
Wasps FC	Nat-1	109	Windermere RUFC	N-CLN	337
Waterloo FC	Nat-2	163	Windsor RFC	SW-SC	521
Waterlooville RFC	L-HA3	475	Winlaton Vulcans RFC	N-DN2	357
Watford RFC	L-HE1	437	Winnington Park RFC	Nat-5N	290
Wath RUFC	N-Y1	361	Winscombe RFC	SW-S2	517
Wearside RUFC	N-DN3	359	Winslow RUFC	SW-BO2	525
Wednesbury RUFC	M-SW2	385	Wirral RFC	N-CLS	345
Wellingborough Old			Wisbech RUFC	L-EC4	447
Grammarians RFC	M-EML2	411	Witham RUFC	L-EC4	447
Wellingborough RFC	M-ME1	397	Withernsea RUFC	N-Y4	367
Wellington RFC	SW-S1	515	Withycombe RFC	SW-D1	497
Wells RFC	SW-S1	515	Witney RFC	SW-BO1	523
Welwyn RFC	L-L3NW	425	Witton RFC	M-NM3	395
Wembley RFC	L-M1	429	Wiveliscombe RFC	SW-GS	505
Wensleydale RUFC	N-DN2	357	Woking RFC	L-SR2	479
West Bridgford RFC	M-ME2	399	Wolverhampton RUFC	M-M1	375
West Hartlepool RFC	Nat-1	115	Woodbridge RUFC	L-L3NE	439
West Hartlepool Technical Day			Woodford RFC	L-L2N	423
School Old Boys RUFC	N-DN1	355	Woodrush RFC	M-MW2	381
West Leeds RUFC	N-Y2	363	Wootton Bassett RFC	SW-BDW1	527
West Leicester RFC	M-EML3	413	Worcester RFC	M-M1	375
West Norfolk RUFC	L-L3NE	439	Workington RUFC	N-CLN	337
West Park (St Helens) RFC	N-N2	331	Worksop RUFC	M-ME2	399
West Park Bramhope RUFC	N-N1	329	Worthing RFC	L-L3SE	453
Westbury RFC	SW-BDW2	529	Wotton RFC	SW-G4	513
Westbury-on-Severn RFC	SW-G3	511	Wulfrun RUFC	M-NM3	395
Westcliff RFC	L-EC1	441	Wymondham RUFC	L-EC1	441
Westcombe Park RFC	L-L2S	451	Yarborough Bees RFC	M-NLD4	407
Westerham RFC	L-K4	461	Yardley & District RFC	M-NM3	395
Westland RFC	SW-S2	517	Yarnbury (Horsforth) RUFC	N-Y1	361
Westleigh RFC	M-M1	375	Yatton RFC	SW-S1	515
Westoe RFC	N-NE2	353	Yeovil RFC	SW-S1	515
Weston-super-Mare RFC	Nat-5S	318	York RI RUFC	N-Y2	363
Westwood RUFC	M-EML3	413	York RUFC	N-N1	329
Wetherby RUFC	N-Y3	365	Yorkshire Copperworks RUFC	N-Y5	369
Weymouth RFC	SW-BDW1	527	Yorkshire Main RUFC	N-Y4	367
Wharfedale RUFC	Nat-5N	288			
Wheatley	SW-BO2	525			
Wheatley Hills RUFC	N-Y1	361			
Wheaton Aston RUFC	M-SW3	387			
Whitby RUFC	N-NE2	353			
Whitchurch RFC	M-M1	375			
Whitehall RFC	SW-GS	505			
Whitehaven RUFC	N-CU	339			
Whitehouse Park RUFC	N-CE	347			

STOP PRESS
Amended address, page 22.
Chairman of National Leagues Organising Committee
Frank Gibbon, 5 Church Row, Wolviston,
Billingham, Cleveland TS20 5LD

LEAGUE
STRUCTURE

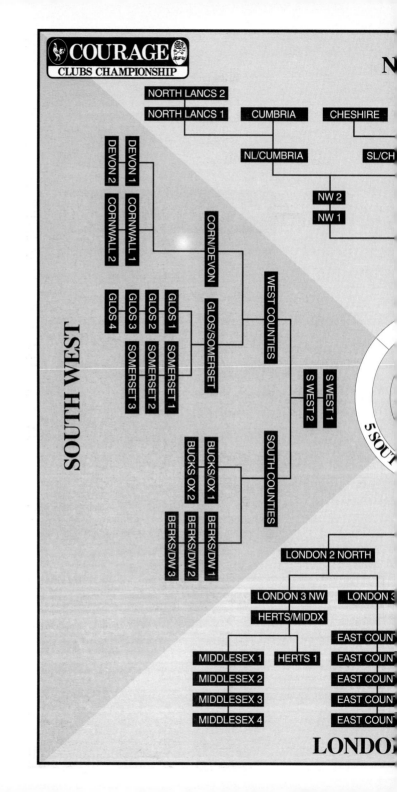

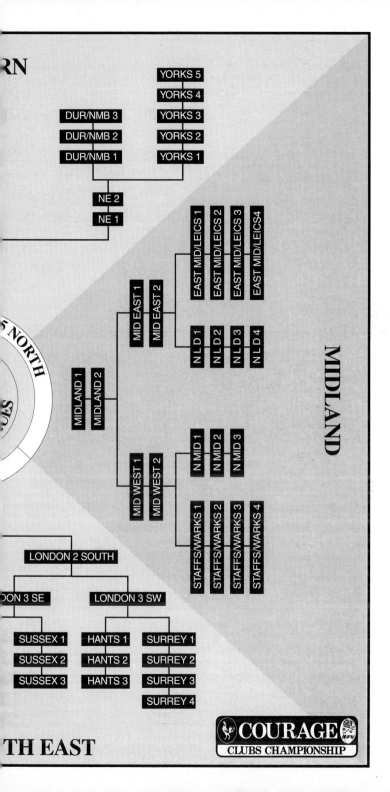

RN

YORKS 5
YORKS 4
YORKS 3
YORKS 2
YORKS 1

DUR/NMB 3
DUR/NMB 2
DUR/NMB 1

NE 2
NE 1

EAST MID/LEICS 1
EAST MID/LEICS 2
EAST MID/LEICS 3
EAST MID/LEICS4

MID EAST 1
MID EAST 2

N L D 1
N L D 2
N L D 3
N L D 4

NORTH

MIDLAND 1
MIDLAND 2

MIDLAND

N MID 1
N MID 2
N MID 3

MID WEST 1
MID WEST 2

STAFFS/WARKS 1
STAFFS/WARKS 2
STAFFS/WARKS 3
STAFFS/WARKS 4

LONDON 2 SOUTH

DON 3 SE
LONDON 3 SW

SUSSEX 1
SUSSEX 2
SUSSEX 3

HANTS 1
HANTS 2
HANTS 3

SURREY 1
SURREY 2
SURREY 3
SURREY 4

TH EAST

COURAGE
CLUBS CHAMPIONSHIP